INTRODUCTION
TO THE
HISTORY OF SCIENCE

VOLUME III

SCIENCE AND LEARNING IN THE FOURTEENTH CENTURY

BY

GEORGE SARTON
Associate in the History of Science
Carnegie Institution of Washington

IN TWO PARTS

PUBLISHED FOR THE
CARNEGIE INSTITUTION OF WASHINGTON
BY
THE WILLIAMS & WILKINS COMPANY
BALTIMORE
1947

CARNEGIE INSTITUTION OF WASHINGTON
PUBLICATION 376

Reprinted 1953

ROBERTO SIMPSON WOODWARD
MATHEMATICO ASTRONOMO
INSTITVTI CARNEGIANI
PRAESIDI ALTERI ALTERIQVE AVCTORI
HVIVS OPERIS FAVTORI PRAECIPVO
PIETATIS PIGNVS
D. D. D.

PREFACE

(1) Truth and peace. (2) Corrections to volume 1. (3) Addenda to volumes 1 and 2. (4) Addenda to volume 3. (5) Classification of contents. (6) To help and to be helped.

1. *Truth and Peace*

The main part of this book was written during the dark days of the war, and this preface, cogitated during days which were darker still. During the war we could dream of peace, and we thought of it as if it would bring happiness and virtue. That would have been possible if the greed for material things and for power had subsided, but it has not by any means, and in a sense one might say that the war is not over. Our technicians are arranging a new world free from the humanities, with a few atomic bombs suspended above it. They seem to think that when bread has been given to the people, the essential has been done, but man cannot live by bread alone. (Millions of men and women lack even bread.) Nevertheless, we should not despair, but work harder, with a deeper faith, cultivate the humanities, and defend the noble traditions without which life, however efficient or comfortable, is hardly worth living.

This may seem sentimental but it is not. We love and need beauty and all the graces of life, but we need reason even more. The only safe ground of unity and peace is clear reason together with its fruits: truth, science, justice, but truth must be tempered by humor, science by humbleness, justice by generosity. One cannot insist too much on the supreme value of rational thinking, the field of which must be steadily increased and deepened (that is what the progress of science amounts to), but our rationalism must always be corrected and restrained by the overwhelming feeling of our ignorance of fundamentals. An ocean of mystery is still surrounding us; the more we push it back, the more it widens; that justifies a good amount of mysticism.[1] Yet we must be rational as much as we can; whenever rational answers are warranted, irrational ones are inexcusable. We need charity as much as justice, yet an appeal to the heart alone is insufficient and dangerous. Does not every tyrant make it? Could any one of them exist for any time without a trusted phalanx of liegemen? Every public crime has been committed by mobs whose emotions had been flattered and whose good will had been corrupted.

Life is certainly more comfortable now, and it is so for many more people, than it was in the past, but it has not been enriched in proportion. In many cases, one cannot escape the impression that it has been actually impoverished. To quote familiar examples, we have plenty of gadgets to save our time, but most

[1] There is no room here for expanding that idea, but the following statement made by Albert Einstein may illustrate it: "The most beautiful emotion we can experience is the mystical. It is the sower of all true art and science. He to whom this emotion is a stranger, who can no longer wonder and stand rapt in awe, is as good as dead. To know that what is impenetrable to us really exists, manifesting itself as the highest wisdom and the most radiant beauty, which our dull faculties can comprehend only in their most primitive forms—this knowledge, this feeling, is at the center of true religiousness. In this sense, and in this sense only, I belong to the ranks of devoutly religious men." As quoted in the excellent biography by Philipp Frank: Einstein his life and times (p. 284, New York 1947).

people cannot use wisely the time which they have saved and now and then they are hard put to it to find means of "killing" it; the speed of communications has been enormously increased, but somehow people have less and less time to see things in a quiet way, to saunter and meditate. They may travel all around the world (it is easy enough if you have money), but somehow they manage to miss the essential and to get everything confused; after a while (often a surprisingly short while), they return with less experience and less wisdom than could be brought home by a mediaeval wight after a short pilgrimage. The tourist's main comment is "The world is small," but the smallness is in himself. The ease of communications is so great that many people seem to think that communications are ends rather than means; they rush ceaselessly from one place to another without having any more to do in the one than in the other. They are always "communicating," but they have nothing worth while to communicate.

Some men have so many time-saving appliances that they have no time left for steady and thoughtful reading. This helps to explain the phenomenal success of such journals as the "Reader's digest," or the "Literary digest," or other journals with different titles but the selfsame purpose, to reduce the need of reading to its minimum.[2]

This book deals with the fourteenth century; that is the Christian way of putting it, but if we considered the matter from the Muslim angle, we should say that it deals with the eighth century; or if we looked at it from the Chinese point of view, we should say that it concerns the end of the Yüan (or Mongol) dynasty and the beginning of the Ming (or Chinese) one; or from the Japanese angle, it is the end of the Kamakura shogunate and the beginning of the Ashikaga. There are many nations, however, to which those descriptions would not apply, and they would require different ones. These remarks are made to suggest that we must always try to look at things from the point of view of our neighbors as well as from our own; if we were unable to do so, we could hardly expect them to have more understanding than we have.

We all know the dangers of political and economic imperialism, and those of religious imperialism ("Our religion is the only true one and hence it is our duty to convert our brothers to it no matter how"). There is also a subtler kind of imperialism which is very common. "Our ways are the best ways, our manners the finest manners, our taste is good taste." Such a state of mind is hopeless. In the field of rationality and science, however, free from sentiment and from cant, some degree of objectivity is attainable, and there can be a consensus of opinion. It is for that very reason that science is the basis of unity and peace. There may come a time when such a consensus will be so evident and compelling that there will be no room left, at least among good people, for injustice.[3] Scientific truth can be

[2] A commercial genius will probably publish sooner or later a "Digest of digests," which will obviate the necessity of reading the "Digests," unless that invention be made superfluous in the meanwhile by the development of the reading machine described by Morris Bishop (New Yorker, March 8, 1947).

[3] The bad people can generally be restricted by laws, but it is far more difficult to restrict good people. One of the main tragedies of life is that bad deeds are often perpetrated by good people in good faith. Rational knowledge is the only cure. We can observe this conflict in ourselves whenever new knowledge enlightens our conscience and imposes on it new duties, which become thenceforth unescapable.

checked, and when it has been checked and found to conform with reality, it is easy enough for every person of any nation to accept it without loss of face, and the acceptance can be continued as long as the truth itself is not refuted by new facts. No basis is more certain and more secure upon which to establish the agreement of mankind and its unity. There have been, of course, discordant and hateful voices in every period, not only in our own, but it is the rational and peaceful ones which have carried humanity forward. Though this book occasionally mentions evil men and describes evil deeds, it is very largely dedicated to the good men of the fourteenth century—saints and thinkers, men of science and men of peace—the very men who, being interested in truth above aught else, transcended their own parochial or national limitations and worked, consciously or not, for the whole of mankind.

Similar feelings and aspirations informed my mind while I was working. The consciousness that what I was doing did not concern myself alone, nor my fellows and my friends, nor even the people of any group however large, but the whole of mankind, has been during the war years my main solace. My efforts for the unification and pacification of mankind are humble enough and perhaps ludicrous in their smallness, yet they were made honestly and lovingly, without prejudice or afterthought; I may have failed to go very far along my chosen path, but I went to the very limit of my strength and gave all I could.

2. *Corrections to Volume 1*

A photographic reprint of volume 1 was issued by the publishers of the original edition, the Williams & Wilkins Company of Baltimore, in the spring of 1946. That reprint, bearing the date 1927, is not easily distinguishable from the original edition, except that connoisseurs are aware of a different surface and appearance of the printed pages. If the author had been warned, he would have asked for the privilege of adding a new preface. That opportunity having been denied to him, he takes advantage of the preface to volume 3 to add a few corrections to volume 1.

If I could rewrite that volume 1 now, the notes devoted to the great figures of ancient science—Hippocrates, Plato, Aristotle, Eudoxos, Euclid, Archimedes, Apollonios, Eratosthenes, Hipparchos, Ptolemy, Galen, Diophantos, Pappos, etc.—would be considerably more elaborate, but that would require another lifetime. Perhaps it was better after all to write it more concisely and thus be able to emerge from antiquity and cover the larger part of the Middle Ages. Students of ancient science have better tools—such as Pauly-Wissowa and many others—than students of mediaeval science.

A few smaller personalities were omitted or else the notes devoted to them were a bit too short. For example, Euclid of Megara was disposed of in a footnote (p. 153), though he deserved a longer notice. He was one of Socrates' best disciples and the founder of the Megarian (or Dialectic, Eristic) school of philosophy.[4]

It would have been well to speak in "The age of Ptolemy" (II-1) of the school established in Rome for scientific and literary studies (ingenuae et humanae artes) by Hadrian (emperor from 117 to 138); it was called Athenaeum in honor of Athens. It is true very little is known about it.

Ptolemy's Geography would require a much longer discussion than was devoted to it; this is a matter of singular complexity. See Leo Bagrow: The origin of Ptolemy's Geographia (Geografiska annaler 27, 318–87, 1945; Isis 37).

[4] See article by Paul Natorp (PW 11, 1000–3, 1907).

It might be remarked in a general way that almost every topic of ancient science calls for a restatement of the mediaeval traditions concerning it; now that I have completed (or almost completed) my survey of mediaeval science, it would not be very difficult for me to prepare that restatement, but I was not equipped to do so before 1927.

The omission of the two Oppianoi—Oppianos I (II-2) the Cilician, author of a Greek poem on fishes and fishing, and Oppianos II (III-1) the Syrian, author of a Greek poem on hunting and on fowling with birdlime—was corrected by Joseph Needham in Isis (11, 413–14, 1928).

The gravest shortcoming concerns the Fathers of the Church; they were not omitted, but dealt with a little offhandedly in a general note (p. 361). Individual notes were devoted to a few of the Greek and Latin Fathers, but not to as many of them as should have been thus treated. Information about them can be found in theological treatises, or in dictionaries of Christian biography, but those reference books do not pay sufficient attention to scientific questions. I should have taken pains to indicate briefly but exactly the contributions (positive or negative, explicit or implicit) of each of those Fathers to scientific knowledge or scientific thought. The following table enumerates for the reader's convenience the Fathers dealt with in volume 1, as well as a few of those who were omitted, all of them in chronological order of death years. Following Christian usage, they are divided into two groups separated by the council of Nicaea in 325, when the Arian heresy was condemned and the Nicene creed established.

Ante-Nicene

(From the martyrdom of St. Polycarpos of Smyrna in 155 to the council of Nicaea in 325)

		Vol. 1
G	St. Justinos Martyr of Samaria (c. 100–c. 165)	(II-2), p. 293
G	St. Irenaeos of Smyrna (?) (c. 130–c. 202)	(II-2), p. 294
G	Clement of Alexandria (c. 150–c. 220)	
L	Tertullianus of Carthage (c. 155–c. 230)	
G	Origenes of Alexandria (c. 185–254)	(III-1), p. 317
L	St. Cyprianus of Carthage (d. 258)	
L	Lactantius of Numidia (c. 260–c. 325–40)	

Nicene and Post-Nicene

G	St. Athanasios of Alexandria (c. 296–373)	
G	St. Basil of Cappadocia (c. 331–379)	(IV-2), p. 361
G	St. Gregory of Nazianzos (c. 327–389)	
G	St. Gregory of Nyssa (c. 335–c. 395)	
L	St. Ambrose of Treves (c. 338–397)	(IV-2), p. 362
G	St. Epiphanios of Palestine (c. 315–403)	(IV-2), p. 362
G	St. John Chrysostom of Antioch (347–407)	
L	St. Jerome of Dalmatia (c. 345–420)	(IV-2), p. 363
L	St. Augustine of Tagaste (354–430)	(V-1), p. 383
G	St. Cyril of Alexandria (c. 376–444)	

This list might be continued; there is no definite upper limit to the procession of the Fathers of the Church; but we may well stop in the fifth century, with St. Augustine and St. Cyril, and the more so because after the fifth century the separation between the Latin and Greek churches never ceased to increase until it became a schism. Of the seventeen Fathers listed above, we devoted special articles to only half. The letter G or L at the beginning of each line refers to the language; eleven are Greek and only six Latin. Four of the Fathers listed above came from Alexandria, three from Syria and Palestine, three from Cappadocia,[5] four from Numidia, and one each from Smyrna, Germany, and Dalmatia. Or else eleven were Easterners and six Westerners, but that has already been said in a different way.

The list of Fathers of the Church is sometimes extended to St. Gregory the Great (VI-2) in the West and to St. John Damascene (VIII-1) in the East, or it may even be extended down to the end of the thirteenth century in the West and to the fall of Constantinople (1453) in the East. Catholic writers have the best of reasons to include St. Thomas Aquinas (XIII-2), who is not only a Father, but the Father by excellence, "doctor communis," of the Roman Catholic church.[6] His scientific views have been frequently discussed in my Introduction.

The main corrections in a book the framework of which is strictly chronological are due to chronological ambiguities. If new investigations make it necessary to change considerably the floruit of a man of science, he must be moved to another chapter, and the conclusions of the old chapter and of the new one have to be modified. For example, my Harvard colleague Werner Jaeger has proved that Diocles of Carystos (IV-1 B.C.) is younger than I thought; he belongs to the age of Euclid rather than to the age of Plato, and some of our conclusions concerning the development of Greek medicine may have to be corrected accordingly.[7]

The uncertainties concerning the chronology of the Alexandrine mechanicians have been insisted upon repeatedly in our volume 1. Ctesibios of Alexandria was placed in II-1 B.C., Philon of Byzantium in II-2 B.C., Heron of Alexandria in I-1 B.C.; that is certainly their relative order, but perhaps each flourished somewhat later than the floruit which I ascribed to him? Many papers have been written on these subjects, but none carries conviction, and my datings may be tentatively preserved.

Similar difficulties exist with regard to the mathematicians who maintained the high level of Greek science until the end of Greek culture, Diophantos of Alexandria (III-2), Pappos of Alexandria (III-2), Theon of Alexandria (IV-2). The date of Diophantos is based on a single statement of Michael Psellos (XI-2); it is possible that Pappos and Theon are closer to each other than my way of placing them would suggest. Pappos' commentary on the Almagest was probably written after 320, and his Mathematical collection even later.[8]

Chronological ambiguities exist also in the Oriental field and are even more difficult to solve than the Western ones. Consider the case of Vasubandhu (IV-1). My doubts were expressed in a footnote (p. 350); they have not been alleviated since. It is possible that Vasubandhu should be placed as late as the second half

[5] In the eastern part of Asia Minor. The three Cappadocians were St. Basil and the two Sts. Gregory; Gregory of Nyssa was Basil's puisne brother.

[6] Introd. 2, 916–21. For the Catholic definition of Fathers of the Church see John Chapman (CE 6, 1–18, 1909).

[7] W. Jaeger: Diokles von Karystos. Die griechische Medizin und die Schule des Aristoteles (252 p., Berlin 1938; Isis 31, 125; 33, 86); Vergessene Fragmente des Peripatetikers Diokles von Karystos, nebst zwei Anhängen zur Chronologie der dogmatischen Aerzteschule (Abhandlungen der Preussischen Akademie, phil. hist. Kl. no. 3, 46 p., Berlin 1938).

[8] Adolphe Rome: Commentaires de Pappus et de Théon sur l'Almageste (vol. 3, Vatican 1943; Isis 36, 255–56).

of the following century, and this would give another twist to the history of Hindu Buddhism.[9]

I owe to my friend Dr. Solomon Gandz the following correction to my note on the Sefer yeẓirah.[9a]

(1) The Sefer yeẓirah dates probably from the early Mishnaic time, the first century after Christ, and perhaps from the first century B.C.; hence between 100 B.C. and A.D. 100. (2) At any rate it is anterior to A.D. 200; for the two oldest Palestinian amoraim, R. Ḥanina and R. Hoshaya, who flourished c. 200, knew of it and made use of it. In A.D. 200 it was already renowned as a holy and ancient thaumaturgical work. See Kaufmann Kohler (JE 12, 602, 1906). (3) It may be considered the earliest Hebrew writing on gnosticism, mysticism, and speculative cosmogony. It is not qabbala. The earliest qabbalists did not understand it. (4) The 10 sefirot have little to do with spheres of emanation. Sefirot are numbers. (5) The basic theory of the book is that God created the world by means of the 10 numbers and the 22 letters of the Hebrew alphabet. These are the 32 mysterious ways and elements of Divine Wisdom. (6) The 10 numbers represent the peg,[9b] beli-mah (nothing), upon which God suspended the earth (Job 26:7), and the 22 letters are the foundation of the earth (Prov. 3:19; Job 38:4). (7) The author of the book was familiar with the calculation of permutations and combinations. (8) The commentary of Saadia Gaon (X-1) upon it is still the best available. (9) For more details cf. Gandz: Saadia as a mathematician (p. 143–50, 158-63, New York 1943; Isis 35, 57).

To return to the West, the main error of my volume 1 concerns Joannes Philoponos (VI-1) and John the Grammarian (VII-1). It seems now established that these two personalities are but one. John the Grammarian lived in VI-1, not VII-1, and is identical with Philoponos.[10] His Aristotelian commentaries and theological writings were translated into Syriac and thus transmitted to the Arabs; the Arabic translations influenced Muslim doctors like al-Ghazzālī and Jewish ones like Maimonides, and thus indirectly most of the scholastic philosophers. The medical writings are apocryphal. Whether John had a share or not in the establishment of the Byzantine canon of Galenic medicine—the so-called "sixteen books of Galen" (Introd. 1, 480)—is uncertain. Various late abridgments of that canon date from the fifth and sixth centuries.

Philoponos is one of the outstanding personalities of the early Middle Ages, and his importance will probably grow as his work is more completely investigated. This will help us better to understand the transmission of knowledge from Alexandria to Baghdād.[11]

[9] U. Wogihara (ERE 12, 595, 1922) gave the dates 420–500, yet another Japanese scholar, Junyu Kitayama, writing twelve years later in his Metaphysik des Buddhismus. Versuch einer philosophischen Interpretation der Lehre Vasubandhus und seiner Schule (284 p., Stuttgart 1934), gives the dates 320–400, much closer to mine.

[9a] In a letter dated Atlantic City, May 18, 1947. This seems to be a correction to vol. 2, for my note on the Sefer yeẓirah appeared in Introd. 2, 367, but it really belongs to vol. 1.

[9b] The old mystics speculated a great deal on how this little planet of ours keeps its balance and stands without falling or collapsing. Is it suspended on a peg? Does it rest on a foundation? So Job says: The earth is suspended on a peg, but the peg is nothing. Proverbs says that Wisdom is the foundation.

[10] The question was surveyed by Max Meyerhof: Joannes Grammatikos (Mitteilungen des Deutschen Instituts für ägyptische Altertumskunde in Kairo, 21 p., 13 pl., 3 fig., 1 map, 1931; Isis 18, 447).

[11] Philoponos is somewhat neglected in Meyerhof's paper Von Alexandrien nach Bagdad (Sitzungsberichte der Preussischen Akademie, phil. hist. Kl., 43 p., Berlin 1930; Isis 16, 540).

The Arabic geographer Ibn Serapion (X-1) should be called Suhrāb.[12] The name Ibn Serapion, or rather Ibn Sarābiyūn, is due to an error in the British Museum catalogue. His Kitāb 'ajā'ib al-aqālīm al-sab'a (Book of marvels of the seven climates) is simply, in spite of its title, a new edition with but few additions and modifications of the Ṣūrat al-arḍ (Face of the earth) of al-Khwārizmī (IX-1). Both texts were edited by Hans von Mžik, the Ṣūrat al-arḍ in Leipzig 1926 (Introd. 1, 564) and the 'Ajā'ib in Vienna 1930 (Isis 19, 527).

Many personalities straddle the half-century divisions (as they would any other division which might be preferred); hence the notices concerning them might be removed to the previous or the next chapter.[13] This does not matter much if the student of any period is careful to examine rapidly, as he should, the two adjoining periods. Bibliographical notes are generally published in Isis under the same heading or period selected in the Introduction, even if the item belongs to another period. For example, apocryphal Hippocratic writings and articles devoted to them are generally placed under V B.C. though they may be much later. This is done for the scholar's convenience; it is much simpler to look for such items under one heading than under a great many possible ones.

Considering the size and complexity of volume 1, it contains very few typographical errors, or other lapsus. Two bad misprints must be mentioned: page 780, read Niẓām al-mulk (XI-2), not Nidhām; page 782, read Nathan ben Jehiel (XI-2), not Jeliel. Jehiel is the Biblical transliteration which I have followed throughout my work in order to accommodate it to the reader's habits; the correct transliteration would be Yeḥī'ēl (God lives). Page 335, the first title quoted under "General criticism" should be canceled, for it refers not to the Neoplatonic philosopher Porphyry (III-2), but to another Porphyry, bishop of Gaza from 395 to 420. There are few mistakes in the index: read diabetes, 77 (not 97), 307; level, 75; lever, 128, 170.

3. *Addenda to Volumes 1 and 2*

Addenda to volumes 1 and 2 have been published in the critical bibliographies of Isis, beginning with the nineteenth for volume 1 (Isis 8, 732–831, 1926), with the thirty-first for volume 2 (Isis 16, 476–584, 1931). The seventy-first bibliography, to appear in Isis volume 38, is now in the course of preparation. Using those bibliographies, it would be possible to produce greatly enlarged editions of volumes 1 and 2. This would not be as easy a task, however, as might appear on the surface. Indeed, it would not suffice to add mechanically the new notes to the old ones (though that would be very useful); in order to do a really good job, the additions should be integrated into the text, and this would require in each case a re-examination of the subject and rewriting of some sentences or paragraphs.

The rewriting of my volume 1 in the light of all these accumulated addenda and of my own increased knowledge and experience would probably take me more time than the original writing, and I prefer to spend my remaining years going forward, opening new paths, rather than cleaning old ones.

[12] On Suhrāb see Brockelmann (1, 227, 1898; suppt. 1, 406, 1937); A. R. Guest (Journal of the Royal Asiatic Society, p. 231, 1932).

[13] An extreme case is that of al-Rāzī (IX-2). The dates concerning him given in Introd. 1, 609, need correction; according to al-Bīrūnī (XI-1), al-Rāzī was born in 865 and died in 925. Hence, it would have been better perhaps to place him in the next chapter (X-1). Max Meyerhof: Thirty-three clinical observations by Rhazes, circa 900 A.D. (Isis 23, 321–72, 1935), including 16 pages of Arabic text. A sheet of corrections to the Arabic text can be obtained by application to G. Sarton.

A compromise solution would consist in publishing all the addenda in supplementary volumes, wherein the addenda relative to each page of the original text would be put together, page by page in their original order. Scholars using the original volume, after reading, say, page 735, would then take the supplement and find immediately the additions to that very page. That simple and excellent method has been followed by Henri Cordier in his Ser Marco Polo. Notes and addenda to Sir Henry Yule's edition (London 1920), and on a larger scale by Carl Brockelmann in the supplementary volumes to his Geschichte der arabischen Litteratur (1898–1902); three supplementary volumes, much larger than the original ones, appeared in 1937, 1938, 1942.

This would be very convenient but is not actually necessary. Bringing the whole work up to date by means of the Isis bibliographies would be an immense undertaking, but few scholars need the whole work. For one interested in a special topic, say, Ibn Sīnā (XI-1), it would not take very long after reading the article ad hoc in volume 1 and exploiting the indexes of the three volumes to consult the sections XI(1) in the bibliographies of Isis, from volume 8 down to the latest one. Somebody having the Isis volumes at his elbow could easily deduce from it, in less than a day's work, an elaborate Ibn Sīnā bibliography completing that given in my volume 1.[14] That bibliography would not be complete, of course, but it would be largely sufficient for a start and would enable the scholar to increase it and to come asymptotically nearer to perfection.

One serious warning must be added here, however. As every trained scholar knows (and superficial bibliographers forget), some of the best information on any subject is likely to be found in books devoted to larger subjects or even to other subjects. For example, valuable information on Ibn Sīnā might be tucked in a general history of Islam or hidden in a medical journal or a metaphysical treatise. How will a scholar find such items? Well, the other items listed in the Introduction and in Isis in the sections XI(1) might lead him to them, and he might find others by examining other sections of Isis such as Islam, Israel, Middle Ages, or astronomy, medicine, etc.

The first draft of his bibliography could be established in a few days; the completion of it by means of the autopsy of the items themselves might take any amount of time, months or years. Good bibliography is slow, very slow; any kind of good work is. Superficial lists can be collected easily and the use of various gadgets may conceivably increase the speed of collection and reproduction, but good bibliography implies the individual analysis and appraisal of each item, and no gadget will ever replace the operations of the human mind, except those which are mechanical and choiceless.

4. *Addenda to Volume 3*

The reader may exclaim, "Addenda to this volume! Is it a new volume, or not? Is it like a suit of clothes already mended and patched up before being worn? Why were the addenda not inserted each at its proper place?" That would have been much better no doubt, but one cannot always do the best thing, especially in times of war and chaos; one must be satisfied, here as elsewhere, with approximations.

A knowledge of how this work was printed may induce the reader to take a more lenient view of the matter. The manuscript was mailed to the Carnegie Institution

[14] By the way, in my volume 1 I failed to mention an important Avicennian edition by August Ferdinand van Mehren: Traités mystiques d'Avicenne (4 parts, Leyde 1889–99), probably because I did not then realize the value of those "mystical" treatises for the historian of science.

on October 8, 1943. During the time when it was being examined and edited for printing, I was able to make many corrections and even to insert or rewrite sundry paragraphs. I began proofreading on January 26, 1945. Many additional corrections were made in the galleys, but once the galleys were returned, no more corrections were possible or desirable except very small ones. It thus became necessary to prepare addenda separated from the text to which they refer. Their separation from the text is unfortunate, but it is better to have them where they are than not to have them at all. These addenda will be indexed and will thus be immediately available to any reader using the index with sufficient care.

The addenda piled up because of the extraordinarily long time consumed in the printing. Delays were due in part to the large size of the work, in part to industrial difficulties of wartime and to postwar readjustments. Moreover, a good many European publications which were not obtained, nor even known of, during the war began to stream in as soon as the war was over. The author was obliged to take them into account, although they reached him too late to be integrated into the main text, and sometimes too late even to be investigated and criticized. Some have not reached him yet, but at any rate, he has done his best to classify and communicate to his readers all the information which he could obtain. Other difficulties were caused by the fact that the capacity of Isis was much reduced and its publication terribly slowed up from the end of 1942 to the end of 1946. The editor's drawers are chuck-full of unpublished MSS. The author has drawn attention to some of these MSS, which will be published sooner or later, but this could be done in relatively few cases. That situation has been recently improved, and it is hoped to publish two volumes (37, 38) in 1947 and thus make up for lost time. Nevertheless, the contents of these volumes will not be incorporated in volume 3 as fully as would have been possible if they had appeared more promptly.

More addenda and errata to volume 3 will appear in Isis twice a year, beginning with the autumn of 1947. The first critical bibliography to include them will be the seventy-first, in volume 38.[15]

5. *Classification of Contents*

The reader may ask himself how much of this work is devoted to this or that field of knowledge. The following table will give him the results of a rough computation which I made to gratify my own curiosity.

Subject	*Pages*	*Percentage*
1. Historical background	55	3.1
2. Religious background	131	7.3
3. Translations	83	4.6
4. Education	30	1.7
5. Philosophical and cultural background	283	15.8
6. Mathematics, astronomy	171	9.5
7. Physics, technology, music	109	6.1
8. Chemistry	56	3.1
9. Geography	131	7.3
10. Natural history	105	5.9
11. Medicine	273	15.2
12. Historiography	164	9.1
13. Law and sociology	49	2.7
14. Philology	153	8.5
	1793	99.9

[15] Not the seventieth bibliography, in volume 37, as is stated below on page 27.

These figures are derived only from the main text (p. 37–1829). The addenda were not taken into account, but if they had been included, the percentages would hardly have been affected.

It would have been interesting to find out as well how many pages are devoted respectively to writings in different languages, such as Greek, Latin, Hebrew, Arabic, Chinese, Sanskrit, but that would require more time than I could afford. The relatively large amount of Greek and Chinese materials is illustrated indirectly by the size of the Greek and Chinese indexes.

The main value of the work, however, lies not in this or that part, but in the integration of all the parts. I hope that the medical or mathematical historians, the Hellenists or Arabists, using my book will not restrict themselves to their immediate needs, but will browse about and try to appreciate the intellectual life of the fourteenth century in its integrity.

6. *To Help and to Be Helped*

The author's main preoccupation has been always to be as helpful to other scholars as was possible, and this explains and justifies the awkward addenda printed at the end of the book and the others which will appear periodically in Isis. As Hippolyte Taine expressed it, "Le plus vif plaisir d'un esprit qui travaille consiste dans la pensée du travail que les autres feront plus tard."[16]

On the other hand, I much hope that other scholars will help me to improve my work by the communication of corrections and additions. I shall be especially grateful to the authors of books or papers relative to the fourteenth century if they will kindly send me copies of them. These will be listed in Isis in good order and be ready for eventual use in a new edition of my work in the fullness of time.

A scholar writes for two audiences. The first and larger one (the larger the better) consists of all the people who may be interested in the whole subject or any part of it and seek information. The second audience is, on the contrary, extremely small, and is made up of very critical scholars, working intensely each in his own field and keenly aware of its special difficulties. The first group may feel sometimes impatient with the extent and length of my investigations, and exclaim, "What an enormous book to be devoted to a single century!"; members of the second group are likely to complain of my superficial and high-handed treatment of their own favorite topics. Some of them could probably compose a large work devoted to the amplification of but a few pages of mine. They are right, but it does not follow that I am wrong. My purpose was to satisfy not one scholar, but the whole Republic of Letters, and this could not be done without sacrificing an abundance of details. In each case, I was careful to give the means of obtaining all these details, of elaborating my text ad libitum, and of proving, or disproving, my conclusions.

Next to doing one's work, there is nothing more pleasant than to hear it discussed and criticized by competent scholars, the true connoisseurs, who alone are able to appreciate its fine points, and who are generally ready to express with equal enthusiasm their agreement or their disagreement, their praise or their condemnation. These connoisseurs may seem at times a little too fastidious; they may be tempted to attach excessive importance to their pet ideas and make mountains out of molehills, but for all that, it is a joy to work for them; it is for them indeed that the author does his very best; it is because of them that he takes endless pains with

[16] Essais de critique et d'histoire, in the preface written for the second edition in March 1866.

regard to matters of which the general reader would hardly notice the presence or the omission, let alone the details. He is anxious to win their approbation and tries very hard to obtain it; it is from them that he expects the most severe and also the most useful criticism.

When such a brother scholar dies, the author is deeply bereft of him. Unfortunately, such bereavements have been often repeated in recent years. One after another, friends, colleagues, rivals, faultfinders (some of them all of that combined) have gone and left me full of sadness. Professor Edmund O. von Lippmann of Halle a.d.S. died sometime at the beginning of the war. In 1943, I lost my old friend and first Arabic mentor, the Rev. Dr. Duncan Black Macdonald of Hartford, Connecticut, and in the same year, Dr. Arnold C. Klebs of Nyon. David Eugene Smith of New York and Don Miguel Asín y Palacios of Madrid died in 1944. Max Meyerhof of Cairo, Henri Renaud of Rabat, Marie Tannery and Paul Pelliot of Paris, Joseph Bidez of Ghent died in 1945. They will not read this book, nor shall I benefit from their criticism. Yet, I hope that other friends and critics will eventually help me to correct it and to improve our knowledge of the fourteenth century.

GEORGE SARTON

Cambridge, Massachusetts
April 1947

CONTENTS

PARTS I AND II

PART I

The Time of Abū-l-Fidā', Levi ben Gerson, and William of Occam (First half of the fourteenth century)

CHAPTER I

CHAPTER I—*Continued*

PAGES

PART II

The Time of Geoffrey Chaucer, Ibn Khaldūn, and Ḥasdai Crescas (Second half of the fourteenth century)

CHAPTER XXVI

LIST OF ILLUSTRATIONS

For further explanations and acknowledgments of courtesies received, see the legends under the illustrations.

PART I

PART II

INTRODUCTION TO THE HISTORY OF SCIENCE

Volume III

Omnes ad quos haec eadem Historia pervenire poterit nostrae nationis legentes sive audientes suppliciter precor ut pro meis infirmitatibus et mentis et corporis apud supernam clementiam saepius intervenire meminerint.

—*Baeda Venerabilis*

(Historia ecclesiastica gentis Anglorum [731 A.D.].
Praefatio Baedae ad Regem Ceoluulfum*)

* Saint Ceolwulf, king of Northumbria 729–37, later monk at Lindisfarne, died 764, commemorated on January 15.

INTRODUCTORY CHAPTER

I. REMINISCENCES

The author of a work to which the best part of his life has been devoted may perhaps be permitted, as the end of it is in sight, to indulge in the pleasure and vanity of reminiscences. His recollections may interest the readers and, what is more to the point, may help them to understand the work and to make the best use of it.

Even in childhood my imagination was kindled by the great intellectual and spiritual deeds which men had wrought. I was thinking gratefully of the heroic men to whose efforts and sacrifices we owe whatever freedom we enjoy and whatever amount of truth has been placed within our reach. They had fought for every bit of that freedom and for the gradual discovery and unveiling of the truth. During my long university studies that enthusiasm became more precise yet more ardent, and soon after I had obtained my doctor's degree (in mathematics, Ghent 1911) the purpose of my life was determined. Not only that, but I knew already how I would try to attain it.

The purpose was to explain the development of science across the ages and around the earth, the growth of man's knowledge of nature and of himself. The means I thought of using were two, the creation of a journal devoted to the history and philosophy of science, and the composition of a manual wherein the main facts would be briefly recorded, together with enough bibliographical information to facilitate further studies.

The first of those means, being by its nature fragmentary, analytical, unsystematic, could be applied almost immediately. The program of the new journal, Isis, was circulated in November 1912 and the first number appeared early in 1913. Since then, its publication has been continued through thick and thin, though it was twice halted and jeopardized by the same merciless enemies. The first German invasion of Belgium stopped Isis from 1914 to 1919; the second German invasion, begun on May 10, 1940, prevented the international distribution of number 84 (completing volume 31) and the publication of volume 32. A journal defending the freedom of conscience and the integrity of thought was highly objectionable to the invaders, but they could not kill it.

The second of those means, implying the building up of a synthesis, required a very long preparation and could not be realized until much later. In 1911, however, my scientific knowledge was much vaster and sounder than my historical learning, and I was thus led to underestimate historical difficulties. This is a mistake common to most scientists; they know well enough how difficult it is to obtain valuable results in purely scientific (say, experimental) investigations, but, being ignorant of historical methods, they fancy that historical work is simply a matter of compilation; they would compare it to the latest stage of scientific research, whereas it should be compared to the whole of it. I visualized the possibility of writing an Introduction to the History of Science extended to 1900, which would be completed in about ten years and would fill two or three volumes. Sancta simplicitas. Such illusions are useful in that they make possible undertakings which would be discouraged if all the obstacles to their realization could be clearly seen at the beginning.

For many years I collected materials for my Introduction, unconsciously at first,[1] then more and more consciously. By 1912, my note-taking was systematized, and inasmuch as a relatively short Introduction was conceived, telling the story down to our own days, the notes steadily accumulated by me covered the whole history of science—everywhere--from the earliest times down to the twentieth century.

This labor was interrupted and almost wrecked by the German invasion of Belgium. It would have been wrecked but for the generous help extended to me by the George Washington University in Washington, D. C., then by Harvard University, and finally by the Carnegie Institution of Washington under the presidency of the mathematician Robert Simpson Woodward (1849–1924), of blessed memory.[2] The labor undertaken in Belgium was resumed, slowly and weakly at first in Washington, then more vigorously in the Harvard Library, where a room had been placed at my disposal. This enabled me to unpack my own library and archives and put them in working order. The first volume of the Introduction, entitled From Homer to Omar Khayyam, appeared in 1927; the second, From Rabbi ben Ezra to Roger Bacon (in two parts), in 1931; and this is finally the third (also in two parts), dealing with the fourteenth century only.

Note the slow progression, getting slower and slower, as was unavoidable, not only because the collection of materials for each volume had begun at the same time and hence more materials had accumulated for each volume than for the preceding one, but also because the advance was more difficult as I became more learned and more fastidious.

Volume 1, covering two thousand years, was a kind of wager, the very idea of which causes me to shudder. I could not write it now in double the time. Perhaps it is well that circumstances obliged me to compose it in a hurry, for this enabled me to reach more rapidly the three centuries (twelfth to fourteenth) to the exploration of which most of my efforts were to be devoted. To sum up, leaving out the years of unconscious or casual preparation for my task, the creation of volume 1 took nine years; that of volume 2, thirteen; that of volume 3, twenty-seven. At the time of beginning the final redaction of volume 2, I had already a complete set of articles (finished within their scale) concerning not only the twelfth and thirteenth centuries, but also the fourteenth and fifteenth. To measure the accumulation of materials in another way, it will suffice to observe that by the time of publication of volume 1, 27 numbers (almost 8 volumes) of Isis had appeared, including 18 critical bibliographies; by the time of publication of volume 2, 46 numbers (almost 15 volumes), including 30 bibliographies; by the time of publication of volume 3, 103 numbers (35 volumes), including 67 bibliographies, plus seven volumes of Osiris. The materials contained in the Introduction, Isis, and Osiris are integrated by means of thousands of cross references. Thus we may say that volume 1 was built on a foundation of eight volumes; volume 2, on a foundation of fifteen; volume 3, on a foundation of forty-two.[3]

[1] One of the notes used in this volume was taken by me as early as 1894, that is, half a century ago. Most of the notes, however, were taken during the past twenty-five years; a good many are quite recent.

[2] The work done under the auspices of the Carnegie Institution has been briefly explained each year in the Year Books of that institution, beginning with no. 18 (for 1919).

[3] It would be foolish to conclude that these three volumes are valuable in the ratios 8:15:42, for there are other factors than experience and learning to take into consideration. My learning increased calculably, but my moral qualities did not. I was probably as wise and honest in 1927 as in 1943, though I became gradually more conscious of my shortcomings, that is, more distrustful of myself.

It is now hardly necessary to explain why this volume must be the last. Working on the same scale, the completion of volume 4 (dealing with the fifteenth century) would cost me at least ten additional years, and more probably fifteen. At my age this would be tempting Providence. It will be wiser from now on to devote the remnant of my life to shorter undertakings, that is, the writing of various smaller books, which have been slowly maturing in my mind, each of which could be finished in two or three years.

Looking back to the dreams of my youth, the creation of a chronological survey of scientific efforts down to the twentieth century, to be followed by two series of complementary surveys (see Introd. 1, 34), I may seem to have failed egregiously, for my Introduction stops five centuries short of the goal. The scholarly reader will agree with me that it is better to do something as well as one can than to do considerably more less well. Other scholars will complete my task and may be able to do it much better.

The situation is even more tragic than appears on the surface, for my main interest as a young doctor in the mathematical and physical sciences was naturally enough modern science, particularly nineteenth-century physics.[4] I never expected to become a mediaevalist, still less an Orientalist, and my conception of mediaeval science was at first that of most scientists. I must have thought (I cannot be more precise, for I am unable to recapture exactly what my reactions to mediaeval science were in my days of ignorance) that a survey of mediaeval science could be carried through easily enough, and that like most historians of science I would simply jump from late antiquity to the sixteenth and seventeenth centuries (say, from Galen to Vesalius, or from Pappos to Descartes). Yet I was already familiar with the mediaeval studies of Pierre Duhem and the Byzantine ones of Paul Tannery, and, what is more important, I was determined to examine everything with my own eyes. My state of mind can best be compared to that of a naturalist who has undertaken to make a biological survey of a large territory, including waterless areas. If he were careless, he might hurry across the arid regions, or simply say "It is a desert," and abandon it to others; if he were more conscientious, he would want to explore the desert himself, and the chances are he would be astonished by the abundance and the tenacity of its denizens. My exploration of the Middle Ages obliged me to study Arabic and much else; I penetrated them as a young man full of misgivings, but found them so rich in ideas that I shall never be able to leave them.

Moreover, if I have failed to reach the Promised Land of my youth—the luxuriant meadows of modern physics—in my Introduction, this does not mean that I have been completely exiled from it, for Isis as well as my teaching in Harvard University has obliged me to make frequent excursions into it. I lived in the Middle Ages, to be sure, but spent many delightful vacations in the later centuries, even in the twentieth.

During the endless investigations which were necessary for the accomplishment of my purpose, I comforted myself with the anticipation of my pleasure when the hour of synthesis should finally ring. The ungrateful travail was only (for me at least) a means to that end—the putting together and comparison of the results, the drawing of conclusions. I was like a husbandman, applying himself for years to the care of his trees, thirsting for their luscious fruits, finding his only solace in

[4] Carnegie Institution of Washington Year Book no. 18, 347–49, 1919.

their vision. When the time of the long-delayed harvest finally approached, my joy was spoiled and ruined by the infinite miseries which fanaticism and cruelty were causing in Germany, Italy, Spain, and other countries of Europe. Then the war raised its ugly head. My work, which had been almost wrecked at the beginning by merciless enemies, was in danger of being wrecked a second time by the same enemies, assailing their neighbors under a new management. For a time I was almost discouraged. The day of Munich (September 29, 1938) marked, I believe, the absolute nadir of my life. Then followed the German invasions of Poland, of Denmark and Norway, of Holland and Belgium, the fall of France and Greece, the attack on Russia. In the meanwhile, China had been violated by other fiends. Pearl Harbor! The occupation of Further India and the East Indies. The slaughter taking place day after day on the plains of China and Russia. It is probable that my Asiatic and European friends envied me; it is certain that my situation was very enviable as compared with theirs. In spite of those calamities succeeding each other almost without a breathing spell, I could jog along and study; I need not fear any brutality, hunger, humiliation, imprisonment, or violent death; but it does not follow that I was free from care. I was terribly handicapped throughout those final years (the years of harvest, and presumably of joy) by the constant evocation of miseries which my body did not share. My body did not share them, to be sure, but my mind did it the more fully that it lacked the catharsis caused by physical pains; at times my heart was so heavy that nothing, not even my sweet labor, could console me.

I often thought of Emile Littré, obliged to end the superhuman work of his great dictionary during the war of 1870 (again the same enemies!) and the period of terror and mortification which followed.[5] Littré suffered more directly than I did, but his sufferings were more limited. He did not have to worry about the perversion of justice over a great part of the civilized world, nor about racial fanaticism, the imprisonment, subjection, humiliation, depravation, the fast or slow killing of millions of innocent people. Truly such horrors had not been witnessed in Western Europe since the Middle Ages, and if mediaeval people could be cruel at times, their barbarity was tempered by ignorance and impotence; German savagery was immeasurably increased by technical efficiency and by pseudo-scientific justifications. Corruptio optimi pessima.

Reading the accounts of mediaeval cruelty, say, the gigantic and inhuman deeds of Tamerlane, brought my mind forward to another Tamerlane, less virile but more cruel, if that be possible, and more hypocritical, whose exploits were related every day in the newspapers. Vice versa, when the papers described the miseries obtaining now in Europe because of wars and persecutions, I recalled the infinite distress caused or aggravated by the Great Schism. Consider only these two statements recorded by A. C. Flick (1, 342; 2, 440, 1930):

"Meyer[6] in his annals of Flanders, under date of 1379, said that it was impossible to give a true sketch of the perjuries, blasphemies, adulteries, hatreds, brawls, debauchery, murder, rapine, thievery, gambling, whoredom, avarice,

[5] He had begun proofreading in 1859 and finished it in 1872. If all the galleys (one set only) of the Dictionnaire de la langue française (without its supplement) were attached end to end, they would measure more than 37½ kilometers. The story has been very well told by himself, Comment j'ai fait mon dictionnaire (Etudes et glanures p. 390–492, Paris 1880). See also Léon Guinet: Emile Littré 1801–81 (Isis 8, 77–102, 1 pl., 1926).

[6] Jacob De Meyer of Bailleul (1491–1552), Flemish historian. See Biographie nationale de Belgique (5, 534–50, 1876).

oppression of the poor, rape, drunkenness, and similar vices. In Ghent within ten months 1,400 murders were committed in the brothels, gambling-houses, and taverns." ... "Luke Wadding[7] described Italy in the first part of the fifteenth century in these words: 'At that time Italy was sunk in vice and wickedness. In the Church there was no devotion, in the laity no faith, no piety, no modesty, no discipline of morals. Every man cursed his neighbour; the factions of Guelf and Ghibelline flooded the streets of the towns with fraternal blood; the roads were closed by robbers; the seas were infested with pirates ... The world was full of sorcery and incantations; the churches deserted, the gambling-houses filled.' "

Or else, the infamous trials of the Templars evoked similar perversions of justice and humanity committed in our own days on a large scale in many countries of Europe.

In short, I was living a double life, the one mediaeval, the other contemporary. The events of the twentieth century helped me to understand those of the fourteenth century and vice versa. Life would have become a very hell but for the redeeming presence in both ages of a number of brave men and women, champions of human rights, defenders of the human conscience, fearless investigators, saints and scientists. My story of the fourteenth century is of course largely restricted to that nobler though less obvious side of the picture, the heroism of good men.

My health broken by anxiety, I was afraid that I would not succeed in bringing my ship to its haven. This caused me to work at times with too much speed or fever. I hope that the final redaction has not been damaged by these worries. Should the reader detect any weakness here or there, I must beg for his indulgence. I would not deserve any except on this particular ground; I hope the reader will not have to extend it to me.

II. STRUCTURE OF THIS WORK AND HOW TO USE IT

Students who have been using volumes 1 and 2 know already how to use volume 3. New readers, however, may require some explanation. It will save them time and trouble to read this section.

Volume 3 is divided into two parts dealing respectively with the first half and the second half of the fourteenth century. These two parts are completely symmetrical. Each contains fourteen chapters, the first of which (chapter I or XV) is a synthesis of the thirteen others. These other chapters deal with: II (XVI), Religious background; III (XVII), The translators; IV (XVIII), Education; V (XIX), Philosophical and cultural background; VI (XX), Mathematics and astronomy; VII (XXI), Physics, technology, and music; VIII (XXII), Chemistry; IX (XXIII), Geography; X (XXIV), Natural history; XI (XXV), Medicine; XII (XXVI), Historiography; XIII (XXVII), Law and sociology; XIV (XXVIII), Philology.

The first chapters (I, XV) of each part are meant for consecutive reading; the other chapters, for consultation. The first chapters were necessary, not only for the sake of synthesis, but also because the classification of my materials in the other chapters was always somewhat artificial. Mediaeval scholars were not so specialized as modern ones; some of them were exclusively mathematicians or physicians, but most of them had many interests. Though the main note devoted to each scientist or scholar must be placed, sometimes a little arbitrarily, in a definite chapter, his activities in other fields must be recalled in the other sections.

[7] Luke Wadding (1588–1657), Irish Franciscan, historian of his order (DNB 58, 407, 1899).

The two synthetic chapters (I, XV) are also symmetrical. Each contains fourteen sections, of which sections II to XIV correspond respectively to chapters II (XVI) to XIV (XXVIII).

The reader wishing to have a general view of science and learning in the fourteenth century need read only chapters I and XV. If he were interested exclusively in mathematics and astronomy, he might restrict himself to chapter I, section VI; chapter VI; chapter XV, section VI; chapter XX. If he were interested only in Arabic (or Chinese) science, the table of contents would enable him to find easily the section of each chapter devoted to Arabic (or Chinese) science. The philological surveys in sections XIV of chapters I and XV would enable him to find documents written in a given language. If his interest were even more restricted, the index would help him to find what he needed. Of course, no index can meet every request, but readers must be prepared to interrogate ours in more than one way.

The survey chapters (I, XV), being summaries, are necessarily sketchy; while writing them the author has been sometimes obliged to simplify the account, but the index will make it possible in many cases to find additional information or precision concerning any given item. In spite of their general and recapitulative point of view, the survey chapters contain facts not included in the special chapters, for the simple reason that additional facts were often elicited in the final process of comparison and synthesis. Hence readers using this work as a dictionary, and consulting only the main note dealing with an individual scientist or scholar, do so at the risk of missing important data and of losing perhaps the best which the author had to offer.

The index to volume 3 is more comprehensive than those of volumes 1 and 2, for it contains at least one reference to each article of the whole work. For example: Archimedes (III-2 B.C.), I, 169–72; III, *x*; Roger Bacon (XIII-2), II, 952–67; III, *y*. The main note may suffice for the reader's purpose, but if he wanted to study, say, Archimedes, he should consult the indexes of the three volumes. Indeed, Archimedes flourished in III-2 B.C., but he influenced other men throughout the ages; his physical life ended in 212 B.C., but his spirit was resurrected each time another mathematician investigated Archimedean problems at their source. Perhaps the simplest way of putting it would be to say that Archimedes flourished from the second half of the third century B.C. on. He is still marching on today.

III. PURPOSE AND SPIRIT OF THIS WORK

The purpose of the whole work is to explain briefly, yet as completely as possible, the development of science and learning (systematized knowledge) throughout the ages everywhere. The present volume is restricted to the fourteenth century; it is a survey of science and learning everywhere in that century, a cross section of the intellectual history of mankind at the level XIV. Such a survey is necessarily incomplete and superficial because of its vastness. Yet every question has been investigated as thoroughly as was possible without jeopardizing the whole. Sometimes the study of a topic had to be abandoned without having been exhausted, when it was realized that a sufficient exploration of it would consume many years. That suggested the torment of Tántalos, a torment which the author deserved to some extent, because of his recklessness in attempting to describe and appraise the intellectual achievements of a whole century. Some subjects, however, have been dealt with pretty thoroughly; others are in different stages of elaboration as conditions of present scholarship permitted; in every case the student is given the available means of continuing the exploration himself. Good luck to him! Should his competent efforts lead him to new conclusions, even to conclusions discrediting or negating the author's, the latter would be the first to rejoice and to give the new conclusions full publicity.

Indeed, the purpose of this work is not simply to describe the knowledge attained or attainable today, but even more, while discouraging futile investigations, to stimulate profitable ones. It is clear that the necessary additions to our knowledge, the desiderata of today or tomorrow, cannot be clearly determined, or even sensed, before the available knowledge is properly mapped and measured.

Though the scholar attempting to survey the fourteenth century is unable ipso facto to attain as deep a knowledge of any single topic as the scholar devoting his life to the study of that topic, he is in a better position to understand the relation of that topic to every other, and may be able to suggest new ways of approaching it.

The author's point of view is that of the naturalist. To be sure, human history is infinitely more complex than natural history, but that is no reason why one should not try to tell the former as methodically and impartially as the latter. The fourteenth century is so far remote from our time that one should be able to analyze and appraise it without prejudice and without passion, or at least with some tranquillity. It is because of that point of view that much emphasis is laid throughout on strict chronology. Indeed, that is what the geologist or the palaeontologist would do. Every deed may influence later ones, it cannot possibly influence earlier ones; that much is certain, and in a sea of doubts we must avail ourselves always of that certainty.

The historian's duty was succinctly expressed a long time ago by the master humanist Cicero (I-1 B.C.): "Quis nescit, primam esse historiae legem, ne quid falsi dicere audeat? Deinde ne quid veri non audeat? Ne qua suspicio gratiae sit in scribendo? Ne qua simultatis?"[8] That duty is the same whether he deals with natural history or with human history, but its accomplishment is vastly more difficult in the latter case. It is relatively easy to treat atoms or stars, or even insects and birds, with impartiality, but it is not so easy to discuss the ideas of other men (however distant in time or space) without prejudice or to review their passions without passion. Indeed, a paradox is implied, for the historian cannot understand the feelings of other men unless he be capable of participating in those feelings (and those of their adversaries), yet he must keep himself under control. His conscience must be the last judge. His readers will not be able to help him, unless they be as well trained as himself; the average reader considers impartial any historian who shares his prejudices, and partial anyone who traverses them. Alas! that melancholy fact is true not only of individuals but of whole nations.

Political historians, it must be admitted, have seldom been unbiased. Many had a lawyer's mentality, rather than the integrity of the scientist. The task of the historian of science is much easier, for the prejudices of his heroes are rarer and their passions less violent. He must try to tell the whole truth without ambiguities or insinuations. Let Pontius Pilatus ask Τί ἐστιν ἀλήθεια; ("What is truth?" John 18:38); let metaphysicians argue endlessly about the meaning of truth; any honest historian knows the difference between a true statement, con-

[8] De oratore (2, 15): "Who does not know that the first law of history is not to say anything false nor to hide anything true? There should not be in the historian's account any suspicion of partiality or of animosity."

gruent with reality, and a false one, incongruent with it. Whether the lie be explicit or implicit makes no difference to him; it is a lie in either case; the subtlest lies and the least obvious are the worst.

To write without passion or prejudice does not mean to write without feeling. The author has not been afraid of expressing his feelings, indeed he has sometimes considered it his duty to express them; but his feelings are always unmistakably separated from the facts. Feelings which exist must be expressed in order that the reader may take them into account and be on his guard; to hide them or to rationalize them is not objectivity, but hypocrisy.

IV. THE PERIOD DEALT WITH: THE FOURTEENTH CENTURY

It does not quite suffice to say that this volume is restricted to the fourteenth century, for the reader has a right to know how the restriction was carried out. It is clear that the fourteenth century (or any other period) cannot be sharply detached from the rest of time. Such a separation, however necessary, is always artificial. For example, some scientists were born in the thirteenth century but died in the fourteenth, others were born in the fourteenth but died in the fifteenth. Some of the former ones have been dealt with in volume 2, and it was enough to refer the reader to those earlier notes. Others had been omitted from volume 2 because their main activities took place in the fourteenth century; their proper place was in volume 3, and the reader will find them there. As to the scientists who lived in both the fourteenth and the fifteenth centuries, a similar procedure has been followed except that in ambiguous cases the author has been tempted to give priority to the fourteenth century, that is, to include such men in this volume, being aware of his inability to prepare the next one. For the sake of compromise, some scientists of the early fifteenth century are not the subjects of separate articles in the technical chapters, but of shorter notes in the introductory ones (I, XV).

The difficulty of chronological cuts reoccurs continuously in a subtler form. In order to explain fourteenth-century thought, it is not enough to deal with fourteenth-century authors; one must deal as well with many authors of earlier times whose thought was still living in the fourteenth century. It has already been remarked that though Archimedes was killed in 212 B.C., his spirit is still living today. As a matter of fact that particular spirit was not much in evidence in the fourteenth century, but older ones, those of Hippocrates, Plato, Aristotle, Euclid were going strong. Mediaeval men were not chronologically minded, they spoke of Hippocrates and Aristotle in the same way as of their own contemporaries, and those ancient sages were indeed to that extent their contemporaries.

The earlier comparison with palaeontology may now be developed. The palaeontologist recognizes the emergence of new plants and animals at different levels, but that does not generally mean that organisms which originated at lower levels disappear. The older and newer organisms may coexist and often do. In the same manner new scientists and scholars appear in each century, but some of the older ones continue to exist or at any rate to function as if they existed. That is the real palingenesia litterarum. The "living" authors of each century are selected from among the authors of that time and of preceding times;[9] the most living, that is,

[9] This was shown very plainly in my investigations on scientific incunabula (p. 202–26, 1938), the authors of incunabula being listed in chronological order from the sixth century B.C. to the second half of the fifteenth century.

the most popular, those having the most readers or the best readers, are not necessarily the latest ones; their bodies may have been disintegrated for centuries. Therefore, mankind becomes greater and richer as it grows older, for the number of "living" thinkers and creative spirits is all the time increasing. Of course, that is even more obvious in the fields of arts and letters, where masterpieces are created for ever, than in the field of science, where even the greatest works are bound to be superseded by later ones. It is the scientists, not the artists, who "stand on the shoulders of giants."[10] Phidias, Sophocles, Michelangelo, Shakespeare, and Bach have lost nothing as the centuries pass, they seem as young as ever, and they grow bigger. On the other hand, the works of Hippocrates and Archimedes have long been replaced by better ones derived from their own. This statement may seem to contradict an earlier one, but it does not. The scientific results of the past may generally be neglected, for they have been incorporated into later ones; the scientific achievements, however, can never be superseded, and they keep their value eternally. Mathematicians have no technical reasons for reading Euclid, but they will never cease to admire him, and their appreciation of his genius is bound to increase together with their own knowledge.

References to science anterior to the fourteenth century are fairly numerous in this book, as they were frequently needed in order to account for the new creations; on the other hand, references to later ages had to be kept down to relatively few exceptional instances, otherwise there would have been no end to them. The opportunities for referring to the past were limited; those for referring to the future, unlimited. We had to bear in mind that our book might be entitled "Survey of the knowledge attained in the fourteenth century"; such a survey could not be complete without an account of the past out of which that knowledge had grown; it should not include the future of which it was to be the foundation, but which, however clear it may be to us, was then unpredictable.

According to some authors the fourteenth century is a part of the Middle Ages, or more exactly the beginning of mediaeval decline;[11] according to others it has the characteristics of a renaissance, it is the beginning of a renaissance or pre-renaissance. Such discussions are futile. Each age is a middle age, for it is included between two other ages, just as each generation is included between two other generations; it may thus be considered ad libitum as the conclusion of one age or the anticipation of another. Even so each age, if not restricted to too small a geographical area or too small a human group, is a very complex mixture of ups and downs. It always is a revival in some respects and a period of somnolence or sloth, of decline or regression, in others. Of course, if the Middle Ages have been formally defined as ending in 1453, or 1492, or 1543, or any date posterior to 1400, then the fourteenth century is a part of them by definition, irrespective of merit. To deny it would be just as foolish as to claim that John Scott, Jr., should not be called junior any more because he is sixty years old.

It is pretty clear, however, especially if one restricts oneself to the Western world and Latin Christendom, that is, to our world, that the fourteenth century was a period of unusual fermentation, of liquidation and chaos, and this becomes even

[10] Sarton (Isis 24, 107–9, 1935), R. E. Ockenden (Isis 25, 451, 1936), Raymond Klibansky (Isis 26, 147–49, 1936).

[11] These views have been well explained by the Dutch humanist Jan Huizinga: Herfsttij der Middeleeuwen (Haarlem 1919), Englished under the title The waning of the Middle Ages, a study of the forms of life, thought and art in France and the Netherlands in the fourteenth and fifteenth centuries (336 p., London 1924). For Huizinga, see Isis (26, 487–89).

clearer if one compares it with the thirteenth century, which was in many respects (not by any means in every one) an age of synthesis, of faith, of relative stability. In contrast, the fourteenth century is an age of incipient doubts, of restlessness and rebellion. Keep that image in mind without attaching too much importance to it, that is, without ascribing to it more truth than it can possibly hold. It may be helpful also to think of the whole Middle Ages as a period of secret fermentation and unconscious preparation, and if you do so, then remember that the fermentation increased considerably during the fourteenth century. The student of that century often feels that matters cannot go on much longer as they do, the frictions and pains are becoming unendurable, disruptions or explosions occur more and more frequently, a social metamorphosis is due sooner or later.

The reader will find in this volume many particular examples of the dissolution and fermentation which obtained in the fourteenth century. Limiting ourselves here to the most obvious and general cases, let us indicate briefly what happened in the religious, political, philosophical, and scientific fields.

The church faced one of the most dangerous crises in its long history, the gradual undermining of papal authority, the growth of discontent and anticlericalism within its own fold, the painful travail which, we now realize it, was leading slowly but surely to the Reformation. It is true that that irreparable schism could probably have been avoided if the leading churchmen had been wiser—as wise, let us say, as the cardinal Nicholas of Cusa (1401–64);[12] alas! the necessary prudence was denied them, and the schism tore the church asunder forever. At the beginning of the century Boniface VIII could still believe in his supreme power and say "Ego, ego sum imperator." It is typical enough of the changing times that his insolence was chastised, not by the emperor, but by the king of France. During the fourteenth century there are no great popes, no great emperors; the kings of France and England become relatively more important but none of them could be called a great king. The empire is disintegrating, and its center of gravity is moving eastward toward Bohemia and Austria. The two main pillars of Western society, the pope and the emperor, are giving way. It is true the sovereigns and lords are still keeping sumptuous establishments, their halls may be filled with courtiers, they travel and hunt in state, yet the glamour is tarnishing, gold changes to tinsel; more and more people see the show for what it is, their eyes open. Chivalry is making a brave face against the rising bourgeoisie, but it is on its decline. The contrast existing between its superficial delicacy and its inner barbarity cannot be hidden much longer. The false values upon which it prided itself and which constituted its defense as well as its glory are beginning to be recognized for what they are; those values are discounted, and it is chiefly for that reason that chivalry is on its way to doom. We should remember that wars were as endemic then as before, but new methods of warfare tended to diminish the importance of the knights and to increase that of the villains. Thus even war itself ceased to be the field of glory of the knights; they were less and less able to protect their own villains against other villains.

The communes are steadily growing in number, size, and power. The town walls are more important than the castle walls, and the town's belfry surges to heaven

[12] Witness Nicholas' treatise De concordantia catholica, written c. 1433 for the Council of Basel, and even more his De pace seu concordantia fidei, of 1453. He had been appointed a cardinal in 1448/9. About the De pace, see George Lincoln Burr: Selections (p. 378–81, Ithaca 1943; Isis 35, 147–53).

and competes with the seignorial dungeon and the church's steeple. The development of trades and industries causes a greater concentration of artisans and workmen and their organization in guilds. Labor troubles occur in many parts of Europe. The guilds try to obtain political rights and privileges, and they do obtain them, little by little to be sure and somewhat precariously, in Worms 1300, Liége 1302, Speier 1304, Ulm 1327, Mainz and Strassburg 1332, Augsburg 1368, Cologne 1370.[13] Parliamentary institutions are developing (chiefly in England), and many kinds of governments, regulations, and administrations are established by states, provinces, communes, or by free groups of traders or artisans. Under the growing resistance and the alternating knocks of so many adversaries—bourgeois, merchants, workmen, administrators and jurists, representatives of this or that institution—the nobility, whether lay or clerical, loses its grip. The fallacious unity which it has imposed upon the people is repeatedly broken, and sometimes chaos ensues. It is no exaggeration to say that waves of socialism were spreading over Western Europe in the fourteenth century. The unrest was enormously aggravated by natural and artificial calamities of exceptional size, such as the Black Death and the Hundred Years' War. The political and ecclesiastical armature of the feudal world was breaking.

The situation was not less critical, nor the unrest less disturbing, in the purely spiritual field. The church's troubles were not only ecclesiastical, political, financial, but spiritual as well. We might even say that those troubles were spiritual in the first place. A deep spiritual unrest had set in in Christendom long before the fourteenth century; for the two preceding centuries see the remarks made in volume 2 (p. 110–12, 280–81, 486–88, 712–14). The periodic insurgencies of Spiritual Franciscans, Flagellants, Penitents, Beghards, Lollards, and other kinds of ascetics are undeniable symptoms of the deepening illness. Men and women are ready everywhere to suffer incredible privations, imprisonments, torture, and death itself in order to vindicate their faith and redeem the church of Christ.

Aristotelianism had been Christianized by St. Thomas for the defense of theology, philosophy, and politics against the dangerous tendencies lurking in the folds of Platonism to the right and of Averroism to the left. There were also here and there danger signs of pantheism, imprudent criticism, skepticism, and even (very rarely) of agnosticism. While the new Aristotelianism was triumphing over Platonism, a new nominalism (Occamism) was gaining ground against realism; rationalism and experimentalism were increasing, slowly and intermittently, yet persistently. Dangerous ideas, or ideas which are considered dangerous, may be driven down, they can never be driven out. Consider, for example, the mediaeval vicissitudes of the atomic and evolutionary theories.[14] When scientific and rational ideas are hastily condemned as subversive, their progress is no longer visible at the surface, but it continues nonetheless underground.

Nothing can be more misleading than to think, as is so often done by thoughtless people, of the Middle Ages in general, or of the fourteenth century in particular, as a period of stagnation, repetition, and uniformity. Of course, matters of faith were generally accepted in good faith without reservation; in addition, there was a good deal of acquiescence in the authorities, for it was unsafe not to comply with them;

[13] Dates as given by Vanderkindere (p. 163, 1879). Similar dates could easily be quoted for other countries.

[14] For the first, see Mabilleau (1895), Pines (1936); for the second, Sarton's preface to Ashley Montagu's Tyson (Philadelphia 1943; Isis 34, 526).

but that outward conformity was offset by considerable individualism, open or secret. The conformity itself was restricted to essentials and left considerable scope to orthodox vagaries, keeping in the same fold without disturbance men as varied as Petrarca, Buridan, Eiximènis, and Geert Groote. Individual objections or discrepancies ran the whole gamut from right to left. The fourteenth century was a great age of mysticism. This is not surprising, because mysticism was the refuge of the choicest spirits, a refuge which was the more necessary that the times were harder.

Aristotelianism was used to bolster up the faith and to determine the limitations of reason, but it was used also to limit the faith itself. It was realized that faith did not have to be proved and that it was likely to be weakened rather than strengthened by indiscreet rationalizations. This gave science a chance of emancipation. Scientifically minded men dared to be more inquisitive and adventurous, they were more ready for experiments.

One of the main difficulties in scientific speculations is to state the problems, that is, to separate clearly some elements from the apparently inextricable context of reality. Nor is it enough to state problems, one must hit upon the right ones, those which are capable of being solved with the equipment at hand. Few problems could be unequivocally stated in those days, but incessant gropings around them helped to make their statement possible in later times. We realize this when we watch a man as intelligent and as well informed as Nicole Oresme, ahead of his time in many respects, yet bewildered by the abundance of foggy ideas which were circulating around him. Such ideas are not immediately useful, they are often confusing, yet it would be foolish to reject them outright; unclear ideas may be and often are all wrong, but they may be potentially right, we might call them then germinating ideas, which will become useful as they mature and clarify. They could never mature if they did not exist vaguely to begin with. We come across them repeatedly in treatises dealing directly or indirectly with mathematics, mechanics, astronomy, physics. The scholars discussing them seem to be turning in circles, yet out of their clumsy efforts will eventually emerge the new physics and the new astronomy of the seventeenth century. It is as difficult to write the history of such travail as it is to describe the conception and elaboration of a scientific idea in a single brain (the discoverer of that idea could hardly do it himself); it cannot be done completely, but only by way of general allusions. Early historians of science were tempted, in their ignorance and their bumptiousness, to consider the science of the sixteenth and seventeenth centuries as a continuation of ancient science, and so it was, but a continuation which would have been impossible or utterly different without the mediaeval gropings which intervened. Galilean physics is the climax of centuries of such gropings, and even the Newtonian fluxions and gravitation have mediaeval roots (whether Newton was explicitly aware of them or not does not matter much). The seventeenth-century mathematicians were generally well acquainted with Greek mathematics down to Diophantos and Pappos, and they believed in good faith that they were taking up the work where those ancients had left it. They did not realize how much they owed to the slow incubation of ideas which was the mediaeval indispensable contribution. This was hidden from them because Renaissance scholars had tried to obliterate the Middle Ages; that obliteration, whether conscious or not, continued in the field of art and letters until the Romantic age, and in the field of science until our very own.

The fact remains, of course, that there did not occur in the fourteenth century any discovery of such radical and trenchant nature that it created a cut in human thought. There was no annus mirabilis in the fourteenth century comparable to 1687 or even to 1637 or 1543. No apparent solution of continuity, which may be called a climax or a new beginning, as you please, for it is both. It does not follow, as so many ignorant persons think, that the mediaeval activities were sterile. That would be just as foolish as to consider a pregnant woman sterile as long as the fruit of her womb was unborn. The Middle Ages were pregnant with many ideas which could not be delivered until much later. Modern science, we might say, was the fruition of mediaeval immaturity. Vesalius, Copernicus, Galileo, Newton were the happy inheritors who cashed in.

The fourteenth century was a period of apparent chaos and confusion, of rebellion and misery, of doubts and searchings apparently fruitless, of material and spiritual unrest. The same definition might perhaps be applied to our own century, and the contrast obtaining between the fourteenth and thirteenth centuries is not greater than that between the twentieth and nineteenth centuries. The fourteenth century was a period of violent social transformations, yet some people already dreamt generous dreams and saw visions of brotherhood and democracy, of good citizenship, of pure religion freely accepted and followed, of material independence and spiritual toleration. Many of those dreams were bound to be squashed in the fifteenth century by a new kind of absolutism, royal and national, but such dreams can never be undreamt and unlearned, eradicated. We are dreaming them again now, more clearly and with greater confidence, for we are a bit closer to the goal. We owe our relative success in part to the unfortunate but necessary efforts of our mediaeval ancestors. We should be very grateful to them and very humble.

On account of the lack of technical means, mediaeval efforts were uncoordinated and inefficient; on account of the poverty or complete absence of communications, these efforts were localized and could never penetrate very far. In that respect we have a great advantage, but that advantage has to be paid for dearly. People often repeat nowadays that our world has become very small, because we can fly from one end of it to another in a short time. That is a legitimate way of looking at it, but another way, equally legitimate, would prompt us to say that our world is much larger than the mediaeval one. The mediaeval man could not be conscious of what was happening except in a very small territory; when news finally reached him from more distant places, it was already so old that it could hardly disturb him. On the contrary, we are able to know almost immediately what is occurring anywhere on the terrestrial globe, but this means that our sufferings are never interrupted, for we are made to feel every human misery wherever it may happen. Thus our social problems are infinitely more difficult to solve; it does not suffice any more to cure our own ills or those of our close neighbors, we can have no real peace until the whole world is at peace. That is an immense task, almost superhuman, yet it must be done, it can be done, it will be done.

V. THE SUBJECT DEALT WITH: SCIENCE AND LEARNING

Though the reader of this volume may be presumed to know its subject in a general way, it is worth while to define it more clearly in order that he may know more exactly what he may expect, and also what he should not expect, to find in it.

Science, that is, systematized positive knowledge, is different from philosophy and theology, and yet in the fourteenth century the separation is not always easy to make. Moreover, almost every philosopher or theologian was induced to discuss scientific questions; sometimes he was able to clarify those questions and, if not to solve them, at least to bring them nearer to their solution. In those days a man was considered especially learned and deep if he could discourse on such subjects as the infinity (vs. the finiteness) and the plurality (or singleness) of the universe, the reality (or nonreality) of universals, the relations between the persons of the Trinity; at present he is considered more profound if he deals with such recondite matters as the age, size, mass, and rotation of the galaxy, the number and size of extragalactic nebulae, the temperature of the sun and other stars, the expansion of the universe, the curvature of space and the length of its radius, the average density of matter in space, etc. Modern disputes are based upon definite observations, but they are not by any means free from speculation; mediaeval disputes were very largely speculative. It is not possible to make the reader understand those unrestrained speculators without saying something of their philosophical and theological activities. He is warned, however, that this book does not pretend to be a history of philosophy, even less of theology, and that my explanations and the documentation relative to them are incomplete. Enormous collections of documents or commentaries have been and are being published by the religious orders, the Catholic universities and seminaries. It was beyond my power to analyze these collections, and I did not attempt to do so. Nevertheless separate memoirs or articles are sometimes quoted, which became known to me occasionally, e.g., when the authors were thoughtful and kind enough to send me reprints. Following my usual method, I have mentioned all the information which had become available to me in one way or another. The reader should remember that reference to a paper included in a collection does not imply that the whole collection has been inventoried or even examined. Historians of philosophy or theology should not expect to find here full accounts of the questions which interest them most, but they may peradventure obtain information not available in their usual reference books.

Doctors in sacra pagina or in theology, rabbis, 'ulamā' were asked to give their opinions on all kinds of questions, not only religious and theological, but also philosophical, scientific, ethical, and social. On the whole they were perhaps better qualified to give such opinions than the Atlantic fliers and other celebrities whom newspaper reporters interview today. Their responsa or fatāwā were often deemed important enough to be carefully preserved and eventually collected, and such collections may contain valuable information for the history of thought. My book contains sundry references to them, but no attempt has been made to exhaust or analyze these forbidding sources.

Science is very different from magic and superstition, yet here again there are plenty of boundary difficulties and mediaeval men were not more consistent than modern ones. The same individuals might be rational at some times and irrational at others. They might exclude or try to exclude some superstitions and accept others. They might kick magic out of the front door and not realize that worse magic was coming back through the window. Should we cast stones at them? Was astrology a superstition, and if so, how much of a superstition was it? Was it wholly irrational? These questions have been considered so often in the body of this volume and the previous ones that they need not stop us again now. The best mediaeval minds as well as the worst were dominated by astrological ideas, though in a different way. Astrological fancies outlived the Middle Ages and, alas! they are still rampant today.[15] It is possible that the church encouraged some superstitions; it is certain that without its restraining influence superstitious practices would have been far more numerous than they were.

Special pains have been taken to explain the emergence of the experimental point of view. This is made difficult because, then as now, many people tended to confuse experiments in the vulgar sense with deliberate and critical experimenting. The distinction is obscured by the existence of an infinity of gradations between the one and the other. The art of experimenting developed very slowly and precariously. The early experimenters advanced somewhat like the dancing pilgrims of Echternach (three steps forward and two steps backward). Men of genius might occasionally make good experiments, but their method did not become explicit until much later. The vulgar sense is well expressed by the Arabic proverb "Is'āl mujarrib lā tas'āl ṭabīb," meaning "Ask the experimenter (or the experienced person), don't ask the physician." Empiricism, often of the crudest sort, was mistaken (and still is today by men lacking scientific training) for experimentalism. The Latin word experimenta, so often repeated in mediaeval recipes, illustrates the same confusion.

True experiments were exceedingly rare in ancient and mediaeval times, they continued to be rare during the Renaissance, they became more common in the second half of the seventeenth century and later. They more than anything else introduced modern science and modern life. The spirit of experimentation, such as it was in the fourteenth century, heralded a new kind of search for the truth, bolder, more adventurous, less inhibited by prejudices, and it made possible the emergence of a new kind of knowledge, mobile, active, dynamic. Where there is a struggle between two systems of knowledge, the one however large and venerable, but fixed, the other however small and contemptible, but growing with accelerated speed, the second is bound to win. That is exactly what happened in Christian Europe; the immense static knowledge of the past was challenged by the new dynamic knowledge—rare in the Middle Ages, more and more abundant later—and the static knowledge was defeated and driven out. Sound scientific knowledge, as derived from methodic experimentation, prudent induction, and restrained deduction, is essentially dynamic, it is always imperfect and knows itself to be so; it is alive, changeable, perfectible, never fixed, always moving in a definite direction.

There is, however, another side to the picture. One might think that mystics would be excluded from this book, but that would have been all wrong. The defenders of positive knowledge, weak and few as they were in the fourteenth century, tended to obscure the Platonic notion that knowledge is essentially incomplete

[15] Remember Kepler! his horoscopes and his De fundamentis astrologiae certioribus (Prague 1601). Among the theses discussed before the faculty of medicine of Paris, we find, as late as 1667, Berger's Est ne imperfectus qui astrologiam ignorat medicus?, and as late as 1707, Le François's Est ne aliquod lunae in corpora humana imperium? It is true both doctorandi answered the questions in the negative, yet it is significant that the matter had to be discussed on such formal occasions. Paul Delaunay: La vie médicale aux XVIe, XVIIe et XVIIIe siècles (p. 508, Paris 1935).

The doctoral thesis of Franz Anton Mesmer (Vienna 1766) was entitled De planetarum influxu in corpus humanum, and the astrological delusions conveyed by mesmerism are still working harm today. G. Sarton: Vindication of Father Hell (Isis 35, 97–105, 1944). Bart J. Bok and Margaret W. Mayall: Scientists look at astrology (Scientific monthly 52, 233–44, 1941).

without love and wisdom. The mystics, we might say, were (and continue to be) the guardians of wisdom. Their knowledge was not meant to supersede positive knowledge, but to perfect it. Thus it is not surprising to find in some of the best minds of mediaeval times mystical ideas combined with purely scientific ones. Moreover, mysticism was often a form of revolt—a revolt of love against indifference and tepidity, a revolt of originality and creativeness against stupidity, pedantism, administration, and routine; it often was a liberating influence. It indicated a new kind of knowledge, different from systematic knowledge to be sure, but like the latter alive, adventurous, dynamic. The mystic, then as now, reaffirmed a king of living truth against a dead or dying one. Therefore, we must take into account many mystics, not only Christian, but also Jewish, Muslim, Hindu, Buddhist, Taoist. Nor does it suffice to take them into account; we should be ready to give them the appreciation, the reverence, and the love which they deserve.

For all that, rational efforts were the most hopeful. Nothing is more certain than this: Men cannot be expected to agree with one another except on clear ideas and tangible facts. On the contrary, dark ideas which cannot be communicated to other people except with plenty of hocus-pocus on one side and credulity on the other—such ideas, however warm and generous in their intention, are bound to become sources of misunderstanding and distress. Obscure ideas are like troubled waters wherein some men may like to fish; the scientist prefers clear water and does all he can to clarify it if it be not clear enough. Obscure ideas are good means of enslaving and exploiting credulous people; in the long run they are not compatible with freedom and justice. We should not reject obscure ideas, but do our best to clarify them.

The history of science is to a large extent a history of rationalism, rationalism in action. It is a history of the gradual emancipation of men from superstition and ambiguities, a history of the growth of light in dark or darkened corners, a history of our salvation not only from lies but also from other evils, from servitude and intolerance. The mediaeval part of that history is meager in tangible results, but such results are not always a fair measure of the efforts. The difficulties which the mediaeval heroes of thought had to overcome were immense. Results are the fruit of all preceding efforts, not only of the latest ones. The triumph of modern science was partly due to mediaeval efforts.

A book like this one is necessarily incomplete in that it tends to direct the attention to relatively few individuals, separate from the mass of the people. This is unavoidable. Thinkers are rare at any time; even in our days, when scientists have become relatively so numerous, the majority of them are routine workers, not thinkers, not creators. Great men were very rare, they always are. There is an old saying that God creates a new contemplator of his work for each century; perhaps we might assume that he creates one for each cultural group, e.g., in the fourteenth century, Dante for the Christians, Levi ben Gerson for the Jews, Ibn Khaldūn for the Muslims, etc. The point remains that such "contemplators" are exceedingly rare at any time. The number of lesser thinkers is much larger, but even they are a small minority among the people. What about the latter?

To begin with, the mass of the people constitute the reservoir out of which men of genius appear from time to time. Men of genius do not belong to definite families; they do not succeed themselves like kings, for genius laughs at heredity and cheats it repeatedly, or seems to cheat it.[16] They may thus be considered as representatives of their social group or nation; they symbolize the potential goodness of that group.

The passions of men were very much the same in the fourteenth century as today. The men themselves were very much the same under their skins. A few saints, a few rascals, and a great mass of people who are good or bad according to circumstances; so it was, so it is, so it will ever be. This is an optimistic view, for it will always be difficult, if not impossible, to change human nature, whereas circumstances can be improved with relative ease and speed. The history of science is very largely a history of great men, but it should include some account of the institutions which help to lift up the standards of all men. Great men were not rarer in the fourteenth century than in the twentieth, but the old institutions (the church and the empire) were shaking and the new institutions (universities, parliaments, etc.) not yet sufficiently well established. It should be noted that the great men represent mainly the living group out of which they emerge, whereas the institutions, outliving many generations, represent the past as well as the present.

No attempt was made to write a social history, yet to the extent that great men are the best representatives of their time and group, this is a history of the people of the fourteenth century.

VI. FOUR GUIDING IDEAS

Readers of the preceding volumes know already that the author's thought is dominated by four fundamental ideas which run through his writings like Leitmotive in a Wagnerian drama. These four ideas may be briefly called (1) the idea of unity, (2) the humanity of science, (3) the great value of Eastern thought, (4) the supreme need of toleration and charity.

1. *The idea of unity.* The unity of nature must be postulated, for if it did not exist, if there were no inherent unity and consistency in nature, there would be no possibility of scientific knowledge. It must be possible to explain a cosmos, but chaos is essentially unexplainable. The existence of science and its astounding consistency (in spite of occasional, partial, temporary contradictions due to our ignorance) prove at one and the same time the unity of knowledge and the unity of nature. The fact that the building up of science has been done in the past and is done today by men of various races and many nationalities, inspired by different faiths, speaking different languages, proves that these men have the same needs and aspirations, reason in the same way, and, as far as they collaborate in the essential task of mankind, are united. Their collaboration has often been unorganized and unpremeditated, various efforts have been made here and there, then or later, without plan or design; yet inasmuch as every scientific effort aims at the same general purpose, all those efforts did converge and harmonize. The unity of mankind is an underlying reality which no civil war can obliterate.

The unity of nature, the unity of knowledge, and the unity of mankind are but three aspects of a single reality. Each aspect helps to justify the others. That

[16] The contradiction between this statement and what we know of heredity is more apparent than real. Let us assume that the offspring of superior people are more likely, let us say 100 times more likely, to be superior than the offspring of common people; the latter are so overwhelmingly more numerous that their total chances must be greater than the total chances of superior people.

trinity is but the dispersion of a fundamental unity, which is beyond our material grasp, but within our loving hearts.

2. *The humanity of science.* Science might be defined as the reflection of nature (of everything that is) by the human mind. Perfect science could be reflected only by a perfect, godlike mind. Human science is of course very imperfect, not only in the past, in the "darkest" ages, but even now and later; it will always be imperfect, but it is indefinitely perfectible. The imperfection of science is explained and to some extent mitigated by its humanity.

Scientific results are always abstractions, and they tend to become more and more abstract, hence they seem to lose their humanity. Such appearances cannot deceive anybody except hard-boiled scientists who care only for results or logical sequences. A scientific theory may be as beautiful as the Parthenon; both are equally abstract if you choose to look at them as they are and do not wonder how they came to be, but as soon as you investigate their genesis and development, the theory as well as the Parthenon becomes human, intensely so. Indeed, both were built up by men, both are primarily and almost exclusively human achievements; because of their humanity they touch us in a way no natural object could.

Science is as human as art or religion, neither more nor less. Its humanity is implicit; it takes a scientifically educated humanist to draw it out, just as it takes a musically educated humanist to draw out the humanity of music. The well tempered historian admires the achievements of science in themselves, but much more so in their becoming, that is, their humanity.

Science is not distinct from religion or art in being more or less human than they are, but simply because it is the fruit of different needs or tendencies. Religions exist because men are hungry for goodness, for justice, for mercy; the arts exist because men are hungry for beauty; the sciences exist because men are hungry for truth. The division is not as clear-cut as that, but it is sufficient to mark out main oppositions. Think of a triangular pyramid; the people standing on different faces near the base may be very distant from one another, but they come nearer as they climb higher. Bigots, little scientists, mediocre artists may feel very distant from one another, but those whose religion is deeper feel very close to the great artists and the great scientists. The pyramid symbolizes a new kind of trinity culminating in unity.

3. *The great value of Eastern thought.* The majority of historians have restricted their attention to Western achievements, and thus they have gradually evoked a conception of Western unity (at least spiritual unity) from which Eastern people were excluded. They seemed to assume a cleavage between East and West.

It is true they could not ignore the Eastern, Jewish, origin of our religion, but that was in their eyes a kind of miraculous exception. All else in our culture was considered Western; the synagogue itself had been superseded by the church, the Western Latin church, out of which all the churches of the West have developed.

We now know that the origins of Western science (not only of religion and art) are Oriental—Egyptian, Mesopotamian, Iranian—and it has been fully proved in the preceding volumes that the Arabic and other Oriental achievements were extremely important during the Middle Ages. Greek science (itself partly Oriental) could not have reached us as soon as it did without the help of Eastern dragomans. Those dragomans—Jews, Eastern Christians, Muslims—did not simply transmit to us the ancient treasure, they enriched it, they gave it a new vitality. I have proved that at least from the ninth to the eleventh century (three full centuries)

Arabic science was supreme. In order to understand mediaeval science and mediaeval thought one must explore the writings of many people, Western and Oriental. For the purely Asiatic traditions the main languages are Sanskrit, Tibetan, Chinese, and Japanese; for the Western tradition the main languages are Hebrew, Greek, Latin, Arabic. Note that even in the case of traditions which are more specially our own, one has to take into account two Oriental languages, Hebrew and Arabic. To judge mediaeval thought on the basis of, say, Latin writings only would be just as unfair as if our times were judged exclusively on the basis of the English or the Russian language; indeed, the unfairness would be greater, because the communications between one linguistic area and another were not as frequent, rapid, and complex as they are now.

During the Middle Ages the linguistic areas were naturally separated from one another as they will always be, but it is misleading to divide those areas into two main groups, Western and Eastern. Some areas to be sure were unmistakably in one of these groups, Latin or Icelandic in the Western group, Chinese in the Eastern one. Others were intermediary. The Greek territory was partly Oriental, the Arabic and Hebrew ones partly Western. Therefore, Arabic and Hebrew studies are not Oriental in the same sense as Sanskrit and Chinese are.

Greek books were translated into Arabic, Arabic ones into Latin, not for the sake of scholarly curiosity, but for practical use. Sometimes the original publications have disappeared, and we must then read Arabic texts to investigate Greek sources, or Latin texts to investigate Arabic ones. We may say that the mediaeval philosophy and science which concern us (Western people) most were written down and are preserved in four languages, Greek, Latin, Hebrew, Arabic; if we wish to go down to bedrock we must be prepared to read these four languages. The artificial classification, Eastern vs. Western, runs across the languages. A Latin text may represent an Oriental tradition, and an Arabic one may represent a Western tradition.

It has been proved in my Introduction with an abundance of detail that down to the fourteenth century the separation between East and West was artificial. It is true the separation between Central and Eastern Asia on the one hand and Europe, Africa, and the Near East on the other was much wider than that obtaining between Christendom and the Dār al-Islām, yet it was far from complete. There were Islamic bridges between the Near East and India, and Buddhist ones between India and China. There was no solution of continuity except for relatively short intervals. Some communities might be isolated (e.g., on islands or in the mountains), but none was completely isolated. The unity of mankind can be broken in some places and some times, but not everywhere and always.

Down to the end of the fourteenth century, Eastern and Western people were working together, trying to solve the same kind of problems; from the sixteenth century on, their paths have diverged, the fundamental if not the only cause of divergence being that the Western scientists understood the experimental method and exploited it, whereas the Eastern ones failed to understand it. Toward the end of the nineteenth century the divergence was extreme. We saw on one side engineers and mechanics together with physicians and missionaries, and on the other side "benighted natives"; that, I repeat, was the extreme division. Even in this connection the classification East vs. West, convenient as it might be to tough Westerners, was not quite correct. There were happily a number of Easterners among us, wise men who upheld mediaeval traditions, helped us to solve the many outstanding problems which are not patient of scientific analysis, and taught us to live well and beautifully. On the other hand, some native Easterners learned our mechanical tricks and were able to compete successfully with our best experimentalists and our most ruthless industrialists.

The Western choice made possible the fantastic development of science and technology; it might have been a pure blessing if it had not been so often divorced from wisdom and generosity. The triumph of science was overwhelming; as it often gave immense power to barbarians over good men, it ended by undermining the very basis of any culture. Everybody except the blind can see that very clearly today, but it is a thousand pities they could not see it more promptly.

The Japanese have adopted our methods and our materialistic point of view with a vengeance. The Chinese are adopting them more wisely. We may look forward after the war to a new period of complete unity as in mediaeval times, when Eastern and Western nations will work together, cultivating the sciences and their applications, but also the arts, above all the art of living. Let us hope—but perhaps this is hoping too much—that men of prey will no longer be permitted to use the applications of science for the enslavement of their fellow men. Perhaps the war calamities will help us to remember that science, however necessary, is utterly insufficient. We cannot live the good life with science alone, not even if our science were a hundred times better than it is. This introduces the fourth idea.

4. *The supreme need of toleration and charity.* No one can study the history of mediaeval science (or the history of science in general) without realizing the supreme need of toleration. Experimental proofs of this have been given repeatedly throughout the ages. Indeed, rulers, lay and ecclesiastical, have often tried to enforce creeds and opinions, and have not hesitated to punish offenders, sometimes with the utmost cruelty. They have often succeeded in killing or torturing thousands of people, but they have always failed in their main purpose. Intolerance is always destructive, not only of its natural and immediate victims, but of the oppressors themselves.

The root of intolerance is self-complacency, the belief that one is right, absolutely right, and that everybody else can be right only if he agrees with you without restriction. Anyone having such a belief will easily slip to the conclusion that it is his duty to oblige his neighbors, if necessary against their own will, to share his belief and its concomitant salvation. Mediaeval intolerance was essentially of religious origin, but it was sometimes extended to other fields, such as philosophy, politics, economics, even science itself.

The church was ever ready to persecute dissenters, not only among laymen, but even more among its own clerics. A long series of books were burned and men imprisoned or murdered during the fourteenth century. In addition to other examples mentioned in this volume, let me quote this general statement published by Victor Le Clerc (1789–1865) in his Discours sur l'état des lettres en France au XIVe siècle (HL 24, 7–9, 1862).

"C'est peu de renouveler l'usage romain de livrer au feu les livres condamnés, comme nous le voyons par les sentences exécutées contre ceux d'Arnauld, d'Amauri, et dans ce siècle, en 1303, contre des livres de magie; en 1323, contre le livre publié par un moine de l'abbaye bénédictine de Morigni; en 1326, contre le commentaire de Pierre Jean d'Olive sur l'Apocalypse; l'année suivante, contre les traités de Marsile de Padoue et de Jean de Jandun; en 1329, contre ceux du dominicain Eckart; en 1348, contre les hérésies enseignées dans la rue du Fouarre par Nicolas d'Autrecour; en 1361, contre les prophéties de Nicolas Janovez sur l'Antéchrist; en 1374, contre le 'Miroir de Saxe,' qu'un bref de Grégoire XI proclame 'exécrable;' en 1376, contre des opuscules de Raymond Lull; en 1382, contre les premiers ouvrages de Wiclef; en 1388, contre celui de Thomas de Pouille, etc. Les écrits du célèbre recteur de l'université de Paris, Guillaume de Saint-Amour, sur les religieux mendiants, après avoir été brûlés d'abord en 1256, durent l'être de nouveau, quand reparut, en 1389, le livre sur les Périls des derniers temps. Mais tous ces arrêts ne purent l'anéantir, puisqu'il fut imprimé en 1633, malgré la haine persévérante qui fit défendre alors, 'sous peine de la vie,' de le lire ou même de l'avoir chez soi.

"Il fut reconnu sans doute que ce vieil usage de brûler les livres proscrits ne suffisait pas, et on décida qu'il fallait, comme par anticipation du feu d'enfer, brûler les auteurs et leurs disciples. Ainsi périrent, en 1308, Dolcino, de Novare, qui prêchait la communauté de tous biens; en 1315, les Cathares d'Autriche; en 1319, à Marseille, quatre frères du tiers ordre franciscain, trois prêtres et un diacre; en 1322, à Cologne, Walter Lolhard, chef d'une secte de bégards ou de fratricelles; en 1325, à Girone, Durand de Valdac, bourgeois de cette ville, avec un de ses complices, déclaré bégard comme lui; en 1337,[17] à Florence, le poète Cecco d'Ascoli, et dans Ascoli même, Dominique Savi, auteur de prédications et d'ouvrages qui lui firent plus de dix mille disciples; en 1353, deux autres fratricelles, frère Maurice et frère Jean de Narbonne; en 1392, à Erfurt, quelques pauvres paysans, déclarés aussi bégards et béguttes.

"On brûlait plus rarement des femmes. L'usage était, quand on les condamnait à mort, de les enterrer vives. Nous ne voyons pas que Priscilla, cette fameuse Montaniste, ni la visionnaire Antoinette Bourignon, ni madame Guyon la quiétiste aient été menacées du bûcher. Le livre de Marie d'Agreda fut seulement condamné en Sorbonne. L'inquisition pontificale fut moins indulgente, en 1308, à Verceil, pour Marguerite, la compagne de fra Dolcino, qui, avant d'être brûlée, avait été écartelée sous ses yeux. On fit aussi expirer dans les flammes, comme plus tard Jeanne d'Arc, *in causa fidei*, par sentence inquisitoriale, Marguerite Poirette, originaire du Hainaut, que le chroniqueur appelle on ne sait pourquoi *pseudo-mulier*, qui avait soutenu, dans un livre écrit par elle, des doctrines assez semblables au quiétisme, et qui fut brûlée sur la place de Grève, *coram clero et populo*, en 1310, le même jour qu'un juif relaps, qu'il sembla tout naturel de brûler d'avance: *incendio concrematur temporali, transiens ad sempiternum.*

"On ne voudrait point voir sous le règne de Charles le Sage, le 4 juillet 1372, conduire en Grève pour y mourir dans les flammes, Peronne d'Aubenton, accusée par un inquisiteur et par l'évêque d'Angers, vicaire de l'évêque de Paris, d'être complice de l'hérésie des Turlupins.

"Jusqu'ici du moins nous voyons jeter au feu des laïques, ou des gens que le clergé avait quelque droit de renier, comme les fratricelles: peut-être y avait-il plus d'imprudence à brûler des hommes d'Eglise, tels que ce prêtre italien condamné en 1399, à titre de flagellant, quoique les flagellants eussent été d'abord encouragés par les franciscains, et même par le saint-siége. Mais ce dut être un grand scandale, quand furent suspendues au gibet dans un sac les cendres d'un évêque de Cahors, Hugues Géraud, dégradé, écorché et brûlé en 1317, à Avignon, par ordre du pape Jean XXII, pour avoir conspiré contre lui.

"Il fallut s'étonner aussi d'avoir à compter dans cette liste funèbre plusieurs religieux des divers ordres, tels que les templiers, victimes, en 1307, de l'accord du

[17] No, 1327.

roi de France et du pape, mais condamnés par l'inquisition, qui n'était pas aux ordres du roi. La papauté ne devait-elle pas épargner surtout ces ordres nouveaux qu'elle venait d'appeler à sa défense? Comment se plaît-elle à briser cette arme qu'elle s'était faite contre les dangers dont la menaçait la transformation du monde féodal? Nous verrons bientôt qu'elle fut sans pitié pour eux, et singulièrement pour les franciscains, quand, après un coup d'oeil rapide sur les papes eux-mêmes et sur le clergé séculier, nous aurons, comme c'est notre devoir, à retracer dans leur ensemble les services rendus aux lettres par les ordres monastiques.

"Pourquoi aussi les religieux, dans l'administration de leur justice claustrale, avaient-ils donné l'exemple de la barbarie des châtiments, qui peut déshonorer la justice même? Déjà Charlemagne avait réprimé les excès de quelques abbés, qui punissaient leurs moines en leur mutilant les membres et en leur crevant les yeux. Quand les révolutions du dehors pénétrèrent dans les monastères et que l'indiscipline les troubla de plus en plus, leurs chefs voulurent y opposer des peines nouvelles. On fit un tel abus de cette prison souterraine appelée *Vade in pace*, affreux cachot, espèce de tombe anticipée pour le prisonnier, qui n'y pouvait voir personne et n'en devait point sortir vivant, que l'archevêque de Toulouse, Etienne, s'en plaignit au roi Jean, et que le roi, par ses lettres patentes, transcrites aux registres du parlement de Languedoc à l'an 1350, ordonna que le coupable soumis à cette peine fût visité au moins quatre fois par mois; ordonnance que les religieux mendiants essayèrent en vain de faire révoquer. 'Certainement il est bien étrange, dit à ce sujet Mabillon, que des religieux, qui devraient être des modèles de douceur et de compassion, soient obligés d'apprendre des princes et des magistrats séculiers les premiers principes de l'humanité qu'ils devaient pratiquer envers leurs frères.' "

This long quotation might easily be enlarged if one added to it the many crimes committed in the very name of Christ in other countries of Europe, but it is more than sufficient. Even if one accepts the abominable doctrine that the end justifies the means, those crimes were not justified, for they did not attain their very purpose. They did not save the offenders, but they doomed to eternal punishment the persecutors. They did not save the church, but increased its peril and paved the way for the Reformation. In a long view nothing is more certain than the uselessness of persecution.

Should you want another experiment on a large scale, consider the history of Spain. As the reconquest proceeded, the kings and lords of Spain and their supporters became more and more impatient of dissent of any kind. Heresy-hunters, calificadores, improved their methods and became gradually more violent, more desperate, and more implacable; they finally ended in persecuting not only heretics and infidels (Jews and Moors), but even their descendants. According to the rulers, lay or clerical, who arrogated to themselves the right to incarnate the conscience of Spain, no one could be a good man without limpieza (purity of blood). The total result of their efforts was the material and spiritual ruin of their country. In spite of that colossal failure, their methods have been imitated in our own times in other countries of Europe; it is not necessary to be a prophet to foretell with almost complete certainty that the final result will be the same as in Spain, to wit, self-destruction.

For another gigantic example which began its sinister development before the end of the fourteenth century, we may now turn to China. The self-complacency and the stupid autarchy of the Ming emperors, and later of their Ch'ing imitators, brought their immense dominions to the verge of irretrievable ruin.

Nothing is clearer to me than that self-complacency and self-righteousness are necessarily self-defeating. Instead of which we should always—either as individuals or as members of a definite group, religious, national, or professional—be very humble and very gentle. Not only is intolerance an evil, but so is contempt of others. In particular, Christians who hate or despise other Christians or even infidels cannot be good Christians according to their own doctrine (Matthew 5:22). Such men are bigots and hypocrites, they are dooming themselves.

Science is unable to teach us toleration and charity, but the history of science (e.g., in the fourteenth century) gives us inductive proofs of their need. If we fail to love our brother and to be patient with him, if we cannot make the effort of understanding him but hasten to condemn him, our knowledge is of little account.

Without tolerance and mercy our civilization, whatever there is of it, is very precarious. Science is necessary but utterly insufficient.

VII. THE PRACTICAL VALUE OF HISTORICAL RESEARCH

The question has often been asked, "Does history teach anything?" We have just answered it. It teaches at least one thing, a very important one: that intolerance is not only criminal but stupid. Intolerance does not even serve its own purpose, which is to protect the group exercising it, for it seldom fails to jeopardize that very group, if not to destroy it.

The history of science proves the value of science for every individual and for society; it also proves the insufficiency of science.

To be sure, historians do not start out to prove such things, but the proof is implied in their recitals. Historical research can have no value unless it be carried out without prejudices, without any desire other than to find the truth (the most probable truth) and to tell it. Nevertheless, when a candid account is completed, it is the historian's privilege to draw conclusions, and such conclusions are true lessons, the lessons derived from the experience of our predecessors.

It is impossible to tell the whole truth, but in this volume special pains have been taken to consider each problem from as many angles as possible.

Our story is not a history of the fourteenth century as a whole, but simply a history of science and learning in that century. Hence it is largely devoted to men of good will, to men having essentially the same purpose as ours, that is, to find and vindicate the truth. These men were of many kinds, but they were all trying in their own ways and with their own genius and limitations to fulfill one of mankind's highest duties. They were the real builders of the new world which emerged from the fourteenth century.

The history of science describes man's exploration of the universe, his discovery of existing relations in time and space, his defense of whatever truth has been attained, his fight against errors and superstitions. Hence, it is full of lessons which one could not expect from political history, wherein human passions have introduced too much arbitrariness. Moreover, it is an account of definite progress, the only progress clearly and unmistakably discernible in human evolution. Of course, this does not mean that scientific progress is never interrupted; there are moments of stagnation and even regression here or there; but the general sweep across the times and across the countries is progressive and measurable. The history of science includes the most glorious, the purest, and the most encouraging deeds in the whole past. The development of knowledge is more tangible in certain fields (say, geography) than in others (say, sociology), but it is always relatively tangible, and the stretches of obscurity or fogginess, such as are met occasionally in the Middle Ages, are likely to be periods of incubation or pregnancy.

The history of science is above all a history of good will, even at times when there was no good will except in scientific research, and of peaceful efforts, even at times when war dominated everything else. A day will come when this will be realized by more people than now—not only by scientists, but by lawyers, statesmen, publicists, even by educators—and when such history will be recognized as the experimental and rational basis of international life, of peace and justice. The history of man's approach to truth is also the history of his approach to peace. There can be no peace anywhere without justice or without truth.

In the better kind of world, which we all hope will be the fruit of this war, the children will be expected to learn the evolution of mankind, and the development of science will be shown to be the very core of that evolution.

"Does history teach anything?" The history of science will teach men to be truthful, it will teach them to be brothers and to help one another. Is not that enough?

VIII. PRINCIPLES OF SELECTION

There is nothing to add to what was said in volume 1, pages 41–43.

IX. BIBLIOGRAPHIC BASIS

To the remarks made in volume 1, pages 39–41, it will suffice to add the three following.

References to volumes 1 and 2 are generally avoided, except that an indication like (III-1 B.C.) or (XI-2) after a personal name does not mean simply "first half of the third century B.C." or "second half of the eleventh century"; it also means that an article is devoted to that person at its proper place in volume 1 or 2. For persons to whom no article is devoted, time is indicated differently (dates of birth and/or death, floruit, or such a statement as "end of the thirteenth century").

References to the location of objects (such as MSS, rare books, paintings, or other monuments) are made with regard to pre-war conditions. Some of these objects may have been destroyed, displaced, or lost during the war.

It is probable that in this volume as in the previous ones the selection of bibliographical references has occasionally been too generous. That is, I sometimes hesitated to cast out a title which seemed negligible to me, because another person might make use of it. You may remember that Pliny the Younger, referring to his illustrious uncle Pliny the Elder (I-2), wrote, "Dicere solebat nullum esse librum tam malum ut non aliqua parte prodesset" (Epistolae III, 5). The wisdom of that remark has often been borne out in my experience, and hence I have tended to become more indulgent.

X. ERRORS OF THIS WORK AND THEIR CORRECTION

See volume 1, page 43; volume 2, page ix. In spite of every effort to avoid errors, there must be many in this work, for the opportunities for making them were innumerable. One of the first books I ever read, entitled "Mésaventures de Monsieur Touche-à-tout," described the accidents happening to a child who is too inquisitive and cannot keep his hands off things like matches, scissors, etc. I did not realize then that in the composition of a work like this one I should be obliged to be a Monsieur Touche-à-tout of the most inveterate kind, or, to change the metaphor and use a delightful bit of "turtle" slang, that I should be obliged "to stick my neck out" so many times that my chances of escaping unhurt would be very slim. The author of a monograph may be expected to know his subject more deeply than any of his predecessors, but this work deals with such an immense variety of topics that the possibilities of error are necessarily greater.

I have tried to collect relevant facts as completely and to tell them as simply as possible, and I have avoided generalizations, except in chapters I and XV, which are written, and which the reader is expected to read, in a different spirit. Even in those chapters, generalizations, impressions, side remarks are clearly given as such; the reader can easily disregard or discount them should he prefer to do so.

The very care bestowed on this work may be, alas! an additional cause of error. Indeed, when a book has been kept on the stocks for a long period of years, the author may be obliged to copy early statements of his, of which he does not remember the basis and which it has become impossible or very troublesome to recheck.

No one can make as many separate investigations as the author has had to make without becoming rather skeptical in many cases where younger scholars would be tempted to dogmatize. For example, it may be stated that such or such a text could not have been written by so and so, because it contains ideas different from those expressed in his other writings, or because it does not bear the "unmistakable" marks of his own style. The views and style of a man—a growing and living man, not a fossil—change repeatedly throughout his life; a great many examples of unimpeachable authority prove it, every man's own experience confirms it. The argument of consistency is a very weak one in a world full of inconsistencies, and yet critics repeat it again and again. They cannot help it; we should not discard that argument, but use it with prudence and without unnecessary dogmatism.

As years of analysis went by I became more and more cautious, and yet such phrases as "to the best of my knowledge," "as far as I know," "I believe that" will not be found often in this book. They are futile, for they should always be implied. Every statement concerning the past is subject to correction. It goes without saying that the opinions which the author records are his "final" and "best" ones, yet he does not claim that he is always right; the author does his best without being too positive about anything. He has more confidence in the inductions derived from thousands of facts than in any one of those facts. Indeed, the errors which may blemish some of those facts are accidental, not systematic, and we may assume that they do not pile up, but compensate one another to some extent. In spite of this, volume 3 is presented to the Republic of letters with more humility than volume 2, and especially than volume 1 (that volume being a kind of wager which a scholar would risk only in his days of innocence and would not dare repeat in his maturity).

Obvious slips (such as writing that Columbus sailed in 1942) are annoying—like a spot of grease on a new dress—but unimportant, as they cause no deception. The better a mistake is hidden, the more dangerous it is. It is the hidden mistakes which I am most anxious to ferret out and to publish.

I have always taken especial pains to publish and correct my sins, and maybe some of them will be forgiven me on that account. The necessary addenda and errata have been published as soon as known in the critical bibliographies of Isis, those concerning volume 1 in the nineteenth and following (Isis vol. 8 ff.), those concerning volume 2 in the thirty-first and following (Isis vol. 16 ff.). The corrections relative to this volume will begin to appear in the seventieth critical bibliography (Isis vol. 37).

Eleventh-hour corrections have been interpolated into the text, in the form either of footnotes or of bibliographic notes. These notes may contradict the text, or help a critic in contradicting it; nevertheless, they have been added in order to serve the reader as well as possible up to the last moment. The fact that such a last-minute insertion contradicts a previous statement, or refers to a publication which the author himself was not able to use for the correction or amplification of his text, has been generally left unmentioned, because that is clear enough.

The reader is asked to consider that this interlocking of Isis and the Introduction is a rare, and perhaps unique, example of integration in historical work. The Introduction is sufficiently massive and earnest to deserve and invite correction. The author will be very grateful to scholars who will kindly send him reprints of their publications concerning the history of science, or transmit their corrections, and the latter as well as the former will be faithfully registered in Isis for the benefit of the whole Republic of letters. Imperfect and incomplete as it must be, the Introduction is still the best instrument for its own emendation and eventually for its replacement by a better work.

XI. THE AUTHOR EXPRESSES HIS GRATITUDE

The thanks expressed in volume 1, pages 44–46 and volume 2, pages x–xiii are often repeated in the author's own heart but need not be reprinted here. It will suffice to enumerate his new debts, which are hereby gratefully acknowledged.

Dr. Mary Catherine Welborn worked with me from the end of 1930 to the end of 1938. After having helped in reading the proofs of volume 2, she undertook to revise many of the articles already prepared for volume 3. A few articles were entirely her own work; this is acknowledged in footnotes appended to those articles.

The new debts are as follows:

For Arabic, to Philip K. Hitti, professor in Princeton, and to Dr. A. R. Nykl.

For Chinese, to Dr. Alfred Kaiming Chiu, librarian of the Harvard-Yenching Institute; to my Harvard colleague James Roland Ware; and to L. Carrington Goodrich, professor in Columbia University. Though Dr. Arthur W. Hummel, of the Library of Congress, has been mentioned before, I am indebted to him for so many kind offices that I must mention him again.

For Georgian (as well as for Armenian), to my Harvard colleague Robert Pierpont Blake.

For incunabula, to the late Dr. Arnold C. Klebs, of Nyon, Switzerland.

For Japanese, to Dr. Shio Sakanishi, of the Library of Congress (now back in Japan), and to my Harvard colleague Serge Elisséeff.

For Korean, to my Harvard colleague Edwin Oldfather Reischauer.

For mediaeval matters I must reiterate my thanks to Lynn Thorndike, professor in Columbia University. We do not see eye to eye on the subject science vs. magic, but that is no reason (on the contrary) why I should not warmly recognize his great and enduring work. Many facts in this volume are derived from his patient investigation of MSS, most of which are now available to other scholars, in his precious collection of photostats and rotographs.[18] The records of the Mass written

[18] List published in Isis (21, 145–68, 1934), but the collection has been considerably increased since that time. Thorndike wrote to me on Dec. 15, 1943 that it numbered 222 items as against 155 in 1934. Large collections of microfilms are being made in America by the Library of Congress, the Harvard Library, the University of Michigan, the Mediaeval Academy, the Modern Language Association, etc.

by Guillaume de Machaut for the coronation of Charles the Wise (1364) were given me by my former student Mr. I Bernard Cohen.

For Russian and other Slavonic languages, to my Carnegie Institution colleague Dr. Alexander Pogo.

For Samaritan, to Dr. Theodor H. Gaster, of New York City.

For Sanskrit, to Paul E. Dumont, professor in Johns Hopkins University, Baltimore.

For Turkish, to my former student Dr. Aydin M. Sayili, of Ankara.

More specific acknowledgments may be found in the body of this volume in their proper places. Some correspondents to whom I applied to help me clear up special difficulties kindly sent me far more information than could be used in this book. It was sometimes very hard to keep to the straight (but not so narrow) path of the fourteenth century. Their generosity increased my temptations to digress, but I was generally able to resist them.

I obtained considerable assistance not only from the many Harvard libraries, but also from various other libraries in the Boston district, and from libraries in other cities, above all, the Library of Congress, the New York Public Library, the Yale and Princeton libraries, the American Geographical Society, the Jewish Theological Seminary of America, the Pierpont Morgan Library (these three in New York City), the Huntington Library in San Marino, California, the Cleveland Public Library, and others. Much information has been obtained also from museums, such as the Boston Museum of Fine Arts, the William Hayes Fogg Art Museum in Cambridge, the Metropolitan Museum and the American Museum of Natural History in New York, the United States National Museum, the Freer Gallery, and the Dumbarton Oaks Collection in Washington, the Art Institute and the Field Museum in Chicago.

My debts to the Carnegie Institution and to Harvard University are immense. I am especially grateful to Dr. James Bryant Conant, president of Harvard University, for the confidence he placed in me from the beginning. The greatest debt of all, however, and my first loyalty, go to the Harvard libraries, chiefly the main library, called Widener, and the depository of rare books, called Houghton. I am grateful to the librarian, Dr. Keyes DeWitt Metcalf, to the assistant librarians, and to every officer and servant, for the excellence of that treasure house is due to their individual and collective devotion as well as to its intrinsic richness.[19] It may be remarked incidentally that the increasing slowness of my work has been partly caused by the excellence of those libraries, for I felt bound to make the best use of them and have undertaken innumerable side investigations which I would never have thought of entering upon even in the richest European libraries. Sometimes I was thus caught in a kind of trap. I would try to answer a query with the idea that it would hardly delay me, but the solution of one difficulty led to another and "de fil en aiguille" a new investigation was started which might consume days or weeks. These are the joys and perils of scholarship.

[19] According to the latest census the Harvard libraries contained 4,608,862 volumes and pamphlets, duly catalogued. My own library, deposited in rooms 185–89 of the Widener (but not included in the Widener catalogue or census), contains some 3,460 volumes, 13,500 pamphlets, 80,000 cards, and a large quantity of other documents. This library, little as it is, is excellent for my purpose, and its practical value is enormously increased by the proximity and complete availability of the Widener and Houghton libraries.

Finally, I wish to give my best thanks to appreciative and cooperative readers: those who are ready to help me improve this work by pointing out its shortcomings, and also the readers who having found it useful have been generous enough to acknowledge the fact.

GEORGE SARTON

CAMBRIDGE, MASSACHUSETTS
HARVARD LIBRARY, ROOM 185
Thanksgiving Day, 1943

APPENDIX

NOTES ON THE TRANSCRIPTION OF VARIOUS LANGUAGES

These notes complete those published in vol. 1, 46–51; vol. 2, 100–4.

The use of an international phonetic alphabet[20] would seem to establish the required uniformity; but it would introduce endless difficulties. Not only would it require long explanations and cause every familiar word to become unfamiliar, but it would oblige one to consider the spoken language, which varies from place to place and from time to time. A name like Muḥammad is pronounced very differently in various parts of the Arabic world, but it is always written in the same way, and our transliteration enables one to recreate and visualize the original Arabic spelling and to find the name immediately in an Arabic dictionary. Let me repeat the principle expressed in vol. 1, 46:

"The supreme desiderata of any system of transliteration are consistency and simplicity. I have been guided always by the written language, which is relatively fixed, rather than by the spoken, which may vary considerably. That is, I have tried to write foreign words in such manner that the original written form might be easily reconstructed or found in a dictionary."

Only tyros imagine that a general system of transliteration can be devised. It is impossible to be consistent without unbearable pedantism. No matter what your rules are, you will be obliged occasionally to break them. When words have passed through many languages, all kinds of deformation have taken place, and it is a moot question which of the successive forms of the word should be crystallized.

The following languages are dealt with in alphabetical order: (1) Arabic, (2) Chinese, (3) Czech, (4) Greek, (5) Hebrew, (6) Icelandic, (7) Japanese, (8) Korean, (9) Persian, (10) Polish, (11) Russian, (12) Sanskrit, (13) Syriac, (14) Turkish.

1. Arabic

Vol. 1, 46; 2, 101.

2. Chinese

Vol. 1, 47. The Giles numbers have not been given in vol. 3, because the Chinese index in Chinese type printed at the end of the volume makes them unnecessary.

3. Czech

There are very few Czech words in this volume, and Czech letters have been used except when there would be no ambiguity or an English form of the word is generally accepted, as for the word Czech itself = Český. As the Czech alphabet is the same as ours plus a few letters distinguished from ours by diacritical signs, there is never great difficulty in consulting a Czech dictionary.

4. Greek

Vol. 1, 48. Inconsistencies are unavoidable in the modern names, when we must follow the usage of their own bearers. For example, Eleutheroudakis, Venizelos, or even Vénizélos.

[20] Otto Jespersen and Holger Pedersen: Phonetic transcription and transliteration. Proposals of the Copenhagen conference April 1925 (32 p., Clarendon Press, Oxford 1926).

5. Hebrew

Vol. 1, 49; 2, 102.

6. Icelandic

Vol. 2, 103. For modern Icelandic names see the remark made above concerning modern Greek names. No great harm is done when the Icelandic letters þoddn and eð are occasionally replaced by our th, which is sufficiently ambiguous to serve in both cases.

7. Japanese

Vol. 1, 49.

8. Korean

As the Koreans dealt with in this volume wrote only in Chinese and expressed their own names with Chinese characters, these names have been dealt with as if they were the names of Chinese people.

9. Persian

Vol. 1, 49.

10. Polish

Same remarks as for Czech. The Poles themselves have been so often inconsistent in their spellings of proper names in foreign publications that they can hardly expect us to be more fastidious. Letters with diacritical signs (such as the crossed l) are often classified in the dictionary as if those signs did not exist. There are but few Polish words in this volume.

11. Russian

Russian words taken from a Russian context are transliterated as explained in vol. 2, 104. The names of Russian authors of non-Russian books are generally left as the authors (or publishers) spelled them. The same author may have spelled his own name differently in various languages in order to conform to the phonetic habits of each language. For example, the name of the great story-teller Anton Pavlovich Chekhov. The six letters of the Russian family name became Tchékov in French, Chejov in Spanish, Cechov in Italian, Tchehov in Irish, Tschechow in German. The German transcription is the richest in letters; it almost doubles the number of letters of the original name!

12. Sanskrit

Vol. 1, 50.

13. Syriac

Vol. 1, 51.

14. Turkish

Inasmuch as there is now (since 1928) an official romanization of the Turkish language, obligatory in Turkey, it might seem best to use that transcription, for irrespective of its value it has the great advantage of being standard. This is what I would do if I were dealing only with Turkish matters and Turkish men.

Unfortunately, I have to deal at the same time with Arabic and Persian subjects, and this introduces many difficulties and conflicts. To begin with, it is not always easy in the fourteenth century to separate Turks from non-Turks. In the simplest case, that of a Turk writing in Turkish, his scientific works would likely have Arabic titles (even as vernacular works of Europe might have Latin titles). Thus I would be led to the contradiction of writing such a title in one way if the text of the book were Arabic and in another way if the text were Turkish. For example, the titles Tarwīḥ al-arwāḥ and Khulāṣat al-ṭibb would read, according to the modern Turkish spelling, Tervih al-ervah and Hulasat al-tıb. (The i in the last word, tıb, should be dotless.)

This would be very confusing, especially to non-Orientalists, and would give pleasure to nobody except a few Turkish scholars, who do not really need their own transcription, as they will have no difficulty in deducing it from my own, that is, if they have remained sufficiently familiar with the Arabic script.

Thus *ancient* Turkish names and words will be transcribed in the same way as Arabic and Persian ones, with the following exceptions: (1) To the Arabic letters and the four Persian ones (pē, chim, zhē, gef) must be added a purely Turkish one, sāghīr nūn (kāf-i nūnī), a nasal n, which I shall write in the Spanish way, ñ. (This letter is not pronounced or written in modern Turkish otherwise than the plain n.) (2) To the conventional Arabic vowels must be added a few others, as ö, ü, and e. You need them all in the name Ṭāshköprüzāde.

As to the names of *modern* Turkish authors and the titles of their books, they will be spelled just as they spell them themselves. I may recall that the modern Turkish alphabet has been devised primarily for phonetic purposes (every letter is pronounced and the form of the words gives one a good idea of their true pronunciation). Thus is the education of the children greatly facilitated, but at the price of breaking the continuity of the language. That alphabet is rich in vowels (8) but poor in consonants (20).[21] Thus khā, ḥā, and hā are represented by the single letter h; thā, sīn, and ṣād by the single letter s; dhāl, ẓā, and zai by the single letter z; etc.; moreover, hamza and 'ain (which the Turks and Persians hardly pronounced) have been eliminated, and hence the origin of words is sometimes difficult to discover, and the etymology of words including originally a 'ain is almost completely obscured. The phonetic purpose necessitated the creation of new letters not always available to Western printers, such as ö and ü (French eu and u), ğ (a very soft g, hardly heard; e.g., uğur = luckiness; pronounce ughur, the gh very soft), ş like sh in shoe, ç like ch in church (plain c, representing the Arabic jīm, is pronounced like j in jam). The greatest stumbling block to foreign printers and readers is the use of two i's, dotted and undotted. The dotted i is a long i like the Italian or French; the undotted one is a guttural y sound, as in ırmak = river, pronounced yrmak.

In spite of its practical value, the modern Turkish spelling is not acceptable to Western scholars in matters of transcription from Arabic script because of its many ambiguities; our spelling of Arabic, Persian, and Turkish enables one to visualize immediately each word in its original script; with the modern Turkish spelling this is impossible except if one is already familiar with the Arabic form.

[21] As compared with Arabic, but those consonants are sufficient for phonetic purposes. The new Turkish alphabet has simply recognized the fact that many Arabic consonants had become indistinguishable in Turkish speech.

PART I

The Time of Abū-l-Fidā', Levi ben Gerson, and William of Occam

(*First half of the fourteenth century*)

Dante:

Siccome dice il Filosofo nel principio della Prima Filosofia "tutti gli uomini naturalmente desiderano di sapere."* La ragione di che puote essere, che ciascuna cosa, da provvidenza di propria natura impinta, è inclinabile alla sua perfezione. Onde, acciocchè la scienza è l'ultima perfezione della nostra anima, nella quale sta la nostra ultima felicità, tutti naturalmente al suo desiderio siamo soggetti. Veramente da questa nobilissima perfezione molti sono privati per diverse cagioni che dentro dall'uomo, e di fuori da esso, lui rimuovono dall'abito di scienza.

(Beginning of *Il Convivio*, c. 1308)

Omnium hominum in quos amorem veritatis natura superior impressit, hoc maxime interesse videtur, ut quemadmodum de labore antiquorum ditati sunt, ita et ipsi posteris prolaborent, quatenus ab eis posteritas habeat quo ditetur.†

(Beginning of *De monarchia*, c. 1311)

Ma già volgeva il mio disiro e il velle,
Si come rota ch' igualmente è mossa,
L'Amor che move il sole e l'altre stelle.

(End of *Paradiso*, c. 1321)

*Reference to the first line of Aristotle's Metaphysics, "All men by nature desire to know."

†Compare with the quotation from Seneca (I-2) printed in volume 2, page 484.

CHAPTER I

SURVEY OF SCIENCE AND INTELLECTUAL PROGRESS IN THE FIRST HALF OF THE FOURTEENTH CENTURY

I. GENERAL BACKGROUND

As our readers may be expected to have some knowledge of the political history of the Middle Ages, a few indications will suffice to refresh their memories and evoke the atmosphere wherein science and learning could and did develop.[1] Political and economic factors are obviously important; we might even say that they are fundamental. Primum vivere deinde philosophari. If men are killed in battle or during the sack of a city, or if social chaos or tyranny starves their bodies or their minds to death, their spiritual intentions become futile. What chances did the people of the first half of the fourteenth century have of accomplishing their manly duty, the creation of spritual values? Well, let us see.

Let us turn first of all to Riome, which was still, at the beginning of the century, the head of Western Europe. We shall speak of the Jubilee of 1300 later, but that was a political event as well as a religious one. The same could be said of the bull Unam sanctam wherein Boniface VIII proclaimed in 1302 his political superiority over the lay rulers of Europe. Italy itself, papal and nonpapal, gave a good example of political chaos. Even Florence was torn asunder by quarrels between factions, the Neri and Bianchi. Its business was jeopardized by increasing labor troubles, and its international financiers, among the earliest of their kind, were driven into bankruptcy by Edward III's repudiation of his debts; the Peruzzi failed in 1343 and the Bardi in the following year. In spite of that chaos, during the first quarter of the century lived two of the noblest Italians of all times, Dante (1265–1321) and Giotto (c. 1276–1337), both Florentines. Who has done most for posterity, the Peruzzi or the Alighieri? the Bardi or the Giotti? Petrarca (1304–74) and Boccaccio (1313–75) had already shown their merit before the middle of the century. In the meanwhile, Rome had been deserted by the popes, misery and confusion grew there as well as in the rest of Italy. Remember the short-lived revolution of Cola di Rienzi.

In contrast with Italy, France was remarkably unified, and the king of France was becoming the most important ruler of Western Europe. In 1302, Philip the Fair summoned the first national representative assembly of France and defied the pope. It is true that in that same year occurred the Battle of the Golden Spurs, near Courtrai (Kortrijk), won by Flemish burghers and laborers over the French chivalry, whose "golden spurs" were found scattered all over the battlefield. This for a time secured Flemish democracy against the growing autocracy of the French kings. The heroic struggle of the Flemish people during the first half of the fourteenth century reminds one of the early battles of the French Republic at the end of the eighteenth. The Flemings were fortunate in having then a great

[1] Their orientation may be facilitated also by the use of Miss M. Morison's Time table of modern history, A.D. 400–1870 (oblong album, 160 p., 2d ed., London 1908), or by the excellent revision of Karl Ploetz' Epitome, "An encyclopaedia of world history," compiled under the direction of William L. Langer (1250 p., Boston 1940). Such books are as necesssary to historians as finders to astronomers.

and wise[2] leader, Jacob van Artevelde of Ghent (d. 1345). His politics was pro-English (he caused Edward III to assume the title of king of France in Ghent 1340), democratic, and "Belgian." Indeed, he tried to unite Flanders, Hainaut, and Brabant and thus to create a buffer state of sufficient strength, but could not overcome municipal, provincial, and class jealousies.

The establishment of the popes in Avignon (not within French territory, but within French power) began during Philip's rule and lasted almost seventy years ("Babylonian captivity"). The same monarch organized in 1307 the infamous trial of the Templars, their suppression, and the confiscation of their wealth. He might have said before Louis XIV (1655), "L'Etat c'est moi"; if he did not say that (any more than Louis, for that famous saying is decidedly apocryphal), he thought it and was sure of it. In 1328, Philip's family, the old Capetian line, came to an end and was replaced by the lateral line of Valois, Philip VI being the first ruler (against the pretensions of Edward III). This is the beginning of a new period, a sad one, in French life.

Spain was far from unified except against the Muslims, who had nothing left in the peninsula except the little kingdom of Granada. The victory of Salado de Tarifa,[3] won in 1340 by Castilians and Portuguese over the Moors, put an end to Moroccan interventions. The fate of the Naṣrī rulers of Granada was then sealed, yet they managed to hold their ground for another century and a half (until 1492, to be precise).

The main events in English history, outside those already suggested apropos of Jacob van Artevelde, are constitutional developments like the Confirmatio cartarum of 1297, the Carta mercatoria of 1303, the establishment of the Inns of Court under the three Edwards. The opposition to papal encroachments is steadily growing, especially with regard to provisions and annates.[4] In 1346 the English longbowmen won a great victory at Crécy (near Abbeville, Somme) over the French crossbowmen. In 1347 Calais was taken, to remain in English power until 1558. Artillery was used by the English probably at Crécy, certainly at Calais.

There was a long interregnum or civil war in the Holy Roman Empire (1314-30), Louis IV of Bavaria (Wittelsbach) being elected emperor in 1314 by one party, Frederick the Handsome of Austria (Hapsburg) by another party. Louis was backed by the German people and the leading publicists (Marsiglio da Padua and William of Occam); Frederick, by the pope. The latter excommunicated Louis and laid an interdict upon all cities supporting him. Nevertheless, Louis IV was finally crowned in Rome 1328 (lay coronation) and remained emperor until 1347.

An episode of the imperial civil war was the defeat of Leopold the Handsome at Morgarten 1315 by Swiss infantry. This was the first battle for Swiss independence, consecrating the creation but twenty-four years earlier (in 1291) of the Swiss Confederation.[5]

Two events of immense importance have not yet been mentioned, because they occurred toward the end of the period and cast their shadows over the following

[2] According to Froissart, who devotes considerable space to him.

[3] In the southernmost part of Spain, southwest of Gibraltar.

[4] Provisions were papal appointments to benefices before they became vacant; annates were the first fruits of those benefices, to be paid to the pope.

[5] The original members of 1291 were the three forest cantons, Uri, Schwyz, and Unterwalden. To these added themselves Lucerne in 1332, Zürich in 1351, Glarus in 1352, Bern in 1353. At the time of writing (May 1942), the small Confederation (650 years old) is still a beacon of light and freedom in devastated Europe.

one: the Hundred Years' War and the Black Death. The outbreak of the Hundred Years' War in 1337, and Edward III's coronation in Ghent 1340 as king of France, initiated a long cycle of misery and sufferings (1337–1453). The Black Death of 1348–49 devastated the whole of Europe. This gigantic calamity introduced a sharp discontinuity in the fourteenth century; it cut that century down to the midriff.

A few architectural achievements may help us to complete our general view of the Christian West. In 1304 the Cloth Hall of Ypres was completed. In 1312, the cathedral of Gerona. In 1324, the west front of the York Cathedral. In 1327, the Town Hall of Siena. In 1328, the Gothic lantern of Ely Cathedral. In 1335, the transept and choir of the Gloucester Cathedral. In 1350, the spire of the Salisbury Cathedral and the nave of the Glasgow one. This list could easily be lengthened, but it is sufficient for our purpose.

On account of his readiness to "collaborate" with the Tatars and his virtuosity in double-crossing them, Ivan I Kalita succeeded in increasing considerably the power of the Moscow principality. This Ivan Danilovich (1304–40) was a grandson of Alexander Nevski (1236–63, prince of Novgorod and later of Vladimir); he was duke of Moscow (1325) and grand duke of Vladimir (1328). He led Tatar armies against Russian princes, collected tribute from the latter for the Tatars, and used some of it for his own purposes (hence his name Kalita = moneybag); he succeeded in shifting the political center of gravity to Moscow—the religious center as well, for he transferred the metropolitan Peter from Vladimir to his own capital. The monastery of the Trinity (Troitse-Sergieva lavra) near Moscow, founded c. 1335 by St. Sergius, became under Ivan Kalita's rule (1325–40) the second religious center of Russia in antiquity and importance (the first being St. Sophia[5a] in Kiev, founded during the rule of Yaroslav the Wise, 1019–54).

The supreme ruler in the Balkans was the Serbian tsar Stephen Dushan (1331–55), who took full advantage of the Byzantine civil war to increase his own power. In 1346, he set up his capital at Skoplye[6] and proclaimed himself emperor of the Serbs, Greeks, Bulgars, and Albanians. He established a separate patriarchate at Ipek (Slavonic, Peč), not far from Novibazar. He ordered the preparation of a new code of law, Zakonnik (1349–54).

The sack of Constantinople by the Latins in 1204 and the Latin domination which followed it (1204–61) were terrible blows from which Byzantine culture was never able to recover completely. The deliverance in 1261 was followed by endless economic and political difficulties. In spite of all that, the fourteenth century witnessed a remarkable cultural revival. It was perhaps in the field of art that the renascence was greatest; indeed, the artistic renascence of the fourteenth century might be compared to those of the sixth century and of the ninth/tenth century. Was this due to foreign influences, Occidental or Oriental? To be sure, such influences were received, but the primary causes of a revival are always in-

[5a] We call the church St. Sophia, because it is not like Hagia Sophia dedicated to an abstraction, Divine Wisdom, but to a woman, the widow Sophia, mother of Faith, Hope, and Charity; the children suffered martyrdom under Hadrian (117–38); Sophia herself died three days later; her feast is celebrated on September 30. The cult of St. Sophia and her children is very popular in the Orthodox churches.

[6] That is the Serbian name; more people know it under its Turkish name, Uskub. The ancient name was Scupi; it was the capital of the Roman province of Dardania. On account of its having been the birthplace of Justinian the Great (VI-1), it was also called Justiniana prima.

ternal. The fact is that the empire of the Palaeologoi, in spite of its political weakness, was still one of the main strongholds of culture in the world. It was not progressing and it was encumbered with all kinds of superstitions and corruptions, but at its best its spiritual level was very high.

Oriental influences need no explanation, for Constantinople was always more than half Oriental. Occidental influences under the Palaeologoi might come from Italy[7] or from France, particularly through Cyprus and Rhodes. From 1192 on, Cyprus was ruled by the French family of Lusignan (after 1267, Antioche-Lusignan). In the fourteenth century the island was considerably enriched by international commerce;[8] some of the wealthiest merchants of the world were then established or represented in Nicosia and Famagusta; luxury and the corruption inseparable from it were prevailing among them. It was said,[9] "fastus gallicus, syra mollities, graecae blanditiae ac fraudes quae unam videlicet in insulam convenere." Such eminent men as St. Thomas Aquinas (XIII-2), Guillaume de Machaut, Philippe de Mézières (XIV-2), Boccaccio (XIV-2) worked for the kings of Cyprus or dedicated writings to them. As to Rhodes, it was never ruled by a French family, but it was taken in 1310 by the Knights of St. John of Jerusalem,[9a] and the majority of the grand masters were Frenchmen. Cyprus and Rhodes were the Oriental outposts of French culture, whence it radiated all around.

A new Turkish power appeared in the Near East, succeeding to the Saljūq (1037–1300) and destined to become even more redoubtable. The house of 'Uthmān emerged from obscurity at the very end of the thirteenth century, and during the first half of the fourteenth century its power remained restricted to a small part of Anatolia. The Turks penetrated Europe for the first time in 1345 upon the treacherous invitation of John VI Cantacuzenos, who gave his daughter Theodora in marriage to the second 'Uthmānlī sulṭān, Urkhān.

The main Muslim rulers in the Near East were the Baḥrī Mamlūk, who dominated Egypt and Syria. The reigns of al-Nāṣir Nāṣir al-dīn Muḥammad (1293, 1298–1308, 1309–40) constitute a golden age of Muslim art.

The first īl-khān to rule Persia was a grandson of Chingiz Khān (XIII-1), Hūlāgū, who sacked Baghdād in 1258. That powerful dynasty fizzled out at the very end of this period, with a prince (Nūshīrwān, 1344–49) bearing one of the most glorious names in Iranian history.[10]

While the sons of 'Uthmān were preparing to rule Anatolia, another Turkish dynasty was invading and dominating the best part of Hindūstān. Muslim rule in India goes back to the second half of the tenth century, and Turks often took part in the invasions of that country. The second Muslim dynasty of India, Khaljī (1290–1320), was Turkish. The Turkish dynasty which we have now in mind, however, is the one founded by Taghlaq or Tughluq, which lasted from 1320

[7] Flourishing Genoese, Venetian, Pisan colonies existed in Constantinople and the Archipelago. Members of the Palaeologos family traveled to Venice, Florence, Avignon, and contracted matrimonial unions with princely Italian families, such as Malatesta, Savoia, Monferrato (Diehl p. 741, 1926).

[8] See enthusiastic account by John of Mandeville (XIV-2).

[9] By a contemporary quoted but unnamed in Sir Ronald Storrs and Bryan Justin O'Brien: Handbook of Cyprus (9th issue, p. 20, London 1930).

[9a] Driven out of Acre in 1291, they first moved to Cyprus. From 1310 to 1523 they were settled in Rhodes and were then called Knights of Rhodes. From 1530 to 1798 they were in Malta and called Knights of Malta (Introd. 2, 160).

[10] The reference is to Nūshīrwān the Just, or Chosroës, the most illustrious Sāsānī ruler, 531–79 (Introd. 1, 435).

to 1412. The golden age of that dynasty was the reign of Muḥammad ibn Taghlaq (ruled 1325–51), whose empire extended so far southward that he felt obliged to move his capital from Dihlī (Delhi) to Deogīrī, which he renamed Dawlatābād ("the seat of government"; northwest part of Ḥaidarābād).[11] Muslim dynasties were flourishing all over North Africa, the Baḥrī Mamlūk in Egypt, the Ḥafṣī in Tunis, the Ziyānī in Algeria, the Marīnī in Morocco. Moreover, this period witnessed the climax of the Mandingo empire in the western Sūdān (i.e., Western Africa, main city Timbuktu) under the rule of Gongo Mūsā (1307–32). The religion and culture of that empire were Muslim, but the masses remained faithful to their naturalistic cults as well as to their native language.[12]

Thus in the fourteenth century Muslim power and culture extended over a large part of the known world: the whole of known Africa, the Near and Middle East, a good part of Central Asia, the best part of India. The Mongols, though largely Lamaists, were not unfavorable to Islām and did not put too many obstacles in the way of its diffusion in Eastern Asia. A number of splendid monuments scattered from the Atlantic to the Bay of Bengal, from Morocco to India bear witness to this day to the greatness and prosperity of the Dār al-Islām in the fourteenth century.

Under the pressure of repeated Muslim onslaughts, Hindu culture might have been almost obliterated in India but for the existence of the Vijayanagar empire. This had been created in 1336 by two Canarese (or Telugu?) brothers, Harihara and Bukka (d. 1376), sons of Saṅgama. They finally dominated a large part of southern India. Their capital, Vijayanagar (= city of victory),[13] became one of the most splendid cities of India; it was a center of Hindu resistance to foreign ideals and of Vedantic Sanskrit studies.[14] The Vijayanagar empire lasted until 1565, when the last emperor, Rāma Rāja, was defeated by Muslims at Tālikota and his capital utterly destroyed. Fragments of the empire continued to exist until 1646, and the present rāja of Anagundi (near the ruined capital across the river Tungabhadra) is a representative of Rāma Rāja. The prosperity of the Portuguese establishments was intimately connected with that of Vijayanagar; both fell together, never to rise again.

Vijayanagar was described by Niccolò Conti c. 1420, by 'Abd al-Razzāq of Herāt in 1442, and more elaborately by two Portuguese chroniclers, Domingo Paes c. 1520 and Fernão Nuniz c. 1535. The Portuguese chronicles were edited by David Lopes: Chronica dos reis de Bisnaga (213 p., 2 pl., Lisboa 1897). Robert Sewell: A forgotten empire (450 p., 15 ill., 3 maps, London 1900), including full translation of the Portuguese texts. S. Krishnaswami Ayyangar: Sources of Vijayanagar history (414 p., University of Madras 1919). N. Venkata Ramanayya: Vijayanagar. Origin of the city and of the empire (Bull. Department of Indian history no. 4, 196 p., University of Madras 1933). B. A. Saletore: Social and political life in the Vijayanagar empire (2 vols., Madras 1934). Vijayanagar sexcentenary commemoration volume (394 p., ill., Dharwar 1936), 32 essays. T. V. Mahalingam: Administration and social life under Vijayanagar (492 p., Madras University 1940).

[11] Agha Mahdi Ḥusain: The rise and fall of Muḥammad ibn Tughluq (300 p., London 1938). Reviewed by H. Dodwell (Bull. London School of Oriental Studies 9, 1117–18).

[12] H. Labouret (EI 3, 239–42, 1929). For the Mandingo language, Maurice Delafosse in Meillet et Cohen (p. 463 f., 1924).

[13] Modern Hampi, in the Bellary district of Madras. The ruins of the old city cover nine square miles!

[14] See my notes on Mādhava (XIV-2) and Sāyaṇa (XIV-2).

Many readers will be satisfied with the clear summary in V. A. Smith (p. 299–320, 1923).

The Yüan or Mongol dynasty ruled China from 1280 to 1368. It is thus co-extensive with our period, overlapping it generously at both ends. The Mongol empire was remarkably cosmopolitan and tolerant of foreigners and foreign ways, witness the accounts of Christian travelers, beginning with Marco Polo's; on the other hand, it was never popular with the Chinese themselves. Its first ruler, Kublai Khān (XIII-2), was by far its greatest one. The next in importance to us, though coming far behind him, was Ayuli Palpata, canonized as Jên Tsung, who ruled from 1311 to his death in 1320. Jên Tsung was a learned man; he re-established the Han-lin yüan and favored Buddhism.

In the meanwhile, Japan was completing or trying to complete its cultural independence from Korea and China. The Japanese language was used more frequently by scholars (instead of Chinese); Zen Buddhism combined with Shintō mythology became the favorite religion of unscrupulous soldiers. During the period called Kamakura (1185–1333), the military government seated at Kamakura (in Sagami, Tōkaidō) became far more important than the imperial court of Kyōto (in Yamashiro, Kinai). The military government remained in the hands of the Minamoto families until 1219; Minamoto Yoritomo, the first shōgun[15] of that clan, died in 1199; in 1219 the power was assumed by the Hōjō family, whose chiefs were shikken (regent) of the Kamakura shōgun. The Hōjō rule lasted until 1333; it was able to fight off the Mongol invasions of 1274 and 1281, but at a ruinous cost. Imperial power was restored in 1331 by Go-Daigo-tennō (emperor 1319–38). In 1336 began what is called the Ashikaga (or Muromachi) period, which lasted until 1568; civil wars continued throughout the fourteenth century, military brutalities being curiously blended with Buddhism of the Zen and Amidaist varieties.

Even as the Mongols had been driven out of Japan, they were driven out of Java by the Mājapāhit rulers, who created during the fourteenth century a Malay empire, extending over Java, Borneo, Sumatra, parts of the Malay peninsula, and the Philippine Islands. The capital was near the present Modjokěrto (in Soerabaja, Java) from 1294 to 1400. The culture was Hindu, the religion Buddhist. Many archaeological remains are gathered in the Modjokěrto museum. See note on Nāgarakṛitāgama (XIV-2), a Javanese poem describing Mājapāhit conditions c. 1365.

Encyclopaedie van Nederlandsch-Indie (2d printing, 2, 193, 634, 's-Gravenhage 1918). Bernard H. M. Vlekke: Nusantara. A history of the East Indian archipelago (Harvard University Press, Cambridge, Mass. 1943; Isis 35, 77), chiefly ch. III, Gajah Mada, founder of the Javanese empire, 1331–64 (p. 49–67).

Historians reading this summary and recognizing familiar names such as Crécy, Morgarten, or Salado de Tarifa, then coming across less familiar or outlandish ones, such as Skoplye, Mājapāhit, or Vijayanagar, may think that my selection is very arbitrary. Of course it is arbitrary; every selection is, but it is far less so than they may think. It might be argued that the author did not select the facts, but it was rather the facts that selected him. Indeed, the political events which have just been enumerated are those which forced themselves repeatedly upon his attention. They have been put together here in the hope of helping historians of

[15] Short for Sei-i-tai shōgun, commander in chief against the barbarians; dictator. Yoritomo was the first hereditary shōgun.

science who would certainly come across them sooner or later and would be unprepared to understand their implications and their relations. Enough has been said to put them on their guard and enable them to obtain without great difficulty as much additional information as they may need or wish for.

II. RELIGIOUS BACKGROUND

A. *Western Christendom*

1. *The government of the church*

Looking backward across more than six centuries, we realize that the Great Jubilee decreed by Boniface VIII in 1300 (Introd. 2, 823) was a sort of apotheosis of the mediaeval church, which then reached a climax never surpassed or attained in later times. The very success of the Jubilee tempted greedy popes to increase their frequency and to abuse the sales of indulgences, and thus undermined the church committed to their care.

Earlier popes had been obliged to try conclusions with their single rivals, the emperors, but in the meanwhile "nationalities" had been awakened and powerful nations such as France and England had risen.[1] The pope's authority was now challenged, not only by the emperor, but by kings whose power was gradually increasing while his was not. The first statutes of mortmain were issued in England in 1279, 1285, 1391, to prevent the alienation of estates to religious foundations. When Boniface VIII was raised to St. Peter's chair in 1294 he found himself confronted with two strong rulers, Edward I Longshanks (1272–1307) and Philip the Fair (1285–1314), as jealous of their prerogatives as he was of his, and equally determined to increase them at his expense. It will suffice to recall two final incidents. In April 1303 Boniface excommunicated Philip and prepared to depose him, but in September he himself was seized in Anagni by the king's men, roughly handled, and imprisoned.[2] The pope was rescued and brought back to Rome, where he died of grief soon afterward (October 11).

These events followed each other as swiftly as the crimes and deaths in a tragedy. The papacy never recovered completely from the blow of Anagni, and the Italian Boniface was the last of the Hildebrandine popes.[3] After him and his friend, the Italian Dominican St. Benedict XI, whose rule was but a brief interlude (Perugia 1303–4), St. Peter's chair was occupied by a succession of Frenchmen.[4]

The first of these, Bertrand de Got, was born near Bordeaux, in Guyenne, and hence was not a subject of the king of France, but he was easily won to Philip's

[1] Also smaller nations, which were equally vigilant in the defense of their material or spiritual freedom. For example, the Swiss Confederation (1291).

[2] "Veggio in Alagna entrar lo fiordaliso
E nel vicario suo Cristo esser catto
Veggiolo un'altra volta esser deriso;
Veggio rinnovellar l'aceto e'l fele,
E tra vivi ladroni esser anciso."
(Purgatorio XX, 86–90)

Alagna is the same as Anagni.

[3] The followers of Hildebrand, Gregory VII (pope 1073–85), who asserted papal supremacy.

[4] Elaborate accounts of their lives and writings in the Histoire littéraire de la France: Clement V, pope 1305–14, by Ernest Renan (28, 272–314, 1881); John XXII, pope 1316–34, by Noël Valois (34, 391–630, 1914); Benedict XII, 1334–42, and Clement VI, 1342–52, by Paul Fournier (37, 174–209, 209–38, 1936).

party. He was archbishop of Bordeaux at the time of his election (1305), when he assumed the name Clement V. The king and pope met in Lyon and understood each other very well (comme larrons en foire); Philip was the master mind, obliging his partner (e.g., in the trial of the Templars) to go much farther than the latter intended. Clement resided in Lyon, then in Poitiers; he could not return to Italy, yet wished to be a little more out of Philip's reach; therefore he established himself (1309) at Avignon, in the comtat Venaissin (which had belonged to the papacy since 1274). This was the beginning of the "Babylonian captivity," which lasted sixty-seven years (1309–76) and aggravated the downfall of the papacy. To be sure, the popes of Avignon were in their own territory; they were as independent of French power as the inhabitants of the free Vatican City are of Italian power. Clement made a brave show of freedom about some matters, but in essentials he was the king's creature. At the council of Vienne (1311–12) he abolished the Templars for Philip's benefit. If he was a weak and pusillanimous pope, he showed some interest in science and learning. He protected Arnold of Villanova (XIII-2) and William Corvi (XIII-2); through his bull Deus scientiarum (September 8, 1309, Avignon) he reorganized medical studies in Montpellier on Greek and Arabic foundations; in another bull, Inter sollicitudines, he discussed the teaching of Hebrew, Syriac, and Arabic as recommended by the council of Vienne (little came out of that); in another still (Vienne 1312) he defended Arnold of Villanova.

Jacques Duèse (or Duesa in Provençal) was also a secular, and came from Guyenne,[5] from Cahors, in the pays de Querci, where he was born c. 1244. He was a jurist and rose gradually in the hierarchy, becoming a cardinal in 1312. He was seventy-two years old when he was elected pope in 1316, yet governed the church with a firm hand for eighteen years. John XXII, such was his pontifical name, was a great administrator who centralized excessively the administration of the church, and especially its fiscality.[6] Much of his time was devoted to fighting heresies, repressing the Spirituals, that is, the radicals of the Franciscan order, and defending his prerogatives against the emperor Louis of Bavaria, whom he finally excommunicated. He was a learned man and a patron of learning. He favored universities in many countries and even helped to establish a Latin college in Ayās, Armenia (of course the purpose was propaganda but in a decent manner); he continued his predecessor's efforts for the teaching of Oriental languages. He deprecated vain scholastic subtleties. In spite of his zeal for orthodoxy, he was treated as a heretic by the Fraticelli and also by his opponents on the subject of beatific vision. Strangely enough, he was accused of being an alchemist, and a treatise on the subject was wrongly ascribed to him, De arte metallorum transmutatoria.[7] As a matter of fact he was strongly opposed to magic, and especially to alchemy, which he condemned implacably (Extravagantes communes, lib. V, lit. VI, De crimine falsi, year 1317) (HL 34, 417–20, 628). He died in 1334.

The third of the Avignon popes, Jacques Fournier, came from the county of Foix; he assumed the Cistercian habit, which he continued to boast when he was cardinal (in 1327); hence he was called the "white cardinal." He was pope for

[5] He was so much of a southerner that he never learned to speak French (langue d'oïl) well. In his old age (1323) he caused a letter written to him by Charles le Bel in French to be translated into Latin in order that he might be sure of its meaning (HL 34, 394).

[6] The people of Cahors—the Cahorsains—were renowned for their financial cleverness.

[7] It was also ascribed, equally wrongly, to another pope, John XXI, Peter of Spain (XIII-2). The French translation is entitled L'élixir des philosophes, autrement l'art transmutatoire des métaux, écrit en latin par Jean XXII (Lyon 1557).

eight years (1334–42) under the name Benedict XII. His main interest was the defense of orthodoxy and the unmasking of heresies. In his bull Benedictus Deus (1336), he condemned the views of his predecessor on beatific vision. His writings are restricted to Biblical commentaries (as Postillae super Matthaeum), sermons, treatises against the Fraticelli and Meister Eckhart, etc.

Pierre Roger, who succeeded him in 1342 under the name of Clement VI, ruled until 1352. He belonged to a noble family of Limousin and became a Benedictine, but being patronized by the French kings and popes he rose quickly in the hierarchy, was entrusted with various diplomatic missions, and was cardinal before he was fifty. He was a diplomat and a humanist, who embellished Avignon, befriended Petrarca, and patronized artists, a kind of forerunner of the Italian popes of the following century. He was interested in the reform of the calendar, about which see my notes on Levi ben Gerson, Jean de Meurs, and Firmin de Beauval. His writings are of no importance, but we know that during his theological studies in Paris he was strongly influenced by Thomas Aquinas, whom he defended publicly against Pierre Auriol and François de Meyronnes. In 1323, he received his master's degree in theology from the University of Paris, six years ahead of his time, upon the order of John XXII; a few weeks later St. Thomas was canonized. Thomism became the official philosophy of the church.

In order to appreciate the activities of these popes, it is well to bear in mind that the government of the church was only a part of their duties, and the defense of orthodoxy but another part; their main business, whether they liked it or not, was the defense of the church against the states—an endless struggle between churchmen and politicians, or rather between clerical and lay politicians, to which it was necessary at times to subordinate everything else.

To the credit of the papacy it must be added that it used its spiritual power to fight superstitions such as magic, astrology, and alchemy. That is, it stigmatized every superstition except those compatible with its own dogmas and traditions (e.g., intercession of saints, vicarious sacrifices), and hence it canalized the irrepressible love of the miraculous and kept it under control. As we have already indicated, the role of John XXII was especially conspicuous in that line; he denounced occultism, alchemy, and astrology (Thorndike 3, 18–38, 1934); Clement VI was equally outspoken against the mathematici and the philosophi naturales (HL 36, 236). To that extent the Catholic church fought for rationalism against promiscuous irrationalism; irrationalism was severely restricted to a few premises and to innocent rites and customs.

2. *The Crusades*

The Crusades are generally numbered from one to seven, eight, or nine, the last one being in any case that led by St. Louis and Edward I, which failed completely. The fall of Acre in 1291 seemed to close forever that kind of adventure. As a matter of fact the crusading spirit was quite strong in the fourteenth century, being fed and stimulated by a long series of pamphlets. That literature reminds us of the literature appearing today in defense of freedom and democracy. The evils are correctly seen, but the nations cannot be sufficiently united nor accept the common sacrifices without which victory remains elusive or precarious.[8]

Kings and popes, aided by publicists, were strong enough to organize new crusades—there were half a dozen of them in the fourteenth century—but they were

[8] This paragraph was written before Pearl Harbor.

not strong enough to subordinate divergent interests to the common good of Christian Europe. Hence all those crusades failed. An excellent account of them has been given by A. S. Atiya (1938).

We are interested not in the crusades themselves, but in the "propaganda" literature which prepared and discussed them. Most of the publicists were French or wrote for the king of France, for that country remained the main leader in that field. See my notes on Pierre Dubois, Guillaume Durant of Mende, "Brocard," Guillaume Adam, Pierre de la Palu: the first of these, a lawyer in the king's service; the second, a secular; the last three, Dominicans. To these Frenchmen may be added five Italians, Ricoldo di Monte Croce, Galvano de Levanto, Giacomo da Verona, Marino Sanudo il Vecchio, and Guido da Vigevano; one Westphalian, William Boldensele; one Catalan, Ramon Lull; and one Armenian, Hayton the Monk. The points of view of these men were not by any means identical, but there is no point in insisting here on their differences. Each of them explained in his own way the necessity and possibility of a new crusade and defended the methods which he thought to be the most efficient.

One may wonder whether propaganda literature circulating in the form of MSS, which were relatively rare, could be very effective. It was far more effective than we should imagine, because the literate people read less and probably with more attention than we do. Moreover, as each MS was rare, it was treated with greater respect than we treat our journals and books, and was used more thoroughly. One often speaks of mediaeval illiteracy and darkness, but one forgets that there prevails today a new kind of darkness or confusion due to excessive and thoughtless reading. There was no radio, but "the grapevine telegraph" was not an invention of the Civil War, it has functioned beautifully at all times and everywhere, especially when passions were aroused. Neither should we underestimate other forms of oral tradition—reading aloud, discussions, etc. The pilgrims were often, consciously or not, excellent disseminators of the crusading ideals.

There was counterpropaganda, but no effort was made to influence the enemy. That is, Christians were satisfied to reach other Christians, they did not try to undermine Muslim faith and morale with Arabic publications. Neither did the Muslims try to explain their case in Western languages.

3. *Trial of the Templars*

We have recalled above the violent struggle between Philip the Fair and Boniface, which ended in the pope's disgrace and death (1303). The king needed money and coveted the immense wealth of the Knights Templars. In order to be able to dispossess them, it was necessary to prove their indignity, but for a long time the new pope, Clement V, docile as he was, refused to abandon the order to the king's vengeance. Finally they compromised, the king promising to drop his attacks on the memory of Boniface VIII if the pope ceased to protect the Templars. This may seem an oversimplified statement of a very complex matter, but it is, I believe, substantially correct. One must not forget that the Templars were as greedy as they were rich. Renan speaks of them as of a gigantic camòrra (HL 28, 285). People were persuaded to bequeath their estates to the Temple for protection, and if poor they acknowledged themselves men of the order "pro commodo et utilitate et ad vitanda futura pericula." The Temple had the means of protecting its men against church and state. It is easy to see how readily their financial and spiritual power could be abused. It was abused. Nevertheless, the process which led to the suppression of the order was a gigantic miscarriage of justice. This was felt by some contemporaries as deeply as by ourselves, witness Dante's cry for vengeance (not later than 1319):

> "Veggio il novo Pilato sì crudele
> Che ciò nol saziä: ma, sanza decreto
> portar nel tempio le cupide vele.
> O signor mio, quando sarò io lieto
> a veder la vendetta, che, nascosa,
> fa dolce l'ira tua nel tuo secreto."
> (Purgatorio XX, 91–96)[9]

For another account, somewhat later, but still echoing contemporary reactions, see the De casibus virorum illustrium of Boccaccio, or Lydgate's Fall of princes.[10]

The persecution of the Templars and the parody of justice which it implied are comparable in many respects to the persecutions of the Jews which have taken place in Central Europe within our own time.

4. *Religious orders*

The only order of importance created in the first half of the fourteenth century was that of the Olivetans, which was simply a reform of the Cistercian order, a blending of Benedictine and Franciscan ideals, accomplished in 1313–19 by St. Bernard Tolomei, who died of the plague in 1348, a victim of his devotion to other patients.

The main religious conflict of the age raged within the order of St. Francis, between the more conservative friars and the more radical or enthusiastic ones, the Spirituals, Zelanti, or Fraticelli. That conflict spread far beyond the Franciscan walls, setting popes, theologians, and friars by the ears. It was even extended to the imperial court, where condemned Spirituals took refuge. It is an episode of the eternal conflict concerning the apostolic virtues and the counsels of perfection which Christ gave, and which Christianity has never been able to follow, even in the monasteries, very completely or for very long.

5. *Regulars versus seculars*

Another perennial conflict was that between the seculars (that is, the clergy) and the regulars (members of orders). That unavoidable conflict had grown considerably because of the immense success in the universities and elsewhere of those late-comers the Franciscans and Dominicans, or Friars Minor and Friars Preachers. Any theological or philosophical dispute might be (and often was) suddenly envenomed by such jealousies, or else by jealousies between rival orders.

We need not consider the effects of that rivalry on the religious life of the people; as to their intellectual life, it was largely led by regulars, who held chairs in the universities and had probably more time to think and write than the clergy. The seculars, however, were neither inactive nor mute. Their cause had been defended in the previous century by William of Saint Amour (d. 1272), Nicholas of

[9] The "novo Pilato" is Philip the Fair, and "ciò" in the second line refers to the imprisonment of Boniface VIII, for which see previous quotation from the same canto, footnote 2.

[10] For Boccaccio I consulted the princeps, Strassburg c. 1474 (fol. 143v–144v), and the only edition of the second version, Augsburg 1544 (book IX, ch. 21, p. 260–62). For Lydgate, Henry Bergen's edition (3, 979–82, 1923; Isis 33, 361).

Lisieux (fl. 1270), Gerard of Abbeville (d. 1271); it was defended again, among others, by Conrad von Megenberg and by Jean de Pouilli. The latter, however, was defeated by the embattled friars, condemned by John XXII, and obliged to recant in 1321. We have little pity for him, for he had no mercy either for the Templars or even for such a gentle soul as Marguerite Porrette.[10a]

Conventual life was often relaxed, sometimes to the point of immorality; this statement is borne out by a good many contemporary satires, the authors of which were not only laymen but also members of the clergy or monks. We shall come across a few examples of such texts, and more information has been collected by Coulton (vols. 2, 3, 1927, 1936).

6. *Biblical commentaries and homiletic writings*

Though I made no efforts to explore religious literature, I could not help coming across many writings occasionally composed by men of science or philosophers either for their own consolation or for the edification of others. Biblical commentaries are far too many to be quoted, for almost every clerk wrote some. It will suffice to mention a few examples.

One of the most remarkable specimens of religious literature is the "Ovide moralisé" composed at the turn of the century by the Champenois poet Chrétien Legouais. That French poem is more than six times longer than Ovid's Metamorphoses, which it purports to explain and to adapt to the needs of Christian readers. It is a splendid illustration of the clerical tendency to exploit pagan literature for Christian purposes.

Then let us consider two Franciscans, Pierre Auriol and Vital Dufour. Pierre wrote a conciliatory treatise on poverty, and two in defense of the Immaculate Conception (an idea especially dear to Franciscan hearts), but the most popular of his writings was a commentary on the Holy Bible, which was frequently printed under different titles. The Speculum morale of Vital Dufour was equally popular; it may be called a dictionary of Biblical ethics. It was also many times reprinted until the seventeenth century. The Benedictine Pierre Bersuire composed a work of the same kind which met with similar success, a fact which proves that there was then already a genuine demand for Biblical encyclopaedias. Bersuire's encyclopaedia was divided into two parts, the Reductorium morale and the Repertorium morale. Note the insistence on ethics; but the contents were more comprehensive than the title suggests.

I have kept the most important name for the end. The Franciscan Nicholas of Lyra was the greatest Biblical scholar among the Christians not only of his time but of the Middle Ages, and his Postilla litteralis (1322–32) was for centuries the outstanding book of its kind.

It is very remarkable that all the scholars named in this section are Frenchmen, for I selected them without regard to nationality, and it is only now that I realize they belong to a single country. To be sure, Biblical scholars existed in other countries, but the French were apparently more distinguished.

7. *Apologetic writings, especially those written against heresies*

We must expect to find many books written by clerks in defense of their church, and such defense is generally composed with reference to other churches. The apology degenerates very easily into an attack. Indeed, it has always been more

[10a] The name is written also Poirette and Porète (Biographie nationale belge 18, 60, 1905).

expedient to lead people by taking advantage of their prejudices, dislikes, and hatreds than by banking on their sympathies, for the latter are generally weaker than their aversions.

Thus there are numberless tracts written by Jews against Christians and (or) Muslims, or by Christians[11] against Jews and (or) Muslims, or by Muslims against Jews and (or) Christians; and within each religion other tracts are launched by each sect against the other sects. Some men are naturally keen on suspecting and denouncing nonconformities or heresies, and under the influence of theological disputations and of inquisitorial practice, that keenness was enormously developed. Thus even a pope might fall under suspicion. This happened to John XXII, himself a jealous searcher after difference and dissent, when he claimed that the saints would not enjoy the beatific vision[12] until the Last Judgment. He was ready enough to punish theologians who thought differently on the subject, but was promptly and roundly denounced by the University of Paris, the king of France, the emperor, and other such "defenders of the faith," who are the more anxious to demonstrate their orthodoxy, the more their own conduct is open to reproach and their own conscience apprehensive of punishment. John recanted in extremis (1334) and his views were formally condemned by his successor, Benedict XII, in 1336.

Scholars who feel called to defend their own faith, or more often to attack other people's faith, differ greatly. You will find among them the whole gamut extending from gentle apologetics to ferocious denunciations, or from love to hatred.

The most important treatise directed against a particular error is the one of Thomas Bradwardine against Pelagianism. At the first view the occurrence of this treatise may seem strange, for Pelagianism, after a long fight which occupied the first third of the fifth century, was refuted by St. Augustine and finally condemned, together with Nestorianism, at the council of Ephesos in 431. Pelagian "errors," however—that is, faith in man's soundness and perfectibility and in free will (vs. the Augustinian ideas of peccatum originis and grace)—are bound to reappear time after time, no matter how often they are beaten down. We may note in passing that one of the fundamental and irremediable differences between Western and Eastern Christendom was precisely of this kind, the Orthodox church affirming freedom while the Western one was dominated by Augustinianism.[13]

The German Conrad of Megenberg discussed the errors of Beghards and Beguines;[14] these good people gave trouble, often because of their lack of discipline, and sometimes because of their enthusiasm and their Lollard tendencies.

[11] The crusading propaganda literature reviewed in section 2 was naturally anti-Islamic. The leaders of anti-Islamic propaganda per se were Ramon Lull and Ricoldo di Monte Croce.

[12] This is not a metaphor, but a technical term meaning "the immediate sight of God in the glory of heaven, as enjoyed by the blessed dead" (Webster).

[13] In addition to references given elsewhere in this book, see R. G. Parsons: Pelagianism and semi-Pelagianism (ERE 9, 703–11, 1917).

[14] Semimonastic associations of laymen (Beghards) or laywomen (Beguines) which began in the Low Countries in the first half of the thirteenth century and developed considerably in the following centuries. They lived in communities but retained some property and independence, and took no final vows. Joseph Greven: Die Anfänge der Beginen. Ein Beitrag zur Geschichte der Volksfrömmigkeit und des Ordenswesens (243 p., Münster i.W. 1912). H. Hoornaert: Ce que c'est qu'un béguinage (quarto, 176 p., Bruges 1921), with drawings by Louis Reckelbus. Eugenie Theissing: Over klopjes en kwezels (thesis, 254 p., Utrecht 1935), "On beguines and bigots," in Dutch, dealing mainly with modern conditions. Dayton Phillips: Beguines in medieval Strasburg. A study of the social aspect of beguine life (264 p., Stanford University 1941; Isis 34, 278).

The Catalan Carmelite Guiu Terrena wrote against the Spirituals, but is best known by his Summa de haeresibus, a history and condemnation of many sects, more zealous than critical. To the Galician Franciscan Alvaro Pelayo we owe a similar work entitled Collyrium adversus haereses. The French Clunisian Guillaume de Montlauzun was primarily a canonist, yet he showed some interest in other religions and gave an account of Jewish and Muslim beliefs, as well as a biography of the Prophet.

The main work of the period, a masterpiece of its kind in mediaeval literature, was produced, as we might expect, by a Dominican, Bernard Gui. His Practica officii inquisitionis heretice pravitatis was mainly a treatise of inquisitorial procedure, but it included a large amount of materials and authentic documents concerning definite sects and individual heresies such as witchcraft. It records the trials and condemnation of almost a thousand people!

Its publication in 1323 is a landmark in the history of witchcraft, which it helped to define, classify, and repress. Witchcraft was rife in those days, and every political or ecclesiastical scandal was generously seasoned with it. Accusations of witchcraft were the best means of getting rid of disagreeable adversaries or of people whose thought was not sufficiently conventional.

8. *Criticism of the church. Early reformers vs. conservatives*

By far the most interesting facts and the most impressive are those which reveal the growing pains of the church, that is, the growth of the Christian conscience in spite of clerical formalism and of clerical abuses. These facts appear everywhere—in Italy, Spain, Germany, England, France. We shall consider a few examples in that order, but let us first examine a popular phaenomenon of international importance.

I am thus referring to the strange people called Flagellants (Flagellatores), representatives of a movement already dealt with (Introd. 2, 821–23) in its Italian form.[15] This was a popular revolt against unbearable pains and evils, which reached a climax (the revolt as well as the pains) at the time of the Black Death and soon afterward. It was condemned by Clement VI in 1349. The Italian Battuti were also called Laudesi, because of their poetic effusions, and their leading poet, one of the best of the Middle Ages, Jacopone da Todi, belongs to our period, for he died in 1306. The beautiful hymn Stabat mater is ascribed to him.[16] In the fourteenth century the Flagellants spread in the Low Countries, singing in Flemish, German, or French, and their morbid exaltation disturbed the lay and clerical authorities. Curious information concerning them is given by the Belgian chronicler Le Muisit (XIV-2), and their rebellious and heretical tendencies are proved in a number of documents collected by the great Flemish historian Paul Fredericq (1850–1920) in his Corpus documentorum inquisitionis haereticae pravitatis Neerlandicae (Gent 1889–1906) and other works. More documents are analyzed or quoted by Alfred Coville in the Histoire littéraire (37, 390–411, 1938).

To go to another extreme, consider the letters written by Petrarca wherein he criticized in beautiful but forceful language the popes of Avignon. The Flagel-

[15] See also Rufus M. Jones (ERE 6, 49–51, 1914).

[16] In both forms, the original one, Stabat mater dolorosa, and the derived one, Stabat mater speciosa. The original hymn is ascribed also to Innocent III (d. 1216) and to others. T. H. Henry (CE 14, 239–40, 1912).

lants expressed in their crude way the despair and disgust of plain people; Petrarca, in his elegant manner, the dissent of the humanists; they anticipated the more disorderly phases of the Reformation, whereas he was a forerunner of Erasmus.

Still another Italian voice, perhaps more redoubtable than any other, was heard in the Defensor pacis completed by Marsiglio of Padua in 1324. Marsiglio anticipated not only the Reformation, but even in some respects the French Revolution. One might be tempted to discount his violent criticism of the church because of his natural radicalism, and because he was a rebel, but in that year 1324 neither he nor his collaborator John of Jandun had yet fallen out of grace with the curia. Their first condemnation occurred two years later.

Moreover, if you impugn their evidence as inimical, consider that of the Spanish Franciscan Alvaro Pelayo, who was a man of influence in Avignon and the pope's own penitentiary; his De planctu ecclesiae was as severe a criticism of the church as any moderate reformer would have written two centuries later. He spared nobody, neither pope, nor monk, nor layman, and found evils and shortcomings in every part of the church's decaying body. It must be added, to the credit of the church, that the writing of that book was encouraged by John XXII.

Conrad von Megenberg wrote a poem bearing the same significant title, Planctus ecclesiae. It is far less comprehensive than Pelayo's treatise, as it deals mainly with the troubles arising from the conflicts between papal and imperial power, and between seculars and regulars.

English opinion is represented by two Franciscans, both of whom were very outspoken. Hugh of Newcastle was a defender of apostolic poverty, and he wrote a memorial against the sale of indulgences. William of Occam was one of the leaders in the opposition to the temporal power of the pope, and he showed up with special vigor the abuses of the Avignon court and of the ecclesiastic hierarchy. He is one of the main forerunners of the Reformation.

Though the popes were submitted to French influence, they found many of their most dangerous adversaries among the French clerks and laymen. We meet among the latter a new powerful class of enemies, the professional lawyers employed by the king to conduct his political machinations, very much as corporations today retain the best legal talent available to them in order to be able to play their game more successfully. The best specimen of this type was Pierre Dubois, a crafty, pettifogging, and not overscrupulous agent of the king of France against the pope, the emperor, the Templars, or anybody else who might be in his master's way or whose own place in the sun might appeal to the king's fancy. These tendencies led him to denounce the vices and abuses of the church without fear or mercy, and to suggest reforms of the most drastic type. The Dominican John of Paris used Thomism as a siege engine to undermine the papal power and lay bare clerical abuses. He was a herald of the Reformation in another more technical aspect, for he defended a theory of the Eucharist anticipating Luther's (impanation vs. transubstantiation or consubstantiation). To be sure, another Dominican, Hervé Nédélec, used other arguments out of the same Thomist arsenal to defend the pope's unrestricted power and clerical privileges in general and to fight the Spirituals. One of these, the Franciscan Bernard Délicieux, having witnessed inquisitorial evils in Languedoc, became an outspoken enemy of the system which made such iniquities possible. Here we have a forerunner not of the Reformers, who could be as intolerant and fanatical as Catholic inquisitors, but of the liberal-minded people of our own days, like Paul Fredericq, Henry Charles Lea, George Gordon Coulton, and others, who place truth and justice above creed and party.

Finally, consider two men as moderate as the Benedictine Pierre Bersuire, who spent five years in Avignon and was not blind to the goings on in and about the palace, or the younger Guillaume Durant, bishop of Mende, who criticized the shortcomings of the Avignonese court and of the clergy and the abuses in the sale of indulgences, and suggested reforms from top to bottom.

The mass of these criticisms originating from many countries and all kinds of people is impressive enough, especially when we find them confirmed by the vox populi as expressed in contemporary literature, or in the sayings of simple pious men who had no ax to grind, except that they suffered from the church evils as they would have suffered from family ones. Read the Roman de la rose of John of Meung (XIII-2), who lived until 1305, and you will be surprised by the occasional outspokenness against the church. We may say more generally that a certain amount of anticlericalism is an ordinary ingredient of the lay literature of the fourteenth century; this will be even more true of the second half of the century than of the first. The tendency grows as the church becomes more corrupt, yet more obstinate against the very suggestion of reform.

Some of the best examples of that tendency are found in the story of St. Louis completed by Joinville in his old age, in 1305–9. We read (§670 of the text edited by Natalis de Wailly) that the bishop Guy of Auxerre declared to the king in the name of all the other bishops, "Sire, Christendom is decaying and getting lost in your hands, and it will decay even more if you do not take care, for nobody today fears excommunication." I suppose that many bishops have felt obliged to give such warnings to their lay rulers, especially in our unbelieving days, but note that Guy's statement was made before 1270,[17] that is, in the so-called age of faith! But by 1270 the climax was already passed, and, as Coulton has wisely remarked (p. 458, 1938b), the Middle Ages was an age of acquiescence rather than an age of faith. Joinville tells the story (§445) of an old woman who was seen in Acre crossing the street holding in her right hand a chafing dish full of live charcoal and in her left a flask of water. Friar Yves asked her, "What are you carrying these for?" She answered, "I mean to burn paradise with the one and to quench hell fire with the other." "Why?" said he. "So that no man might henceforth do right for the hope of heaven or for the fear of hell, but only for the pure love of God, who is so worthy and can do for us what is best."

Such stories are particularly impressive, because Joinville was not in the least an anticlerical or a satirist, but a pious and kind man, reminiscent of the good old days.

B. *The Byzantine Church*

9. *Union of the churches*

The misintelligence between the Western church and the Eastern one began as early as the fifth century; it was soon remedied, but not for very long, and the cleft separating them gradually increased. By the end of the eighth century, there were facing one another two enemy churches, the Catholic centered in Rome, and the Orthodox centered in Constantinople. During the following centuries, the enmity was constantly aggravated, and it was allowed to grow beyond the possi-

[17] Guido II de Mello was bishop of Auxerre from 1247 to his death in 1270; St Louis died in the same year.

bility of healing by a series of outrageous crimes, the main one being the sack of Constantinople in 1204 by the Crusaders (Osiris 2, 439–43, 1936).

The Orthodox and Catholic Christians did not merely disagree, they hated each other with a burning hatred. Their conflict was not simply a conflict of opinions, which could have been solved by persuasive discussions; it was a conflict of temperament and character (ἦθος), between a kind of Orientalized Hellenism on the one hand and Italianized barbarism on the other. Such conflicts cannot be healed and have a tendency to get worse and worse. In the fourteenth century, however, the Catholic church managed to have some defenders of its cause in the enemy camp, and for various reasons, chiefly the growing weakness and jeopardy of the Eastern Empire, those defenders obtained some kind of hearing. Thus originated a new quarrel between the Latins and Latinizing clerks and the Orthodox; the latter are generally called Hesychasts, for reasons which we shall explain in another chapter, when we are to deal with the theological aspects of that controversy.

The Latinizing party was often named Barlaamite after its main leader, Barlaam, a Calabrian monk. Barlaam was a Greek hailing from "Magna Graecia," coming back East with new ideas from the West. He was supported by the basilissa Anna, and was actually employed in negotiations with the papal legates to explore the possibilities of union. Unfortunately, the anti-union party was and remained considerably stronger. One has the impression that the Barlaamites were never more than a small and artificial minority out of touch with the great mass of the faithful. Indeed, the fundamental difference between the Latin and Orthodox churches must be looked for not in the minds of the theologians, but in the hearts of the people; the theological explanations of it are epiphaenomena rather than causes.

No wonder, then, that Barlaam was defeated in 1341, and again in 1346. The people and monks were arrayed against him, and the leading theologians, Nicephoros Chumnos, Neophytos Prodromenos, Gregorios Palamas, Nicephoros Gregoras wrote treatises against the Latins. The union of the churches was doomed, and so was ultimately the Eastern Empire.

10. *Defense of the Orthodox faith*

Andronicos of Constantinople wrote an apology against the Jews in the form of a dialogue. To the geographer Andreas Libadenos we owe a confession of faith. There must be many other such documents which we did not consider, because their authors had done nothing else to justify being included in our survey.

Abundant information concerning the theories and practices of the church may be found in the Syntagma of Blastares, in the Hexabiblos of Armenopulos, and in other writings of these men. Blastares composed many treatises discussing theological or ecclesiastical matters or denouncing Jewish and Latin errors. Armenopulos discussed Christian heresies, including of course the Latin one!

C. *Other Eastern Christian Churches*

11. *Missionary efforts*

The history of the Eastern churches can be approached in two ways, from the inside and from the outside. The outside point of view is that of missionaries sent to them by other churches, but the only missionaries I came across were Catholic ones (I do not recall a single Orthodox one, which is puzzling me!).

The Catholic missionaries were almost all Dominicans or Franciscans. Yet the first to occur to my mind in this period is Hayton the Monk, of Armenian birth, who assumed the Premonstrant habit in Cyprus; perhaps we should call him a convert rather than a missionary, but even that would be misleading, for under the Rupenian dynasty, the Armenians of Cilicia had drawn nearer to Rome, and in the early years of the fourteenth century they had submitted to it in order to save their kingdom from utter ruin. That submission was neither genuine nor popular,[18] but that is another question which we need not discuss.

To return to missionaries, the Dominicans were Brocard, who traveled for at least twenty-four years preaching the gospel in Eastern Europe and the Near East; William Adam and Bartholomew of Bologna, both of whom went to Persia and were engaged in Catholic propaganda among the Armenians. Bartholomew's efforts were particularly successful, because he took the trouble to translate books from Latin into Armenian with the help of a native convert, John of Karīn. The latter became the leader of the United Brethren or Uniters (Unitores), that is, the Romanized Armenians, the Uniat[19] minority of the Armenian people.[20]

As to the Franciscans, Andrew of Perugia and Peregrine of Castello, they continued the tradition of their order in China. They were sent to that country by Clement V to become suffragans to the first Catholic bishop of Peking (1307), John of Montecorvino (XIII-2). Andrew of Perugia replaced him, and was replaced in his turn by James of Florence, who died a martyr in 1362. Thus ended that brief Catholic effort, made possible by Mongol toleration and stopped short by Chinese (Ming) intolerance.

12. *Nestorian church*

The Nestorians had been activated from the beginning (in the fifth century) by an intense missionary zeal, and they had spread all over Muslim and Buddhist Asia, anticipating and outstripping Catholics everywhere. This was especially true of China, where the Nestorians had tilled the field more than five centuries earlier than the Catholic missionaries; in fact, when the latter finally arrived their efforts were devoted at least as much to converting the Nestorians as to converting non-Christians. At the beginning of the fourteenth century the Nestorian patriarch was assisted by twenty-five metropolitans and some two hundred fifty bishops.[21] The Nestorian achievements were told by various chroniclers, notably

[18] The Roman supremacy was acknowledged at the Armenian synod of Sīs in 1307, and this led to rioting and the murder of king Leo III. Catholic proselytism continued creating further trouble. As to the genuineness of the Armenian submission, see Brocard's extraordinary statement quoted by Atiya (p. 106, 270, 1938).

[19] Meaning a group recognizing the Roman authority in matters of dogma, but preserving its own rites and traditions. From the fourteenth to the eighteenth century many orders established missionaries among Armenians, and thus created many kinds of Catholic Armenians, yet these did not constitute a united body until the middle of the eighteenth century.

[20] The combined efforts of Bartholomew and John of Karīn were emulated by John of Erzinjān (XIII-2), who translated St. Thomas' treatise on sacraments for John XXII (hence after 1316) and lived until 1326. On the other hand, the Armenian opposition had been well represented by Stephen Orbelian (XIII-2), who had written a manual (dserhnarg) against the Latin church and addressed it in 1302 to the catholicos Gregor VII of 'Ain zarba (Anazarba), whose successor, Constantine III of Caesarea, submitted to Rome in 1307.

[21] For the Asiatic distribution of the Nestorian churches and their history, see P. Yoshio Saeki: The Nestorian documents and relics in China (550 p., 96 p. in Chinese, 52 ill., 5 maps, Toho Bunkwa Gakuin, Maruzen Co., Tokyo 1937). Arthur Christopher Moule: Nestorians in China. Some corrections and additions (44 p., London 1940). For Nestorianism in general, Introd. (1, 381–82), and A. J. Maclean (ERE 9, 323–32, 1917).

in our period by ʻAmr ibn Mattā of Ṭīrhān and Ṣalībā ibn Yūḥanna of Mūṣul, who wrote in Arabic c. 1317–30.

13. *Coptic church*

In spite of persecutions, the Coptic church, which continued the Eutychean[22] (Monophysite) heresy condemned in 451, was still flourishing in the fourteenth century; in fact, it is still flourishing today, being the national Christian church of Egypt. It had been able to withstand so many enemies and to weather so many storms throughout the centuries because of the administrative and financial abilities of individual Copts (the Muslim government could not function without them), and also because of the protection secured for them occasionally by the Byzantine emperor, the kings of Aragon, or best of all the Negus of Aethiopia,[23] threatening to deflect the waters of the Blue Nile from the Egyptian plain.

A good amount of information on the Coptic church can be derived from the Coptic writings of Abū-l-Barakāt (d. 1324), some of which deal with ecclesiastical subjects. One is an apology against the Jews and Muslims.

For the Abyssinian church see Enno Littmann (ERE 1, 57–59, 1908); for the Coptic church, P. D. Scott-Moncrieff (ERE 4, 113–19, 1912).

D. *Israel*

14. *Biblical and Talmudic commentaries. Homiletics*

Even as Christian scientists and learned men devoted a good part of their time to the study of the Old and New Testaments, even so—or rather even more—did the Jewish scholars spend much of their time and energy in the study of the Old Testament and the Talmud, and in the writing of commentaries. These commentaries are so numerous[24] and their bulk so enormous that they are forbidding to the modern reader. Happily we are not obliged to read them, or at any rate to read all of them, but some of them must be mentioned to give a true idea of the religious life of that time.

The Portuguese David ben Yom-ṭob ben Bila wrote Biblical commentaries somewhat in the style of Abraham ben Ezra. In Spain, Vidal de Tolosa was commenting on the Mishneh Torah of Maimonides; Baḥya ben Asher wrote a famous commentary on the Torah and a book on practical religion; other commentaries were composed by Abudraham and by Abner of Burgos before his apostasy.

[22] Eutyches was an archimandrite in Constantinople, who combated the Nestorian heresy (Introd. 1, 381) with so much passion that he fell into the opposite heresy, Monophysitism (Introd. 2, 501). Nestorianism was condemned at the council of Ephesos (431). Later Eutyches was deposed, but vindicated again at the synod of Ephesos (449), packed with his own partisans. Eutychianism or Monophysitism was finally condemned at the council of Chalcedon (451), and Eutyches exiled to Egypt. For a general discussion of Monophysitism see Gustav Krüger (ERE 8, 811–17, 1916), and also the same author's article on Monotheletism (ERE 8, 821–25, 1916).

[23] The Abyssinian church was founded by Frumentios of Tyre, who was consecrated bishop of Aksūm c. 330 by St. Athanasios of Alexandria (Introd. 1, 347). Since the creation of the Coptic church the heads of the Abyssinian church have always been Copts and have always been consecrated by the Coptic patriarch of Alexandria. The Aethiopian version of the Bible (Introd. 1, 381), traditionally ascribed to Frumentios, must be somewhat later. Frumentios was called abūnā (our father) or abbā salāma (father of peace); these titles are still given to the head of the Abyssinian church, who is generally referred to as the abūnā.

[24] In spite of the fact that many were destroyed, and that the mass extant is only a fraction of the total.

The religious activity of the Jews was equally remarkable in France. This may seem puzzling when one remembers that they were expelled from France in 1306, but happily for them "France" at that time did not yet include the county of Orange nor the whole of Provence and Languedoc. Large Jewish colonies had existed in southern France since the beginning of our era. As the persecutions increased, more Jews withdrew their attention from the world and concentrated it on the holy writings, anxious to interpret them as well as possible. The most prolific of these southern French commentators was Joseph Kaspi, who flourished mainly in Tarascon; the most illustrious of course was Levi ben Gerson, but his activity as a Biblical scholar, though considerable, is eclipsed by his fame as a philosopher and scientist. We should mention also David ben Samuel Kokabi and Moses ben Joshua of Narbonne.

All these men were orthodox Talmudists who had inherited the glosses of Rashi (XI-2) and the postillae (tosafot) of his followers.[25] These tosafot were collected during the fourteenth century by an anonymous compiler; they are appended to the printed editions of the Bible and of the Babylonian Talmud, at the end of each tractate. While this Talmudic work was engrossing the minds of the great majority of Jewish scholars, another movement was going on, much more restricted geographically but quite as deep, that is, the kind of anti-Talmudic or rather anti-rabbinic reformation initiated by Anan ben David (VIII-2) and Benjamin Nahawendi (IX-1) and called Qaraism. This was now represented by Aaron ben Elijah of Constantinople, the greatest and last of the Qaraite doctors, "the Maimonides of Qaraism," and also by the North African teacher Israel ben Samuel al-Ma'arabi, who had established himself in Cairo.[26] Another doctor, Shemariah ben Elijah ha-Iqriṭi, who was a Qaraite himself or familiar with Qaraite doctrines, flourished in Crete and then at the court of Robert of Anjou. He wrote Biblical commentaries, but interests us mainly because of the efforts he made in his old age to reconcile the Qaraites and rabbinists of Spain. These generous efforts were rewarded with imprisonment; he probably died in a Spanish prison.

15. *Persecutions of the Jews*

Many cruel persecutions of the Jewish minorities testify to the barbarity of that age in spite of a veneer of Christianity. Let us recall a few dates. In 1288 thirteen Jews were burned to death at Troyes,[27] in Champagne; in 1290 the Jews were ex-

[25] For a general account of the tosafists of the Bible and Talmud, see Neubauer-Renan (p. 433–49, 1877).

[26] For the history of Qaraism see Introd. vols. 1, 2 by index. Good introductions to the subject by Abraham de Harkavy and Kaufmann Kohler (JE 7, 437–47, 1904), by Samuel Poznanski (ERE 7, 662–72, 1915), and by I. Markon, Josef Heller, and M. Balaban (EJ 9, 923–54, 1932). According to the estimate made in 1932 the Qaraites numbered then about 12,000, most of them in Russia. Since the publication of Introd. vol. 1, the edition of one of the outstanding Qaraite books, the Kitāb al-anwār wal-marāqib of al-Qirqisānī (X-1), has been completed by Leon Nemoy (vols. 1–5, New York 1939–43; Isis 33, 89, 357; 34, 44; 35, 57). A great many original documents covering a period of eleven centuries (ninth to nineteenth) have been published by Jacob Mann (1935).

[27] Elégies sur l'auto-da-fé de Troyes en 1288 (Neubauer-Renan p. 475–82, 1877). Apropos of two elegies, Hebrew and French, in the Vatican; the text of the French one is reproduced. The Hebrew elegy was composed by Jacob ben Judah of Lorraine. James Darmesteter remarked apropos of the French text, written in Hebrew script by an unknown poet: "La langue maternelle de ce paria ce n'est pas un patois hébreu, c'est le français de la France, et la plus ancienne élégie française, la plus belle peut-être qui ait été composée en notre langue, a été écrite dans un ghetto à la lueur d'un bûcher" (Essais orientaux p. 274, Paris 1883).

pelled from England (Introd. 2, 825); in 1298 occurred the extermination of the Würzburg and Nuremberg communities; in 1306 the Jews were expelled from France (again in 1322); in 1328 they were massacred in Navarre; in 1336–38 they were persecuted in Alsace, Swabia, and Franconia.[28] Finally, the Black Death of 1348 being blamed on them furnished the best pretext for new oppressions. It is to the credit of the Catholic church that Clement VI was one of the rare sovereigns who dared defend the Jews, and he did so effectively. Avignon remained one of the few peaceful havens open to them.

The general state of mind is well illustrated by a saying of St. Louis (Joinville §53). A layman should not argue with a Jew, nor try to defend the Christian law against him except with the sword, "pushing it into his belly as deep as it can go." If such a good king thought like that, what could one expect of others, or of their underlings?

Many Jews were converted to Christianity, and, as will always happen, some of the neophytes tried to prove their zeal by accusations of their former brethren. The outstanding apostate was Abner of Burgos, alias Alfonso of Valladolid, many of whose Hebrew and Spanish publications are strongly anti-Jewish. He was answered in Hebrew by Isaac ben Pulqar, who was the author also of an elaborate treatise in defense of Judaism.

E. *Islam*

16. *Muslim brotherhoods*

The same human needs which led to the creation of monastic orders, tertiaries, and other religious communities in Christendom were answered in the Dār al-Islām by the development of mystical brotherhoods. The Muslim equivalent of Christian monkhood appeared much later and was probably influenced to some extent by Christian examples (Asín Palacios 1931). The essentials are the same in both cases; men came together in closer union, abandoning more or less completely their property rights for the sake of the community, and other individual rights for the sake of discipline. Their association is caused by negative forces, distrust of the world and disgust with it; and by positive ones, love of God, desire for solitude and for undisturbed contemplation and meditation, preparation for the hereafter. Sometimes, though less frequently in Islām than in Christendom, there were added to these attractions philanthropic purposes and religious propaganda.

The Muslim brotherhoods were generally inspired and sustained by mystical conceptions, and many of the Arabic writings on taṣawwuf (mysticism) were composed by members of such brotherhoods. We shall deal with that ṣūfī literature in the chapter on philosophy. At present it suffices to draw attention to the religious organizations which were the cradle of that literature and made its luxuriant development possible.

The earliest ṭuruq cannot be traced back earlier than the twelfth century. At least five important ones were already flourishing before 1300. Two more were established before 1350, the Ṣafawīya and the Baktāshīya, both of which are of special interest for the history not only of Islamic mysticism in general, but also of Turkish culture in particular. Strangely enough, the first was also the root out of which sprang, two centuries later, the Ṣafawī dynasty of Īrān.

[28] Dates taken from Margolis and Marx (p. 765, 1927).

17. *Explanation of the Qur'ān*

The Biblical commentaries which afforded learned Jews and Christians a means of satisfying their religious hunger were replaced in Islām by commentaries on the Qur'ān (tafsīr). It is not always easy to distinguish between such commentaries and theological treatises, for the former imply necessarily the discussion of theological questions. Nevertheless the general point of view is different. The commentaries are mainly concerned with the Holy Scriptures or Reading (= qur'ān) and with elucidating them as completely as possible.

The best mufassirūn (commentators) of this age were perhaps Quṭb al-dīn al-Shīrāzī (XIII-2), Niẓām al-a'raj, Multānī, and Abū Ḥaiyān. To call them the best is a little risky, for such a judgment would presuppose a comparative study of a large class of bulky writings, but they are certainly good representatives of the contemporary tafsīr. The first three were Persians, the fourth a Spaniard. The first two were mathematicians, the third a theologian, the fourth a philologist. The second and fourth wrote exclusively in Arabic, while the first and third wrote also in Persian. It would seem that Quṭb al-dīn became more interested in religious and mystical matters toward the end of his life; it is thus probable that his commentaries on the Qur'ān were written in this century (he died in 1311).

Niẓām al-a'raj wrote a large commentary on the Qur'ān. Multānī, who flourished in northern India, compiled a collection of Persian explanations of the outstanding terms of each sūra. Abū Ḥaiyān, who was established in Egypt, composed a commentary which was so comprehensive that it was called "the ocean" (al-baḥr al-muḥīṭ fī tafsīr . . .). As he was a grammarian, his explanations were to a large extent grammatical, but we have pointed out many times already that this was a necessity readily accepted everywhere. A text cannot be exactly understood unless it is possible to give a grammatical account of every word, vowel, or accent; grammar is thus the handmaid of exegesis.

18. *Puritanism or fundamentalism in Islām*

The intense study of the Qur'ān produced the same psychological results as the study of the Bible. Some doctors steeped themselves so deeply in the sacred text that they were fascinated by it and lost count of everything else. This was a dangerous fallacy, for even if one admits the perfection of the divine text, its establishment and the interpretation of its obscurities, being human, are bound to be imperfect and erroneous in many respects.

A good example of textual fanaticism was given by the Syrian theologian Ibn Taimīya, who tried to bring Islām back to the literal purity of its infancy. Being outspoken and violent, he made many enemies but also enthusiastic supporters. His influence is strongly felt to this day, in the Wahhābī doctrines of modern Arabia and also in the efforts which liberal Muslims are making to cleanse their faith from the superstitions which defile and smother it.

19. *Muslim apologetics*

The Syrian cosmographer Muḥammad ibn Ibrāhīm al-Dimashqī wrote a defense of Islām directed against the Christians of Cyprus, that is, against Catholics and Orthodox. I am not aware that Muslims attached much or any importance to the theological differences separating so profoundly the Latins from the Orthodox. Their fundamental objection was to Trinitarianism in all its forms, for they are absolutely unitarian. For other apologetic writings in Arabic consult Steinschneider (p. 426, 1877).

F. *Buddhism*

20. *Buddhism in Ceylon and Burma*

Buddhism ceased to develop in its native country in the eighth century, and gradually it even ceased to exist there at all. By the fourteenth century it was extinct except in Ceylon, Burma, and Nepal.[29] So far as we know from the Chinese records (which are our main source for the later stages of Hindu Buddhism), its slow and imperceptible extinction was due much less to definite persecution than to the overwhelming competition of polymorphic and ubiquitous Hinduism. Long before its destruction the original Hīnayāna Buddhism had been transformed into something very different, Mahāyāna. Aśvaghosha (II-1) and Nāgārjuna (III-1) are often quoted as the founders of the new religion, the enormous canon of which was built up within six centuries (second to seventh). But even Mahāyāna, catholic and eclectic as it was, could not resist the pressure of Hinduism, and it was submerged and canceled by it in the same way that a beautiful temple is swallowed up by the exuberant and irrepressible jungle.[30]

The Buddhism which conquered China and the Far East was almost exclusively Mahāyāna, but, by a sort of miracle, Hīnayāna Buddhism was preserved in Ceylon and Burma. We have for each of those countries a good witness.

Vedeha thera, who lived at the great minster of Anurādhapura, compiled a collection of Buddhist stories, which has remained very popular to this day. A similar task was performed in Burma by Medhaṃkara, who wrote a series of legends illustrating different stages of existence. These works, whether written in Ceylon or in Burma, were naturally in Pāli, the vehicle of Hīnayāna Buddhism.

21. *Chinese Buddhism*

Nien ch'ang wrote a history of Buddhism down to 1344. We may assume that he belonged to the Ch'an tsung (or Dhyāna sect, Zen), for he attaches special importance to its history from its foundation by Bodhidharma (VI-1) to his own days. That school was very popular in China.

The development of Tibetan Buddhism (Introd. 1, 466–69) in China is proved by the fact that the translation of the Kanjur from Tibetan into Mongolian was completed within the first quarter of the century.

22. *Japanese Buddhism*

Before the end of the thirteenth century the evolution of Japanese Buddhism was essentially completed; that is, all the main sects had been constituted, the two latest ones being the Nichiren-shū (1253) and the Ji-shū (1275)—though some subsects branched off from the main ones in later times. For example, in the fourteenth century there appeared new branches of the Rinzai-shū (the mother stem of Zen), Shin-shū, and Nichiren-shū.

[29] We shall say a few words of Ceylon and Burma presently. As to Nepalese Buddhism, it was soon mixed up with Hinduism beyond recognition.

[30] We may say that by the end of the seventh century, when I-ching (VII-2) visited India, the creative age of Mahāyāna was already over in that country, and by the tenth century there was hardly any Buddhism left there. Yet religious traditions are hard to kill; they continue if necessary a kind of underground or parasitic life. Thus there was in India as late as the eleventh or twelfth century a Buddhist writer called Advayavajra, author of didactic poems on Mahāyāna and Vajrayāna (that is, a queer mixture of monism, magic, erotics, Buddhism). The Advayavajrasaṃgraha was edited by Haraprasāda Shāstrī (Gaekwad's Oriental series no. 40, 108 p., Baroda 1927). Winternitz (2, 375, 388, 1933). Emeneau (no. 3673, 1935).

We cannot insist on such matters (the early history of all these sects was given in previous volumes), but it is worth while to remark that the whole of Japanese Buddhism was almost exclusively Mahāyāna (daijō). The only Hīnayāna (shōjō) sects were the two early ones, Jōjitsu-shū and Kusha-shū, introduced respectively in 625 from Korea and in 658 from China, both of which were soon superseded by daijō sects (Introd. 1, 470, 492).

The greatest Buddhist teachers of this age were Gen-e, who harmonized Buddhism with Confucianism, and Kitabatake Chikafusa, who harmonized it with the national mythology Shintō, and was the inventor of the peculiar national religion of Japan, which is a mixture of Buddhism and Confucianism with deification of the emperors and mystical exaltation of the country above all others.

One of the most elaborate documents for the history of Buddhism, the life of Hōnen-Shōnin (XII-2), founder of the Jōdo-shū in 1175, was written by a Tendai abbot, Shunjō Hōin, at the beginning of the fourteenth century at the request of the retired emperor Go-Fushimi.

G. *Hinduism*

23. Rāmānanda, fourth successor of Rāmānuja (XI-2), created a new Vaishṇava sect, the Rāmāwat or Rāmānandī, far more charitable and tolerant than the previous ones, open to all without distinction of caste. The two main principles of his faith, the love of God and the love of man, remind us of two commandments of Christ (Matthew 22:37–40).

III. THE TRANSLATORS

One of the simplest ways of appreciating the general trends in cultural exchanges is to examine the translations made from each language into others. A single translation might be due to accidental causes, a whole group of them can only be explained by general needs. In accordance with the method followed in our previous volumes, we shall now proceed to determine those general needs and tendencies before attempting to weigh the scientific contributions of each people.

By the beginning of the fourteenth century the intellectual streams passing from one nation to another, or, more exactly, from the people speaking one language to people using other languages, were already so many (I counted thirty-four of them) that our account has to be very systematic or else it would soon be confusing.

Thus I shall consider one by one the nine languages from which the streams flowed into other languages, transmitting knowledge and ideas from one section of mankind to another. These languages are Arabic, Persian, Greek, Latin, Hebrew, French, Spanish (and Catalan), Sanskrit, and Tibetan. There were possibly others still which escaped my observation, but if so, they were not very important.

1. *Arabic*

1a. *From Arabic into Latin*

When one remembers the flood of earlier Latin writings translated from the Arabic, it is a surprise to realize their fewness in the fourteenth century. This is a good example of a cultural river, once very broad and deep, now gradually diminishing to a brook.

Some of the translations dealt with in volume 2 may belong to this period. That is the case for some of the many translations bearing the name of Arnold of Villanova (Introd. 2, 896) and for at least one of those ascribed to Armengaud son of Blaise (XIII-2), who lived probably as late as 1313. He translated Maimonides' treatise on poisons for Clement V in 1307. This translation is a good illustration of the transitional age, for although it was made from the Arabic it is probable that Armengaud took advantage of the Hebrew version by Moses ibn Tibbon (XIII-2) or of another Hebrew version.

Similar remarks might apply to the medical translations made from the Arabic (or from the Hebrew?) into Latin by Simon of Genoa (XIII-2) with the assistance of Abraham ben Shem-ṭob (XIII-2). The only other translations were made by one Stephen son of Arnold, who flourished in Montpellier and produced versions of two works, the one astronomical and the other medical, both by Qusṭā ibn Lūqā (IX-2).

1b. *From Arabic into Italian*

Bencivenni's translations of al-Farghānī (IX-1) and al-Rāzī (IX-2) were made from the French, not from the Arabic. They may be counted as indirect translations.

1c. *From Arabic into Spanish or Portuguese*

Dinis the Liberal (king of Portugal from 1279 to 1325) did for his country what Alfonso el Sabio (king of Castile and León from 1252 to 1284) had done for his own a little earlier. He caused a number of books to be translated from Arabic, Spanish, and Latin into Portuguese. I do not know whether the translations from the Arabic were direct or not. These translations constitute the earliest monuments of Portuguese prose.

At the same time Jacme II (king of Aragon from 1291 to 1327) employed Judah ben Astruc Bonsenyor to translate a collection of proverbs and an unidentified book of medicine from Arabic into Catalan. The collection of proverbs was translated a century later (1402) from Catalan into Castilian.

1d. *From Arabic into Hebrew*

This is by far the largest group of translations, so large, indeed, that it is convenient to divide it into smaller groups, according to the nationality of the translators. Except for one Italian, these were Provençaux or Spaniards.

One of the greatest of the Hebrew translators, Jacob ben Maḥir ibn Tibbon (XIII-2), scion of an illustrious family of scholars, died in Montpellier c. 1304. His translation of Ibn Rushd's commentary on Aristotelian zoology was completed in 1302. Other translations of his have come down to us revised by other scholars, to wit, that of Ibn Rushd's commentary on the Organon, revised by Marsilli ben Judah at Tarascon in 1329, and that of the Iṣlāḥ al-majisṭī of Jābir ibn Aflaḥ, corrected by Samuel ben Judah in 1335.

Other Provençaux: Jedaiah ben Abraham of Béziers revised the Hebrew version of a philosophical book of al-Fārābī. Moses ben Solomon of Beaucaire translated the longest commentary of Ibn Rushd on the Metaphysics. Samson ben Solomon completed in 1322 a translation of the sixteen books of Galen. It is a pity we do not know more about him (his origin is unknown, and my placing him among the Provençaux is a matter of guess, not of certainty), for that translation was of special importance. Qalonymos ben David translated Ibn Rushd's famous treatise against al-Ghazzālī, The destruction of the destruction. To another member of the same family, Qalonymos ben Qalonymos, we owe a whole library of translations of Greek and Arabic mathematicians and physicians, too many to be enumerated here. The same can be said of Samuel ben Judah of Marseille, whose list is shorter yet includes commentaries on Plato's Republic and on Aristotle's Logic and Ethics. Ṭodros Ṭodrosi of Arles restricted himself to philosophical writings, those of al-Fārābī, Ibn Sīnā, Ibn Rushd.

The achievements of their Spanish contemporaries are no less astonishing, especially if one bears in mind (as one always should) that these Jewish scholars were a persecuted minority. Solomon Bonirac translated the De crisibus of Galen; Solomon ben Paṭer, the short astronomy of Ibn al-Haitham; Israel ben Joseph, brother of Isaac Israeli the Younger, various texts for Asher ben Jehiel. Isaac ben Pulqar completed the translation of al-Ghazzālī's famous treatise on The meanings of the philosophers, begun by Isaac Albalag (XIII-2). Other philosophical and theological treatises by al-Ghazzālī, Maimonides, Joseph ibn 'Aqnīn, Muḥammad al-Tabrīzī were put into Hebrew by Isaac ben Nathan of Cordova. The philosophic or scientific poem of Mūsā ibn Ṭūbī was translated by Solomon ben Immanuel Dapiera (the translation dates from the middle of the century, whether before or after 1350 I cannot say). Finally, we may recall that one Joseph ibn Waqar (possibly identical with the qabbalist of that name) had made a new Hebrew translation of the surgery of Abū-l-Qāsim at the end of the thirteenth century.

The single Italian translator, Samuel ben Solomon ha-Me'ati, Hebraicized Galen's commentary on Hippocrates' regimen in acute diseases and a medical work of Ibn Zuhr.

The fact that all these translators were Westerners and that none came from the East is natural enough, for Easterners would know their Arabic so well that they would not wish for Hebrew versions; all that they might need would be transcriptions of the Arabic text in Hebrew script, and in the case of scientific and lay writings they would sometimes prefer to keep the Arabic script as well as the language.

1e. *From Arabic into Aethiopian*

Considering the dependence of the Aethiopic church on the Coptic one, it is not surprising that the clerks of Abyssinia derived their knowledge and inspiration partly from Arabic writings. In fact, those clerks, or at any rate the leading ones, were likely to be Egyptians. This was the case with Salāmā, who revised the Ge'ez version of the Bible on the basis of Arabic editions, and translated from the Arabic homilies, liturgical and monastic books, lives of saints and martyrs. Other books of the same category were translated by other men. The most remarkable of those versions and the most important from the point of view of international scholarship is the anonymous one of the strange historical chronicle called Sefer Yosippon.

2. *Persian*

It is natural to pass from Arabic to Persian, so natural that it is sometimes difficult to draw the line between these two languages.[1] In spite of their belonging to very different families, they have in common a very large vocabulary; in particular, the philosophic and scientific terms are generally the same (Arabic) in both languages. Translations from Arabic into Persian were hardly needed by real scholars

[1] That is, in the case of translations mentioned only by title, for the titles would probably be Arabic in both cases.

(I do not recall a single one in this period); when they occurred at all, they were prepared in answer to popular needs, even as the early versions from Latin into sundry vernaculars.

On the other hand, the Byzantine empire was always in communication with the Persian one, or with the Persian kingdoms, or the Persian provinces of the Dār al-Islām, and hence we come across some translations from Persian into Greek.

2a. *From Persian into Greek*

The natural center of Persian-Greek exchanges was the city of Trebizond,[2] at the southeast corner of the Black Sea, which was also for the Arabs and the Persians the main Greek bazaar, the one most convenient to them. The place had so much importance in their eyes that they often called the Black Sea after it, Baḥr Ṭarābazanda. The Greek emperors of Trebizond were all the time menaced and jeopardized by the Turcomans of Asia Minor, yet their capital continued to be a center of Greek culture. Under the rule of Alexios II (emp. 1297–1330) a kind of academy was constituted in Trebizond and some efforts were made to investigate Persian scientific literature. Gregorios Chioniades was sent to Persia and returned to Trebizond with a load of Persian books. Some of these books were investigated and translated or elaborated into Greek by the priest Manuel, his disciple Georgios Chrysococces, and Georgios Choniates. Chrysococces was primarily interested in astronomy; Choniates translated a treatise on antidotes.

Thus Trebizond was in the middle of the century the center of a Persian renaissance. The supremacy of Persian thought is established by the fact that we hear of translations from Persian into Greek, but not of a single one from Greek into Persian.

This will be less astonishing if we take the word Persian in a national rather than strictly linguistic sense. Indeed, I strongly suspect that among the Persian books brought to Trebizond, some at least, and probably the most important, were in Arabic. As the script is essentially the same in both languages, the average man and even the average scholar (non-Orientalist) could not see any difference, and the term Persian would be good enough to designate the Arabic books as well as the Persian ones, considering their common (Arabic) provenance. This matter deserves investigation; it is possible that that Persian renaissance should be called an Arabic one.

The ambiguity was increased by the fact that the Greek writers, wishing to Atticize, called the Arabs or Turks, Persians. Thus did Cinnamos (XII-2).

2b. *From Persian into Armenian*

Though there were many Greek and Muslim merchants in the bazaars and aswāq of Trebizond, the majority of the traders were Armenians. It was already so in the time of Ibn Ḥawqal (X-2). The Armenians then as now did not need translations, as they were ready enough to master any language which would improve their business. Catholic missionaries, however, would be anxious to publish their own sacred literature in Armenian, and one of them, Bartholomew of Bologna, preached sermons in Persian and then translated them into Armenian.

[2] Τραπεζοῦς; in Arabic, Aṭrābazund or Ṭarābazanda; in Turkish, Ṭarabzun. See article by J. H. Kramers (EI 4, 660–62, 1929).

2c. *From Persian into Turkish*

In the meanwhile the Anatolian world west of Trebizond was witnessing the chaotic growth of various Turkish nations and the beginning of Turkish literature. That literature was derived from foreign models, which were in the first place Arabic and Persian. The needs of the theologians called for the Arabic language itself rather than for translations, but the case of Persian was different. Arabic was an exceptional, divine language, but Persian was not nobler than the people's own language, and hence it was natural enough to pour out ideas from the Persian vessels into Turkish ones. Gülshehrī composed in 1317 a Turkish version of the famous mystical poem, Reasoning of the birds, of Fārīḍ al-dīn 'Aṭṭār.

3. *Greek*

Beginning in the thirteenth century, a small and slowly increasing group of Western scholars was coming to realize the supremacy of Greek sources and the advantage of drinking from them directly.

3a. *From Greek into Latin*

The example of Robert Grosseteste, Bartholomew of Messina, and William of Moerbeke was followed by two Italians, Pietro d'Abano and Niccolò da Reggio. Pietro translated the Problems of Aristotle, Alexander of Aphrodisias, Cassios the Iatrosophist, and various treatises of Galen. Leaving out the disputable translation of the Dynameron of Nicholas Myrepsos, Niccolò translated a large collection of Hippocratic and Galenic writings. Neither was of equal stature with the great Fleming, William of Moerbeke, yet Niccolò's translation of Galen's De usu partium (1322) was an event in the field of Galenic tradition comparable to William's translation of the Politics, Economics, etc. (1260, etc.) in the history of Aristotelian ideas.

3b. *From Greek into Hebrew*

Apparently the Jews were much slower than the Christians in realizing the superiority of direct translations from the Greek over indirect ones via Arabic intermediaries. The comparative ease with which they dealt with Arabic texts made it perhaps harder to abandon them. Considering the number of Oriental Jews who must have been familiar with the Greek language, however, it is strange that direct translations from Greek into Hebrew occurred so late and remained so rare. The earliest mediaeval Jew to translate from Greek into Hebrew was *perhaps* the Cretan Shemariah ben Elijah, but if so, we have no definite information on the subject beyond his own vague testimony.

4. *Latin*

In earlier centuries a vast amount of literature had been translated into Latin, chiefly from or through the Arabic, but now Latin is becoming itself a source equivalent to Arabic, whence knowledge is gradually transferred into other vessels.

4a. *From Latin into Hebrew*

Among all those transfers, none are more characteristic of the new era than those from Latin into Hebrew. They illustrate the established supremacy of Western Christendom over Israel, a supremacy which was natural enough, for whereas the Christian doctor, as long as he was sufficiently orthodox, conformist, and decorous, might count on the support of state and church, the Jewish one could shine only in the ghetto and was treated with contumely by most of the population, rich and poor alike. His life was always in danger, and the leisure required for intellectual work was to him a gift as rare and precarious as it was needed. The increase in the number of translations from Latin into Hebrew (for previous ones see Introd. 2, 723) was largely due, of course, to the fact that the Western Jews were becoming more and more ignorant of Arabic.

This is especially true of the Provençal Jews who composed most of those translations. Jacob ben Joseph ha-Levi translated medical treatises by Arnold of Villanova, Mesuë the Third, and Agilinus; Estori Farḥi, two other medical texts, the one by Armengaud son of Blaise, and the other of uncertain (Jewish?) authorship; finally, Israel ben Joseph Caslari and Hezekiah of Milhau each translated a separate medical treatise by Arnold of Villanova. Note that all these translations are medical; their occurrence may be explained by the fact that Jewish physicians practicing amid Christian populations and competing with Christian doctors needed introductions to the latter's terminology.

Passing to Italy, the situation is different. There we find only one Jew engaged in this kind of activity, but he was interested in philosophy, and we owe him Hebrew versions of the De causis, Boetius, Ibn Rushd (from the Latin version of Michael Scot), and even a short treatise by Thomas Aquinas. This was Judah ben Moses ben Daniel, better known under the name of Judah (or Leone) Romano.

As Muslim Spain was contracting, the number of Jews with a good knowledge of Arabic must have diminished in proportion, and hence here too we find a couple of them engaged in the transmission of Latin writings. Hezekiah bar Ḥalafta (was he really a Spaniard? if not, leave him out) translated the logic of Peter of Spain; Samuel Benveniste, physician to the Aragonese court, the Consolation of Boetius and Maimonides' treatise on asthma (from a Latin version of it); finally, the Portuguese David ben Yom-ṭob ben Bila, a strange tract dealing with the virtues of pulverized snakeskin.

4b. *From Latin into French*

As Latin rose to greater importance, French followed at some distance behind, being undoubtedly the first European vernacular to assume the dignity of an international vehicle of scientific knowledge. Jean de Prouville translated the surgical treatise of the mysterious abbé Poutrel; Pierre of Paris, the Psalms, Aristotle's Politics, and Boetius' Consolation. Much of Pierre's work was done in Cyprus.

The prestige of the French language is shown by the fact that a French translation of Seneca's Letters to Lucilius was made by an anonymous south Italian (Bartolommeo Siginulfo?) for Charles II (king of Naples to 1309).

Arnold of Quinquempoix is chiefly known as a translator of astrological books from Hebrew into Latin, but he is credited also with similar versions from Latin into French. Another astrological work, Guido Bonatti's, was Frenchified by Nicolas de la Horbe.

Various historical works, ancient and mediaeval, were translated by Jean de Vignai. Some of these versions are important, because of their length (the Speculum historiale of Vincent of Beauvais) or because the Latin originals are lost. Together they constitute a remarkable French library of historians. They were soon eclipsed, however, by Pierre Bersuire's translation of Livy's Decades. That particular translation was made after the middle of the century (1351–55), but Bersuire was really a man of the first half of the century, having been born c. 1290.

4c. *From Latin into Italian*

The translation of Aristotle's Ethics into Italian by Taddeo Alderotti, criticized by Dante (Convivio 1, 10), belongs probably to the thirteenth century, though Taddeo lived until 1303. His example was not imitated.

4d. *From Latin into Dutch*

The father of Dutch literature, Jacob van Maerlant, died in 1299, leaving behind a collection of books translated from Latin and French into his own Flemish language. What is equally important, he left disciples, Philip Utenbroeke and Lodewijk van Velthem, who continued his free translation of the Speculum historiale.

4e. *From Latin into German*

The first great scientific writers in German and in French, Conrad von Megenberg (c. 1309–74) and Nicole Oresme (c. 1323–82), are almost contemporary, though the latter is sufficiently younger than the former to be placed in the second half of the century, whereas Conrad's two main works belong undoubtedly to the first half. These two works may be considered free versions of the Latin works of Thomas of Cantimpré and John of Holywood.

4f. *From Latin into Icelandic*

The Norwegian judge Haukr Erlendsson translated the algorism of Alexandre de Villedieu, one of the most popular books of its kind in mediaeval times.

4f. *From Latin into Greek*

The many translations prepared by Maximos Planudes have been discussed before (Introd. 2, 973), but we should bear in mind that he lived until 1310. As it was not till 1296 that he was sent as ambassador to Venice, it is probable that many of his translations were made at the end of the thirteenth century or the beginning of the fourteenth.

The translation of the Semita recta, an alchemical treatise ascribed to Albert the Great, by one Petros Theoctonicos (XIII-2?), otherwise unknown, may date from this time.

The Provençal Dominican Guillaume Bernard and twelve of his brethren were delegated to Constantinople with the obvious purpose of helping to convert the schismatic Greeks. This could not be done without studying the Greek language, and brother Guillaume learned it so well that he was able to translate St. Thomas into Greek! This is hard to believe, for such ability would imply a very deep knowledge of Greek, but the intention is worth recording, and moreover Guillaume may have been helped to any extent by native proselytes. A similar story concerns Gregorios Acindynos, whose name was long attached to a Greek translation of St. Thomas. It is now generally accepted that that particular translation dates from the second half of the century.

4h. *From Latin into Armenian*

The Catholic church early took a strong interest in the Armenians who were living among Muslims or schismatics, and tried to wean them from their ancient church.[3] Those living in the New Armenia (Cilicia) were particularly amenable to

[3] It goes back to Gregory the Illuminator, evangelist of the Armenian people and first catholicos of Echmiadzin (302–25).

Latin influences, whether political or religious. Under the rule of Leo III (1301–7) and Ochin (1308–20), and the patriarchate of Constantine III of Caesarea (1307–22), the council of Sīs decided on the union with Rome (1307–8); this was the cause of violent troubles, to which we have already referred. John XXII (pope 1316–34) sent St. Thomas' treatise on sacraments to Cilicia; it was translated twice intó Armenian, by Zacharias, bishop of Dsordsor, and by John of Erzinjān (XIII-2).

More translations were made for the same religious and political purposes by the Dominican Bartholomew of Bologna, helped by United Brethren (i.e., Catholicized Armenians) such as John of Karīn, Jacob the Dragoman, and a little later Nerses Balì.

5. *Hebrew*

Translations from the Hebrew had been remarkably numerous in the second half of the thirteenth century (Introd. 2, 721); in the fourteenth century they become insignificant.

5a. *From Hebrew into Latin*

The Hebrew tables of Montpellier (1300) by Jacob ben Maḥir ibn Tibbon (XIII-2) were soon translated, obtaining much popularity under their Latin title. Armengaud son of Blaise (XIII-2) used Hebrew texts in his translations from Arabic into Latin. Qalonymos ben Qalonymos, chiefly known for his translations from the Arabic, translated Ibn Rushd's Destruction of the destruction from Hebrew; John de Planis, a medical treatise by the same author; Arnold of Quinquempoix, various astrological books; Abraham ben Shem-ṭob (XIII-2) helped Simon of Genoa (XIII-2) to translate Arabic medical books, probably from Hebrew versions, or at any rate with the help of such versions. These last-named translations may have been made in the thirteenth century or not until the fourteenth. All these translators, excepting of course Simon, were Provençaux.

5b. *From Hebrew into French*

This same Arnold of Quinquempoix translated various books from Hebrew into French; and on the other hand his translation of Abraham ben Ezra from Hebrew into Latin was probably made with the help of the French translation by Hagin Deulacres (XIII-2). This illustrates the linguistic perplexities of a Jew employed by the kings of France. He was clearly trilingual (Hebrew, French, Latin).

5c. *From Hebrew into Arabic*

Joseph ben Isaac Israeli abbreviated his father's Yesod 'olam in Arabic (c. 1324–31); this abridgment was soon retranslated into Hebrew! This is a good additional example of the linguistic difficulties in Toledo, which have been brilliantly illustrated by Angel González Palencia (1926–30). Don Angel's documents extend only to 1315, but polyglottic complications did not stop then.

6. *French*

The growing superiority of the French language is well shown by its use as a source. Latin and Hebrew books (but no others) were translated into French; on the other hand, French books were translated into English, Dutch, and Italian, and there was even some trickling back into Latin.

6a. *From French into English*

The most pregnant of these translations from the general point of view are those made in English: the Handlyng synne adapted from an Anglo-Norman original by Robert Mannyng, and the Ayenbite of inwyt translated from the purest langue d'oïl by Michael of Northgate.

6b. *From French into Dutch*

Continuing the effort of his master, Jacob van Maerlant, Lodewijk van Velthem completed the Dutch book of Merlin, derived from French romances.

6c. *From French into Italian*

Zucchero Bencivenni translated various French texts into Italian; it is said that some of these texts were themselves translated from the Arabic. We are thus given here a curious example of learning transmitted from Arabic to Italian, via French; it is not the first one; see my notes on Aldobrandin of Siena (XIII-2) and Brunetto Latini (XIII-2), though in their cases the transmission became more complicated,

$$\text{Arabic} \rightarrow \text{Latin} \rightarrow \text{French} \rightarrow \text{Italian.}$$

6d. *From French into Latin*

Pietro of Abano translated one of Abraham ben Ezra's astrological treatises from the French version by Hagin Deulacres, and similar tasks were performed by Arnold of Quinquempoix and by Henry Bate (XIII-2).

7. *Spanish (Castilian) and Catalan*

For the sake of simplification we shall deal with Spanish and Catalan together, though Romance philologists might seriously object to that. I do so only because my account of translations is already so long that I am afraid of discouraging my gentle readers.

7a. *From Spanish into Latin*

The fables of Kalīla wa-Dimna were translated from Castilian into Latin by Raymond of Béziers. An Arabic medical text was translated from Catalan into Latin by a certain mysterious Berengarius.

7b. *From Castilian into Italian*

There is in the Vatican a MS translation of the Libro di astrologia of Alfonso el Sabio (XIII-2) made in 1341 by one Gueruccius (Isis 13, 93, 1929).

7c. *From Castilian into Portuguese*

Some of the translations ordered by Dinis the Liberal (king of Portugal 1279–1325) were made from the Spanish, the most important being the Cronica general of his grandfather, Alfonso X.

8. *Sanskrit*

The complicated history of the translations which concerned the development of European culture is now completed, and we pass to a very distant field, that of India and Buddhist Asia. The key language of India is Sanskrit, whose authority has always been, and continues to be, so great that it can be detected not only in the Aryan languages derived from it, but also in the non-Aryan languages of India and of all lands ever submitted to Hindu influences.

8a. *From Sanskrit into Persian*

Moreover, in mediaeval times there were many points of contact between Hindu culture on the one hand and the Persian-Arabic on the other. This field has not yet been sufficiently explored, because the scholars equally familiar with Sanskrit, Persian, and Arabic are few, and thus every bit of information relative to it is very welcome, even if it is relatively unimportant in itself.

The shaykh al-Nakhshabī derived (directly or indirectly) from a Sanskrit original a collection of stories called the Book of the parrot, which was destined to enjoy in different forms and languages considerable popularity in Eastern lands. He adapted a treatise on erotics from another Sanskrit text.

8b. *From Sanskrit into Telugu*

The translation of the Mahābhārata begun in the eleventh century was completed by the Śaiva poet Errāpragaḍa. Translations of the Mahābhārata have almost the same cultural importance in the Hindu world as translations of the Bible in the Christian one.

8c. *From Canarese into Telugu*

A popular cosmography written by Raṭṭa-kavi in Canarese at the turn of the thirteenth century was translated into Telugu by one Bhāskara. This is a relatively rare example of the literary and scientific influence of one Dravidian people upon another.

8d. *From Sanskrit into Chinese*

The translation of thousands of Buddhist texts from Sanskrit into Chinese was largely completed before the fourteenth century, yet it continued during that century. It is worth while to insist again upon these translations, which in their totality constitute the largest and most important cultural flow in the history of mankind.

9. *Tibetan*

From Tibetan into Mongolian

The translation of the Kanjur and Tanjur into Mongolian which Kublai Khān had wished for was not undertaken until c. 1310 under the rule of Kublai's great-grandson, the emperor Wu-tsung. I do not know how much of it was accomplished, but a set of the translations thus made in the period 1310–68 exists to this day in Mukden.

10. *Conclusions*

The most interesting queries in any comparative study of these translations would naturally relate to their contents. What kinds of texts were translated more often? which were the favorite authors? what were the contributions of each century to the translations of the fourteenth century? We need not worry about that now, however, for the answers to such queries will be found in the following chapters. The mathematical translations will be compared and discussed in the mathematical chapter, and so on.

The previous account is so complex that it is useful to summarize it in a symbolical way, as is done in the following table:

Table 1

Linguistic classification of translations (XIV-1)

1. A → L	4. L → H*	6. F → E
→ I	→ F*	→ D
→ Sp	→ I	→ I
→ Po	→ D	→ L*
→ H*	→ Ge	7. Sp → L
→ Aeth	→ Ic	→ I
2. P → G	→ G*	→ Po
→ Arm	→ Arm	8. S → P
→ T	5. H → L*	→ Tel
3. G → L*	→ F	→ Ch
→ H	→ A*	Can → Tel
		9. Tib → Mong

The symbols used need no explanation; in case of doubt refer to the text above, the order of which is preserved.

These 34 combinations are not equally important. The most important by far are A → H and L → H; that is, translations into Hebrew were on the whole the most numerous. Then come L → F and H → L. The asterisks in table 1 refer to the reversible translations. It is clear at once that these are the exception (4 pairs out of 34 units); most translations were not reversed. That is, books were translated A → L but not L → A, but we have the four pairs

A ⇄ H   G ⇄ L
L ⇄ H   L ⇄ F

Even here the transmissions are very unequal, except for G ⇄ L, where the two languages are almost equal or seem to be so. In every one of these four cases the predominant language is the one on the left side.

To show that G and L were not really on an equal footing, one must introduce a new distinction, between natural and artificial translations. The natural translations are those which are actually needed and called for by the people using them. For example, there were many medical versions from Latin into Hebrew because Jewish doctors created a demand for them. On the other hand, the versions from Latin into Greek and into Armenian were decidedly artificial, for they were created for propaganda purposes, somewhat like the hundreds of Biblical versions issued by the Bible societies.

A final comparison should be made between the languages into which translated texts poured from more than one other language. This is shown in table 2.

Three languages, A, Sp, P, were translated from but a single language (respectively H, A, S) but were translated into various others, A into six, Sp and P into three each. The other languages, Ge, E, Ic, Mong, Ch, Aeth, were used for only one kind of transmission, to wit translations from L, F, L, Tib, S, and A, respectively, without reciprocity.

The growing superiority of Latin appears in its double connection as a reservoir filled from the largest number (five) of other sources and as a source transmitting influences in the largest number (eight) of directions.

Table 2

(Reverse of table 1)

L	was translated from	A	G	H	F	Sp		
I	" " "	A			F	Sp	L	
H	" " "	A	G				L	
{G	" " "						L	P
{Arm	" " "						L	P
F	" " "			H			L	
D	" " "				F		L	
Po	" " "	A				Sp		
Tel	" " "	S	Can					

Appendix

This section was already written when I became aware of other translations which I had not considered. I speak of them here in order to avoid the recasting of the whole section and of its conclusions.

John of Montecorvino (XIII-2) wrote in 1305 from Peking, "I have obtained a working knowledge of the Tatar language and script, have translated into it the whole of the New Testament and the Psalms, and caused my translation to be carefully copied." Thus sometime before 1305 a translation of the New Testament and Psalms had been completed from Latin into Mongolian. Moreover, John had the intention of translating into Mongolian the whole Latin ritual, and when he celebrated mass he used to say the words of the praefatio and of the canon in Mongolian. I do not know whether these translations of his are extant. (Laufer p. 256, 1907.)

Some Buddhist texts were translated from Chinese into Uighūr. The sūtra of the Great Bear constellation (Pei t'ou ch'i hsing ching) was thus translated and printed in Uighūr in 1330 in an edition of a thousand copies, none of which is known at present. That sūtra is not listed by Nanjio (1883) or Bagchi (1927–38); it was translated into Tibetan in 1336 and the Tibetan text is available in MS and printed form, though not included (on account of its late date) in the Kanjur or Tanjur.

This item is curious in many respects. On the basis of it one may put back the beginning of Turkish printing at least to 1330! What is more important, it enables us to fix a date in the history of the Uighūr people in relation to Chinese culture and to Buddhism.

Thus to the translations listed above should be added translations from Latin into Mongolian, from Chinese into Uighūr, and from Chinese (or Uighūr?) into Tibetan.

IV. EDUCATION

A. *Christendom*

1. *Introductory remarks*

It is worth while to give our readers some idea of the efforts which were made not only to create knowledge, but also to preserve and diffuse it. We cannot, however, devote too much space to a part of the subject which is almost endless. There were schools all over Christendom, we may say all over the civilized world, schools of various grades and kinds, and each of these schools had its own peculiarities and suffered its own vicissitudes. On the other hand, the greatest and most successful teachers of mankind, then as always, were not the deliberate and professional teachers, but other men, poets and scholars, doing as well as possible their self-appointed task without much thought of anything else. As an illustration of my meaning, think of Dante, who saw and knew everything, and influenced more men than all the grammarians of Europe put together.

Now we shall deal with Dante, Petrarca, and other great "teachers" presently, in a very full manner, but we shall hardly insist here or later on their function as educators of the people, for that goes without saying. The great poets and seers are the first and last teachers.

2. *Creation of new universities*

The universities, or studia generalia as they were called, continued their triumphal development begun at the end of the twelfth century. Ten new ones were added to the roll: Rome and Avignon in 1303, Perugia in 1308, Treviso in 1318, Cahors in 1332, Grenoble in 1339, Pisa in 1343, Prague in 1347–48, Florence in 1349, Perpignan in 1350. The most important universities of this period, however, were the earlier ones, which were already enjoying the prestige of seniority.

In contrast with the older institutions, which grew up like Topsy or existed ex consuetudine, the new studia were deliberately created, most of them by papal bulls. Yet even in their case what we call the creation was sometimes nothing but the official recognition of an existing situation. All these universities were essentially guilds of students or guilds of teachers, that is, associations of men grouped together for the defense and promotion of their common interests. By this time the value of universities was well understood in France, Italy, England, Spain, but not yet in Germany, unless Prague be called a German city. There was an increasing need of them because of the demand for educated theologians, lawyers, physicians, and administrators. Their propaganda value was also recognized by their patrons, the heads of church and state.

3. *English colleges*

In England the organization of the two old universities was continued and supplemented by the creation of new colleges: Exeter, Oriel, and Queen's in Oxford; King's, Michaelhouse, Clare, Pembroke, Gonville, and Trinity Hall in Cambridge.

4. *Parisian colleges*

There were plenty of colleges on the Continent, but they seldom attained a relative importance comparable to that of the English colleges, nor did they achieve a similar independence. On the other hand, their abundance was equaled by their diversity. In Paris alone there were by 1350 very nearly fifty colleges of all kinds, most of them, it is true, small and rudimentary, hardly more than hostelries for students. A few became the nurseries of a relatively large number of distinguished people and rendered the same service to France that the main English colleges rendered to England. The three leading houses were probably Cardinal Lemoine, Navarre, and Montaigu.

5. *Educational reforms*

The most original educator was the Norman lawyer Pierre Dubois, who advocated the study of Oriental languages for colonial purposes, and public education for the needs of the state. He went so far as to recommend the training of girls, even for special professions such as medicine. His ideas did not materialize because they were too far ahead of his time, and perhaps also because they were too socialistic in an age of Catholic individualism.

Diniz the Liberal (XIII-2), who did so much for the education and the spiritual growth of Portugal, lived until 1325. The University of Lisbon, founded by him in 1290, moved eighteen years later to Coimbra, which was destined to become after many more vicissitudes its final home.

The Catalan visionary Ramon Lull was also in his own strange way an outstanding educator. He was by temperament a missionary and a teacher, and some of his books, the Liber de militia, the Liber doctrinae puerilis, and the Liber de prima et secunda intentione, were educational books which exerted much influence in their Catalan, Spanish, Latin, French, and English editions. These books were written before 1300, but Lull lived until 1315/16. As far as the Spanish world was concerned, his influence was transmitted partly by Don Juan Manuel.

The earliest Spanish code, Las siete partidas, compiled for Alfonso el Sabio, was not promulgated until 1348,[1] at the cortes gathered by Alfonso XI (king of Castile and León 1312-50) in Alcalá de Henares.[2]

This Ordenamentio de Alcalá is a landmark in the history of universities. It included the first legal definition of a studium generale, and explained the main rules of its administration and the privileges of its members. It has been called the earliest educational code of Europe. Its contents were handed down, with occasional modifications, from one Spanish code to another until the end of the Middle Ages.

B. *Israel*

Until recent times the Jewish schools, yeshibot, were almost exclusively theological and Talmudic schools, though considerable importance was always given of necessity to the Hebrew language. Their history can be traced back to early Talmudic days in Palestine and Babylon, and it can be followed more or less closely in many countries of North Africa, Western Asia, and Europe throughout the Middle Ages.[3]

The main teachers of Israel were not necessarily found in the yeshibot, however, for here as everywhere the most influential teachers are as likely as not outside the schools; in the long run the best teachers are those who teach not, but simply accomplish their own heroic purpose. From this point of view, we may say that the leading teachers of Israel in the first half of the fourteenth century were, for the orthodox, Levi ben Gerson in southern France, and, for the Qaraites, Aaron ben Elijah in Turkey.

The most original views on education were set forth by Joseph Kaspi in the ethical testament which he wrote in Valencia 1332 in accordance with an old Jewish custom. This contains moral advice to his son Solomon and outlines a course of study and education from the fourteenth year to the twentieth and later in life. It is a very interesting document of a rare kind in mediaeval literature, which enables us to visualize as it were the spiritual progress of a Jewish adolescent of noble family.

[1] Not 1338, as was printed in Introd. 2, 838.

[2] Some 33 km. from Madrid. It was in that city that a university was founded in 1499 at the request of cardinal Ximenes. It was there also that Cervantes was born in 1547.

[3] For general guidance on this subject see the articles by Judah David Eisenstein (JE 12, 595-600, 1906) and S. Assaf (EJ 9, 25-42, 1932).

C. *Islām*

The most remarkable pedagogue of the previous century was Muḥammad ibn Aḥmad al-Riqūṭī of Murcia. We do not know the circumstances of his life, nor the date of his death. The latter may have occurred in the fourteenth century. As far as we know he did not write any book, and this suggests that other original teachers may have distinguished themselves without leaving any trace of their activities. Men deeply interested in teaching would do but little else, and have no time left for writing. Their contemporary fame may be considerable, but it hardly survives their pupils.

The main teachers of this period whose memory has come down to us are all in the East. The most significant by far is the Persian Rashīd al-dīn of Tabrīz, who used his wealth to patronize learning and art. He was himself an outstanding scholar, one of the greatest of the Middle Ages, and he took special pains to diffuse and preserve his writings. Considering the originality of his mind, it is remarkable that it did not occur to him to take advantage of the art of printing, which he was acquainted with, for that diffusion.

In the previous section I spoke of the "student's guide" prepared by the Provençal Jew Joseph Kaspi for his son Solomon. Similar works were compiled by Muslims. One of them, the Ta'līm al-muta'allim, had been written at the beginning of the thirteenth century by Burhān al-dīn al-Zarnūjī (XIII-1); that was simply a collection of sayings culled from earlier writers, but on account of its attractiveness and brevity it enjoyed much popularity in the East, including Turkey.[4] More elaborate guides were prepared by the Syrian Ibn Jamā'a in 1273 and especially by the Iraqian Ibn al-Akfānī. The latter's Irshād al-qāṣid ílā asnā'-l-maqāṣid seems to be one of the most remarkable books of its kind, of special interest to us because of the historical and bibliographical information which it contains. That guide did not remain unnoticed, but it was too elaborate and too learned to be as popular as the earlier and humbler Ta'līm.

D. *Far East*

The author of the most popular schoolbook of China, Wang Ying-lin (XIII-2), died in 1296, hence he does not belong to our story, but his Three character classic (San tzŭ ching) began in our period its triumphal career. Millions of people have been conning that short text (560 words) ever since, while scholars, a much smaller but devoted band, have been consulting Wang's greater work, the Sea of jade (Yü hai). I did not come across any other representative of Chinese education, and therefore I recalled Wang's humble but popular contribution.[5]

For educational progress we must turn to Japan. The powerful Hōjō family had created in Kanazawa (near Yokohama) a rich Chinese and Japanese library which became a center of learning of increasing value until 1333, when the fall of that family jeopardized their efforts for the sake of learning. The Kanazawa-bunko continued to exist, however, ready for better use a century later.

Japanese education was based on Confucianism and Buddhism. The leading exponent of the new Confucianism, mixed with Buddhism—the so-called hsing-li, brought to its perfection by Chu Hsi (XII-2)—was the monk Gen-e, who was able to impart these teachings not only to his followers of the Tendai and Rinzai sects,

[4] To my note in Introd. 2, 598 add a reference to M. Plessner (EI 4, 1218, 1934).

[5] It should be added, however, that the ascription of the San tzŭ ching to him has been disputed. The far more important Yü hai is undoubtedly his.

but also to the members of the imperial court. Another great teacher of the Rinzai-shū (a branch of Zen) was Soseki, but his teaching was primarily if not exclusively Buddhistic. Other monks of this age might be named, but Gen-e and Soseki represent it almost completely. We should also mention Yoshida Kenkō, whose influence was of the literary type. His Tsurē-zure-gusa, a collection of essays, was the pleasant vehicle of Buddhism and Confucianism, not only to his own contemporaries (he died in 1350) but to every following generation. He is an excellent symbol of the Japanese humanities of his time.

V. PHILOSOPHICAL AND CULTURAL BACKGROUND

1. Definition

As the title indicates, this section deals not only with philosophy, but with a number of activities which are not of a very technical nature and hence cannot be grouped in the following sections devoted to special sciences, and yet which influenced, sometimes deeply, the mental climate of this period. Economic and artistic activities are generally omitted, not because we fail to appreciate their importance, but simply because these are treated elaborately in other books and our field is already too large and too complex as it is.

Moreover, the title implies that I am not attempting to write a history of philosophy (or of theology) as such, but simply to describe the "philosophical and cultural background." This is of course very desirable, but even if it were not, it would be unavoidable, as many of the scientists were primarily philosophers. It was thus impossible to deal with science without dealing at the same time with philosophy and theology.

As philosophy was inseparable from theology, the account had to be divided according to the theological systems (Jewish, Christian, Muslim, etc.), and the large number of personalities involved made further subdivisions necessary, according to geographical regions or nationalities. This is natural, for each region represents a mental climate determined partly by ethnical conditions, partly by geographical ones, partly by religion and philosophy. Nevertheless, another kind of classification would have been conceivable, for various categories of mediaeval philosophy cut across racial, national, and even religious boundaries. The quarrel between nominalists and realists, for example, was not by any means restricted to Christian philosophers; neither was the encyclopaedic point of view, or the mystical one, the appanage of a single creed or nation. Therefore, it will be useful to indicate some of the main philosophical viewpoints and controversies before attempting our description of the cultural backgrounds of the main human groups.

Some of the more technical problems discussed by philosophers are reserved for later sections devoted to the special sciences concerned. For example, ideas on infinity and continuity will be reviewed in the mathematical and physical sections, and relations between theology and canon law on the one hand, and between philosophy and politics on the other, will be examined in the section on law and sociology.

As far as the Latin West was concerned, I did my best to investigate the activities of the leading doctors, but I realize that in spite of my efforts much has necessarily escaped me. Indeed, the journals devoted to scholastic philosophy are as numerous as they are bulky; every Catholic college or institution publishes at least one, and almost every religious order publishes not only its own annals and biographical collections, but also periodicals devoted to scholastic learning and discussion. It was clearly impossible for me to examine all those files, though I keenly realized the probability of obtaining valuable materials in each of them. The reader will find occasional references to papers issued in monastic journals, because such papers were given to me by the authors or otherwise brought to my attention; these references should be considered as exemplary rather than exhaustive.

2. The need of unity, encyclopaedic tendencies, classification of the sciences

The main purposes of philosophy are to unify knowledge and to harmonize it with one's religious creed. When philosophy and theology are inextricably combined, as they were in the Middle Ages, these two purposes become a single one. It was very strong in the Christian West in the fourteenth century in spite of increasing criticism and even of a small amount of skepticism, and it was almost equally strong elsewhere. There were many differences between, say, Muslim and Christian, and even between different schools of Christian theology, but everyone believed in the existence of absolute values. Thus mediaeval doctors of different schools or of different churches spoke more nearly the same language than do, let us say, professors teaching philosophy today in the same faculty.

On that basis the attempt to write a history of comparative philosophy in the Middle Ages would be justified and worth while, though it has never been made.[1] Comparisons thus far have been restricted to the Jewish, Christian, and Muslim philosophies, which are closely connected in many ways, being branches of the same Greco-Judaic tree. The philosophical treatises written in the same century in Arabic, Hebrew, Latin, and Greek, by men very remote from one another in space and outwardly very different, are nevertheless singularly congruent.

The need of unity takes two forms. It may lead one to determine the first principles of one's knowledge and of one's faith; that is the more strictly philosophical form. Or it may lead one to review, analyze, and synthetize all the knowledge available on every subject; that is the encyclopaedic form. Both forms were equally well represented in mediaeval times, and almost everywhere. In my account of the cultural background of each country I am thus obliged to deal concurrently with two different kinds of purposes, the purely philosophical or theological, and the encyclopaedic. It is practically impossible to separate them, because they were often united in the same individuals, and sometimes in the same books. It is not necessary to give examples; the reader will come across plenty of them in the following pages. He should not blame me for calling an encyclopaedist a philosopher, or vice versa, for I could not well avoid it without creating artificial difficulties. The logician sharpening his intellectual tools, the theologian introducing more rigor into his definitions, and the encyclopaedist unifying available knowledge are each of them philosophizing in his own way.

The fundamental convergence of their thinking, in spite of divergent methods, is proved by the existence of similar by-products appearing and reappearing almost everywhere. I am referring to the treatises (or chapters) on the classification of the sciences (or branches of science) which occur in every learned language. The original purpose of the classification may be logical, or theological, or encyclopaedic; the fruits are similar. Many examples of such classification may easily be found in this volume by means of the index, and a detailed comparison of them would be instructive.

[1] Except for a brilliant and incomplete sketch by Masson-Oursel (1923).

The subject is a fascinating one; it has exercised the minds of modern philosophers as well as of mediaeval ones. A study of it would be out of place here, and, however short, it would take too much space. Faute de mieux I mention the main *modern* books devoted to it.

It is expedient to begin with Auguste Comte: Cours de philosophie positive (vol. 1, Paris 1830), for that work revived the subject more than any other. André Marie Ampère: Essai sur la philosophie des sciences, ou Exposition analytique d'une classification naturelle de toutes les connaissances humaines (2 vols., Paris 1838–43); both volumes were published after Ampère's death (1836), the second being edited by his son Jean-Jacques Ampère. I have used a reprint of vol. 1 dated 1856, and the first edition of vol. 2. Herbert Spencer: The classification of the sciences, to which are added reasons for dissenting from the philosophy of M. Comte (48 p., New York 1864). Edmond Goblot: Essai sur la classification des sciences (296 p., Paris 1898). Camillo Trivero: Classificazione delle scienze (292 p., Hoepli, Milano 1899). Joseph Mariétan (Augustinian canon): Problème de la classification des sciences d'Aristote à St. Thomas (203 p., St. Maurice, Switzerland 1901), largely devoted to the history of mediaeval Christendom. Adrien Naville: Nouvelle classification des sciences (185 p., Paris 1901), first published in Geneva 1888; the second edition is so different from the first that it is more like a new work. Robert Flint: Philosophy as scientia scientiarum and a history of classification of the sciences (Edinburgh 1904). Edmond Goblot: Le système des sciences (260 p., Paris 1922; Isis 4, 565). Paul Oppenheim: Die natürliche Ordnung der Wissenschaften. Grundgesetze der Wissenschaftslehre (288 p., Jena 1926; Isis 9, 565). Henry Evelyn Bliss: The organization of knowledge and the system of the sciences (453 p., New York 1929; Isis 13, 378–79). Georges Clergué: Etude sur le problème de la classification des sciences (Clermont thesis, 78 p., Paris 1930).

Most of these studies are deductive rather than inductive. Historical data are generally avoided except by Mariétan, Flint, and Bliss. For the Middle Ages these studies are utterly insufficient, even Mariétan's, restricted to Christendom. More special and more valuable studies (e.g., Wolfson's) will be found in the editions and commentaries of the texts ad hoc quoted in this volume. I think it can be said that every tendency developed in the modern books on classification of sciences can already be found in their mediaeval prototypes, whether Arabic, Hebrew, or Latin.

The Chinese classification of knowledge can be inferred from their schemes of bibliography, the earliest of which, Pieh-lu, was devised by the director of the Han imperial library, Liu Hsiang, and by his son and successor, Liu Hsin (I-2 B.C.). All the books in the library were classified under the seven outlines (ch'i lüeh), (1) general introduction, (2) classics, (3) philosophy, (4) poetry, (5) military science, (6) astronomy, occultism, etc., (7) medicine. That system was accepted by Pan Ku (I-2), except that the latter reduced the number of classes to six by distributing the contents of class 1 among the other six. A new system was devised by Hsün Hsü (III-2) for the catalogue of the Wei imperial library. That system, called ssŭ pu (four categories), recognized four main divisions, (1) classics and philology, (2) philosophy, military science, mathematics, and divination, (3) history, anecdotes, state reports, and miscellaneous records, (4) poetry, eulogies, and treatises found in the Wei tombs. The modern names of these four divisions, to wit, ching, shih, tzŭ, and chi, were first used in the first half of the seventh century in the bibliographic section of the standard history of the Sui dynasty (Sui shu), and two new divisions were added concerning tao (Taoism) and fo (Buddhism).

Other modifications were made from time to time during the T'ang and Sung dynasties. A better classification was proposed by the historian Chêng Ch'iao (XII-2); it was based on twelve divisions, (1) classics, (2) rituals, (3) music, (4) linguistics, (5) history, (6) philosophy, (7) astronomy, (8) numerology, (9) fine arts, (10) medicine, (11) encyclopaedias, (12) belles-lettres. The old ssŭ pu triumphed, however, and after some improvement of its subdivisions served as basis for the imperial catalogue of the Ch'ing dynasty, the famous Ssŭ k'u ch'üan shu, compiled in 1773–81 by order of Kao Tsung (Ch'ien-lung), and remained the official classification until the end of that dynasty (1912).

The earliest Japanese classification, compiled in 889–97, was based upon that of the Sui shu; this was natural enough, for it was used to classify the 1,579 Chinese works then existing in Japan. The second Japanese classification (the first dealing with Japanese books as well as Chinese ones), completed c. 1440, included c. 500 works by Japanese authors, which were divided into twenty classes. The third Japanese classification appeared in 1791, and was followed through the nineteenth and twentieth centuries by various others more and more elaborate; all those classifications were specifically Japanese. After the Meiji restoration (1868) Western methods were introduced.

To return to the mediaeval systems, the Chinese and Japanese do not seem ever to have risen above the level of classification needed for library or bibliography; they never faced the epistemological problems which exercised the minds of the ancient and mediaeval philosophers of the West.

For further details on the history of Chinese and Japanese classification, see A. K'ai-ming Ch'iu: A classification scheme for Chinese and Japanese books (385 p., Washington 1943; Isis 36).

3. Internationalism or universalism of mediaeval philosophy

The most striking feature of mediaeval thought is its universalism, so strong that it overcame not only national boundaries, but also to a large extent religious ones. Arguments developed by Jewish or Muslim scholars could be reproduced almost verbatim by Christian ones. To be sure, the consensus was deeper and broader within each faith, but in any case it transgressed national boundaries and ethnical divisions. Thus Buddhism spread a definite ideology from India across the whole of Central and Eastern Asia. Islām diffused another ideology, common categories of thought, from Arabia to India and across the Mediterranean world to the Far West.

In the Latin West, which concerns us more directly, the main centers of intellectual diffusion were the universities, and as we have seen the majority of these were licensed by the pope. There were far more individual differences among mediaeval scholars than most people imagine, yet these scholars had in common a goodly stock of fundamental ideas and identical aspirations. They were very cosmopolitan; when we read their biographies, we find that they studied and taught in many places and very often in many countries. The population of the universities—masters and students—was drawn from everywhere, so much so that it was found expedient for administrative purposes to divide it into "nations."[2] Etienne Gilson has given us (1937) a striking picture of the internationalism obtaining in Paris. It so happens that during its period of glory—the thirteenth century—the

[2] The choice and number of "nations" and the rules ad hoc varied from one university to another. See Rashdall (1936, passim)

leading teachers in the University of Paris were almost all foreigners, whether English like Alexander of Hales or Roger Bacon, or German like Albert the Great, or Italian like St. Bonaventure and St. Thomas, or Scot like John Duns, or Belgian like Siger of Brabant. This was less surprising than it seems at first view, for the University of Paris was not a Parisian or a French institution; it was neither regulated nor subsidized by town or country; its ideals were Christian ideals, and it was controlled by an international organization, the Catholic church. It is true the situation is far from being the same in the following century, especially when the popes are "captive" in Avignon under the thumb of the French kings; indeed, in the fourteenth century the main teachers of Paris are no longer foreigners, but Frenchmen. As there were many differences between universities, we may expect conditions as to nationalism vs. internationalism to vary also from one to another. In each of them various "nations" were represented, but the relations between the nations were more or less harmonious; sometimes they were not harmonious at all (as in Prague) and became inimical; the exceptions, however, do not invalidate the rule. The spirit of Western Christendom, and particularly of the universities, was not nationalistic to begin with, but during the fourteenth century there are ominous signs here and there of increasing nationalism and sectarianism. In this respect as in many others the best mediaeval ideals are becoming tarnished.

4. The Book of sentences

Almost every schoolman wrote a complete or partial commentary on the Sententiarum libri IV composed by Peter the Lombard (XII-2). These commentaries occur in innumerable MSS which may be simply the notes taken by students (reportationes), or the text edited by the commentator (ordinatio), or later abridgments of that text (abbreviationes). How is it that such MSS are so numerous? Simply because the teaching of theology in every university was based essentially on two books, the Bible and the Sentences (this affords another illustration of mediaeval universalism). Of course subsidiary texts were used, notably the Historia scholastica, a manual of sacred history by Peter the Eater (XII-2), but during his fifteen or sixteen years of theological preparation the student's main pabulum was the Bible and the Sentences, and some people complained that the students devoted far more time to the latter than to the former!

In Paris, the attainment of the bachelorship in theology involved three steps: (1) biblicus ordinarius or cursor (according as the candidate was regular or secular); for this he had to lecture on the Bible; (2) sententiarius; for this he had to lecture for nine months on the Sentences; (3) the final degree of baccalarius formatus. As each bachelor was thus obliged to deliver a good many lectures on the Sentences, and as his lectures were attended by small or large bodies of students, it is natural enough that every ancient library has a good number of manuscripts of reportationes, ordinationes, and abbreviationes.

Neither is it surprising that after a century or more of that practice the Sentences occupied in the theologian's estimation a place hardly second to that of the Bible.[3] An outstanding scholar like Albert the Great, discussing the amount of knowledge possessed by the Mother of Christ, concluded that she must have been acquainted

[3] Compare the story concerning the Kitāb al-fuṣūl wal-ghāyāt written by the Syrian poet Abū-l-'Alā' (973–1058) in imitation of the Qur'ān. When he was rebuked because of his arrogance, he replied that his work would lose its inferiority if it were ceremoniously read for a few centuries!

with the trivium and quadrivium and have had a summary knowledge of the Bible and Sentences.[4] After Albert's time the practice continued for three more centuries at least. Every theologian lectured on the Sentences. Plenty of examples will be found in this volume (see index); let me quote two. No less a doctor than St. Thomas Aquinas wrote a very elaborate commentary on the Sentences.[5] On the other hand, Luther's earliest production was a partial commentary on the same work.[6] It should be remembered that mediaeval writers (and this includes Luther) did not have the same shame or self-consciousness that we have with regard to authorities. The modern scientist would not think of intitulating a treatise on relativity "Commentary on Einstein." The mediaeval tendency was rather the opposite; the works of Aristotle furnished various categories of thought; instead of writing a treatise on morals, one wrote naturally a commentary on the Ethics; a treatise on geography took easily the form of a commentary on Ptolemy; to lecture on Euclid was the same as to lecture on geometry; and the words "theology" and "Book of sentences"[7] tended in the same way to become synonymous.

It remains to explain how Peter the Lombard had managed to assume such a fundamental importance. He had not invented theology? Of course not. The question is highly pertinent, and the answer very instructive to the observer of human affairs.

Modern theologians agree that the Sentences is not in any sense an original and creative work; but it has the necessary qualities of a good textbook, of an educational best seller. It is sufficiently moderate and eclectic and displays no offensive superiority of any kind. The Magister Sententiarum had been very much influenced by Peter Abaelard (XII-1), especially by the latter's Sic et non, and his effort to organize the teaching of theology is very similar to that of his predecessor. Yet the spirit is utterly different, and it is because of that difference that the first Peter failed egregiously, whereas the second obtained such unbelievable and, it must be admitted, such undeserved fame. Peter Abaelard was critical and aggressive; he enjoyed showing up contradictions and did not bother to solve them; he was a trouble-maker and a rebel, irreverent and mischievous. On the contrary, Peter the Lombard was essentially conservative and compromising; he was obedient and deferent to each authority and found ways of solving the difficulties separating them almost without criticizing them, as if they were always right even when they contradicted one another! As always happens in such cases, because of his aggressiveness Peter Abaelard was often suspected of mischief or heresy even when he was innocent, whereas Peter the Lombard could get away with everything, even with heresy itself. For example, the two Peters shared the heretical idea of nihilianism (quod Christus secundum quod est homo non est aliquid; the human nature of Christ is nothing). Abaelard was thrice condemned (1121, 1141, 1142);

[4] "Beatissima Virgo Bibliam et Sententias in summo habuit" (Opera XX, 80, Lyon 1651). Quotation derived from Rashdall (1, 474, 1936). Considering the place held by the Sentences in the universities, we may expect Rashdall to give abundant information on the subject. See index, s.v. Peter the Lombard. Main account in his vol. 1, 474–78.

[5] I have in hand the Scriptum super libro tertio Sententiarum de incarnatione et de virtutibus et donis nobis per Christum collatis. New edition by Maria Fabianus Moos (O.P.). This represents only one-quarter of the whole work, yet covers 1374 pages (Paris 1933).

[6] Paul Vignaux: Luther, commentateur des Sentences, livre 1, dist. XVII (115 p., Paris 1935); La pensée au Moyen âge (p. 65, collection Colin, Paris 1938; Isis 30, 165).

[7] This makes sense of the saying of Albert the Great quoted above. Taken literally it is absurd, but what Albert meant was, "Our Lady had an intuitive knowledge of the Bible and of theology."

Peter the Lombard was reproved too, but far more gently. In 1121 Abaelard was obliged to burn his own treatise with his own hands, whereas the Sentences became the holiest of textbooks!

The main and indisputable merit of the Sentences was that it provided a well ordered exposition of the whole of theology. The student was given not only the principles, but for each of them a whole body of controversial arguments; he was provided with a commodious frame of reference. For people endowed or afflicted with dialectical tendencies, and such people were but too frequent in mediaeval times, the Book of sentences was as stimulating as a stamp album for a collector of stamps. The results were some of them good, most of them deleterious. It was good to provide theological knowledge; it was very bad to encourage excessive discussions, most of which were naturally futile and sterile. Some Franciscan doctors could think of nothing else but such controversies, and yet what would their masters, Christ and St. Francis, have thought of them?

This reminds me of the Buddha's reaction to similar extravagances of the Hindu schoolmen arguing endlessly on such questions as "Is the world eternal or not? Is the world finite or not?" Said the Buddha:[8] "These questions are not calculated to profit, they are not concerned with the Dharma, they do not redound to the elements of right conduct, nor to detachment, nor to purification from lusts, nor to quietude, nor to tranquilisation of heart, nor to real knowledge, nor to the insight of the higher stages of the Path, nor to Nirvāṇa. Therefore it is that I express no opinion upon them."

Similar reactions against scholasticism occurred in Christendom, and we shall come across some of them later on.

In the meanwhile let us consider a few of the main causes of conflict.

5. Nominalism vs. logical realism

The opposition expressed by the words nominalism and realism is an ancient one, but it is not expedient to insist on the Greek origin. To be sure, Plato's theory of ideas (as archetypes, transcendent essences) is the source of realism, but Aristotle's philosophy is not the source of nominalism. The problem of universals was formulated in Boetius' translation of Porphyry's Isagoge, a favorite mediaeval textbook. Under the influence of Plato, Proclos, Dionysios, etc. (Isis 29, 423–28), early mediaeval thought was realist, and that point of view was made explicit by St. Anselm (XI-2): universals exist before the individual things modeled upon them (universalia ante rem). The opposite point of view—universals do not correspond to any objective realities, they are mere words, flatus vocis (universalia post rem)—was expressed at about the same time by Roscelin of Compiègne (XI-2). From then on, the issue was one which no philosopher could eschew. By the end of the thirteenth century realism was triumphant in a moderate form in the writings of St. Thomas Aquinas, and in a more extreme form in those of Duns Scotus. Both of them derived the individual from the universal, though in different ways.[9]

[8] According to the Poṭṭhapāda sutta (B. C. Law 1, 93, 1933), as quoted by Suzuki (1, 125, 1927). Poṭṭhapāda was the name of a paribbājaka or wandering teacher who met the Buddha.

[9] For St. Thomas' and Duns Scotus' views on individuation, see De Wulf (2, 12, 74, 1926). The principium individuationis was a subject of predilection to the schoolmen of the thirteenth century, but they had not invented it. The idea of individuation is already formulated in the metaphysics of Ibn Sīnā, being called tashakhkhuṣ. Amélie Marie Goichon: La distinction de l'essence et de l'existence d'après Ibn Sīnā (p. 460–82, Paris 1937; Isis 33, 326–29); also Goichon (no. 310, 1938).

In the first half of the fourteenth century occurred what might be called a second nominalist reaction, led by the English Franciscan William of Occam. This was part of a complete system of philosophy implying a theory of knowledge. Occam's nominalism (Occamism) was moderate, and because of that it obtained a success comparable to that of St. Thomas' moderate realism; it is often called terminism, because he so often used the word terminus in his analysis of logical operations. He tried to give a psychological interpretation of universals, and therefore terminism might be considered an early kind of conceptualism (see below). He was supported by other English Franciscans such as Adam Wodeham, and even by an English Dominican, Robert of Holcot.

Duhem claimed that Occamism was a purely English perversion and that the views of the contemporary French "physicists" were essentially different. There are differences between the views of Buridan and those of Occam, but they are secondary, and not larger than those separating Occam from his English followers. Buridan was moderate, but so was Occam himself; the exaggerations of radical nominalism were not his, but as usual due to the zeal of lesser men.

In the meanwhile a sort of intermediary doctrine, conceptualism (universals exist in the mind; they are more than signs, they are forms or operations of thought) was developed by such Frenchmen as the Franciscan Pierre Auriol and the Dominican Durand of Saint Pourçain, by the Augustinian Thomas of Strassburg, and by other members of the schola aegidiana.

The nominalist revival was part and parcel of the renewed interest in logic as a universal method. The old logic (logica antiqua or vetus) was based on the Isagoge, the Categories, De interpretatione, and Boetius; the new logic on the two Analytics, the Topics, the Elenchi, and the Summulae logicales of Peter of Spain[10] (XIII-2). Irrespective of content, the new logic was more rig orous, and was studied with greater predilection. It was the favorite technique of the time; it was applied to everything with fancy expectations, somewhat like logistics today. It was the outstanding scientific method of the fourteenth century.

There is no doubt that at that particular stage nominalism was favorable to the progress of science, and it is easy to prove that the new method attracted on the whole the most original and vigorous minds. On the other hand, it was less favorable to religion, or to religious feeling; it increased the rationalistic impact on blind obedience and superstition. It tended to lead philosophy toward science and away from theology. It created a kind of radicalism, fortifying Averroism and incredulity, but not necessarily concerned with social matters.

We may say that Occamism was a powerful factor both in the disintegration of mediaeval thought and in the slow elaboration of modern science, but both statements require qualification. As to the first, we must remember that mediaeval thought was very complex and that Occamism did not affect equally every aspect of it. Then even as now a man might be a radical in philosophy and religion, yet a conservative in politics (lay or ecclesiastical), or vice versa. As to the second, one must beware of exaggerating the innovations of nominalism or of comparing

[10] More exactly, the seventh part of the Summulae, De terminorum proprietatibus (parva logicalia), the six earlier parts being a summary of the Organon (see Introd. 2, 890), though already colored with nominalism. I have given a different description of logica nova vs. logica vetus in my note on Raoul Le Breton, and will not try to harmonize the two descriptions. The term logica nova (or vetus) is naturally a relative one, which was understood somewhat differently in different places or times, or by different persons.

it with its modern phasis, the so-called "scientific" nominalism.[11] Again, though Occam was always asking himself whether a sentence was true or not "de virtute sermonis" (Michalski p. 255–61, 1937), it is misleading to consider him a forerunner of modern semantics.

6. Rationalism in Jewish, Muslim, and Christian philosophies

Under the pressure of Aristotle, which increased gradually as the writings of his school became better known, there was a greater tendency everywhere, and especially in scientific circles, to rationalize more freely and more abundantly. It is very remarkable that we can observe the growth of this tendency equally well in Jewish, Muslim, and Christian writings. In every case, it leads to the same attitude. The religious frame must be accepted without restriction, but within that frame superstition should not be tolerated. That is what we call the rationalistic attitude, an attitude objected to by other adherents of the same religion, who were not satisfied with a minimum of dogmas, but tended to increase continually the number of irrational, marvelous, and magical elements clustering around their faith. Thus we witness in the fourteenth century three major conflicts: Maimonidism vs. anti-Maimonidism, Averroism vs. anti-Averroism, Thomism vs. anti-Thomism. These conflicts are naturally different, not only because each has its own sacred domain wherein rationalism is not permitted to apply (the three domains have some elements in common); yet each is a conflict between more rationalism and less rationalism (I do not say between pure rationalism and irrationalism). Each of these conflicts has been discussed in volume 2. Indeed, the first two developed throughout the thirteenth century, and the third one began in the last quarter of that century. It will thus suffice to say a few words about each of them, the main point of this note being to call attention to their coexistence.

The Jewish conflict is independent of the one between Rabbinism and Qaraism already mentioned (section II, subsection 14); it was largely restricted to rabbinic circles, and raged particularly in southern France and Spain. In 1234 the conservative rabbis of southern France had gone so far as to cause Maimonides' works to be burned by the Christian authorities. The main leaders of the reaction at the beginning of the fourteenth century were Solomon ben Adret (XIII-2) and Abba Mari ben Moses. For a brief appreciation of the situation, reread my note on Maimonides' rationalism and influence (Introd. 2, 374–75).

The struggle between the Averroists and their enemies is very much the same, with the strange peculiarity that it was fought not so much in the Muslim world as in the Jewish and Christian ones. Moreover, on account of a series of misunderstandings Averroism took the appearance not only of what it really was, to wit, Aristotelian positivism, but of what it was not—at least originally—namely, radicalism in the mischievous sense. Under the stress of persecution some Averroists became as troublesome as they had been misconstrued to be and lived up (or down) to their fame; all kinds of subversive elements conglomerated around the views of Ibn Rushd as distorted by his bigoted adversaries.

Thus, while St. Thomas was fighting for Christian rationalism and using many

[11] Modern and mediaeval nominalism have enough in common to justify a common name, yet they are different, and the name should be qualified with different adjectives. It is not the place here to discuss scientific nominalism as developed by Edouard Le Roy, Pierre Duhem, and others. For a discussion of one of its latest phases see Herbert Dingle: Science and the unobservable (Nature 141, 21–28, 1938).

of the weapons forged by Ibn Sīnā, al-Ghazzālī, and Ibn Rushd himself, he was fighting also the subversive Averroism which was then current in Latin writings.[12] Among other things, Averroism had come to mean free thought in the sense of irreligion; its supporters were accused of questioning the fundamental doctrines of the church, especially of doubting the dogmas of creation and of the immortality of the soul, of being materialists, etc. Moreover, Averroists had the bad reputation of being scientifically minded and prone to dialectics. This was the crowning irony. Humanists like Petrarca hated Averroists for the very qualities and defects which the latter shared with the Christian schoolmen; he considered them ill-mannered and conceited pedants, always ready to insist on terms but unable to appreciate letters.

Thus St. Thomas found himself in the position of fighting at the same time Muslim rationalism and Christian irrationalism. He followed a via media between the Averroists of the left and the Scotists and Augustinians of the right. It is largely because of that conciliatory attitude that St. Thomas obtained so much prestige. At their general chapter held at Metz in 1313 the Dominicans designated his teachings as the "doctrina communis Thome," and from then on the Order took special pains to prevent deviations from them. For example, c. 1316 Pierre de la Palu and John of Naples were charged with the mission of examining the writings of one of their brethren, Durand of Saint Pourçain, with regard to his Thomist orthodoxy. These two theological detectives worked so well that they discovered two hundred thirty-five points about which Durand was swerving, however slightly, from the straight road of Thomism. Happily the new pope, John XXII, came to Durand's rescue, appointing him bishop of Limoux (later of Puy) and thus withdrawing him from his Dominican obedience.

This story is significant, but one should beware of exaggerating its meaning. In spite of occasional rebellions from the left or from the right, Thomism remained the main doctrine of Christian compromise and unity in the fourteenth century. It is foolish to deny unity; it is equally foolish to deny the reality of many divergent streams. There are on one side the nominalists and the extravagant dialecticians who argue for the sake of argument and can never stop; there are also skeptical tendencies, as exemplified in the astounding sayings of John of Mirecourt and of Nicholas of Autrecourt, "the mediaeval Hume." Indeed, it is only people who are ignorant of mediaeval philosophy who can speak of its uniformity and monotony; there was a great deal of diversity in it, but the centripetal forces were correspondingly strong, and these forces were largely supplied by Dominican and Thomist discipline.

7. Mystical reaction

When the scientific and dialectical pressure increases, it is sooner or later too strong for certain temperaments and becomes unendurable to them. Their reaction is universally the same: mysticism. We find it in all the literatures of the East and West, the terms being sometimes so much akin that interinfluences are suggested when in all probability there is nothing but similar reactions to identical actions.

[12] Thus the triumph of Thomism was represented as a triumph over heresy and over Averroism. Remember the Pisa altarpiece painted by Francesco Traini, for which see Introd. 2, 736, and below.

In the Latin West, Augustinianism as developed by St. Bonaventure (XIII-2) and other Franciscans is largely a mystical movement, but in addition we witness a marvelous eclosion of mystical writings by inspired "friends of God" such as Eckhart, Tauler, Suso in German lands, Ruysbroeck in Brabant, and Richard Rolle in England. Many sayings of Eckhart are astonishingly close to Vedantic or Buddhist statements, and these similitudes can hardly be explained by the assumption of borrowings; the only plausible explanation is convergence due to the essential alikeness of human beings all over the world.

Other mystical developments can be witnessed in contemporary Mahāyāna Buddhism, where they are endemic, and in ṣūfī literature, the latter being considerably encouraged in this period by the multiplication of darwīsh orders. The great Spanish Arabist Don Miguel Asín Palacios has claimed (1931) that Muslim mysticism (taṣawwuf) was largely derived from Christian examples. His brilliant defense of that hypothesis lends some plausibility to it, but we hardly need it to understand the reaction of human hearts to any kind of intellectual oppression.

One universal characteristic of mystical thinking is the distrust of intellectualism. We find it in St. Bonaventure and his followers, in all the Western mystics already mentioned, in the Jewish qabbalists, and in every one of their Oriental brethren, whether Arabic, Turkish, Persian, Hindu, Chinese, or Japanese. It is well expressed in a Christian text of a somewhat later date, the Imitation of Christ (I, 3): "Quid prodest magna cavillatio de occultis et obscuris rebus, de quibus nec arguemur in judicio, quia ignoravimus? . . . Et quid curae nobis de generibus et speciebus?" That is the genuine mystical taunt to dialecticians, and even to scientists; it belongs to all times and all places.

The great weakness of mysticism, always and everywhere, is its individualism. It is necessarily and paradoxically dogmatic, for the mystic, however sincere and convinced he may be, cannot give his reasons. His conviction cannot be communicated to others, except if they are exactly in the same mood. He cannot completely justify himself; he can only oppose intuitive dogmatism to dialectical dogmatism. As Gilson has shrewdly observed (p. 17, 1937), "Deep intuition is always my own intuition; good taste is always my own taste, sacred feelings are my own feelings, and, in the long run, lawful interests are always my own interests."

Sensitive men, reading mystical treatises and sharing intuitively the author's thoughts, cannot help suffering because these cannot be shared with others, except when the sharing has become almost unnecessary. Mysticism was always in part a revolt against the hard facts of life and against logical necessities, in part also an escape from everyday men to everlasting God. Its popularity almost everywhere in mediaeval times is not surprising, because misery and cruelty were rife and the wheel of fortune turned faster than it does today. But dare we criticize? It remained for our times to invent more refined cruelties and to introduce a new kind of national mysticism less rational and infinitely more pernicious than any form of mediaeval mysticism known to us.

8. Philosophical and cultural background of various countries

We may now pass to the consideration of regional or national conditions. The careful reader will recognize patterns which reappear in more than one region, but the most common have been indicated in the preceding pages.

A. *Western Christendom*

The number of "philosophers" or "thinkers" in Western Europe is so large that we have to divide them into seven national groups: Italian, Spanish, French, English, German, Flemish, and Icelandic. In a final section we shall then mention a couple of works which could not be classified in the previous ones.

A1. *Italy*

Let us begin with the poets. The earliest is the Umbrian Jacopone da Todi, who takes us back almost to the days of St. Francis, yet lived until 1306. He was the leader of the Spiritual Franciscans, and a popular poet as well as a mystic. He represents Franciscan (vs. Dominican) mysticism. His Laude belong to world literature even as the Confessions of St. Augustine or the writings of the German mystics to be considered presently.[13]

The second poet is Dante, of whom it is almost superfluous to speak here, for every reader of this book is aware of his fundamental importance for the study of fourteenth-century thought. The writings of Dante Alighieri, and especially his Divina commedia (written c. 1314–21), may be considered as the testament of early mediaeval thought, but also as the beginning of a new age. His encyclopaedic knowledge included philosophy; he was anything but a systematic philosopher, yet many trecentiste derived from him their vision of life.

The monumental nature of the three poems, Inferno, Purgatorio, and Paradiso, whether they be considered as records of the past or as apocalyptic literature, was soon realized by Dante's own contemporaries, and commentaries began to appear soon after his death (1321). The first two were those by Ser Graziolo and Guido da Pisa, but the most important of the early commentaries was composed by one of Dante's sons, Jacopo (after 1326). It is clear that in Jacopo's eyes the Divina commedia was essentially a mirror of human conduct. He, or his elder brother Pietro, composed also a kind of popular encyclopaedia in verse, called Il dottrinale.

The third poet is Petrarca, who straddled across the century, and whose influence was second only to Dante's. Though Petrarca and Dante belong to two successive generations, they seem to be separated by a whole world. Nothing illustrates better the transitional age with which we are dealing and the speed of its vicissitudes, for if we visualize the Middle Ages and Modern Times as two mountains, Dante stands upon the summit of the first, while Petrarca is guiding the way up the lower slopes of the second. Both are Christians, but the older is a schoolman, and the younger, for good and evil, a humanist.

To return to the first half of the fourteenth century (Petrarca being more typical of the middle of the century), we may now consider the schoolmen, who belonged to four orders, Dominican, Franciscan, Carmelite, and Augustinian.

The monasteries of the Friars Preachers were dominated by the gigantic figure of St. Thomas, standing at the door of Catholicism like a new apostle, or rather like a new father of the church. When he died, on March 7, 1274, he was already famous and legendary. He was given the title "doctor communis" at the council of Vienne. 1311, and was canonized by John XXII (in 1323) less than half a century

[13] To complete the information given in Introd. 2, 822, there were two incunabula editions of the Laude: Florence 1490, Brescia 1495. The Florentine edition is the basis of the modern edition by Giovanni Ferri (Roma 1910), often reprinted. The best introduction is Evelyn Underhill: Jacopone da Todi, poet and mystic, 1228–1306 (534 p., London 1919), with selected aude in Italian and English verse.

after his death. In the altarpiece which the Tuscan artist Francesco Traini painted for Santa Catarina in Pisa (c. 1341–46), St. Thomas is represented triumphing over heresy and especially over Ibn Rushd, prostrated at his feet. That painting is the best symbol of contemporary opinion; it proves that St. Thomas' triumph was almost complete at that time, and his fame second to none in the church militant.

It is not necessary to speak as lengthily of the three outstanding Italians in the Dominican order who were actually flourishing in those days as we have of him who was already dead in the flesh. John of Naples and Graziadei d'Ascoli were Thomist commentators who happened to attract a little more attention than others. John of Naples, who took a prominent part in the process of canonization of St. Thomas, wrote on the Sentences and attacked the radical views of the Franciscan Vital du Four on monastic poverty. Graziadei continued the Thomist discussion of Aristotle. The third Italian Dominican, Bartholomaeus de Sancto Concordio, or Bartholomew of Pisa the Elder, is of very little importance, except that a textbook of his on cases of conscience enjoyed some popularity among confessors (seven incunabula). It is clear that such a textbook *might* be of great interest to psychologists.

So much for the Dominicans. The three other orders had less to show. The Italian Franciscans could boast only one distinguished doctor, brother Alexander of Alexandria, who wrote commentaries on the Sentences and on the Metaphysics. The latter was translated into Hebrew. The Carmelite Gerard of Bologna wrote a Summa organized on the same pattern as St. Thomas'. Though brother Gerard lived until 1317, it is probable that his Summa is anterior to 1300, or even to 1297, when he was elected prior general of his order. We should have dealt with him in volume 2, even as we did with the Augustinian Giles of Rome (general of his order 1292, died 1316). Two other Augustinians deserve mention, however, to wit, Petrarca's friend Dionysius de Rubertis, astrologer and humanist, and Gregorio da Rimini, whose masterpiece was a commentary on the Sentences.

With the single exception of Dionysius de Rubertis, all these men had very much in common in spite of their different monastic affiliations. Their Thomism might vary in purity or intensity, their manner of thinking was substantially the same.

The men of the two following groups, whom I call respectively the humanists and the encyclopaedists, are strikingly different from the schoolmen.

The humanists, with whom the Augustinian Dionysius would gladly have associated, were more interested in history and the bonae litterae than in philosophical or theological subtleties. Yet those whom I mention here were not simply historians or men of letters, and they managed to influence the cultural atmosphere by their writings or by other activities. We need not dwell upon them at present, for we shall come across them again. They stand here as representatives of a definite pattern of thinking—humanism.

The historian and diplomat Albertino Mussato wrote philosophical dialogues on the vicissitudes of life. Cino of Pistoia was one of the early "commentatores," that is, he belonged to the new generation of civilians whose commentaries were more philosophical than those of the "glossatores"; moreover, he was a friend of Dante and Petrarca and somewhat of a poet. Ferreto de' Ferreti was deeply influenced by the Roman historians as well as by Dante, and his main ambition was to revive the classical atmosphere. Giovanni de Matociis had a similar ambition, and his study of ancient literature enabled him to distinguish from each other the two Plinii, whom careless tradition had allowed to become fused together. The last man of this group is unexpected, being none other than the famous tribune—the "duce" of that time—Cola di Rienzo. Cola's interest in Roman antiquities was very genuine indeed, and his example is perhaps more significant than the others. He makes it clear to us that that new conception of life which we call humanism, a revival of ancient ideals, was in the air. All these men were north Italians, except Cola, who was a Roman. Their social positions were very different; Albertino was a notary, Cino a lawyer of noble birth, Giovanni a priest, Ferreto a wealthy dilettante, Cola a man of the people become a dictator; yet they had common aspirations which were prophetic of the future. Under the guidance of Dante and even more of Petrarca, they were the harbingers of the Renaissance.

Two physicians whose life was spent mainly in the thirteenth century, but who lived, the first, Taddeo Alderotti (XIII-2), until 1303, and the second, Guglielmo Corvi (XIII-2), until c. 1326, constitute a curious subgroup, which may be placed between the humanists and the encyclopaedists. Alderotti was more of a humanist, Corvi of a schoolman; both tried to explain medicine in the accepted scholastic manner.

The final Italian group is perhaps the most interesting of all and certainly the most pregnant. They predict the future in a deeper way than the humanists. They are the men whom I have called the encyclopaedists, but who might be called also the scientists or the rebels. Their main interest is not a definite pattern of thought to which everything has to be reduced, as it was for the schoolmen; nor is it beautiful form and the noble traditions of antiquity, as it was for the poets and humanists; it is rather knowledge, we might say scientific knowledge, bearing in mind that the conception of such knowledge was not the same then as now, and that they were still groping after it and thus unable to agree among themselves except on vague aspirations.

I counted five in that group, to which might possibly be added Jacopo di Dante Alighieri because of his Dottrinale. The first in point of date, Pietro d'Abano, composed (c. 1310) the Conciliator, wherein he attempted to solve the moot problems of science and philosophy of his time. Cecco d'Ascoli composed a didactic poem, L'acerba, in Italian. His unifying thoughts, like Pietro's, were astrological. The third of these scientifically minded philosophers was, strangely enough, a Servite brother, Urbano of Bologna, a precursor, with Pietro, of the Averroistic school of Padua. The most illustrious member of the group was Marsiglio of Padua, whose scientific radicalism was applied in the Defensor pacis (1324) to questions of government and religion, church and state. Though Maino de Maineri, astrologer and physician, dabbled with philosophy, he does not completely deserve the honor of being considered together with the four men previously named. Finally, mention may be made of an anonymous encyclopaedic treatise, the Multifarium, compiled at Bologna in 1326 and largely derived from the Speculum of Vincent of Beauvais (XIII-2).

Marsiglio was a student of politics; the others were students of science in the ordinary sense. Their main purpose was to explain the "nature of things," and their explanations were largely Averroistic and astrological. It is noteworthy that all of them, except Urbano, came to grief. Pietro d'Abano was twice in trouble with the Inquisition, and his remains were ordered to be destroyed. Cecco d'Ascoli was burned at the stake in Florence in 1327. Marsiglio was excommunicated in 1326 and ten years later he was cast out by his protector, the emperor Ludwig, as heretic and schismatic.

A2. *Spain*

As compared with that of Italy, the intellectual life of Christian Spain was poor, and most of it was Catalan rather than Spanish in a stricter sense. To begin with, two of the greatest scholars of the Middle Ages, Arnold of Villanova and Ramon Lull, were Catalan. Both have been discussed in volume 2, but we should bear in mind that Arnold lived until 1311 and Ramon until 1315/16. In spite of his great originality, the latter should be described as a conservative; he was an extreme realist, anti-Averroist, and a Franciscan tertiary. On the contrary, the layman, Arnold, was comparatively speaking a liberal. Some of his writings were innocent enough, notably the Regimen sanitatis which he edited for Jaime II of Aragon in 1307; others, dealing with forbidden subjects, such as astrology and magic, savored of heresy. Arnold had twice been warned by the Inquisition (1299, 1305) and many of his writings were posthumously condemned in 1317 by the inquisitor of Tarragona.

In addition to these two great men, who could not help creating trouble because of their genius, Catalonia gave us three humbler and quieter doctors: the Franciscan and Scotist Antonius Andreae, whose innocuous commentaries were exceedingly popular; the Carmelite Guiu Terrena, whose activity was of the same kind if less successful; and the Augustinian Bernat Oliver, whose Excitatorium mentis ad Deum was the most important work of its kind in the peninsula. Bernat, it is true, was a Valencian, that is, a Catalan not in the strict political sense, but in the linguistic one. His Excitatorium was soon translated into Catalan, the Catalan version being one of the early classics of that language.

The only real Spaniard, Vargas of Toledo, was also an Augustinian, that is, a disciple of Giles of Rome (XIII-2), trying carefully to steer a middle course between extreme realism and nominalism.

A3. *France*

The two most active countries in Western Christendom, next to Italy, were France and England. The Frenchmen are so numerous that it is necessary to subdivide them into smaller groups: Dominicans, Franciscans, Cistercians, seculars and laymen. That division is natural enough.

Dominicans. These Dominicans were most of them Thomists, as we might expect, but not all of them, as we shall see in a moment. John of Paris was one of the earliest defenders of Thomism. He really belongs to the previous period, but he lived until 1306. He was followed by Hervé Nédélec, who died in the year of his master's canonization (1323), and by Durand of Saint Pourçain (d. 1334), but the latter developed anti-Thomist tendencies. This is interesting, for it illustrates a remarkable freedom of thought in the very order to which St. Thomas had given so great a fame. Another friar Durand, Durand d'Aurillac, wrote a treatise on the reality of time. Pierre de la Palu was the conventional theologian and administrator, who was a Thomist because Thomism was the orthodox philosophy of his day and of his order; he tried to persecute Durand of Saint Pourçain, but his main interest lay in theological controversies and in political and administrative problems. We close this account of Dominican achievements with a reference to the Speculum morale, completed c. 1310–25. The author is unknown, but we may safely assume that he was a Dominican delegated to compile this companion volume to the three other Specula of his spiritual brother, Vincent of Beauvais (XIII-2).

Franciscans. The most remarkable of the Franciscans was Pierre Auriol, who was trying to compromise between Scotism and Thomism, and was thus coming close to the Dominican Durand of Saint Pourçain. The other Franciscans are primarily commentators on the Bible, the Books of sentences, or the Aristotelian corpus: François de Meyronnes, Vital Dufour, Nicholas Bonet. To these must be added the outstanding Biblical scholar Nicholas of Lyra.

Cistercians. There are only two Cistercians worth mentioning, and they form a violent and singular contrast. The first, Guillaume Deguilleville, was a pious individual whose "pilgrimages," edifying and hortatory poems, enjoyed much popularity not only in their original French form, but also in various translations. He was a simple man helping other men like himself to live the good life. His brother Cistercian John of Mirecourt was, on the contrary, a highly sophisticated logician, who went so far as to doubt man's free will on the one hand and the principle of causality on the other.

Seculars. The Cistercians whom we have named were exceedingly different, but no conclusion can be drawn from two cases. The Dominican and Franciscan groups were each, as we should expect, fairly homogeneous. We cannot expect the remaining group, the seculars, to be equally homogeneous, and it is not.

We have in it seven canons or prebendaries: Peter of Auvergne (XIII-2), who wrote quodlibeta and Thomist commentaries on Aristotle; Raoul le Breton, who taught logic, the old and the new; Jean de Pouilli, disciple of Godfrey of Fontaines (XIII-2), that is, an independent Thomist but more interested in theological controversies than in philosophy; then two very great men, Jean de Jandun, Averroist, Marsiglio's friend and peer, and Jean Buridan, one of the main builders of the new Occamist structure; finally, Thomas Le Miesier, Lullist, and Nicholas of Autrecourt, "the mediaeval Hume." That little group, one out of many others, might be exhibited to those ignorant scholars who complain of the uniformity of mediaeval thought! Due allowance being made for a number of factors, the main one of which was the greater dangers involved in nonconformity, mediaeval thought was not more uniform than our own. There was more acquiescence, especially concerning matters about which it would have been suicidal not to acquiesce; the domain of free thought was superficially restricted, but in that domain there was still considerable room for multiple and wide divergences of opinion.

It might have been possible for those seven learned canons, different as they were from one another, to come together, and they would have had as many interests in common as, say, the members of a university faculty today. It is probable, however, that they would have resented the intrusion of two other men, who did not write in Latin, but in French. These other men were a generation older anyway, for they lived at the turn of the century. The first is Jean de Meung (XIII-2), a layman who completed the Roman de la rose, and the second, the author (Jean Bonnet?) of the dialogue entitled Placides et Timéo ou Livre des secrets aux philosophes (written before 1304). These two works (of which the former is incomparably the more important) were of great value for the "popularization" of scientific or critical thought among the increasing number of people whose Latin was too elementary (if it existed at all) or too rusty for comfort.

A4. *England*

English philosophers and scholars being as numerous as the French, we are obliged to subdivide them also into groups: Franciscans, Dominicans, other regulars, and seculars. In this case, however, we must give the place of honor, not to the Dominicans (as we did with the French and Italians), but to the Franciscans. Indeed, the Gray Friars had a magnificent tradition in England. It began very early with Bartholomew the Englishman, Alexander of Hales, Adam Marsh, all of whom flourished in the first half of the thirteenth century. To these should be added Robert Grosseteste,[14] who was the first lecturer to the Oxford Franciscans (1224). The second and third generations were no less honorable, for they included such men as Thomas of York (d. 1260), Richard of Middleton (fl. 1286), William of Ware, Roger Bacon (d. 1292), John Peckham (d. 1292), William de la Mare (d. 1298), and Duns Scot (d. 1308).[15] The English Franciscan tradition was especially remarkable in its freedom. It was not composed of a single stream like Dominican Thomism; in addition to smaller rivulets, it included two large streams, the experimental (or scientific) tradition of Grosseteste, Peckham, and Bacon, and the tradition of Duns Scot, "Scotism," which itself was broad enough to sympathize with the seraphic doctor St. Bonaventure on the one hand and to give birth to Wycliffe and Lollardy on the other. The English Franciscans had one intellectual taste or passion in common—anti-Thomism.

Duns Scot lived until 1308, and some of his best work was done at the beginning of the century. Hence, he fully belongs to our story; his influence was in many ways as great as St. Thomas'; in addition, he was for many years (of the fourteenth century) a living teacher, not simply a ghostly presence. Down to the middle of the century there were living men who had known him personally and heard him speak. Two of the English Franciscans were his immediate disciples, Hugh of Newcastle and John of Bassoles;[16] the latter was said to be his favorite.

To the two Franciscan streams running out of England, the Baconian and the Scotist, was added now a third one, which became larger and larger as the century rolled out of the womb of time, and which exerted a deep influence upon the progress of rationalism and of science. I am referring to the school initiated by William of Occam (d. 1349); its main features were its individualism and its symbolic conception of knowledge, which anticipated some of the boldest ideas of modern thought. Occam's main English disciples were John Rodington and Adam Wodeham. His intellectual initiatives were as dangerous as they were bold; they introduced a ferment of decomposition into the mediaeval atmosphere. We shall not be far wrong in saying that it was Occamism combined with Averroism which prepared the gradual dissolution of mediaeval continuity and the beginning of a new age. In the northern countries that double ferment played somewhat the same part as humanism and the love of sensual beauty in the south. One is startled to realize that the inventors of the most powerful engines against the older kind of mediaevalism, to wit, Baconianism and Occamism, were sons of St. Francis; it is equally remarkable that these two harbingers of the future were Englishmen.

The English Dominicans are more commonplace. Thomas Jorz was one of six brothers every one of whom assumed the Dominican habit; two of them became archbishops of Armagh, and a third one, Thomas, provincial of his order and cardinal. In spite of being primarily a prelate and diplomat, he managed to com-

[14] I seize this opportunity of citing and praising the recent work of Samuel Harrison Thomson: The writings of Robert Grosseteste, bishop of Lincoln (Cambridge 1940; Isis 33, 93). I wish it had been available to me when I wrote the Grosseteste article (Introd. 2, 583–86).

[15] All of them dealt with in Introd. vol. 2.

[16] I assume here that Bassoles was an Englishman; that is not certain.

pose a number of commentaries. More commentaries on the Bible and the Sentences were written by Thomas of Sutton, Nicholas Trevet, and Robert of Holcot. All these men were Thomists, but Robert had been exposed to the teachings of the via moderna (Occam, Gregory of Rimini) and to those of Bradwardine, and hence was not as pure a Thomist as the three others.

If the Franciscan and Dominican groups fail to be completely homogeneous, we must not be surprised at the heterogeneity of the remaining groups of other regulars and of seculars.

Robert Mannyng, Gilbertine canon, wrote in 1303 an edifying poem Handlyng synne, adapted from the French. The Benedictine Richard de Bury composed the Philobiblon in 1345, when he was bishop of Durham. John Baconthorpe was more of a philosopher in the technical sense; he was an intimate friend of Bradwardine and his point of view was that of moderate Averroism; he is the philosopher par excellence of the Carmelite order. The fact that the same order, whose official philosophy was so close to Averroism, or at any rate so independent, became hardly more than two centuries later the spiritual family of St. Theresa of Jesus and St. John of the Cross proves sufficiently its relative freedom and the unpredictability of human genius. Finally, the Cistercian Richard Swineshead, though he wrote the usual commentaries on Aristotle and the Sentences, distinguished himself chiefly in the field of mathematics and physics.

And now the seculars. Simon of Faversham was a good Thomist, or came very close to it. Four others had in common the distinction of being Merton men, and we shall have other opportunities for emphasizing the valuable services rendered to science by that noble house. They were Walter Burley, Thomas Bradwardine, John Dumbleton, and William Heytesbury. We shall meet them again in the physical chapter, except Dumbleton, whose main work was a treatise on logic and natural philosophy, the contents of which have not yet been sufficiently explored. This English section may end fittingly with the evocation of the gentle mystic Richard Rolle, of whose masterpiece Lydgate said a century later (c. 1434):

> "In parfyt lyvyng, which passith poysye,
> Richard Hermyte, contemplatyff of sentence,
> Drowh in Ynglyssh the Prykke of Conscience."[17]

A5. *Germany*

We have seen that the spiritual fame of England was due to Franciscans; even so the spiritual fame of contemporary Germany was due to Dominicans. The latter accomplished more in that country than all the other orders together.

They may be divided into two groups: the physicists and the mystics. To the former belong Dietrich of Freiberg, one of the leading opticians of the Middle Ages, and Berthold of Mosburg. Both were independent philosophers combining Thomism with Neoplatonism, such as was transmitted in the elements of theology (i.e., metaphysics) of Proclos.

The mystical group derived its pabulum partly from the same source, which was easy enough, for by 1300, Neoplatonic doctrines had reached the West through many channels (Isis 29, 423-28). Thus the difference between the two groups was not essential, they shared the same philosophy; it was simply a difference of emphasis. Dietrich and Berthold were genuinely interested in physics, whereas the

[17] The fall of princes (book IX, 3412-14). Edition by Henry Bergen (3, 1016, 1923).

others were so deeply concerned with metaphysics and theology that they could spare but little attention for physical matters except the beauty of nature reflecting the perfect beauty of God.

The names of these men, Meister Eckhart, Johann Tauler, Heinrich Suso, and especially of the first, are widely known, even outside philosophical circles and outside German ones. Their writings have brought peace and understanding into many hearts. Eckhart was the most learned of the three, and because of his status as a master of theology and as a monastic teacher and administrator, his views were scrutinized more carefully; ecclesiastical proceedings were instituted against him in 1326 and he was still under a cloud at the time of his death, in the following year. Tauler belonged to a little company, centered in Basel, who named themselves "the friends of God," but he preached their message far and wide in the German lands. If we call Eckhart the doctor of the group, and Tauler its preacher, we should call Suso its poet, "der Minnedichter der Gottesliebe," but we should bear in mind that the three of them were teachers, preachers, and poets. Their Christian message was so deep that it rejoined unconsciously Hindu messages set forth in some of the Upanishad or of the Mahāyāna scriptures. To the writings of Eckhart, Tauler, and Suso should be added an anonymous one, which shared their burden and their fame, the Theologia germanica. This dates from the same period (or perhaps a bit later, say, middle of the fourteenth century), but was first revealed to the world by Martin Luther.

The other Germans—those who did not wear the Dominican habit—are of two kinds. In the first place, we have two regulars, the Benedictine Engelbert of Admont, and the Augustinian Thomas of Strassburg. Engelbert was essentially a moralist, that is, a psychologist, a student of the soul and of man's conduct; his countrymen called him, rather inaptly but with pardonable pride, the Austrian Albertus Magnus. Thomas continued the tendencies of the Aegidian school—eclectic Thomism, a kind of via media between realism and the growing nominalism of his time.

There remain to be considered three men representing the didactic type on the vernacular level, for all of them wrote in German, that is, for their own people. The first two, Eberhard von Wampen and Ulrich Boner, distributed their knowledge in verse, in order that it might be more easily memorized. They belonged to the frontiers of German culture. Eberhard was a Balt, who had been taken into the service of the Swedish court and wrote his "mirror of nature" in Low German. Ulrich was near the southern frontier, in Bern, and composed in German a collection of fables. Eberhard was interested primarily in nature; Ulrich, in practical morals, in what were then called exempla (fables or stories illustrating virtues and vices and their divers consequences). The third and greatest, Conrad of Megenberg, was a true encyclopaedist and the first scientific writer of importance in the German language. We shall come back to him many times. In addition to his scientific writings, he devoted others to theological, ecclesiastical, and political questions. Eberhard seems to have been a layman, a court physician; Ulrich was some sort of monk; Conrad, a canon of the Ratisbon cathedral.

A6. *Flanders*

Flanders being even in the broadest sense a small country, we cannot expect the Flemish thinkers to form a large company, but it is a very distinguished one. I say Flemish advisedly, for the people to be named presently belonged exclusively to the southwestern part of the Netherlands—the county of Flanders and the duchy of Brabant. To put it otherwise, I have to deal only with people who lived in that region, and whose vernacular speech was Flemish, that is, the southern dialects of Netherlandish. The first three, however, Henry Bate, Siger of Courtrai, and Bartholomew of Bruges, addressing themselves to the international public of Western Europe, wrote in Latin.

My five Flemings are as different from one another as it is possible to be. Henry Bate of Malines was an astronomer and astrologer. Siger, a parish priest in Courtrai and later a member of the Sorbonne, was primarily a modista, which means that his main interest was in reconciling grammar with logic and thus reviving an ancient tradition. Bartholomew of Bruges was a physician, writing commentaries on Aristotle. The two others, who used the Flemish language, came from the country around Brussels. Jan van Boendale was a city clerk in Antwerp; primarily a historian, he composed didactic poems. Jan van Ruysbroeck was a mystic, the peer of Eckhart, Tauler, and Suso; in fact, their Flemish counterpart. Like them he belongs to world literature. The name of Ruysbroeck is familiar to every student of mediaeval mysticism. He has been popularized in the modern world of letters by two powerful writers, Ernest Hello and Maurice Maeterlinck.

There were no contemporary philosophers in the Walloon part of modern Belgium, unless we take into account Godfrey of Fontaines (XIII-2), who died c. 1303, and the Dominican Giles of Lessines (XIII-2), who died c. 1304. Both were Thomist philosophers, but Giles was a more thoroughgoing Thomist than Godfrey, in fact one of the best expounders and defenders of the unity of substantial form. It should be noted that the Fleming Henry Bate was for a time canon in Liége, hence he may have been acquainted with Godfrey of Fontaines.

A7. *Icelandic*

The general knowledge of that time was treasured and transmitted in the Icelandic language by Haukr Erlendsson.

A8. *Alia*

The popular encyclopaedia Lumen animae, dealing mainly with ethical topics, was written about this time by an unknown author. We are obliged to place it here, because its local origin is unknown. Its importance is very small. The Lumen animae is briefly described in the text below. Mention might be made here also of another encyclopaedic work we have not dealt with at all. It is an anonymous Latin treatise in six books on metaphysics and natural philosophy, written probably after 1323 (Thorndike 3, 568–84, 761–76, 1934).

B. *Eastern Christendom*

Our account of general thought in the non-Latin or non-Roman Catholic parts of Christendom will be divided into four sections. The first two deal with the great controversy which was agitating the Byzantine empire, and which has already been discussed in the section on "Union of the churches" above (section II, subsection 9). The third and fourth sections treat respectively other Byzantine philosophers and representatives of other Eastern churches.

B1. *The Latinizing party*

The intellectual differences (not to speak of nonintellectual ones which were deeper and more powerful) between the theologians who advocated the union with

Rome and those, far more numerous, who resisted that union can be easily imagined from the conflict existing in the West between the scholastic theologians, whether Thomist or Scotist or Aegidian, on the one hand, and the Neoplatonists and the mystically minded on the other hand. The very fact that the conflict was sometimes difficult to locate exactly and to define increased its acuity and its rancor. The main appellation of the anti-Latin party was the Hesychasts (meaning, the quietists), which was perhaps as good a definition of them as can be given in a single word. We shall come back to them in a moment. Let us first consider their enemies.

At this time they were headed by Barlaam, whose personality dominated the controversy to such an extent that the Latinizers were called after him, Barlaamites. However, he was by no means the inventor of the idea of reconciliation with Rome. He had been preceded by such men as the patriarch Joannes Beccos, who wrote many books to promote the union, and Georgios Metochites, archdeacon of Hagia Sophia, both of whom might be called martyrs of the Latin cause, for they died in prison because of it (Joannes in 1293; Georgios after 1308). We may recall also Maximos Planudes (XIII-2), who translated into Greek some books of St. Augustine, Boetius, and St. Thomas; he died in 1310. Barlaam, however, was more active and turbulent, and he succeeded remarkably well in setting the Orthodox priests and the caloyers by the ears. He was powerful at court and there were cogent political reasons for listening to him; yet he was condemned and anathematized in 1341. We need not insist on the Barlaamite philosophy; it was simply a form of Thomism, not too pure, however, for Barlaam was a very complex individual and somewhat of a humanist; in fact, he was so complex and unstable that some of his writings contradict others on fundamental questions. The main ally of the Calabrian Barlaam was the Bulgar Gregorios Acindynos; the latter, however, has lost much of his importance, since the Thomist treatise on the essence and activity of God formerly ascribed to him has been proved to be apocryphal. It was written by Prochoros Cydones (XIV-2).

B2. *The Hesychasts*

The theology and philosophy of the Hesychasts or Palamites can be defined as a combination of orthodoxy—right thinking by definition, needing no rational justification—with quietism. The proportion of the ingredients might vary considerably, the amount of mysticism being reduced to the liturgical minimum at the extreme left, or exalted beyond measure at the extreme right. The extremists of the right are well characterized by their nickname ὀμφαλόψυχοι or umbilicanimi, because they tried to reach ecstasy by a kind of autohypnotization; they sat in a rigid posture gazing on the middle of their body, controlling their breathing, and repeating endlessly the same sacred words. According to their leader Palamas (who became later one of the most popular saints of the Orthodox church), a sufficiently prolonged contemplation of their navel, together with short prayers repeated according to the rhythm of respiration, itself slowed up to the limit, enabled them to see a light comparable to the Uncreated Light which the three most intimate disciples of Christ saw above his head at the time of his transfiguration on Mount Tabor.[18]

[18] Matthew 17; Mark 9. Biblical scholars are not agreed on the mountain where the Transfiguration occurred. Mount Tabor or Thabor is the location accepted by the Greek Church, which celebrates the Transfiguration on August 6 under the name τὸ Θαβώριον or Μεταμόρφωσις.

It is not necessary to insist on these spiritual extravagances, which take us out of the field of theology, not to speak of philosophy, but it is interesting to note their great likeness to the practices of other religions, chiefly those described in the Yoga-sūtra of Patañjali (fourth or fifth century?),[19] or other forms of Hindu yoga, Muslim dhikr, etc. The likeness is the more impressive because these methods of religious intoxication and self-hypnosis have been developed independently by so many different peoples.

For the Greek method of prayer and attention, μέθοδος τῆς ἱερᾶς προσευχῆς καὶ προσοχῆς, see Karl Holl: Enthusiasmus und Bussgewalt beim griechischen Mönchtum (Leipzig 1898); Irénée Hausherr: La méthode d'oraison hésychaste (Orientalia christiana 9, 99–210, Rome 1927). Both writers deal with texts ascribed to Symeon the New Theologian,[20] but father Hausherr claims that the μέθοδος published under Symeon's name is a later Hesychastic fabrication. For a comparison of Hesychastic practices with the Hindu āsana (posture), prāṇāyāma (breathing exercises), ekāgratā (concentration), etc., and with other Oriental forms of yoga, see the excellent book of Eliade (1936). For the Taoist methods of "nourishing the vital spirit" (yang hsin) and obtaining immortality (ch'ang shêng, shih chieh), see Maspero (1937).

The leading Hesychasts and anti-Latins were Nicephoros Chumnos, high official at the Byzantine court under Andronicos II; Gregorios Sinaites,[21] who flourished during the same rule; and later Gregorios Palamas, who was the main doctor of the sect and the organizer of its victory. We should also mention Nicephoros Gregoras, the greatest writer not only of his time but of the whole Palaeologoi age (the two last centuries of Byzantine independence). This Nicephoros took part in the theological controversies but tried to keep some sort of neutrality, and that Erasmian attitude caused him to be persecuted and to end his life in monastic confinement. These three men wrote commentaries on Plato and Aristotle; on the whole, they were Platonists, but only so far as their orthodoxy permitted. Their faith made it impossible for them to share the Neoplatonic point of view without many restrictions, and the elder Chumnos wrote a treatise against Plotinos. All of them were deeply interested in psychology, which means that they were bound to discuss

[19] James Haughton Woods: The yoga system of Patañjali (425 p., Harvard Oriental series no. 17, 1914; Isis 4, 60). This Patañjali should not be confused with the grammarian Patañjali (II-2 B.C.). For a scientific evaluation from the point of view of today's psychophysiology, see Kovoor T. Behanan: Yoga (292 p., London 1938; Isis 32).

[20] Συμεών ὁ νέος θεολόγος. Born in Paphlagonia in 949, came to Constantinople c. 960, entered the Studion tentatively in 963, finally in 977, but passed soon to the St. Mamas monastery, of which he became the hegumenos in 980; after many difficulties with his own monks and others he was exiled in 1009, founded the St. Marina monastery, and died in 1022. This Symeon exerted a great influence on Greek monks, his writings being read considerably on Mount Athos in Greek and Russian. The most popular of his works, however, is the Method quoted above, which is apocryphal. His life was written after 1052 by Nicetas Stethatos, edited and translated into French by Irénée Hausherr and Gabriel Horn (Orientalia christiana 12, 351 p., Rome 1928). The dates of birth and death (c. 1025–after 1092) given by Krumbacher (p. 152–54, 1897) are wrong.

[21] This Gregorios was born near Clazomenae, on the Gulf of Smyrna, and was made prisoner by the Turks. After his redemption, he went to Cypros, then to Mount Sinai, where he became a monk. He went to Mount Athos, where he is considered to have been the founder of Hesychasm. He traveled much and wrote little. The main work ascribed to him is a collection of 137 chapters (κεφάλαια) dealing with dogmas, virtues, and chiefly ἡσυχία (quietness) and προσευχή (prayer). Krumbacher (p. 157, 1897).

and rediscuss Platonic and Neoplatonic ideas on the soul from the point of view of orthodoxy and Hesychasm.

B3. *Other Byzantine theologians or philosophers*

A Byzantine scholar not interested in theological or ecclesiastical controversies would be almost impossible to find, and in this particular period the Hesychastic dispute was so intense and absorbing that it was inescapable. Yet there were a few scholars who in spite of that pressure continued to be primarily interested in other matters and who managed to remain outside the turmoil. Such a one was the venerable Georgios Pachymeres, who wrote Aristotelian commentaries and lived until c. 1310. Two younger contemporaries of his, Joannes Chumnos and Joannes Pediasimos, escaped the tumult probably for the simple reason that they died before it had reached its climax. Joannes, who was the son of Nicephoros Chumnos, wrote philosophical letters in a Platonic vein, and to Pediasimos we owe a number of Aristotelian scholia, as well as rhetorical exercises on various subjects. Other Aristotelian commentaries were contributed by Theodoros Metochites and Leon Magentinos. The latter's were restricted to the Organon and to Porphyry, but Theodoros, in spite of being a high court officer of Andronicos, found time to paraphrase a good many Aristotelian treatises on philosophical and physical questions, and to write many essays of his own. He shared his sovereign's disgrace in 1328 and spent the end of his life in the monastery of St. Saviour in Chora together with him and Nicephoros Gregoras. St. Saviour must have been a delightful place of retirement for those old men, who could reminisce and philosophize together on the vicissitudes of sublunar things and the permanent glory of God. They could also enjoy the lovely mosaics with which Theodoros had adorned the monastic church when he was still the grand logothete. Indeed, he could see himself in one of those astounding mosaics, offering to Christ the church which he had caused to be restored (see fig. 11). These mosaics can be enjoyed to this day, and draw many visitors to the charming little mosque of Kahrie jami.

We may perhaps mention also the jurist Constantine Armenopulos, who tried to compromise between the Hesychasts and their enemies, and thus provoked the anger of both parties. His Hexabiblos was so popular in Greek lands, almost to our own days, that it concerns the historian of thought as well as the historian of law.

B4. *Theologians of other Eastern churches*

The theologian 'Abhd-Īshō' bar Bĕrīkhā (XIII-2), who was to the Nestorian Syrians what Abū-l-Faraj was to the Jacobites, lived until 1318, and thus he belongs to our period though his main work, the Margānīthā (Pearl), a theological summa in the Syriac language, was completed before the end of the thirteenth century.

In the meanwhile Coptic (Monophysitic) theology was explained in elaborate Arabic treatises by Abū-l-Barakāt (d. 1324).

This ends our account of Eastern churches, but we may perhaps recall the work done by a Catholic theologian, the Dominican Bartholomew of Bologna, in order to bring the Armenian church to the Roman obedience. Bartholomew was helped by Armenians such as John of Karīn and Jacob the Dragoman. That activity was not original; it was largely restricted to the translation of Latin treatises into Armenian. John of Erzinjān (XIII-2) employed himself in a similar way, for he translated St. Thomas' treatise on sacraments, the original of which had been sent to Cilicia in or after 1316, but in addition he wrote treatises on religious and ethical subjects; he was a theologian in his own right.

The purely Armenian thought (vs. the Latinizing tendencies) was represented at the beginning of the century by a scion of the illustrious Orbelian family, Stephen Orbelian (XIII-2), who was primarily a historian, yet composed, in 1302, a theological treatise defending the Armenian church against Rome.

C. *Israel*

The number of Jewish scholars is far smaller than that of Christian ones, yet the Jews form the second largest of the main religious groups, being followed at some distance by the Muslims. This is the more remarkable if one bears in mind that the Western Jews were now restricted to southern France, Spain, and Italy, and were submitted to many kinds of limitations, humiliations, and vexations. In spite of these terrible handicaps they continued their intellectual activities and their creative work, being sustained by their religious faith and by their love of wisdom and knowledge. We shall consider successively the Jews of southern France, of Spain, of Italy, and of Eastern countries.

C1. *Southern France*

The Jews of southern France were much devoted not only to rabbinical learning, but also to philosophy. Many of them were rather liberal in their outlook. I shall deal with the more liberal group first, reserving for the end a small group of diehards.

The liberal group was headed by two survivors from the preceding century, the mathematician Jacob ben Maḥir ibn Tibbon (XIII-2), who defended with especial zeal the Maimonidean party and rallied to it the community of Montpellier, and Levi ben Abraham ben Ḥayyim (XIII-2), who lived at least until 1315; indeed, one of his two encyclopaedias, the Liwyat ḥen, was revised and expanded by him at Arles in that very year. It deals with the lay sciences as well as with metaphysics, theology, and prophecy. Levi was the liberal leader of his age in Languedoc and Provence. The philosophical interests of contemporary Jews often materialized in the form of translations of Arabic texts, for they realized the fundamental importance of those texts, and a sufficient knowledge of Arabic, far from being assumed as a matter of course, was becoming more and more exceptional among them. The philosophical texts which attracted most of their attention were Ibn Rushd's commentaries on Plato and Aristotle and his Tahāfut al-tahāfut, then Alexander of Aphrodisias, al-Fārābī, Ibn Sīnā. The main philosophical translators were Moses ben Solomon of Beaucaire, Qalonymos ben David, Qalonymos ben Qalonymos, Samuel ben Judah of Marseille, Ṭodros Ṭodrosi, Jedaiah ben Abraham of Béziers.

More original works were written by Joseph Kaspi, Jedaiah ben Abraham of Béziers, Levi ben Gerson, Moses ben Joshua of Narbonne, and Judah ben Isaac Kohen. Joseph wrote books discussing the philosophy of Plato, Aristotle, al-Fārābī, Ibn Rushd. We have already referred to his testament wherein he outlined for his son (in 1332) an elaborate course of philosophical studies. The Sefer ha-pardes (Book of paradise) of Jedaiah (written by him c. 1287; he lived until c. 1340) is an encyclopaedia of religion and ethics, the fourth and last part of which is devoted to scientific knowledge. Moses' main activity was the writing of commentaries on Ibn Rushd, commentaries so elaborate that they might be called original treatises. We must not be deceived by the form of a work; some of the most original works of the Middle Ages appeared in the shape of commentaries, whereas others ostensibly independent were hardly more than plagiarisms. Moses commented also on various books of al-Ghazzālī, Ibn Ṭufail, and Maimonides. Another commentary on the logic of Ibn Rushd was contributed by Judah.

Thus far we have not yet spoken of the greatest of these philosophers and critics, to wit Levi ben Gerson, the outstanding Jewish thinker in the period between Maimonides and Crescas, one of the giants of mediaeval thought.

Thanks to his deep knowledge of the commentaries of Ibn Rushd, Levi was a more thoroughgoing Aristotelian than Maimonides; he was also more rationalistic; yet he had been strongly influenced by Plato, and he defended realism (as against nominalism) for the sake of maintaining the principle of immortality. This peculiar mixture of realism (unique in Jewish-Muslim philosophy) and Averroism gives to his personality a strange relief. Levi took great pains to reconcile Jewish orthodoxy with philosophy, and revealed considerable ingenuity in these efforts; he expressed his conclusions with strength and clearness not only in his main work, the Milḥamot Adonai, and his Averroistic commentaries, but also in his Biblical studies.

While these five men, Joseph, Jedaiah, Moses, Judah, and above all the great Levi, were thus working to liberate Jewish minds within the frame of their religion, there were many other Jews who were scandalized by those liberal efforts and did all they could to frustrate them and to protect their flocks against such dangerous thoughts. It is probable that the majority of the rabbis were rather conservative, and more likely to indulge in superstition than in rationalism, but we cannot be sure, for many of them did not write; their main defense was passive inertia and forbidding ritual. Here are two examples of the more conservative and superstitious type. Isaac ben Judah Lattes was a Talmudist and astrologer, a muddle-headed thinker who used talismans. The conservative reaction had been exacerbated at the beginning of the century by the growing prestige of Maimonides and the waxing strength of the Maimonidean party. In the very influential Montpellier district that party was led at the turn of the century by Jacob ben Maḥir ibn Tibbon (XIII-2); later it received the support of the liberals of whom I have just spoken, above all, Levi ben Gerson. The main leader of the anti-Maimonidean party was Abba Mari ben Moses (Don Astruc of Lunel), who published a collection of letters relative to that passionate controversy.

C2. *Spain*

Let us deal with the Spanish Jews as we have with the Provençal ones, taking first the more scientifically minded and the more liberal, then the others. Most of these Spaniards were translators, but it is highly significant that the language from which they decanted philosophical knowledge into Hebrew was no longer exclusively the Arabic, but also the Latin.

Two of them translated from Arabic into Hebrew: Isaac Albalag (XIII-2) and Isaac ben Nathan of Cordova. The first Isaac translated, in 1292 or at the beginning of the fourteenth century, the Maqāṣid al-falāsifa of al-Ghazzālī, one of the most important texts of Arabic metaphysics. He also wrote a commentary on the physics of Aristotle and Ibn Rushd. Isaac ben Nathan translated a series of important philosophical texts by al-Ghazzālī, Maimonides, Joseph ben Judah ibn ʻAqnīn, and Muḥammad al-Tabrīzī. It is clear that these two Isaacs were earnest students with a flair for the essential.

The two translators from the Latin, Hezekiah bar Ḥalafta and David ben Yom-ṭob ben Bila, were especially interested in logic. Hezekiah translated a commentary on the Parva logicalia of Peter of Spain, and David wrote a logical treatise. As a translator the latter was contemptible, for he devoted his attention to the Salus vitae, a wretched text on the magical virtues of snakeskin. David rendered no good service to his brethren by making that collection of superstitions available to them.

There remain to be considered two authors, Vidal de Tolosa and Mūsā ibn Ṭūbī, who wrote in Arabic. Vidal used both languages; he wrote in Hebrew a commentary on the Mishneh Torah of Maimonides, and in Arabic marginal notes to the Maqāṣid al-falāsifa of al-Ghazzālī, the importance of which has already been mentioned. To the second writer, Mūsā ibn Ṭūbī, we owe an Arabic poem in praise of philosophy, including a classification of the "seven" sciences. Mūsā did not write in Hebrew at all, but his philosophical poem was soon Hebraicized by Solomon ben Immanuel Dapiera.

This Spanish group of scientifically minded philosophers is small but distinguished, even if it is somewhat disgraced by the presence of David ben Bila. Leave that astrologer and magician out, and there remain five outstanding men, Isaac Albalag, Isaac ben Nathan, Hezekiah bar Ḥalafta, Vidal de Tolosa, and Mūsā ibn Ṭūbī.

The group of Spanish qabbalists is equally remarkable. To begin with, it includes the master of the Zohar, Moses of Leon (XIII-2) or whoever he be. Moses died at Arevalo in 1305, and the Zohar was not completed until about the beginning of the fourteenth century. Then we have Joseph ben Abraham Giqaṭilia (XIII-2), who was almost the exact contemporary of Moses of Leon and whose works influenced Christians as well as Jews; then many more (I have not the patience now to discriminate among them), such as Isaac ben Jacob ha-Kohen, Shem-ṭob ben Abraham ibn Gaon, Elḥanan ben Abraham, Joseph ben Abraham ibn Waqar, and the Palestinian exile Isaac ben Samuel.

The leader of conservative Judaism, keeping clear from philosophy on the left as well as from qabbalistic extravagances on the right, was Solomon ben Adret (XIII-2), el rab d'España, who died in 1310. As late as 1305 he managed to unite the rabbis of Barcelona in a joint excommunication of the young men who studied philosophy, unless they were physicians or were preparing themselves for the medical profession. The last years of his life were devoted to fighting the growing rationalism. He was able to communicate his fervor to the German tosafist Asher ben Jehiel, c. 1303, when the latter passed through Barcelona on his way to Toledo. From 1304 to his death in 1327, Asher was the chief rabbi of Toledo and the defender of orthodoxy against any kind of innovation. This leadership was continued by his sons Judah and Jacob. The latter compiled a new code, Arba' ṭurim (four rows), which superseded the Mishneh Torah of Maimonides and remained the standard work of its kind for all Jews, except Qaraites, until the publication of the Shulḥan 'aruk (1565).

The most conservative side of Judaism was represented also by a man of humbler type, Baḥya ben Asher (not related to Asher ben Jehiel), a pupil of Solomon ben Adret. Baḥya composed a commentary on the Pentateuch, but is known chiefly because of a book of ethics and practical religion, the Kad ha-qemaḥ (Flour jar). The commentary was completed as early as 1291, and the "Flour jar" may also belong to the thirteenth century, but Baḥya flourished in Saragossa until 1340.

C3. *Italy*

Italian Judaism can boast two great men, both Romans. The poet Immanuel ben Solomon (Manoello Giudeo) was influenced by Dante and other interpreters of the "dolce stil nuovo"; he reintroduced into Hebrew poetry conceits which were of Oriental origin, and helped to integrate Italian with Jewish thought. His satirical verve caused him to be nicknamed "the mediaeval Heine" or "the Jewish Voltaire," two comparisons which are incorrect, yet suggestive of qualities less rare in the Middle Ages than most people imagine (cf. history of carving and limning). The other Roman, Judah ben Moses (Leone Romano), was primarily a translator, and a philosopher rather than a poet. Like Immanuel he was a transmitter of Latin lore into Hebrew; strangely enough, he translated texts such as the De causis, and the Substantia orbis of Ibn Rushd, which Oriental or Spanish Jews could obtain more directly from Arabic originals; his translation into Hebrew of purely Latin texts like the De unito et unitate of Boetius, and of various treatises of Catholic theology, is even more remarkable. It illustrates once more the direction of the main current of European culture.

C4. *Eastern Jews*

The Eastern Jews taking part in the progress of philosophy or of thought are so few that it would be unnecessary to classify them, except that the separation of the orthodox from the Qaraites is too natural to be avoided.

One of the two Talmudists we have already met in Spain; that is, Isaac ben Samuel, who was driven out of 'Akkā by the Muslim conquerors in 1291 and moved westward. By the way, his exile is strange, for the Muslims were generally more tolerant of Jews than the Christians. The consequences of it were equally strange, for he met Moses of Leon in Valladolid and thus became a qabbalist! The other one was the physician 'Abd al-Dā'yim, who wrote a catechism on physics and metaphysics. Isaac wrote in Hebrew; 'Abd al-Dā'yim, in Arabic, but of course in Hebrew script.

This was a golden age of Qaraism, the age of the two Aarons, for it witnessed the final years of Aaron ben Joseph, author of the Mibḥar (Choice), a famous commentary on the Torah. The Mibḥar was written in Constantinople 1294, but Aaron the Elder lived in that city until 1320. As to Aaron ben Elijah, or Aaron the Younger, who flourished also in Constantinople, but a generation later, he was the greatest as well as the last of the Qaraite doctors, the "Maimonides" of Qaraism. The Qaraites were representatives of the older philosophical traditions which had been superseded by al-Ghazzālī and still more by Ibn Rushd; they rejected most of the Talmudic and rabbinical commentaries, trying to establish their faith and knowledge more exclusively upon the Scriptures.

D. *Islam*

As I was putting in order my notes concerning the philosophical and cultural background of the Muslim world, I was astonished to find not a single reference to a Western theologian. This is sufficient evidence of the decline which had set in in Western Islām, partly because of the increasing pressure of the Christian princes, partly for internal reasons. The only Muslim rulers able to hold their own in Spain were the Banū Naṣr (1232–1492), whose domain was restricted to the kingdom of Granada, a small territory in the southeast of the peninsula. In Morocco the Marīnī dynasty (1195–1470) was ruling, in Tunis the Banū Ḥafṣ (1228–1534), and in Algeria the Banū Ziyān (1235–1393), but the latter were to be absorbed before the end of the century by their Marīnī neighbors. For the period under consideration none of these four Muslim courts could boast a single philosopher or theologian of moderate eminence.

In the Eastern world, on the contrary, there were a number of distinguished men. We shall divide them into six national (or regional) groups: Yaman, Mamlūk (Egypt and Syria), Anatolia, 'Irāq, Persia, and Muslim India.

D1. *Yaman*

The kingdom of Yaman in southwestern Arabia enjoyed a good measure of prosperity under the Banū Rasūl (1229–1454). The latter had wrested the government of the country from the foreign Ayyūbī dynasty, which had held it for over half a century (1173–1228). The Banū Rasūl ruled over the whole southwestern quarter of Arabia from Ḥaḍramawt in the east to Mecca in the north. In the thirteenth century they had had some trouble with the Rassī a'imma, Zaidī (Shī'a) rulers of Ṣa'da and Ṣan'ā, but the last imām[22] ruled about the end of that century.

That Arabian kingdom was graced with the presence of two distinguished theologians. The first, al-Mu'aiyad billāh, wrote the Kitāb al-intiṣār, which is the outstanding book of Zaidī theology and jurisprudence. The second, al-Yāfi'ī, who spent most of his life in the two holy cities, belonged to the Shāfi'ī school and was a great admirer of al-Ash'arī (X-1). However, under the influence of Ibn 'Arabī (XIII-1), he became more and more of a mystic. He preached and wrote considerably, and from c. 1318 to his death in 1367 was the main spiritual guide of Yaman.

D2. *Mamlūk*

By far the largest group of scholars in the Dār al-Islām was the one that flourished under the Mamlūk rulers of Egypt and Syria. It is impossible to deal separately with each of these two countries, for many scholars began their career in Egypt and completed it in Syria, or vice versa, and sometimes they oscillated many times between the leading cities, such as Damascus, Jerusalem, Cairo, which were then the most active centers of Muslim thought and the main nurseries of talent and learning.

The scholars flourishing under Mamlūk patronage are so many that I must divide them into smaller groups, and the most natural classification is by schools (just as we divided the Christian doctors according to the orders to which they were affiliated, as Dominicans, Franciscans, etc.). We shall deal first with the Shāfi'ī, then with the Ḥanbalī, finally with a few others.

The Shāfi'ī school originated in Egypt in the first half of the ninth century (see Introd. 1, 550) and never lost its grip on the people of that country; it has remained to this day one of its leading schools, and the tomb of the imām Muḥammad ibn Idrīs al-Shāfi'ī (IX-1) has been venerated in Cairo for more than seven centuries. The Shāfi'ī school is remarkable for its relative eclecticism and moderation.

No less than six distinguished leaders of thought belonged to the Shāfi'ī school. Ibn Jamā'a is best remembered for his book on government and constitutional theory, a subject closely connected with Muslim theology, but he had written also, among other books, a general guide for students, which we have mentioned in our

[22] A new series of a'imma related to the first began to rule in 1591 and is represented to this day. Ṣa'da was the capital of the earlier a'imma (893–c. 1300), Ṣan'ā the capital of the later ones (c. 1591 ff.). Ṣa'da is on the pilgrim road from Ṣan'ā to Mecca.

account of education. Ibn Jamā'a is a good illustration of the facility with which scholars of his time and nationality passed from Syria to Egypt and vice versa, for after he left his native city, Ḥamāh, his career was spent in Damascus, Jerusalem, Cairo, Damascus, Cairo. Al-Nuwairī was a government secretary and the author of a single book of encyclopaedic scope and enormous size, the Nihāyat al-arab fī funūn al-adab. Various encyclopaedias were composed by Mamlūk subjects of this age; we shall have opportunities of dealing later on with others put together by Abū-l-Fidā' and Ibn Faḍlallāh al-'Umarī (al-Shāfi'ī). Al-Nuwairī came from Upper Egypt, and so did al-Adfuwī. The latter was more of a historian than a theologian, yet he has a few theological or legal books to his credit. The Syrian Ibn al-Wardī was also a historian, but with encyclopaedic tendencies. He wrote legal commentaries, a mystical treatise, and a book on the interpretation of dreams. The last named belongs to an important mediaeval category the classification of which is delicate. To dismiss oneiromancy as superstition pure and simple would be easy enough, but misleading. There were philosophical and psychological theories at the core of it, whose unrecognized erroneousness invited the sedimentation of all kinds of fanciful data. In spite of that, oneiromancy remained an integral part of a man's outlook, of his philosophy. Finally, the Egyptian 'Alī al-Subkī and his sons distinguished themselves as theological teachers, judges, and authors.

We took the Shāfi'ī group as a matter of course; the Ḥanbalī one, second in point of importance, is rather unexpected. Indeed, the Ḥanbalī sect has almost disappeared from Egypt and Syria and is now to be found only in Arabia and, in a new form, in the Wahhābī brotherhoods. The imām Aḥmad ibn Ḥanbal (IX-1), who created that sect, was curiously enough a disciple of al-Shāfi'ī, but he soon developed and inculcated in his followers fanatical and puritanical tendencies. In the fourteenth century, the Ḥanbalī sect was very active in Syria and Egypt and caused considerable trouble because of its zeal and turbulence. The great leader was Ibn Taimīya, whose outspokenness and fervor gained him the support of devoted friends and the hatred of many enemies. His most ardent disciple was Ibn Qayyim al-Jawzīya, who explained Ḥanbalī ideals in a long series of books. At one time Ibn Taimīya and Ibn Qayyim were together in a prison of Cairo, a fine place for zealots to commune and to recruit their strength for further sacrifices. Still another Ḥanbalī theologian was the Baghdādī Ibn Rajab.

There remain four scholars whom I cannot associate with any school. The first is Muḥammad ibn Dāniyāl (XIII-2), one of the most original writers of his time and the only representative of dramatic poetry in Islām. He is a very good witness to Egyptian culture at the end of the thirteenth century and the beginning of the fourteenth. Two others are encyclopaedic writers, Muḥammad ibn Ibrāhīm al-Waṭwāṭ (XIII-2), who died in 1318, and Muḥammad ibn Ibrāhīm al-Dimashqī, who died eight years later. The latter is especially famous as the author of one of the elaborate cosmographies of the Middle Ages. He also composed a treatise on physiognomy, a popular subject which deserves consideration on grounds similar to those set forth above apropos of oneiromancy. The Ḥanbalī Ibn Qayyim had also dealt with it.[23] Nor were oneiromancy and physiognomy the only fantastic subjects drawing the curiosity of mediaeval scholars. There were many other forms of divination or "mancy," for example, the jafr, for which camel membranes

[23] More treatises on physiognomy may be found by means of the index.

provided the instrument. The fourth of the independent Mamlūk scholars, Muḥammad ibn Sālim al-Khallāl, wrote a book on that branch of knowledge ('ilm al-jafr).

We should not judge these aberrations too severely, because they were not quite as irrational, ridiculous, and inexcusable at a time when few physical laws had yet been ascertained as they would be today. Moreover, they were not mediaeval in origin, but far more ancient; in fact, they continued hoary traditions, the purification of which would require many more centuries of painful effort.[24] Finally, we should always remember with due humility that these aberrations continue to exist around us to this day, at least in dark corners, and that they would soon flourish abundantly if scientific control of them were relaxed even for a short time. As new fools are born every day, superstitions can never be completely suppressed, but only subdued.

D3. *Anatolia*

There are especially good reasons for dealing with the Anatolians separately, for they represent a very definite nationality, which we call Turkish. In the fourteenth century, that nationality was very far from being unified. The fall of the Saljūq dynasty (a Turkish dynasty by the way) in 1300 had created a political chaos. The whole of Anatolia was divided among a number of feudal states, ten of which assumed gradually some importance. The political vicissitudes of these rival states are very complicated and do not interest us, but we are very much interested in the fact that the populations of all these states were presumably Turkish. It may be very difficult to separate Turks from Iranians in the territories farther east, as far east as Central Asia, where Turkish dialects (e.g., Uighūr) had been spoken for centuries, and some of the men quoted in section D5 (Persia) may be of Turkish origin; but when it comes to Anatolia we are on safer ground. We may assume that an Anatolian is some kind of Turk, unless he is proved to be something else, and if he prefers the Turkish language to either Arabic or Persian our assumption becomes stronger.

Before dealing with these Anatolians I should like to tell a story[25] illustrating the contemporary use of the Turkish language as far east at least as the Bahr Khwārizm (Aral Sea): The shaykh Sharaf of Urganj (or Jurjānīya, in the region of Khwārizm, south of the sea) received a request from the people of Khiḍr Īlī, Balkhān, Manqishlāgh, and vicinity for translations of Arabic books into Turkish. "It is so difficult," they said, "for us Turkish folks to read the Arabic books, understand their meaning, and act accordingly. If you were kind enough to translate them for us into Turkish you would obtain merit (thawāb)."[26] It was because of that request that the shaykh Sharaf wrote in Turkish the Mu'īn al-murīd in 1313 or before. A copy of it including marginal notes has been found in one of the Brusa libraries.[27] The story is especially interesting because of its date. Beginning with the fourteenth century there is a growing awareness of the Turkish language and of

[24] For the Greek legacy, chiefly as reflected in Byzantine documents, see Armand Delatte (vol. 1, 1927); La catoptromancie grecque (Liége 1932; Isis 20, 478–80).

[25] I owe this story with its sources to Mr. Aydin M. Sayili (January 1941).

[26] As quoted in the Shajara-i Tarākima of Abū-l-Ghāzī Bahādur Khān. See Zapiski of the Russian Archaeological Society (18 [1907–8], 0162–63, St. Petersburg 1908). Text in Turkish and Russian.

[27] Mehmed Fuad Köprülü (or Köprülü zade Mehmed Fuad): Türk edebiyatı tarihi (p. 340–41, Istanbul 1928/29).

its possible value and dignity. Until that time it had been completely kept down by more learned languages like Syriac and Persian, not to speak of Arabic.[28]

To return to Anatolia, four or five men arrest our attention. 'Āshiq pāshā wrote a Turkish poem entitled Ma'ārif-nāma (Book of the sciences). He was a ṣūfī and the first teacher of taṣawwuf in the Turkish language. He was also the first Turkish poet of any importance, though his Ma'ārif-nāma, completed in 1330, was preceded by the Turkish poems of Jalāl al-dīn-i-Rūmī and the latter's son Sulṭān Walad. There were also a number of popular poets, the greatest being Yūnus Emre. Both 'Āshiq pāshā and Yūnus Emre were said to be friends of Ḥājjī Baktāsh, eponymic founder of the darwīsh order Baktāshīya, a peculiarly Turkish organization, the importance of which in the history of Turkish literature and culture can hardly be exaggerated. The third poet, Gülshehrī, wrote a Turkish version of the Manṭiq al-ṭayr (Reasoning of the birds), a mystical allegory originally written in Persian by Fāriḍ al-dīn 'Aṭṭār (XIII-1). Gülshehrī was not a Baktāshī darwīsh, but more probably a Mawlawī (= whirling dervish).

'Āshiq pāshā and Yūnus Emre wrote exclusively in Turkish; Gülshehrī wrote in Turkish but also in Persian. A fourth man, Dā'ūd ibn Maḥmūd al-Qaiṣarī, wrote in Arabic. This is not surprising, for he was a regular Muslim teacher, the founder of the first 'Uthmānlī madrasa (in Iznīq, Nicaea), and Arabic was the sacred language of Islām. All these men were ṣūfī (mystics), but it is one thing to write mystic poems in Turkish for the education of the people, and quite another to teach the elements of religion and theology in a regular school. For such teaching Arabic was at that time and long afterward the only acceptable language.

D4. *'Irāq*

The Iraqian group is less homogeneous than the Turkish one, and this is natural, for 'Irāq (and this means generally Baghdād) was far less separated from the rest of the Muslim world than was Anatolia. It is true al-Qaiṣarī had been educated in Egypt, but voyages from Anatolia to Egypt were exceptional, save as part of the Pilgrimage, whereas all kinds of relations, political and economic as well as spiritual, existed continuously between the great Eastern cities, Baghdād on the one hand, Damascus, Jerusalem, Cairo, Alexandria on the other. Moreover, 'Irāq was in constant communication with Persia. The characteristic features of that country are due to its being a kind of bridge between the great Arabian centers and Persia, and the Oriental sea traffic converging in the Persian Gulf and the Shaṭṭ al-'Arab; they are due also to the juxtaposition of Sunnī and Shī'a elements.

The first 'Irāqī in point of time is precisely a Shī'a, Ibn al-Muṭahhar al-Ḥillī, who wrote a long series of theological treatises, widely circulated and commented upon in Arabic and Persian. The second is a ṣūfī, 'Abd al-Razzāq, whose main work was a dictionary of the technical terms used by the mystics. He was the author of various philosophical treatises in which he helped to "unveil" the doctrines generally associated with the name of Ibn 'Arabī (XIII-1). Al-Khaṭīb al-Irbilī, best known as a theorist of music, composed a treatise on the definition of the sciences. Finally, Ibn al-Akfānī, who was born near Mūṣul but practiced medicine in Cairo, wrote an encyclopaedia dealing with sixty sciences and aiming to guide the student in his exploration of them.

[28] In the introduction to his Kitāb al-ṣaidana fī-l-ṭibb, al-Bīrūnī remarked on the polyglottism of the Khwārizm region and spoke of polyglot dictionaries used in Central Asia, one of them referring to ten languages; the Nestorians used Greek-Syriac-Arabic-Persian dictionaries. Max Meyerhof: Das Vorwort zur Drogenkunde des Bīrūnī (Berlin 1932; Isis 20, 451–54).

These four men among them covered the totality of Muslim philosophy and theology. The first looked at it from the Shī'a point of view, the second from the mystical one, the two others from that of knowledge in general, Muslim and lay. All of them wrote in Arabic, but al-Ḥillī may have used the Persian language as well.

D5. *Īrān*

The Iranian group is second in point of numbers to the Mamlūk one, but we must bear in mind the possibility that some of its members were of Turkish origin. Our classification is meant to be geographical rather than ethnical, for ethnical distinctions are often hopelessly complicated in Central Asia.[29]

The great mathematician and physicist Quṭb al-dīn al-Shīrāzī was also a philosopher, one of the representatives of the mystical school called ḥikmat al-ishrāq which originated in Spain in the first half of the tenth century (Introd. 2, 362, 596). He wrote a commentary on one of the earliest Eastern treatises on the subject, written by another Persian, Yaḥyā al-Suhrawardī (XII-2).

Rashīd al-dīn was a historian and a patron of learning, but so great a man that one cannot explain the cultural background without referring to him. As long as he lived (that is, until 1318) he dominated art and learning in the regions of Tabrīz and Sulṭānīyah. Aḥmad ibn al-Ḥasan al-Jārabardī, a Shāfi'ī theologian, was considered the most learned man in Tabrīz in the first half of the fourteenth century. Passing to Khurāsān and farther east, we come across the Ḥanafī theologian 'Abdallāh ibn Aḥmad al-Nasafī (XIII-2), the enigmatic Shams al-dīn Mīrak of Bukhārā, who wrote philosophical commentaries, and the encyclopaedist Ṣadr al-Sharī'a al-thānī. Returning to Persia proper, the most distinguished theologians were al-Ījī and al-Taḥtānī.

All these men wrote in Arabic, except Rashīd al-dīn, who wrote primarily in Persian. Rashīd al-dīn was by far the greatest man, but he was not a philosopher, hardly a theologian, and we include him in this section only because of the considerable influence which he wielded. We must still name in addition to him, however, two outstanding men writing in Persian. The first of these is the historian and encyclopaedist Ḥamdallāh Mustawfī (al-Qazwīnī), to whom we shall be obliged to refer repeatedly in the following sections, and the second was another encyclopaedist, more philosophically minded, Muḥammad ibn Maḥmūd al-Āmilī. Both of them were Shī'a,[30] and between them they opened to the Shī'a elite and to Persian readers a large mass of philosophical, theological, and scientific information which had hitherto been available only in Arabic.

[29] In his monumental bibliography of Arabic literature, Carl Brockelmann entitles one of the chapters (2, 410–14, 1902) "Īrān and Tūrān," making no attempt to distinguish between these two entities. He has followed the same practice in the supplement (1938). For Tūrānian difficulties see V. Minorsky: Tūrān (EI 4, 878–84, 1931).

[30] I did not discuss the Shī'a in the chapter on religion, because it would take too long and is not sufficiently relevant to my purpose. See Hughes (p. 572–79, 1885) and R. Strothmann (EI 4, 350–58, 1926). The origin of the Shī'a separation was political; the members of that sect claim that 'Alī, first cousin of the Prophet and husband of his daughter Fāṭimah, should have been elected to succeed the Prophet, being the first legitimate imām or khalīfah; they reject the first three khulafā', Abū Bakr, 'Umar, and 'Uthmān, as usurpers. The separation thus begun was gradually widened and exacerbated by other political events and by deep temperamental differences between Arabs, Turks, etc. on the one side and Iranians on the other. The Sunnī point of view was on the whole more tolerant and conservative; the Shī'a became more and more secretive, intolerant, dramatic, messianic.

D6. *Muslim India*

To the two Persian authors whom we have just mentioned at the end of the preceding section might be added a third, al-Multānī, who flourished in the Punjab. He was primarily a theologian, and not a Shī'a, but a Sunnī of the Ḥanafī sect, the earliest sect to take a definite form (see Abū Ḥanīfa, VIII-1). This fact (his Sunnī orthodoxy) explains his use of the Arabic as well as of the Persian language. He illustrates Persian influence of a moderate kind, not the fanatical and exclusive zeal of the Shī'a.

E. *Hindu India*

Our knowledge of Hindu thought in the fourteenth century is very incomplete for many reasons. To begin with, Hindu culture was stifled, if not stamped out, in many places by the Muslim conquerors. The patronage of Muslim courts went naturally to Muslim scholars. The worst impediment to our knowledge is the fact that the writings in Sanskrit and other Hindu languages are generally undated. That impediment, however, applies to every period of the Hindu past, and it never created as complete a desert as it does in this case. For I cannot quote a single Sanskrit writer of this period who might be called a philosopher or theologian, or whose activities are of cultural importance.

The Burmese writer Medhaṃkara, educated in Ceylon, wrote in Pāli the Lokadīpasāra, a collection of stories illustrating different stages of existence.

Raṭṭa-kavi composed in Canarese a kind of popular cosmography or encyclopaedia, and this was soon translated by one Bhāskara into Telugu. Another poet of southeastern India, Errāpragaḍa, completed the translation of the Mahābhārata, which is the outstanding monument of Telugu literature. This is culturally important, for the history of the non-Aryan civilizations of India is largely dominated by the assimilation of Sanskrit and Pāli elements, even as our own culture was determined by the gradual assimilation of Greek and Hebrew elements.

F. *China*

The natural classification of the Chinese scholars is in three groups, Taoists, Confucianists, and Buddhists, but we should always bear in mind that these groups are not by any means exclusive. This fact can be well illustrated by the story[31] of Fu hsi (497–569), the inventor of revolving bookcases, who is generally represented wearing a Taoist cap, Confucian shoes, and a Buddhist scarf across the shoulder! When he was introduced to the emperor Wu Ti (Liang dynasty, ruled 502–49), and the latter asked him whether he was a Buddhist priest, Fu pointed to his Taoist cap; when Wu asked him whether he was a Taoist, Fu pointed to his Confucian shoes; when Wu finally asked him whether he was a Confucianist, Fu pointed to his Buddhist scarf. Nevertheless, the classification is not useless and it is often expedient to make it. We may call Confucianist one who wrote mainly Confucian commentaries, Buddhist one whose main works are included in the Tripiṭaka or Buddhist patrology,[32] Taoist one whose main works are included in the Tao tsang or Taoist patrology.

[31] As told by Nanjio (p. xxvi, 1883).

[32] Following father Wieger's advice (p. 5, 1911), I use the word patrology in lieu of canon, for these collections not only have no canonic authority, but are very heterogeneous from any dogmatic point of view.

We have already dealt with the main Buddhist doctor, Nien ch'ang, in the religious section of this summary. Two of his contemporaries are represented in the Tao tsang, and we may thus call them Taoists: the alchemist Ch'ên Kuan-wu, and Wu Ch'êng, who prepared an annotated edition of the Tao tê ching and of the Nan Hua chên ching.

By far the main group is the Confucian one,[33] which constitutes the real Chinese orthodoxy, and, true to the orthodox pattern, tends but too often to smugness. Buddhists, and Taoists even more, are comparatively heterodox and savor of heresy unless they be prudent enough to obtain good Confucian titles to fame. This was done by Wu Ch'êng, who edited Confucian classics as well as Taoist ones. In addition to Wu Ch'êng, the three outstanding Confucianists were Ch'ên Li, Hsü Ch'ien, and Ch'ên Hao. The first of these, being primarily a historian, was more interested in the Shang shu than in the other classics, yet he wrote a treatise in which he discussed various schools of philosophy. The two others compiled commentaries on the classics.

The Confucianism which engrossed the minds of the contemporary Chinese literati was not the pure Confucianism of ancient times, but the neo-Confucianism developed by the "five philosophers" (wu tzŭ) of the Sung dynasty and especially by the last one, Chu Hsi (XII-2). It is a Confucianism which has been somewhat exposed to Taoist and Buddhist ideas, and has become a kind of philosophy of nature (hsing-li), and this helps us to understand how one could be at the same time a Confucianist, a Buddhist, and a Taoist without unbearable contradictions. The same ideology dominated the countries submitted to Chinese influence, such as Korea, Japan, and Indo-China, though with somewhat of a lag, varying from one country to another. For example, it took a considerable time for the more eclectic Confucianism to reach Korea. One may not realize that at once, because Confucianism had deep roots in that country. By the sixth century, if not before, the Confucian classics were already the basis of Korean education. The first Confucian "fathers" (of Korea), Hsieh ts'ung and Ts'ui Chih-yüan, flourished as early as the beginning of the eighth century and the end of the ninth. The Confucian cult received a great impulse c. 983, when Jên-ch'êng-lao brought back plans and records describing the chief temples of the Sung capital and the rites there practiced. Soon after this, Confucian temples spread throughout the land, and beautiful editions of the Classics were printed which excited the admiration and covetousness of the Sung court. Yet for centuries the cult was eclipsed by the Buddhist cult, which enjoyed considerably more popularity. Korean chronicles speak of a Confucian revival led by Ho Ch'ung c. 1068. Yet all that was definitely anterior to the wu tzŭ, the first of whom was Chou Tun-i (XI-2).

The next Confucian revival in Korea was led by An Yü, who died in 1306 and was canonized in 1319. It is not sure whether An Yü was already acquainted with the hsing-li, but the next teacher, Li Ch'i-hsien, certainly was, for in the meanwhile (in 1313 ff.) a great many Sung books were imported into Korea. We may say that by the middle of the fourteenth century, neo-Confucianism was fairly well launched in that country, though its complete triumph would require another half-century of efforts and the establishment of a new dynasty.[34]

[33] There is no Confucian patrology, which might be called Ju-tsang, comparable to the Tao-tsang or the Fo-tsang (Tripiṭaka), though the idea of editing one was advocated by Chou Yung-nien (1730-91) (Giles no. 430). There are of course the Five Classics (wu ching), the Six Classics, the Nine Classics, and the Thirteen Classics (Couling p. 122, 1917), and a number of indexes to them are now available, but there is no Ju-tsang.

[34] Youn (1939).

G. *Japan*

The main characteristic of Japan at this time, as contrasted with either China or Korea, is the more complete amalgamation of Buddhism with Confucianism. In Korea, Buddhism and Confucianism were facing each other as rivals for public favor and almost as enemies. In Japan, on the contrary, the main Buddhist teachers made it a point to teach also the new philosophy, hsing-li[35]. Japan has always exhibited a remarkable genius for synthesis, even for purely formal synthesis of irreconcilable elements.

The main teacher of both Buddhism (Rinzai-shū) and Confucianism was the bonze and imperial tutor Gen-e. For example, we know that on the 22d day of the 7th month 1319 Gen-e lectured on the teachings of Chu Hsi before the emperor Go-Daigo. Kitabatake Chikafusa was in the audience.

The Buddhist sects realized the great practical importance of printing[36] and used the new art to diffuse Buddhist and Confucian doctrines. It is proper to speak of that here, as the contemporary development of printing in Japan is less interesting from the purely technical point of view than from the cultural one. Printing had begun in Japan more than five centuries before. To be sure, an expanding craft would suggest and solve an endless series of technical problems, but the essential was known, and well known. The main point of interest to us is that the Sung culture was diffused in Japan (as in Korea) with the help of the printing art, and this was made easy because of the cooperation of the Buddhist clerks. The Buddhist Tripiṭaka, an enormous collection of books, had been printed in Japan in 1278–88. The first Confucian text printed in Japan was the Rongo shūchū, in ten volumes, completed in 1247.[37] A large biography of the Buddha was printed in 1322, and the Analects in 1364. A great many other items issued in the fourteenth century from the Japanese presses, distributing with impartiality the favorite sūtra of various Buddhist sects and Confucian teachings. Hsing-li texts, however, were printed relatively late in Japan, the first being Chu Hsi's four commentaries on the Confucian classics, printed in 1599. Apparently no Taoist book was printed in Japan during the fourteenth century; however, the Sankyō shiki, by Kōbō Daishi (IX-1), in two volumes printed in 1253, contains a long essay on Taoism. Chinese poems were not printed until after the middle of the fourteenth century, the first being the collection Fan Tê-chi shih-chi, by Fan P'êng (1272–1330), in seven volumes printed in Kyōto in 1361. In the same year or perhaps even a little earlier (1360) was printed the Dontetsu-shū, a collection of Chinese poems written by a Japanese priest. A purely secular work entitled Rekidai Teiō hennen goken no zu

[35] Hsing-li was introduced very rapidly in Japan, by Shunjō (1167–1227), a priest of the Tendai-shū. Shunjō went to the Sung court in 1199 and remained there for twelve years. He could not study very long under Chu Hsi (d. 1200), but he studied under the latter's disciples. He brought back to Japan 256 works on Confucianism and lectured in Kyōto on Chu Hsi's teaching. In his diary Kimitsugu Tokudaiji, minister of the left, sums up Shunjō's lectures. (Shio Sakanishi.)

[36] Even as the Catholic church was to be, in the fifteenth century, the first institution which realized its importance in the West (Sarton p. 63, 1938).

[37] Rongo shūchū. This was the text of the Analects (Lun yü = Rongo) with brief commentaries collected from various Chinese sources. No copy of that edition of 1247 has been seen since the beginning of the sixteenth century, and some scholars, questioning its reality, claim that the Rongo shūkai of 1364 is the first edition of the Analects printed in Japan. The edition of 1364 is in ten volumes and contains no commentary. It is the most famous edition, and because it was printed in the nengō Shōhei (1346–70) it is generally called the Shōhei Rongo (Shōhei edition of Rongo).

(Handy chronological table of the successive emperors) was printed in Kyōto in 1376.

As to printing in Japanese, I obtained from Dr. Shio Sakanishi the following information (in her letter of Jan. 22, 1941): Two monks of the Jōdo-shū (Pure land sect) collected the sermons of the founder of their sect, Hōnen-Shōnin (XII-2), and had them printed in 1321 under the title Kurodani Shōnin wago tōroku. As far as I know (she writes), this is the earliest example of a printed Japanese text, i.e., a combination of Chinese characters with hiragana. Twenty-two years later a small volume entitled Muchū mondō, by Soseki, posthumous name Musō-kokushi (1275–1351), was printed in Kyōto. This is the earliest example of a text combining Chinese characters with katakana.[38]

VI. MATHEMATICS AND ASTRONOMY

Having cleared the ground and explained the political and religious events and the philosophical ideas which influenced the scientific atmosphere, the translations by means of which the accumulated knowledge of some groups became available to other groups, and the educative methods insuring the transmission of science to the new generations, we may now proceed to consider more carefully the development of separate branches of science and learning. It is natural to begin with mathematics. We shall pass in review the men who created, organized, or taught mathematics and astronomy, and we shall examine their writings.

Mathematics is not separated from astronomy, because the subjects grew together (e.g., trigonometry remained a branch of the latter as much as of the former) and, generally speaking, the same men were responsible for their progress or diffusion. Neither can astrology be conveniently detached from astronomy, nor meteorology from both. Questions of optical meteorology, however, will be reserved for the section on physics.

A. *Western Christendom*

A1. *Italy*

The Italian mathematicians are so numerous that we must divide them into five groups: the mathematicians proper, the astronomers, the astrologers, then the writers of books on medical astrology, and the critics of astrology. These groups are not mutually exclusive, except in a first approximation.

Three men seem to have taken an exceptional interest in mathematics, Jacob of Florence, Paolo Dagomari, and Gregorio da Rimini. The first is unknown except as the author of a treatise on algorism written in 1307, continuing without distinction the tradition of Leonardo da Pisa. Paolo, absurdly praised by Boccaccio and other Florentines, was an astronomer and astrologer as well as a mathematician, but his main work is a kind of mathematical encyclopaedia, Trattato d'abbaco, d'astronomie e di segreti naturali e medicinali, composed in 1339. The arithmetical and algebraical parts recall Leonardo's Liber abaci and Jacob's Tractatus algorismi, adding nothing new.

The books of Jacob and Paolo just referred to were written in Italian, and both men were specialized mathematicians. On the contrary, the third author, Gregorio da Rimini, was primarily a philosopher or a theologian, and he wrote exclusively in Latin. He was an Augustinian hermit and became eventually the general of his

[38] For the history of the Japanese syllabaries see Introd. 1, 519, 553.

order. His tendencies were Occamist. He discussed mathematical continuity and infinity.

To return to Jacob and Paolo, their mathematical activities were partly determined by commercial needs. For example, Jacob proposes and solves a series of problems on exchange, interest, and partnership; similar problems as well as tables of weights and measures are given by Paolo. We find again the same kind of problems in an anonymous Italian text of the same age. It is clear that the commercial prosperity of the Italian cities created a need for such books, and the fact that they were written in Italian, not in Latin, proves that the people needing them were not clerks or scholars, but merchants or bankers. These three Italian texts anticipate and prepare those which will be multiplied a century later by the early printers, such as the first great commercial arithmetic, the Nobel opera de arithmetica, printed by Ratdolt (Venice 1484),[1] often reprinted and imitated and leading to the climax of that tradition, the Summa de arithmetica of Luca Paciolo (Venice 1494).

Another mathematical tradition which was developed at this time in northern Italy, but which would require another century of gestation (in Italy and Flanders) before attaining sufficient maturity, was the study of perspective. This was needed by painters, especially those who tried to represent the outside or inside of buildings and to create illusions. The beginnings of a deliberate use of central projection may be seen in paintings by Ambrogio Lorenzetti of Siena, e.g., in the Annunciation (Accademia, Siena) dated 1344. Either Lorenzetti or his mathematical advisers had been able to apply to the solution of his artistic needs the knowledge explained by Euclid, Ibn al-Haitham, and Witelo.

Guido Joseph Kern: Die Grundzüge der linear-perspektivischen Darstellung in der Kunst der Gebrüder Van Eyck (36 p., 14 pl., Leipzig 1904); Die Anfänge der zentralperspektivischen Konstruktion in der italienischen Malerei des 14. Jahrhunderts (Mitt. Kunsthistorischen Instituts, Florenz, 2, 39–65, 1912; Mitt. 14, 250). Heinrich Wieleitner: Zur Erfindung der verschiedenen Distanzkonstruktionen in der malerischen Perspektive (Repertorium für Kunstwissenschaft 42, 249–62, 1920; Isis 4, 140). Gino Loria: Storia della geometria descrittiva (Milano 1921; Isis 5, 181–82); Loria neglects the origins. For a history of perspective see Introd. (1, 86, 95, 721; 2, 23, 509, 761, etc.); for Egyptian origins see Isis (33, 71–73).

The main geometrical work of this period is the Practica geometriae written by Dominicus de Clavasio in Paris 1346. This Piemontese mathematician was especially concerned with measurements—measurements of lengths, areas, and volumes. His Practica includes trigonometrical measurements as well as purely geometrical ones. Dominicus was well acquainted not only with sine, cosine, and versed sine, but also with cotangent and tangent; he realized the practical value of tangents. That treatise was often copied, which proves that it was appreciated, yet it was never printed.

In an account of fourteenth-century mathematics Dante may be left out, but the historian of astronomy cannot neglect him. Dante's ideas on astronomy were not up-to-date; he had derived them almost exclusively from the Latin versions of al-Farghānī (IX-1); nevertheless, they must be taken into consideration because they represent the astronomical and cosmological knowledge not only of his educated (not specialized) contemporaries, but also of many following generations.

[1] Analyzed by David Eugene Smith (Isis 8, 41–49, 1926).

He was the first Western writer to refer to the Southern Cross. If he was the author of the "Quaestio de aqua et terra," he discussed the shape of the earth, refuting the alleged coexistence of two excentric land and water spheres.

At the beginning of the century the main theorist of astronomy in a general, nonmathematical way was Giles of Rome (XIII-2). After his death (1316) and Dante's (1321), astronomical work was done by John of Genoa, who was interested in eclipses and compiled tables ad hoc, and by the Umbrian Dominican Hugh of Città di Castello, who wrote in Florence 1337 a commentary on the most popular astronomical textbook of the Middle Ages, the Sphere of John of Sacrobosco (XIII-1). An incomplete Italian translation of the Alphonsine astronomy (or astrology?) was made in 1341 by one Gueruccius (Isis 13, 93). The geometer Dominicus de Clavasio wrote commentaries on the Sacroboscan Sphere and the Aristotelian De coelo. The trigonometrical features of his Practica have already been mentioned.

The separation of astrologers from astronomers is sometimes easy but in most cases difficult, if not impossible. Their purposes were different but their methods to some extent the same. For example, the same astronomical tables might be compiled or used for irrational purposes and for rational ones. The very terms astrologi, astronomi, even mathematici were used promiscuously. This source of confusion goes back to classical times; the terms astrologus, astrologia were first used to mean what we call astronomer, astronomy (Introd. 2, 760). When Cicero (I-1 B.C.) spoke of a mathematicus he meant a mathematician, but for Tacitus (I-2) the same word had already a very bad connotation (Historiae 1, 22), the same as our astrologer or charlatan. Bearing these ambiguities in mind, we are nevertheless safe in calling Pietro d'Abano, Cecco d'Ascoli, and the Augustinian Dionysius de Rubertis astrologers in the bad sense.

The Lucidator compiled by Pietro d'Abano in 1310 was an elaborate astronomical treatise, defending Ptolemaic theories. It illustrates well what was said above, that the difference between astrology and astronomy was a difference between intentions rather than between methods. For the treatise is a good summary of astronomical knowledge, yet Pietro was primarily an astrologer, if a moderate one. Cecco d'Ascoli wrote a number of astrological commentaries in Latin, and his Italian poem L'acerba was encyclopaedic in purpose but thoroughly imbued with astrological prejudices. Dionysius de Rubertis was an astrological adviser of the king of Naples, and one of Petrarca's friends.

Medical practice, e.g. bloodletting, being dominated by astrological considerations, we must expect to find a number of treatises devoted to what might be called astrological medicine (or medical astrology). The astronomer Hugh of Città di Castello wrote one of these in Perugia 1338 (or 1358?), De diebus criticis secundum astrologos. Similar books were written by Niccolò di Paganica, Andalò di Negro, Augustine of Trent, Thaddeus of Parma, and Maino de Maineri. The occurrence and diffusion of the plague, a scourge the capricious developments of which completely baffled even the most experienced physicians, increased the relative importance of medical astrology; this particular consequence will become more tangible in the second half of the century.

Though the general outlook of all people, rich or poor, learned or ignorant, was astrological, or at least colored with astrological views, the intensity of the dye varied from one individual to another, the one extreme being represented by a mixture of all kinds of superstitions in their wildest forms, the other extreme by comparative rationalism. Astrological tenets and extravagances were attacked by such men as the Augustinian Agostino Trionfo and the great humanist Petrarca, and we have already recalled that the Catholic church exerted a moderating influence. It was precisely in the name of religious orthodoxy that Trionfo condemned the astrologers and other soothsayers; Petrarca's objections were those of common sense and humanism. To many people of his training and mood, astrology appeared as an exaggeration of science instead of a perversion of it. He disliked astrology because it was too scientific and too pedantic, whereas we condemn it because it is not scientific at all.

A2. *France*

The French group of mathematici is smaller than the Italian, but on the whole more distinguished. This does not mean that the French eschewed to any considerable extent the main intellectual disease of their time, that is, the astrological delusions. In fact, some of them did their best to increase it. For example, Arnold of Quinquempoix translated some of the astrological treatises of Abraham ben Ezra (XII-1), and Nicolas de La Horbe translated the Liber astronomicus of Guido Bonatti (XIII-2). It is curious that Arnold translated from French (not Hebrew) into Latin, and Nicolas translated from Latin into French! The two languages could serve the same purpose in France, except that Latin was more highbrow and exclusive.

The new arithmetic made remarkable progress in France. I was very much impressed to find a lucid explanation of the new numerals and of the principle of position, not in a mathematical treatise, but in a surgical one written in French for unlearned people, the Chirurgie of Henri de Mondeville (Nicaise edition, p. 8–10). That a surgeon thought it worth while to include this new arithmetic in his treatise is more significant than if we had a number of such explanations in purely mathematical MSS. Henri explains that the value of each numeral increases tenfold for each move to the left, and that it is so because Arabs and Jews, from whom we received these numerals, write from right to left.

The decimal idea was fermenting, but with incredible slowness. Al-Nasawī (XI-1), John of Seville (XII-1) in his translation of an unknown Arabic text, and Jordanus Nemorarius (XIII-1) had repeated at century intervals operations of this kind:

$$(1) \qquad \sqrt{a} = \frac{1}{10^n}\sqrt{(a\cdot 10^{2n})}$$

though they spoiled it all by expressing the final results in degrees, minutes, and seconds. This shows that the decimal idea had not yet been able to shake off the sexagesimal one (we should judge these mediaeval mathematicians with indulgence, for we have not yet succeeded in disentangling ourselves completely from the same Babylonian conventions!). John of Seville had already recognized that the value of the sexagesimal system lay in the orderly system, not in the number sixty; Nemorarius expresses the same idea even more clearly.[2] For all that, in the fourteenth century there were only two kinds of fractions, the so-called physical or sexagesimal ones, and the vulgar or common ones. Various treatises bearing such titles as "algorismus de minutiis (tam vulgaribus quam physicis)" were written to set forth the use of both kinds of fractions. One of these treatises is ascribed to

[2] Text given by Gustav Eneström (BM 14, 172, 1913).

the French astronomer Jean de Linières. In none of them is any mention made of decimal fractions. An adumbration of these fractions occurs in the Quadripartitum (1343) of Jean de Meurs, where, after having extracted the square root of 2 according to the method represented by formula (1) above, he remarks that if we say that 1414 is the root of 2, the first unit of that number is to be regarded as an integer, the following 4 as tenths, etc.... How tantalizing! Yet decimal fractions did not completely emerge until 1585, almost two centuries and a half later![3]

At any rate, from the writings of the surgeon Henri de Mondeville, and of the astronomers Jean de Linières and Jean de Meurs, we can safely conclude that the French scientists were interested in the new arithmetic and realized some of its possibilities.

In the meanwhile, astronomical thought was developed on Arabic models, and Stephanus Arlandi (was he French or Catalan?) translated one more treatise from Arabic into Latin, the Sphaera solidis of Qusṭā ibn Lūqā (IX-2). Yet it could obtain more help from the fine experimental and theoretical traditions of the Parisian school. No wonder that a remarkable group of French philosophers was eager to investigate more deeply the motions of stars and planets.

In his commentary on the Sentences, the Franciscan François de Meyronnes reported that according to an unnamed doctor it would be simpler to assume that the earth rotates and that the heavens are at rest rather than the opposite. This was a very bold suggestion, which he did not press, but it is very remarkable that it was made at all and that he was willing to transmit it.[4] The Books of sentences obliged every theologian to contemplate astronomical theories, and gave them opportunities to discuss them if they were so inclined. Thus the Dominican Durand of Saint Pourçain took advantage of that obligation to ventilate his own views, which were the Ptolemaic ones as restored by Ibn al-Haitham (XI-1) and vindicated by the Franciscans Richard of Middleton (XIII-2) and Bernard of Verdun (XIII-2).

The two leading philosophers, Jean de Jandun and Jean Buridan, were deeply interested in astronomy and both defended Ptolemaic theories. It should be noted that every French astronomer of that time was a Ptolemaist, in spite of the fact that Aristotle was then at his zenith. The shortcomings of the Almagest had been recognized by Arabic astronomers, and various corrections had been proposed, but none of them, e.g. those of Jābir ibn Aflaḥ (XII-1) or al-Biṭrūjī (XII-2), had been satisfying. Ptolemaism, however imperfect, was proved to be better than Alpetragianism. It is easy for us moderns to see that no improvement could be of much value, short of the Copernican revolution, and the latter was still hidden deep in the womb of time.

Buridan has another title to our admiration. He and the Italian Franciscan Francis of Marchia were the first to assume that ordinary mechanics could be legitimately extended to celestial bodies and that celestial mechanics was not essentially different from the sublunar. This was only a prophecy, the verification of which could not even be attempted before the beginning of the seventeenth century. To speak of the French astronomers and philosophers of the fourteenth century as forerunners of Galileo is silly, even though some of their guesses were eventually verified by Galileo and by Newton.

[3] Tropfke (1[3], 172, 1930). Sarton (p. 168, 203, 1935).

[4] I have been wondering whether the "quidam doctor" quoted by Meyronnes was not himself?

To return to practical astronomers, Jean de Linières compiled a catalogue of stars and determined the obliquity of the ecliptic with remarkable precision; he and his pupil John of Saxony revised the Alphonsine tables, the printed form of which (1483) embodied their corrections. Following the example of many thirteenth-century predecessors, Jewish, Christian, and Muslim, he devised new instruments. More tables were compiled by Jean de Meurs, whose activities are generally of the same nature as those of Jean de Linières, though with stronger leanings to astrology.

Jean de Meurs' most valuable work concerns the calendar. The insufficiency of the Julian calendar had been pointed out in the preceding century by Robert Grosseteste and Roger Bacon; the Julian year being a little too long, the civil dates of astronomical landmarks (say, the equinoxes) were more and more retarded and the calendric out-of-gearness became more obvious and more annoying as each century passed by. In 1318 a new calendar and a scheme of a perpetual one were presented by the Dominican Pierre Vidal to John XXII. Nothing was done about it, but twenty-six years later Clement VI requested Jean de Meurs and Firmin de Beauval to investigate the need of calendric reform; they reported to him in the following year (1345). Their report is still extant; it devotes considerably more attention to the problems of the ecclesiastical calendar than to those of the civil one.

Jean de Meurs was much of an astrologer; he wrote various prognostications and may be the author of an anonymous treatise on astrological medicine (Paris 1344). Firmin de Beauval also wrote a prognostication, but his main astrological effort is the De mutatione (sive de impressionibus) aëris, which may be called a treatise of astrological meteorology, though it includes a discussion of astrology in general. In fact, it is so comprehensive that one at least of the many MSS is entitled Colliget[5] astrologiae. In spite of their astrological business, Jean de Meurs and Firmin de Beauval must be considered men of science; with Geoffroi de Meaux, author of many prognostications, we come down to a lower level, and with Jean de Bassigny, astrological charlatan, we fall lower still. Among them these four men give us a general idea of astrological theory and practice in France. To complete the picture, we ought to take into account some criticisms of astrology, which were largely if not exclusively of ecclesiastical origin. The church condemned the fatalism and materialism of the astrologers. The Avignonese popes (especially John XXII and Clement VI) were quite outspoken on such matters; whatever their shortcomings may have been as shepherds of the Catholic flock, the historian of science must give them some credit for their fight against astrology and superstition and their interest in the reform of the calendar. Thorndike has recently analyzed an anonymous treatise against astrology[6] which may be a French or Avignonese production of this time. For example, it might have been written by the English Franciscan Walter Catton,[7] who was penitentiary to the pope and wrote "adversus astrologos." Unfortunately, the astrological tide was too strong for the popes to halt it. The church could not defeat the astrologers; it could only scold them, punish the worst offenders, compromise with the others, and minimize the scandal.

[5] The word colliget is explained in Introd. 2, 356.

[6] Lynn Thorndike: A hitherto unnoticed criticism of astrology. Liber de reprobatione iudiciorum astrologiae (Isis 31, 68–78, 1939).

[7] Gualterus Chattodunus (d. Avignon 1343), Franciscan in Norwich, mathematician, distinguished Aristotelian, whose commentary on the Sentences and other writings are lost. T. A. Archer (DNB 9, 325, 1887).

A3. *England*

The English school was mathematical rather than astronomical. To be sure, schoolmen like Duns Scot (XIII-2) would discuss astronomical theories in general. Scot's views were modeled upon those of his Franciscan brethren. To put it in the briefest form, they were Ptolemaic, anti-Aristotelian. The English group of mathematicians is impressive, because of its early specialization. We meet here a number of men who are decidedly mathematicians, rather than philosophers; we might consider them almost professionals. Their enthusiasm was sustained by a regular school, Merton in Oxford (Introd. 2, 863), which might be called the earliest school of mathematics (and astronomy) in Christian Europe. Of the ten leading mathematicians in England in the first half of the fourteenth century, five were certainly, and two or three others probably, connected with Merton.

Before speaking of their achievements, we may remark that there is less evidence here than in France of a wide interest in the new arithmetic. We have two algorisms written in English, both anonymous and incomplete. The first is a commentary on the popular Carmen de algorismo of Alexander of Villedieu (XIII-1), the other is a small fragment (550 words) dealing with numeration only.[8] Bradwardine's Arithmetica speculativa does not stoop to explain the new numerals.

To return to Merton College, it was a nursery not simply of mathematicians, but also of physicians, and one might add of archbishops, for in a little more than a century six primates of England were Merton men. Unfortunately, our knowledge of the early Mertonian scientists is very insufficient, because a good part of the Merton library and archives was sold as waste paper about the middle of the sixteenth century. According to the mathematician Thomas Allen (1542–1632), a cartload of valuable MSS was taken out of the library; he managed to save only a few of them, which had belonged to Rede and others. These few, now in the Bodleian, constitute our best source of information.

John Mauduith is the real initiator of Western trigonometry, for his Parvus tractatus was written in Merton as early as 1310, and was thus a little anterior to the Quadripartitum of Richard Wallingford, not to speak of the Latin translation of Levi ben Gerson's treatise, which did not appear till 1342, that is, a full generation later. As the Quadripartitum was presumably derived from the Parvus tractatus, it is proper to speak of Wallingford now, though his connection with Merton is uncertain. His trigonometrical treatise was the first original and fairly complete work of its kind in the West, and suffices to give him a place of honor in the history of mathematics. In 1326, he became abbot of St. Albans, and we may assume that much if not all of his scientific work was then already done. In addition to his two trigonometrical treatises, he wrote (or edited?) the Exafrenon, a collection of astrological rules, and described his astronomical instruments. His popular fame was naturally derived from those instruments, especially from the most comprehensive of them, an astronomical clock yclept Albion. Walter Odington was, like Wallingford, a Benedictine, yet he was mentioned in a Merton account dated 1330. This is puzzling. May we not assume that regulars interested in astronomy were welcome in Merton for consultation or study, even as various monks and nuns are welcome in Harvard today? In 1301, Walter compiled an almanac for his abbey, Evesham in Worcestershire, but in 1316 he was making

[8] The first was edited by David Eugene Smith: An ancient English algorism (Archiv für die Geschichte der Naturwissenschaften 1, 301–9, 1909). The second, by Halliwell (p. 29–31, 1839). Benedict (nos. 30, 31, 1914).

astronomical observations *in Oxford*. Surely that would bring him into touch with the local astronomers, that is, with Merton College. Various mathematical and astronomical treatises are ascribed to him.

The two following, Richard Swineshead and Thomas Bradwardine, may be considered together. Both were Merton alumni but continued their careers elsewhere. Richard assumed the Cistercian habit in Swineshead (Lincolnshire) and became somewhat of a philosopher, commenting on the Sentences and the Aristotelian Ethics, and discussing astronomical matters and the "increase and decrease of forms," about which more anon. Thomas' evolution was somewhat similar, except that he was a secular priest destined to die[9] archbishop of Canterbury. He was much interested in the old arithmetic, geometry, and theory of proportions, and investigated geometrical continuity. In Richard's main work, the Calculator, wherein the increase and decrease of forms were discussed, Thomas was mentioned. As far as we can make out, both men were groping for the graphical representation of functions. Their hesitations, to be continued for three centuries, help us to measure the depth and inherent difficulty of notions with which we are so familiar that we take them too much for granted, as we take the rising of the sun and the love of our friends.

John of Ashendon was the author of a large astrological treatise, the Summa iudicialis (or anglicana), completed in 1348, which prolonged his fame almost to the end of the seventeenth century. Simon Bredon continued the purer Merton tradition in trigonometry and astronomy. He must have been a man of some wealth, for he had accumulated a remarkable collection of books and instruments, which he bequeathed (in 1368) to the six Oxford colleges.

We have already called attention to the relation obtaining in this period between astrology and meteorology. Thus, some astrologers would specialize in meteorology, but in most cases they would do that without bothering over much about observations. The English priest William Merle, rector of Driby in Lincolnshire, was one of the first men to realize the fundamental need of systematic, regular, and protracted observations. His weather record extending over seven years (1337–44) is the first of comparable length in the whole world (aside from records in monastic and other chronicles restricted to anomalies). In 1340, he wrote a treatise on weather forecasting which conforms more closely to the tradition of astrological meteorology, but is far less precious to us than his weather journal. A similar work had been composed a little earlier (1325) by the Dominican Robert of York, "Perscrutator," and much of it was eventually absorbed in the more ambitious Summa anglicana of Ashendon. Various astrological treatises were produced by another Dominican, Robert of Holcot.

The English achievements can be summed up thus: first organization of trigonometry in the West, new meteorology, and tentative efforts concerning the increase and decrease of forms.

A4. *Germany*

The contrast between the German group and the English one is striking. The English group included a sufficient number of men who were primarily, if not exclusively, mathematicians and astronomers to have almost a professional appearance. On the contrary, among the Germans I can only find John of Saxony who may be called a mathematician. Some of the English devoted themselves to

[9] I put it that way, for he died thirty-eight days after his consecration as archbishop.

astrological meteorology, and, what is far more important, one of them began the practice of regular meteorological observation. In contrast, two of the Germans are meteorologists, but only in the Greek, Aristotelian sense, and they continue the tradition of Proclos in metaphysics and of Ibn al-Haitham in physics. As these two men, Dietrich of Freiberg and Berthold of Mosburg, were primarily concerned with optical meteorology, it will be better to deal with them in the physical section. Dietrich had made a survey of astronomical facts and theories, and with the majority of his contemporaries he had concluded in favor of the theory of excentrics and epicycles. In spite of his Neoplatonism, as far as physics was concerned, he realized the priority of experimental data.

Conrad of Heinrichau, who flourished in a Cistercian monastery not very far from Breslau, wrote in Latin various astronomical and calendric tracts of no importance, except to illustrate the spiritual life of Silesia. He seems to have been more of a German than a Pole, but I am not sure. Of far greater significance is the work of his Bavarian contemporary Conrad of Megenberg, who translated the Sphaera of John of Sacrobosco (XIII-1) into German. This was the first astronomical textbook in that language; it attracted but little attention, as scientifically minded Germans were prepared to read astronomy in Latin and unprepared, if not unwilling, to read it in their own dialect. Nevertheless the Deutsche Sphaera is a landmark in the history of German culture, even as Oresme's Espère in that of France.

We now come to the one German mathematician, John of Saxony, who, however, did not flourish in Germany, but was a very distinguished member of the Parisian school; I would have been justified in speaking of him in my account of French astronomy, when I dealt with his master, John de Linières. These two Johns indeed worked together and were largely responsible for the introduction of the Alphonsine tables in Paris. John of Saxony elaborated them and added the necessary explanations (1327). Ephemerides, as well as astronomical and astrological commentaries, are ascribed to him; he was active as a professional astronomer from 1327 to 1355. He was the outstanding German astronomer, but as there was no mathematical center in Germany at that time, his fame was added to the fame of the Parisian school.

A5. *Netherlands*

The contemporary mathematical culture of the Netherlands was not particularly brilliant. I cannot quote a single mathematician of the northern provinces. In the southern provinces, we should consider separately the Flemings and the Walloons.

As to the Flemish part, I know of only two astronomers, both in the diocese of Malines (Mechelen, near Antwerp). The first, Henry of Brussels, was a monk in the Benedictine abbey of Afflighem; he wrote calendric and astronomical tracts of little value, and seems to have been a very mediocre individual. The canon Henry Bate (XIII-2), who lived in Malines until 1310 or later, was a distinguished astronomer, a good observer (he observed the annular eclipse of the sun of 1310), and an astrologer of lasting reputation.

It should be noted that Henry Bate flourished in Liége as well as in his native place, Malines, and hence belongs to Walloon as well as to Flemish history. The main part of his scientific work, however, was done in Malines. There were no astronomers of repute in the bishopric of Liége, but the chronicler Jean de Hocsem noted meteorological phenomena, and the physician Simon of Couvin composed an astrological poem apropos of the plague of 1348.

In short, there was but a single astronomer in the Netherlands, Henry Bate, and he belongs rather to the thirteenth century than to the fourteenth.

A6. *Scandinavia*

Haukr Erlendsson, who held the dignity of a judge in Norway and in Iceland, translated the famous algorism of Alexandre de Villedieu (XIII-1) into Icelandic. The Swedish master Sven was authorized by the University of Paris to lecture on spherics.

A7. *Catalonia*

I am not aware of any mathematical or astronomical work done in Christian Spain, but mention should be made of two famous Catalans, Arnold of Villanova (XIII-2) and Ramon Lull (XIII-2). Villanova, who lived until 1311, was one of the best representatives of the astrological thought of his time. Lull (d. 1315) wrote treatises apparently devoted to astronomy and mathematics, but dealing with astrology and with his own extravagant logic. The titles of these books, Tractatus novus de astronomia and Liber de nova et compendiosa geometria, would deceive us but did not deceive his contemporaries, for most of them, even when they called themselves mathematici or astronomici, were as muddleheaded as himself.

B. *Eastern Christendom*

With the exception of the Armenian John of Erzinjān (XIII-2), all the Eastern Christian mathematicians and astronomers we are dealing with belonged to the Greek community. John of Erzinjān wrote an astronomical treatise in Armenian in 1284; I do not know of any mathematical writing of his posterior to that date, but he lived until 1326. It is probable that the end of his life was devoted chiefly, if not exclusively, to theology and religion.

Two of the leading men of the previous century, Maximos Planudes (XIII-2) and Georgios Pachymeres (XIII-2, Introd. 2, 972), lived through the first decade of the fourteenth century. Pachymeres wrote a treatise on the quadrivium[10] and Planudes a commentary on the first two books of Diophantos. Perhaps the most remarkable feature of Byzantine mathematics is the attention paid to arithmetic, both the old and the new. As to the old, that is, the theory of numbers, we have a treatise on magic squares composed by Manuel Moschopulos. This is a purely scientific work explaining how to arrange n^2 numbers in a square, in such a manner that the sum of the numbers in each row, column, or diagonal be constant, equal to $\frac{1}{2}n(n^2 + 1)$. As contrasted with Arabic works like that of al-Būnī (XIII-1), there is no magic in it, no magic whatsoever, not even in the title, for Manuel does not speak as we do of "magic squares," but simply of square numbers (*τετράγωνος ἀριθμός*), which is unfortunately ambiguous. Manuel's treatise was, I believe, the first of its kind in any language.

On the other hand, Manuel's friend Nicolaos Rhabdas was interested particu-

[10] The Greek text, *Σύνταγμα τῶν τεσσάρων μαθημάτων*, the edition of which was begun by Paul Tannery (Osiris 4, 704) and continued by others, was finally published by father E. Stéphanou (Studi e testi 94, 565 p., Vatican 1940; Isis 34, 218–19).

larly in numeration and computation. I have explained before (Introd. 2, 973) that Maximos Planudes introduced the "Hindu calculation" (as he called it, Ἰνδικὴ ψηφοφορία) into the Greek world.[11] It is noteworthy that the same service had been rendered to the Latin world at least a century and a half earlier, by Adelard of Bath (XII-1), if not before; it is equally noteworthy that these numerals were called Hindu by the Greeks (as well as by the Arabs and Persians), whereas the Latins called them Arabic (or Jewish). This suggests that the traditions carrying these numerals respectively to the Greeks and to the Latins were independent. Planudes' treatise was revised by Rhabdas, who wrote other dissertations on numeration and computation. He set forth the use not only of the new numerals, but also of the Greek letters and of finger notation. In his computations he continued to use fractions of the Egyptian model (sum of fractions of the type $\frac{1}{n}$ and $\frac{2}{3}$). The melancholy but inescapable conclusion to be drawn from Rhabdas' writing and from contemporary anonymous documents is that the Byzantine mathematicians of the fourteenth century were acquainted with the Hindu numerals but did not yet fully understand their properties and their use.

This is the more puzzling because the two essential features of the new numerals had been known to the Greek world for a long time, though independently and only in particular and disconnected cases. The grammarian Herodian (II-2) had a very limited understanding of "place value" (as in the Roman numerals IV and VI). Of course the "place value" was perfectly clear to early Babylonians, who had even extended it to submultiples as well as to multiples of their number basis; unfortunately, that basis was sixty rather than ten. The Greeks inherited that tradition, but very imperfectly; they inherited only its worst feature, the sexagesimal basis, and lost the real treasure which it carried, the idea of place value. Thus Ptolemy (II-1) used sexagesimal fractions with a real zero to indicate absent items. The Greeks used the zero[12] only in sexagesimals, not in other numbers! To illustrate Byzantine confusion of thought with regard to the meaning and use of various kinds of numerals, let us consider the following four examples:

1. The combination of alphabetic numerals with place value, as $\frac{\alpha\gamma}{\beta\eta} = \frac{13}{28}$ (of course, the alphabetic system excluded place value).

2. Lambros[13] has edited a fragment attached to an Athenian MS (see fig. 1; Βουλή library no. 32; the MS is of the fifteenth century, but the παραφύλλον to which I refer is of an earlier date, fourteenth century?) exhibiting a similar aber-

[11] Heiberg pointed out the presence of Arabic numerals in a Viennese MS of scholia to Euclid X, a MS which he declares to be without doubt of the twelfth century (Euclidis elementa 5, xix, Leipzig 1888). This would be the earliest appearance of Arabic numerals in a Greek MS. In MSS of the scholia of Georgios Pachymeres (XIII-2, Introd. 2, 972) to the same book of Euclid, Arabic numerals including zero are noted, their use is explained, and they are actually used in the figures to indicate dimensions. There was some additional reason for doing so, because Greek letters were used to denote geometrical points, and their simultaneous use for numbers would have been confusing. Hence Arabic numerals are used in the figures, though not in the text, where the same numbers are expressed by means of the conventional alphabetic numerals (Tannery 4, 201, 1920); Stéphanou's edition (p. LIV, 1940). It is thus clear that Planudes' formal introduction was preceded by partial introductions. Note that Pachymeres and Planudes died about the same year, 1310. Finally, one of the mosaics in St. Saviour in the Fields, Istanbul, bears a date (= 1303) in Arabic numerals; see the note on Theodoros Metochites.

[12] Heath (1, 39, 45, 1921; p. 23, 1931). The zero was simply an omicron, abbreviation for οὐδεμία μοῖρα, οὐδὲν ἑξηκοστόν, etc.

[13] Spyr. P. Lambros: Κατάλογος κωδίκων τῆς Βιβλιοθήκης τῆς Βουλῆς (Νέος Ἑλληνομνήμων 2, 228–30, Athens 1905), including a facsimile, which we reproduce.

ration: *δο* means 40, *βζςδηο* = 276,480, *γδεςοο* = 345,600.[13a] I have marked with a cross the lines of the facsimile containing these examples, but note that what I have transcribed as a zero is written there like a kind of y. This is a strange mixture of alphabetic numerals, place value, and use of a zero!

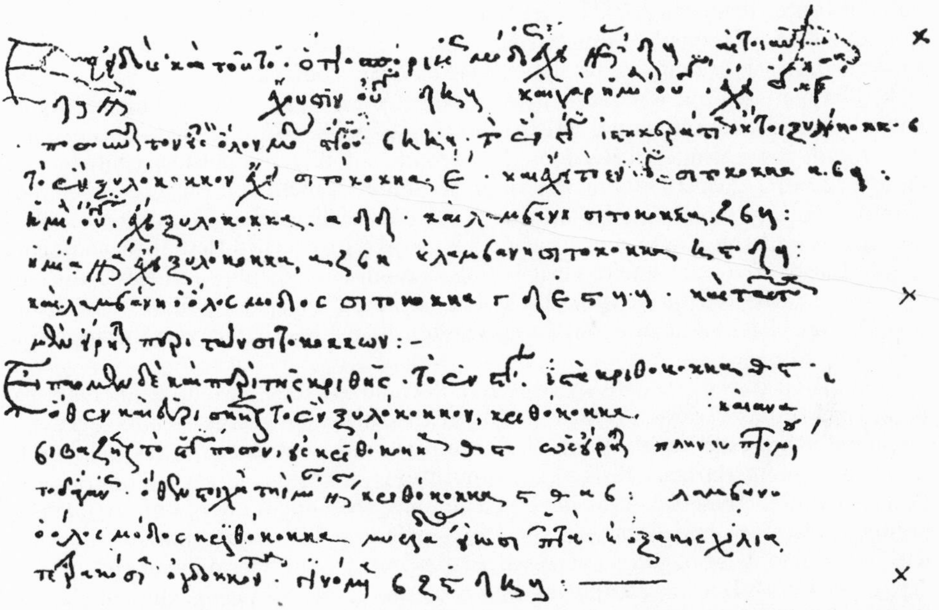

FIG. 1. Hindu-Byzantine numerals (fourteenth century?) in MS no. 32, Library of Greek Parliament, Athens. Κατάλογος κωδίκων τῆς Βιβλιοθήκης τῆς Βουλῆς (Νέος Ἑλληνομνήμων 2, 229, 1905).

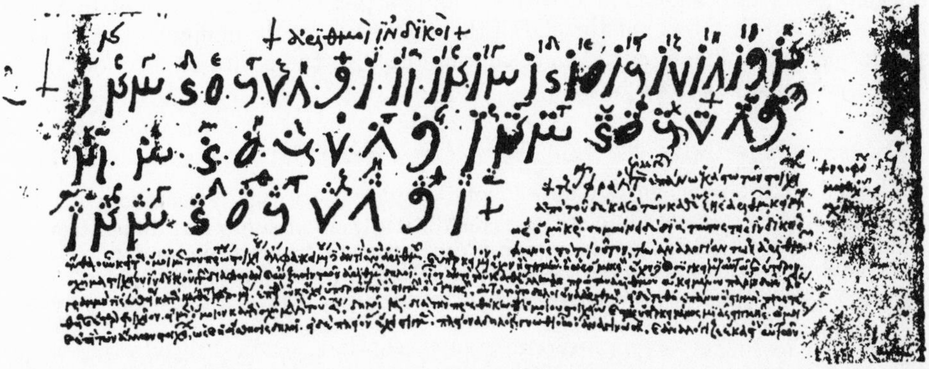

FIG. 2. Hindu-Byzantine numerals (fifteenth century) in MS fonds grec 1928, fol. 15, Bibliothèque nationale, Paris. Tannery: Mémoires (4, 22, 1920).

3. Tannery has published (4, 22, 1920) a scholium by a monk called Neophytos, describing Hindu numerals (ἀριθμοὶ ἰνδικοί). I reproduce the fragment ad hoc (fig. 2; Bibliothèque nationale, Paris, Greek MS 1928, fol. 15 recto; that MS dates

[13a] The figure 6 in the last two numbers is represented by a final sigma, because we lack a stigma, with which the Greeks replaced the sixth letter, digamma.

from the fifteenth century; the text is probably earlier, and may be anterior to Planudes). Neophytos explains the use of the zero (τζύφρα; the word is of Semitic or Latin origin, cifra, ziphra, etc.) as a kind of exponent placed over the numerals (see our facsimile). One zero placed over a numeral multiplies it by ten, two zeros (or dots) by one hundred, three dots by one thousand; the final symbol 1 with four dots on top of it means 10,000. The Arabic numerals are explained by the use of Greek letters. It should be noted that the Arabic five (same shape as our zero or the old Greek seventy) must have increased the confusion.

4. The copyist Andreas Darmarios in the Escorial MS (ΦII, 17) mixed alphabetical and Hindu numerals, writing ἐν τῷ ,αφ70 (= 1570). That is the limit. And mind you Darmarios lived in the second half of the sixteenth century (see Sandys 2, 161, 205, 1908), in the time of Simon Stevin, but he continued the stupid traditions which had begun three centuries earlier, when Byzantine scholars had discovered the Hindu numerals. This helps us to realize that their confusion of mind was essentially due to their trying to assimilate the new numerals without disregarding the old ones; they did not understand the new numerical tradition (hinging on place value and zero) well enough to realize that it was incompatible with the old one.[14]

In addition to the treatises by Moschopulos and Rhabdas, we have arithmetical notes by Joannes Pediasimos as well as a treatise of his on geometry and surveying continuing the tradition of Heron of Alexandria, and there is also a very elaborate logistica wherein Barlaam discusses computations of various kinds. The fractions dealt with in all these texts (as in the Latin ones, see above) are of only two types, ordinary fractions and sexagesimals. In particular, pro rata repartitions which with us would be generally expressed in percentages (or permillages, etc.) were expressed by Byzantine computers in sexagesimals or, strangely enough, in six-thousandths. Thus was the Sumerian tradition re-established even on its weakest side.[15] The immediate reason for that repartition was that the Byzantine golden solidus (νόμισμα) was divided into 6,000 copper pence (λεπτά or ἀσσάρια). Hence the computers had to be familiar with the aliquot parts of 6,000 and prepare tables ad hoc. Alas! that was not the end of their troubles, for the nomisma was divided also into twelve miliarenses (μιλιαρήσιον), and each of these into twenty-four obols (φόλλις, ὀβολός). Thus we have

$$1 \text{ νόμισμα} = 6{,}000 \text{ λεπτά} = 288 \text{ φόλλεις}.$$

These two subdivisions did not dovetail, but we are not concerned with the aberrations of Byzantine numismatics, only with their arithmetical difficulties.

Paul Tannery: Le scholie du moine Néophytos sur les chiffres hindous (Revue archéologique 5, 99–102, 1885; Mémoires 4, 20–26, 1920); Les chiffres arabes dans les MSS. grecs (Revue archéologique 7, 355–60, 1886; Mémoires 4, 199–205); Le

[14] In order to appreciate fairly their difficulties, it is necessary to remember how deeply the numerical value of letters was rooted in their minds, and had been for a great many centuries. To illustrate: it was a simple kind of pun for them to write the two letters koppa theta at the end of a prayer instead of amen, for their value is 90 + 9, while ἀμήν = 1 + 40 + 8 + 50 = 99. That pun is already found on a papyrus of the fifth or sixth century (P. Oxyr. 925). See A. S. Hunt and C. C. Edgar: Select papyri (1, 441, London 1932). John Garrett Winter: Life and letters in the papyri (p. 189, Ann Arbor 1933).

[15] Indeed, the Sumerian basis was not 60 alone, but a combination of 60 and 10, the various orders being represented by 10, (10 × 6), (10 × 6) × 10, etc. See F. Thureau-Dangin: History of the sexagesimal system (Osiris 7, 95–141, 1939).

calcul des parties proportionnelles (Bull. sciences mathématiques 30, 59–60, 1906; Mémoires 4, 283–93).

Viktor Gardthausen: Griechische Palaeographie (2d ed., 2, 374–81, Leipzig 1913).

To the arithmetical revival which has been outlined corresponded an astronomical revival. Byzantine mathematicians made a fresh study of the Almagest. Barlaam discussed the theory of solar eclipses explained by Ptolemy. Pediasimos wrote scholia to Cleomedes (I-1 B.C.), and his other writings exhibit the extent of his ill digested astronomical knowledge. Theodoros Metochites composed an introductory astronomical treatise in the form of a commentary on the Almagest. Nicephoros Gregoras wrote two treatises on the astrolabe and a third one on the projections of spherical triangles upon a plane.

Theologians could not help taking an interest in the calendar for the exact determination of the fixed and movable holidays. For example, Rhabdas tried to determine the Orthodox Easter without reference to the Jewish Passover. What is more important is that Nicephoros Gregoras in 1324 submitted a treatise on the reform of the calendar to Andronicos II. The accumulated excesses of the Julian year over the tropical year were beginning to annoy Byzantine astronomers as they annoyed their Latin colleagues.[16]

A new direction was given to astronomical studies at the court of Trebizond during the rule of the eighth emperor, Alexios II. That empire, being considerably closer to Persia than to the Roman empire, was more open to Oriental influences. Alexios II sent one of his familiars, Gregorios Chioniades, on a scientific mission to Persia. Chioniades came back with a collection of Persian (and Arabic?) MSS. One of these treatises, ascribed to one Shams al-dīn al-Bukhārī, was fully translated from Persian into Greek in 1323. This marks the beginning of a kind of astronomical renaissance which occurred in Trebizond and reached its maturity with the work of Georgios Chrysococces, a generation later, in 1346. The "astronomy of the Persians" (ἡ σύνταξις τῶν Περσῶν), as Chrysococces' treatise was called, had a strange success in the East. It helped the Greeks to appreciate more deeply the achievements of their own ancestors. Moreover, after Chrysococces' work had been superseded in Greek by those of Theodoros Meliteniotes and Isaac Argyros, it continued to exert an influence in Eastern Europe and the Near East through Hebrew translations and commentaries.

The astronomical treatises written in Constantinople and Trebizond naturally contained astrological sections, but I do not know of any contemporary Greek treatise representing the most blatant kind of astrology. Here, as well as in Western Europe, the church seems to have moderated astrological extravagances.[17] We have, however, a dialogue by one Joannes Catrarios, largely derived from Abū Ma'shar (IX-1), wherein naïve attempts are made to reconcile astrological fancies with Christian miracles.

Byzantine cosmology is a hotchpotch of Ionian, Aristotelian, Platonic, Neoplatonic, and patristic ideas, the ingredients varying somewhat from one text to another. A good example (of indeterminate date) is the one partly edited by Delatte and represented by eight MSS.

[16] For Byzantine chronology see Paul Tannery: Noms des mois attiques chez les Byzantins (Revue archéologique 9, 23–36, 1887; Mémoires 4, 223–39, 1920). Viktor Gardthausen: Griechische Palaeographie (2d ed., 2, 442–83, Leipzig 1913). Ginzel (3, 288–327, 1914).

[17] As much as it could! It was not easy. Other superstitions were rife. See Paul Tannery: La géomancie chez les Byzantins (4, 354–72, 1920), texts on ῥαβδόλιον, i.e., Arabic raml. Armand Delatte (vol. 1, 1927; Isis 12, 328–30).

Armand Delatte: Geographica (Byzantinische Zeitschrift 30, 511–18, 1929/30), Greek text of second part only; Un manuel byzantin de cosmologie et de géographie (Bull. Académie royale de Belgique, lettres, 18, 189–222, 1932; Isis 23, 563). Franz Cumont: Catalogus (8, part 4, 108–14, 1921), extracts from the text as given in Paris. 2219, ascribed to a monk called Paul; date, eleventh to fifteenth century.

Note on Mediaeval Accounting in Europe

This note is placed in appendix to the Christian sections A and B, because it concerns many countries of Europe. The need of accounts increased in proportion as business extended, became more international and complex, and involved more partners.

Italy. The earliest (mediaeval) commercial accounts that have come down to us concern the winding up of three partnerships between Genoese merchants for the years 1156–58.[18] The oldest preserved account book is a fragmentary libro delle ragioni (= livre de raison, commonplace book) kept by an unknown Florentine banker in 1211; it contains a series of memoranda written without order except chronological succession. The accounts kept by another Florentine, Riccomanno Jacopi, from 1272 to 1277, as tutor of the children of his brother Baldovino Jacopi, are of the same primitive kind. We have also accounts of the Sienese firm Ugolini relative to their business in the fairs of Champagne from 1249 to 1263, of Sienese drapers from 1277 to 1282, and of the Sienese banking firm Bonsignori covering the end of the thirteenth century; and an inventory drawn c. 1280 to liquidate a rich company of which Bernardino Ugolini was the main partner, with offices in Siena and Pisa. The only progress perceptible in all these early accounts consisted in the simultaneous use of many books, such as libro dell' entrata e dell' uscita (cash book), libro dei creditori e dei debitori (current accounts), libro a devito e a richolti (debits and credits), libro a vendite (sales book), libro dei capitali (partners' accounts), etc. As long as double-entry accounting had not been invented, a multiplicity of books were needed, each of which helped to check the others.

Thus by the beginning of the fourteenth century the commercial and banking concerns of northern Italy had already obtained much experience in accounting. They had learned to keep the accounts as clearly as possible and to separate them. The firm Alberto del Giudice of Florence had realized the value of periodic inventories (every two years), and many such inventories are preserved in their Libro piccolo dell' asse begun in 1304. Among other documents preserved in Italian archives are those relative to the liquidation in 1322 of the firm Francesco del Bene, member of the Arte di Calimala[19] of Florence, including elaborate inventories; the accounts of the international banking firm Peruzzi, which was bankrupted in 1343; the five hundred commercial registers of another international firm, founded by Francesco Datini (c. 1335–1410) in Prato.[20] In the meanwhile a new method of keeping accounts had been invented in Venice, the idea being to post credits and debits face to face on opposite pages or in two columns of one page. (This was not yet double-entry bookkeeping, for there was no double posting of each trans-

[18] Florence Edler de Roover: Partnership accounts in twelfth century Genoa (Bull. Business Historical Society 15, 87–92, Boston 1941).

[19] One of the major guilds of Florence, L'arte e università de' mercanti di Calimala, so called because its offices were located in the Via di Calimala. Edgcumbe Staley: The guilds of Florence (p. 105–38, London 1906).

[20] See end of the note on Pegolotti.

action and no balancing, but it led to double entry.) The earliest mention of that method appears in a Florentine account book of 1382 kept by one Paliano di Falco, a partner of Giovanni Portinari; Paliano wrote debits and credits face to face "alla veneziana." That Venetian method was used in Genoa from the beginning of the century; the Genoese may have thought of it independently. The earliest Venetian examples extant date from the fifteenth century.

An abundance of collateral information on Italian mercantile methods may be found in the Practica della mercatura written c. 1340 by Francesco Pegolotti (see the special note devoted to him). Pegolotti did not explain methods of accounting, but gave valuable tables for accountants, such as tables of exchange reckonings, tables of interest, tariffs.

We shall come back to Italy presently to witness the birth and early development of double entry, but let us first describe the development of single entry in other countries.

Germany. The oldest accounts extant are (1) some inventories of the Teutonic Order (XII-2) dating from the end of the thirteenth century and the beginning of the fourteenth. Then follow various commercial accounts: (2) Holzschuher, drapers in Nuremberg, 1304–7; (2) Hermann and Johann Wittenborg, Hanseatic merchants[21] in Lübeck, 1329–60; (4) Johann Clingenberg and Hermann Warendorp, merchants in Lübeck, 1330–36; (5) Johann Tölner, Hanseatic merchant, 1345–50; (6) Vicko von Geldersen, in Hamburg, 1367–92; (7) Runtinger, in Regensburg (Ratisbon), 1383–1407.

The earliest of these accounts are very rudimentary, like the Italian ones of the thirteenth century, mere memoranda jotted down as they came, without method. The latest ones are more and more methodical, but there is no trace of current accounts nor of the Venetian method, except occasionally in Runtinger's books.

France. (1) The earliest French accounts are the Hebrew accounts of a Jewish association located in Vesoul (Haute-Saône; Franche-Comté), for the years 1300–6, 1310–18. They are of great interest from many points of view (e.g., French philology, Jewish sociology, coins, weights and measures) and have been studied by Isidore Loeb: Deux livres de commerce du commencement du XIVe siècle (Revue des études juives 8, 161–96, facs., 1884; 9, 21–50, 187–213, 1884).

The earliest account in French is that (2) of an unknown Lyon draper, 1320–23. Then follow (3) Ugo Teralh, draper and notary in Forcalquier (Basses-Alpes; Provence), 1330–32; (4) Jean Saval, draper in Carcassonne, 1340–41; (5) Frères Bonis (= Bonis Bros.), merchants and bankers in Montauban (Tarn et Garonne), 1345–69; (6) Jacme Olivier, merchant in Narbonne (Aude; Languedoc), 1381–91; this includes many separate travel accounts for business ventures in the Near East.

A feature common to all the early account books is the lack of continuity in the modern sense. A merchant engaged in international business did not consider all his undertakings as one, but rather as separate ventures. For one thing, he might have different partners for each of them. For overseas trade there were two kinds of contract, called societas maris and commenda. In both cases the traveling partner received one-fourth of the profits, the investors three-fourths. In commenda the traveling partner did not invest; in societas maris he supplied one-third of the capital, and thus his full share of the profits amounted to one-half.

The Venetian manner remained as little known in France before the fifteenth

[21] For the Hanseatic League (XIII-2), see Introd. 2, 1063, 38.

century as in Germany. The Bonis and Olivier accounts, however, were in very good order.

England. Matters were even worse in England, where but a single commercial account anterior to 1400 has beeen found, that is, the account of Gilbert Maghfeld, kept in French and without method. Chaucer was one of Maghfeld's customers.

Flanders. The situation was considerably better in Flanders, and this is not surprising, for the cities of Flanders were almost as active commercially as those of northern Italy. Moreover, Italian firms had offices in Bruges, and hence Italian methods of accounting might easily be transmitted from one country to the other.

There have come to us six ledgers and two daybooks kept by two money-changers of Bruges, Collard de Marke and Guillaume Ruyelle, during the years 1366–70. The accounts were single entry, but they did use the Venetian method. R. De Roover: Le livre de comptes de Guillaume Ruyelle (Annales de la Société d'émulation 77, 15–95, Bruges 1934; Isis 24, 481).

The accounts of Johannes Plige, factor of the Teutonic Order in Bruges, for 1391–99 have also been preserved. They are simple accounts, well kept for submission to the chief of the Order in Königsberg, East Prussia.

Double-entry bookkeeping. The earliest example of double-entry bookkeeping occurs in a Latin account book of 1340, kept by the massari (financial stewards) of Genoa; that method may have been introduced in 1327, when the Genoese administration was reformed and it was decided to keep the city accounts ad modum banchi. The diffusion of that method is obscure for more than a century. Its earliest example in Venice is to be found in books of the firm Donado Soranzo e fratelli, for 1406–34. During the fifteenth century the method spread a little faster across Europe and the Near East, wherever Italian, Genoese, and Venetian factors were located. It was not adopted by every merchant, however, not even by every Italian merchant. For example, consider the account books and business papers of the junior branch of the Medici family, drapers in Florence; those papers have been donated by H. Gordon Selfridge of London to the Harvard School of Business Administration in Cambridge, Mass. The Medici ledger of 1431–34 is very much like the Datini books of half a century earlier; by 1441 we find in the Medici books examples of the Venetian method, but not yet of double entry.

The double-entry method was first published by the Franciscan Luca Paciolo of Borgo San Sepolcro in his Summa de arithmetica (printed Venice 1494). From that time on it spread more rapidly all over Italy, the Low Countries, France, Germany, England, etc. (Isis 21, 264).

State accounting. References have already been made to the municipal accounts of Genoa. The accounts of the Teutonic Order were partly administrative, partly commercial. The line is not always easy to draw, for every national or municipal, royal, seignorial, or ecclesiastical administration has commercial aspects, and every business concern of sufficient amplitude has administrative aspects.

Leonardo Fibonacci (XIII-1) was employed by the city of Pisa in 1202, 1220, 1250 to audit its accounts. There have come down to us Milanese accounts of 1225 ff., Florentine accounts of c. 1250, the accounts of Nicholas III (pope 1277–80), and a good many accounts of Italian cities during the fourteenth century. The earliest account of the city of London is dated 1334; there are many fourteenth-century accounts of the livery companies of London, of the Scottish burghs, of the priory of Finchale in the county of Durham (1354 ff.), etc. Examples and facsimiles of such accounts are given by Brown.

The need of separating personal royal or seignorial accounts from impersonal state accounts was recognized dimly at first in the fourteenth century, then more clearly but very slowly during the following centuries. Simon Stevin was the first to explain these matters clearly, in his Livre de compte de prince à la manière d'Italie . . . (Leiden 1608; Isis 21, 263, 298), written at the request of his own sovereign, prince Maurice of Nassau, and dedicated to Sully, minister to Henri IV.

Modern methods (double entry and the rest) were introduced with incredible slowness in state accounts, especially in conservative England. For example, it is said of Sydney Olivier, assistant comptroller of exchequer (1917–20), that he found the national accounts kept still as in the days of king John (ruled 1199–1216) and introduced the startling novelty of bookkeeping by double entry! That story, being told by Hesketh Pearson in his delightful biography of G. Bernard Shaw (p. 227, New York 1942), should be taken cum grano salis.

Use of Hindu numerals. There remains to be examined a question which may seem accessory, but which is really of essential importance. Therefore, the author does not apologize for discussing it again, though other aspects of it have already been dealt with many times.[22] What kind of numerals were used in all these accounts?[23] In spite of Leonardo Fibonacci (XIII-1), the numerals used until the sixteenth century were almost always cursive Roman, not Hindu. The latter were said to be unclear (Introd. 2, 985) and to lend themselves too easily to falsification. The true explanation of the resistance to the Hindu numerals is that they were considered an integral part of the Arabic script, whereas the Roman ones were inseparable from the Latin script. This shows that the accountants and even the majority of mathematicians had not yet understood the principle underlying the new numerals, a principle independent of their shape. Yet the simple arithmetical operations easy enough with Hindu numerals were very difficult with the Roman ones. How did they fail to see that? Simply because they did not try. This is one of the best examples of human inertia blocking the fruition of a fundamental discovery for centuries.

According to Brown (p. 107), the oldest ledger wherein Hindu numerals are employed is one kept by Jacob Badoer in 1436–39; that ledger was kept by him in Constantinople, where those numerals had been transmitted by Greeks and Jews.

D. E. Smith and L. C. Karpinski (1911). George Francis Hill: Development of Arabic numerals in Europe (125 p., Oxford 1915). Richard Brown: History of accounting and accountants (476 p., ill., Edinburgh 1905). Raymond De Roover: La formation et l'expansion de la comptabilité à partie double (Annales d'histoire économique nos. 44–45, p. 171–93, 270–98, Paris 1937; Isis 28, 580). The many accounts cited in this note have been published or analyzed; references to such publications will be found in Brown or De Roover or both.

The Cour des comptes (French Audit Office) continued to use Roman numerals until the eighteenth century (Encyclopédie des sciences mathématiques 1, 1, 14, 1904).

Mediaeval banking practice differed essentially from our own in that no checks were used, these being replaced by transfer orders given orally and taken down by

[22] Introd. 2, 4, 747, 985. Article Abū-l-Fidā'; note on Byzantine arithmetic just above this one, etc.

[23] Leaving out the Hebrew accounts, wherein Hebrew letters were naturally used. See facsimile in Revue des études juives (8, facing 161, 1884) and transcription (9, 203–6, 1884).

the banker at the transferer's dictation. The journals of banks were given the status of a notarial register, and this implied that they had to be kept in strict chronological order, without blanks, without erasures, without interpolation of any kind; the pages had to be numbered and none could ever be torn out. The French Ordonnance du commerce of 1673 and the Code Napoléon reaffirmed these restrictions, and therefore the countries influenced by French law attach more importance to this day to the journal than to the ledger, and forbid the use of loose-leaf books, without which accounting machines cannot be profitably employed.

Abbott Payson Usher: The origins of banking; the primitive bank of deposit 1200–1600 (Economic history review 4, 399–428, 1934); The early history of deposit banking in Mediterranean countries (2 vols., Cambridge, Mass. 1943–44). Raymond De Roover: The lingering influence of medieval practices (Accounting review 18, 148–51, 1943; Isis 35, 73).

C. *Israel*

Jewish mathematicians flourished in Provence and Spain, and hardly anywhere else.

C1. *Provence*

Just before the opening of the century, on March 1, 1300, Jacob ben Maḥir ibn Tibbon had completed his ephemerides for the longitude of Montpellier. These tables were promptly translated from Hebrew into Latin, and under their new name, Almanach perpetuum Prophatii, enjoyed considerable popularity.

Such a translation could only be made by a Jew. In the meanwhile, other Jews were continuing to translate Arabic books into Hebrew, for as the Arabic language ceased to be known among them, these translations were becoming more and more necessary. The outstanding mathematical translators were Qalonymos ben Qalonymos and Samuel ben Judah of Marseille. Qalonymos translated books of Archimedes, Apollonios, Hypsicles, Nicomachos, Ptolemy, Eutocios, al-Kindī, Thābit ibn Qurra, Ibn al-Samḥ (treatise on cylinders and cones, lost in Arabic), Jābir ibn Aflaḥ, "Abū Sa'dān" (treatise on the triangle, unknown in Arabic). Samuel ben Judah completed Qalonymos' version of Hypsicles; he translated Ibn Rushd's commentary on the Almagest, and astronomical treatises by Muḥammad ibn Mu'ādh and al-Zarqālī; he obtained the translation of the Iṣlāḥ al-majisṭī by Jacob ben Maḥir and revised it (Aix 1335). This list of translations is impressive enough, the more so because it includes some of the choicest fruits of Greek and Arabic mathematics and astronomy, and because it does *not* include astrology, except a couple of items, the Centiloquium ascribed to Ptolemy and a treatise by al-Kindī. Clearly these Provençal mathematicians wanted the best that their predecessors had to offer; this implies that their own knowledge was sufficiently pure and deep.

We are given a general view of that knowledge in the encyclopaedic treatises of Levi ben Abraham ben Ḥayyim (XIII-2), and glimpses of it in the writings of Estori Farḥi; we see that he was acquainted with the works of Ptolemy, Abraham bar Ḥiyya, and Jacob ben Maḥir. Abba Mari ben Eligdor wrote an introduction to the first book of Euclid. This is of little importance and might be dismissed without loss, but it would be impossible to overlook Levi ben Gerson, one of the leading mathematicians and astronomers of the Middle Ages.

Levi wrote in 1321 the Sefer ma'aseh ḥosheb, dealing with arithmetic and algebra, combinatorial analysis, computation. This book contains novelties but is unfortunately deficient with regard to a fundamental concept, the new numerals. Levi shared with his Arabic, Latin, and Greek contemporaries the inability to understand the new method (place value and zero), his inability being due to the same reason as theirs; he did not discard the old method, and did not realize that the old and new methods were incompatible. He tried to explain the idea of place value, but used no numerals except Hebrew letters contradicting that idea.[24] Another arithmetical treatise of his, known only in Latin, dealt with harmonic numbers in the Euclidean manner. He determined the number of simple permutations of *n* objects (factorial *n*) by the use of mathematical induction; I think he was the first to use that method, which was not formulated until much later, incompletely by Maurolico (1575) and better by Pascal (after 1654; printed 1665).

Levi wrote a commentary on the first five books of Euclid, and tried (vainly of course) to eliminate the axioms. He devoted a separate discussion to the fifth (parallel) postulate. His most valuable work, however, was in the field of trigonometry. His treatise was the first *independent* one in Hebrew, as distinguished from the chapters relative to spherical trigonometry which served to introduce astronomical tables. It was soon translated into Latin (1342), though not soon enough to anticipate Wallingford's Quadripartitum (c. 1326). It is significant that these two treatises were almost simultaneous. They answered the same purpose—the transmission of Arabic trigonometry into Hebrew or Latin, its Westernization. Wallingford's influence was largely restricted to the English school; Levi's treatise was the model of Regiomontanus' De triangulis (1464; printed 1533), which is the basis of modern trigonometry.

Though Levi's trigonometry served to introduce the Hindu-Arabic ideas on sines and cosines (but not tangents!), it still continued to deal with chords in the old Greek manner. This is another illustration of the singular inertia which prevents old traditions from being discarded even when they are clearly superseded, and are nothing more than hindrances and sources of confusion, jeopardizing the new ideas and preventing their development.

Levi ben Gerson invented (or improved materially) a new astronomical instrument, the cross-staff, which remained for centuries one of the main tools of navigators. He compiled astronomical tables (1320) and wrote a treatise explaining in detail the motions of stars and planets, criticizing the Almagest, Jābir ibn Aflaḥ, and al-Biṭrūjī. These works and many others were available to him in Hebrew, and it is clear that he had studied them with the independence of a man capable of repeating and correcting their observations and their computations. Yet he ended by confirming Hipparchian astronomy, and thus it is very misleading to call him a forerunner of Copernicus. That would be expecting too much of him anyhow. He was a good observer, a learned and intelligent astronomer, fully able to discuss and weigh one against another the theories of his time; not sufficiently bold and original to invent a new one. As his astronomical writings were soon available in Latin as well as in Hebrew and were very well received, he influenced Western astronomy strongly and rapidly. The other Jewish mathematicians I have quoted are important chiefly, if not exclusively, from the Jewish or Hebrew point of view;

[24] The use of Hebrew letters is similar to the use of Greek letters; certain letters are used for the numbers 1 to 9, others for the decades (yod = 10, kaf = 20, · · ·), others for hundreds (qōf = 100, rēsh = 200, sīn = 300, tāw = 400). The letters are selected on a decimal basis, but the decimal order is determined by the letter itself, not by its place.

Levi ben Gerson is one of the leading mathematicians and astronomers of the European Middle Ages, Christian as well as Jewish. Levi's attitude toward astrology was the most enlightened of his time; that is, he did not deny the astrological premises, but handled them with great circumspection and humility.

C2. *Spain and Morocco*

The Spanish record is not quite so good as the Provençal, not only because there was no Levi ben Gerson south of the Pyrénées, but also because the general level of mathematical thinking was (or seemed to be) lower.

Solomon ben Paṭer ha-Kohen translated, or rather retranslated, an astronomical treatise by Ibn al-Haitham (XI-1) from Arabic into Hebrew. That is the only translation I know of, but we should bear in mind that Spanish Jews were less likely to need such translations than their trans-Pyrenean brethren. In fact, some of the Spanish astronomers not only were able to read Arabic, but continued to use that language, rather than Hebrew, for scientific purposes.

The outstanding astronomical treatise, Yesod 'olam, was written in Toledo 1310 by Isaac Israeli the Younger. It is very elaborate, and includes as usual a trigonometrical introduction and tables. It was written in Hebrew, but the author's son, Joseph ben Isaac, began (c. 1324) an Arabic abridgment of it, interrupted by his death. That abridgment was soon translated into Hebrew, and a commentary on the Yesod 'olam was composed by Solomon ben Abraham Corcos in the same language. Another Hebrew astronomical work, the Ḥuqqat ha-shameyim, is ascribed to Judah ben Asher ben Jehiel (d. 1349) or to the latter's grandson, Judah ben Asher II (d. 1391). In the meanwhile the Nūr al-'ālam was written in Arabic by Joseph ben Joseph Naḥmias of Toledo, and translated into Hebrew within the same century. It is clear that in Spain, and particularly in the cosmopolitan and polyglot city of Toledo, Arabic held its own against Hebrew.[25]

Apparently more astrology and superstition were rampant in the Hispanic peninsula than in Provence. The Portuguese David ben Yom-ṭob ben Bila thought it necessary to translate from Latin into Hebrew the Salus vitae, a wretched account of the magical virtues of snakeskins, and he discussed astrological medicine. The apostate Abner (or Alfonso) of Burgos wrote a defense of astrology against Isaac ben Pulqar. The latter had not hesitated to attack astrological tenets both in Spanish and in Hebrew. His outspokenness is rare in mediaeval literature (Isis 11, 172), for even men like Levi ben Gerson among the Jews and Agostino Trionfo among the Christians were very cautious in their criticisms of the predominant and fashionable superstition.

The Jews had calendrical difficulties even as the Christians, though for a different reason. The Christian year is essentially a solar year, yet it has to take the moon into account for the determination of Easter and of all the movable feasts. The Jewish year, on the contrary, is essentially lunar, yet it is not independent of the sun. In both cases the difficulties originate from the necessity of counting time with two celestial clocks which do not harmonize. The Muslims escaped these difficulties by the use of a purely lunar year (instead of a "bound" one); they deliberately discarded one of the clocks. In order to bring back the Passover feast into the month of the wheat harvest (determined by the sun), and have the first month, Abib, begin with the spring as prescribed in the Torah (Exodus 12:2, 13:4; Deuteronomy 16:1), it was necessary to lengthen the year every two or three years with an intercalary month.

[25] For further information on conditions in Toledo, see González Palencia (1926–30).

To be precise, the lunar month averages 29 days 12 hours 793 parts,[26] and the lunar year of twelve months equals 354 days 8 hours 876 parts, which is shorter by 10 days 21 hours 204 parts than the solar year. The calendrical problems consist then in arranging suitable cycles of months containing 29 or 30 days and in deciding when a thirteenth month (second Adar) should be added (the principle of intercalation of a thirtieth day or thirteenth month is called sod ha-'ibbur); in addition, there are many liturgical complications which need not be enumerated here (JE 3, 498–508, 1902). These problems were almost exclusively ecclesiastical ones, and they exercised the mathematical ingenuity and the religious scrupulousness of many theologians throughout the ages.

The fourth part of the Yesod 'olam contains an exhaustive account of the Jewish calendar in all its ramifications. A briefer and humbler account was given by Abudraham in a book on liturgy and prayers (Seville 1339). It would not be difficult to find other contemporary examples, for almost every theologian or liturgist was bound to study and teach the calendar, and every mathematician might be consulted about it.

A Jewish astronomer, Jacob ben Ṭafīruh, constructed an astrolabe in Fès 1316. We know nothing about him, but the name Tapiero, which may be considered a modern form of Ṭafīruh, is not uncommon among North African Jewish families See H. P. J. Renaud: Quelques constructeurs d'astrolabes en Orient musulman (Isis 34, 20–23, 1942).

C3. *Eastern Jews*

The only Oriental Jews whom I can think of are Estori Farḥi and Israel ben Samuel Ma'arabi. The first has already been mentioned in the Provençal section, for he spent his boyhood and youth in southern France and went to the Near East about 1313. He immortalized himself with his study of Palestinian topography and archaeology; this task required a certain amount of mathematical and astronomical knowledge, which he had probably obtained before his emigration, for his main sources, Abraham bar Ḥiyya and Jacob ben Maḥir, were Western. The other Eastern scholar, Israel ben Samuel Ma'arabi, was also (as his name indicates) of Western origin, but he had become a leader of the Qaraite community of Cairo. He wrote a treatise on the calendar which is of special interest because it explains the Qaraite views on moot questions. Of course, we may expect other Qaraite doctors, such as Aaron ben Elijah, to discuss calendric questions also, because any commentary on the Torah implied a discussion of the Biblical injunctions which constitute the basis of the Jewish calendar.

D. *Islam*

The mathematical documents written in Arabic (and occasionally in Persian) are so numerous that we shall divide them into six groups. The simplest subdivision is geographical; that is, we shall deal with these mathematicians in groups according to physical proximity, for we may assume as a first approximation that those living in a definite region had more opportunities for influencing one another than they had for influencing foreigners. Moving from the Far West to the East, our groups are (1) Maghrib, (2) Spain, (3) Mamlūk (Syria and Egypt), (4) Persia, (5) 'Irāq, (6) Turkey. The three last groups are the least satisfactory from the point of view of classification (mutual exclusiveness), but the last two are so small that the reader will perhaps be willing to consider (4, 5, 6) together.

[26] The hour being divided into 1,080 parts (ḥalaqim).

D1. *Maghrib*

The greatest Maghribī mathematician, Ibn al-Bannā', has already been dealt with (Introd. 2, 998–1000), because he was forty-five years old when the fourteenth century began. Yet he lived on to 1321, and his influence continued for at least a couple of centuries. He wrote books on every branch of mathematics and astronomy, the most famous one being the Talkhīṣ fī a'māl al-ḥisāb, dealing with calculation and explaining the use of the new numerals. After his death his teachings were transmitted by Muḥammad ibn Ibrāhīm al-Abulī of Tlemcen and by the Islamized Berber 'Abd al-'Azīz al-Huwārī, who wrote one of many commentaries on the Talkhīṣ.

Two other Moroccans deserve mention, whose writings belong respectively to two popular types of Arabic compositions in the astronomical field. They are Muḥammad ibn al-Jazūlī, who wrote treatises on the use of astrolabes, and Abū Muqri', author of a poem on the calendar and astrology.

D2. *Spain*

The Spanish Muslim record is apparently much poorer than the Moroccan, but the latter's brilliancy is partly due to Ibn al-Bannā', who was a relic of the preceding century. Moreover, we should not forget that Morocco (or more generally North Africa west of Egypt) was a large territory enjoying political and cultural independence, whereas Muslim Spain was restricted to the small kingdom of Granada. It would seem that the mathematical and astronomical activities of the learned people of Granada were reduced to the bare necessities, that is, the practical needs of ordinary life and the liturgical needs, requiring lunar observations and the determination of the praying times. This involved some knowledge of astrolabes and other instruments, plus stellar and planetary observations for astrological purposes. The main representatives of that art in Granada were Ibn al-Raqqām, and two members of the Ibn Bāṣa family, the father, al-Ḥasan ibn Muḥammad, and the son, Aḥmad ibn al-Ḥasan, who succeeded each other as chief time-computers (muwaqqitūn) in the cathedral mosque.

The Muslim accountants of Spain were acquainted with the new numerals; they would know of them through the Talkhīṣ of Ibn al-Bannā', not to speak of earlier Arabic books probably available to them. Ibn al-Bannā' used ghubār numerals, that is, the Western form of the Arabic numerals, and this raises the question whether he really understood the new arithmetic or not, a question which cannot be solved without deeper investigation of his writings than I am able to undertake at present.[27] On the other hand, archival documents prove that the Mozarabs of Toledo used numerals functionally similar to the Arabic abujad numerals, though different in form.[28]

Our judgment of the Hispano-Muslim mathematicians will not be too severe if we compare their activities with those of the other inhabitants of the peninsula. To be sure, the Jews, persecuted as they were, did considerably better (see section C2 above). You need think only of Isaac Israeli or of Joseph Naḥmias, who are like giants in the presence of the Granada time-computers; Joseph Naḥmias, by the way, wrote in Arabic, and hence his Nūr al-'ālam could have been used by the

[27] The difficulties of that question will be appreciated after reading Solomon Gandz: The origin of the ghubār numerals, or the Arabian abacus and the articuli (Isis 16, 393–424, 1931).
[28] González Palencia (vol. prel. p. 48, 1930).

contemporary Muslim.[29] We should not compare the Muslims with the Jews, however, but with the Christians who at that time controlled almost the whole peninsula. And what did they produce in mathematics? Nothing. I was not able to find a single mathematician in the whole of Christian Spain, and the only item which might be quoted to illustrate astronomy is a Portuguese almanac for the year 1321 and the meridian of Tortosa, derived from another one for 1307 translated from Arabic into Latin.[30]

D3. *Mamlūk*

Summaries of astronomy are contained in the Taqwīm al-buldān (c. 1318) of the Syrian prince Abū-l-Fidā' and in the first part of the Nihāyat al-arab (c. 1320) of the Egyptian official al-Nuwairī. In the tables of Abū-l-Fidā' the indications of latitudes and longitudes are given in Arabic letters, not in numerals (fig. 19). I was so astonished to find the abujad symbols used in the very cases where the new numerals would prove most useful that I investigated the matter and found that it was the rule rather than the exception. Of course, I have not been able to examine every table, but in the few tables I have seen numbers are expressed by means of abujad letters, not by means of Hindu numerals. That is the case not only in the Taqwīm of Abū-l-Fidā', but also in the Risāla-i-sī faṣl of Nāṣir al-dīn al-Ṭūsī (XIII-2) and in the Nuzhat al-qulūb of Ḥamdallāh Mustawfī.[31] When were Hindu numerals first used in Arabic (or Persian) tables, I wonder, or in books dealing with non-arithmetical subjects?

This aberration seems to prove that the Arabic writers themselves did not understand the true function and merit of the new numerals. They preferred to follow the old abujad system, that is, the use of Arabic letters, even as other nations used Greek or Hebrew letters for the same purpose. That preference was consecrated not only by long usage, but also by religious and mystical traditions associating each of these letters (and corresponding numbers) with all kinds of qualities, such as one of God's names, one of the four elements, a sign of the zodiac, a planet. For a good Muslim the letters were richer in content than the new numerals, and richer in magical virtue, and of course long habit made it possible for him to read them as easily as we read our numerals. For us the practice is confusing, and the more so because the letters do not have the same numerical values in the Maghrib as they have in the Mashriq. Learned Muslims must have been aware of that difficulty, but tradition was so strong that they were willing to overlook ambiguities for its sake, even as the defenders of the English weights and measures seem to prefer their very discrepancies to the logic and uniformity of the metric system.

[29] Not necessarily, for if his treatise was written in Hebrew script, it was closed to the Muslims.

[30] MS 3349 Biblioteca nacional, Madrid. Published mistakenly among the Alphonsine tables, by Manuel Rico y Sinobas: Libros del saber (vol. 4, Madrid 1866). José Millas Vallicrosa: Un almanaque Portugués del siglo XIV (IIIe Congrès international d'histoire des sciences, Portugal 1934, 160–66, Lisboa 1936; Isis 28, 135–38).

[31] Since writing the above I have found the same aberration in the Qānūn al-Mas'ūdī of al-Bīrūnī (XI-1) as edited by A. Zeki Validi Togan (New Delhi 1941; Isis 34, 31), and yet al-Bīrūnī was one of the best exponents of the Hindu numerals. Al-Karkhī (XI-1), famous algebraist, did not use numerals at all, but wrote the names of the numbers in full. My interpretation of Roman numerals in the Latin Alphonsine tables (Introd. 2, 5) must then be modified. The Latin numerals did not replace Hindu numerals, but abujad numbers.

For the differences in value of the Arabic letters East and West see Silvestre de Sacy: Grammaire arabe (1, 74–76, Paris 1810). The author gives in plate VIII the corresponding figures abujad (East and West), Hindu, ghubār, Coptic (often found in Egyptian MSS), and dīwānī (initials of Arabic number words). The abujad numbers are written like the Arabic words, from right to left, whereas the Hindu numerals are written from left to right.

For the mystical interpretations of abujad numbers see article da'wah in Hughes (p. 72–78, 1885) and Weil (EI 1, 68, 1908).

I cannot think of a single geometer living at this time in the Mamlūk countries, but came across a few time-computers, constructors of astrolabes, and compilers of treatises and tables ad hoc. These occupations were generally combined and implied a fair amount of arithmetical, algebraical, and trigonometrical knowledge, as well as familiarity with the elements of astronomy. The outstanding Mamlūk muwaqqitūn were Muḥammad ibn Sam'ūn, al-Mizzī, al-Karakī. Al-Mizzī's treatises were especially popular, and an astrolabe made by him in Damascus 1333 is kept to this day in the national library of Leningrad. Al-Karakī worked in a mosque in Jerusalem.

A discussion of the various kinds of calendars was included by al-Ṣafadī in the introduction to his monumental biographical dictionary.

D4. *Persia*

The Persian mathematicians are of two kinds, arithmeticians and astronomers. As usual, these two groups are not exclusive. For example, the astronomer Niẓām al-a'raj wrote a treatise on computation (ḥisāb).

The famous optician Kamāl al-dīn al-Fārisī wrote a commentary on Ibn al-Khaddām's treatise on arithmetic and mensuration, and, what is more remarkable, he devoted a special tract to amicable numbers. The first writer on this subject was Iamblichos (IV-1), who ascribed knowledge of the first pair of amicable numbers (220, 284) to Pythagoras and Aristotle; but after Iamblichos the subject disappeared completely from Western literature (Latin, Greek, European vernaculars) until Nicolas Chuquet (1484). It was taken up, however, by Arabic writers, Thābit ibn Qurra (IX-2), who gave a general formula, the Ikhwān al-ṣafā' (X-2) and their Western interpreter Maslama ibn Aḥmad al-Majrīṭī (X-2), then Kamāl al-dīn in Arabic and his contemporary Qalonymos ben Qalonymos in Hebrew (Sefer melakim 1320); later Ibn Khaldūn (XIV-2) and the Spaniard al-Qalaṣādī (d. 1486).[32]

Other arithmetical treatises were composed by al-Abharī and al-Kāshānī.

Astronomical studies flourished for a while because of the considerable influence exerted by Nāṣir al-dīn al-Ṭūsī (XIII-2). The latter had died in 1274, but some of his disciples and assistants in the Marāgha observatory were still alive in the fourteenth century. Two of his sons, Ṣadr al-dīn and Aṣīl al-dīn (d. 1315), succeeded him in the direction of that observatory, which seems to have died out with them. The most famous of Nāṣir al-dīn's followers, Quṭb al-dīn al-Shīrāzī (XIII-2), lived until 1311. He wrote an elaborate astronomical treatise, the Nihāyat al-idrāk fī dirāyat al-aflāk, which is derived from Nāṣir al-dīn's Tadhkira, but is far more than a commentary upon it and contains many novelties. He con-

[32] Though the first pair of amicable numbers was known to early Pythagoreans, the second pair (17,296, 18,416) was not discovered until Fermat (statement made by Mersenne in 1636). A century later, in 1750, Euler quoted sixty pairs of them! For the history of that strange topic, see Dickson (1, 38–50, 1919). Ferdinand Rudio (BM 14, 351–54, 1914).

sidered it worth while to discuss at length whether the earth is at rest or not, and concluded that it is an immobile sphere concentric with the universe. His theories were Ptolemaic but not blindly so; he had studied the Almagest and various criticisms of it and satisfied himself that Ptolemy was more nearly correct than his reformers. He wrote various other books on astronomy, but the Nihāyat is the most important. Another disciple of Nāṣir al-dīn, Niẓām al-a'raj, completed in 1305 a commentary on the Almagest as edited by his master, and in 1311 a commentary on the latter's Tadhkira. His activities were a direct continuation and explanation of the great work begun in Marāgha, though he himself does not seem to have lived there except perhaps as a student and apprentice. This matter may be cleared up when his astronomical works are published or investigated.

After the death of Nāṣir al-dīn's sons, the center of astronomical work seems to have moved from Adharbāijān eastward to Khurāsān, Khwārizm, and beyond the Oxus. At any rate, the other astronomers to be named presently do not seem to have had any direct connection with Marāgha, and they flourished farther east. The mysterious Shams al-dīn Mīrak lived in Bukhārā; he wrote encyclopaedic treatises and at least one astronomical commentary. He may be identical with the Σάμψ μπουχαρής whose astronomical lectures were studied by Greek students in Trebizond or elsewhere. Maḥmūd ibn Muḥammad al-Jaghmīnī of Khwārizm wrote on astronomy and astrology. His "quintessence of astronomy" enjoyed some popularity in the Arabic world and was translated into Persian. Ṣadr al-Sharī'a al-thānī, who flourished in Bukhārā (c. 1333), wrote a scientific encyclopaedia, the Ta'dīl al-'ulūm, of which the third part, dealing with astronomy, is sometimes considered a separate treatise.

Finally, we may mention the qibla table included in the Nuzhat al-qulūb of Ḥamdallāh Mustawfī. It is interesting to note that that work was composed in Persian, whereas all the other works thus far mentioned in this "Persian" section were written in Arabic.[33] This shows that the Arabic language continued to enjoy the same privileged status in Islām that Latin did in Western Christendom.

To return to the qibla, that is, the direction of Mecca, it was necessary to determine it as exactly as possible for every Muslim place, inasmuch as the Muslims were obliged to say their prayers in that direction (Qur'ān 2, 136–45). Thus, in the building of a mosque, the miḥrāb indicating that direction to the faithful has to be exactly oriented. This involves the solution for each place *A* of a problem of spherical trigonometry, to wit, to determine the angle formed by the great circle passing through *A* and *M* (Mecca) with the meridian of *A*.[34] The fundamental data were the coordinates of *A* and *M*; these data, especially the longitudes, were very imperfectly known. Consider the coordinates of Mecca itself. Abū-l-Fidā' (Renaud 2, 114), according to his habit, gives many values (in this case five for each coordinate), varying from 67° to 67°31′ for the longitude (from the Fortunate Islands) and from 21° to 21°40′N. for the latitude. The modern values are 39°54′E. from Greenwich (or 56°54′ from Madeira, the most favorable interpretation of Fortunate Islands) and 21°25′N. The latitude was perhaps sufficiently well known, but the longitude was ten degrees off.

[33] Except that Quṭb al-dīn occasionally used the Persian language.

[34] That particular angle is called in Arabic inḥirāf, meaning the deflection (from the meridian), for the earliest qibla (after the rejection of Jerusalem), the Prophet's qibla in Medīna, was the meridian itself (the difference of longitude between Mecca and Medīna being only one minute). The term inḥirāf is used by mariners for the deflection of the true course, and inḥirāf al-sha'ā'i means the refraction of a ray of light.

Wishing to obtain a clearer idea of Muslim accuracy on the subject, I selected at random fifteen important Islamic places[35] and compared their latitudes and longitudes as given in the Times Atlas (London 1922) with the data given by Abū-l-Fidā' (Renaud's edition). Abū-l-Fidā' generally gives many values for each coordinate (values which may vary by more than 1°); sometimes he indicates one of these as the best; in such cases I have adopted the value chosen by him; otherwise I have calculated the averages. In order to avoid difficulties due to our uncertain knowledge of his first meridian, I have considered only differential longitudes; that is, I have reduced every longitude to its value from Mecca. A single item was proved to be correct, the latitude of Damascus (33°30′N.); all other latitudes and longitudes are either too large or too small. The average error in latitude is −15′12″, the average absolute error 45′. The average error in longitude is +14′30″, the average absolute error 5°16′.[36]

Given such errors in latitudes and longitudes, it is clear that the inḥirāf of each place was likely to be incorrect, sometimes very much so. Some of the astronomers attached to the principal mosques might realize that, suffer from it, and try to obtain better results. This was a serious incentive to astronomical progress, but unfortunately it was felt only by exceptional individuals. The average Muslim accepted without question the direction indicated by the nearest miḥrāb. During my travels in Islamic countries, East and West, I was shocked to discover that the maḥārīb were sometimes very wrongly placed; in some cases, it is true, this was corrected by a line drawn upon the floor or upon the miḥrāb, and the true direction was made clear by the imām directing the prayers.

Hughes (p. 480–81, 1885). Carl Schoy: Aus der astronomischen Geographie der Araber (Isis 5, 51–74, 1923). John Kirtland Wright: Notes on the knowledge of latitudes and longitudes in the Middle Ages (Isis 5, 75–98, 1923). A. J. Wensinck and C. Schoy: Qibla (EI 2, 985–99, 1927). Sarton: Orientation of the miḥrāb in mosques (Isis 20, 262–64, 1933); Henri Terrasse (Isis 24, 109–10, 1935); H. P. J. Renaud (Isis 34, 24, 1942); Sarton (Isis 35, 176, 1944). Additional remarks in the geographical section below.

D5. *'Irāq*

The only 'Irāqī astronomer to draw my attention was 'Abd al-'Azīz ibn Sarāyā al-Ḥillī, who wrote a curious treatise on musical astrology, that is, on the advantage of composing melodies according to the signs of the zodiac (burūj al-aflāk) which may happen to dominate. This was not a novelty, but the continuation of an Islamic tradition going back at least to the ninth century.

D6. *Tūrān*

I am not sure that I am right in putting in a separate section the Turcoman Aḥmad ibn 'Uthmān al-Jūzjānī, who wrote an astronomical treatise. I do so to

[35] In order of increasing longitudes, from west to east, Fez, Granada, Tlemcen, Tunis, Cairo, Jerusalem, Beirūt, Damascus, Mecca, Baghdād, Tabrīz, Ispahān, Nīshāpūr, Bukhārā, and Samarqand.

[36] It is the average *absolute* error which matters. Otherwise, enormous errors compensating one another would give one a false idea of precision. For example, the average of two longitudes in error by $+m°$ and $-m°$ is correct, irrespective of the size of m. Should one take the signs of the errors into account, the longitudes would seem to be a little more accurate than the latitudes; as a matter of fact, the errors in longitude were at least seven times greater than those in latitude. Of the fifteen places selected by me at random, the latitude was given within half a degree for eight, and within a degree for ten; the longitude was given within half a degree for only one (Tabrīz), and within a degree for one more (Beirūt).

emphasize the fact that some astronomical work was done by non-Persians living near the river Oxus, and also because I do not know where to place him otherwise. Al-Jūzjānī died in Cairo 1343, and may thus have flourished in Egypt. Yet I did not like to group him with the Egyptians, nor with the Persians.

This completes my account of Islamic mathematics. Instead of the six divisions adopted by me, I now realize that it would have been simpler to divide it into three parts: (1) the Maghrib including Spain, (2) the Mamlūk kingdom, (3) the rest of Eastern Islām. The reader can easily do that for himself, however, by combining some of my subdivisions (1+2, 3, 4+5+6).

E. *India*

Hindu mathematics and astronomy of this period are almost a complete blank. The Muslim invaders, if they did not destroy Hindu culture and what remained of Buddhist culture, were utterly indifferent to any culture but that of Islām. They encouraged their own learned men and drew their knowledge and inspiration exclusively from western sources—that is, Arabic and Persian. The languages used by them were Persian and Urdu.

Under these circumstances, it is not surprising that Hindu astronomy degenerated into the art of calendar-making and astrology, and that the lack of scientific control gave a new vitality to palmistry and other superstitions. The state of Hindu culture and learning was particularly bad under the cruel rule of Muḥammad ibn Taghlaq (1325–51). It improved somewhat, as we shall see in another chapter, under Fīrūz Shāh (1351–88).

N. N. Law (1916, beginning). Bibhutibhusan Datta: The algebra of Nārāyaṇa (Isis 19, 472 ff., 1933).

F. *China*

Under the Yüan dynasty much of the astronomical work was entrusted to Nestorian or Muslim mathematicians. For example, we have spoken in volume 2 (p. 1021) of 'Īsā tarjamān (meaning Jesus the interpreter, in Chinese Ai-hsieh), who was appointed director of the astronomical bureau by Kublai Khān in 1263, and was still flourishing at the end of the century; his four sons, Nestorians like himself, held important posts at the imperial court. Another astronomer in the Mongol service, Cha-ma-lu-ting (Jamāl al-dīn), devised a calendar for Kublai in 1267, the Wan-nien li, and introduced Muslim instruments; one does not know how long he lived, but his influence, if not himself, survived the century. The tendencies of Muslim astronomy were continued by a Chinese disciple, Kuo Shou-ching, who in 1280 compiled for Kublai a new calendar, Shou-shih li, which remained in use until the end of the Yüan dynasty. Two of the astronomical instruments used by him, dated 1279, are remarkable because of their subdivisions of the circle into $365\frac{1}{4}$ degrees, each degree into 100 minutes, each minute into 100 seconds. Their vicissitudes are no less remarkable, for they were removed from Peking in 1900 or 1901 by the Germans, taken to Potsdam, and returned to their original place by order of the Treaty of Versailles in October 1920. What will happen to them now?

Ruins of a "tower for the observation of the stars" and of a "standard for the measurement of the sky" constructed by him may be seen to this day in Kao-ch'êng (ancient Yang-ch'eng), Honan. Astronomical observations had been made there from the time of the Chou dynasty (1122–255 B.C.); a tower was used as a gnomon. That gnomon was lengthened by Kuo from 8 to 40 ch'ih (feet), and thus the determination of the solstices could be made with greater accuracy. The "standard for the measurement of the sky" was the stone-built level surface upon which the shadow was measured. The "tower for the observation of the stars" was used mainly for the observation of the polestar. The ruins of these instruments have been recently investigated and the results published in Chinese in the Report on Chou-kung's tower by C. P. Tong, T. C. Liu, and P. C. Kao (Shanghai 1939; Isis 34, 68).

Kuo Shou-ching was a skillful observer, but, his writings being lost, it is impossible to appraise his trigonometrical and astronomical knowledge. He lived until 1316.

In 1328, the Mongolian government issued a large quantity of printed almanacs —3,123,185 of them—in three different sizes, including information on lucky and unlucky days, etc. A special kind of almanac was printed for the use of Muslims. This confirms the presence of a large number of Muslims in China, and Mongolian interest in them. Indeed, Islām was prejudiced against printing until modern times, and no copy of the Qur'ān was printed even in China. Thus the Muslim almanacs owed their existence to Mongolian, rather than Muslim, initiative. It should be added in this connection that there is no trace of mediaeval Christian printing, whether Nestorian or Catholic, in China. With the exception of the Muslim almanacs just mentioned, early Chinese printing was restricted to Confucian and Buddhist writings, and to a smaller extent to Taoist ones.[37]

Henry H. Howorth: History of the Mongols (1, 274, London 1876). Carter (p. 66–69, 1925).

In spite of Christian and Muslim influences, the latter being especially strong, a thoroughly original stream of Chinese mathematics[38] was flowing. Algebraic methods, apparently independent from the Greek-Arabic ones but continuing purely Chinese traditions, were developed by Ch'in Chiu-shao (XIII-1), Li Chih (XIII-1),[39] Yang Hui (XIII-2). The latter flourished c. 1275. He was succeeded by Chu Shih-chieh (fl. 1280–1303).

Strangely enough, these four men following one another in less than a century are less closely related than one would expect. Ch'in Chiu-shao invented or perfected the method of the celestial element (t'ien yüan shu, or li t'ien yüan i) for the solution of equations. Li Chih's method was different, though his general purpose was the same. Yang Hui quoted neither of them, but mentions another mathematician, Liu I, about whom we know nothing else. Finally, Chu Shih-chieh quotes none of his three predecessors, though there is internal evidence that he knew the work of at least one of them, Yang Hui. All this suggests that our own knowledge of that mediaeval Chinese school is still very fragmentary. We know only a few of the treatises, and even those few have not yet been sufficiently

[37] Let me repeat that the Confucian classics were printed in China as early as 953 and the Tripiṭaka as early as 972. A Taoist patrology was completed in 1016, but not immediately printed, and the first edition of it is lost. However, several eleventh-century reprints of Taoist books exist.

[38] I am thinking of arithmetic and algebra, not of the theory of numbers (magic squares), neither of the fantastic conceptions clustering around numbers and artificial groups of x units which became one of the diseases of the Chinese mind. For a summary and discussion of these conceptions, see Marcel Granet: La pensée chinoise (p. 151–299, Paris 1934).

[39] The name Li Yeh used in Introd. 2, 627 should be replaced by Li Chih.

investigated. It should be noted that not a single one is available in a critical edition, nor is there a complete translation of any one properly annotated by Sinologists and mathematicians. This shows that a very large amount of work remains to be done, and in the meanwhile, we cannot help guessing instead of knowing. When a few of these treatises have been properly edited, translated, annotated, it will be possible to assess their respective value, to compare them, to determine their genealogy and their various relationships, and to find out whether they represent purely Chinese traditions or contain foreign elements, either Arabic brought by Muslim astronomers attached to the Mongolian court, or Western in a general way carried by the Nestorian refugees, or Hindu introduced by the Buddhists, or Manichaean introduced through Taoist or Buddhist channels. As you see, the possibilities are many.

Let us consider the last mentioned. Some idea of Manichaean cosmogony is given us in a Syriac book of scholia (Kethābā dheskōlyōn)[40] by Theodoros bar Kōnī, who flourished at an uncertain time (seventh to ninth century). As persecuted Manichaeans drifted eastward, they carried their scientific conceptions with them as well as their religious ones. The early Taoist patrology contained two Manichaean treatises (Introd. 1, 333); another one has come down to us in the form of a Buddhist sūtra.[41]

A Manichaean astronomer arrived in China in 719 and is said to have greatly influenced Chinese astronomy. Manichaean influence seems to have increased and declined together with Uighūr power. From the early eighth century on, the followers of Mo-ni were sufficiently numerous and obnoxious to invite new persecutions; a number of imperial edicts were issued against them, in 732 by Hsüan Tsung, c. 769 by Tai Tsung, c. 843 by Wu Tsung (Introd. 1, 552). This last persecution was particularly severe, yet Manichaeism continued underground at least until the end of the Ming dynasty (Couling p. 325, 1917).

The Buddhist writings transmitted other mathematical and cosmological ideas of Hindu origin. One of their features was their insistence on the use of fantastically large numbers (10^{50} and beyond), and the mention of very large or very small sizes, periods of time, etc. The Hindu mind loved to play with the idea of infinity and to illustrate its inexhaustibleness. This, however, does not seem to have influenced Chinese mathematics to any extent.

For a summary of Buddhist arithmetical, metrological, and cosmological views, see McGovern (p. 39–48, 56 f., 1923).

To return to Chu Shih-chieh, he wrote a general treatise on arithmetic and algebra in 1299, but his main work, the Ssŭ-yüan yü-chien (Precious mirror of the four elements), was not completed until 1303. It explains the method of four elements

[40] I should have spoken of it in Introd. vol. 1, and probably neglected it because it was so difficult to place chronologically. It was edited by Henri Pognon: Inscriptions mandaïtes des coupes de Khouabir. Appendice II, Extraits du Livre des scholies (p. 181–93, Paris 1898). Franz Cumont: Recherches sur le Manichéisme. I, La cosmogonie manichéenne d'après Théodore bar Khôni (80 p., Bruxelles 1908). Baumstark (p. 218, 1922).

[41] Edouard Chavannes et Paul Pelliot: Un traité manichéen retrouvé en Chine, traduit et annoté (Journal asiatique 18, 499–617, 1911; 1, 99–199, 261–394, 1913), fundamental and very elaborate memoir (354 p.) including the Chinese text and many other Chinese-Manichaean documents. This Buddhist-Manichaean sūtra is an acephalous treatise written in a script of the eighth century, one of the MSS found by Pelliot in Tun-huang, 1908. See also Pelliot: Mo-ni et les Manichéens (Journal asiatique 3, 461–70, 1914). The mediaeval Chinese name of Manichaeism was ming chiao (religion of light).

(ssŭ-yüan shu), which is an application of the t'ien-yüan shu to a system of four linear equations with four unknown quantities; it is practically the same as the method of elimination and substitution, except that the concept of determinant has not yet emerged. That concept was first brought out of the Chinese tradition and discovered by the Japanese mathematician Seki Kowa before 1683; it was rediscovered independently by Leibniz in 1693. The Precious mirror contains other startling items, to wit, a method of solving numerical equations of any degree, anticipating to some extent the Ruffini-Horner procedure;[42] a diagram giving the binomial coefficients up to the eighth power, equivalent to the Pascal triangle; a discussion of the summation of integral finite series.

Chu Shih-chieh was probably the greatest Chinese mathematician, as he is one of the greatest of the Middle Ages. He was certainly the greatest Chinese mathematician of his time, but he was not the only one. That is, I can name at least another one, Chao Yu-ch'in, author of an astronomical treatise wherein a remarkably accurate value of π is found by the inscription of a polygon of 16,384 sides in a circle.

That mathematical efflorescence is intrinsically important; it is also of great interest for the student of comparative mathematics.. How can one account for these independent Chinese discoveries, anticipating Western ones of a much later date? Unfortunately, that Chinese tradition was not allowed to continue in sufficient freedom; the introduction of Western mathematics by the Jesuits in the second half of the sixteenth century stifled it and finally killed it.[43] It was then continued for a few centuries in Japan, until it was stopped and extinguished in that country also by the overwhelming competition of Western mathematics. The Western tradition was on the whole superior, yet the Chinese one was very remarkable and for a brief time ahead of the other.

Excellent materials concerning some of the Ch'ing restorers of mediaeval mathematics will be found in Hummel (1943–44); some of those mathematicians are listed in Isis 34, 519–20, see also Hummel (p. 1086, 1944).

As I finish the writing of this chapter, I realize that its last section, dealing with India and the Far East, will tease the learned reader rather than satisfy him, but this cannot be helped. A tremendous amount of work remains to be done, and even when a sufficient number of texts are properly edited, translated, interpreted, it will take a man's lifetime to explain the origin and development of Chinese mathematics.

VII. PHYSICS, TECHNOLOGY, AND MUSIC

It will be more convenient to divide this chapter, not along geographical or political lines, but according to subjects. This is natural enough, because it deals with a number of subjects, the connection of which was far from clear in the fourteenth century. Their order is of no importance, for a logical order is out of the question on the basis of the knowledge then available.

The chapter is divided into twelve parts, as follows: (1) Optics and optical meteorology. (2) Weights and measures. (3) Magnetism. (4) Early mechanical clocks. (5) Arms and armor. Note on dinanderie. (6) Development of printing

[42] This had been done before by Ch'in Chiu-shao (XIII-1).

[43] Henry Bernard: Matteo Ricci's scientific contributions to China (108 p., 6 pl., Peiping 1935; Isis 26, 164–67, 2 fig.). Ricci was in China from 1582 to his death in 1610.

in the East. (7) Hydrostatics. (8) Canals. (9) Mechanical theories. (10) Discussions concerning the vacuum. (11) Various technical improvements and their social impact. Guilds. Particular inventions. (12) Musical theories: (A) In the Latin West, (B) Byzantine, (C) Muslim.

1. *Optics and Optical Meteorology*

Meteorological books were discussed in the previous chapter because meteorology is naturally connected with astronomy, and became part and parcel of the astrological literature of that time. In addition, the mathematical school of Merton awakened an interest in meteorological observations of a more scientific kind (see note on William Merle). However, a number of queries relative to optical phaenomena (chiefly, the rainbow) may be separated from the rest of the highly heterogeneous meteorological literature and must be considered in any history of optics. There were also queries concerning the nature of light, e.g., in the very obscure Liber de lumine of Ramon Lull (XIII-2) and the De intentionibus in medio of Giles of Rome (XIII-2).

The interest in optical questions was particularly great in the period 1250–1350, both in the Muslim East and in the Latin West, witness the Latin works of Roger Bacon, John Peckham, Witelo, John of Paris, Dietrich of Freiberg; the Arabic works of Aḥmad ibn Idrīs al-Qarāfī, Quṭb al-dīn al-Shīrāzī, Kamāl al-dīn al-Fārisī; and the Hebrew ones of Levi ben Gerson. How shall we account for such ubiquitous and simultaneous efflorescence? The explanation is that all these scholars were drinking from the same source, which became available to them (or which they were ready to use) at about the same time. That source was the Kitāb al-manāẓir of Ibn al-Haitham (XI-1), known to the Latin public as Opticae thesaurus Alhazeni, a book which must be listed among the leading classics; indeed, it influenced scientific thought for at least six centuries.[1] Ibn al-Haitham's great book and other writings included the discussion of such a medley of topics as the structure of the eye, optical illusions, perspective, binocular vision, vision of outlines, shadows, and colors, the ancient catoptrics and dioptrics with new developments, atmospheric refraction, length of twilight and height of the atmosphere, apparent increase of size of the moon near the horizon, camera obscura, Alhazen's problem (Introd. 1, 721), mirages, comets, the Milky Way, rainbows, halos, etc.; that is, it dealt with questions which would now be classified in at least seven different compartments, anatomy, physiology, psychology, mathematics, astronomy, physics, meteorology. The Christian, Jewish, and Muslim commentators on the Kitāb al-manāẓir were induced to discuss all these topics, and did so in various measure according to their own inclinations.

One topic found special favor among them, namely, the rainbow; naturally enough, for it is one of the most marvelous phaenomena as well as one of the most common everywhere. In Genesis (9:14–17) the bow (qesheth) is represented as the token of the everlasting covenant between God and every living creature, and in Ezekiel (1:28) it symbolizes the glory of the Lord. Hence a discussion of the rainbow was one of the necessities of Biblical scholarship; no meteorologist, astrologer, or physicist could avoid it. To speak only of the events of our period, the commentary

[1] Of course, the Kitāb al-manāẓir was itself derived from many older sources, the chief of them being the Meteorology of Aristotle (Isis 6, 138), Euclid, and Ptolemy, the study of which was continued by Ibn al-Haitham's successors together with that of the latter's own works. Sarton: The tradition of the optics of Ibn al-Haitham (Isis 29, 403–6, 1938; 34, 217).

on the Meteorology of Aristotle begun by St. Thomas Aquinas was continued by another Dominican (John of Paris?), who included in it a treatise de iride. The leading optician in the West was another Dominican, Dietrich of Freiberg. He accounted for the rainbow by the assumption of two refractions and one reflection in spherical drops of water, a theory which was transmitted to posterity by Regiomontanus and held the ground until the law of refraction expressed by Snel and Descartes (1618, 1637) introduced a slight modification. The same theory was proposed at about the same time by Quṭb al-dīn al-Shīrāzī (XIII-2) and by Kamāl al-dīn al-Fārisī. Quṭb al-dīn was probably the first in point of time to expound it, but Dietrich discovered it independently. Considering the slowness of communications in their time and the enormous distance separating them (Quṭb al-dīn was a Persian and never traveled farther west than Egypt; Dietrich lived in France and Germany), their discoveries were practically contemporary, and furnish us with one of the earliest examples of simultaneity due to the pressure of identical circumstances. Quṭb al-dīn and Dietrich had derived their information from the same source, and they were facing the same queries; their knowledge matured with the same speed, because in their time Western Europe and the Near East were almost on the same cultural level.

Dietrich wrote other optical treatises, but as they dealt with subjects which were still in the metaphysical (or rather prophysical) stage—the theory of light and the theory of colors[2]—they are insignificant.

The main work of Kamāl al-dīn was a very elaborate commentary on the treatise of Ibn al-Haitham, containing many novelties, e.g., remarks on aerial perspective adumbrating those to be made two centuries later by Leonardo da Vinci, and a recognition of the fact that the speed of light, however great, cannot be infinite. The use of a camera obscura, initiated by Ibn al-Haitham, was developed at about the same time by Kamāl al-dīn, writing in Arabic in Persia, and by Levi ben Gerson, writing in Hebrew in southern France. Levi distinguished between the clear images obtained with a pinprick aperture and the blurred images obtained through a larger one. He used the camera obscura for astronomical purposes, in particular for the measurement of variations in the apparent diameters of sun and moon.

A number of northern lights were observed in the fourteenth century, but apart from the indication of their occurrence and jejune descriptions, there is no literature concerning them. The authors of optical treatises just mentioned did not speak of them because they lived in such low latitudes that they had no sufficient opportunities for observing them. The best accounts are probably those found in Russian chronicles, and they do not amount to much, beyond the dating of occurrences, which may be of value for the study of long-range periodicity.

Some of the earliest Western accounts of spectacles date from the beginning of the fourteenth century, and the earliest illustration occurs in a Treviso fresco by Tommaso de Modena, dated 1352.[3] As the invention was probably made in the last quarter of the thirteenth century, it is discussed in Introd. 2, 1024–27. The development of that invention was very slow, for many technical difficulties

[2] Of course, Newton's experiments on the dispersion of color might have been made much earlier; but they were not made. It was not experimental difficulty, but only inertia and lack of imagination which delayed them until 1672. Sarton: Discovery of the dispersion of light (Isis 14, 326–41, 1930), with facsimile of Newton's original paper.

[3] Reproduced in Geschichtsblätter für Technik (3, 127, 1916).

had to be overcome before spectacles were really useful, and as many psychological difficulties before they were actually used by many people.

2. *Weights and Measures*

Information concerning metrology may be extracted from many classes of books, such as (1) Biblical and Talmudic commentaries, (2) medical writings, (3) Arabic treatises for the guidance of market inspectors, (4) cosmographies, (5) annals, (6) codes of law, regulations.

An excellent example of the second kind is the De ponderibus et mensuris of Dino del Garbo. It was published separately, but that did not change its nature; its main source was the Qānūn of Ibn Sīnā, and its point of view medical.

One of the best guides for the market inspector or muḥtasib is the one written by Ibn al-Ukhuwwa, which contains miscellaneous information on weights and measures, their use and abuse.

I did not come across any Chinese or Japanese text of this time devoted to metrology, but the people of the Far East continued their own metrological traditions, the investigation of which is still almost impossible to Western students.

3. *Magnetism*

The compass described by Peter the Stranger in 1269 was already an instrument of sufficient elaboration to be of practical use in navigation. Various improvements were brought to it by sailors, who may have been Italian or even Amalfian, but we do not know. That history is very obscure. The main improvement consisted in adding the wind rose to the magnetic needle and making a single instrument of the two. Another improvement of great pregnancy was due to the awareness that the needle did not show the true north, but pointed a little away from it to the east or to the west. We do not know when the declination was discovered; that happened probably long before Columbus' time, and yet was not really integrated into our knowledge before the sixteenth century.

As indicated in the first section of this chapter, northern lights were observed, but their influence on the magnetic needle remained unnoticed until four centuries later. We should expect northern sailors, who we are sure used compasses, to have observed their disturbance during auroral displays; at any rate, they did not publish their experiences.

The Austrian Benedictine Engelbert of Admont wrote a treatise on fascination, wherein magnetic influences were discussed as a pertinent part of the subject. Thus began (or continued) the confusion between genuine magnetism on the one hand and metaphorical magnetism ("animal magnetism," "personal magnetism") on the other. That confusion was greatly increased by Franz Anton Mesmer in the second half of the eighteenth century, and was (and is being) fostered by many other people, even unto our own days. Engelbert had been shown a mariner's compass in Venice, and he compared the ability which some men have of influencing and "fascinating" others to the mysterious power holding the needle in a definite direction.

4. *Early Mechanical Clocks*

Mechanical clocks (as distinguished from clepsydrae and sundials) might have developed a little earlier than they did but for the fact that there was no urgent need of them. The need grew with the importance of cities vs. monasteries and the creation of a new economy of open markets of widening scope, national and international traffic as against the closed, self-contained economy of earlier days. As long as public and private life was almost exclusively regulated by the church, the day was divided into hours of unequal length and the times of appointment were determined by the church bells.

Clocks began to make their appearance in the second half of the thirteenth century, and it is probable that their first purpose was private rather than public. That is, they were first devised to wake up the monks whose duty it was to ring the bells for matins. The first clocks were alarm clocks, but of a primitive nature. The two essential characteristics of a simple mechanical clock are the weight drive and some kind of escapement. A kind of weight drive was already used in water clocks, and the simplest escapement, the foliot balance, was discovered early in the fourteenth century, if not before.

There is much information concerning public clocks in the first half of the fourteenth century, and one cannot escape the conclusion that clocks were in use before the middle of the century, yet there is not a single case for which the literary and archaeological evidence is completely convincing. We may perhaps say that the Milano clock of 1335 was the first genuine striking clock, but it is lost; as to the Dover clock of 1348, it is most probably of a later date.

It is significant that quite a few people appear on the stage who are called clock-makers, clock-keepers, etc. The reader will find references in our book to some of them, such as Roger de Ropford, Bartholomaeus Orologiarius, Peter Lightfoot, Richard Wallingford, Giacomo de' Dondi.

In short, we may say that clocks were probably discovered at the beginning of the fourteenth century, and that their use increased slowly during the first half of the century.

5. *Arms and Armor*

The explosive property of gunpowder was first applied to the propulsion of missiles in the first half of the century, and firearms were used for military purposes in the second quarter of it. These early firearms were very inefficient, to such an extent that the making of armor continued its development with little, if any, reference to them.

The discussion of firearms suggests the consideration of other metal work, especially monumental brasses and "dinanderie," so called after the Belgian town of Dinant, where the making of objects in copper, brass, and bronze reached a new climax in those days. In later times the recurrent need of metal for the casting of guns caused a great many of these beautiful objects to be destroyed, yet enough of them remain to witness to the artistic and technical ability of the smiths and founders who produced them.

6. *Development of Printing in the East*

The old art of printing books instead of writing them by hand was continued not only in China, but also in Korea and in Japan. It had not been restricted to religious and philosophical purposes, but extended to the reproduction of scientific books and, of course, of bank notes. Xylography did not involve in this period any tangible improvement, and hence its history is of literary, rather than of technical, interest.

With regard to typography, invented in China in the first half of the eleventh century, the situation is a little different, for material progress was accomplished about 1314 by Wang Chên. He made new experiments with metal and wooden type and finally used the latter for the printing of his book on agriculture. His rejection of metal type was probably due to inking difficulties, that is, to the lack of an oily ink. In addition, he invented revolving type cases, which were almost a necessity for Chinese typesetters on account of the many thousands of characters which had to be always within their reach.

Though printing had traveled west as far as Tabrīz in 1294, it did not go any farther in the fourteenth century, and the Tabrīz incident remained isolated in the story of Islamic printing.[4] There was as yet no trace of printing in the Christian West, even in the form of block books, not to speak of typography. It is one of the curiosities of history, that typography was invented and practiced for centuries by Far Eastern people, who needed it least on account of their lack of alphabet, before being rediscovered by Western people, for whom it was incomparably more expedient. This proves once more that discoveries are not made only because of their usefulness, or made more promptly where they can be most useful. We must assume that the early Chinese inventors and practitioners of typography enjoyed the beauty of the invention rather than its economy, which remained for them highly problematic until modern times.

7. *Hydrostatics*

The Archimedean tradition of hydrostatics and its application to the determination of specific densities had been revived by the author of the De ponderibus (Introd. 2, 615, 957), by Jordanus, and by William of Moerbeke. It was continued by John of Meurs and by the anonymous author of a short text De insidentibus aquae, but nothing new was added to it.

8. *Canals*

It is a curious fact that the remarkable activity in canal and sluice building which characterized the thirteenth century came almost to a stop during the fourteenth century, to be revived only in the fifteenth. This may perhaps be better explained in terms of economic and political history than in terms of technological development. The people of the fourteenth century knew how to build canals but did not build any of importance.

8 bis. *Metallurgy and Mining*

Mining is so closely connected with geology, and metallurgy with mining, that these two topics will find a more appropriate place in chapter X (or section X of chapter I), on natural history.

9. *Mechanical Theories*

The history of mechanical theories is curious because of its discontinuities. They began as a part of Aristotelian philosophy, but were soon lifted up to the mathematical level by the genius of Archimedes. Then one has to wait seven centuries and a half for the emergence of new ideas. Simplicios (VI-1) and Philoponos

[4] Prejudices against printing caused Islamic countries to be very backward in this respect (Isis 33, 561). It is not true, however, that Islamic printing began only in 1825, for at least eighteen books were printed before 1825 by Chinese Muslims. Ollone (p. 389-419, 1911).

(VI-1) in their commentaries on Aristotelian mechanics adumbrated the notions of impetus and inertia. Another period of seven centuries was needed for the germination of those seeds, but then—that is, in the thirteenth century—we witness a new mechanical efflorescence.[5] Let me recall the main points of it. Jordanus Nemorarius (XIII-1) introduces the idea of a kind of gravity potential (gravitas secundum situm) and formulates what Duhem called "Jordanus' axiom": "that which can lift a certain weight up to a certain height, can also lift a weight k times heavier to a height k times smaller." The same Jordanus or one of his disciples used a notion comparable to that of statical moment for the study of the angular lever and of the inclined plane. With sufficient good will one can even read in the writings of the Jordanus school an anticipation of the principle of virtual displacements.[6] In the meanwhile another mechanician, Gerald of Brussels (XIII-1), was struggling with the difficulties to be solved later by the distinction between linear and angular velocities. In the latter part of the same century, two Franciscans, Roger Bacon (XIII-2) and Peter Olivi (XIII-2), distinguished themselves in the same field. Peter revived the Philoponian conception of impetus; Bacon, influenced by Grosseteste even more than by Nemorarius, pondered on the nature of mechanical force and the possibilities of its transmission. Peter the Stranger (XIII-2) and Villard de Honnecourt (XIII-2) were speculating on perpetual motion.

Note the internationalism of this movement. Nemorarius was a German, Gerald of Brussels a Netherlander, Robert Grosseteste and Roger Bacon were Englishmen; Peter Olivi, Villard de Honnecourt, and Peter the Stranger, Frenchmen. Moreover, this mechanical crisis was not restricted to Europe. We find it also in Persia; 'Alī ibn 'Umar al-Kātibī (XIII-2) and Quṭb al-dīn al-Shīrāzī (XIII-2) discussed the diurnal rotation of the earth and rejected it on mechanical grounds.

The mixture of mechanics with astronomy is not surprising. In some respects celestial mechanics is older than terrestrial mechanics, and the planets gave us examples of pure resistless motion long before similar ones could be observed below the moon. In order to appreciate the confusion of ideas which was inhibiting progress, we must remember that the Aristotelian conception of motion was considerably broader than ours. When we speak of the motion of a body we think simply of its displacement, but Peripatetics and the schoolmen thought of it as any kind of change (physicochemical as well as mechanical). In that sense it is correct to say that Aristotelian physics is essentially a theory of movement (motion, change).[7]

[5] The sources of that efflorescence are not easy to determine, for in the thirteenth century Philoponos' physics was not known in the Latin West, except through Simplicios' quotations. This has been shown by Martin Grabmann: Mittelalterliche lateinische Übersetzungen von Johannes Philoponos, Alexander von Aphrodisias und Themistios (München 1929; Isis 15, 446). It may be, however, that the quotations were sufficient to stimulate mechanical thinking and switch it to a new direction. If not, Philoponian ideas must have reached the Latin West through Arabic channels. These questions are being investigated by Salomon Pines: Les précurseurs musulmans de la théorie de l'impetus (Archeion 21, 298–306, 1938); Etudes sur Awḥad al-zamān Abū-l-Barakāt al-Baghdādī (Revue des études juives 104, 1–95, 1938; Isis 31, 148). The main author studied by Pines is the Baghdād Jew Hibatallāh ibn Malkā (XII-2), who turns out to be far more important than was realized when I wrote my note on him (Introd. 2, 382).

[6] In his interpretations, Duhem was carried away by his enthusiasm and by his desire to magnify the schoolmen and belittle Galileo. That bias of his has been unconsciously emphasized by his panegyrists (e.g., Isis 27, 161). Benjamin Ginzburg: Duhem and Jordanus Nemorarius (Isis 25, 341–62, 1936).

[7] Jules Barthélemy Saint-Hilaire: Physique d'Aristote (vol. 1, p. ii, Paris 1862).

Quṭb al-dīn lived until 1311, and hence he belongs definitely to our period. His rejection of the diurnal rotation of the earth was based on the a priori idea that circular motions are characteristic of the heavenly bodies and exclusive to them; sublunar bodies can have only rectilinear motions. It is hard to understand how such a prejudice can establish itself; yet it dominated and inhibited the human mind throughout the Middle Ages and down to the seventeenth century.

To return to the main mechanical tradition: Greek in origin and twice interrupted for seven centuries, it was finally restored in the Latin West. We have summarized the contributions of Latin doctors of the thirteenth century; their work was continued in the fourteenth century. French scholars connected with the University of Paris had a good share in that renaissance. Pierre Duhem, who devoted the third series of his studies on Leonardo da Vinci (1913) to the "Parisian forerunners of Galileo," did proudly inscribe the following dedication: "Ad maiorem gloriam mechanicae nostrae scientiae vere genetricis, facultatis artium quae in universitate parisiensi XIV° saeculo florebat." Let us now consider these Parisian forerunners, as well as their rivals in other scientific centers of the West.

John of Jandun (d. 1328) continued Bacon's cogitations on action at a distance and concluded that it was impossible; that led him to conceive magnetic attraction as caused by a kind of transmission throughout the field, a vague foretaste of Faraday's conceptions. He also denied the possibility of gravity potential postulated by Jordanus. Jandun's deep interest in such questions was characteristic of his time and of his own personality, yet we must admit that his mechanical thinking was, on the whole, reactionary.

On the contrary, John Buridan (d. 1358) was the leader of the nominalistic revolt against Aristotelian dynamics, and developed the Philoponian ideas of impetus and inertia far more boldly than Peter Olivi had done a generation or two before. His explanation of magnetic attraction, however, was similar to Jandun's. The most original feature of Buridan's mechanics was his recognition of the essential likeness of celestial and terrestrial laws. He was almost alone (with Francis of Marchia) in postulating that identity, which remained unproved until the seventeenth century.

The mechanical work of the mathematician John of Meurs (d. after 1350) was more traditional. The first two treatises of his Quadripartitum numerorum were devoted, respectively, to the defense of Aristotelian dynamics and the explanation of Archimedean hydrostatics.

Finally, the Cistercian monk Pierre Ceffons, discussing the Sentences and probably stimulated by the mechanical controversies of his day, solved the astronomical difficulties in a curious manner. Boldness invites boldness. Buridan's speculations, we may assume, helped him to realize that mechanical ideas were not sacrosanct. Ceffons denied the use of Intelligences to move the celestial spheres, and considered carefully all the objections to the diurnal motion of the earth, refuting them, yet unaccountably rejecting the theory itself or at least refusing to accept it. Think once more of Quṭb al-dīn going through the same intellectual anxieties at the same time—Pierre Ceffons in Clairvaux and Quṭb al-dīn in Tabrīz!

A similar fermentation of ideas was engrossing English minds; the coincidence is natural enough, if we remember the international spirit animating the universities, and especially the University of Paris. As Merton College was a great mathematical center, we may expect it to have been also a center of physical thinking, and so it was. Richard Swineshead, who was like Ceffons a Cistercian, had been educated in Merton. He was deeply interested in the subject then called "increase and decrease of forms" (intensio et remissio formarum), which was, as far as we can make out, a vague anticipation of the study of physical changes in function of variables. Whether he was really the originator of that line of thinking, or only its main mediaeval exponent, I do not know, but considering the vagueness and obscurity of his thought, it is astounding to find him praised not only by Jerome Cardan, but by Leibniz as late as 1696! The same subject exercised the minds of two other Merton men, William Heytesbury and Thomas Bradwardine. The latter's Tractatus proportionum was a notable summary of dynamics and cinematics, which remained a standard book until the end of the Renaissance.

The most original teacher of Oxford was William of Occam. Being a Franciscan, he was not connected with Merton, but in a place as small as Oxford how could he have remained unaware of the work done by the Mertonians, or they of his? He led the nominalistic revolt against Aristotelianism in England, even as his peer Buridan did in Paris. On the other hand, he opposed the views of John of Jandun on action at a distance, admitting the possibility of such action, and thus establishing himself as a forerunner of Newtonian mechanics. These internal conflicts between the leading physicists reveal the complexity of the age, so far removed from the mediaeval "uniformity of thought" complacently described by historians who have never taken the trouble to analyze the endless divergencies of that thought.

The mechanical speculations of the Franciscan brethren Peter Olivi, Roger Bacon, William of Occam were continued in Italy by other brethren of the same order, Francis of Marchia and Giovanni da Casale. We know little about the latter, but Francis was apparently a man of great originality who did not hesitate to question the Aristotelian dogmas on the motion of projectiles or the existence of laws restricted to the sublunar world. Francis assumed that celestial mechanics was not essentially different from terrestrial.

When one tries to sum up what these mechanicians accomplished, one is bound to be disappointed. Indeed, there was a great deal of discussion, but no results of lasting value were definitely attained; much groping in the dark and little light. We should bear in mind, however, that these mechanical questions were difficult in proportion as they seemed simple, and that many centuries of controversy would still be required before the fundamental notions could be disentangled from the rest and the essential questions correctly stated.

10. *Discussions Concerning the Vacuum*

There was another perennial cause of strife between the Aristotelians and their adversaries, that is, the theory of vacuum. In fact, the quarrel ad hoc was already well started in Aristotle's time. Democritos (V B.C.), leading the atomists, distinguished between the full (*πλῆρες, στερεόν*) and the empty (*κενόν, μανόν*); a vacuum, he argued, was necessary for the motion of the atoms. Others, led by Anaxagoras (V B.C.), claimed that there could be no vacuum. Anaxagoras even thought that he had proved the impossibility of the vacuum; he had simply proved (as Aristotle remarked, Physics, IV, VI, 213a) the materiality of air. Plato and Aristotle followed Anaxagoras; Aristotle analyzed the dilemma in such a masterly way that he dominated scientific thinking on the subject almost until yesterday. As against Anaxagoras and others, he defined the notion of absolute vacuum; men were always deceived by their language, they called a thing empty when it was empty of that which they were interested in;[8] he taught them the idea of absolute emptiness, an idea assuming the existence of space and naught else—space that is absolutely vacant. Such an idea, he claimed, was as remote from reality or realization as nothingness or chaos. Vacuum, far from being necessary for motion, would make the kind of motions[9] which we observe impossible. For example, in a vacuum, once a body was started it would never stop; the differences between movements which are more or less rapid according to the greater or smaller weight of the moved bodies, or to smaller or greater resistance of the medium, would cease to exist. These objections are immensely interesting, for they presaged in reverse the idea of inertia. Aristotle's argument concerning the impossibility of vacuum was so strong that Descartes adopted it two thousand years later, and belated Cartesians continued to defend it until last century.

There is no point in enumerating the philosophers who refused to accept the idea of vacuum, and the list would be too long. It is more significant to name the few who accepted the idea. First we have Straton of Lampsacos (III-1 B.C.), who tried to reconcile the theories of Aristotle with those of Democritos. Straton realized the scientific plausibility of the latter's thinking, and failed to understand how light and heat could be transmitted without vacuum.[10] Then Philoponos, the admirable Philoponos (VI-1), whose prophetic genius has already been illustrated with reference to the theory of the impetus. Western science comes out, directly or indirectly, of Philoponos' commentaries. It is possible that the transmission was made, as in so many other cases, via the Arabic channels.

The tradition of the vacuum is to a large extent parallel to the tradition of atomism, and atomism was introduced relatively early in Muslim kalām (scholastic philosophy). It was explained by al-Rāzī (IX-2), al-Bāqilānī (XI-1), and many others.[11] One of the best expositions is found in the Guide of the perplexed of Maimonides (XIII-2), who, however, rejected it.[12] The earliness of Arabic atomism and its relative popularity in Islām for a considerable time suggests that that theory reached the Arabic scholars possibly from more than one source. It may have come to them not only from Greece but also from India, where Jaina and Buddhist doctrines included atomistic ideas (for Jaina atomism, see Introd. 1, 69; for Buddhist atomism, Macdonald, Isis 9, 343–44). Certain it is that atomistic ideas were explained in Ismā'īlī circles, where a good deal of Asiatic syncretism was going on. One of the main books on the subject, the Kitāb zād al-musāfirīn, was written in Persian by the Ismā'īlī missionary Nāṣir-i-Khusraw (XI-2), and Nāṣir quoted as his main sources al-Rāzī and a mysterious Īrānshahrī. We know little about Abū-l-'Abbās al-Īrānshahrī[13] except that he must have flourished in

[8] For example, they would call a wine bottle or a fishpond empty when the former contained no more wine and the latter had no more fish.

[9] Motion is understood here in the broad Aristotelian sense; it refers not only to displacement, but to dilatation, contraction, growth, vaporization, etc.

[10] Georges Rodier: La physique de Straton (p. 60, Paris 1890).

[11] The terms used for atom were many, e.g., al-juz' alladhī lā yatajazza' (this is the literal translation of the Greek word; the *a* privative, having no Arabic equivalent, must be expressed by a negative sentence), al-juz' al-wāḥid, al-jawhar al-wāhid alladhī la yanqasim, al-jawhar al-fard (pl. al-jawāhir al-fardah), or more briefly al-juz' or al-jawhar. The Democritean voidness and fullness are called al-khalā wal-malā'.

[12] Munk's edition (1, 375 ff.). D. B. Macdonald: Continuous re-creation and atomic time in Muslim scholastic philosophy (Isis 9, 326–44, 1927).

[13] Īrānshahrī probably means "he of Nīshāpūr," in Khurāsān, for the title Īrān shahr (the city of Īrān) was sometimes given to that city.

the tenth or eleventh century, and that he had given explanations of the Jewish, Christian, and Manichaean religions, *and of Hindu doctrines.*[14]

To return to the West, a curious revival of atomism combined with pluralism and Neoplatonism occurred in the twelfth century under the guidance of Hugh of Saint Victor (XII-1) in Paris and of William of Conches (XII-1) in Chartres. The great majority of the Christian schoolmen, however, were hostile to atomism, as they were to the idea of vacuum, because of their Aristotelian orthodoxy, which was carried just as far as was consistent with Christian theology, just as far but no farther.

Thus all kinds of arguments are introduced, e.g. in the commentaries on the Sentences or on Aristotelian physics, to prove the impossibility of the vacuum. For example, John of Jandun argues that the extreme difficulty of separating two polished surfaces closely pressed against each other is a consequence of that impossibility, and hence an experimental confirmation of it. This argument was quoted again by Albert of Saxony (XIV-2) and Marsilius van Inghen (XIV-2). As independent a man as John Buridan accepted implicitly the impossibility of vacuum. The queerest argument for that prejudice was introduced by the English Franciscan John the Canon, but we need not insist on that. When a prejudice is sufficiently well entrenched—and this one, the horror vacui, had been allowed to grow for over sixteen centuries—no argument is needed, or every argument is good enough, to defend it.

It should be noted that the impossibility of a vacuum had been given astronomical significance by being mixed up with another famous controversy. Is the universe unique or not? Theologians rejected instinctively the conception of other universes. There is but one God; there can be but one universe. If there were a vacuum, there might be other universes behind it; on the contrary, if there be no vacuum, there is no possibility of discontinuity in nature; everything holds together, there is but one universe. The believers in vacuum were thus put under suspicion of heresy, as potential believers in the plurality of worlds.

Enough has been said to show that a defender of the idea of vacuum had to be a brave and independent spirit. We cannot expect to find many, and, as a matter of fact, I can only name one for the first half of the fourteenth century, to wit, the Englishman Walter Burley. Burley was a Merton man, tutor to the Black Prince. In his commentary on the Physics, he had the boldness to affirm that the possibility of a vacuum and of a plurality of universes was not incompatible with the power of God. In short, he was turning the gun the other way around, exactly as had been done by the early Muslim schoolmen (mutakallimūn). There is no limit to the creative power of God. That power may be conceived as a continuous re-creation on an atomic basis, and it is conciliable with "vacua." Why not? Nevertheless the orthodox view of Christendom remained for many more centuries the conception of a single continuous world without holes and without atoms.

11. *Various Technical Improvements and Their Social Impact*

This section is very difficult to write because of its endless complexities, but fortunately the author of a history of science cannot be expected to deal minutely

[14] A longer discussion of the multiple origins of atomism would be out of place here. For further information see Mabilleau (1895), Wilhelm Kroll, Hermann Jacobi, Tjitze de Boer, and John Henry Poynting (ERE 2, 197–210, 1910), Keith (1921), Pines (1936). Though the latter deals primarily with Islamic atomism, he has a whole chapter on its Greek and Hindu origins.

with the history of inventions. The history of science is relatively simple, for its basic materials are texts which, even if they be anonymous, are sufficiently tangible. In the majority of cases they are the productions of men of whom we know, not always as much as we should wish, yet enough to locate them in space and time. Technical inventions are generally difficult to locate, even when their practical importance was considerable. This difficulty is due to the facts that the inventors were often illiterate or inarticulate, and that secrecy was their best protection. In spite of secrecy, a valuable invention has a tendency to spread, and that tendency may be strong enough to overcome almost every kind of geographical and political boundaries. This has been proved repeatedly by ethnologists, e.g., with regard to the diffusion of cultural items across the Americas.[15] Some examples will be discussed in other parts of this volume, the most remarkable perhaps being the one concerning the new method of preserving and packing herrings, an invention the economic value of which can hardly be exaggerated. It dates probably from the beginning of the fourteenth century, but was it made in Dutch Zeeland, as I am inclined to think (see article on Beukels), or in Norway, or Sweden? Perhaps it was partly made in each country. Indeed, an invention is seldom final, but rather a link in an endless series. Each link has its own origin, its own story; it is always difficult and sometimes impossible to weigh its relative importance.

Though some inventions travel far and fast, and stimulate changes, that is, new inventions, others are more static in every sense. They do not develop, and they remain of local interest.

Finally, human inertia is often strong enough to block innovations, irrespective of the latter's usefulness. Thus the examination of the tools used by a people at a definite time only proves that those tools were invented either then or before. The tools used at any one time may date from any and every preceding age. This is a fact of common experience. One of the foremen employed by the French Egyptologist Mariette pacha (d. 1881) was still shaving himself with a flint razor![16] I have seen in France primitive instruments which should have been relegated to museums, yet were actually used, and they were used in the vicinity of electric devices. It was common enough in Syria to witness mediaeval caravans proceeding along the same roads as motorcars. Every traveler could tell similar stories. Moreover, almost every person could discover a few "fossils" in his own surroundings, if not in his own kit.

The following circumstance is even more disturbing. We have no pains in understanding that a better individual tool may remain unobserved for a long time, especially if the inventor wishes to monopolize the fruits of his invention, but how does it happen that inventions of public importance are so difficult to trace? To illustrate, consider the compass. Its early history is extremely difficult to write, but this may be due to the secrecy of the sailors who were the first to benefit from it. Now consider guns and clocks. Their early history is equally mysterious, yet guns and clocks were from the first not individual but social tools. The first mechanical clocks were established in church towers or belfries. We ought to know them very well (from the accounts and other archival documents), yet our knowledge of them is extremely imperfect.

[15] Clark Wissler: The American Indian. An introduction to the anthropology of the New World (2d ed., New York 1922; Isis 9, 138–42).

[16] Louis de Launay: La conquête minérale (p. 47, Paris 1908). Other similar anachronisms are quoted by him.

The history of technology is as much a part of economic history as of the history of science. At any rate, the social impact of new inventions—and that impact may be sufficient to change a culture and to upset the balance of power between nations—concerns the political historian and the economist more directly than ourselves. We should not trespass upon their territory. The history of tools is intimately connected with the history of capital and labor. This leads us to the history of mediaeval guilds. That history is very fascinating; it did not begin in the fourteenth century nor even in the Middle Ages, for some kind of guild organization existed already in the Roman and Byzantine empires.[17] Nor were guilds a purely Western development, for we find guilds in the Islamic world, in India, China, and Japan.

Western guilds

As far as the Christian West is concerned, the importance of guilds increased considerably during the fourteenth century because of the growing urbanism and the progress of trade and industries. It is noteworthy that in Ghent, Bruges, Bruxelles one counted already at that time from fifty to sixty guilds, which is the best proof of the increasing division and specialization of labor. Not only were the main arts and trades separated, as the weavers, fullers, shearers (of cloth), dyers, butchers, fishmongers, bricklayers, roofers, plumbers, bakers, furriers, haberdashers, tanners, etc., but many of these arts were already subdivided. For example, the tanners of black leather were separated from the tanners of white leather and from the men preparing leather with warm water, from the glovers, from the pursemakers; the furriers handling domestic furs were organized apart from the furriers using foreign furs; the dyers were divided according to the dyes, etc. Each technical advance tended to create a new art and a new guild, until the process of disintegration had been carried so far that it had to be compensated by new amalgamations. Then, in Flanders, various guilds were combined into "members" or "nations" (Vanderkindere p. 122, 1879). Similar evolutions occurred in other countries, not necessarily as early, but according to the technical progress of each.

One can see that the history of guilds would provide valuable information concerning arts and even sciences (e.g., medicine and pharmacy were generally counted among the arts), but we must abandon those gleanings to other scholars. It must suffice here to indicate some of the main books of reference.

Generalities for the Western guilds. ERE (6, 214–21, 1914). Rudolph Eberstadt: Der Ursprung des Zunftwesens und die älteren Handwerkerverbände des Mittelalters (204 p., Leipzig 1900; 2d ed., 336 p., Leipzig 1915). Georges Renard: Guilds in the Middle Ages, with introduction by G. D. H. Cole (165 p., London 1919). Gennaro Maria Monti: Le corporazioni nell'evo antico e nell'alto medio evo (362 p., Bari 1934). Gunnar Mickwitz: Die Kartellfunktionen der Zünfte und ihre Bedeutung bei der Entstehung des Zunftwesens. Eine Studie in spätantiker und mittelalterlicher Wirtschaftsgeschichte (Societas scientiarum fennica, Comm. hum. litt. vol. 8, no. 3, 250 p., Helsinki 1936).

Italy. Edgcumbe Staley: The guilds of Florence (645 p., ill., London 1906). Giovanni Monticolo: I capitolari delle arti veneziane dalle origini al 1330 (3 vols., Roma 1896–1914). Gina Fasoli: Le compagnie delle arti a Bologna fino al prin-

[17] Some papyri refer to guilds. E.g., the Oxyrhynchos pap. 85 reprinted in A. S. Hunt and C. C. Edgar: Select papyri (Loeb library, vol. 2, 378–80, 1934). Sworn declarations by the guild of coppersmiths (*παρὰ τοῦ κοινοῦ τῶν χαλκοκολλητῶν*) and the guild of beersellers (*παρὰ τοῦ κοινοῦ τῶν ζυθοπωλῶν*), dated A.D. 338.

cipio del secolo XV (72 p., Bologna 1936). Gonippo Morelli: Le corporazioni romane di arti e mestieri dal XIII al XIX secolo (333 p., Roma 1937).

France. See my article on Etienne Boileau (XIII-2), who collected the Etablissements des métiers de Paris c. 1268. Alfred Franklin: Les corporations ouvrières de Paris du XIIe au XVIIIe siècle (Paris 1884). René de Lespinasse: Les métiers et corporations de Paris du XIVe au XVIIIe siècle (folio, 3 vols., Paris 1886–97). Etienne Martin Saint Léon (1860–): Histoire des corporations de métiers depuis leurs origines jusqu'à leur suppression en 1791 (681 p., Paris 1897; 2d ed., Paris 1909; 3d ed., 903 p., Paris 1922; 4th ed. posthumous, 588 p., Paris 1941). This last edition is identical with the third but for the critical bibliography by Emile Coornaert added to it (p. 557–67).

England. George Unwin: The guilds and companies of London (413 p., 37 ill., London 1908; 2d ed., London 1925). John Charles Thornley: The guilds of the city of London and their liverymen (498 p., London 1911). Frederick Armitage: The old guilds of England (230 p., London 1918). Stella Kramer: The English craft-guilds, their progress and decline (New York 1927).

Netherlands. Jules Huyttens: Recherches sur les corporations gantoises, notamment sur celles des tisserands et des foulons (240 p., Gand 1861). Herman Van der Linden: Les gildes marchandes dans les Pays-Bas au Moyen âge (Gand 1896). Guillaume Des Marez: L'organisation du travail à Bruxelles au XVe siècle (532 p., Bruxelles 1904).

Germany. Rudolf Wissell: Des alten Handwerks Recht und Gewohnheit (2 vols., Berlin 1929). Elisabet Thikötter: Die Zünfte Bremens im Mittelalter (Bremen 1930). Manfred Weider: Das Recht der deutschen Kaufmannsgilden des Mittelalters (540 p., Breslau 1931).

For Germanic and Scandinavian countries, see article Gilde (RGA 2, 253–58, 1914).

Switzerland. Werner Krebs: Alte Handwerksbräuche mit besonderer Berücksichtigung der Schweiz (322 p., 18 pl., Basel 1933). Werner Schnyder: Quellen zur Zürcher Zunftgeschichte, 13. Jahrh. bis 1798 (2 vols., 930 p., Zürich 1936).

Spain. Robert Sidney Smith: The Spanish guild merchant, a history of the consulado 1250–1700 (179 p., Durham, N.C., 1940).

Islamic guilds

The organization of the European guilds was semireligious; the amount of religious interests mixed with purely economic ones varied from time to time, from country to country, from place to place, from guild to guild. Similar guilds existed in Islamic countries, and were deeply permeated with religion and mysticism (taṣawwuf). Many of the darvishes were workingmen or craftsmen, and Islamic guilds were very closely associated with the orders of darvishes discussed in another chapter.

Islamic guildsmen are generally called in Arabic ahl al-ṭarīq (people of the road), and their knowledge is called 'ulūm al-ṭarīq (sciences of the road). Ṭarīqa (pl. ṭuruq), meaning the road, the way, is the technical name for a religious brotherhood, an order of darvishes. Hence you see that the two ideas of religious brotherhood and guild are very well combined. Similar ambiguities existed in the French compagnonnages (of very ancient, Oriental? origin), which survived the Revolution under various rival forms. One of the compagnonnages was patronized by Jacques de Molay, last grand master of the Templars. Similar parallelisms between arts and crafts and religion have been fostered also by the freemasons, but it would be out of place here to tell even briefly the history of the compagnonnages or of freemasonry.

To return to the Dār al-Islām, the system of guilds[18] was greatly stimulated by the growing urbanism during the 'Abbāsī caliphate, especially thanks to the Qarmaṭī propaganda, a mixture of socialism and mysticism (see Introd. 1, 593). That propaganda found a very fertile soil in 'Irāq during the first half of the tenth century, because of labor troubles in Baṣra and Baghdād and of anti-Arabic fermentation (shu'ūbīya; see Introd. vol. 1; EI 4, 395). Because of their Qarmaṭī origin, guilds flourished particularly well in Fāṭimī Egypt (909–1171). On the other hand, when the last Fāṭimī ruler was conquered by the Ayyūbī Ṣalāḥ al-dīn, in 1171, guilds fell under suspicion and disfavor, and were persecuted. Their peculiar organization continued, however, in Turkey, the Panjāb, Persia, Turkestān until the end of the last century. As that organization remained essentially the same for centuries in the Ottoman empire, the elaborate description of the guilds of Constantinople in the time of Murād IV (1623–40) given by Evliyā Čelebī (1611–c. 1680) helps us to understand mediaeval conditions.[19]

The earliest description (very brief) of Muslim guilds is to be found in the writings of the Brethren of Purity (X-2), Rasā'il ikhwān al-ṣafā', composed in Baṣra after 983. That description suggests Byzantine influences in addition to the Qarmaṭī ones. There are a number of catechisms of initiation, called in Arabic Kutub al-futūwa (Books of youthful generosity; EI 2, 123, 1914), in Turkish futuwwetnāme, which help us to understand the spirit of these religious fraternities of craftsmen. The degrees were ṣāni', muta'allim, khalīfa, finally mu'allim (master craftsman). The chief or syndic of the ṣinf was called naqīb (also pīr, 'arīf, amīn). The muḥtasib (inspector of markets) kept a close watch on the guilds, which were conservative organizations up to a certain point yet secreted revolutionary ferments. Treatises on ḥisba (q.v.) may include information on the aṣnāf.

The mention of futūwa suggests another filiation of guild ideas in Islām. The caliph al-Nāṣir lidīnillāh (ruled 1180–1225) granted the hereditary rank of futūwa to various men, the ceremonies of initiation including the putting on of a pair of trousers (sarāwīl al-futūwa, or libās al-futūwa) and drinking the knight's cup (ka's al-futūwa). Other members of al-Nāṣir's family had the right to grant the futūwa and even the khirqat al-taṣawwuf (the woolen robe of a ṣūfī, a kind of licentia docendi). Thus were new brotherhoods created. According to Ibn Baṭṭūṭa in his chapter on al-akhiyya al-fityān, such brotherhoods existed all over the country inhabited by Turks in Anatolia (al-bilād al-turkumāniyya al-rūmiyya); he was received in many of them (Defrémery 2, 260–65, 281, etc.) and describes the manners and dress of the members (fityān). Men belonging to the same trade or craft and other bachelors lived together in the same phalanstery (zāwiya); they helped one another and were hospitable to strangers.

Each postulant was instructed by a teacher (kabīr), and the group of postulants instructed by the same teacher was called ḥizb. Many aḥzāb formed a bait in charge of a wakīl; many buyūt assembled in their meeting house (manzil) for guild celebrations and the entertainment of strangers. The head of a manzil was called naqīb or turjamān (interpreter); indeed, he it was who interpreted all the technical terms. There were three initiation steps celebrated at general meetings, shirb, shadd, and takmīl. At the first, shirb (drinking), the apprentice drank with his

[18] In Arabic, ṣinf, pl. aṣnāf. The word ḥirfa, pl. ḥiraf, meaning "métier," is also used.

[19] Narrative of travels in Europe, Asia and Africa in the seventeenth century, by Evliya efendi. Translated from the Turkish by Joseph von Hammer (2 vols., London 1846–50; see vol. 1, part 2, 104–250). J. H. Mordtmann (EI 2, 33–34, 1913).

prospective brethren and was assigned to a kabīr; at the second, shadd (binding), he became a companion (rafīq); at the third, takmīl (completion), his initiation was completed and he was ceremoniously dressed with the sarāwīl al-futūwa.

It would seem that some forms of futūwa and also of taṣawwuf existed before the creation of the first darwīsh orders; it is possible that both led to that creation as well as to the creation of guilds. The same complex of influences (futūwa, taṣawwuf, aṣnāf) can easily be detected in the organization of the janissaries (Turkish, yeñi-cheri, new troops), the infantry created by the second 'Uthmānlī sulṭān, Urkhān (ruled 1326–60). These soldiers were soon affiliated to the Baktāshīya order; the names of their officers were taken from the various departments of the kitchen, and their main symbol was a great caldron (qazān) of bronze. See Cl. Huart (EI 2, 572–74, 1921).

Hermann Thorning: Beiträge zur Kenntnis des islamischen Vereinswesens auf Grund von Basṭ madad et-taufīq (Türkische Bibliothek, vol. 16, 288 p., Berlin 1913). Study based upon a guild tract called Basṭ madad al-taufīq fīmā yata'allaq bi aḥkām al-ṭarīq (Explanation of the Lord's help concerning the rules of the guild). Thorning's book contains a partial translation of the text, explanations, glossary, bibliography. Many studies on Islamic guilds (chiefly as they exist at present) have appeared in the Revue du monde musulman under the direction of Louis Massignon. E.g., Enquête sur les corporations musulmanes d'artisans et de commerçants au Maroc, avec des tableaux synoptiques et une bibliographie sommaire de l'histoire du travail en Islam (260 p., Paris 1925). See his summary with references (EI 4, 436, 1927). C. Van Arendonk: Futūwa (EI 2, 123, 1914).

Guilds in India

Hindu society is based on the existence of castes. Though castes are connected with occupations, they are very different from guilds.[20] Buddhism did not recognize castes, but allowed divisions of the people according to their occupations, and this led to the organization of groups similar to guilds in some respects. "Hinduism by adding occupational categories to already existing castes, assimilated the economic structure of Buddhism without destroying its own" (Halidé Edib: Inside India p. 250, London 1937). The Muslim invaders of India introduced their own corporative usages. Hence the Indian situation is extremely complex. There may be guilds of Buddhist or Muslim origin, purely Muslim guilds, also guilds within castes.

K. R. R. Sastry: South Indian gilds (54 p., ill., Madras 1925).

Chinese guilds

Guild organizations are very old in China. The main type is the kung so, associations of craftsmen of one kind for mutual protection. This type, which comes closest to the Western type of trade union, is traced back to the Han dynasty, and even to the Chou.

Another type, hui-kuan, is rather an association of fellow provincials in an alien province. It is traced back to the T'ang dynasty. In spite of the fact that the name means something like guild hall, this type does not correspond to the Western guild. Finally, there are in China associations of merchants comparable to the mediaeval hansa or to our modern chambers of commerce.

[20] Emile Senart (1847–1928): Les castes dans l'Inde. Les faits et le système (280 p., Paris 1896; reprinted Paris 1927; Englished London 1930).

These Chinese guilds should not be confused with the many secret societies, which are purely religious or political, and never restricted to any single craft or trade.

Couling (p. 123, 219, 501, 1917). John Stewart Burgess: The guilds of Peking (270 p., Columbia University Press, New York 1928). Hosea Ballou Morse: The gilds of China, with an account of the gild merchant or co-hong of Canton (100 p., New York 1909; 2d ed., 120 p., London 1932); the Cantonese co-hong dates only from 1720.

For the secret societies (ssŭ-hui) see J. J. M. De Groot: Sectarianism and religious persecution in China (2 vols., Verhandelingen der Konink. Akademie van Wetenschappen, Afdeeling Letterkunde, deel 4, c. 600 p., Amsterdam 1903–4). Ball (1926, 605–18). Lieut. Col. B. Fabvre: Les sociétés secrètes en Chine (222 p., Paris 1933), without Chinese characters. John C. De Korne: The fellowship of goodness (t'ung shan shê), a study in contemporary Chinese religion (109 typewritten pages, Grand Rapids, Mich. 1941; Isis 34, 67), study of a modern secret society, including information on ancient ones.

Japanese guilds

As I had no means of approaching the study of Japanese guilds, I applied to Dr. Shio Sakanishi, who answered kindly (May 27, 1941):

"In the early clan system of the eighth century, there was a unit called be which was composed of householders associated not by common ancestry, but usually by a common occupation, such as weaving, the making of tools, or the performance of religious rites. This be is often translated as 'guilds.' Their membership and their position in the group were hereditary. We have the Tanabe, guild of agricultural laborers, the Amabe, of fishermen, the Hasebe, of potters, and so on.

"The widespread warfare of the fourteenth century strengthened earlier trade guilds and similar organizations. Because the times were unsafe, merchants and artisans were obliged to cooperate in devising safeguards for their own interests. They usually placed themselves under the patronage of some powerful person or institution. For example, the cotton clothiers' guild was composed of parishioners of the powerful Gion shrine; the Tendai monastery on Mount Hiei was patron of the warehouse keepers. The paper makers of Kyōto were protected by the strong Bōjō, and the gold-leaf makers by the Konoe family. But with the centralized feudal bureaucracy after the fourteenth century, the trade guilds were gradually deprived of their liberties."

Particular inventions

After this necessary digression on the social aspect of labor—a digression which in spite of its length does hardly more than scratch the surface of an immense subject—we may now consider a few individual inventions. It will suffice to mention the compass, the mechanical clock, the earliest firearms, and Chinese typography, which have already been discussed in this volume, and spectacles, discussed in volume 2 (p. 1024–27). Practically all the tools used in the fourteenth century were discovered before; many, a long time before. Some improvements in design or construction may have been made in this period, but if so they are intangible.

I may recall the stimulating studies published by a retired French calvary officer, commandant Lefebvre des Noëttes. In one of them, L'attelage et le cheval de selle à travers les âges (2 vols., ill., Paris 1931; Isis 19, 300), he proved the inefficiency of animal power in antiquity and the enormous increase of that power in mediaeval times due to three coordinate inventions: the rigid horse collar, the metal horseshoe, and harnessing in file. In another book, De la marine antique à la marine moderne. La révolution du gouvernail, contribution à l'étude de l'esclavage (Paris 1935; Isis 26, 484–86), he claimed that the invention of the rudder caused a revolution of equal importance in maritime transportation. That second claim was not as well established as the first, because, important as the rudder was, it was possible to steer without it by means of a lateral oar or paddle, or better still by means of lateen sails, fore-and-aft rig, and other improvements in rigging. In any case, all these inventions were completed long before the fourteenth century. As shipbuilding was considerably developed in the twelfth and thirteenth centuries, it is possible that other improvements in ship design or rigging were made in our period, but we are unable to specify which and when.[21]

As textiles played a tremendous part in the economic history of Europe, we may wonder whether any improvements were made in spinning, weaving, fulling, or dyeing, but again I cannot think of any. Economic historians are agreed, however, that the use of linen increased considerably, so much so that the fourteenth century has been called "le siècle de la chemise" (Vanderkindere p. 390, 1879).[22] It is certain that the use of body linen and bed sheets increased enormously in the fourteenth century. This was one of the fruits of urbanism and of the urbanity that grew with it. The use of linen was pregnant with unforeseen consequences. The advantages to personal and public health are obvious, but not so obvious the fact that an abundance of rags led to the manufacture of rag paper and thus prepared the age of printing.[23] The incunabula were born in a cradle stuffed with linen! Who would have thought that the humble "chemise" helped to introduce the Renaissance?

The consideration of clothing suggests that the use of buttons, if it did not begin at about this time, at any rate became far more common. More people used them and more of them were used on each garment.[24]

It is time to stop this survey. It is clear enough that even an invention as simple as the use of buttons to fasten pieces of clothing might have unexpected consequences. It is equally clear that the history of such inventions is bound to be infinitely complex and to discourage the investigator and the reader alike by its endlessness and its vagueness.

Allow us one more example, which illustrates another endless group of possibilities. It would seem that table forks began to be used in the fourteenth century. To be sure, there are earlier examples quoted by Feldhaus (p. 347–50, 1914), but the forks which are the direct ancestors of our table forks were still a great novelty

[21] S. C. Gilfillan: Inventing the ship. A study of the inventions made in her history between floating log and rotor ship (294 p., 80 fig., Chicago 1935; Isis 24, 450–53).

[22] The word camisia (whence chemise is derived) is relatively old. See Ducange s.v. camisa, camisia. Words are of not much use, however, in such investigations. The name remains, but the thing changes. E.g., according to Ducange's Glossarium gallicum (p. 93, Paris 1850), chemise de Chartres meant a coat of mail.

[23] Luce (p. 79, 1876). The whole chapter "La vie privée au XIVe siècle" is very interesting. Luce shows that before the Black Death and the Hundred Years' War (1337–1453) France was remarkably prosperous, and that luxury in clothing was never greater. The main glory of the age was the generalized use of linen; its main turpitude, the cruelty and immorality of feudal justice.

[24] A. Parent: Le bouton à travers les âges (Paris 1935). Not seen by me, but quoted by L. White (p. 148, 1940).

at the beginning of the fourteenth century. They were real luxuries and treated as such. In 1321, a goldsmith of Avignon, named Pelegrin, made two forks for the pope's individual use (Brun p. 209, 1928). Fancy forks of silver and gold, sometimes adorned with precious stones, were used to eat figs or to toast cheese. Gradually more forks were made and cheaper ones, and their use was generalized; this took a very long time, however.[25] The invention of forks was a social as well as a technical one.

With the exception of a short section on Oriental guilds, this chapter has dealt only with Western technology. If the history of Western development is tantalizing because of the lack of definite information, the history of Asiatic technology is doubly so.

I have spoken in volume 2 (p. 1034) of the Muslim engineers who were taken into the service of Cathay during the Yüan dynasty. Some of them lived until the fourteenth century. A-lao-wa-ting died in 1312, and was succeeded by his son Ma-ha-sha; I-ssŭ-ma-yin died in 1330 (?) and was succeeded by his son Ya-ku.

We do not know exactly what these men did in the Mongol service, but they certainly helped to transmit Muslim (and perhaps other Western) ideas to China.

A model study of the Chinese tools was published recently by Rudolf P. Hommel: China at work (quarto, 378 p., Doylestown, Penna. 1937; Isis 31, 219). It is based on a collection made by the author in China, and thus represents the tools used today, yet we may be sure that many of them were already used under the Yüan dynasty and even in earlier times. As it is, it may help us to visualize the life of Chinese farmers and artisans in the fourteenth century.

12. *Musical Theories*

A. *In the Latin West*

The history of Western music, that is, our music, is much easier to write than that of the other arts and crafts because there is an abundant literature explaining its progress from century to century. This is due to old traditions of musical learning and to the fact that music was considered from the beginning a branch of mathematics. The Pythagoraean Archytas of Tarentum (IV-1 B.C.), speaking of the mathematicians (*οἱ περὶ τὰ μαθήματα*), remarked, "They have handed down to us clear knowledge about the speed of the stars, their risings and settings, and about geometry, arithmetic and sphaerics, and not least, about music; for these branches of knowledge (*μαθήματα*) seem to be sisters."[26] Music continued to be a part of the quadrivium throughout the Middle Ages, and thus enjoyed the status of a science as well as of an art. The Pythagorean ideas of the harmony of the spheres and of harmonic progressions were transmitted by Plato, and to the Christian world by the Wisdom of Solomon (I-1 B.C.)[27] and later by Boetius (VI-1). Boetius distinguished three kinds of musica: mundana, harmony of the macrocosmos; humana, harmony of the microcosmos; and instrumentalis, music proper.[28] We are concerned here, however, only with musica instrumentalis.

In spite of many dated treatises, authentic scores, and the survival of not a few

[25] The earliest quotation in OED (s.v. fork, p. 455) is dated 1463.

[26] Hermann Diels: Die Fragmente der Vorsokratiker (1^3, 330, 1912), translated by Heath (1, 11, 1921).

[27] "Thou hast ordered all things in measure and number and weight" (11:20).

[28] Isis 34, 182. Manfred B. Bukofzer: Speculative thinking in mediaeval music (Speculum 17, 165–80, 1942).

of the instruments described in mediaeval texts, the historian's path is made arduous by many difficulties and pitfalls. The main difficulty is to determine to what extent musical practice preceded musical theory. Did it always precede it?

Another difficulty concerns the origins of the new music (ars nova). Was it due to Muslim influence? This has been discussed in volume 2 (p. 24–26 and passim), and we need not discuss it any longer, for the Muslim influences were much anterior to the fourteenth century.[29] At the beginning of that century the ars nova was already well established both in practice and in theory, but that century witnessed its blossoming out. If the production of the six-part canon "Sumer is icumen in" (Introd. 2, 634) in England c. 1240 is a landmark in the history of polyphonic music, the compositions of Guillaume de Machaut constitute another one of equal moment.

The best proof that polyphony was used, and even abused, in the church services is given us by the famous bull of John XXII, dated 1322 (or 1324/25). In that bull the pope forbade not only the addition of motetus and triplum parts to the plain song, but practically all kinds of polyphony. On special occasions, that is on high festivals, one might add consecutive fourths, fifths, and octaves, but the plain song must always be heard. Musicians could not be completely repressed, however, and they tried new experiments such as faburden and gymel. I give the English terms, for these innovations seem to have come from England. Faburden (faux-bourdon) was a type of polyphony in which the upper and middle voices moved chiefly in parallel sixths and thirds above the lower one; gymel (gemellum) "appears to have been a plan for inverting intervals . . . it was concerned with the doctoring of consecutive thirds into sixths. The upper singer read the lower part but transposed it up an octave."[30]

The musical instinct of our ancestors led them irresistibly to polyphony and to harmony—to vertical vs. horizontal writing. The church exerted in this field as in others a moderating influence, without which music might have degenerated into a kind of mediaeval jazz, and the masterpieces of Palestrinian music might have been sidetracked.

To return to musical theories, the most significant fact is their wide dispersion. The ars nova was a European efflorescence, its advocates are to be found not in a single country, but simultaneously in many, Italy, England, the Pays de Liége, and last but not least in France. Does this not prove conclusively that it realized not a personal need, but a social one? We are left with a final impression not of individual theorists trying to guide music according to their own wishes, but of music itself fulfilling its natural growth.

A comparative study of all these writings would be too heavy a task, not sufficiently germane to our purpose to be justified here and now. It will suffice to recall to the reader's mind the leading masters. In Italy, it was Marchetto of

[29] The protagonist of the theory of Muslim influence on Spanish music was Julian Ribera y Tarrago (1858–1934), who showed that the Cantigas de Santa María of Don Alfonso el Sabio (XIII-2), the music of which had been preserved, represented a very rich collection of Arabian music, vocal and instrumental, as it existed in the second half of the thirteenth century. Ribera developed his views in La música de las cantigas (folio, 502 p., Madrid 1922). Abridged translation by Eleanor Hague and Marion Leffingwell (302 p., Stanford University 1929; Isis 34, 46). See also Ribera's Disertaciones y opúsculos (2, 3–174, Madrid 1928; Isis 12, 161–63), for an extension of the same methods to the study of troubadour and Minnesänger music.

[30] Cecil Forsyth in Charles Villiers Stanford and Forsyth's History of music (p. 140, New York 1930).

Padua, who flourished at the beginning of the century and wrote the Lucidarium in arte musicae planae (1274, revised c. 1309) and the Pomerium in arte musicae mensuratae (after 1309). In England, there were two outstanding teachers of music: the Benedictine Walter Odington of Evesham, who wrote the Speculatio musices and practiced what he taught (he illustrated his treatise with examples of his own composition); and Robert de Handlo, who wrote a learned commentary on the theories of Franco of Cologne (XII-2). This may help us in reconstructing the growth of mensural music. The encyclopaedic-minded Engelbert of Admont discussed musical questions. Hugo Spechtshart of Reutlingen paraphrased the teachings of Guido of Arezzo (XI-1); his Flores musicae is rather in the nature of a countercurrent to the novelties. That is why I did not name Austria and Germany above in the list of countries where the ars nova grew during this period; I have no evidence that it did.

But let us pass to the Pays de Liége and France, where the new art prospered exceedingly. The Pays de Liége is important because of the mysterious Jacques de Liége, to whom the Speculum musices is now ascribed (c. 1330). This is one of the most important treatises of the age in spite of its being rather conservative. The mathematician Jean de Meurs, who was formerly praised for that very treatise, wrote many others and experimented with new instruments which foreshadowed the clavichord. Though the Speculum musices was written in Liége, it might be credited to the French school, for Jacques de Liége was a pupil of Pierre de la Croix in Paris. The French school is sufficiently vindicated, however, by the greatest musical theorist of the age, Philip of Vitry, bishop of Meaux. Philip was a composer as well as a theorist, but unfortunately his compositions are lost. The theories of this famous exponent of the ars nova, however, are abundantly and most beautifully illustrated by the compositions of his fellow Champenois, the poet Guillaume de Machaut. In his French poems Machaut listed many of the instruments used in his day. This suggests that the study of the contemporary theories should be completed with an investigation of the instruments which musicians were playing on and with, but I must leave that very difficult task to others.

The names of Marchetto, Odington, Jacques de Liége, Jean de Meurs, Vitry, and Machaut evoke a period of intense musical fermentation.

B. *Byzantine music*

The lower substrata of Byzantine and Latin music are the same, to wit, Greek, Jewish, Syrian; but on account of the growing estrangement of the Orthodox and Catholic churches and of the increasing hostility between Greeks and Latins, the musical development of either group was largely independent from that of the other. Thus was a gigantic experiment instituted, the results of which are of deep interest to the philosophically minded historian.

One of the fundamental difficulties in the study of Western music is to determine the extent of the Muslim influences, if any, on the growth of organum and descant, and on all the novelties of the ars nova. That kind of difficulty does not worry the student of Byzantine music, which remained more faithful to its origins, more conservative in every way. Islamic influences may have operated on Byzantine and Balkanic folksongs, but much later, and we need not consider these here.[31]

[31] A deeper study of the folksongs might reveal earlier influences than we are aware of now, not only in the Balkans and the Islands, but also in Asia Minor, e.g., in Trebizond. Samuel Baud-Bovy: La chanson populaire grecque du Dodécanèse. I, Les textes (Institut néohellénique de l'Université de Paris, vol. 3, 408 p., Paris 1936).

Even if the Orthodox had heard of the musical experiments of the Roman church, they could not have been influenced by them, except negatively. That is, any novelty accepted or approved by the Catholic hierarchy or laity would have been ipso facto obnoxious to them. The outstanding Byzantine instrument was the organ, which did not lend itself easily to innovations.[32] Their church songs remained monodic.

The connection between Greek and Byzantine music was never broken. The leading Byzantine theorists were very well acquainted with the treatises of the classical age and with Greek prosody,[33] so much so that their commentaries are valuable today for the interpretation of the ancient texts.

The study of musical theories in the fourteenth century may be begun with the Tetrabiblon of Georgios Pachymeres (XIII-2, Introd. 2, 972), who lived until c. 1310. The Tetrabiblon is so called because it deals with the four branches of mathematics (the quadrivium). In the introduction Pachymeres explains, after Plato (Laws, end of book XIII), the deep cohesion of those four branches which constitute together the basis of philosophy. He divides the four branches, curiously enough, into two groups dealing respectively with continuous quantities (geometry, astronomy) and with discontinuous ones (arithmetic, music). The fourth part of the Tetrabiblon is a treatise on Greek music. At about the same time as Pachymeres or a little later, Joannes Pediasimos wrote a brief justification of the numerical names given to musical intervals. Still another musician flourishing under the same emperor, Andronicos II (ruled 1282–1328), was Manuel Bryennios, author of the latest Byzantine treatise on music. His Harmonica, partly derived from Pachymeres, and in any case depending on the same Greek sources, is a very elaborate treatise, which is remarkable because it does not profess to teach anything new (as do the contemporary Latin treatises), but on the contrary reaffirms and re-explains the doctrines of the ancients. It is typical that for Bryennios the musical past was divided into three periods (see first section of his treatise), pre-Pythagorean, Pythagorean, and post-Pythagorean; there was for him no essential discontinuity between the time of Aristoxenos (IV-2 B.C.) and his own.

A younger contemporary of these three, the greatest scholar of the age of the Palaeologoi, Nicephoros Gregoras, carried the cult of antiquity even farther in that he tried to complete the musical treatise which Ptolemy had left unfinished. His reconstruction was criticized by his rival Barlaam.

All these writings are severely technical, and though they are little more than reflections of ancient Greek music, they leave out one aspect of the latter which is probably expressed in philosophical books of the same period, that is, the ethical aspect. Plato ascribed to music a ruling power over the building up of character. According to him and to his followers, there is inherent in music a certain morality (ἦθος), which may be transmitted to individuals and to society. The ancient Greeks distinguished between good music and bad music, but not at all as we do. Certain modes they thought were better suited than others for the inculcation of virtue. The educational value of good music is supreme. It should be noted that this ethical theory of music was almost completely forgotten in the Latin West. The Roman church recognized the value of music as an instrument to achieve good purposes, but it did not consider that music could be (morally) good

[32] No Byzantine instrumental music has come down to us.

[33] This is important, because the musical rhythm was based on the poetical rhythm. The prosodic "foot" was comparable to our "bar" or "measure."

in itself. On the other hand, a theory very similar to the Platonic theory had been developed by Confucius (VI B.C.) and exerted a deep influence on Chinese rites and education.[34] This coincidence between Greek and Chinese thinking is the more remarkable because Greek and Chinese music are otherwise as different as it is possible to be.[35]

In my discussion of Byzantine and Latin music, I have left entirely out of account the very important subject of notation. This was unavoidable, because musical palaeography is so technical a subject that it can hardly be summarized. Moreover, its connection with musical theory is not sufficiently close to warrant discussion in this place. To put it otherwise, for the investigator of Byzantine music, palaeography is absolutely fundamental, but the student of Byzantine thought need not worry over much about it.

For the study of Byzantine music, see Stephen Georgeson Hatherly: A treatise on Byzantine music (quarto, 168 p., London 1892), with many musical specimens. Georgios Ioannes Papadopulos: Ἱστορικὴ ἐπισκόπησις τῆς βυζαντινῆς ἐκκλησιαστικῆς μουσικῆς ἀπὸ τῶν ἀποστολικῶν χρόνων μέχρι τῶν καθ' ἡμᾶς (Athens 1904). Mme Melpo Mercier: Etudes sur la musique byzantine. Le premier mode et son plagal (Bibliothèque musicale du Musée Guimet, vol. 2, 66 p., Paris 1935; printed 1931–32, dated 1935, published 1936). Reese (p. 57–94, 1940).

The most valuable collection of documents has been published in Copenhagen since 1935 under the auspices of the Union académique internationale, Monumenta musicae byzantinae, edited by Carsten Höeg, H. J. W. Tillyard, Egon Wellesz, in four series: (I) Principal series, quarto. Facsimiles of MSS. Vol. 1, Sticherarium (1935) (a στιχηράριον is a list for the ecclesiastic year of the στιχηρά[36] or short hymns sung after each day's στίχος or verse of the Psalter or of the nine odes); vol. 2, Hirmologium (εἰρμολόγιον)[37] Athoum (1938). (II) Subsidia, octavo.

[34] The Chinese idea was beautifully expressed by Ssŭ-ma Ch'ien (II-2 B.C.): "He who knows music is close to the rites. To know music and rites means to possess virtue," quoted by W. Hartner (Isis 29, 72, 1938).

[35] Chinese music will not be discussed here, because I am not aware of any progress in it in the fourteenth century. It is true, a modification of the pentatonic scale had been accomplished under Kublai Khān (XIII-2); I do not know of any musical treatise of the first half of the fourteenth century. The first Western study on Chinese music was that of the Jesuit father Joseph Marie Amiot (1718–93): Mémoire sur la musique des Chinois, tant anciens que modernes (Pékin 1776), included in the Mémoires concernant les Chinois (Paris 1776–89; vol. 6). Later writings, J. A. Van Aalst: Chinese music (88 p., Shanghai 1884; reprinted 1933). Georges Soulié: La musique en Chine (119 p., Paris 1911). Maurice Courant: Essai historique sur la musique classique des Chinois, avec un appendice relatif à la musique coréenne (Encyclopédie de la musique d'Albert Lavignac 1, 77–241, Paris 1913), very elaborate, with Chinese characters. Couling (p. 385–90, 1917). John Hazedel Levis: Foundations of Chinese musical art (246 p., Peiping 1936). Willy Hartner: Some notes on Chinese musical art (Isis 29, 72–94, 1938). R. H. van Gulik: The lore of the Chinese lute, an essay on ch'in ideology (Monumenta nipponica, 250 p., 9 fig., 16 pl., Sophia University, Tokyo 1940; Bull. Ecole française d'Extrême Orient 40, 460). For Japanese music, especially as contrasted with Chinese music, see the review by Yoshio Mikami (Isis 4, 77–81, 1921), based on the Japanese memoirs of S. Kanetsune (Tokyo 1912) and H. Tanabe (Tokyo 1919). For Korean music see Courant (1913) and Mrs. J. L. Boots: Korean musical instruments and an introduction to Korean music (Transactions of the Korea branch of the Royal Asiatic Society 30, 1–31, Seoul 1940).

[36] τὸ στιχηρόν = τὸ τῆς ἡμέρας τροπάριον = the day's modulation.

[37] The Greek church has from the earliest times added to the Psalter nine canticles (ᾠδαί) extracted from the Bible, to wit, Exodus 15:1–19; Deuteronomy 32:1–47; I Samuel 2:1–10; Habakkuk 3:2–19; Isaiah 26:9–20; Jonah 2:3–10; Daniel 3:26–51; Daniel 3:52–88; Luke 1:46–55, 68–79. Special hymns called canons are adapted to these canticles. Each canon (κανών) includes a certain number of versets (τροπάρια), and all the versets of a given canon belong

Vol. 1, Tillyard: Handbook of the middle Byzantine notation; Höeg: La notation ekphonétique (1935). (III) Transcripta, octavo. Vol. 1, Wellesz: Die Hymnen des Sticherarium für September (1936); vol. 2, Tillyard: idem for November (1938); vol. 3, Tillyard: Hymns of the octoechus[38] (1940). (IV) Lectionaria, octavo. Vol. 1, Höeg and Günther Zuntz: Prophetologium (1939–40). The continuation of this great effort has been interrupted by the German invasion of Denmark.

C. *Muslim music*

Muslim interest in the theory and practice of music is proved by the publication of various writings, such as didactic poems on melodies by Muḥammad al-Khaṭīb al-Irbilī and by al-Dhahabī, the treatise on the science of music and the knowledge of melodies by the latter's son, Ibn al-Ṣabbāḥ, and a treatise on melodies and rhythms by Ibn Karā. Unfortunately, the most important by far of these writings, an elaborate commentary on the Kitāb al-adwār of Ṣafī al-dīn, is difficult to place. I am inclined to credit it to the Persian philosopher and astronomer Shams al-dīn Mīrak, but Farmer (no. 241, 1940) would ascribe it to another Persian, al-Jurjānī (XIV-2). It is certainly a work of the fourteenth century, but may belong to the second half rather than the first. It is valuable, because it includes a large mass of detailed information and because it continues the main tradition of Islamic music, which had been brought to a first climax by al-Fārābī (X-1) and to a second one by Ṣafī al-dīn (XIII-2). Moreover, it is easy to study it in baron d'Erlanger's corpus, La musique arabe (vol. 3, Paris 1938; Isis 30, 334).

To these Arabic writings might be added the Rabāb-nāma (Book of the rabāb),[39] composed in West Turkish in 1301 by Sulṭān Walad, son of the illustrious Jalāl al-dīn-i-Rūmī (XIII-2). Of course, this is simply poetry, but for the Muslims poetry and music were intimately connected. These poems were meant to be sung with the accompaniment of a rabāb. To be sure, a good many Arabic books would deserve to be quoted on the same ground as the Rabāb-nāma. Let this one stand as a representative of all the others.

In addition to the technical writings and to the books of poetry, there is still a large class of writings on music which we owe to theologians discussing whether listening to music is licit or not. I have already mentioned some of these theological-musical writings (Introd. 2, 26); to begin with, a whole chapter of the Iḥyā 'ulūm al-dīn of al-Ghazzālī (XI-2). In our period, I came across four of them, by Ibn al-Firkāḥ, al-Adfuwī, Ibn Qayyim al-Jawzīya, and al-Yāfi'ī. All of them belonged to the Shāfi'ī school of religious law, except Ibn Qayyim, who was a Ḥanbalī.

The idea of the more austere doctors was that music was a snare of the world

---

to the same musical mode, and have the same metrical structure and the same melody. If one knows the melody of the first verset, called hirm (εἱρμός), one can sing the whole canon from a text containing no musical notation. The tradition of the canons is thus double. Some books give the full text of the canons with every troparion but without music, others give only the hirms with music. These latter are called hirmologia (εἱρμολόγια). The hirmologion of Mount Athos (Cod. monast. Hiberorum 470, not posterior to c. 1150) is particularly precious.

[38] Ὀκτάηχος, book containing the troparia or modulations for weekdays and ordinary Sundays; also called παρακλητική.

[39] In Introd. 2, 874, I called it book of the rebec, which was misleading. The rabāb is one of the earliest Arabic string instruments. The rebec, a string instrument used in the Christian West, was different from the flat-chested rabāb used in the East; it derived from the Arabic 'ūd (lute) and was more like the Moorish vault-chested rabāb. Francesco Salvador Daniel (1831–71): Music and musical instruments of the Arab, translated with notes by Henry George Farmer (p. 229–37, London 1915).

and of the devil, a cause of danger to a man's salvation. It should be noted that such a fear of music is the best proof that the Muslim people loved music or were at least highly susceptible to it.[40] Of course, the allurements of music could not be separated from those of poetry and of the dance, for the three arts were closely interrelated.

It is very curious to compare the reactions of different human groups to music. The Greeks and Chinese considered it an essential part of education—an essential part also of the good life. Western Christians used music as a ritual means of leading men to God; they thought that music was not good in itself, but only in so far as it could be used for good purposes. Finally, the more puritanical of the Muslims feared music, and permitted the use of it, if they permitted it at all, only under special conditions. In short, for the Greeks and Chinese music was good; for the Catholics, it was indifferent; for the austere Muslims (as for some of our Protestants later on), it was dangerous.[41]

The Muslim attitude was due to the austerity, exclusiveness, and totalitarian nature of their religion, not to ignorance of the Greek arguments. Indeed, al-Fārābī was well acquainted with these, and every Muslim theorist of music began his education with the writings of al-Fārābī. Moreover, the Arabic musicians accepted the Greek premise that every chord or mode (shadd, pl. shudūd) has a certain effect upon the soul; one chord will "expand" it and generate pleasure and courage, another will "contract" it and cause sadness and languor, etc.[42] Their religion made it impossible for them to accept the Greek conclusion. From their point of view, music was at best a means of amusement and relaxation; education was the task and privilege of religious doctors, not of musicians.

Muslims were agreed with the Greeks and the Chinese, however, in recognizing relations between musical chords and other physical phaenomena. The "music of the spheres" was not with any of them an idle metaphor. Byzantine treatises on music contain many astronomical parallels. Similar comparisons appeared early in Arabic literature, e.g., in al-Kindī (IX-1), and were naturally exploited by the astrologers. The best example of astrological music in our period was a treatise wherein 'Abd al-'Azīz ibn Sarāyā al-Ḥillī explained how to compose melodies in harmony with the zodiac.

In the course of writing this summary I was surprised to discover that every author mentioned by me is an Easterner. This is not the result of any parti pris. It so happened that the only treatises which drew my attention were written in the East. It would be unwise to conclude that musical theories did not interest the Moorish authors any more; nevertheless, if their interest had been greater, it would have manifested itself in the kind of treatises that could not be overlooked. There is at least one aspect of the subject in which their 'ulamā' could not fail to be

[40] Additional proof of Muslim susceptibility to music was given by H. G. Farmer: Music, the priceless jewel (Journal of the Royal Asiatic Society, 1941, p. 22–30, 127–44), being translated extracts from Al-'iqd al-farīd, an anthology collected by the Cordovan poet Abū 'Umar Aḥmad ibn Muḥammad ibn 'Abd Rabbihi (860–940). Ibn 'Abd Rabbihi was defending music against the puritans. See also Farmer's study on The music of the Arabian Nights (Journal of the Royal Asiatic Society, 1944, p. 172–85; 1945, p. 39–60, 2 pl.).

[41] The perils of musical sensuality were realized by some Catholic doctors, notably St. Augustine (V-1), in his Confessions (book X, 33, "Voluptates aurium tenacius me implicaverant"). As to the Protestants, Luther was favorable to music, but not so Zwingli, and Calvin was decidedly antagonistic. These questions are well discussed by P. H. Láng (p. 207 f., 256 f., 1941).

[42] See the commentary on the Kitab al-adwār mentioned above. Erlanger (3, 543–50, 1938).

interested, no matter what the torpor of their minds might be; namely, the licitness or illicitness of music. Such a topic would be sure to arouse them. As a matter of fact, Henry George Farmer, to whom we owe so many studies on Arabic music, has investigated a tract Kitāb al-imtā' wal-intifā' fi mas'alat samā' al-samā' (The book of joy and profit on the question of listening to music), written in April 1301, by one Muḥammad ibn Ibrāhīm al-Shalāḥī. The tract is noteworthy, because al-Shalāḥī had been carried away by his subject to the extent of giving a very interesting list of musical instruments.[43]

VIII. CHEMISTRY

1. *Alchemical Traditions*

The study of the chemical or alchemical literature is very difficult, because in addition to its hermetic nature, which it shares with astrological writings, it is generally undated and often undatable. Internal evidence which enables one to date many astrological writings is of little help for the alchemical ones, and we must often be satisfied with the determination of termini a quo and ad quem too widely separated to be very useful. By the end of the thirteenth century, and the beginning of the fourteenth, a number of Latin treatises were reflecting and diffusing Arabic knowledge. Some were of a purely philosophical nature, like the Tabula smaragdina and the Turba philosophorum; others were a little more practical, like the De compositione alchimiae ascribed to Khālid ibn Yazīd, the Liber claritatis ascribed to Jābir, the Secreta secretorum and the De aluminibus et salibus ascribed to al-Rāzī, the Liber sacerdotum, the Magisterium of Michael Scot (XIII-1).[1] The most important of these writings was the Summa perfectionis ascribed to Jābir (or Geber). Whether apocryphal or anonymous, it is certain that these Latin treatises were derived directly or indirectly from Arabic models. In many cases the Arabic origin is made obvious by strange Latin phrases which any Arabist will recognize at once as the equivalents of Arabic idioms or the expression of Arabic conceits.[2] The Arabic originals may have been inspired to some extent by ancient Greek models, yet no Greek text (of the proper kind) has thus far been discovered. The Greek influences to which the Arabic alchemists were exposed were probably of the vaguest nature.

An analysis of the Summa perfectionis will be found in volume 2 (p. 1043–44). The tradition of the other writings just mentioned has been studied with great perspicacity by Julius Ruska. For the Tabula smaragdina, see Isis 9, 375–77; for the Compositio alchemiae, Isis 13, 221; for the Turba philosophorum, Isis 20, 302–5; for the Liber claritatis, Isis 24, 207; for the Secreta secretorum of al-Rāzī, Isis 25, 189–90; 27, 506–7; for the De aluminibus et salibus ascribed to the same, Isis 25, 144–45; for the apocryphal literature bearing his name, Osiris 7, 31–94; for the Liber sacerdotum, Isis 27, 125. For Jābir, see the elaborate work of the late Paul Kraus (1904–44): Jābir ibn Ḥayyān. Contribution à l'histoire des idées

[43] H. G. Farmer: A Maghribī work on musical instruments (Journal of the Royal Asiatic Society, 1935, p. 339–53; Isis 24, 480). Following Casiri, I had placed that writer in (XIII-1); see Introd. 2, 633. If Farmer's dating is correct, al-Shalāḥī belongs to the beginning of the fourteenth century.

[1] Edited by Charles H. Haskins: The alchemy ascribed to M. Scot (Isis 10, 350–59, 1928), and by Dorothea W. Singer (Isis 13, 5–15, 1929).

[2] E.g., in the Turba philosophorum occurs the sentence "Dico tamen quod Deus unus est nunquam genuit nec genitus est," which is derived from the Sūrat al-ikhlāṣ (no. 112, 1).

scientifiques dans l'Islam (quarto, 2 vols., Mémoires présentés à l'Institut d'Egypte, vol. 44, 280 p., vol. 45, 420 p., Le Caire 1943–42; Isis 35, 213–17). The same Kraus published a biography of his master Julius Ruska (b. 1867) and a discussion of the latter's investigations with full bibliography (Osiris 5, 5–40, 1938).

These Latin writings of Arabic origin are interesting to compare with other Latin writings wherein Arabic influences are scarcer or have not been detected at all. I am now referring to some of the writings ascribed to Michael Scot, Vincent of Beauvais, Albert the Great,[3] Roger Bacon, etc. It is possible, however, that a deeper investigation of these texts by Arabists would reveal Arabic influences which have escaped the attention of Latinists. We should not forget that some Arabic treatises were available in Latin before the thirteenth century, and that it was thus possible to drink Arabic knowledge from Latin vessels, perhaps without being aware of it or without being able to avoid it. The Compositio alchemiae had been translated by Robert of Chester (XII-1) in 1144, the Emerald table by Hugh of Santalla (XII-1), the De aluminibus by Gerard of Cremona (XII-2); the chemical part of the Kitāb al-shifā' of Ibn Sīnā was translated about the turn of the twelfth century by Alfred of Sareshel (XIII-1). This last-named treatise was particularly influential. Avicenna's opinions are quoted in almost every Latin treatise of the thirteenth century or later. Consider, e.g., the short Tractatus de metallis et alchimia included in the Fritz Paneth MS dating from the first quarter of the fourteenth century (see Isis 13, 433, 498).[4]

In his great work on Magic and science (vol. 3, ch. 3, 1934), Thorndike refers to various other Latin writings, possibly anterior to the fourteenth century, which are either anonymous or ascribed to enigmatic authors. To wit, the treatise addressed by Rosinus (corruption of Zosimos?) to Euthesia; tracts by Alfidius (Alphidius), Rodianus (Rudianus), Senior, Gratian the Alchemist, who wrote a commentary on the Turba philosophorum and a treatise super lapidem philosophicum componendum. Then there is the Liber compostella multorum experimentorum veritatis ascribed to the Franciscan Bonaventura de Iseo of Brescia, who composed it in the monastery of the Brethren of St. Mary in Venice, and the Liber Platonis de XIII clavibus sapientie maioris translatus de arabico in latinum A.D. 1301.

In other words, there was available in Latin at the beginning of the fourteenth century an abundance of writings derived directly or indirectly from Arabic writings, but it should be noted that the Arabic writings thus represented were all of them anterior to the thirteenth century, and some of them much anterior to that century. Later Arabic writings failed to be translated. Hence after 1300 Arabic and Latin alchemy must be considered as continuing their development independently, though on the basis of a common (Arabic) stock.

The fourteenth century witnessed a high production of Latin alchemical treatises, many of which were arbitrarily ascribed to such illustrious authors as Vincent of Beauvais (d. 1264), Thomas Aquinas (d. 1274), Albert the Great (d. 1280), Alfonso el Sabio (d. 1284), John of Meung (d. 1305), Duns Scot (d. 1308), Arnold of Villanova (d. 1311), and Ramon Lull (d. 1315). The three last-named authors died after the beginning of the fourteenth century, hence some chemical writings bearing their names may have been composed by them in our century. The proba-

[3] Pearl Kibre: An alchemical treatise attributed to Albertus Magnus (Isis 35, 1945). Apropos of the treatise beginning "Calistenus [Callisthenes?] unus de antiquioribus post Hermetem artis nostre inventoribus dicit." Text with long introduction.

[4] One must bear in mind, however, that the Avicennian alchemy was largely apocryphal. Julius Ruska: Die Alchemie des Avicenna (Isis 21, 14–51, 1934).

bility that all these writings are apocryphal, however, is very large. Lull was obviously the favorite of the fourteenth-century chemical pseudographers, and no less than eighty writings were ascribed to him; so much so that the words "Lullian art" or "Lullian philosophy" acquired alchemical implications.

The alchemical writings are very obscure, because the subject itself was obscure and the early chemists could not help groping in the dark. Their differentiation of substances was very crude, but we should bear in mind that it was still crude enough in the mind of Robert Boyle, and that the fundamentals of chemistry were cleared up only at the end of the eighteenth century. Even when the early students refined their experiments up to the limit of their technical means, they could not understand what they were doing nor repeat exactly the circumstances which they described. They were obliged to postulate the existence of various kinds of mercury and sulphur, because their own samples might vary considerably. Modern chemists will be more likely to overestimate these difficulties than the opposite, for they know well enough how hard it is to obtain pure substances and how deeply the properties of each can be modified even by the smallest impurities. The unavoidable obscurity was increased because of the sense of secrecy and mystery dominating the minds of the early experimenters, and in many cases because of their own confusion and ignorance. And alas! this is not all. To the natural and artificial obscurities could be added but too often ominous suggestions of negromancy, nefariousness, and nefandousness. Some of those alchemists, it must be admitted, were nothing but charlatans and rascals, to whom the darkness was a welcome camouflage.

It is not surprising, then, that the church was frightened by their activities and took umbrage at them. About the year 1317 John XXII issued a decretal (not a bull) "de crimine falsi," wherein alchemy was forbidden and alchemists as well as their abettors were ordered punished. That decretal has been repeatedly quoted with disapproval by anticlerical writers who did not take the trouble to read it. For example, White spoke of it (1, 384, 1896) as having dealt a terrible blow to the beginnings of chemical science. As a matter of fact the decretal Spondent[5] was directed not against legitimate alchemy (or chemistry), but only against the gold makers promising riches to others; they were ordered to forfeit to the poor as much gold and silver as they had produced; if they were contumacious and went so far as to coin counterfeit money from alchemical gold or silver, their goods should be confiscated and themselves considered as criminals and excommunicated. All considered, John XXII should be praised rather than blamed for having issued that decree against men whose purpose was evil and dangerous, even if they honestly believed in their power to make gold out of base metals. I may recall that the same pope issued a few years later the bull Super illius specula, condemning magical practices or the reading of books on magic.[6] There can be no doubt that John XXII was fighting not science, but superstition and the exploitation of superstitious minds by swindlers. Unfortunately there are so many greedy men, even among princes and popes, that persuasive swindlers could always obtain the patronage they needed, and therefore John's decretal was not very efficacious. The golden days of alchemical imposture were yet to come. As to chemistry itself,

[5] Corpus universi iuris canonici. Extravagantes Ioannis XXII. I have used the Francfort edition (4, 548, 1586). "Spondent" is the first word of that decretal; "De crimine falsi" is a kind of title given to it by editors.

[6] Walsh (p. 146 f., 1913). The book contains Latin and English texts of the bull, and also of the decretal quoted before.

the decretal did not stop it and did not mean to stop or to slow it up in any way; there were then already a sufficient number of legitimate fields of research for honest chemists.

2. *Treatises on Colors*

The most popular of these fields was the study of pigments, oils, varnishes, and siccatives for the sake of painters and decorators, of whom the church, be it noted, was the main employer. This was not by any means a new field, and its literature had old traditions. Leaving out of account Hellenistic treatises, remember the Compositiones ad tingenda (VIII-2);[7] the Mappae clavicula (VIII-2); the books of Heraclius (X-2) de coloribus et artibus Romanorum; the De clarea, by the Bernese anonym;[8] the Diversarum artium schedula, by Theophile the Priest (XII-1); finally, closer to our period, the Liber de coloribus faciendis, by Peter of Saint Omer (XIII-2), and the Portuguese treatise written in Hebrew script by Abraham ben Judah ibn Ḥayyim (XIII-2). This written tradition was probably of much less importance than the spoken or manual one. Indeed, considering the inarticulateness of the average artist, and his tendency to hide his successful tricks rather than broadcast them, the number of treatises echeloned from the eighth century to the thirteenth is very remarkable.

The literary tradition continued with greater force in the fourteenth century, culminating finally in the Libro dell'arte composed by Cennino Cennini in or before 1437. Regarding the many fourteenth-century treatises, it is generally impossible to date them exactly or even to say, for example, whether they belong to the beginning, the middle, or the end of that century. One of the pioneer students of that subject was Mrs. Mary Philadelphia Merrifield, who translated Cennini in 1844, and a few years later published the "Original treatises dating from the twelfth to the eighteenth centuries on the arts of painting in oil, miniature, mosaic, and on glass; of gilding, dyeing, and the preparation of colours and artificial gems" (2 vols., 1230 p., London 1849). The treatises edited by her are most of them anterior or posterior to our period, though the collection of recipes, Segreti per colori (MS 165, S. Salvatore, Bologna), may come close to it. Mrs. Merrifield was the first to edit it (op. cit. p. 340–600), and it was again edited, independently, by Olindo Guerrini and Corrado Ricci: Il libro dei colori (Scelta di curiosità letterarie, no. 222, 335 p., Bologna 1887). An earlier text, De arte illuminandi (Biblioteca nazionale, Naples) was first edited by Demetrio Salazaro: L'arte della miniatura nel secolo XIV (Napoli 1877), then again by Lecoy de la Marche: L'art d'enluminer, manuel technique du quatorzième siècle (Mémoires de la Société nationale des antiquaires de France 7, 248–86, 1886; Paris 1887). Discussion of both texts from the chemical point of view by Icilio Guareschi: Osservazioni sul De arte illuminandi e sul manoscritto bolognese, Segreti per colori (Atti della R. Accademia delle scienze di Torino 40, 663–90, 1905).

The comparative study of these collections of recipes (for these treatises are hardly more) would be an exceedingly long and tedious task. This might enable one to put them in some chronological order, and then perhaps to determine the approximate date of this or that recipe. One of the novelties of the fourteenth

[7] I take advantage of this opportunity to mention two important contributions published after my note (Introd. 1, 533) was written. Hjalmar Hedfors: Compositiones ad tingenda musiva, herausgegeben, übersetzt und philologisch erklärt (thesis, 245 p., Uppsala 1932; Isis 20, 517). Rozelle Parker Johnson: Compositiones variae (116 p., Urbana, Ill. 1939; Isis 32).

[8] Dating from the second half of the eleventh century. Edited by Daniel V. Thompson, Jr. (Technical studies in the field of the fine arts vol. 1, 1932; Isis 20, 521).

century seems to have been "mosaic gold" (aurum musicum, musivum, color purpurinus; oro musaico, musivo; or mussif), serving as an imitation of gold, one among others, for mediaeval limners and painters were very fond of using gold in their miniatures, or if gold was beyond their reach, as it often was, something like it. "Mosaic gold" is a stannic sulphide, SnS_2. That substance (or its use for decorative purposes) may have been discovered before 1300, but its use became more frequent in the fourteenth century, and almost every treatise of that century contains a recipe for it. The recipe given in the Bolognese MS of which we have just spoken was discussed by J. R. Partington: The discovery of mosaic gold (Isis **21**, 203–6, 1934). See also D. V. Thompson (p. 181–84, 1936).

In recent years, many such texts have been investigated by Daniel Varney Thompson. He re-edited and Englished Cennini's Libro dell'arte (New Haven 1932–33), and with George Heard Hamilton translated the De arte illuminandi, mentioned above (82 p., New Haven 1933). He edited and translated the Liber de coloribus illuminatorum sive pictorum from Sloane MS no. 1754 (Speculum 1, 280–307, 1926), and later concluded that it was probably of English origin and of the beginning of the fourteenth century (Speculum 1, 448–50, 1926). He edited the Tractatus qualiter quilibet artificialis color fieri possit from Paris Bibliothèque nationale MS Latin 6749^b (Isis 22, 456–68, 1935) and the Tractatus de coloribus from Munich, Staatsbibliothek MS Latin 444 (Isis 24, 382–96, 1936).[9] Many more MSS including similar texts have been listed by Dorothea Singer (2, 589–621, 1930), and others may be found in every large collection of mediaeval MSS.

For the sake of comparison, one should examine also the Byzantine treatise on Christian iconography Ἑρμηνεία τῶν ζωγράφων or better Ἑρμηνεία τῆς ζωγραφικῆς (Explanation of painting, The painter's guide), written by the monk and painter Dionysios of Phurna (Φουρνᾶ τῶν Ἀγράφων) and dedicated τῇ θεοτόκῳ καὶ ἀειπαρθένῳ Μαρίᾳ. According to the first Greek editor, the MS was written in 1458, but that early date is no longer accepted. According to Diehl, the book was not written until the beginning of the eighteenth century. However that may be, it represents a much older tradition. In his preface Dionysios explains that he studied painting in his childhood in Salonica and tried to imitate the paintings of the illustrious master Manuel Panselinos (Ἐμμανουὴλ Πανήλιος ὁ Πανσέληνος)[10] of that city. In order to facilitate the task of other painters, he wrote this guide with the assistance of his disciple Cyrillos of Chios. The first part of the work explains the preparation of colors and painting materials, how to gild or to reproduce definite colors, etc.; the second part explains iconographic traditions relative to the Old and the New Testaments; the third part deals with the distribution of paintings in the churches.

This text was discovered by Alfred Napoléon Didron in Mount Athos in 1839, and a French translation of it by Paul Durand was edited by Didron: Manuel d'iconographie chrétienne (532 p., Paris 1845). First edition of the Greek text,

[9] The Paris text is a later (fifteenth century) abbreviation of the Munich one (fourteenth century). Thompson describes the latter as a kind of link between the Michael Scot text edited by Dorothea W. Singer (Isis 13, 5–15, 1929) and the Paris text. However, Michael Scot (XIII-1) was more interested in the broad problems of alchemy than in art recipes.

[10] Very mysterious individual, "the Giotto of Byzantine painting," to whom Athonite traditions ascribe the most beautiful paintings on the Holy Mountain, those in the Protaton of Karyes. According to Diehl his floruit would be c. 1540, which does not tally at all with the alleged date of the MS, but other scholars would place him in the eleventh century, the twelfth, the thirteenth, or the fourteenth. (Diehl p. 841–44, 1926.) The paintings of the Protaton are not earlier than the sixteenth century, but it does not follow that the Manuel Panselinos to whom they are ascribed did not exist many centuries before.

Ἑρμηνεία τῶν ζωγράφων (274 p., Athens 1853); no editor is named. Second edition by A. Konstantinides (Athens 1885). German translation by Godeh. Schäfer: Das Handbuch der Malerei vom Berge Athos (480 p., Trier 1855).

Krumbacher (p. 1117, 1897). Diehl (p. 854–55, 1926). J. R. Partington: Chemical arts in the Mount Athos manual of Christian iconography (Isis 22, 136–49, 1934), concluding that the range of chemical subjects is small as compared with Heraclius (X-2) and Theophilus (XII-1).

For Panselinos, see Gabriel Millet: Recherches sur l'iconographie de l'Evangile aux XIVe, XVe, et XVIe siècles d'après les monuments de Mistra, de la Macédoine et du Mont Athos (874 p., 670 ill., Paris 1916; p. 656 ff.).

One of the most controversial questions in the history of mediaeval technique is that concerning "oil painting." I have already pointed out (Introd. 2, 219) that Theophilus (XII-1) gave recipes for oil painting in his Schedula, and we know that linseed oil, hempseed oil, and walnut oil were used in mediaeval painting; the fourteenth-century Italians used what we now call "fat oils" (D. V. Thompson p. 65–69, 1936). The discovery of oil painting ascribed to the brothers Van Eyck and to other painters of the Renaissance was certainly something more than the use of oil, for oil had been used before and in more than one way (e.g., the glazing of metal surfaces, oil glazes over tempera). The Van Eycks discovered a *better* use of oil. It is interesting in this respect to recall that the Japanese used an oil technique very early and then abandoned it. Indeed, the small panels of the Tamamushi-no-zushi (shrine of jewel beetles) in the Kondō of Hōryū-ji appear to have been painted in oil on wood; they would then be the earliest existing examples of oil painting (seventh century). Japanese scholars who have investigated the matter conclude that the painting was probably done on a ground of white clay, or possibly lead white but not lime white; a vegetable oil called egoma being used as a binding medium, and massicot or litharge, a yellow lead, as a drier or siccative. A similar technique is preserved to this day in Korea.[10a]

Sir Charles Lock Eastlake (1793–1865): Materials for the history of oil painting (2 vols., London 1847–69). Charles Dalbon: Lés origines de la peinture à l'huile (Paris 1904). Ernst Berger: Quellen und Technik der Fresko-, Oel- und Tempera-Malerei des Mittelalters von der byzantinischen Zeit bis einschliesslich der Erfindung der Ölmalerei durch die Brüder Van Eyck (2te Aufl., 311 p., Munich 1912; 1st ed. 1897). Rokuro Uyemura: Studies on the ancient pigments of Japan (Eastern art 3, 47–60, 3 pl., Philadelphia 1931). Edward W. Forbes: Materials used in Japanese painting (Bull. Fogg Art Museum 1, 48–52, Cambridge, Mass. 1932). Daniel V. Thompson (p. 65–69, 1936).

3. *Manufacture and Use of Glass*

The making of glass is an art of immemorial antiquity which was brought to a high climax under the Romans and was spread by them over a great part of Europe.

[10a] A letter kindly written to me by my Harvard colleague Langdon Warner, of the Fogg Museum (Feb. 21, 1945), and further discussion and correspondence with him show that the Tamamushi problem is more complicated than I realized. The theory outlined above has been challenged by one of the best lacquer artists in Japan, who believed the Tamamushi painting to be a true lacquer painting like that of the famous "painted basket" found in a tomb of the third century in Lo-lang and now kept at the Keijô Museum (Korea). Other theories have been suggested. Finally H. Yoshida has come back to the oil-litharge explanation, and called the technique used mitsuda-é. A summary of his Japanese paper of 1926 will be found in Technical studies in the field of the fine arts (1, 165–75, Cambridge, Mass. 1940). That technique is called in Persian murdār-sang or murdāsang (litharge), and has long been known in Japan as the Persian method. Of course in the mediaeval Far East "Persian" might refer to almost any region west of China, north of India.

The art never died out, for when the Romans stopped practicing it, barbarians were already trained to continue it. The Western technique was well explained by Theophilus the Priest (XII-1). That technique was improved by the Venetians in the thirteenth century; it is probable that they learned much from the Syrian glass makers and also from the Byzantine ones after the sack of Constantinople (1204). At any rate, during that century Venice established her position as the leading glass market of the world, and various regulations were decreed from time to time by the Venetians to protect their supremacy. In 1291, the industry was moved from the città di Rialto (the city proper) to the island of Murano. After the return of Marco Polo and others from remote and fabulous countries, the Venetian glassmakers were actively employed in the making of beads and "costume jewelry." This may account for the almost complete absence of fourteenth-century specimens[11] of Venetian glass in the museums. The corporation of vitrarii, founded in 1268, became so important in the community that by 1376 the noble character of glassworking was recognized, and a nobleman could marry the daughter of a vetraio without jeopardizing the nobility of their offspring.

In the meanwhile the "ars tam nobilis" had spread to other Italian cities and to other countries. There is a document showing that the art was actually *taught* in Pisa as early as 1308 by one Bartholinus fiascarius, and other documents show that the Pisan glassmakers imported soda from Provence.[12] Inventories refer to glass obtained in Flanders, but this may be Venetian or Oriental glass imported by Flemish merchants. There is evidence, however, that glasshouses existed in the Low Countries, Germany, Bohemia, Silesia, England, France, and Spain. To cite a few examples, glasshouses were functioning in the Vendômois as early as 1316, and in the Dauphiné in 1338. An account of 1302 refers to the cutting of ferns in the woods of Normandy. Bracken was burnt to ashes to provide the alkali necessary in glassmaking. "Verre de fougère"[13] was a poor and light kind of glass. See Hartshorne (p. 100 and passim, 1897); Dillon (p. 234, 1907). An edict of 1324 forbade the construction of glass furnaces in the center of the town of Barcelona because of fire risks.[14]

The fourteenth-century glass industry in Western Europe was not necessarily derived from Venice or from Italy, for there was during that century a steady exportation of glasses from the Near East (Constantinople, Damascus, Alexandria) to the West, and many of these Oriental glasses are preserved to this day in European collections. Venice, however, was the leading center of glassmaking in the fourteenth century, and though it gradually lost much of the trade, especially of the cheaper trade, its artistic supremacy was undisputed at least until the sixteenth century.

Thus far we have spoken chiefly of the glass used in glass vessels. Stained-glass windows originated in France, probably under Byzantine influence via the Limoges trade. The earliest authenticated example of stained glass was presented by Suger (XII-1) to the church of St. Denis. It was made according to the recipes given by Theophilus the Priest (XII-1), and similar glass continued to be made until

[11] There are two beautiful specimens in the British Museum, one signed by magister Aldrevandinus. See Hartshorne (p. 25, pl. 7, 1897).

[12] Peleo Bacci: L'importazione della "soda provenzale." Contributo alla storia dell'arte del vetro in Pisa nel secolo XIV (Archivio di storia della scienza 1, 243, 1919–20).

[13] Waldglas. Documents speak of feucheria ad faciendum vitrum. Une fougère in ancient French meant a drinking glass, as well as the fern itself.

[14] René Jean: Les arts de la terre (p. 287, Paris 1911). Robert Schmidt: Das Glas (2d ed., p. 380, Berlin 1922). Alice Wilson Frothingham: Hispanic glass. With examples in the collection of the Hispanic Society (222 p., 125 ill., New York 1941).

the middle of the thirteenth century, as is proved by specimens in Angers, Sens, Chartres, Bourges, Canterbury, Lincoln, Salisbury, etc. (Hartshorne p. 125, 1897). Many of the English painted windows were imported from France, but some were of English manufacture.

By the beginning of the fourteenth century the style and technique of glass painting had changed materially in France. Said Emile Mâle, "Rien ne ressemble moins à un vitrail du XIIIe siècle qu'un vitrail du XIVe."[15] For a complete analysis of the differences, which are artistic as well as technical, I must refer to Mâle's study. The differences in style were partly determined by architectural changes (the Gothic windows being divided into spaces more and more narrow and of increasing height), partly by the possibility of obtaining larger pieces of glass; hence the stained-glass window lost its early mosaic aspect. New colors were used by the masters of the fourteenth century, who seemed less interested in the rich colors of the preceding century and favored combinations of gray, white, and yellow. The makers of stained glass began to use immoderate quantities of white glass (was this because good white glass was a relative novelty?) and a newly invented pigment, yellow of silver. This was really a new technique, for the glass was not colored in its mass, but the places where the yellow color was desired were covered with a light coating of yellow ochre mixed with silver chloride, then the glass was cooked again and yellow stains appeared on its surface.[16] This easy process was abused, and because of that, fourteenth-century glass is often given a tawdry look by too many yellow stains instead of the purer colors of earlier glass. It was also in the fourteenth century that the process of damasquinage on double glass was introduced; that is, two different sheets of glass are attached together (this had been done long before); then if one sheet is, say, red and the other white, the red glass may be worn out in places with emery, and the white color shows through. The evolution of stained glass may be studied with some precision because of the existence of a whole series of dated examples in the French and English churches; the series is particularly rich for the fourteenth century.

For information on English glass see Christopher Woodforde: English stained glass and glasspainters in the fourteenth century (Proceedings British Academy **25**, 29–49, 8 pl., 1939; Isis **35**, 227).

It may seem strange to speak of stained glass before speaking of unstained panes; but it would seem that that was the chronological order. Of course, glass had been used for centuries as a means of shutting windows, but that glass was translucid, not transparent. For example, in Roman times panes of glass were made by pouring the molten metal upon a slab of marble, the result being panes smooth on one side and rough on the other; such panes let the light through, but only in a diffused state. The crown glass or bull's-eye glass was not much better; this was much used in the West and continued in use for a considerable time. When and where was white transparent glass first made? It is not possible to answer the question,

[15] Emile Mâle, in André Michel: Histoire de l'art (2, 502, 1906). On the technique of glass painting, see D. V. Thompson (1936).

[16] The invention of the use of yellow of silver is sometimes ascribed to Jacob Griesinger (1407–91), called Jacob of Ulm after his birthplace, though his career as a Dominican and glass painter was pursued entirely in Bologna, where he created a school of glass painters and died. The blessed Jacob of Ulm was called by the Italians Giacomo Alemanno (ADB 9, 667–68, 1879). Pieces of stained glass preserved to this day prove that the French used yellow of silver a century before him.

but such glass, transparent or nearly so, was incorporated in painted-glass windows of the fourteenth century. In 1333, a nobleman of Normandie called Philip de Cacqueray was granted the privilege of making panes of glass. Were those panes transparent? (Hartshorne p. 100, 109, 1897).

At any rate, the use of glass panes in windows increased materially in the fourteenth century in France and England, though only the richer people could afford it. Moreover, we may assume that that glass was generally opaque and its use restricted to the closing of relatively small apertures (Luce p. 58, 1876).

As to the state of glass manufacture in the East, we are very well informed because there are a number of datable specimens. The outstanding examples of the Eastern glazier's virtuosity are bottles and mosque lamps of enameled glass. Some three hundred or more are scattered in the museums. The richest collection by far is in the Arabic Museum of Cairo, which has no less than 118 objects, including 78 lamps; the Metropolitan Museum of New York has 13 lamps, the Boston Museum has 3 important pieces.[17] These objects are of great archaeological value, because so many of them bear the names, titles, or blazons of known umarā' and hence are datable. The Cairene collection is so comprehensive that we may restrict ourselves to it.[18] Out of the 118 objects in the Cairo Museum, 87 are datable. The oldest object is a bottle bearing the name of Ṣalāḥ al-dīn al-Ṣaghīr, sulṭān of Damascus and Aleppo, 1250–60; this shows that the technique of enameled glass was already established by the middle of the thirteenth century. The latest objects bear the name of the sulṭān Qā'it-bey (r. 1468–95), but they are of inferior quality (Dillon p. 168, 1907). Objects of the thirteenth and fifteenth centuries are relatively rare, the great majority belonging to the fourteenth century. In the Cairo Museum there are only three objects of the thirteenth century and two of the fifteenth; all the other datable ones, i.e. 82, are of the fourteenth century. No less than 39 (including 35 lamps) bear the name of the sulṭān Nāṣir al-dīn Ḥasan (ruled 1347–51, 1354–61), and 24 (including 22 lamps) bear the name of the sulṭān Ẓāhir Barqūq (ruled 1382–89, 1390–98). Out of the 13 lamps in the Metropolitan Museum, 8 bear the names of rulers, enabling one to date them exactly. The earliest is earlier than 1277, the 7 others date from the fourteenth century.[19]

A lamp made in Aleppo, now in the Louvre, has been described in great detail by Paul Ravaisse: Une lampe sépulcrale en verre émaillé au nom d'Arghūn en-Nāṣirī (73 p., 16 pl., Paris 1931); the amīr Arghūn al-Nāṣirī died in Aleppo 1331.

The art declined rapidly after the fourteenth century, probably because Tīmūr sacked Damascus in 1400 and took the Syrian craftsmen prisoners with him. They do not seem to have continued their craft in Samarqand, or else their creations have disappeared. The rulers of Egypt and Syria were less magnificent in the fifteenth century than in the fourteenth.

These mosque lamps prove that the technique of glass manufacture was very advanced in the Near East, far ahead of the Western technique. Indeed, there are no contemporary specimens of Venetian glass which begin to compare with these superb Syrian (or Egyptian?) glasses.[20]

[17] Courtesy of my friend Ananda K. Coomaraswamy (letter of June 16, 1941), who gave me much information on the subject.

[18] This has been made easy by Gaston Wiet's elaborate study in Catalogue général du Musée du Caire, Lampes et bouteilles en verre émaillé (folio, 200 p., 92 pl., Cairo 1929).

[19] Information kindly given by M. S. Dimand, curator of Near Eastern Art (letter dated New York, June 27, 1941).

[20] My long account of them is justified by the fact that the Mamlūk mosque lamps constitute a very rare, large yet homogeneous, imposing group of dated objects.

4. *Manufacture and Use of Paper*

The invention of paper made of "[mulberry] tree bark, hemp, rags, and fish nets" is traditionally ascribed to the eunuch Ts'ai Lun (II-1). It is certain that paper was invented in China[21] and was used there for centuries before it was used anywhere else. Some specimens of Chinese paper extant date back to the second century. During the following centuries paper gradually displaced bamboo and silk as writing material. By the fifth century, paper was generally used all over China and eastern Turkestān, and its quality had been steadily improved.[21a] In the sixth century it had penetrated Kashmir, witness Sanskrit texts written on paper found at Gilghit by the Citroën mission (Sylvain Lévi, in Blum p. 15, 1935). The first manufacture of paper outside China occurred in Samarqand (757), where it was probably introduced by Chinese craftsmen. From Samarqand the use and manufacture of paper spread over the Muslim world, including the Maghrib.[22] Paper was used in Spain by the middle of the tenth century. Two important MSS, the Breviarium et missale mozarabicum, preserved in the monastery of Silos (near Burgos), and the Latin-Arabic glossary in Visigothic script, preserved in Leiden, are written partly on paper. They date from the tenth or the beginning of the eleventh century.[23]

It is clear that paper was introduced into the Christian world via the Arabic-speaking people, and the main channel of introduction was the Maghrib. By the end of the twelfth century, there were some four hundred paper mills in Fās alone. In Spain, the main center of fabrication was Shāṭiba (Spanish, Játiva), near Valencia, and the Shāṭiba paper gained a great reputation in the Muslim world, being exported as far as Egypt; it can be recognized in ancient Arabic documents because of its watermark. Shāṭiba remained a Muslim city until its conquest in 1238–39 by Jaime I of Aragon. The paper business was in Jewish hands, witness ordinances of Jaime I dated 1238, 1273.[24] It is curious that one of the earliest references to true paper in the West is found in the treatise against the Jews written by Peter the Venerable (XII-1), abbot of Cluny.

[21] Egyptian papyrus (whence our word paper is derived) was not true paper. Papyrus was made of longitudinal strips of the stem of Cyperus papyrus, placed crosswise, soaked, and pressed together. The basis of true paper is a pulp wherein the original fibers are disintegrated; on the contrary, papyrus is a laminated substance. Judging from the very large number of documents in archduke Rainer's collection, by the middle of the tenth century paper had almost completely superseded papyrus in Egypt. The last papyrus in that collection dates from 936. By the end of that century the exportation of papyrus had ceased (Carter p. 99, 1925). The last recorded use of papyrus by the curia was in 1057 under Victor II.

[21a] The early history of Chinese paper can be easily investigated on the basis of the MSS found in the Tunhuang oasis (Introd. 1, 604), a collection of some 13,500 paper rolls dating from the beginning of the fifth century to the end of the tenth. The best paper is found in the rolls of the Sui dynasty and early T'ang (say, 589 to 718). Lionel Giles: Six centuries at Tunhuang (50 p., 8 pl., London 1944; Isis 36).

[22] Chiefly in Syria, Egypt, Morocco. "Charta damascena" referred to the Damascene origin; "charta bombycina," another early name for paper, referred to the substance. Bombyx = linteorum aut aliae quae vis quisquiliae (Ducange).

[23] My dating of the second (Introd. 1, 783) is probably too late. Walter Muir Whitehill: Date of the earliest Latin-Arabic glossary (Isis 26, 370–72, 1937).

[24] The connection of Jews with that industry is not surprising, for Jews were always deeply interested in learning and everything connected with it. There are Hebrew documents on paper dating from the eighth century (Blum p. 28, 1935). Jews may have been responsible for the transmission of paper use and manufacture from Samarqand to the Dār al-Islām, hence to Christendom.

It is remarkable that Western languages do not reveal more clearly the Arabic transmission of paper to the West. This reticence is due to the accident that paper was wrongly assimilated to papyrus, on account of their identical function, and that there was no very striking Arabic word for the new product. Qirṭās (pl. qarāṭīs), from χάρτης, designated papyrus (e.g., in Qur'ān VI, 7) but was used later for paper as well. Waraq (pl. awrāq) meant originally a leaf (similar analogy in liber); one distinguished between Chinese paper waraq ṣīnī, made of vegetable fibers (ḥashīsh), and waraq khurāsānī, made of linen (kattān). The most definite word for paper was the Persian kāghad or kāghadh,[25] which was adopted in Arabic (Arabic pl., kawāghid) and in Turkish (the kāghad khāna, popularly kiat-hāne, on the Sweet waters of Europe, near Istanbul, was so called because it had been formerly the site of a paper mill). That word is probably of Central Asian or Chinese origin. There is an Arabic word, however, which has attained considerable popularity in the paper business and testifies to the Arabic origin of that business in the West; that is the word rizma, meaning a bundle of merchandise, which has been adopted in almost every Western language to mean a bundle of paper: raxma de papiro in an ordinance of Peter III of Aragon 1280; Spanish and Portuguese resma, Latin risma, French rame, Catalan raima, German ries, English ream (480 sheets, or 472, 500, 516).

There is an early Arabic treatise dealing with papermaking, the 'Umdat al-kuttāb wa 'uddat dhawī' l-albāb (The support of the scribes and the preparation of the intelligent people),[26] ascribed to the amīr al-Mu'izz ibn Bādīs, a ruler of the Zayrī dynasty (1015–61) in Tunis. Ch. XI of that treatise, dealing with paper, has been edited, translated, and elaborately discussed by the foremost student of Arabic paper, Josef Karabaček: Neue Quellen zur Papiergeschichte (Mittheilungen aus der Sammlung der Papyrus Erzherzog Rainer, folio, vol. 4, p. 75–122, 1 pl., 4 fig., Wien 1888), a supplement to his fundamental investigations, Das arabische Papier (ibid. vols. 2–3, p. 87–178, 1 pl., 2 fig., 1887).[27] The 'Umdat al-kuttāb explains how to prepare the pulp, make the sheets, wash and bleach them, color, polish, and paste them, and give them an antique appearance (ṣifat ta'tīq al-kāghad). I know of no text comparable to this in any other language of so early a date. There is no reason for doubting its date, though the text as it has come to us, in late MSS from a copy dated 1204, may contain twelfth-century interpolations.

To return to Spain, it is possible that paper was already manufactured in Christian localities before Shāṭiba was conquered (1238–39); it was certainly used in many places, and was called pergamino de paño (or de trapo), as distinguished from real parchment, called pergamino de cuero.[28] Under the kings of Aragon Játiva continued to be the main center of manufacture in the peninsula. From Spain the industry moved to Italy, where the main center was established in Fabriano (prov. of Ancona), c. 1268–78. The papers of Fabriano were soon famous. As the quality of paper may vary considerably according to the method of preparation, it was important for the manufacturers to identify their products by means

[25] More specifically, kāghad Samarqandī or kāghad khurāsānī. Cl. Huart (EI 2, 624, 1036).

[26] I should have spoken of that treatise, one of the greatest importance in the history of technology, in Introd. vol. 1, but I did not know of it. It is not too late to correct myself now. Brief references in Brockelmann (1, 268, 525, 1898; suppt. 1, 473, 1937).

[27] See also the catalogue of the exhibition prepared in the K. K. Oesterreichisches Museum für Kunst und Industrie, Vienna, by Josef Karabaček, Jakob Krall, and K. Wessely: Papyrus Erzherzog Rainer. Führer durch die Ausstellung (318 p., 20 pl., Wien 1894).

[28] It was the misfortune of paper to be confused with parchment, just as it was confused elsewhere with papyrus, hence the mixed terminology.

of watermarks. We have an interesting text ad hoc, praising the Fabriano papers and referring to their special signs, in a treatise of the great legist Bartolus (XIV-2), Tractatus de insigniis et armis, rub. 8, quoted by Augustin Blanchet: Essai sur l'histoire du papier (1, 62, Paris 1900). The papers of Fabriano were still famous in the sixteenth century, but in the meanwhile some of the craftsmen had swarmed off to other cities: Bologna 1293, Padua 1340, Colle val d'Elsa 1349. The fabrication began very early also in Genoa (thirteenth century), where it developed considerably. In the fourteenth century, however, the paper mills of Fabriano were supreme. The Fabriano pulp was made of linen and hemp, not essentially different from the Játiva pulp, but the process of manufacture was improved. From Italy the industry spread to other countries. Documentary evidence proves the existence of paper mills in 1348, 1354, and 1357 in and near Troyes (a great Jewish center).[29] The earliest German mill was established in 1390 near Nuremberg, by Ulman Stromer (XIV-2), helped by Italian craftsmen.

In the meanwhile, various measures were taken to protect the Italian paper industry. In 1366 and 1374, the Venetian senate was doing its best to protect the paper mills of Treviso. In the following century Genoa took more drastic measures, but it is interesting to note that it was only in 1481 that the guild of papermakers could establish itself in that city, because of the opposition of the ragsorters and of the parchmentmongers.

One may wonder why it took paper so long to displace parchment, much longer than to displace papyrus. It was known in Spain in the tenth century, and in Constantinople and Sicily at the beginning of the twelfth century, yet its manufacture was established in Spain and Italy only in the thirteenth century, and in France and Germany only in the fourteenth. The reasons are that the parchment trade was well entrenched, that paper was at first very expensive (almost as expensive as parchment), and perhaps that it was the fruit of a Jewish industry. It is probable also that the main materials, linen and hemp, remained too rare as long as there was no other use for them. The situation changed completely as the need of linen became more general; when the mass of the people began to use linen shirts, there was an abundance of rags. Now, that domestic revolution happened in the fourteenth century, and it made possible the typographic revolution which occurred a century later. The "siècle de la chemise" introduced the century of printing. On the other hand, the growing practice of printing, increasing immeasurably the need of writing materials, later caused the final establishment of paper, the only material which could be produced in unlimited quantities and with sufficient cheapness.

Early papers are dated by means of the documents written on them, of chemical analysis, and of the study of their appearance and their physical characteristics. The most precise data are given by their watermarks, i.e., filigranes and wire marks (the horizontal vergeures or chain lines and the vertical pontuseaux or laid lines). The Játiva and Fabriano watermarks have already been mentioned; others appeared at the end of the thirteenth century, and many more during the fourteenth and fifteenth centuries. The subject of watermarks is a very complicated and extensive one which I do not wish to tackle. Many references ad hoc will be found

[29] For more information on paper manufacture in France, see Alexandre Nicolaï: Histoire des moulins à papier du sud-ouest de la France (1300–1800), Périgord, Agenais, Angoumois, Soule, Béarn (2 vols., Bordeaux 1935). Though the earliest reference is 1302, the first paper mill about which definite information has survived appeared only in 1470, Périgord. Volume 2, including 147 plates, deals with watermarks.

in Blum (p. 37–46, 1935) and in Dard Hunter: Paper making through eighteen centuries (375 p., 214 ill., New York 1930).

5. *Discovery of New Chemical Substances*

It would be very convenient if we could state when various substances—say, acids like nitric acid and aqua regia (nitrohydrochloric acid, capable of dissolving gold)—were discovered, but that would require an endless series of investigations which we cannot undertake at present lest our synthesis be indefinitely postponed. It would be necessary to reread all the mediaeval chemical texts and excerpt them from this particular point of view. One would thus find that aqua regia was first mentioned in this or that text, the date of which would be a terminus ad quem. When the history of a science is written with sufficient completeness and accuracy, its contents may and should be redistributed in such manner that one could tell the history of each particular item or idea. This has been done admirably by Johannes Tropfke (1902 ff.) for elementary mathematics and by Mary Elvira Weeks for the chemical elements (1933). It will be done some day for the chemical substances. In the meanwhile this section will serve to indicate a gap in our knowledge.

6. *Alchemists in the Latin West*

The word alchemist in this section, and more generally in the whole work, is used without malice. When we are dealing with mediaeval times it simply means "chemist"; or it may be a briefer way of saying "mediaeval chemist." There were bona fide alchemists just as there were mala fide ones; even as today there are good chemists and bad ones. Some alchemists of the past, even as some chemists of today, were blinded by their greed. Making gold was to them, then as now, the supreme purpose of life. Some alchemists were rascals, thieves, and criminals, others were mystics, dreamers, and seers; some were good scientists, or not so good; some were greedy and worldly, others were unworldly and generous.

The main centers of alchemical thinking in this period were in Italy and England.

A. *Italy*

The social importance of alchemy is reflected in the writings of jurists, whether civilians or canonists. It is clear that any art making it possible, either immediately or eventually, to transmute base metals into noble ones would undermine the economic organization of society and weaken its political structure. Moreover, such possibilities would be exploited by impostors. No wonder, then, that theologians and jurists were on the alert.

Oldrado da Ponte wrote a consilium wherein he discussed the arguments against and for alchemy, concluding that it was a legitimate art. Similar opinions were delivered by another civilian, Alberico da Rosciate, and by the canonist Giovanni d'Andrea. It is clear that these men considered that the transmutation of base metals was possible, if difficult; yet they recognized the possibility of false claims. There is nothing wrong, they decided, in making gold, if the gold is pure; but palming off counterfeit gold is wicked.

The astrologer Cecco d'Ascoli discussed alchemy in his didactic poem L'acerba. To a mind dominated by astrological tendencies, and almost every contemporary mind was more or less dominated by them, the alchemical thesis was only a particular case of transmutation in nature, as plausible or possible as any other.

A physician of Ferrara named Pietro Buono wrote c. 1330 a large alchemical compilation, the Pretiosa margarita novella. This contained nothing new and was too undiscriminating and eclectic to point out a new way, but it was a valuable summary of the knowledge then available.

Petrarca's criticism of astrological and alchemical medicine was a part of his Christian rationalism and of his revolt against scholasticism and against everything suggesting Arabic influences. The opposition of humanists to science and Arabism was comparable to the form of modern anti-Semitism associating Jewishness with radicalism.

More information on Italian alchemy may be found in the collection made by Giovanni Carbonelli (1925). Edmund O. v. Lippmann: Quellen zur Geschichte der Chemie und Alchemie in Italien (Isis 8, 465–76, 1926).

B. *England*

The character of English alchemy is very different from that of Italian alchemy· We do not hear of English jurists taking as strong an interest in the matter as their Italian colleagues, dreading alchemical abuses and seeking ways of preventing them, nor do we hear of humanists fighting alchemy in the name of urbanity and common sense. Yet a number of alchemical texts were written by Englishmen during this period: the Correctorium alchimiae, ascribed to Robert of York (but possibly a later work), the Icocedron, composed by Walter Odington, and a whole series of treatises written by (or ascribed to) John Dastin. This last-named author is somewhat mysterious, but the two others are fairly well known. Robert was a Dominican primarily interested in meteorology and astrology; Walter, a Benedictine, was a student of astronomy and music. They both represent the group of mathematical alchemists, without exemplar in contemporary Italy.

The physician John of Gaddesden investigated methods of distilling fresh water out of sea water.

C. *France*

The attitude of the popes has been discussed above. This concerns the intellectual history of France, for the curia was located in Avignon and the contemporary popes from Clement V to Gregory XI were Frenchmen. John XXII (1316–34) was a protagonist in the fight against any kind of superstition which was not profitable to the church.

The papal hostility to alchemy, or more exactly to alchemical superstition and imposture, was shared and vigorously supported by the Dominican order, at least by the French province of that order. Hervé Nédélec, who became master general in 1318, was responsible for the decision taken at the Dominican chapter held in Barcelona in 1323, when every monk studying alchemy and refusing to destroy his alchemical books was excommunicated.

Considering the power of papal and Dominican opposition, it is not surprising that no alchemical treatises were written by contemporary Frenchmen.

D. *Catalonia*

The alchemical treatises ascribed to Arnold of Villanova (XIII-2) and Ramon Lull (XIII-2) have already been mentioned. Most of them are apocryphal, but it is probable that some are genuine, and if so they should be considered here, for Arnold lived until 1311 and Ramon until 1315. Both men were interested in alchemy. Strangely enough, Ramon's own attitude was rather a skeptical one. That is, in the writings which are undoubtedly his he rejected the possibility of transmutation of metals. Many of the alchemical writings bearing his name (there are all together some eighty!) were written by the Jewish apostate Raimundo de Tárrega (XIV-2).

7. *Byzantine Alchemy*

The most remarkable Greek treatises on alchemy are, in the first place, the translation of the Semita recta, ascribed to Albert the Great, by one Petros Theoctonicos, whom I have placed somewhat arbitrarily in the second half of the thirteenth century (Introd. 2, 1042). The MS of it (Bibliothèque nationale, Paris 2419) was copied as late as 1462. In the second place, the anonymous treatise on the metallic art (περὶ μεταλλικῆς τέχνης),[30] written probably before 1350, certainly before 1378. With this second text we are, chronologically speaking, on safer ground. Though it is not (as far as we know) a direct translation from the Latin like the first, it is obviously derived from Latin sources. It was written in southern Italy, the only region where there was sufficient anastomosis between the Latin and Greek cultures. That union did not extend to theology, to be sure, but it is typical that it did include alchemy, whose promises emulated and even outbid those of religion. This second Greek treatise is comparable to the Latin Sedacina totius alchimiae, composed c. 1378 by Guillem Sedacer. The latter and the Greek author probably utilized the same Latin sources.

8. *Muslim Alchemy*

There has come to us, together with a number of Arabic and Persian treatises of a more pretentious nature, a Persian text written in 1300 by 'Abdallāh ibn 'Alī al-Kāshānī, explaining the manufacture of faïence, the ingredients needed, their mixtures, the kiln processes and implements, the methods of glazing and decorating. This account is especially valuable because it is based on actual and traditional practice and also because it is unique of its kind in world literature until the sixteenth century. Indeed, the earliest Italian account, Piccolpasso's, dates from c. 1557, and the earliest Chinese account, concerning i-hsing pottery, is later still.

The contemporary Arabic and Persian writers were as interested in alchemy as their Christian colleagues, and thus we may expect almost every scientifically minded author to deal occasionally with that subject and any encyclopaedic treatise to devote some space to it. Here are a few examples:

The great historian Rashīd al-dīn described alchemical practice in Mongol Persia and expressed his distrust of the alchemists who were courting Hūlāgū's favor. Rashīd al-dīn must thus be added to the relatively small group of fourteenth-century writers who were sufficiently intelligent and courageous to expose the alchemical racket. The large encyclopaedic work Nukhbat al-dahr, of al-Dimashqī, contains in part 2 much information on metals, their properties and influences. As usual in Arabic treatises, chemistry is mixed up with mineralogy and geology. Al-Dimashqī was rather hostile to alchemy, yet he had accepted the Neoplatonic views on the transmutation of metals, and he explained the possibility of "educating" base metals up to a higher level. A book on alchemy, Shudhūr al-dhahab fī-l-iliksīr, is ascribed to the grammarian Abū Ḥaiyān, but it may be of an earlier date. The true contents of that treatise have not yet been ascertained; in spite

[30] Catalogue des manuscrits alchimiques grecs (1, 65, 1924).

of its alchemical title, it might turn out to be simply an essay on happiness or a metaphysical disquisition.

We are on safer ground with regard to the Egyptian al-Jildakī, who wrote not one, but many alchemical treatises. He was the last important Arabic writer on the subject, but irrespective of their intrinsic value, which cannot yet be determined, his writings are of relatively little importance to the historian of chemistry because they arrived too late to be translated into Latin and hence exerted no influence whatever on the main chemical tradition.

It is noteworthy that all the alchemical writers mentioned in this section were Easterners, with the partial exception of Abū Ḥaiyān. That exception is a partial one, because his authorship of an alchemical treatise is uncertain, and also because, in spite of his having been born and educated in Spain, he spent the best part of his life (from 1280 to 1344) in Egypt.

9. *Alchemy in Buddhist Asia*

Atomic theories developed very early in India, witness their discussion in the Vaiśeshika and Nyāya systems (Introd. 1, 88) and by Jaina theologians (Introd. 1, 69), and further discussion in Buddhist writings.[31] The latter spread atomism and alchemy throughout Buddhist Asia. For some interesting (though very incomplete) information on the subject, see McGovern (p. 125–28, 1923) and Eliade (p. 254–75, 1936).

I do not know how many writings of the Buddhist patrology contain atomistic and alchemical considerations, but we have a little more information concerning the Taoist patrology. Indeed, father Wieger has attempted a rough classification of the Taoist writings, and out of a total of 1,464 lists some 130 under "alchemy" (p. 226, 1911). This gives one an idea of the immensity of the task awaiting the student of Chinese alchemy. These writings, it should be remembered, are spread over a period of many centuries, and we could consider only those pertaining to the fourteenth century. A great many, if not the majority, are decidedly anterior to that century. Indeed, when the great scholar Chêng Ch'iao (XII-2) made a catalogue of them, he found it already necessary to subdivide that abundant literature into twenty-five groups, some of which have alchemical implications: no. 16, "nourishing the vital spirit," yang-hsing (Maspero 1937); no. 21, chemical cures; no. 23, special diet for candidates to immortality (Wieger p. 24, 1911).

The only one of these Taoist writings which I can ascribe to our period is the Chin tan ta yao (Essentials of the gold medicine), by Ch'ên Kuan-wu (no. 1053 in Wieger list, but not included by him in his alchemical group, which suggests that there may be many more alchemical treatises in the Taoist patrology than he says). The Chin tan ta yao, dealing with theoretical alchemy, was composed during the Chih Shun years (1330–32) of the rule of Wên Ti. An alchemical poem by Kao Hsiang-hsien (date unknown) was commented upon in the same years, say c. 1331, by Tai Ch'i Tsung. This commentator was a Confucian scholar, but a Confucian of that age might dabble in alchemy and Taoism, and often did. The poem is supposed to be similar to the lost essay Chih hsüan p'ien (Guide to the mystery), by Chang Po-tuan (983–1082; Isis 33, 90). It was translated and discussed by Tenney L. Davis and Chao Yün-ts'ung (Isis 30, 236–40, 1939).

In addition to these alchemical treatises, we have Chinese texts dealing with subjects which would be classified today under chemistry. For example, Lu Yu

[31] General statement of atomic theories in India by Hermann Jacobi (ERE 2, 199–202, 1910).

wrote a treatise on ink, Mo shih, wherein he deals with the history of ink manufacturers. Ink being to the Chinese mind a very precious substance, because it was one of the tools kept in the wên fang, it was worth while to write the history of its production. Such histories, however, whether Lu Yu's or others, are generally of purely literary interest, and include little information, if any, on the manufacture itself, the different kinds of ink, and other chemical realia. The wên fang is the place where a scholar reads, writes, and meditates; it is from the Chinese point of view a sacred place, and all the tools needed by a scholar for his task are to some extent sacred tools. A treatise Wên fang ssŭ p'u, written in 986 by Su I-chien, describes the furniture of a Chinese wên fang, such as existed then and many centuries later, even to this day. The scholar's main tools are writing brushes of many kinds (at least five and often twelve kinds, different in materials as well as in size), ink palettes or ink slabs, the ink itself, paper;[32] but he also needed many accessories, such as brush rests, brush holders, water holders, water droppers, paper rests, ink screens, wrist supporters, not to speak of flower holders and of at least one musical instrument, the lute or ch'in. All these tools were meant to be as beautiful as possible. For example, the ink cakes were fashioned in elegant shapes and bore suitable decorations and inscriptions. Books on ink deal with such artistic matters as well as (if not more than) the many ingredients used in the manufacture of ink. There are collections of ink cakes in the Government and Palace museums in Peking, and in many other public and private places. For further details and illustrations, see John C. Ferguson: Survey of Chinese art (p. 130-32, Shanghai 1939). The best collection of ink cakes and other writing tools known to me is in the Chinese section of the Chicago Natural History Museum. It was gathered in China 1923 by Berthold Laufer. The latter's history of ink in China and other parts of Asia was written in 1922 and is included in Frank B. Wiborg: Printing ink (p. 1-76, New York 1926; Isis 9, 134-38).

A complete wên fang, of later date (eighteenth century), but illustrating the same features as the earlier ones, has been reconstructed in the Philadelphia Museum. Brief description by Laurence Roberts (Pennsylvania Museum Bull., March 1934, p. 65-66; ibid., November 1934, May 1938).

Another chemical subject is the preparation of salt. We have a treatise on that written c. 1334 by Ch'ên Ch'un, who was then commissioner of the salt gabelle (Ar. qabāla). The name treatise is perhaps too pretentious for it; it would be better to call it an album, for it is simply a set of forty-seven illustrations with explanations.

IX. GEOGRAPHY

Our account of geographical progress will be divided, according to the main cultural types, into five parts: (A) Latin West, (B) Byzantine, (C) Jewish, (D) Muslim, and (E) Chinese. The first of these parts is by far the largest, so much so that we must subdivide it into six sections dealing respectively with (1) Italy, (2) France, (3) Spain, (4) Western Isles (i.e., Ireland and England), (5) Germany, (6) Knowledge of polar and antipodal regions.

Of course, a topical division might be preferred to the geographical one, and in one case at least it is essential. We must speak separately of the development of cartography. Happily, we can do that easily without disturbing our other arrangement, for the cartographical development was due largely, if not exclusively, to Italians. We shall thus begin with an account of the early portolani.

[32] Thus the Wên fang ssŭ p'u is divided into four parts, dealing respectively with brushes, palettes, ink, and paper (Wylie p. 145, 1922).

A. *Latin West*

A1. *Italy*

Portolani. The genesis of marine maps or portolani has been discussed in volume 2 (p. 1047–50). It is difficult to decide which of the multiple origins ascribed to them by various scholars—Scandinavian, Byzantine, Catalan, Italian (Pisan or Genoese?), Mediterranean, Muslim—is the true one. It is quite possible that crude maps were first made and used more or less casually in many places, for similar needs would create similar inventions. What is certain is that a "normal" Mediterranean portolano existed in the second half of the thirteenth century, and that the Carte pisane appearing at the end of that century had many unknown predecessors. I have given sufficient proofs of that (Introd. 2, 1048).

In the second decade of the fourteenth century, a number of early maps or atlases are connected with the name of Pietro Vesconte. The first is dated 1311 and has the distinction of being the earliest dated portolano. It was probably made in Genoa, for Vesconte was a Genoese and no other city is mentioned; yet his third and fourth atlases are dated Venice 1318. Thus honors are shared by the two rival cities, as they were a generation before apropos of the great traveler Marco Polo, a Venetian who dictated his astounding narrative in Genoese captivity. This time the roles were reversed, for Vesconte was enticed to move his studio from Genoa to Venice. Thus we find him not only preparing his later portolani in the second city, but also cooperating with the Venetian publicist Marino Sanudo il Vecchio, of whom we shall speak again and again.

A more important map was produced about 1320 by another Genoese, Giovanni di Carignano. Not only is this portolano markedly superior to earlier ones, but it contains new data concerning the Tāfīlālat (or (Tāfīlālt), a fertile region of southeastern Morocco, south of the Atlas mountains, and concerning the Berber traffic across the Sahara. This illustrates the deep interest which Genoese merchants were taking in the unexploited riches of the African continent. We know from other sources that they had had since 1223 a fundaco in Tunis. This excited the jealousy of the Venetians, whose doge Michele Dolfin (Delfino) obtained for them in 1320 from the Ḥafṣī sulṭān a general privilege of sending caravans in every direction and enjoying all the needed facilities and security for their business. Other portolani were designed in 1325 (or 1330) by the Genoese Angellino Dalorto and in 1339 by Angellino Dulcert in Majorca. The two portolani have many features in common, but the second illustrates the progress made in twenty years with regard to the Canaries and northwestern Africa. It is highly probable that the two Angellini are one and the same man. In any case we witness the moving of the cartographic studio from Genoa to Majorca, where it continued its growth in the second half of the century.

So much for the portolani. The progress made from the Carte pisane to the Majorcan map of 1339 was very great indeed. In the meanwhile a few other maps appeared relative to the lands themselves, the terra firma, not primarily to coast lines like the portolani; but these maps, a few of which will be cited in this section, represent independent traditions. The most original of all are those drawn c. 1335 by the Pavian priest Opicinus de Canistris.[1] In addition to precise geographical details, Opicinus' drawings contain moral and theological data; they are *moralized* maps, the only ones of their kind that I know of.

The study of portolani involves the query, When did the map makers become

[1] For an analysis of them see Richard Salomon: Opicinus (1, 52–81, London 1936; **Isis 26**, 460–63).

aware of magnetic declination? Investigations ad hoc have not yet yielded definite results.

To the references on portolani already given (Introd. 2, 1049) add R. D. Oldham: The portolan maps of the Rhône delta (Geographical journal 65, 403–28, 10 figs., 4 maps, 1925; Isis 8, 746). Charles Du Bus: L'art des portulans à la Bibliothèque nationale (Trésors des bibliothèques de France 3, 17–24, 8 pl., 1929). Richard Uhden: Die antiken Grundlagen der mittelalterlichen Seekarten (Imago mundi 1, 1–20, 1935; Isis 26, 486).

Many portolani have been magnificently reproduced in La Roncière (1925–27), Kammerer (1929–35), and the gigantic work of the Egyptian prince Yūsuf Kamāl (spelled in French Youssouf Kamal): Monumenta cartographica Africae et Aegypti (vol. 4; Isis 30, 335). The sumptuous publication of this atlas, private and restricted to 100 copies, began in 1926 (Isis 12, 393; 19, 562; 29, 270). The same author has discussed his Monumenta in two other publications, Quelques éclaircissements épars sur mes Monumenta (Leiden 1935; Isis 24, 453–55); Hallucinations scientifiques, les portulans (93 p., 39 pl., Leiden 1937; Isis 28, 144–46).

Expeditions to the Madeira, Canaries, and Azores islands. Madeira: It is probable that the Madeira and Porto Santo archipelagoes were discovered about this time by Italian (Genoese) sailors, for their Italian names (Isola de lo Legname, Deserte, Porto Santo) appear in the Libro del conosçimiento (c. 1348) and in the Medicean atlas of 1351.

The English discovery of Madeira, ascribed to one Robert Machin (or Macham) fleeing from Bristol with his mistress, is a pretty romance, but without sufficient foundation. It is not intrinsically impossible, but it is unproven, and if it occurred at all it left no trace and exerted no influence. It is dated c. 1344 by C. L. Kingsford (DNB 35, 110, 1893); Beazley (3, 441–42, 1906) places it in the latter days of Edward III (c. 1370?).

To complete the early history of the Madeira archipelago, its effective discovery was made relatively late, by João Gonçalves Zarco. He discovered the islands of Porto Santo in 1418 with Tristão Vaz Teixeira, and the main island of Madeira in 1419 with Bartholomeu Perestrello. This Perestrello belonged to a noble family of Piacenza which had emigrated to Lisbon in the fourteenth century. He received from Dom Henrique o Navegador the hereditary captaincy of Porto Santo, and died there c. 1457. His third wife was a noblewoman from the Algarve province, Dona Isabel Moniz. About 1479 Christopher Columbus married their daughter, Dona Felipa Perestrello e Moniz, in Lisbon (S. E. Morison: Admiral of the ocean sea 1, 49–51, 58, Boston 1942; Isis 34, 169–72).

Canaries: As to the Canaries, their earliest Christian discoverer was the Genoese Lanzarote Malocello (XIII-2). One of the northeastern islands is called Lanzarote after him. Another Genoese, Nicoloso da Recco, in Portuguese service, discovered other islands of that archipelago in 1341 and spent four months in them. The account of Nicoloso's expedition by Boccaccio contains the first description of the Canaries.

These Genoese and Portuguese successes stimulated not only their political rivals, but even the curia. Clement VI urged the conquest of the Fortunate Islands (Beneventuradas, as the Canaries were then called), and in Avignon, November 15, 1344, he had the impudence to crown Luis de La Cerda[2] their ruler, the Prince of Fortune. In 1342 a Majorcan expedition had visited the Canaries, led by Ffrancesch

[2] "Luis de España," member of the princely Castilian family La Cerda; direct descendant of Alfonso X el Sabio (XIII-2); admiral of France, 1341; died after 1360.

des Valers. In 1345 Humbert, dauphin du Viennois,[3] was preparing another. The English became anxious. Many other expeditions followed, Majorcan 1346, 1352, 1360, Spanish 1377, 1382, 1386, 1393; it is not worth while to give a detailed account of them (see La Roncière 2, 7–10, 1925). The rush for colonial spoils had begun in full earnest, and though it necessarily entailed geographical discoveries, it more directly concerns political history.

The effective discovery of the Canaries was finally made by two French noblemen, the Norman Jean de Béthencourt and the Poitevin Gadifer de La Salle, who sailed together from La Rochelle on May 1, 1402. There are two conflicting sources for the study of their conquest: (1) Le Canarien, composed probably in great part on the spot before the close of 1404 by the chaplains of both lords, Pierre Bontier, Benedictine, and Jean Le Verrier, secular priest. It magnifies the part played by Gadifer. The MS was acquired by the British Museum in 1888 and edited by Pierre Margry: La conquête et les conquérants des Canaries. Nouvelles recherches sur Jean IV de Béthencourt et Gadifer de La Salle. Le vrai ms. du Canarien (328 p., 3 pl., Paris 1896). (2) Le Livre de la conqueste et conversion des Canariens. This account is apparently the same text by the same authors, but edited c. 1625 by Galien de Béthencourt in order to magnify the achievements of his ancestors. It was printed by Pierre Bergeron (Paris 1630) from the MS preserved in the Béthencourt family until 1874 at least, when a new edition of it was prepared by Gabriel Gravier: Le Canarien. Livre de la conquête et conversion des Canaries (1402–22) par Jean de Béthencourt (Société de l'histoire de Normandie, 342 p., Rouen 1874). In the meanwhile Bergeron's text had been Englished by Richard Henry Major: The Canarian . . . (Hakluyt Society, 288 p., pls., London 1872).

By the treaty of Alcaçovas (1480) the Canaries were given to Spain, and West Africa, Guinea, and the other islands were conceded to Portugal. The Canaries have remained Spanish ever since, and the Azores and the Madeiras have remained Portuguese.

Azores: Dom Dinis o Lavrador (XIII-2), the great Portuguese king so often mentioned in this book, may be said to have created the Portuguese navy c. 1317, and he did so with the technical assistance of Genoese pilots and captains. The Genoese admiral Manuel Pezagno and his successors were bound by contract to maintain Genoese sailors in Portuguese service. The achievement of Nicoloso da Recco was very probably a fruit of that contract. It is possible that another fruit was the discovery of the Azores, first represented in the Medicean atlas of 1351. (It is true this may be a later interpolation.)

The effective discovery of the Azores was made a century later, Santa Maria in 1432 and São Miguel in 1444, by Gonçalo Velho Cabral, whom Dom Henrique had commissioned to explore the Atlantic. The Azores were then colonized by Portuguese (they have remained a Portuguese colony to this day) with the help of Flemings. In particular, Terceira was colonized by one James of Bruges c. 1450; São Jorge, by Willem van der Haegen[4] of Maestricht; Fayal, by Job Huerter of Moerbeke.[5] A fourth Fleming often quoted, Josuah (or Josse) van den Berg of

[3] Humbert II (1313–55), last independent ruler of Dauphiné; abdicated in 1349 in favor of the king of France's grandson, the future Charles V. From that time on the eldest son of the king of France was titled Dauphin.

[4] The name became Vandaraga in Portuguese speech, then was replaced by the Portuguese equivalent Silveira, and Willem was called Guilherme da Silveira.

[5] Job or Jobst (Jodocus). In Portuguese Joz Dutra or Jorge de Utra. Alphonse le Roy: Biographie nationale de Belgique (9, 623–26, 1887).

Bruges, is mythical. The reality of that Flemish colonization is confirmed by topographical names and especially by the name given to the whole archipelago before the end of the fifteenth century, Insulae flandricae, Insulae flemengorum.[6] These Flemings were acting as private adventurers; they were subject to Portuguese, not Burgundian, regulations. There is an abundant literature on the Azores and other islands, much of it in Spanish and Portuguese. For the Flemish colonies see Jules Mees: Histoire de la découverte des îles Azores et de l'origine de leur dénomination d'îles flamandes (146 p., University of Ghent 1901), with six facsimiles extracted from the portolani from Dulcert 1339 to Andrea Bianco c. 1448 and Christofalo Soligo c. 1455. Beazley (vol. 3, 1906).

The mediaeval discoveries of Madeira, the Canaries, and the Azores were largely made before 1350, but these discoveries remained generally as ineffective as the Norse discoveries of America. In every case, the effective discoveries were completed after 1400 and before 1450. The main preparatory efforts were made in the first half of the fourteenth century, not in the second half. Dinis o Lavrador was the forerunner of Henrique o Navegador.

Travelers to the Near East. Before dealing with various Italian travelers to the Near East, we may recall the Liber . . . pro recuperatione Terrae Sanctae written by the Genoese Galvano de Levanto in 1295 for Philippe le Bel, and including originally a map of Palestine. A book informed with a similar purpose was composed a little later by the Venetian Marino Sanudo il Vecchio. I am referring to the Liber secretum fidelium crucis, or Secreta, completed by him in 1313, illustrated with maps in 1321 or before. Marino was well acquainted with the Near East, for he went thither five times and spent there a good part of his life. His Secreta is a rich source of information especially from the commercial point of view. This introduces the Practica della mercatura, a commercial treatise put together c. 1340 by the Florentine merchant Francesco Balducci Pegolotti. As Pegolotti had spent many years in Famagusta, he was exceptionally well acquainted with the economic geography of the Near East. His book is not restricted to that part of the world, however; it is a general book of reference for international bankers and merchants, the first of its kind, a fitting symbol of growing mercantilism. The best proof that the age was calling for such a book is given by the appearance soon afterward of another one, the Venetian Tarifa of c. 1345. The Tarifa is not plagiarized from Pegolotti's, though its author may have borrowed details from the latter; however, the use of common sources (original tariffs and regulations) would necessarily cause many convergences between the two texts.

Many Italian pilgrims visited the Holy Land and incidentally other parts of the Near East, the most important being the Augustinian James of Verona in 1335 and the Franciscan Niccolò da Poggibonsi, whom we might call a Sienese, ten years later. Indeed, both left interesting accounts of their journeys; James wrote in Latin, Niccolò in Italian. There are many other accounts, too many and too repetitive to be dealt with separately. It will suffice to cite rapidly a few more after Röhricht (1890), whose list contains many errors, and Golubovich (vols. 3–5, 1919–27).

1320. Bernardus Thesaurarus: De acquisitione Terrae Sanctae, including article on Antioch (Röhricht p. 69).

[6] This name was first given in 1494 by the famous geographer Martin Behaim of Nuremberg. Born c. 1459, he was first engaged in business activities in Malines and Antwerp. After 1478, he traveled to Portugal and perhaps to the Azores; at any rate c. 1488 he married the daughter of Job Huerter, head of the Flemish colony and first captain donatary of Fayal and Pico; Martin died in Lisbon 1507.

1320. Franciscus Pipinus de Bononia: Tractatus de locis sanctis Terrae Sanctae (Röhricht p. 71).

[The Francesco Giorgi quoted by Röhricht under 1324 should be canceled. Francesco Giorgi of Venice was a famous Minorite of the fifteenth century, who did not write on the Holy Land. Golubovich 3, 289.]

1327, 1330. Antonio de' Reboldi (or Riboldi) of Cremona, Franciscan: Itinerarium ad sepulcrum Domini (1327) et ad Montem Sinaï (1330). This Franciscan traveled twice to the Near East, the first time to Syria and Palestine (March–September 1327), the second time to Egypt, Sinaï, and Palestine (October 1330–March 1331). Both itineraries printed by Golubovich (3, 326–42).

[c. 1330. Giovanni Fedanzola (or Fidanzola, Bichini) of Perugia. Franciscan, master of theology of Assisi, inquisitor in the Roman and Umbrian provinces, finally provincial of the Holy Land (?). Did *not* write Opusculum descriptionis Terrae Sanctae. Golubovich 3, 367–69.]

c. 1348. "Questi sono i viaggi che debbono fare li pellegrini che vanno oltra mare per salvare l'anima loro." First edited by Michele Melga: I viaggi in Terra Santa descritti da un anonimo trecentista e non mai fin qui stampati (16 p., Napoli 1862). Reprinted by Carlo Gargiolli: Viaggi in Terra Santa (p. 443–50, Firenze 1862). Third edition by Golubovich (5, 34–37). Golubovich thinks that this text is a copy of an earlier text written after Ṣalāḥ al-dīn's conquest (1187) and before the entrance of the Franciscans into the Holy Land (1333). This is the only Italian text in addition to that of Niccolò da Poggibonsi, all others being in Latin. For further study of these questions, father Golubovich is the best guide.

East Africa. In May 1291, two Genoese sailors, the brothers Vivaldi (XIII-2), Ugolino and Vadino, sailed from Genoa with the ambitious purpose of circumnavigating Africa. They never returned. Sometime before 1315, Ugolino's son, Sorleone, undertook various expeditions with the hope of finding and rescuing them. In the course of one of these expeditions he is said to have reached the coast of Italian Somaliland. All of which would be very remarkable if we could believe it, but unfortunately none of the Vivaldi accounts is trustworthy (Hennig 3, 94–103, 1938).

Middle East. Two Italian Dominicans traveled as far as Mesopotamia and even beyond. Ricoldo di Monte Croce (XIII-2) proceeded from Syria to Lesser Armenia, then to Erzerum, Tabrīz, then back to Mūṣul and Baghdād, where he spent many years. The account of his experiences is very rich in information; he also wrote a refutation of Islām which was used considerably by Christian doctors, Orthodox as well as Catholic and Protestant. Ricoldo returned in 1301 to his native city, Florence, and lived twenty more years. The other Dominican, John of Cora, became archbishop of Soltania in 1329. He is probably the author of a substantial book on China, preserved in a French version, Livre de l'état du Grant Caan, dated c. 1331. It is not proved that John visited Cathay himself, but of course more information ad hoc would be available to him in Persian 'Irāq than in Western Europe. He may also have had a share in the Directorium ad faciendum passagium ad Terram Sanctam ascribed to the pseudo Brocard.

China. Far-off Cathay exerted a tremendous attraction on the Italian adventurers of those days, and no wonder when we remember the fame of the Poli brothers (XIII-2) and of the Franciscan John of Montecorvino (XIII-2). The latter lived until c. 1328, but was unable to return home; he died in the Far East, probably in Peking. Marco Polo's wonderful book did not appear until the very end of the thirteenth century. Peter of Abano alluded to it in his Conciliator (c. 1303, 1310).

Except for John of Cora, Dominican, whose presence in China is uncertain, the Italian visitors of this period, those at least whose purpose was religious propaganda, were Franciscans. They followed in the footsteps of their brother, John of Montecorvino. This is not accidental; the curia was then already avoiding the competition of religious orders by restricting each territory to a single one. Thus, as we have seen, the Middle East was given over to Dominicans, the Far East to Franciscans. Among John's successors was Peregrine of Castello, who was appointed John's suffragan in 1307 and proceeded to join his post with his own suffragan, Andrew of Perugia. Both friars died in China, probably in Zaiton, Peregrine c. 1322 and Andrew a few years later. The activities of these men and of their brethren are known mainly from their official letters to their community. However, a far more elaborate account of Franciscan experience in the Far East and of his own journeys thither and back was bequeathed us by Odoric of Pordenone. Odoric was more fortunate than the three brethren previously mentioned, John, Peregrine, and Andrew, in that he was able to spend his last days in his own paese of Friuli, at the northern end of the Adriatic. During his last year, 1330–31, he dictated a relation which is one of the most important of its kind in mediaeval times. It deals with the journey itself and offers abundant information on the Middle East, India, various parts of the Malay peninsula and archipelago, and China itself. Further information was made available by John of Marignolli, a noble Florentine, who had assumed the Franciscan habit and was a member of the very large embassy sent by Benedict XII in 1338 to the Mongol emperor. His reminiscences, a curious mixture of truth and fancy, have been preserved in the form of an interpolation in the Chronicle of Bohemia which he wrote for the emperor, Charles IV.

All these men were followers of John of Montecorvino; was no one impelled to follow Polo's example? Yes, a single man, the Genoese merchant Andalò da Savignone, who traveled to China with Venetian goods, chiefly glass beads and "costume jewelry." We should remember that trading in China was a risky business and that each merchant adventurer had to face all the dangers alone, whereas the friars were supported, spiritually if not materially, by their whole order and by good Catholics everywhere. I do not wish to minimize their courage, which was great, but in most cases the initiative was not their own. They were soldiers of Christ, obeying their instructions and prepared for any sacrifice (many died martyrs of their faith); the merchants like the Poli and Savignone had nothing to support them, except their own courage and perhaps their greed.

Geographical thought. The travelers of whom I have spoken had no geographical purpose, they were simply missionaries or merchants, but as soon as they began to register their experiences, they contributed, some of them richly, to geographical knowledge. If their curiosity was sufficiently deep and comprehensive, or original, they were eventually able, like Odoric of Pordenone, to enrich our knowledge, not only of foreign lands, but of foreign people, of man.

There were other people, however, who were interested in geography for its own sake, that is, who tried to imagine how the surface of the earth and the seas was divided and to describe it as well as they could. Every encyclopaedist of course is obliged to deal with geographical ideas; in addition, some men were more particularly interested in them and devoted special treatises to them. Thus the chronicler Riccobaldo da Ferrara wrote a Latin account of the face of the earth divided into twelve zones. The outstanding treatise on geography in the broad sense is the mysterious Quaestio de aqua et terra, recording Dante's disputation at Verona in

1320. The ascription to Dante and even the date of that treatise are doubtful; no witness of the original text remains except the princeps, printed as late as 1508. The date, however, is plausible enough. It discusses a problem which exercised the minds of many ancient and mediaeval thinkers. How are the areas of land and water distributed, and why are they distributed as they are? One of the sources of mediaeval cogitations on the subject, perhaps the main one, was the apocryphal Apocalypse of Ezra (II Esdras of the Authorized version, ch. 3–14), composed c. 85 A.D. (see 6:42–47). For example, there is no doubt that Columbus was deeply influenced by it.[7] In the thirteenth and fourteenth centuries a strange theory had gradually found acceptance among scholars. The distribution of lands and waters was explained on the assumption that the land sphere and the water sphere were not exactly homocentric. We find that theory, e.g., in the commentary on Genesis of Nicholas of Lyra.[8] Now the Quaestio bearing Dante's name was largely devoted to its refutation. The same conclusion was reached by Andalò di Negro in his Tractatus spere (before 1340). It is typical of philosophical presumption that such questions were argued at a time when a large part of the earth's surface was still as unknown as the other side of the moon is today.

It is said that Petrarca and Robert of Anjou together drew a map of Italy in 1341. That story is not very plausible, but we know that Petrarca was, like Boccaccio later, interested in ancient geography. People anxious to understand a text (for example, an ancient Latin one) wish to identify and locate the places named in it; this leads to the study of "historical geography," a subject which always enjoyed so much popularity in European countries that it actually delayed the development of geography proper. That is, on account of a long and perverse tradition, scholars were wasting their time comparing old maps, or, worse still, comparing names, instead of studying the face of the earth itself. Political boundaries have always been so important for practical reasons that physical geography was entirely subordinated to political geography; the latter was often studied for its own sake and in a historical spirit rather than a practical one. The endless vicissitudes and aberrations of political boundaries had to be investigated for the understanding of history, and hence geographical atlases (and thoughts) tended to become political and historical atlases (and thoughts). Similar remarks apply, with even greater force, to geographical dictionaries. The substitution of history for geography, and of words for things, is only an example of a familiar disease, rampant in many old scientific books (particularly the herbals).

To return to Petrarca, he owned ancient maps and is credited with a treatise on the classical geography of Italy. What is more noteworthy, he made in 1336 the ascent of Mount Ventoux, a mountain over six thousand feet high not very far from Avignon. That feat is almost unique in mediaeval times. To be sure, his concern was literary rather than sporting, yet it took some courage in those days to do what he did. He was perhaps more "modern" in that alpine deed than in any other. In order to appreciate this we should bear in mind that the mediaeval reaction to mountains was one of fear and superstition, very remote from our own reverence and aesthetic pleasure.[9] The first European to look at them as an artist and scientist was Leonardo da Vinci, and Conrad Gesner's letter on the Admiration of mountains, written in 1541, is I believe the earliest text of its kind in European

[7] Salvador de Madariaga: Columbus (passim, New York 1940; Isis 33, 95).
[8] See my note on him for a discussion of it.
[9] Coulton: Medieval panorama (p. 104, 1938).

literature.[10] Chinese and Japanese artists were much prompter than their Western colleagues to appreciate the beauty of landscapes, and especially of mountains. Buddhist thought, especially that of the Dhyāna school (Ch'an; Zen) helped them in that; whereas the Jewish, Christian, and Muslim ways of thinking tended to take man's mind away from natural beauties, and to represent mountains as regions of terror, inhabited only by devils and infidels.

To conclude this section on geographical ideas, I may recall once more the name of Opicinus de Canistris, who carried geographical abstractions to the limit. He devised moralized maps wherein geographical and ethical views were strangely mixed, and he indulged in games of tabular and graphical symbolism which are unexpected in his surroundings.

A2. *France*

The account of geographical achievement in other Christian countries than Italy will not detain us very long.

The outstanding geographical treatise in the French language was written, not by a Frenchman, but by the Armenian monk Hayton. Lesser Armenia was deeply influenced by France, and Hayton had been to that country as a pilgrim (reversing the main direction of the great pilgrimages to the Holy Land!). After his return he assumed the Praemonstratensian habit in Cyprus, another country dominated by French rulers and by French patterns. No wonder, then, that Hayton wrote the Fleur des histoires de la terre d'Orient in the French language (1307); the first part of that book is a geographical and ethnographical introduction to the rest. The Fleur des histoires was one of the most popular works of its kind. It was soon translated into Latin, and in the course of time other versions appeared in German, Dutch, English, Italian, Spanish, and Armenian.

Jordan Catala, a Dominican monk, was sent as a missionary to Persia and India, and after his return c. 1328 wrote the Mirabilia descripta, full of valuable or curious observations, particularly with regard to India.

The third French traveler, Nicholas Bonet, was a member of the mission sent by Benedict XII to China in 1338, already referred to apropos of Giovanni de' Marignolli. His writings were restricted to philosophy and theology.

Two other Frenchmen, both Dominicans, Guillaume Adam and pseudo Brocard, traveled considerably in the Near and Middle East and wrote books of propaganda for new crusades. The authors had in common many ideas, especially a fierce hatred not so much of the Muslims as of the Greeks—and they spoke of Christian union! The historian of geography may find much to glean in their books.

I did not come across documents concerning humbler kinds of pilgrims, itineraries written by them or guides prepared for them. Except perhaps the anonymous guide in the town library of Evreux (MS Latin 36) edited by Henry Omont;[11] the author is unknown, but may have been a Frenchman, which would account for the preservation of his guide in a small library of Normandy. Its sources must be the

[10] Isis 6, 65. Gesner's Epistola ad Jacobum Avienum de montium admiratione, written in 1541, was first printed at the beginning of Gesner's Libellus de lacte et operibus lactariis (Zürich 1543). Text with French translation in W. A. B. Coolidge (p. i–xvii, 1904). English translation by H. B. D. Soulé (de luxe ed., San Francisco 1937). Jacobus Avienus was a physician of Glaris (a Swiss canton); his real name may have been Vögler or Vögeli, but I cannot identify him.

[11] H. Omont: Un guide du pèlerin en Terre sainte au XIVe siècle (Mélanges offerts à Gustave Schlumberger p. 436–50, Paris 1924). Latin text with brief notes.

same as those used by Philip Brusseri of Savone, Franciscan, in his Descriptio terrae sanctae,[12] for there are a good many verbatim similarities between the two compositions; or the anonymous author may have used Philip's own work, which was larger than his and is far better known (at least thirteen MSS).

A3. *Spain*

The Spanish roll of honor is short but very distinguished. The word Spanish is taken in a broad sense, referring to the Hispanic peninsula. Indeed, the three men of whom I am going to speak were, the first a Basque Franciscan, the second a Catalan (Majorcan) adventurer, the third a Castilian Franciscan.

Pascal of Vitoria traveled to the Lower Volga region (the steppes of the Golden Horde), then to Khwārizm and Transoxiana. In 1338 he addressed an account of his journey to his brethren in Vitoria, and in the following year suffered a martyr's death.

Jaime Ferrer sailed from Majorca in 1346 to explore the western African coast, rounded Cape Bojador, and reached the Rio de Oro region. To appreciate the meaning of this, remember that the brothers Ugolino and Vadino Vivaldi (XIII-2) were said to have reached Cape Nun (c. 29°N.) in 1291 before vanishing; Sorleone Vivaldo, Ugolino's son, searched for them in vain (before 1315). Cape Bojador (c. 26°N.), three degrees farther south, remained the southernmost limit for more than a century (in 1455 Alvise Cadamosto, Venetian navigator in Portuguese service, reached the mouth of the Gambia River).[13]

About the middle of the century an unknown Spanish Franciscan wrote, on the basis of the portolani, of travelers' tales, and perhaps to some extent of his own experience, a book of geographical knowledge (Libro del conosçimiento) containing a good amount of information on many countries of the world, as well as a collection of their arms and flags, drawn in colors. According to that Libro some knowledge had already been obtained concerning parts of West Africa south of Cape Bojador, as far as Sierra Leone and even far enough to realize the eastern tendency of the West African coast. This does not contradict the statement made in the previous paragraph, for the knowledge we owe to the Franciscan monk concerning that coast is uncertain, and does not reappear until a century later in the Este mappa mundi.

The pilgrim literature is represented by two texts, the one in Latin of c. 1340 by Nicolas Rossell, Catalan (Majorcan) Dominican: Liber locorum sanctorum Terre Jerusalem; the other in Spanish of c. 1342 by Blas y Buysa, Franciscan: Relacion verdadera y copiosa de los Sagrados Lugares de Jerusalem (122 p., Madrid 1622; reprinted Salamanca 1624). Both texts are quoted by Röhricht (p. 85–86, 1890); neither by Golubovich (vol. 4, 1923), which is disquieting.

A4. *Western Isles*

The geographical work done in Great Britain and Ireland is very small as compared with that done in Italy or France, and it is of a very humble nature as contrasted with the heroic efforts of Spanish adventurers.

Let us consider the maps first. The English Benedictine Ranulf Higden wrote a chronicle (Polychronicon), the first book of which bears the significant title

[12] Text edited by P. W. A. Neumann (Oesterreichische Vierteljahrschrift für katholische Theologie 11, 1–78, 165–74, 1872). Listed by Röhricht (p. 60, 1890) under date 1285–91; Chevalier (p. 718, 1905) gives the date 1340.

[13] Bathurst is in latitude 13°28′N.

Mappa mundi. It is a sort of geographical introduction illustrated with a map of the world. Both the text and the map were antiquated, being derived from Biblical and patristic knowledge, from Isidore of Seville (VII-1), and from a thirteenth-century dictionary, the Geographia universalis. The map is of the old wheel type with Jerusalem in the center, according to the divine injunction, "Thus saith the Lord God: This is Jerusalem; I have set it in the midst of the nations and countries that are round about her" (Ezekiel 5:5).

Independently of that Biblical tradition, a new and more scientific tradition of map making had been remarkably initiated by Matthew Paris (XIII-2), who drew the first detailed maps of England. Another map of Great Britain was drawn in the period 1325–50 by an unknown cartographer. It is preserved in the Bodleian, to which it was bequeathed in 1799 by the topographer and antiquary Richard Gough (1735–1809), hence it is often called the Gough map. The study of these precious documents is facilitated by the existence of excellent facsimiles. Four maps of Great Britain designed by Matthew Paris about 1250, reproduced from three MSS in the British Museum and one at Corpus Christi, Cambridge (London, British Museum, folio, 1928). Facsimile of the ancient map of Great Britain in the Bodleian, A.D. 1325–50, Oxford (1 sheet, 26 × 42 in., Southampton, Ordnance Survey Office, 1935), with an overprint in red of the names transcribed in modern characters. For a comparative study of them, Miss J. B. Mitchell and R. A. Pelham: Early maps of Great Britain (Geographical journal 81, 27–39, see also 40–45, 1933; Isis 22, 337).

Related studies. James Field Willard: Inland transportation in England during the fourteenth century (Speculum 1, 361–74, 1926; Isis 11, 430). J. B. P. Karslake: Further notes on the old English mile (Geographical journal 77, 358–60, 1931; Isis 24, 205). William Rees: Historical map of South Wales and border counties in the fourteenth century (4 sheets with handbook, Southampton, Ordnance Survey, 1932), modern compilation with overprints in red, black, and blue indicating (1) English penetration, (2) survival of Welsh tenure, (3) church property. Elaborately reviewed by H. J. Randall (Antiquity 7, 329–36, 1933). Coulton (p. 317–31, 1938b).

Information concerning the Ordnance Survey facsimiles kindly sent to me by C. B. Hitchcock of the American Geographical Society (Aug. 11, 1941).

As to pilgrimages to the Holy Land, we have two noteworthy accounts. The first refers to the journey undertaken by two Irish Franciscans, Symon Simeonis and Hugh the Limner, who left Kildare county in 1322 and visited Egypt together; Hugh died in Cairo 1323, and Symon proceeded alone to Jerusalem. An unknown Englishman pilgrimed to the Holy Land in 1344 and traveled via Italy, Greece, Rhodes, Cyprus. He left an account, written, like the preceding one, in Latin.[14]

English texts of geographical interest may be investigated under the guidance of Wells' manual (p. 432–37, and supplements ad hoc).

A5. *Germany*

Three narratives of journeys to the Near East were written in Latin by German pilgrims. The earliest and by far the best of these we owe to William Boldensele of Cologne, who was first a Dominican yet was permitted to unfrock himself and

[14] Itinerarium cuiusdam Anglici Terram Sanctam et alia loca sancta visitantis. Röhricht (p. 86, 1890). Text edited by Golubovich (4, 427–60, 1923). G. B. Cao: Il viaggio in Italia di un pellegrino inglese nel 1344 (Boll. R. Società geografica 4, 476–96, 1927; Isis 13, 163).

become a knight of St. John. His account is more critical than most; his journey, undertaken c. 1332 at the request of a French cardinal, was probably more of a political undertaking than a pilgrimage pure and simple. The Westphalian priest Ludolf of Sudheim spent many years (1336–41) traveling in the Mediterranean and the Near East, and after his return wrote a story partly derived from the Hodoeporicon of his predecessor William Boldensele, but with additions of his own, many of which illustrate his intellectual inferiority to his model. His account was soon translated into German, possibly by himself, and the German text was better in some respects than the Latin original; the German translation is lost, and we know it only through a retranslation into Latin made before the end of the century by the Cistercian Nicholas de Hude.[15]

The third German pilgrim was a Bavarian, Rudolf of Frameinsberg, who traveled to Palestine and the Sinaï, and wrote an insignificant account of his journey. He left Landshut in 1346 with 350 florins and came back with four!

To these may perhaps be added the text called by Röhricht the Anonymous Coloniensis. It is a German text beginning "Dar na dat geschreven is van deme heilgen lande ind von allen landen over mer . . . " It is preserved in a single incomplete MS (Cologne archives no. 261) and was edited by Röhricht and Meisner: Ein niederrheinscher Bericht über den Orient (Zeitschrift für deutsche Philologie 19, 1–86, 1886). Röhricht (p. 85, 1890). Aside from its philological importance, the text is valuable because it illustrates the commercial interest of the city of Cologne in oversea trade. The author was obviously a citizen of Cologne; in 1338 he was in Egypt, in 1340 in Tabrīz, and a little before 1348 in Armenia. He wrote his account at his home in Cologne during the Jewish persecutions which occurred in that city in 1350.

A6. *Knowledge of antipodal and polar regions*

It may seem strange to put together the antipodal and polar regions, but they were almost equally inaccessible to the great majority of men. We shall see that the arctic region was not completely inaccessible, but the antarctic was.

The existence of antipodes was assumed on theoretical grounds from early times. The first to propound it clearly was Crates of Mallos (II-1 B.C.). According to him the oikoumene is but one of four similar inhabited masses of land, separated from one another by two orthogonal oceans, and antipodal two by two. The Cratesian theory, implying sphericity of the earth, was obnoxious to some fathers of the church (Isis 8, 212–13), but it was supported by Macrobius (V-1) and Martianus Capella (V-2), and through them it obtained very broad currency, if not always acquiescence, throughout the Middle Ages. It was known to Isidore of Seville (VII-1), Bede (VIII-1), St. Virgil of Salzburg (VIII-1), William of Conches (XII-1), Adelard of Bath (XII-1), Bernard Sylvester (XII-1), Lambert of Saint Omer (XII-1), Gerald the Welshman (XII-2), Godfrey of Viterbo (XII-2)—who considered the golden orb divided by two orthogonal bands, one of the regalia of the Holy Roman Empire, a symbol of the Cratesian world!—Geoffrey of Breteuil,[16] Robert Grosseteste (XIII-1), etc. It would take too long to indicate the reac-

[15] G. A. Neumann: Archives de l'Orient latin (2 B, 305–28, 1884).

[16] I overlooked this Geoffrey (or Godfrey) of Breteuil or of Saint Victor in Introd. vol. 2. He was subprior of Ste Barbe-en-Auge 1173, canon of St. Victor, Paris, and died in 1196. He wrote the Microcosmus and Fons philosophiae. HL (15, 69–85, 1820). A. Bonnetty: Le Fons philosophiae de Godefroi de Saint Victor (Annales de philosophie chrétienne 86, 201–62, 1874), text and analysis of the whole poem, consisting of 209 monorhyme stanzas of 4 lines each. Chevalier (p. 1702, 1905).

tions of each of these men to the theory. They varied all the way from verbal and timid acceptance to genuine belief.[17]

With the Cratesian ideas were mixed, throughout mediaeval times, ancient beliefs concerning rivers of the underworld, Elysian fields, Islands of the blessed, etc., which were often located in antipodal regions. It will suffice to recall Dante's conception. He placed Purgatory at the exact antipode of Jerusalem, Paradise being of course in heaven (see our fig. 8).

Strangely enough, though the Cratesian theory implied belief in the sphericity of the earth, some modifications of it could be reconciled with the hypothesis of a flat earth. That hypothesis, by the way, had never been completely ostracized, except in purely astronomical writings; it reappeared from time to time in patristic and mediaeval literature. Now the fourth (antipodal) continent is clearly indicated on the Mappa mundi of St. Beatus (VIII-2) and the other so-called Beatus maps (e.g., the St. Sever map, middle of eleventh century; Introd. 1, 768), but the antipodal continent on these maps is simply an austral continent, and many people may have imagined the earth as flat but divided into two halves, known and unknown, by the equator. Other authors, like Lambert of Saint Omer (XII-1), played with both ideas, that of an inaccessible austral continent and that of a continent antipodal to the known one. Belief in antipodes and antichthons was largely a matter of belief in Macrobius and Capella.

The mention of antichthons suggests the main difficulty, from the theological point of view, which lay in the acceptance not of the antipodal regions, but of antichthons or inhabitants of those regions. The idea of antichthons was ridiculed and anathematized by the Christian Cicero, Lactantius (d. c. 325?), and the opposition to it was neatly formulated by St. Augustine (V-1).[18] How could the gospel have been preached in "the four quarters of the earth," if some children of Adam had been utterly separated from others? and how could that separation have taken place? how could the text of Romans 10:18 be true?[19] No wonder that many Christian doctors could not follow Macrobius and Capella as far as that. Though the list of believers in antipodes is fairly long, the number of doctors countenancing antichthons was much smaller, and their adhesion was likely to be hedged. Inasmuch as Arabic astronomers such as al-Battānī (IX-2) and al-Zarqālī (XI-2) were willing enough to accept the habitableness of every climate and to extend it to inaccessible parts of the earth, the more scientific writers such as Petrus Alphonsi (XII-1), Lambert of Saint Omer (XII-1), Robert Grosseteste (XIII-1), and Roger Bacon (XIII-2) shared somewhat their indulgence, but William of Conches (XII-1) sat on the fence, and Manegold of Lautenbach (XII-1) voiced his disapproval in unmistakable terms. As late as 1327 belief in antichthons was one of the dangerous ideas which were imputed to Cecco d'Ascoli and led to his execution. It is typical of scholastic reasoning that such questions were discussed at all, solved in one way or another, and even used as touchstone of orthodoxy, at a time when direct knowledge of the earth was still restricted to a small part of it.

Practical knowledge of the Arctic. With regard to the arctic region we are on safer ground, for a not inconsiderable group of people had obtained an experimental

[17] For details see Armand Rainaud: Le continent austral. Hypothèses et découvertes (491 p., Paris 1893). J. K. Wright (1925).

[18] I quoted the main text ad hoc in Introd. 2, 45.

[19] *Μενοῦνγε εἰς πᾶσαν τὴν γῆν ἐξῆλθεν ὁ φθόγγος αὐτῶν, καὶ εἰς τὰ πέρατα τῆς οἰκουμένης τὰ ῥήματα αὐτῶν.*

knowledge of it. Let us briefly recall the facts concerning the discoveries of Iceland, Greenland, and the northeastern coasts of America related in our volume 1.

Iceland had been discovered by Irish sailors before 795, perhaps a long time before; it was rediscovered by Vikings about the middle of the ninth century and colonized by them c. 870. The Vikings were then in the middle of their golden age (c. 800–c. 1050) and admirably well equipped for sea adventures. Witness the great ship and archaeological treasure found in Oseberg farm (Sem parish, Jarlsberg and Larvik, west of the Oslo fjord) in 1903.[20] These objects may date back to the time of queen Åsa, mother of Halvdan Svarte (king of Norway 827–60). According to Stefansson,[21] by 930, when the Icelandic Republic was founded, there were some 50,000 Europeans in the island. That country was the first European democracy north of the Alps, or, if one considers Iceland as a part of the Americas, the first democracy in the New World.

In the meanwhile, the Norwegian Ohthere (IX-2), in the service of Alfred the Great, sailed northward along the Norwegian coast c. 880, passed the North Cape (c. 71°), discovered the Polar (or Barents) Sea, the White Sea, and the mouth of the Dvina (Arkhangelsk).[22] It is probable that Greenland was discovered from Iceland by the end of the same century. The first attempt at colonization, however, was made much later by the Norwegian Eric the Red (X-2). In 982, being outlawed from Iceland for three years, he explored Greenland, and in 986 he went back there with twenty-five ships; fourteen ships arrived, carrying some 400 people. By 990 the Greenland republic was functioning, being the first American democracy;[23] ten years later its parliament voted that Greenland should become Christian. From that date we have thus two primary sources of information concerning that country, the Icelandic sagas and the records of the Catholic church.[24]

In 1000, Leif the Fortunate (X-2), son of Eric the Red, trying to go from Norway to Greenland without stopping in Iceland, reached the northern Atlantic coasts of North America and explored them. In 1003–6, Thorfin Karlsefni (XI-1) established an Icelandic colony in "Wineland," but the colony promptly failed and disappeared. (Introd. 1, 676, 724.)

The Icelandic culture continued vigorously, however, not only in Iceland but also in Greenland, where it reached its peak in the twelfth and thirteenth centuries. The Greenlanders raised large numbers of domestic animals. They paid taxes to Norway and tithes to Rome. They did business not only with Iceland and Norway, but also with England (Bristol, Lynn), exporting walrus and seal oil and

[20] The publication of the Osebergfundet announced in Introd. 1, 576 was prepared by A. W. Brøgger, Hj. Falk, and Haakon Schetelig. I have seen thus far four folio volumes, all published in Kristiania (Oslo): vol. 1, 1917; vol. 2, 1928; vol. 3, 1920 (art); vol. 5, 1927 (anthropology). In addition to the ship, the treasure includes wagon, sledges, furniture, wooden objects, looms and other tools, shoes, combs, etc.; many objects are beautifully carved. The reports are written in Norwegian, but English (or German) summaries are added to some of the copies.

[21] Vilhjalmur Stefansson: The three voyages of Martin Frobisher, 1576–78 (2 vols., London 1938; Isis 30, 284–89); Unsolved mysteries of the Arctic (ch. 1, New York 1939; Isis 32, 212–14); Ultima Thule (New York 1940; Isis 34, 80); Iceland (New York 1939); Greenland (New York 1942; Isis 34, 379–80).

[22] For further exploration of the White Sea region and the lower course of the Dvina (Bjarmeland) c. 920, c. 965, c. 1026, c. 1090, and especially in 1217–22, see Introd. 2, 638.

[23] Or the second if Iceland is considered a part of the Americas.

[24] Greenland had its own bishop beginning c. 1122, and the bishopric continued until 1520 without interruption (Gams p. 334, 1873). The bishop of Greenland was under the jurisdiction of the archbishop of Hamburg (cf. Adam of Bremen XI-2), later (c. 1150) of the archbishop of Nidaros (= Trondhjem).

hides, wool, and, by way of luxury, polar bears and falcons.[25] Unfortunately, after almost three centuries (271 years) of political freedom, Greenland ceased to be an independent republic and became a province of Norway (1261).

There were two large areas of settlement in Greenland, both of them on the west coast, but on account of imperfect knowledge of the direction of that coast the southern one was erroneously called eastern (see map, fig. 3). This so-called "Eastern settlement" began near the southern tip of the island and ran north along the western coast about 100 miles (now Julianehaab district); it was separated from the "Western settlement" by an uninhabited coast of about 170 miles to latitude 63°45′. The "Western settlement" (now Godthaab district) extended

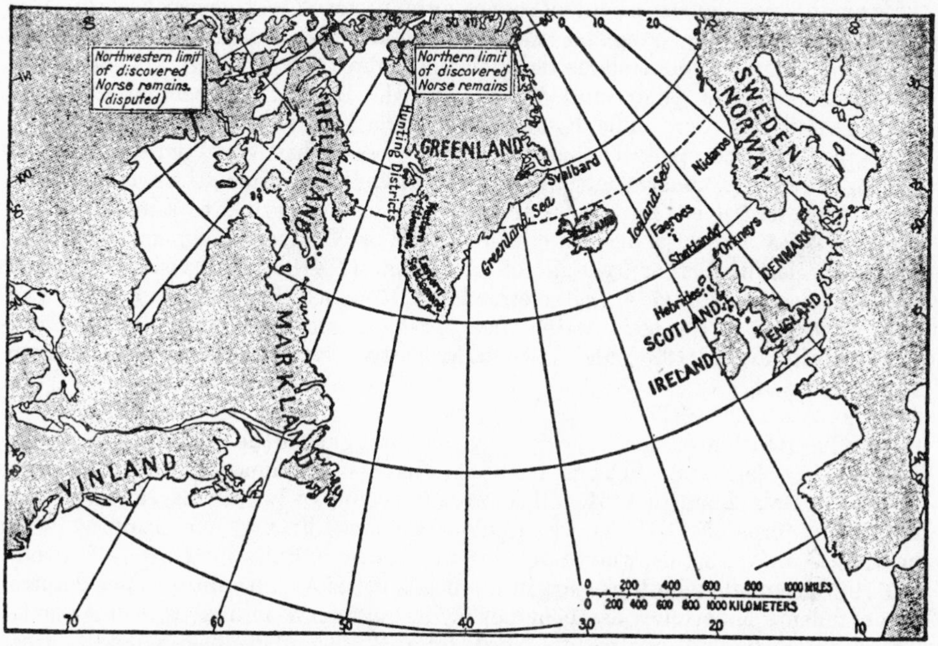

FIG. 3. Map illustrating the position of the Western and "Eastern" Icelandic settlements in Greenland. From Vilhjalmur Stefansson: Unsolved mysteries of the Arctic (p. 3, Macmillan, New York 1939), with kind permission.

to latitude 65°. Farther north for at least 300 miles beyond the Arctic Circle (66°30′) extended the northern outposts (nordurseta). In the twelfth and thirteenth centuries, there were in the "Eastern settlement" twelve churches, an Augustinian monastery, a Benedictine nunnery, and about a hundred and ninety farms; the "Western settlement" boasted four churches and some ninety farms. The members of that settlement were less devoted to husbandry and depended more on hunting; the best hunting grounds were in the nordurseta, hence a relatively

[25] The falcons of Greenland were considered the best and reserved for kings and princes. They could not be domesticated (no falcon breeds in captivity), and hence every one had to be captured in its native haunt. Of course the exact localities were unknown to southern princes, who only knew that some of their most precious birds came from "remote, inaccessible regions of the extreme north." Thus Frederick II (XIII-1) in his De arte venandi (book 1, ch. xxiii F; Wood's edition p. 51, 1943; Isis 35, 182). At the disastrous crusade of Nicopolis, 1396, Jean de Nevers, son of the duke of Burgundy, Philippe le Hardi, was made prisoner by Bāyazīd Yildirim and ransomed for twelve Greenland falcons.

large number of people obtained considerable experience of arctic conditions.[26]

According to Ivar Barðarson (XIV-2), the "Western settlement" was destroyed by the Eskimos in 1345. He was probably wrong, however, in thinking that. It is more probable that the "Western" colonists were not destroyed, but that as their hunting and nomadic habits developed they assimilated themselves to the Eskimos. It is certain that the colonists, not only in the north but also in the south, experienced terrible difficulties after their loss of political freedom. They became less and less able to pay their tithes; this is evidenced in letters exchanged between the Roman curia (1279, Nicholas III; 1282, Martin IV; 1448, Nicholas V; 1492, Alexander VI Borgia) and their bishops.

Many theories have been advanced to account for the destruction of the two European colonies in Greenland about the middle of the fourteenth century or for their serious and continuous deterioration from that time on. The Eskimos were blamed (by Barðarson and others), also the Black Death, climatic changes making victualing more difficult, malnutrition (lack of vitamins!), breakdown of commerce with Europe. The extermination theory has been developed by a number of scholars, chiefly Danish; the assimilation theory (viz., the colonists were not actually destroyed, but "went native" and have survived to some extent to this day) is favored by a succession of Icelandic or Norwegian scholars, beginning with the Icelandic missionary Egill Thórhallason (1734–89), who visited the ruins of the settlements in 1774 (Efterretning om Rudera, Copenhagen 1776). The latest advocates of the assimilation theory, which seems the more plausible one, are Fridtjof Nansen (1921) and V. Stefansson (books cited above), whom I have closely followed.

Some information on arctic geography was brought to the continent by Scandinavian travelers and pilgrims such as Nikulás Saemundarson (XII-2), who visited the Holy Land in 1151 and wrote an account of his journey in Icelandic; Rafn Sveinbjörnsson (XIII-1), who went to England, France, and Spain c. 1202; the Franciscan Mauritius, who traveled from Norway to Palestine 1270–73 (Introd. 2, 1051); Icelanders who took part in a crusade in 1292 (Antiquités russes d'après les monuments historiques des Islandais et des anciens Scandinaves, édités par la Société royale des antiquaires du Nord, folio, 2, 382, Copenhague 1852). One of these last named may be the author of an Icelandic description of Jerusalem dating from the end of the thirteenth century or the beginning of the fourteenth. Icelandic text with Latin version in Erich Christian Werlauff: Summa geographiae medii aevi ad mentem Islandorum (Copenhagen 1821) and in Antiquités russes (2, 416–20). Röhricht (p. 89, 1890).

Further proof that arctic data were available in Western Europe is afforded in the Libro del conosçimiento written by a Spanish Franciscan c. 1348. He claims that he traveled to Scandinavia, ascended lofty mountains in Norway, and was told of an uninhabited country to the north, where the year "makes one day for six months and another six months night" (p. 10).[27] Farther on (p. 35) he refers to the Antarctic Pole, "where they say that the terrestrial paradise is." There are lofty mountains at that pole, whence the four rivers flow. "Wise men say that

[26] Norsemen traveled as far north as 79°, witness cairns and eider-duck shelters (which Eskimos never built). A runic inscription, dating from c. 1333 (?), has been found north of present Upernivik in latitude 72°55′, about 450 miles above the Arctic Circle. V. Stefansson: Greenland (p. 110, 184, 1942), with reproduction of the runic inscription.

[27] My references are to the English edition by Sir Clements Markham (Hakluyt Society, 1912).

as far as the Antarctic Pole there is a great land forming a tenth part of the whole earth" (p. 43). That is, he conceived the African continent, of which many travelers realized the immensity, as stretching all the way to the South Pole.

Then we have the De casibus virorum illustrium of Boccaccio, who searched out stories of worthy princes not only in the West and East but even in the arctic and antarctic regions. Said Fortuna to him (beginning of book VI), "Tu nunc ab Eoo cardine in occiduum solem, nunc ab arcthico in antarcthicum polum . . ." (after the princeps, Strassburg c. 1474). Or, to quote from the Fall of princes (book VI, l. 92–95), Lydgate's quaint version (Bergen's edition, p. 677; Isis 33, 361):

> "Summe duellid vndir the pool Artyk,
> Be my fauour vpreised to the sterris;
> Othir vndir the pool Antartik,
> Which in contrarye from vs so ferr is."

In short, thanks to the reports coming from Iceland and Greenland, via the merchants, bishops, falconers, etc., and the news brought by northern travelers and pilgrims, educated men of the fourteenth century had some general idea of arctic conditions and realized that people lived in northern regions who were not essentially different from themselves. The Antarctic was fabulous, but the Arctic was brought home to them in many ways.

B. *Byzantine Geography*

For a proper appreciation of the Byzantine geographical ideas of this period one might begin with the Συναγωγή of Maximos Planudes (XIII-2); moreover, Maximos claimed to have rediscovered Ptolemy's geography without maps and to have reconstructed the maps on the basis of the text. If that be true, it is possible that the three oldest MSS of the Ptolemaic maps may be traced back to him.[28] Then one should take Nicephoros Gregoras, who was especially interested in mathematical geography and is said to have written a commentary on the γεωγραφική ὑφήγησις of Ptolemy. Similar work was being done at the academy of Trebizond by Georgios Chrysococces, who compiled tables giving the latitudes and longitudes of the main cities. Georgios was also interested in archaeological geography, and wrote a treatise on the names of those cities.

Another kind of preoccupation is revealed by the anonymous treatise published and analyzed by Armand Delatte to which I have already referred in this chapter,[29] dealing with cosmogony and the place of the earth in the universe, the shape of the earth and the cause of its stability, its size (the Eratosthenian value is quoted). The second part of the treatise is devoted to physical geography, describing briefly the twelve mountains, the four seas, the Ocean, paradise (in the East), climates, earthquakes and how they originate, hot springs, and finally the four elements. All this is very brief, far too brief, and unfortunately undatable; it might be much earlier than the fourteenth century and perhaps a little later (the eight MSS date from the fifteenth century). The unknown author rejects the idea of antichthons on physical and religious grounds; he concedes, however, that the antipodes may be inhabited by birds or reptiles. He gives a "physiological" theory of hot springs which he ascribes to Aristotle but which cannot be found in the Aristotelian writings.

[28] Aubrey Diller: The oldest manuscripts of Ptolemaic maps (Transactions of the American Philological Association 71, 62–67, 3 pl., 1940; Isis 34, 43).

[29] Byzantinische Zeitschrift 30, 511–18, 1929/30; Bull. Académie royale de Belgique, lettres, 18, 189–222, 1932 (Isis 23, 563).

His explanation of earthquakes conforms more to that of the Meteorologica, which has been copied with slight modifications by all Byzantine writers; earthquakes are compared to spasms or palpitations of the human body.[30] He insists that earthquakes have natural causes, excepting of course the one which occurred at the time of the Passion.

Whereas Georgios Chrysococces was concerned mainly with mathematical geography, another member of the remarkable Trebizond group, Andreas Libadenos, chief recorder of the metropolitan church, wrote a rhetorical itinerary from Constantinople to Egypt and Palestine and back to Constantinople and Trebizond. This kind of literary exercise became a favorite one among humanists; we find it practiced as late as the sixteenth century, e.g., by such a man as Busbecq, the first of whose famous Turkish letters appeared under the title Itinera Constantinopolitanum et Amasianum (written 1555, princeps Antwerp 1581).[31]

Though many Orthodox clerics and laymen must have pilgrimed to the Holy Land, I do not know any pilgrim literature in Greek, except the itinerary of Libadenos just mentioned, which is somewhat different from the kind of books generally written by or for pilgrims. There is, however, a genuine pilgrim account written in Russian by Stephen of Novgorod, who left Great Novgorod with eight companions c. 1348 in order to visit the Holy Land. They actually reached Constantinople, but, Stephen's account stopping there, we do not know what happened to them after that.

C. *Jewish Geography*

The Jewish group is small but variegated and distinguished. We should begin with a reference to the Yesod 'olam, written at Toledo in 1310 by Isaac Israeli junior. The second part of it includes a geographical summary. The Yesod 'olam was soon abbreviated in Arabic by the author's own son, Joseph ben Isaac, but that abbreviation is known only through a retranslation into Hebrew by another member of the same family.

The outstanding achievement of Jewish geography in this period—and one of the greatest of all times—is the Kaftor u-feraḥ completed in 1322 by Estori Farḥi. Farḥi belonged to an Andalusian family established in southern France. When the Jews were expelled, in 1306, he moved to Perpignan, to Spain, finally to the Near East. He established himself in the Holy Land and devoted seven years to the study of Palestinian topography. The Kaftor u-feraḥ was the first elaborate work on the subject, and it remained the best until the eighteenth century, or even the nineteenth.

Twelve years later (1334), another Western Jew who had come to Jerusalem to settle, Isaac ben Joseph Ḥelo, wrote an itinerary and topographical essay entitled Shebile di Yerushalim.

A Jew of Barcelona named Jucefe Faquin (= Joseph Faquin) had traveled considerably before coming to Majorca, where he married and established himself. We know of this traveler accidentally because of a petition which he presented to Jacme II, the last king of Majorca, in 1334. He may stand here as a representative of a large group of travelers thanks to whom geographical information was gradually accumulated in Majorca. We shall come back to that in chapters XV and XXIII. Alfred Morel-Fatio: Notes et documents pour servir à l'histoire des

[30] Symeon Seth (XI-2) compared them even to sneezings!

[31] Sarton: Brave Busbecq (Isis 33, 557–75, 1942).

Juifs des Baléares sous la domination aragonaise du XIIIe au XVe siècle (Revue des études juives 4, 31–56, 1882; p. 53). Nothing ad hoc in Rubió y Lluch (1908–21).

An anonymous work of c. 1345 (EJ 7, 263), Ẓel ha-'olam (Shadow of the world), is a cosmographical treatise adapted from the French Image du monde by Gautier of Metz (XIII-1). The Hebrew text was developed by Mattithiah ben Solomon Delaqruṭ, a Polish Jew, who studied at Bologna and wrote on science and qabbala about the middle of the sixteenth century (Delaqruṭ's adaptation was printed in Amsterdam in 1733).

To these men writing in Hebrew may perhaps be added one who wrote in Arabic. I am now referring to the author of the Kitāb al-ṭibb al-qasṭālī, presumably identical with Samuel ben Waqar, physician and treasurer to Alfonso XI of Castile. The most remarkable feature of that book is the chapter devoted to what might be called medical geography.

D. *Muslim Geography*

This section may properly be entitled "Muslim geography," for every man considered in it was a Muslim. We could not have done that if we had included Samuel ben Waqar in it, and that would have been embarrassing, for this section could not be entitled "Arabic geography" either, as some of the writings were in Persian. On the other hand, if Samuel ben Waqar had been listed with the Muslims, then the previous sections could have been entitled "Hebrew geography" as well as "Jewish geography." These remarks are made to indicate the difficulty of classifications, and their artificial nature. Classifications are always necessary and always imperfect.

Our Muslim geographers are so numerous that we must subdivide them into four groups: (1) Mamlūk, (2) 'Irāq, (3) Persia, (4) Maghrib.

D1. *Mamlūk geography*

By Mamlūk we mean the combination of Syria and Egypt then united under the government of the Baḥri Mamlūk dynasty. This subgroup is by far the most important in Islām, even as the Italian group was by far the largest in Christendom.

Before speaking of individual geographers it is well to draw attention to a cadastral survey of Egypt made in 1315 during the third rule of sulṭān Malik al-Nāṣir Muḥammad ibn Qalā'ūn (1309–40). That survey was carried out with considerable care and detail, but is administrative, financial, rather than geographical. For example, the positions of the places are not determined except to say that they are on the outskirts (al-ḍawāḥī) of Cairo, or the province of Qalyūb, etc. (21 provinces are enumerated). For each village the area is given, the nature of the soil, the income which appanagists derive from it, the taxes. That kind of Egyptian "Domesday book" was called, after the sovereign who had ordered it, al-rawk al-Nāṣirī. It remained the administrative standard for a long time, being still so considered by the Egyptian historian al-Maqrīzī (d. 1442), who called it the "last cadaster." It was corrected and modified from time to time, however, as changing conditions required, for example in 1375, 1378, and 1403.

The Rawk Nāṣirī as revised in 1375–76, toward the end of the rule of Malik al-Ashraf Sha'bān (1363–76), grandson of al-Nāṣir Muḥammad, is available in many Arabic and Turkish MSS. It is simply an extract from the original rawk, wherein the names of the new landowners have replaced the names of the old ones, and the revenues have been newly evaluated. That extremely interesting text was edited by Silvestre de Sacy in an appendix to his French translation of the description of Egypt by 'Abd al-Laṭīf (XIII-1) (p. 581–704, Paris 1810). In the determination of place names the editor made use of Yāqūt (XIII-1) and Fīrūzābādī (XIV-2); for each place he indicates the total area (expressed in faddān), the area devoted to foundations (awqāf, pl. of waqf) or pensions (azrāq, pl. of rizq), the total income in danānīr (pl. of dīnār). In the MSS all these numbers are written in full words, without the use of numerals. This is another proof that the "Arabic" numerals were hardly used, even in those Arabic documents where they would have been most helpful. Of course, the writing in words may have been adopted in this case to make falsification more difficult, yet if the value of Arabic numerals had been properly appreciated they would have been added to their verbal transcriptions.

The greatest geographer of the age, not only in Islām but anywhere, was the Syrian prince best known under the name of Abū-l-Fidā' (d. 1331). His Taqwīm al-buldān (Tables of the countries), composed in 1316–21, is an elaborate geographical treatise describing almost the whole of the known world, and especially valuable with regard to North Africa and Asia. In the generalities placed at the beginning the author remarked (being the first to do so) that traveling around the world entails the loss (or gain) of a day. His descriptions of each country are followed by tables listing the main cities, and giving their coordinates and other data patient of brief statement (fig. 19). The longitudes and latitudes have been established experimentally, or deduced approximatively from the distances to other places the position of which was exactly determined. He was keenly aware of the imperfection of his coordinates, for he had consulted for that special purpose earlier books such as the Kitāb rasm al-rub' al-ma'mūr (Description of the civilized quarter), translated from the Greek for al-Ma'mūn;[32] the Kitāb al-aṭwāl wal-'urūḍ (Book of longitudes and latitudes), written by an unknown author in the tenth or eleventh century before 1030; al-Qānūn al-Mas'ūdī of al-Bīrūnī (XI-1), written c. 1030; finally, the book of Ibn Sa'īd al-Maghribī (XIII-2). Now the data obtained from these books were generally different, and sometimes the differences were considerable. Abū-l-Fidā' was so honest that he gave them all, but no wonder his confidence was shaken. See other remarks made on this subject in the astronomical section above.

We may now deal more rapidly with the other Mamlūk geographers. I noted seven of them who wrote geographical or cosmographical treatises. Aḥmad al-Ṭīnī is a mysterious personality perhaps identical with Muḥammad ibn Ibrāhīm al-Waṭwāṭ (XIII-2), who died in 1318. At any rate the latter wrote an encyclopaedia of natural sciences and geography, and a book bearing almost the same title is ascribed to the former and many times referred to by al-Dimashqī. These two books may be identical even if the authors are not. Al-Dimashqī, who lived until 1326, composed an encyclopaedia of the same kind, but far better known, perhaps the best of its time; though very inferior to Abū-l-Fidā's Taqwīm al-buldān from the mathematical standpoint, the Nukhbat al-dahr is much richer in every other respect.

Al-Nuwairī and Ibn Faḍlallāh al-'Umarī represent a different type of encyclopaedist, characteristic of Mamlūk culture. They both compiled large works con-

[32] I quote this book and the following exactly as Abū-l-Fidā' quotes them (Reinaud's Arabic text, p. 73–75, 1840). The Rasm al-rub' al-ma'mūr is probably a translation or adaptation of Ptolemy's geography, maybe that prepared by al-Kindī (IX-1), to whom al-Mas'ūdī (X-1) ascribes a Risālat rasm al-ma'mūr min al-arḍ (Brockelmann 1, 210, 1898)?

taining not only materials like those collected by al-Dimashqī, but also a mass of information on ethics and politics, history, biography, and literature. Their purpose was to provide all the knowledge which an administrator or chancellor might need in any eventuality, with a view not only to efficiency, but also to literary prestige. Al-Nuwairī wrote the Nihāyat al-arab fī funūn al-adab, Ibn Faḍlallāh al-'Umarī the Masālik al-abṣār fī mamālik al-amṣār. On account of their enormous size, neither of these works is as yet completely published. Excellent editions of both, prepared by the late Aḥmad Zakī pasha, are in course of publication by the Egyptian government, but thus far only a small part of each is available. It would be difficult to compare these works in their totality, even if we had complete and convenient editions of them; at present one must restrict oneself to comparing them with reference to definite topics as the opportunities arise. One of the superiorities of the Masālik al-abṣār lies in the treatment of Abyssinia, North Africa, and the western Sūdān (Mandingo empire). Some of the Mandingo salāṭīn were interested in Atlantic voyages of discovery, and thus continued Muslim traditions going back to the tenth or ninth century. Ibn Faḍlallāh's work is therefore of special value for the history of geographical explorations.

Two geographers are connected with the city of Ṣafad in Galilee. One of them, generally called al-Ṣafadī, is immortalized by his immense biographical dictionary, but he wrote various other works, including one on geography bearing the same title as that of Ibn Faḍlallāh. His given name and patronymic were Khalīl ibn Aibak, whereas the other al-Ṣafadī, to whom we owe a description of Egypt, was named al-Ḥasan ibn 'Abdallāh. This al-Ḥasan flourished in Egypt c. 1294–1312; Khalīl died in Damascus 1363, after having served the government in many cities of the Mamlūk empire.

Of a much humbler kind was the activity of Ibn al-Firkāḥ, who praised the beauty of Damascus and wrote a guide for Muslim pilgrims to the holy places in Palestine.

D2. *Geography in 'Irāq*

The two men whom I classify under the label 'Irāq might have been treated with their Mamlūk colleagues, for relations between Syria and Mesopotamia were abundant. In fact, both men spent part of their lives in Egypt and Syria. The reader may thus cancel mentally the separation which I have established between these two groups.

Ibn Shabīb wrote an encyclopaedia of geography, natural history, and folklore which was almost forgotten as such, but is well known (not only in Arabic but also in Persian and Turkish translations) as a part of the Kharīdat al-'ajā'ib put together a century later by the younger Ibn al-Wardī (fl. 1446). The writing of large encyclopaedias (not only in Islām, but in Christendom and China) was greatly facilitated by the absorption of other works, sometimes in their entirety. Ibn al-Wardī did so, and, in the usual style of plagiarists, he quoted many sources, omitting only to mention his main victim, Ibn Shabīb!

The other 'Irāqī, 'Abd al-Mu'min ibn 'Abd al-Ḥaqq, compiled a summary of the vast dictionary of Yāqūt (XIII-1), restricting himself to the geographical data. I can testify to the usefulness of that summary, the Marāṣid al-iṭṭilā', because I use it repeatedly. Though it is considerably smaller than Yāqūt's Mu'jam al-buldān, it contains some geographical data not to be found in the older work.

D3. *Geography in Persia and in Persian*

If the separation of 'Irāq from Syria was a little artificial, the separation of Persia from either or from both of them is very natural. The difference is accentuated by the use of another language, Persian instead of (or in addition to) Arabic, and in the case of the second man it is aggravated by a difference in religion, Shī'a instead of Sunnī.

The first is our old friend Quṭb al-dīn al-Shīrāzī (XIII-2), who died in 1311. He wrote mainly in Arabic, but could and did write also in his native language. His Nihāyat al-idrāk fī dirāyat al-aflāk deals not only with astronomy, geodesy, and mathematical geography, but also with physical geography, describing the seas and climates, in the manner of al-Bīrūnī. When Buscarello de' Ghizolfi, a Genoese in the service of Arghūn (īl-khān of Persia, 1284–91), was on his way to Europe in 1289, Quṭb al-dīn explained the journey to him by means of a map. What a pity that that map is lost!

The Nuzhat al-qulūb of Ḥamdallāh Mustawfī al-Qazwīnī, completed by him toward the end of his life (1340), is an elaborate Persian encyclopaedia of natural history and geography. The geographical part is concerned mainly with the holy cities of Arabia and Palestine and with Īrān. Other countries are disposed of more rapidly. This was a logical arrangement in a book written in Persian for Persians.

D4. *Geography in the Maghrib*

The geographical literature of the Western Muslim world is entirely different from that of the Eastern, which, as we saw, was almost exclusively of the encyclopaedic type. The Eastern writers whom we have passed in review were trying to give an account of the world, explaining the sphericity of the earth, the distribution of seas and mountains, the different climates, the coordinates of main cities, the peculiarities of each country. They were always writing geographical textbooks, which might be part, or not, of larger encyclopaedias.

The Moors of that time were more interested in itineraries, which contained usually, according to Muslim tradition, accounts of the important or learned men of the cities where the travelers had stopped. Books of that class may vary according to the amount of biographical information included in them, but there is always some amount of it; in general, information relative to plants and animals is scanty, if not negligible. Their geography was primarily, if not exclusively, human. They traveled to see people, especially learned people, and they were likely to be indifferent and blind to the rest. Under the combined influence of their deep faith in God and their unfailing interest in the servants of God, they could easily overlook the hardships and perils of their long journeys.

Muḥammad ibn Rushaid (XIII-2), who died in Fās 1321, composed three itineraries relative to Spain, Africa, and the two holy cities. Al-Tijānī left Tunis in 1306 to accomplish the Pilgrimage, but illness obliged him to stop his journey at Tripoli of Libya. He returned home after an absence of almost three years. The account of his journey, though restricted to a relatively small part of North Africa, is very full and valuable, being one of our best sources for the study of contemporary conditions in the Ḥafṣī domains. Muḥammad ibn Rushaid and al-Tijānī were Moroccans; our third traveler, al-Balawī, was an Andalusian. He wrote an account of his pilgrimage (1335–40), devoting most of his space to the learned men whom it had been his privilege to meet.

In spite of the facts that the motive of the Pilgrimage was primarily religious, and that the pilgrims who recorded their experiences (as distinguished from the great mass of them who could not or did not record them) were deeply interested in theological discussions and in every aspect of *Muslim* life, we gather from a multiplicity of sources that the average pilgrim did not lose interest in earthly matters, particularly in women and business. It was not unusual for a pilgrim to bewive himself repeatedly during the long journey, nor was it unusual for him to indulge in trade. Of course the temptation was great for any individual, if he was in the least mercenary, to carry with him some of the products of a city in order to resell them in another whereto he was bound in any case. Even scholars or poets did it, witness the case of 'Abd al-bāsiṭ ibn Khalīl,[33] who took advantage of his literary prestige to wheedle tax exemptions and other commercial privileges out of his hosts, the rulers of Tunis and Oran.

E. *Geography in the Far East*

1. *Relations between the Far East and the West*

Before speaking of geographical knowledge in the Far East, especially China, it is well to recall how much the knowledge of China had increased in Western countries. To avoid repetitions, I shall simply send the reader back to what I said above about the Italians in China; to my notes on the Arabic accounts of Quṭb al-dīn al-Shīrāzī, al-Dimashqī, al-Nuwairī, Abū-l-Fidā', Ibn Shabīb; and to the Persian accounts of Rashīd al-dīn, al-Banākatī, Ḥamdallāh Mustawfī al-Qazwīnī. The trade roads connecting the Far East with the West across the lands and the seas were many. The sea road was in Muslim hands, and Christians had to travel inland. In addition to these relations between Asia and Europe (and North Africa), there was also much internal (Asiatic) traffic between China on the one hand, and Central Asia and India on the other. That internal traffic was neither Christian nor even Muslim, but, if a religious name must be given to it, Buddhist. We have much indirect information about it. For example, the famous Russian explorer Petr Kuzmich Kozlov (1863–1935) found many proofs in the ruins of Kara Khoto that that city had been in touch with Tibet, India, even Persia, as well as with China. Witness also the two hexaglot inscriptions on the monumental door of Chü yung kuan in the Nankow pass, on the road from Peking to Kalgan. These inscriptions, dating from 1345, were written in Sanskrit, Tibetan, Mongol in Phagspa (XIII-2) script, Uighūr, Chinese, and an unknown language.[34]

Embassies were circulating between China and the West, and reports were being sent to and from the popes. Not only were the Mongol rulers, the great khān, of China in touch with the West, but also their vassals, the īl-khān of Persia. There is preserved a letter dated 1305 from Uljāi'tū Khudābanda (īl-khān 1304–16) to Philippe le Bel of France, and in the annals of al-Maqrīzī (d. 1442) there is a brief

[33] 'Abd al-bāsiṭ ibn Khalīl (1440–1514) does not belong to our period, but manners and customs were essentially the same in the fourteenth and fifteenth centuries. Robert Brunschvig: Deux récits de voyage en Afrique du Nord (p. 93, 112, Paris 1936; Isis 34, 26).

[34] P. K. Kozlov: Mongolei, Amdo und die tote Stadt Chara-Choto. Die Expedition der Russischen geographischen Gesellschaft 1907–9 (Berlin 1925). Prince Roland Bonaparte: Documents de l'époque mongole des XIIIe et XIVe siècles (Paris 1896).

account of an embassy sent in 1338 by the "king" of China with a letter addressed to the sulṭān Muḥammad ibn Qalā'ūn asking for enlightenment concerning Islām.[35]

As to the relations with the curia, see my notes on John of Montecorvino and on other Franciscans, Peregrine of Castello, Andrew of Perugia, Odoric of Pordenone, John of Marignolli. The latter was a member of a mission sent in 1338 by Benedict XII to Hui Tsung in return for an imperial mission received in the same year.

2. *The place of geography in Chinese learning. Topographical literature*

In order to understand the progress (or lack of progress) of geographical studies in China, one must realize that those studies were given a very definite and very large place in the dynastic histories, under the title ti-li. The section so entitled included essays on historical geography, gazetteers or local histories, and much information on each district or locality, chiefly historical, administrative, anecdotic, biographical, archaeological; subsidiarily physical (natural features and products, climate, hills and rivers, etc.). See my note in Introd. 1, 676, and Gardner (p. 102, 1938). The same remarks apply to the place of geography in Korean historiography (Courant 1, clxvi, 1894; Trollope p. 30, 1932). That mixture of history and geography, or rather complete subordination of geography to purely human factors, was not typical of China and Korea alone, but also of Europe almost until our own days. The Chinese way of doing it, however, was very different from the European one. Their great fondness for gazetteers and topographical studies began very early and developed luxuriantly. The oldest extant gazetteer, the Hua yang kuo chih, was written in 347 by Ch'ang Chü, and is devoted to a country now in southern Shensi and northern Ssŭch'uan. Some 400 gazetteers (out of which only 28 are extant) were compiled during the Sung dynasty, and some 79 (11 extant) during the Yüan.

An elaborate history and catalogue raisonné of the ti-li literature was published in 1930 by Ch'ü Hsüan-ying in his Fang chih k'ao kao (Preliminary studies in gazetteers), but many more gazetteers have come to light since then. The numbers quoted in the preceding paragraph were obtained from Mr. Chu Shih-chia,[36] who is now the leading authority on the subject.

As an example of topographical literature in the first half of the fourteenth century, it will suffice to mention the book written by Huang Chin, born in I-wu, Chehkiang, in order to describe his native country. It was presumably composed after 1315, when Huang received his chin shih.

3. *Cartography*

Chinese cartography is at least as ancient as topography, if not more so. Pei Hsiu (III-2) has been called the father of scientific cartography in China! The earliest maps extant, however, date only from 1137 (Introd. 2, 225, 41). An elaborate map of China, called Yü-t'u, was drawn in 1311–20 by Chu Ssŭ-pên; following old traditions, it was divided into squares the sides of which measure a definite number of li. Such division was generally decimal but independent of map projection. This suggests that the Chinese cartographers had not even

[35] Hennig (3, 133–35, 187–90, 1938).

[36] Cataloguer of the Chinese collection of the Library of Congress. Information obtained through the courtesy of Dr. A. W. Hummel (letter of Aug. 29, 1941). For an analysis of the Fang chih k'ao kao see Report of the Library of Congress for 1931–32, p. 189. For the continuation of that tradition in our own days see Isis (34, 29).

thought of the curvature of the earth's surface. The Yü-t'u is lost, but its main features were traditionally continued in all succeeding maps of China until the end of the sixteenth century, when new principles were introduced by the Jesuit father Matteo Ricci (1584).

An anonymous map of Central Asia was included in the administrative encylopaedia Ching shih ta tien (1329–31).

Many Chinese books deal with rivers and waterways. That tradition, introduced by the "water classic," Shui ching, can be traced at least to the beginning of our era. About the middle of the fourteenth century Wang Hsi composed a treatise of that kind devoted to the River supreme, the Yellow River (Huang ho).[37] This might have been listed in my note on topographical literature, but I speak of it here because it includes six charts representing the floods and erratic changes of the mighty river, which has throughout the ages dispensed with complete impartiality to millions of people her bounties or punishments—plenty or starvation, life or death.

4. *Descriptions of foreign countries*

We owe to an Annamite scholar, Li Tsê, a history of his country written in or before 1307 in Chinese and according to the Chinese historiographical tradition. Thus his treatise included a geographical introduction and even a map (the latter, however, is lost). There are also items of geographical interest (e.g., notes on natural products) in the rest of the volume, and a geographical poem at the end.

Wang Ta-yüan wrote c. 1349 an account of many parts of the Malay archipelago.

5. *Relations between China and other parts of the East*

This title suggests that we might end this Chinese section as we began it. We began with an account of the relations between the Far East and Europe; we shall now ask ourselves what were the relations between China and other parts of the Far East. The previous paragraphs have already given us a part of the answer. It is clear that the Chinese had some knowledge of Indo-China and of the Malay countries. How did they cultivate relations with their Eastern neighbors?

The oldest as well as the crudest method was war. In 1309 the Mongols tried to land in Hakata (northern part of Kyūshū, one of the largest Japanese islands, the one nearest to Korea); it was in that very neighborhood that the fleet sent by Kublai Khān (XIII-2) in 1281 had been destroyed. To the national wars should be added the private ones conducted by pirates. Some of the latter must have obtained a good practical knowledge of the coasts. In 1301, Chinese pirates attacked Satsuma. The compliment was returned by Japanese pirates (wakō), who attacked the coasts of Korea and China (chiefly in 1308). More wakō attacks occurred along the Korean coast in 1350, so much so that that date is sometimes quoted as the beginning of the wakō invasions.

There are also many accounts of peaceful sailing vessels. In 1305–7, Japanese junks sailed to Ning-po. In 1317, a vessel sailing from Miyako-jima (Ryūkyū) ran aground in Chehkiang. In 1325, Japanese junks were restricted to the Ningpo harbor, needed special authorization, and were assumed to bring tribute to the emperor of China. Commerce was mixed with religion. We hear in 1325 of a Kenchōji-bune being sent to China; that is, a ship sent by the temple Kenchō-ji of Kamakura (Rinzai-shū, Introd. 2, 559). In 1341, we hear for the first time

[37] A detailed description of the Yellow River, Huang Ho yüan wei, was begun at the same time by Su T'ien-chio, who died in 1352 before completing it.

of the Tenryūji-bune, ships sent to China by the Tenryū-ji, another Rinzai temple, in Saga near Kyōto. Two left in 1341, a third in 1342. They carried probably gold, copper, sulphur, fans, and swords, and brought back sapecs (cash), religious books, incense, tea, and textiles.

The main and best links between these countries were probably supplied by monks, who traveled either singly or in small groups from monastery to monastery, and did almost as much for the integration of Buddhist Asia as did the ḥujjāj (pl. of ḥājj) for the integration of Islām. In 1308, 1331–36, 1342–49, monkish goings and comings increased between China and Japan. A Japanese monk went to China in 1320, and a Chinese one arrived in Japan in the following year; more Japanese monks sailed to China in 1323–24. In 1326, Japanese monks returned home, and another traveled to China in order to obtain the Fu-chou edition of the Tripiṭaka.[38] In 1350, monks returned to Japan on a Chinese commercial junk. Moïse C. Haguenauer: Encore la question des Gores (Journal asiatique 226, 67–115, map, 1935; chiefly p. 94).

As the geographical literature published in Chinese, Japanese, and perhaps in other Eastern languages is more deeply explored, we shall be able to appreciate more correctly the knowledge which each Far Eastern country had of the others by the middle of the fourteenth century. It is probable that that knowledge was more elaborate than we realize today.

X. NATURAL HISTORY

One might think that the history of "natural history" would invite a topical subdivision of the subject, but so many of the writers to be mentioned in this chapter, whether Christian, Jewish, Muslim, or Chinese, were interested in natural objects of every or any kind—stones, plants, animals—that a topical subdivision would oblige us to reconsider at least thrice the same individuals. Therefore, we must compromise. We shall first review the main naturalists in geographical order, then consider a number of subjects in topical order. Some of the authors mentioned in the geographical survey, but not by any means all of them, will reappear in this or that section of the topical survey.

Geographical survey

A. *Latin Christendom*

A1. *Italy*

The largest group of Christians, and by far, is the Italian one. It is headed by two outstanding personalities, Pietro dei Crescenzi and Dante. Though Pietro was already seventy years of age at the beginning of the century, he did not complete his main work (the most popular book on husbandry down to the middle of the sixteenth century) until c. 1306. His Ruralia commoda are one of the classics of mediaeval science. As to Dante, one must always return to him when one investigates the thought of the century. A number of monographs have been written concerning his knowledge of plants, of animals, of embryology, etc. An analysis of them would take too much space and would be somewhat irrelevant. We fully expect the greatest poet of the age to speak of nature, and it is wise to ask oneself with reference to every special item whether Dante spoke of it or not; at present we can only refer to him in a general way.

[38] Two editions of the Tripiṭaka had then already been printed in Fu-chou, Fuhkien, the first in 1080–1100, the second in 1150–1215 (information kindly given to me by my Harvard colleague George Elisséeff, letter dated Sept. 9, 1941).

Then consider the herbalists (to whom we shall return more elaborately presently). There is the physician John of Milano, who compiled an illustrated herbal for Philippe de Valois sometime before the latter's accession to the throne of France (as Philippe VI in 1328). Matthaeus Sylvaticus, who kept a botanical garden in Salerno and observed plants in many localities, is known to posterity because of his Pandectae, a dictionary of simples, completed in 1317. Guido da Vigevano, the anatomist, made experiments on the properties of aconite (monkshood).

Dino del Garbo, "expositor Avicennae," applying his scholastic methods to biology, was thus led to ascribe a priori the birth and development of living beings to a kind of fermentation. Another Florentine Dino, the chronicler Dino Compagni, wrote a didactic poem, Intelligenza, wherein he discusses the virtues of precious stones.

Finally, we have an impressive group of travelers, whose writings contain many observations of interest to the naturalist: Marco Polo (XIII-2); Giovanni de Montecorvino (XIII-2); Odorico da Pordenone, who observed in the Far East many things which had escaped Polo's attention (I have already remarked on the very curious omissions in the latter's curiosity, Introd. 2, 1058); and Niccolò da Poggibonsi, who kept his eyes open for strange animals while traveling in the Holy Land, but was always even more ready to listen to fancy tales.

A2. *Spain and Portugal*

"A tout seigneur tout honneur"; the good king Dinis o Lavrador (XIII-2), who lived and ruled until 1325, initiating so many of the best features of Portuguese culture, appeals particularly to the naturalist. Indeed, he was in a practical way a great teacher of husbandry; he improved the methods of cultivation, and planted pine forests along the coast of the district of Leiria (in Estremadura). This was done primarily in order to stop the movement of sand dunes tending to invade fertile lands,[1] but the timber of those forests made possible later (this, Dinis could not have foreseen) the building of the ships needed for the colonial expansion of Portugal. Another Portuguese deserves mention, Giraldes, Dinis' physician, who wrote a treatise on poultry.

The leading Spanish writer of the same age was a prince of royal blood, Don Juan Manuel of Castile. He composed the earliest book on the chase in Castilian.

A3. *France*

The French doctors seem to have paid but little attention to nature. The Franciscan Vital Du Four was somewhat of an exception in that respect, that is, if one of the works bearing his name, the Pro conservanda sanitate, is truly his. At any rate, the author of that health manual showed a modicum of natural curiosity.

I have already told how Petrarca inaugurated "alpinism" with his ascent of Mount Ventoux in 1336. He may have been emulated and even preceded on that same mountain by Buridan.

A4. *Germany*

The German record, though short, is far more distinguished. Eberhard von Wampen wrote a didactic poem, "The mirror of nature," in Low German. The first great scientific writer in German, however, was the Bavarian Conrad of Megenberg, whose Buch der Natur, composed c. 1350, was a free translation of the De

[1] A similar task was accomplished four and a half centuries later (1786) by Nicolas Théodore Brémontier (1738–1809) in the French Landes. See his Mémoire sur les dunes, 1796 (NBG 7, 317–18, 1855).

natura rerum of Thomas of Cantimpré (XIII-1). That book is one of the outstanding scientific works of the Middle Ages in any European vernacular.

B. *Byzantium*

The interest of common people in living things is illustrated by animal and plant stories written in vulgar Greek, such as the Pulologos, dealing with birds, "The children's story of the four-footed animals," "The ritual of the honorable ass," "The beautiful story of the ass, the wolf, and the fox," "The story of the fruits." The intention of these writings was ethical and satirical, but they reveal curious aspects of botanical and zoological folklore.

Similar aspects are shown us in a more sophisticated form in some of the didactic poems of Manuel Philes.

A botanical glossary was compiled by Neophytos Prodromenos sometime in the fourteenth century.

C. *Armenia*

A treatise on the botany and zoology of Cilicia, of doubtful age and practically unknown, is ascribed to one Thomas of Cilicia. Its production may be connected or not with the translations of hippological books from Arabic into Armenian made by order of king Hayton. These matters need investigation. The little I say of them should be considered simply as a question mark.

D. *Israel*

Ibn Rushd's commentary on the zoology of Aristotle was translated in 1302 from Arabic into Hebrew by Jacob ben Maḥir ibn Tibbon (XIII-2). His commentary on the pseudo-Aristotelian De plantis was translated, together with the text itself, by Qalonymos ben Qalonymos.

Bible commentators would be led inevitably to the discussion of natural questions. The bulky results of their inquiries and meditations have not yet been sufficiently explored from our point of view. Our knowledge of mediaeval folklore will increase materially when such explorations are made more completely and more thoroughly by scientifically minded scholars. To illustrate, consider the verse "And ye shall take you on the first day the boughs of goodly trees, branches of palm trees and the boughs of thick trees and willows of the brook, and ye shall rejoice before the Lord your God seven days" (Leviticus 23:40). These words caused Baḥya ben Asher of Saragossa to remark, "Not only among palm trees are there male and female, but among all the species of the plants as well as of the minerals there is to be found the division of male and female in a natural way." Solomon Gandz: Artificial fertilization of date-palms in Palestine and Arabia (Isis 23, 245–50, 1935; p. 246).

E. *Islām*

The most prolific and creative writers on natural history were Muslim. So many were they that it is necessary to divide them into four groups: (1) Maghrib, (2) Yaman, (3) Mamlūk (Syria and Egypt), (4) Persia.

E1. *Maghrib*

The itineraries of the Moroccan Muḥammad ibn Rushaid (XIII-2) are remarkable in that he pays some attention to natural history and does not almost completely restrict himself, as most Muslim travelers did, to humanities.

Muḥammad al-Shafra and Ibn Luyūn continued the fine horticultural traditions of Muslim Spain. The former was a renowned herbalist and created a botanic garden in Cadiz. Ibn Luyūn wrote a poem on agriculture.

E2. *Yaman*

One of the members of the Rasūlī dynasty, the fifth sulṭān, al-Mujāhid 'Alī, composed c. 1327 an important treatise on the care and breeding not only of horses, but also of other animals, such as asses, mules, camels, elephants, buffaloes, sheep, and cattle.

E3. *Mamlūk*

The Mamlūk group is as usual the most important, its members being more numerous than the rest of the Muslims of the Mashriq and those of the Maghrib put together.

Most of the naturalists flourishing under Baḥrī Mamlūk patronage were of the encyclopaedic type, of which there were two kinds, the purely scientific type (al-Dimashqī, Abū-l-Fidā', Ibn Shabīb[2]) and what might be called the administrative or humanistic type (al-Nuwairī, Ibn Faḍlallāh al-'Umarī).

The Taqwīm al-buldān of Abū-l-Fidā' contains occasional notes on minerals, plants, and animals, though much fewer than one would wish. He took pains to define the climate of each country, but apparently did not yet realize that the study of the flora and fauna offers us one of the best means of appreciating its climatic possibilities. Al-Dimashqī's cosmography is considerably richer in natural history, and the same can be said of Ibn Shabīb's. Both the Nukhbat al-dahr and the Jāmi' al-funūn would deserve to be thoroughly analyzed by mineralogists, botanists, and zoologists. I do not expect that they would find great treasures, but a good many curious facts.

The two other encyclopaedists, al-Nuwairī and al-'Umarī, were more ambitious in that they planned to cover the whole field of natural history and human history combined. Their immense works, the Nihāyat al-arab of al-Nuwairī and the Masālik al-abṣār of al-'Umarī, are also rich in "naturalia." A comparative analysis of the five works would be very desirable.

Arabs have always been deeply interested in horses, camels, sheep, and a few other domestic animals, and hence we may count on finding in their literature a number of books dealing with these subjects or centered upon them. To consider only the horses, their study branched out in many directions—their normal care and breeding, that is, natural history and husbandry; the treatment of their ailments, that is, veterinary medicine; the use of them in peacetime, that is, horsemanship, or in wartime, that is, a part of the military art; the study of their names, that is, philology, or of the traditions concerning them, that is, a part of law and of ḥadīth; finally, the study of the virtues of the men using them, that is, chivalry (mark the word). I am not inventing these categories; they come naturally to my mind, because I have examined books illustrating each of them, or various combinations of them, up to the combination of all of them. One of the most remarkable books on horses has already been quoted in the paragraph on Yaman,

[2] Ibn Shabīb was born in 'Irāq but flourished in Egypt.

the one composed by one of the salāṭīn of that country. Four more in this half of a century were produced in Syria and Egypt, and no wonder, for the Mamlūk rulers were famous for their cavalry.

'Abd al-Mu'min al-Dimiyāṭī wrote the Kitāb faḍl al-khail, a collection of hippic traditions. Lājīn ibn 'Abdallāh (d. 1337) composed a treatise on cavalry tactics. The prolific author Ibn Qayyim al-Jawzīya devoted at least one of his works to horses and to equitation in peace and war. By far the best of these authors was Ibn al-Mundhir, who wrote the most elaborate hippic treatise of the Middle Ages, the Kitāb al-Nāṣirī.

Ibn al-Akfānī, who was an 'Irāqī but who may be placed in this section because he flourished in Cairo, wrote an account of fourteen precious stones and their virtues.

E4. *Persia*

The only Persian writers I can think of in this connection are 'Abdallāh ibn 'Alī al-Kāshānī, Rashīd al-dīn, and Ḥamdallāh Mustawfī. The three of them wrote in Persian. We have already spoken of the first apropos of his account of the glazing of earthenware. That account constitutes the last chapter of a treatise of his on precious stones, and thus differentiates that treatise in the most remarkable manner from every other lapidary known to me.

One of Rashīd al-dīn's minor writings, the Book of animals and monuments, discussed a number of questions related to husbandry, such as the cultivation of flowers and trees, beekeeping, the destruction of pests, stockbreeding, etc. Unfortunately, that text has not yet been found. His other writings occasionally include items of interest to the naturalist, for he was a man of endless curiosity but quick to focus his attention on essentials.

The Nuzhat al-qulūb of Ḥamdallāh Mustawfī is a scientific encyclopaedia comparable to those produced at the same time in the Mamlūk countries, but written in Persian. The comparative analysis of these works, which I suggested above, should be extended of course to this Persian one, and a correct appreciation of their respective values would be possible only when that analysis was completed. Of course, Ḥamdallāh's information was largely derived from Arabic sources, indeed from the same sources used by his Mamlūk colleagues, hence we cannot expect essential differences between his compilation and theirs. The first part of it is devoted to the three kingdoms of nature, but the primary aim is medical. The zoological part is superior to the same part in Arabic encyclopaedias in at least one respect: it is more naturalistic, less philological. This may be due to the author's medical purpose, or to his position as a state accountant, for both those conditions discouraged wordiness and invited scientific realism.

F. *China*

The Chinese have distinguished themselves from time immemorial as untiring and ingenious farmers.[3] It is not surprising, then, that they have published many books on agriculture, the class of such writings being called nung chia;[4] it is rather more surprising that these writings appeared relatively late. The earliest is a

[3] For a general account of their immemorial methods see Franklin Hiram King: Farmers of forty centuries, or permanent agriculture in China, Korea and Japan (452 p., ill., Madison, Wis. 1911). Revised ed. by Joseph Percy Bruce (380 p., 209 ill., New York 1927).

[4] Wylie (p. 93–95, 1922). The titles of many books of that class beginning with "nung" will be easily found in my Chinese index.

tract on the construction of plows, Lei ssŭ ching, by Lu Kuei-mêng, of the T'ang dynasty; other early ones being the Nung shu of Ch'ên-fu (XII-1) and the album Kêng chih t'u shih by Lou Shou (XII-2).

Two important additions to that literature were made in the year 1314. The first was a new Nung shu in twenty-two chüan (twelve of which were devoted to illustrations), compiled by the great inventor Wang Chên. That treatise was transmitted to us in the encyclopaedia Yung Lo ta tien, compiled a century later, whence it was extracted and reconstructed again three centuries later under Ch'ien Lung. In Wang Chên's time the leading book on agriculture was still the Nung sang chi yao, which had been written in 1273 at the request of Kublai Khān (XIII-2), and might thus be called the imperial treatise, the standard textbook of the Yüan dynasty. A supplement to it, entitled Nung-sang-i-shih ts'o-yao, was published by Lu Ming-shan in 1314. It is a farmer's calendar wherein the latter's occupations are described month by month.

For the study of Chinese folklore on rocks, plants, and animals it may be profitable to consult Arthur de Carle Sowerby: Nature in Chinese art (204 p., beautifully illustrated, New York 1940), but with due caution on the historical side (L. Carrington Goodrich, Journal of the American Oriental Society 60, 580–84).

Special subjects

1. *General surveys. Theory of evolution*

Many scholars were interested in the whole of creation and tried to describe it in its diverse aspects and modalities, and thus there were published a series of books wherein the three kingdoms of nature were surveyed. We came across five Arabic ones, one Persian, and one (or two) in German. The combination of these languages, Arabic, Persian, German, is curious; it is the first time we meet it.

Other scholars and theologians, though lacking the encyclopaedic tendencies of those just mentioned, were trying to solve what would be called today biological problems, or even more general problems dealing with the origin and evolution of things. That is natural enough. Every thinking man must ask himself such questions, and, if he be so inclined, finally write a book *περὶ φύσεως* or de natura rerum. In the fourteenth century such tendencies would not take the form of monographs, but would appear more often within the context of Biblical, Talmudic, Qur'ānic, or Aristotelian commentaries.

The fundamental problem was the general problem of evolution. Granted the creation, how did it develop and become gradually what we are witnessing today? We may recall that Christian doctors like St. Augustine (V-1) and Muslim ones like al-Naẓẓām (IX-1) had already postulated a dynamic creation instead of a static and final one. They assumed that God had created an evolving world. According to Ibn Rushd (XII-2), God's creative efforts never cease. His creation is not a matter of a moment, or of six days, but of eternity. He never stops creating, and hence his creatures must continue to change as time unrolls.[5] This conception of creative evolution, or rather of evolutive creation, tallied very well

[5] D. B. Macdonald: Continuous re-creation and atomic time in Muslim scholastic theology (Isis 9, 326–44, 1927).

with the Aristotelian scala naturae. The "ladder of nature" appealed to Muslim imagination; their theologians and cosmographers liked to outline the progress of nature from mineral to plant, from plant to animal, from animal to man, and to insist on the interrelations existing between all the objects of creation because of their common union with the Creator. That outline is clearly expressed by al-Mas'ūdī (X-1). The next problems raised by any such outline were relative to the transitions from one order of beings to another. How do minerals change into plants? plants into animals? animals into men? Where are the "missing links"? A famous answer was given c. 1155 by the Persian Niẓāmī-i-'Arūḍī (XII-2) suggesting as links the corals, the date palms, and some kind of monkey.[6] The date palms were selected because they had the animal virtue of sexuality. It has been shown before (Introd. 2, 62) that St. Thomas Aquinas (XIII-2) had curiously adumbrated the view of plant sexuality. The Jewish mystic Baḥya ben Asher postulated the existence of sexuality not only among plants but even among minerals (text quoted above). The idea of a sexuality pervading the whole of nature may be found in mystical books of many peoples and is often embedded in their languages.[7] As to the other link, conceived as a monkey, an anthropoid ape, or a pygmy, its history can be traced back to ancient times. This is not the place to relate that very curious story. It suffices to insist that the idea of a ladder of nature, and implicitly of evolution, was not uncommon, if sporadic, throughout the Middle Ages, especially among Muslims. In spite of the uninterrupted growth of Neoplatonism and Augustinianism in Christendom, that idea was perhaps rarer among Christians than among Muslims, yet it never died out. We find it, e.g., in the Liber de ascensu et descensu intellectus which Ramon Lull wrote in Montpellier 1304. It is true Lull knew Arabic and he may have obtained it from Arabic writings.

Evolutionary views were more congenial to mystically minded people, to all those (and they were many) whose hearts had been warmed up by Neoplatonism, Christian mysticism, Jewish qabbalah, or Muslim taṣawwuf. No wonder, then, that some of the Islamic brotherhoods or ṭuruq were hospitable to them. The best illustration of this is given us by the Baktāshīya, though the chronology of their views is obscure. That brotherhood is said to have been founded before the middle of the fourteenth century, yet it is probable that its curious views on evolution—down and up—were not immediately developed. They might very well date from the fourteenth century, however, for their constituent parts are each and all more ancient. These Baktāshīya views are clearly explained by Birge (p. 115, 1937):[8]

"This development is pictured in terms of two Great Arcs, one downward, the Arc of Descent, *kavsı nuzul*, descending from the Divine Source in emanations containing ever-diminishing elements of Reality and an ever-increasing proportion of appearance or Non-Being until the elements of the world of physical matter at the bottom of the arc come into apparent being; then follows the other arc upward, the Arc of Ascent, *kavsı uruç*, aş matter takes on more and more aspects of Real Being until in the Perfect Man there is a complete return into the God-head. Graphically represented in detail the succession is as follows:

[6] I quoted relevant texts of al-Mas'ūdī and Niẓāmī in my foreword to M. F. Ashley Montagu's study on Edward Tyson (Philadelphia 1943; Isis 34, 526).

[7] Arabic examples given by S. Gandz (Isis 23, 246).

[8] The Oriental terms in Birge are Turkish; in spite of the modern spelling, the Arabist will readily identify many words.

Arc of Ascent		Arc of Descent
The Perfect Man *Insanı Kâmil*		The First Intelligence, *aklı evel.*
Stage of Man *Mertebei Insan*		The Nine Intelligences, *ukulu tısa.*
Ape, Monkey *Nesnas maymum*		The Nine Souls, *nufusu tısa.*
Kinds of Animals *Envai Hayvanat*	ARC	The Great Sphere, *feleki âzam.*
Palm of the Date *Nahılı hurma*	OF	Sphere of the Constellations, *buruç.*
Fruit Trees *Aşcari Musmire*	ASCENT	Sphere of Saturn, *zuhal.*
Plants with seed *Nebatat ca tohum*		Sphere of Jupiter, *muşteri.*
Plants without seed *Nebatat bi tohum*		Sphere of Mars, *merih.*
Substance of Coral *Cevheri mercan*	ARC	Sphere of the Sun, *şems.*
Minerals, stones *Maaden ahcar*	OF	Sphere of Venus, *zühre.*
Minerals completed *Maaden mukantara*	DESCENT	Sphere of Mercury, *utarit.*
Volatile toughness *Tayri lezeç*		Sphere of the Moon, *kamer.*
		Condition of Heat, *keyfiyeti hararet.*
		Condition of Cold, *burudet.*
		Condition of Moisture, *rutubet.*
		Condition of Dryness, *yubuset.*
		Fire, *kürei nar.*
		Air, *kürei hava.*
		Water, *kürei ma.*
		Earth, kürei hak.

FIG. 4. Cycle of evolution according to the Baktāshī cosmology. From Birge (p. 116, 1937). With permission of the author and of the Hartford Seminary Foundation.

"It must not be supposed that the cycle of existence is thought of in these exact terms by all Bektashis. There are different terms and ways of picturing the process."

Similar views might probably be found in other books, Arabic, Hebrew, or Latin, but the Turkish example will serve for all.

First Kingdom: Minerals

2. *Geological theories*

No material addition or change was made to the theories explained by al-Mas'ūdī (X-1), Ibn Sīnā (XI-1), and al-Bīrūnī (XI-1). The former's statement at the beginning of his Murūj al-dhahab was astounding: "We have said that what was a river became a sea and what was a sea became dry land, and what was dry land had been changed into a sea in the course of time and that was the result of astronomical and physical causes." The views of Ibn Sīnā were more influential, however, for his Kitāb al-shifā' was partly translated into Latin by John of Seville (XII-1), whereas the works of al-Mas'ūdī and of al-Bīrūnī remained for centuries unknown to Western readers. Al-Bīrūnī repeated with more concreteness and strength the statements of al-Mas'ūdī. For example, in the Taḥdīd nihāyāt al-amākin fī tasṭīḥ masāfāt al-masākin, written by him in 1025,[9] he spoke again of the alternations of dry land and sea, and in another text he remarked that the Indus

[9] Brockelmann (suppt. 1, 874, 1937).

valley should be considered an ancient sea basin filled with alluvium. Similar views appeared in Albert the Great (XIII-2) and Ristoro d'Arezzo (XIII-2). The latter even referred to fossil fishes, and so did al-Bīrūnī in the Taḥdīd, and Joinville in his life of St. Louis.[10]

3. *Lapidaries*

The tradition of lapidaries, that is, of texts dealing with the virtues of precious stones, continued almost everywhere. We have already remarked on their universality in the twelfth and thirteenth centuries (Introd. 2, 48), and cited lapidaries in Latin, Hebrew, Anglo-Norman, French, Danish, Spanish, Arabic, and Persian! Interest in precious stones pervaded every country and every class of people; it was, like astrology, an integral part of mediaeval thought. There are English lapidaries of the fourteenth century,[11] and, on the other hand, we find a cautious Florentine, the chronicler Dino Compagni, paying as much attention to the virtues of stones as did the poets recording folklore in Middle English verse. A comparative study of these Italian and English texts would probably reveal many common superstitions. Then we have an Arabic treatise by Ibn al-Akfānī and a Persian one by 'Abdallāh ibn 'Alī al-Kāshānī, not to speak of the lapidaries included in the cosmographies and encyclopaedias already mentioned.

Beyond the names of stones, the identification of which is not always possible, these lapidaries contain little of value to the historian of mineralogy.

4. *Earthquakes and volcanoes*

It is convenient to speak of earthquakes and volcanic eruptions together because they were generally connected in mediaeval thought. Herodotos (V B.C.), Aristotle, Posidonios (I-1 B.C.), Strabon (I-2 B.C.) had made a number of correct observations. Herodotos and Strabon ascribed the formation of the defile of Tempe (in northern Thessaly) to an earthquake, and Posidonios had recorded the elevation of a new volcanic islet among the Lipari islands.[12] The theory most generally accepted under different forms by Greek philosophers and their mediaeval followers was that quakes and volcanic explosions were caused by the sudden decompression of fluids (water, fire, air) confined in caverns and underground passages. The motions of these fluids under the surface of the earth were soon compared with the motions of fluids inside the human body. Seneca (I-2) was I think the first to make that particular comparison between the macrocosmos and microcosmos, one which was eminently suggestive in many respects (e.g., it enabled one to generalize from medicine to seismology!) and captured the mediaeval imagination, not only until the time of Leonardo da Vinci but even for a long time afterward.

[10] The earliest reference to fossil fishes was made by Xenophanes (VI B.C.), see Arthur Stanley Pease: Fossil fishes again (Isis 33, 689–90, 1941). For al-Bīrūnī's mention of them in the Taḥdīd in 1025, see Eugene V. Prostov (Isis 34, 24). For Ristoro d'Arezzo's in 1282, Frank D. Adams (Isis 33, 335, 1941). For Joinville's in 1309, Sarton (Isis 33, 56–58, 1940).

[11] P. J. Heather: Precious stones in the Middle-English verse of the fourteenth century (Folk-lore 42, 217–64, 345–404, 1931); much of this concerns rather the second half of the century.

[12] The same islands (Isole Eolie, near Sicily) thirteen centuries later attracted the attention of Michael Scot (XIII-1), in his astrological introduction called Liber particularis.

Ancient views on earthquakes have been reviewed by Wilhelm Capelle (PW suppt. 4, 344–74, 1924). K. W. Ringhausen: Posidonius, Asklepiodotus, Seneca und ihre Anschauungen über Erdbeben und Vulkane (Diss. Munich 1930).

Perhaps the best accounts of ancient scientific views[13] will be found in Aristotle, Posidonios, Lucretius, and Seneca. One of the best accounts in our period was given by Conrad of Megenberg.

The winds imprisoned in caverns were supposed to be affected by the outside winds, hence the growth from early Greek times of what might be called meteorological seismology. That is, earthquakes were thought to be connected with and influenced by almost every kind of meteorological phaenomenon.[14] Aristotle, who rationalized these ancient views, went so far as to say that the winds on the surface of the earth, the quakes beneath, and the thunder above were all the same thing (Meteorology, book II, 9). From meteorology to astrology the step was easy. Like any other terrestrial objects, the fluids or vapors moving within the cavities and conduits of the earth might be influenced by the stars. Hence we have an astrological theory of earthquakes the development of which began I don't know exactly when, but very early. The influences of celestial bodies were especially strong when they combined in the case of conjunctions, and particularly of eclipses. Aristotle pointed to a relation between quakes and solar eclipses (Meteorology, book II, 8). We find astrological seismology also in the Bṛihatsaṃhitā of Varāhamihira (VI-1) and throughout mediaeval literature, even in Kepler![15]

The tendency to synthetic explanations establishing relations with as many different facts as possible was carried even farther. As subterranean air is often foul, it was natural to assume that its sudden release by a quake might liberate miasmas and cause diseases. The violent quakes all over Europe on January 25, 1348[16] were adduced as causes of the Black Death (e.g., by Conrad of Megenberg). The seismic interpretation of diseases continued for a long time. We find it defended as late as the beginning of the eighteenth century in the Tractatus medico-physicus de terrae motuum genere of Marco Antonio Faventino Melli (Forli 1708).[17]

Conrad of Megenberg described different kinds of earthquakes and thus continued another branch of seismology (description and classification of quakes), which was much developed in later centuries, e.g., in the publications which followed the disastrous Italian quakes of 1570 (Adams p. 405 f., 1938).

[13] The adjective "scientific" is used here to differentiate these views from others, equally popular in ancient and mediaeval times, associating earthquakes with fantastic animals or prodigies. For a description of these superstitions, see Montessus de Ballore (1923). Bede (VIII-1) recalled such explanations, but classified them under the heading dubia et spuria; Conrad von Megenberg recalled them too, but only in derision (Adams p. 403, 1938). Montessus has shown that superstitions relative to earthquakes are spread all over the world, some of the most definite and strangest being found in countries widely distant from one another. This suggests prehistoric contacts and commerce between those countries.

[14] Relations with meteorological phaenomena should not be rejected a priori; they are possible though thus far unproven. It has been suggested that tidal forces might cause volcanic explosions by a kind of trigger action, and that atmospheric tides might also cause earthquakes. Such suggestions were made as late as 1937 (Isis 30, 499).

[15] Kepler saw a relation between a little quake in Thuringia, political events of 1598, and the solar eclipse of March 7, 1598 (Opera, Frisch, vol. 8, 15, 1870).

[16] According to Mallet (p. 40, 1852), the date January 25 is sure, but the year is not. It varies in different sources from 1343 to 1349. Various prodigies were observed during the quakes of 1348, e.g., a rain of blood was seen in several localities; Giovanni Villani in his Historie fiorentine says that the quake in Carinthia, January 25, 1348, cracked the land in the shape of a cross near the church of Villach, caused a blood spring to surge, moved the castle of Lemberg ten miles away.

[17] Quoted by Montessus de Ballore (p. 27, 1923); not available to me.

It is not surprising that Conrad and his contemporaries paid attention to earthquakes, for many occurred during the first half of the fourteenth century, some of them of sufficient violence to cause destruction of houses or affect the landscape.

Some of them were almost certainly connected with volcanic disturbances. That is especially the case with the earthquakes felt in Iceland in 1300 and in 1338–39, when the Hecla and other volcanoes erupted either before or after the quakes. There were quakes in Italy the following years (sometimes many times in the same year): 1301 (twice), 1302, 1304, 1306, 1317, 1320, 1321, 1322 (violent), 1325 (violent), 1328 (twice, once violent), 1331, 1334 (twice), 1335 (immense landslip, the Arno troubled for more than two months), 1336, 1337, 1339 (twice), 1343 (twice, once violent), 1345 (four times), 1346, 1348 (very violent, beginning January 25 and the shocks recurring at intervals for 40 days;[18] this was felt over a good part of Europe), 1349 (twice, violent), 1350.

It is not necessary to give similar lists for other countries, all of which, except Iceland, were far behind in the number and intensity of quakes. It will be better to mention a few quakes of exceptional strength. An exceedingly violent one was felt in Germany on May 25 (or June 1), 1322. In 1344 (or 1339?), much destruction was caused in Iceland and Norway, as well as the disappearance and reappearance of a river, and a flood. In 1345, a shock caused the emergence of a rock in Iceland. In 1346, many buildings were thrown down in Switzerland, chiefly Basel. In 1350, a Swiss mountain was cleft by a quake.

The wonder is that people did not discuss these strange and frightening events more fully. The main reason for their silence was probably the fact that the astrological explanation satisfied them, stilled their queries, and discouraged further investigations.

These data are taken from Mallet's list (1852), which is certainly incomplete, though the more violent quakes which could not escape notice are probably all included. I know that the list is incomplete, for many other quakes have since been recorded in lists relating to separate countries and thus derived from a larger mass of local documents. For example, according to George H. Boehmer,[19] there were quakes in Iceland in 1300, 1308, 1311, 1332, 1339, 1340, 1341, 1343, 1349 (six of them unrecorded by Mallet). According to Charles Davison,[20] there were only three quakes in Great Britain, to wit in 1318, 1319, 1349, none of them of any gravity (Mallet does not mention the second). What is more remarkable, William Merle refers to a quake which took place in Lincolnshire on March 28, 1343, strong enough to bring down chimney stones. That particular quake is not listed by Mallet or Davison. Now Merle was not an uncritical chronicler, but a trained meteorologist.

Turning to the Near East, a violent quake shook it on August 8, 1303. The walls of Ḥamāh and Alexandria were partly thrown down (Abū-l-Fidā'). In 1319, a very violent quake occurred in Armenia; the famous town Ānī and many villages

[18] The mention of forty days which often occurs in the description of secondary quakes following the main one is suspicious. It occurs in Aristotle (Meteorology, book II, ch. 8), also in Pliny (Natural history, book II, 84). Its frequency in mediaeval writings suggests that "forty days" had become a standard duration. In fact, the epiphaenomena may be damped quickly or they may last for months and even years. Aristotle (Met. II, 8), whose account is magnificent, remarked that small vibrations might go on for as much as two years; Pliny, copying him, said the same.

[19] Volcanic eruptions and earthquakes in Iceland within historic times (Smithsonian Report for 1885, p. 495–541), derived from many MS sources.

[20] History of British earthquakes (434 p., Cambridge 1924; p. 14).

were completely ruined (Mallet p. 37, 1852; EI 1, 355, 1910). Quakes occurred in Constantinople in 1332, 1344, 1346 (Nicephoros Gregoras); the last one destroyed many buildings. There was a quake in Tripolis of Syria in 1339 (?). Al-Dimashqī observed earthquakes and connected them with the formation of mountains and of springs.

There is no other country about which we are as well informed concerning the past tremors of its good earth as we are about China. This is partly due to the care of its annalists, continued imperturbably for millennia, but partly also to a native interest in the subject. Indeed, the earliest inventions of seismoscopes are credited to two Chinese, Ch'ao-Ts'o (II-2 B.C.) and Chang Hêng (II-1). The old chroniclers did their task so well that it was possible for father Hoang to compile a catalogue (published 1909–13) of some 3,500 earthquakes which occurred in the Far East, primarily in China. For the first half of the fourteenth century, no less than 139 items are recorded! (Hoang, p. 130–46, 1913). Strangely enough, Japanese quakes preceded by about a year the Chinese cataclysms of 1303, 1318, 1324, 1326, 1332, 1336, 1337.

In spite of that seismic agitation, I am not acquainted with Chinese or Japanese publications of the fourteenth century devoted to earthquakes or volcanic phaenomena.

5. *Mining and Metallurgy*

Metallurgy is an application of the physical sciences and hence would have been dealt with in the physical section, but for the fact that it was not expedient to separate it from mining. There is very little to say about it anyhow.

Mining as it was practiced in a great many places in the fourteenth century was largely traditional in its methods. Many of the miner's ways, even as the farmer's, were immemorial; his experience was partly mythical and his knowledge imbued with superstitions. The history of mining goes back in many countries (e.g., England, France) to prehistoric times. Our understanding of prehistoric mining is helped by the archaeological remains of it, and also by the study of methods used by primitive people to this day.[21] In Roman days mining was extended over a great part of the world and very much improved. There is much information about that in Pliny (I-2). That mining was often very elaborate and deep, and Roman prospectors were so clever and so lucky that it was generally considered a good omen in recent times to find traces of Roman preoccupation in a lode.[22] The disintegration of the Roman world stopped much of that, and the mining practiced in the fourteenth century was to some extent a new departure. The immemorial traditions had not been completely lost everywhere, but formed a dim background to newer traditions, which were seldom more than a few centuries old and were sometimes counted in years. These new departures were naturally made in the richer mining districts, where traces of Roman work were frequently found. They suffered a tremendous setback at the time of the Black Death, and another one when the discovery of richer veins in the New World about the middle of the sixteenth century caused the exploitation of many European silver and lead mines to become unprofitable.

[21] A model study of this kind is that of Waltér Cline: Mining and metallurgy in Negro Africa (quarto, 155 p., Menasha, Wis. 1937; Isis 28, 522–28).

[22] For an elaborate survey of Roman mining, divided by provinces, consult Oliver Davies: Roman mines in Europe (304 p., 49 ill., 6 maps, Clarendon Press, Oxford 1935; Isis 25, 251).

But we must not anticipate. We have only scraps of knowledge with regard to mediaeval mining before the fourteenth century. In the fourteenth century, the information increases somewhat, but very little of it is of technical interest. The sites and veins exploited in the fourteenth century had generally been known before (or similar ones had been known in the vicinity), neither were the methods new, or if there was any novelty it was hardly tangible. The abundant literature concerning mediaeval mining is of greater importance for the student of economics or sociology than for the historian of technology. I have examined a good deal of it, almost fruitlessly, and I realize that there is considerably more which has escaped my attention, e.g., monographs published in mining journals or in the archives of provincial antiquarian societies. It remains possible, however, that a deeper investigation and more thorough sieving of those widely scattered writings would bring to the surface new facts concerning the history of mining and metallurgy.

Many of the investigations have been made by legal historians, for the customs of miners were soon codified in many districts. The mining profession was regulated before many others. Complicated sets of duties, rights, compensations, etc. had to be devised. A comparative study of these legislations and regulations in different parts of the world would be interesting, but I am not aware of its having been realized or attempted. There are many special studies,[23] and every student of mediaeval mining must pay some attention to its legal aspects.[24]

An indirect proof of the paucity, not to say nullity, of information on the technical aspects of mediaeval mining is given by the excellent catalogue of the South Kensington Museum in London. The two sections devoted to Mining and ore dressing (96 p., 3 pl., 1920) and to Metallurgy by A. J. Spencer (70 p., 11 pl., 1925) contain nothing relevant.

A few indications concerning the history of mining in various countries will help the reader to orient himself.

England. In 1299 Edward I leased silver-lead mines of Devonshire to the Frescobaldi. The latter were representatives of a Florentine family of merchants and financiers who played a prominent part in international affairs (especially in the thirteenth and the first half of the fourteenth centuries); they lent money to Philippe le Bel of France, and to Edward I and II of England; their names occur frequently in the Patent Rolls from 1277 to 1311 (Enciclopedia italiana 16, 70, 1932). In 1314, one Hermann de Allemania was working in a mine near Dulverton, Somerset. In 1324, Thomas de Almaigne was appointed to examine the king's mines in Cumberland and Westmorland. Sometime before, he had obtained from Edward II permission to use the dross and slag thrown aside at the silver mines of Devonshire; he paid twenty shillings per year for that concession (Rickard p. 535). The presence of two German "mining engineers" in England in this period is noteworthy; it confirms the theory ascribing the revival of European mining to craftsmen of the Harz Mountains, Saxony, Bohemia; these regions were the most active

[23] One of the earliest concerning England we owe to Sir John Pettus (1613–90): Fodinae regales, or the History, laws and places of the chief mines and mineral works in England, Wales, and the English pale in Ireland, as also of the mint and mōny, with a clavis explaining some difficult words . . . (small folio, 126 p., London 1670). Sir John was deputy governor of the royal mines under Charles I, and also under Cromwell. Adolf Zycha: Das böhmische Bergrecht des Mittelalters auf Grundlage des Bergrechts von Iglau (2 vols., Berlin 1900).

[24] For a very incomplete summary, see Rickard (p. 571–639, 1932). Philippe Rondeau: La mine à l'inventeur (thesis, 232 p., Paris 1915), discussing the development of regalian rights in mines, rights which, be it noted, are of Germanic, not Roman, origin.

mining districts and the best mining "school" of Europe, but it does not follow that there were no other sources of mining and metallurgical experience.

To return to England, consider the Mendip district (north of Wells) and Cornwall. The Mendip mines, already exploited in Roman days, were worked in the fourteenth century, chiefly for lead and also for iron. Other ores, e.g. calamine (hydrous zinc silicate), were obtained there but did not become important until later.[25] As to the Cornish mines, they constituted one of the main sources of tin of the Old World. Their history illustrates well my remark as to the existence of a wide gap between ancient and mediaeval mining. The literary history of the Cornish mines begins with Herodotos and ends with John the Almoner (Ἰωάννης ὁ Ἐλεημοσυνάριος, patriarch of Alexandria) in Acta sanctorum (c. 600). Then after an eclipse of half a millennium it begins again about the middle of the twelfth century. The earliest charter concerning the stanneries is dated 1201. The mining and metallurgy of tin progress throughout the thirteenth century. In the fourteenth century great quantities of tin were used for the making of brass cannon (a climax occurs in 1337). Tin was used also for the making of church bells, and in the Near East for the inside plating of copper utensils; its use for pewter did not assume great importance until much later, for pewter was still an article of luxury; yet by 1348 the trade was already controlled to some extent by the London "craft of pewterers." At that time tin was exported via Bruges, Venice, and Marseille.[26]

France. Though we have considerable information on prehistoric and Roman mining in Gaul (Davies lists 198 mining sites in France and the Rhineland), we know very little about mediaeval conditions. Rickard (p. 512) speaks of silver mines exploited in 1316 at La Caunette, Languedoc (dépt. Hérault).

Louis Joseph Gras: Histoire économique générale des mines de la Loire (2 vols., St. Etienne 1922), dealing almost exclusively with coal measures, includes very few facts anterior to the Revolution, almost none concerning the fourteenth century.

German lands. The richest source of silver was in Goslar and the mines of Rammelsberg (Harz Mountains).

Konrad Wutke: Schlesiens Bergbau und Hüttenwesen, Urkunden, 1136–1528 (Codex diplomaticus Silesiae vol. 20, quarto, 302 p., Breslau 1900); seventy documents (p. 12–42) concern the first half of the fourteenth century, fifty more (p. 42–64) the second half. Max von Wolfstrigl-Wolfskron: Die Tiroler Erzbergbaue, 1301–1665 (490 p., Innsbruck 1902), listing 593 places where mining was practiced at some time.

For Germanic mining antiquities see RGA (1911–19) passim.

Scandinavia. Considerable mining for metals was already being carried on in the northern countries in the Bronze and Iron Ages. The mediaeval revival of mining in Sweden in the thirteenth century seems to have been due to German initiative. A great development of mining took place in that and the following centuries.

The main mining districts of Sweden were Vermland and Dalarne (Dalecarlia). In the capital of the latter, Falun, was a great copper mine, Fálu grufva, already

[25] John Wiedhofft Gough: The mines of Mendip (278 p., 2 maps, Oxford 1930).

[26] Alfred Kenneth Hamilton Jenkin: The Cornish miner. An account of his life above and underground from early times (352 p., ill., London 1927).

famous in the thirteenth century. The exploitation was considerable in the fourteenth century. There is a mining museum in Falun (Berlagets museum) whence information could be obtained.

Carl Max Maedge: Über den Ursprung der ersten Metalle, der See- und Sumpferzverhüttung, der Bergwerkindustrie und ihrer ältesten Organisation in Schweden (Jena 1916); p. 91–166 deal with the thirteenth and fourteenth centuries. They contain the text of privileges for iron dated 1340 and 1354, and for copper, 1347.

I assume that more publications could be named for the countries dealt with above and that quite a few might be quoted with regard to other countries. Instead of trying to complete my bibliography in that way, I prefer to give a few data concerning the two most important minerals, iron and coal.

Iron. It was probably at the beginning of the fourteenth century that blast furnaces[27] of large size were first used in continental Europe. The invention, or reinvention, may have been made in what is now western Belgium. It has been stated that a furnace was built near Namur in 1340, and that by the year 1400 two furnaces near Liége—Les Vennes and Grivegnée—were well known. This means that by this time the utilization of iron had been greatly improved. One had found means not only of softening it, but of thoroughly melting it so that it could be cast. Assuming that this may have been done sometimes on a small scale before the fourteenth century, it was in this century that the casting of iron began to assume its real importance. That metallurgical revolution passed rapidly from the Continent to England, or the invention may have crossed the Channel before its maturity and have grown to maturity in England independently of the Continent. It developed chiefly in Sussex, or more exactly in the Weald between the North and South Downs, where iron mining had taken place probably from prehistoric times and certainly from Roman ones. It was probably the introduction of the blast furnace which soon led to Sussex' becoming the outstanding iron-producing district of England.

J. Starkie Gardner: Iron casting in the Weald (Archaeologia 56, 133–64, ill., London 1898). Rhys Jenkins: The rise and fall of the Sussex iron industry (Transactions Newcomen Society 1, 16–33, 1921). Hans Grabig: Die mittelalterliche Eisenhüttenindustrie der Niederschlesisch-Lausitzer Heide und ihrer Wasserhämmer (95 p., 31 ill., Breslau 1937; Mitt. 38, 323). L. White (p. 148, note 2, 1940).

Coal. It is clear that coal was used occasionally in early times wherever outcrops of coal measures appeared on the surface. Marco Polo (XIII-2) described its use for heating by the Chinese (Introd. 2, 1058),[27a] but his surprise would probably have been smaller than it was if he had been a Liégeois or an Englishman instead of a Venetian. In his elaborate Annals, Galloway has given many examples of the knowledge of coal from Theophrastos (IV-2 B.C.)[28] on, but its use was sporadic

[27] That is, "a furnace of some height, fed at the open top, and from which at the bottom fluid metal is tapped from time to time" (Rhys Jenkins p. 17, 1921). Accepting that definition, some kind of small blast furnace was already used by African Negroes, see Walter Cline (p. 30–55, 1937). The mediaeval invention seems then to consist in a considerable increase in size.

[27a] There is a reference to coal in the history of the Earlier Han Dynasty by Pan Ku (I-2), a coal seam on fire in 25 B.C. (Homer H. Dubs' edition, 2, 388, 1944; Isis 35, 222). The same work contains a reference to the blowing up of a cupola furnace for iron in the year 27 B.C. (same ed., p. 385).

[28] Theophrastos called it ἀνθρακώδης to signify its similarity to charcoal, ἄνθραξ (De lapidibus 54). Hence our word anthracite.

and inconsequential before the thirteenth century. In that century it increased much in at least three countries, Pays de Liége, Scotland, and England. In the fourteenth century, the profession of coal miner was already well established in the land of Liége,[29] and there as well as in England coal was being used in increasing quantities for industrial as well as for domestic purposes. The growth of iron metallurgy, described above, was probably conditioned by the growth of coal mining.

Robert William Cochran-Patrick: Early records of mining in Scotland (quarto, 274 p., Edinburgh 1878), records of 1210–19, 1291, 1424, etc.; most of them date from the sixteenth and seventeenth centuries. Robert Lindsay Galloway: History of coal mining in Great Britain (285 p., London 1882), superseded by his later work, Annals of coal mining and the coal trade (vol. 1, 545 p., London 1898), elaborate account from beginnings to 1835; for the fourteenth century see p. 35–62. John Ulric Nef: The rise of the British coal industry (2 vols., London 1932). Nef's story begins c. 1550; he admits that the story of the coal industry should begin in England and Liége in the thirteenth century, but the British industry did not become very important until the middle of the sixteenth century. Thomas T. Read: The earliest industrial use of coal (Transactions Newcomen Society **20**, 119–33, 1941).

Superstitions. On account of its mysterious aspects, mining has always been associated with many fables and superstitions. I do not wish to enter into that, but the reader may consult Paul Sébillot: Les travaux publics et les mines dans les traditions et les superstitions de tous les pays (640 p., 416 fig., Paris 1894).

Second Kingdom: Plants

6. *Herbals*

It is hardly possible to separate herbals from botanical glossaries. At their best, mediaeval herbals were philological and medical rather than botanical in purpose. The botanical identification of each plant was replaced by a purely verbal one; the herbalists seemed to think that the more names they could give in many languages, the better the plant would be known! The most important herbal of the period (outside of China) was the Pandectae, completed by Matthaeus Sylvaticus c. 1317. It is a dictionary of simples, most of them plants, and like all the others it was primarily philogical and medical, yet the author—as we shall see presently—was a genuine botanist. Sylvaticus flourished in Salerno, and his work proves that the Salernitan school was still vigorous though its golden age was long over.

It is probable that a systematic analysis of the catalogues of MSS would bring to light many more herbals, some of them illustrated, and other texts enumerating plants and describing their several virtues. For an English example let me quote the poem on the virtues of herbs, beginning "To God that is owre best leche," edited by Thomas Wright and James Orchard Halliwell: Reliquiae antiquae (1, 194–97, London 1845). For that text and a few similar ones in the English language see

[29] The first mention of coal in the Pays de Liége was made by the chronicler Renier, a monk of St. Laurent in Liége, who flourished in the second half of the twelfth century, for the year 1198 (terra nigra ad focum faciendum optima), but surface coal (brixho) was already known in Roman times. At first that terra nigra was used only by poor people and smiths. During the rule of prince bishop Adolphe de La Marck (1313–44) there were already many coal mines, so much so that he had been obliged before 1335 to organize a special court "jurés des charbonnages" to arbitrate labor and industrial troubles. Henri Pirenne: Histoire de Belgique (3d ed., 2, 288 f., Bruxelles 1922). For Renier (Reinerus monachus Leodiensis coenobii S. Laurentii) see Sylvain Balau (Biographie nationale de Belgique 19, 116–18, 1907).

Wells (p. 430, 1273, 1926). A comparative study of them is much to be desired.

For French plant names see the Codex Hamilton 407 (a little before 1328), dealt with below in the section on plant iconography.

Or, traveling across Europe, let us take a Polish example. A Polish MS in the British Museum (add. 22668) contains a collection of texts written in the thirteenth and fourteenth centuries, partly at Ratibor, Silesia, in 1334. One of these texts is the Practica by Roger of Salerno (XII-2), bearing in the margins botanical glosses in Polish. The purpose of the glosses was to identify the plants named in Latin with the native plants known by their popular names. This is one of the oldest, if not the very oldest, botanical text in Polish. Kazimierz Dobrowolski: Science and scholarship in Poland up to the close of the sixteenth century (Organon 1, 43–110, 83, Warsaw 1936; Isis 26, 562; 30, 297–98).

Passing to the Greek world, we find a number of plant lists, for example those enumerated by Margaret Head Thomson in her study of anonymous botanical MSS preserved in Paris[30] (nos. 16, 19, 24, 25, 31–34). Some of them contain medical indications, or the equivalent Latin names (in Greek script). None include Arabic words, though such words are found in two Paris MSS of the following century (nos. 14, 22). It would be dangerous to generalize from the Parisian MSS, and we must wait until all the fourteenth-century Greek botanical MSS have been examined in the same manner. The botanical literature, in Greek and other languages, would be considerably increased if we took into account the botanical chapters of books on natural history, the cosmographies and encyclopaedias mentioned above (under "General surveys"), and the botanical items included, e.g., in Biblical commentaries. This should be done in a book exclusively devoted to the history of botany, but we trust that the reader will make a liberal use of our index and of his own judgment.

All these texts—Latin, French, English, Polish, Greek, etc.—are more interesting from the linguistic than from the botanical angle. This is especially true of the vernacular texts, wherein the plant names are among the earliest forms of such names on record. It is possible, however, that the comparative study of a good many of these texts and a careful sieving of them would yield a residuum of facts which the historian of botany would wish to record.

These texts often contain data of the kind for which folklorists and historians of superstition are hunting. This is perhaps especially true of some Greek texts, wherein the strange beliefs of ῥιζοτόμοι relative to herbs and the most auspicious ways of gathering them have been remarkably well preserved throughout the centuries. Delatte (1936, 1938) has proved the survival of ancient lore and rites in mediaeval times, though the pagan customs were usually camouflaged with the help of Christian accessories.

The Chinese traditions embodied in the pên ts'ao continued their even tenor. At the beginning of the fourteenth century many pên ts'ao were available not only in MS, but in print. The earliest herbal *printed* from blocks,[31] the K'ai-pao hsiang-

[30] Catalogue des MSS grecs de Paris contenant des traités anonymes de botanique (Revue des études grecques 46, 334–48, 1933; Isis 23, 566).

[31] The word "printed" is italicized, because there were of course MSS pên ts'ao of earlier date. Dr. Hummel kindly wrote me (Washington, Oct. 11, 1941): "There are in existence manuscript fragments of herbals older than this. Among the scrolls discovered at Tunhuang, Kansu, in 1907, there is one in the Bibliothèque Nationale, designated Pelliot 3714, which is section (chüan) 10 of the Hsin-hsiu pên-ts'ao compiled at imperial command by Li Chi and others in A.D. 659 (your vol. 1, 498, 539). According to our bibliographer, Mr. Wang Chung-min, the Tunhuang transcription of it was made about the years A.D. 667–69. He informs

ting pên ts'ao, dates back to 973, and other pên ts'ao were printed in 1061, 1108, 1159, 1204, 1249, all of them illustrated! See Introd. 2, 52, 247, 442, and A. W. Hummel: The printed herbal of 1249 (Isis 33, 439–42, 1 fig., 1941). A comparative study of all these Chinese herbals and their comparison, as to text and illustrations, with the Western herbals would be a lifelong task for a botanical Sinologist. Where is he? The work is waiting for him.

It is remarkable that no pên ts'ao was printed or reprinted during the fourteenth century, and that only one was reprinted during the Yüan dynasty (in 1298). No pên ts'ao was printed from 1298 to 1406,[32] when the so-called Famine herbal, the Chiu-huang pên-tsao, appeared, for which see my note on Chu Hsiao (XIV-2).

Of course, the best-known pên ts'ao is a later one, the Pên ts'ao kang mu, first printed in 1596. According to Mr. Wang, it was reprinted in 1603, 1640 (twice), 1655, 1684, 1714 (Japanese edition), 1735, 1846, 1872, 1885, 1892, 1894. Of these editions the Library of Congress has all except one of the two 1640 editions, and the 1684 and 1735 editions. The Pên ts'ao kang mu was compiled by Li Shih-chên (Shih-chên was his personal name; other styles under which he was known are Tung-pi and Pin-hu). The Chinese biographical dictionaries are strangely reticent about him, but I am able to give some of the following information thanks to the courtesy of Arthur W. Hummel (letters of Feb. 20, 21, 1929; Aug. 11, 1942). He was a native of Ch'i Hsien in Hupeh, and held two official posts at different times of his life, (1) attendant at the altar of the prince of Ch'u, (2) magistrate in Ssŭ-ch'uan. He wrote a treatise on the pulse, Ping hu mai (or mo) hsüeh, in 1564. His magnum opus, the Pên ts'ao kang mu, occupied him thirty years, during which he made extracts from 800 authors, selecting 1,518 drugs, adding 374 new ones, the total amounting to 1,892. It is possible that the MS was completed in 1578. The drugs are divided into 62 classes and 16 groups; the total number of prescriptions is said to be 11,896. Syphilis is mentioned as a new disease spreading from the south. The editions contain a large number of illustrations (742?). His son Li Chien-yüan, who held the same magistracy in Ssŭch'uan, in his memorial of presentation of the book to the emperor Wan Li (1573–1620) in 1596 spoke of his father as "my deceased father"; the book was published in the following year. On the other hand, in a preface written by the statesman Wang Shih-chêng (Giles no. 2220) in 1590, it is stated that Li Shih-chên had just come to visit him. Hence Li Shih-chên died between 1590 and 1596.

Western works on Chinese materia medica are derived mainly if not exclusively from the Pên ts'ao kang mu. This is the case for G. A. Stuart: Chinese materia

---

me also that there is a manuscript fragment of this Hsin-hsiu pên-ts'ao in Japan, which was transcribed in A.D. 731; and that among the Tunhuang scrolls in the British Museum (designated Stein 4534) there is part of section (chüan) 17 of this same work.

"Among the British Museum scrolls (Stein 76) there is also a part of a Shih-liao pên-ts'ao compiled by Mêng Shên. Pelliot, in T'oung Pao, 1931, p. 190, says he compiled the work in 706 and died in 713. A Pên-ts'ao shih-i of 739 is reported by Pelliot in the above article, and also by Hagerty in T'oung Pao, 1923, p. 73."

[32] This puzzled me so much that I wrote to Dr. Hummel for confirmation. He kindly answered (Oct. 6, 1941): "The Chêng-lei pên-ts'ao are of two kinds, named after the reign years in which they first appeared. One is the Chêng-ho chêng-lei pên-ts'ao, of which our Chinese bibliographer, Mr. Wang Chung-min, isolates the following editions: 1116, 1249, 1468, 1523, 1552, 1570, 1572, 1587, 1625 (of these the Library of Congress has all but the 1116 and 1468 prints). The Ta-kuan chêng-lei pên-ts'ao has, according to Mr. Wang, the following editions: 1108, 1215, 1298, 1577, 1600, 1656 (of these the Library of Congress has 1577, 1600, 1656)."

medica. Vegetable kingdom. Extensively revised from Frederick Porter Smith's work (564 p., Shanghai 1911). Bernard Emms Read: Chinese medicinal plants from the Pên ts'ao kang mu (3d ed., 406 p., Peking 1936); Animal drugs (9 parts published or at least only 9 are available to me, Peking 1931–39).

Though the Pên ts'ao kang mu is the best known and most used of the Chinese herbals, it is not the most recent, nor the most elaborate, nor the best. The Kuang ch'ün fang p'u of 1630 is said to be fuller and more correct, and it is better printed, but lacks illustrations. Then in the encyclopaedia T'u shu chi ch'êng of 1726, 320 well illustrated books are devoted to botany. Finally, Wu Ch'i-chün (d. 1846; Giles no. 2322) wrote the Chih wu ming shih t'u k'ao, containing 1,800 elaborate drawings, many of which are by his own hand. This is said to be the best Chinese botanical work (Couling p. 56, 1917).

7. *Botanic gardens*

The history of botanic gardens can be traced back to ancient times, though without precision. According to Diogenes Laërtios (III-1), Vitae et placita (book 5, ch. 2), Theophrastos (IV-2 B.C.) had arranged a garden with the help of one of his disciples, Demetrios Phalereos.[33] That garden was probably located close to the Lyceum (Judeich p. 85, 366, 1905). Pliny the Elder (I-2) tells us (Historia naturalis XXV, 5) that he often visited the herb garden of his friend the centenarian Antonius Castor. These stories foreshadow one of our difficulties. When does a garden deserve to be called a botanical garden? For example, is a well kept herb garden a botanical garden, even when plants of the same kind are carefully cultivated together, and doctors may come to it in order to improve their knowledge of materia medica? Such herb gardens existed in every well regulated monastery.

We are given a clear image of one in the detailed plans for the Benedictine monastery of St. Gall (in Switzerland), prepared in 820 by order of Gozbert (abbot 816–836).[34] Gozbert wanted to renovate the abbey on a larger scale. The plan which has been preserved in the abbey library is one of the most precious relics of Carolingian times. It consists of four pieces of parchment sewn together, measuring 110 by 78 cm. A facsimile reproduction of it was published by Ferdinand Keller: Bauriss des Klosters St. Gallen vom Jahr 820 (text 42 p. quarto, plus full-sized facsimile, Zürich 1844). In addition to the kitchen garden (hortus), there was an herb garden (herbularius), and houses were foreseen for the gardener as well as for the leeches (mansio hortolani, domus medicorum). The herbularius located near the doctors' house was divided into sixteen beds, wherein the following plants were cultivated:

Lilium candidum, Salvia officinalis, Ruta graveolens, Rosa rubiginosa, Raphanus raphanistrum, Nasturtium, Cuminum cyminum, Levisticum off., Feniculum off., Mentha piperita, Rosmarinus off., Trigonella foenum graecum, Tanacetum balsamita, Phaseolus vulgaris, Sata regia (Satureia?, mentioned in the Capitulare de villis), Satureia hortensis.[35]

[33] Born c. 345 B.C. A man of immense fame in Athens (360 statues dedicated to him!), later a political refugee in Egypt, where he was probably one of the founders of the great library of Alexandria.

[34] The St. Gall hermitage dated back to the first half of the seventh century (Introd. 1, 657; 2, 55, 154), but the Benedictine house was later. A new charter had been given to it in 818 by Louis the Pious.

[35] After Keller (p. 29). For the plants cultivated in the hortus, see ibid. (p. 31).

Though this plan dates from the ninth century, we may safely assume that a Western herb garden of the fourteenth would not be essentially different. There would be more flower beds or fewer, and some other plants would be favored in other countries, but the general purpose and arrangement would be the same. It is probable that other botanic gardens existed close to medical schools or to the houses of physicians, but we do not hear of any of them, until the time of Matthaeus Sylvaticus. I cannot help feeling that more information on such gardens will gradually emerge when more mediaeval texts have been analyzed by botanically minded scholars.

Matthaeus Sylvaticus organized two botanical gardens at the behest of Robert of Anjou, the one in Castelnuovo, the other in Salerno. He tried to cultivate foreign (Greek) plants. About the same time (c. 1333) we hear of a garden arranged by one Magister Gualterus in Venice "pro herbis necessariis artis suae." This was a garden for the doctor's own purposes. The term "botanic garden," however, suggests an educational function. Later on every medical faculty would have its garden. The earliest of that kind was connected with the University of Prague. It was established soon after the foundation (1347–48) of that university, by the Florentine pharmacist Angelo in 1350 (Schelenz p. 376, 1904).

A botanic garden was created in Cadiz c. 1318 by the physician Muḥammad al-Shafra.

8. *Plant iconography*

The early history of iconography has been reviewed in volume 2 (p. 54–55; see also Isis 15, 368). There is no radical change in the fourteenth century. The struggle continues between what may be called symbolic interpretations of plants and naturalistic interpretations. The latter did not completely supersede the former at any definite date, but they became more numerous as the century grew. Outside of the herbals, naturalistic representations of plants appear in paintings, e.g., of Giotto (c. 1270–1336) and a little later of Spinello Aretino (1333?–1410); they remain exceptional before the fifteenth century. See plates XX–XXIII in Fischer (1929).

Perhaps the most interesting MS of the period is the Codex Hamilton 407 in the Prussian National Library, Berlin, which has the advantage of being exactly datable. It was written for monseigneur Philippe de Valois, sometime before the latter's accession to the throne of France in 1328 (as Philip VI, first king of the Valois dynasty). This large parchment MS (282 folii) contains various texts on materia medica, for example, the Flos medicine (2, 434) by John of Milano, a famous teacher of Salerno, and at the end (f. 229–82) a collection of 210 illustrations of plants (also a few animals and stones) with their names given in French (or sometimes, when the French was unknown, in Latin). This herbal evidences the continuity of the Salernitan tradition, for it is clearly derived from the Circa instans of Matthaeus Platearius (XII-1), and on the other hand its illustrations are very similar to those of the botanical incunabula. We can even go farther and consider it a significant link in the tradition connecting those incunabula across time and space with the Ῥιζοτομικόν of Cratevas (I-1 B.C.).

Charles Singer (1927). Julius Schuster: Secreta salernitana und Gart der Gesundheit (Mittelalterliche Handschriften, Festgabe zu Hermann Degering, p. 203–35, 2 pl., 6 fig., Leipzig 1926; Isis 11, 429).

The study of plant iconography in China is made difficult not by the scarcity of documents, but rather by their abundance. The pên ts'ao printed in many successive editions from the end of the tenth century on were generally illustrated. Many of these illustrations are remarkably realistic (see Isis 33, 440, for one taken from the printed herbal of 1249). How many of these illustrations were reproduced from older MS herbals, or from earlier printed editions, I do not know. It will not be possible to answer such questions until all the pên ts'ao, or at least many of them, have been patiently collated.

In addition, many plants and flowers, especially bamboos, plums, chrysanthemums, pines, orchids, were reproduced by Chinese (and Japanese) artists. I have already spoken of the Chu p'u hsiang lu, a treatise on bamboos written in 1299 by Li K'an (XIII-2). I may add that this Li K'an was born in 1245 in Chi-ch'iu near Peking, and, being a Taoist, was nicknamed hsi chai tao jên, the Taoist of the quiet studio. He died in 1320. It is true that he completed his treatise in 1299, but it does not seem to have been published until 1319 or later. The text was included in the Yung Lo ta tien (1409) and printed in the Chih pu tsu ts'ung shu, edited by Pao T'ing-po in 1808, with three prefaces written respectively by Li K'an in 1299, by Mou Ying-lung in 1307, and by K'o Mu-fu in 1319. The treatise itself is made up of a long introduction followed by seven sections (chüan) including no less than 150 illustrations. The purpose was primarily artistic.[36] Li K'an recognized 332 kinds of bamboo, the picturesque names of which are most intriguing. The differences are artistic rather than botanical, and the names suggest a vast amount of folklore which a foreigner can hardly penetrate. To appreciate the value attached by the Chinese to a book like the Chu p'u hsiang lu, one must bear in mind that the bamboo (chu) was to him an extraordinary plant, not only of great practical value but also of infinite beauty, a source of joy and peace. It is one of the "three friends of winter" (sui han san yu), the two others being the pine (sung) and the plum (mei), and every scholar wishes to have them in his garden as well as paintings of them in his study.[37] It is also one of the "four gentlemen" (chün), the three others being the plum, the orchid (lan), and the chrysanthemum (chü); and no end of essays, poems, and paintings have been devoted to them. The reader will find much information on Chinese bamboo lore in the book of bishop William Charles White: An album of Chinese bamboos. A study of a set of ink bamboo drawings A.D. 1785 (University of Toronto 1939; Isis 33, 389).

Other paintings of flowers and trees were inspired by Buddhist ideals, especially by artists who belonged to the Ch'an tsung (Zen shū). I suppose that Taoists were more inclined to analysis, even if it was of a fantastic kind, and the Buddhists to contemplation, and thus art, science, and religion were differently harmonized in their minds. However that may be, it is certain that the Chinese artists of this time were producing images of plants far more abundant than those available in the West, and most of them of a superior quality.

[36] In contrast with the treatise on bamboo shoots, Sun p'u, of Tsan-ning (X-2) and the section on bamboo in the Nung sang chi yao, compiled in 1273 by order of Kublai Khān (XIII-2).

[37] The three friends of winter are opposed to the friends of spring, to wit t'ao, li, hsing (peach, plum, and apricot). A Chinese couplet often enumerates the two sets of friends on the two pillars of the doors. Information kindly supplied by bishop White (Toronto, Oct. 15, 1941).

9. *Husbandry*

In any history of husbandry a large place would necessarily be made for the accounts of failures—droughts and famines—which are among the main catastrophes which may afflict mankind. These failures help us to realize the fundamental importance of husbandry and also to understand the latter's relative unprogressiveness. The husbandman's success or failure is determined to such a large extent by uncontrollable events that he is likely to become excessively conservative and fatalistic. In Eastern countries famines were largely due to droughts. That is definitely the case for Palestine, witness various references in the Old Testament (I Kings 17:1 f.; Jeremiah 14:2–6; Amos 4:7 f.). It is even more true of India, where the crops are entirely dependent upon the monsoon rains, and where the latter are so badly distributed that there is almost always a drought in one district or another. One of the worst famines occurred in 1344 throughout Mālwā and was particularly severe in Delhi. It lasted for years, and the sulṭān Muḥammad ibn Taghlaq (ruled 1325–51) was unable to save many of his people from destruction.

In Egypt a famine would be likely to occur whenever the level of the Nile was too low to flood the country properly. That was the case in 1200, and the resultant miseries and horrors (anthropophagy) were realistically described by 'Abd al-Laṭīf (XIII-1).

A few other famines have been referred to in previous volumes: the one of 1031, described in moving words by Raoul Glaber (XI-1); the famine of 1181 in Japan, described by Kamo Chōmei (XIII-1); and those chronicled by Matthew Paris (XIII-2). These are only the examples which arrested my attention. In the West there was little danger of drought, but crops might fail for other reasons, or they might be destroyed by insects or other pests or more often by men (during wars or revolts); or a plague such as the one of 1348 might dispose of the harvestmen. There was a terrible succession of crop failures in England in the early fourteenth century (Coulton's Panorama p. 92, 1938). Famines will be treated at greater length in the medical section below.

It is even more difficult to date agricultural inventions than technical ones. In all probability the real invention cannot be dated at all, and one becomes aware of it only when it is sufficiently diffused. For example, who first thought that the good earth might be exhausted with regard to the needs of a particular crop but not necessarily with regard to others? The idea of leaving the land fallow was immemorial, but who thought first of rotating crops? Coulton states (ibid. p. 89) that "the modern rotation of crops, by alternating roots with corn, was common in Flanders as early as the beginning of the fourteenth century; with us [in England] it became general only four hundred years later."

To be sure, agricultural customs and techniques can be reconstructed to some extent on the basis of contemporary documents, especially when many such documents are analyzed and compared. Let me quote one set of them by way of illustration. We have the accounts (or at least some of them) concerning the estates of Thierry d'Hireçon (Hireçon en Berry) in the province of Artois. This Thierry, after having been in the service of Robert II of Artois and of king Philippe le Bel, became the chief adviser to Mahaut, countess of Artois and Burgundy; he was elected bishop of Arras in 1328 and died in the same year. His farming accounts make it possible to determine, sometimes with considerable detail, his agricultural methods. This has been done by Jules-Marie Richard: Thierry d'Hireçon, agriculteur artésien (Bibliothèque de l'Ecole des chartes, vol. 53, 383–416, 571–604, 1892). That study deals successively with (1) modes of exploitation, (2) cereals and leguminous plants, (3) grassland, (4) woods, (5) gardens (jardins et courtils); this includes a list of the vegetables, fruit trees, flowers which were cultivated, (6) animals, (7) buildings and tools, (8) farm laborers.

The greatest agricultural event of the period which can be ascribed to a definite personality is the forestation of the dunes of Leiria by king Dinis o Lavrador (XIII-2), who ruled until 1325. That was not his only service to the community, for he fostered agriculture in all its branches. His physician, master Giraldes, wrote a book on poultry in Portuguese.

For early (i.e., before the eleventh to twelfth centuries) agriculture in England, Germany, Scandinavia, see RGA (1911–19), passim.

The outstanding treatise on husbandry, not only of this period, but, we may say, of the whole Christian Middle Ages, was the Ruralia commoda completed by Pietro dei Crescenzi in his old age, c. 1306. It was very comprehensive in scope and detail and represents the knowledge and wisdom which had accumulated up to that time, excepting unfortunately the rich experience of the agriculturists and horticulturists of Muslim Spain.

By this time the main Arabic work on the subject, the one by Ibn al-'Awwām (XII-2) of Seville, had already been published, though it had appeared too late to be translated. Little was added to his Kitāb al-falāḥa in the Arabic writings of Muḥammad al-Shafra of Elche and of Ibn Luyūn of Almeria, or in the Persian writings of Rashīd al-dīn.

Some knowledge of Oriental gardens may have been brought back from the East by crusaders. We can detect traces of it in the Latin poem De ornatu mundi, ascribed to Hildebert of Lavardin,[38] and also in the first part of the Roman de la rose, written by Guillaume de Lorris in the first third of the thirteenth century (Introd. 2, 932). There was also, however, a tradition of ornamental gardening in Italy and Provence, probably independent of Arabic influences. Such gardens are described in Crescenzi's famous treatise and represented in the miniatures of its MS copies;[39] other glimpses of them are given in the Decamerone and in Il paradiso degli Alberti of Giovanni (or Gherardo) da Prato (c. 1390).[40]

A treatise on agriculture, the Nung shu, was written in 1314 by Wang Chên. Out of the twenty-two books of the Nung shu, six deal with agriculture in general, four with cereals, and the remaining twelve, that is, more than half, are devoted, in a typically Chinese fashion, to a collection of illustrations. Another agricultural book arranged in the form of a farmer's calendar was published in the same year by a writer of Turkish origin, Lu M ng-shan.

The woman Huang Tao-p'o is said to have introduced into China the art of spinning and weaving cotton. It is certain that cotton was known and used in China before her time. The story attached to her name, however, illustrates the growing importance of cotton at the beginning of the fourteenth century.

[38] Hildebert, born in Lavardin (Touraine) c. 1055, bishop of Le Mans 1097, archbishop of Tours 1125; died in Tours c. 1133. His works were edited by Antoine Beaugendre: Ven. Hildeberti Turonensis opera tam edita quam inedita (folio, Paris 1708); for De ornatu mundi, see col. 1187–92, 180 lines. B. Hauréau (NBG 24, 667–69, 1858).

[39] Examples of such miniatures will be found in Pier de' Crescenzi. Studi e documenti (Bologna 1933; Isis 27, 126).

[40] Nordström (p. 137–39, 1933). Sapegno (p. 439, 1934).

10. *Spices*

Spices have been known in Europe from ancient times, though almost all of them had to be imported from remote countries. They were eagerly desired, for there is to some extent a physiological need of them. That need increased when the viands waiting to be consumed had become for one reason or another less appetizing. Some spices were brought to various parts of the Roman Empire from India, China, or beyond. Nobody knew exactly where they came from, for they were handled by a whole succession of caravans or ships and stored in a hundred places before reaching the final buyer. Each of the conveyors or storekeepers might know the immediate provenance of the goods, but not their real origin, and it was to his interest to hide his sources of supply or to accredit fables concerning them. Being handled by so many intermediaries and transported in slow stages from one end of the world to the other, no wonder that spices were very expensive. We are given from time to time a few glimpses of their value. Pliny speaks of the high price of pepper (Hist. nat. XII, 14). When Alaric raised the siege of Rome in 408, three thousand pounds of pepper were part of the ransom (Gibbon ch. 31, Bury's illustrated ed., 3, 329, 1929). And to come nearer to us, when the Venerable Bede (VIII-1) was about to die, in 735, he distributed to his friends the few treasures which he had accumulated in a lifetime, to wit, some pepper, some napkins, and some incense.[41]

Throughout the Middle Ages, as well as in antiquity, the spices from the Orient reached the West through the Near East, where Alexandria was the main emporium, the "forum publicum utrique orbi," as William of Tyre (XII-2) called it. The Asiatic trade was largely in Arab hands, and the treasures which converged on Alexandria by sea and land "from the two Indies, the two Ethiopias, and Arabia" (again William of Tyre, Historia, book XIX, toward the end) were then distributed to the Western countries through the representatives, established in that city, of the merchants of Venice, Amalfi, Salerno, Pisa, Genoa, Montpellier, Marseille, Narbonne, Barcelona, etc. According to al-Idrīsī (XII-2), the main articles of trade were musk, pepper, cardamom, cinnamon, galingale (khalanj), myrobalan, camphor, coconut, nutmeg, aloe, ebony, shells, ivory, china, all of which came from Asia, plus incense, myrrh, balsams, and benzoins brought from the Ḥaḍramawt, Somaliland, or the Sūdān. Among all these goods, spices were the more precious, especially pepper, and one of the doors of Alexandria was called the peppergate[42] (Kammerer p. 10–14, 1929).

References to spices and especially to pepper are abundant in the contemporary writings, e.g., Giovanni de Montecorvino (XIII-2), who speaks of ginger, dyewood, cinnamon, and other spices; Marco Polo (XIII-2), Giovanni de' Marignolli. The western coast of Hindūstān, the coast of Malabar, was often called the pepper country; so Abū-l-Fidā' (Reinaud's translation, vol. 2, part 2, 115), but the word Malabar had no definite meaning to Western imagination. Most people had fantastic ideas about the origin of pepper and other spices, thinking for instance that they were floated down the Nile all the way from Paradise and fished out of the river in Egypt. Joinville tells us just that! (ed. de Wailly, §189).

It is not necessary to multiply these examples. A good many more could easily

[41] Raymond Wilson Chambers: Bede (Proceedings of the British Academy vol. 22, 1936; reprint p. 26). Reprinted in Man's unconquerable mind (London 1939).

[42] "Porta del pepe" in the map included in Pierre Belon: Les observations de plusieurs singularitez (Paris 1554). Map reproduced in Gaston Jondet: Atlas historique d'Alexandrie (Mémoires de la Société Sultanieh de géographie, vol. 2, pl. 2, Le Caire 1921).

be found in Heyd (1885–86). Let me simply recall that in old French "épices" (spices) came to mean bribes paid to judges. That history is curious in itself; the "épices" were first spontaneous gifts made by the parties to the judges, either spices or candies, later irregular bribes, then regular ones, exactly graduated, finally emoluments which were suppressed only at the time of the Revolution (1789, 1790).

The exorbitant prices wrested by the merchants engaged in the spice trade were one of the main causes which led the Portuguese, who had no share in that trade, to find a new route to the Indies; after their discovery of a passage around the Cape of Good Hope, in 1498, the value of spices fell considerably, and the trade was monopolized by the Portuguese until the eighteenth century.

All the spices came from the East and from the tropics and were luxuries out of reach of the poorer people—all except one. That one with which the temperate zones were blessed was a very precious one, though it is possible that the people did not use it yet as efficiently as we do. I am referring now to mustard, the humble mustard seeds of the Gospels (Matthew 13:31; 17:20, etc.). To be sure, the biting flavor of mustard[43] is not in the tiny seeds exalted in Christ's parables, but in ground seeds; yet the virtues of "mustard oil" were known long before Christ, and we find many mentions of medicinal mustard in the Hippocratic writings.[44] From that time on at least, mustard of one kind or another (black or white, cultivated or wild) has remained in the pharmacopoeia of every nation. See Meyerhof (1940), articles nos. 218 labsān, 322 ṣināb, 400 khardal. Meyerhof remarks (ibid. p. 201) that mustard, though much used as a drug, is less used as a condiment in the East than in the West.

As to the use of the condiment in the West there are many witnesses. We read of a Breton traveler who drew his sword against an innkeeper because the meat offered to him was not seasoned with mustard! In the French countryside there were generally three wheat mills to one mustard mill (Luce p. 63, 1876). In England the people selling mustard were humble ones (that is, mustard was not a luxury), and we read in one of the Paston letters, "He should never have my good wyll for to make my sustyr to selle kandyll and mustard in Framlyngham."[45] Of course, it is impossible to say whether the condiment used in the fourteenth century in France or England was the same as ours. For one thing, there are many recipes for the making of mustard, and many national and individual differences concerning it, but that does not concern us.[46] The main point is that mustard of some kind was consumed, and the Western people were lucky in having it. There was a deep contrast between the democratic mustard and the aristocratic pepper, but the one spice could do for the other to a large extent. That difference is for-

[43] Due to allyl isothiocyanate ("mustard oil").

[44] The term used in those writings is τὸ νᾶπυ, whereas in the Gospels we find the variant τὸ σίναπι (sénevé in French, Senf in German, etc.); the word νᾶπυ or σίναπι is obviously of foreign (Egyptian?) origin.

[45] James Gairdner: The Paston letters A.D. 1422–1509. New complete library ed. (6 vols., Exeter 1904; vol. 4, 21). The letter wherein the quotation occurs is dated 1469, but conditions were presumably the same in the previous century.

[46] According to Verrill, "it was not until 1720 that mustard meal or flour was invented. The process was discovered by a Mrs. Clements of Durham, and as a result the name of 'Durham mustard' still stands for the best of mustards." A. Hyatt Verrill: Perfumes and spices (320 p., Boston 1940; p. 56).

gotten today, and pepper as readily available to everybody as mustard. When I am lunching in a cafeteria and see a poor man handling a caster in such awkward manner that he spreads pepper on the table, I cannot help thinking of Bede, Marco Polo, and Joinville!

In our study of spices it is well to bear in mind that some plants may have been used as condiments in the Middle Ages which are no longer used for that purpose today. A case in point is lovage, which the Roman agriculturists called ligusticum (probably levisticum officinale); it was listed in Charlemagne's Capitulare de villis and was one of the plants to be cultivated in the herbularius of St. Gall (see above).[47] It is still used as a popular remedy (diuretic), but not as a spice, probably because better spices, such as pepper, are readily available.

For a popular account of many spices, with brief historical notes, see James B. McNair: Spices and condiments (61 p., Field Museum, Chicago 1937). As to perfumes and aromata, see J. A. MacCulloch (ERE 9, 737–39, 1917). For the use of spices in England, see Jack Cecil Drummond and Anne Wilbraham: The Englishman's food (p. 34–35, London 1939; Isis 33, 300). Sister Mary Francis Xavier: Saffron and pepper in fourteenth century Florence (Pharmaceutical archives 15, 37–44, Madison, Wis. 1944).

Third Kingdom: Animals

11. *Falconry*

We have seen that a good many treatises on hunting were published during the twelfth and thirteenth centuries. That is not surprising, for hunting, and especially hunting with hawks and falcons, was the outstanding sport of the time. As practiced in the West, falconry was very expensive and correspondingly exclusive, but this only added to its charm and attraction for those who could afford it. The domestication, training, and care of falcons and other hunting birds involved so many difficulties that textbooks were needed, textbooks which the lazy lords could easily read. This explains the existence of books in many languages.

In my survey of earlier literature (Introd. 2, 58–59),[48] I forgot to recall the famous treatise of "King Dancus" (XIII-2), which was probably written in French (c. 1284) but was soon translated into Latin and Italian. The most important treatise of our time was written by a royal prince of Castile, Don Juan Manuel. His Libro de la caza (1325) may be considered the first of its kind in Spanish. It deals almost exclusively with falconry. Another treatise was written before 1328 in Norman French for Edward II by his falconer Guillaume Twici and John Gifford; see my note on Gaston Phoebus (XIV-2). An English version of it made later, MS Cotton Vespasian A XII (c. 1420), is divided into eleven short chapters giving directions for hunting the hare and the hart, the buck and the boar. Le livre des deduis, which is one of the books of "King Modus and Queen Ratio," does not belong to the first but to the second half of the fourteenth century, and hence I shall discuss it in chapter XV. On the other hand, some Italian books may date back to the

[47] Alfred C. Andrews: Alimentary use of lovage in the classical period (Isis 33, 514–18, 1941). Meyerhof (nos. 196, 203, 283, 337, 1940).

[48] Since the publication of volume 2, a complete English translation of the De arte venandi cum avibus of Frederick II (XIII-1) by Casey A. Wood (d. 1942) has been published posthumously with the assistance of F. Marjorie Fyfe (quarto, 750 p., 186 pl., Stanford University 1943; Isis 35, 182–84). That sumptuous edition includes an abundance of materials on mediaeval falconry, valuable because of Wood's deep knowledge of the realia.

beginning of the century, to wit, the Due trattati del governo e delle infermità degli uccelli in a Vatican MS, the Trattato di falconeria (Trattato del governo, delle malattie e guarigioni de' falconi, astori e sparvieri) in the Ambrosiana, an Italian version of the book of King Dancus, and possibly the Libro del Gandolfo[49] persiano.[50] The last-named text may be somewhat later, though its Italian seems pretty antiquated to me. It begins "Qui se comenza le nature de li falconi, astori e sparavieri, le sue cure de tute infirmitade como se pono sanare," and is divided into 211 brief chapters (two of them missing).

The best falcons had to be brought all the way from Greenland. So great was the desire to obtain these royal birds, which did not breed except in the freedom of their homeland (no falcon does), that the knowledge of arctic regions may be said to have been increased because of the needs of falconers! (See my note in the section on geography.) The gerfalcons of Spain were famous, and when Ruy González de Clavijo was sent on an embassy to Tīmūr in 1403, a mew of gerfalcons was included among the royal gifts of which he was the bearer.

For early (i.e., before the eleventh to twelfth centuries) falconry in Germanic countries, see various articles by Fritz Roeder in RGA, such as Beizvögel (1, 217–18, 1912), Falkenbeize (2, 5–9, 1913); Falkenjagd in Scandinavia, by Björn Bjarnason (2, 610, 1915).

Scenes of hawking, as well as of staghunting, rabbiting, bird snaring with decoy, cockfighting, performing animals are shown in the magnificent Bodleian MS 264 (the most famous illuminated MS in the Bodleian), containing "Li romans du boin roi Alixandre" (the Romance of Alexandre), composed by Lambert li Tors or le Tort (trouvère fl. 1170) and continued by Alexandre de Bernai (in Normandy, dépt. Eure), also called Alexandre of Paris (fl. before 1184). The text, in Picard dialect, was copied by an unnamed scribe in 1338 and beautifully illuminated by Jehan de Grise (of Bruges?), who completed his task on April 18, 1344. The romance was edited by Henri Michelant (584 p., Stuttgart 1846) and by F. Le Court de la Villethassetz and Eugène Talbot (550 p., Dinan 1861). Collotype facsimile of the whole MS Bodleian 264 with an introduction by Montague Rhodes James (folio, Clarendon Press, Oxford 1933). This MS is mentioned here as an example, perhaps the best example of its kind; other MSS (not necessarily of books on falconry or hunting) may contain similar illustrations.

Though falconry is of Oriental origin and was always in great favor in the Orient, we have relatively few early texts ad hoc in Arabic or Persian.[51] To these few may be added the Persian treatise on falcons (bāz-nāma) entitled Qawānīn al-ṣayyād, composed, if we may believe its own preface, by Ibn Yār Muḥammad, known as Khudā Yār Khān Dā'ūd 'Abbāsī, who lived during the time of Tughā Tīmūr

[49] Gandolfo is not an unusual Italian name, but there is no such name in Persian. The early Western writings on falconry acknowledge their indebtedness to their Arabic and Persian sources in many ways, and "Gandolfo persiano" is one of those ways.

[50] Giuseppe Spezi: Due trattati (100 p., Roma 1864). Antonio Ceruti: Trattato di falconeria (Bologna 1870). Francesco Zambrini: Libro delle nature degli uccelli fatto per lo re Danchi (ill., Bologna 1874). Giuseppe Ferraro: Libro del Gandolfo persiano delle medesine de falconi (153 p., Scelta di curiosità letterarie, no. 154, Bologna 1877). Harting (p. 158–60, 1891).

[51] The information given in Introd. 2, 58 concerning the Egyptian origin should be canceled. For the early history see Hans J. Epstein: The origin and earliest history of falconry (Isis 34, 497–509, 1 pl., 1943). The same author is preparing another memoir, "Falconry during the early Middle Ages," to be completed after the war.

(īl-khān of Persia 1337–51).[52] The work is stated to be a simplified translation of the Shikār-nāma-i-Īlkhānī, itself derived from the Ṣayd-nāma i Malik Shāhī[53] of 'Alī ibn Manṣūr. The Qawānīn al-ṣayyād was edited in Persian by Douglas Craven Phillott[54] (470 p., Bibliotheca indica, Calcutta 1908). As represented by two late MSS used by the editor, the text is written in poor Indian Persian mixed with a little Panjabi and Sindhi.

As to the Far East, we know that Accipitres are common in China and of many species, some of them of superior quality for hunting (Couling p. 6, 1917). Marco Polo (XIII-2) spoke of many kinds of falcons observed by him in Asia. It is known that the Chinese have always practiced hawking, but I am not aware of the existence of a single mediaeval book on falconry (fang ying shu). Any amateur of Chinese (and Japanese) art, however, is acquainted with some splendid representations of falcons[55]—some of the best in the whole history of art—and that proves a familiarity with these birds possible only to falconers. Moreover, one of the best-known poems in Chinese literature is "The wounded falcon," by Han Yü (768–824).[56]

Note on Falconry in Ancient China, contributed by Dr. A. W. Hummel

Berthold Laufer has a rather full account of Chinese falconry and its Western parallels in his "Chinese pottery of the Han dynasty" (p. 231–32, Leiden 1909). There is also a discussion of it in William Charles White: Tomb tile pictures of ancient China (Museum Studies, no. 1, p. 59, University of Toronto 1939).

The consensus of opinion is that the Chinese got the practice from Central Asia in the Han period, just as they took from there other habits such as sitting on chairs. Falconry is not mentioned in Chinese classical literature of the Chou period. In bishop White's book there are representations of "falcon-like birds," carved on stone, which White dates in the third century B.C. But there is nothing to show that falcons were used for hunting at that time. The earliest clear pictures of falcons in a hunting scene are in the Han reliefs of Hsiao-t'ang shan, Shantung, which were carved before A.D. 129 at the latest; see Edouard Chavannes: La sculpture sur pierre en Chine au temps des deux dynasties Han (p. 77, Paris 1893). In the Royal Ontario Museum, Toronto, are two pottery figures probably of the fifth century, showing mounted hunters each with a falcon on his wrist.

52 Zambaur (p. 244, 1927). EI (4, 820–82, 1931). Not to be confused with his contemporary the last Yüan emperor Tughān Tīmūr, who ruled from 1333 on and was called by the Mongols Hui Tsung and by the Ming, Shun Ti (Giles no. 1953).

53 Various Saljūq rulers were named Malik Shāh in the period 1072–1192 (Lane-Poole p. 153–55, 1893). I am unable to identify this 'Alī ibn Manṣūr.

54 The same author, lieutenant colonel Phillott, also published the English translation of another Persian treatise, the Bāz-nāma-yi Nāṣirī (220 p., 25 ill., London 1908), which was written by Ḥusām al-daula Taimūr Mīrzā (d. 1874) as late as 1868, but which will be very useful to the historian for the interpretation of the older texts. It is divided into 69 chapters, the first 11 dealing with the "yellow-eyed birds of prey" (hawks, eagle, owl, etc.); the others with the "dark-eyed birds of prey" (falcons, etc.), methods of training and feeding in health and of treatment during the molt or in cases of illness. The Persian text was published in lithographed editions in Teheran, and later in Bombay (dates unknown).

55 The word "falcons" is used here rather loosely for Accipitres in general. According to Arthur de Carle Sowerby: Nature in Chinese art (p. 24, New York 1940; Isis 34, 68), some of the Chinese paintings represent such birds as the Eastern goshawk, the golden eagle, the buzzard, etc.

56 For the Han Yü see Giles (no. 632). English version of the poem in Ball (p. 489, 1926).

J. J. L. Duyvendak cites (T'oung Pao 35, 373, 1940) a veiled literary reference to falcons used in hunting, in a poem written by the astronomer Chang Hêng (II-1), but our Chinese bibliographer, Mr. Wang Chung-min, who is working here now, has pointed out to me an earlier and much more detailed literary reference which was written before 88 B.C. but refers to an event which took place in 208 B.C. The reference is in Ssŭ-ma Ch'ien (II-2 B.C.), Shih-chi, chüan 87. It has hitherto been overlooked by scholars owing to the omission of three characters, reading pei ts'ang yin "with black falcons on our arms," in the texts of the Shih-chi which are now current. The encyclopaedia T'ai-p'ing yü-lan of A.D. 983 (ch. 926, p. 2) quotes the passage in question, and we now know that it originally had the above words. The passage is one giving the last words spoken by the famous minister Li Ssŭ (d. 208 B.C.) to his son just before being led out to be executed. With the text properly emended, the sentence reads, "I had hoped that you and I might once more lead forth the yellow hounds, and with black falcons on our arms, together set out from the East Gate of Shang-ts'ai to pursue the wily hares. But now this cannot be!"

We can thus confidently place falconry in China shortly before the Han dynasties, that is to say, in Ch'in times.

Falconry has been very popular in Japan from early times, witness many books ad hoc (though none of the fourteenth century), paintings, carvings, poems, etc. According to tradition there are (in Japan) forty-eight places where falcons are found, hence the phrase "forty-eight falcons." Under the Tokugawa shōgunate (and perhaps earlier?) young falcons were caught and trained in these forty-eight places and then the twelve best ones were sent to the shōgun. The presentation and acceptance of the twelve falcons (jūni no taka) were the occasion of well regulated ceremonies.[57]

An account of Japanese falconry in early Meiji times is given by Edward S. Morse: Japan day by day, 1877–83 (2, 381–88, Boston 1917; Isis 34, 371–73). Hans Heinrich Vögele: Die Falknerei, eine ethnographische Darstellung (p. 22–25, Königsberg i.Pr. 1931).

For traditional falconry in India, see Richard F. Burton: Falconry in the valley of the Indus (124 p., London 1852).

12. *Fishing*

Not only is fishing essentially the same as hunting,[58] but a natural transition from the one subject to the other is given to us by the Far Eastern practice of cormorant fishing, comparable to falconry. Though the cormorant is found in many parts of the world, its domestication and use for fishing purposes has happened only in the Far East. The Japanese were apparently the initiators, and cormorant fishing did not spread to China until relatively late, though before the tenth cen-

[57] This inspired the creation by Chokichi Suzuki of the twelve bronze falcons which were exhibited at the Chicago World's Fair in 1893. Explanatory pamphlet with twelve plates (Tokyo 1893).

[58] In Arabic the same word, al-ṣayd, is used for both, except that for fishing one often adds the word meaning fish (hunting for fish), ṣayd al-samak.

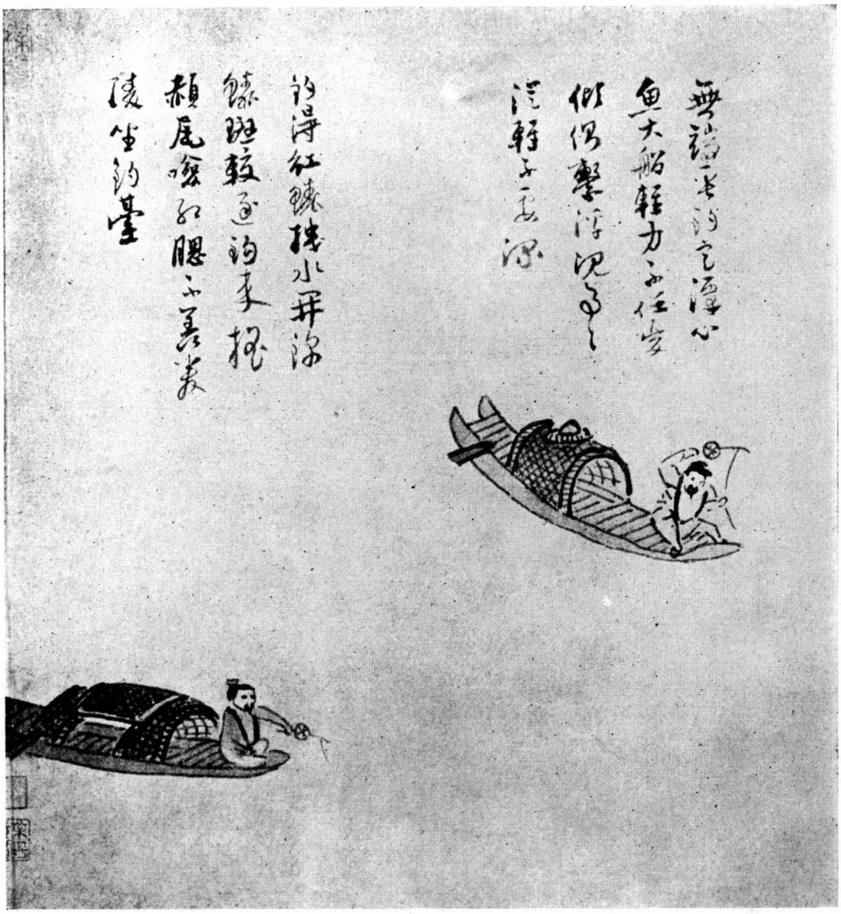

FIG. 5. Chinese fishermen using rod with reel. Painting by Wu Chên (1280–1354). Courtesy of Freer Gallery, Washington. Wu Chên was one of the "Four masters" of the Yüan dynasty. Herbert A. Giles: Introduction to the history of Chinese pictorial art (p. 144, Shanghai 1905). Arthur Waley: Index to Chinese artists (p. 100, British Museum 1922).

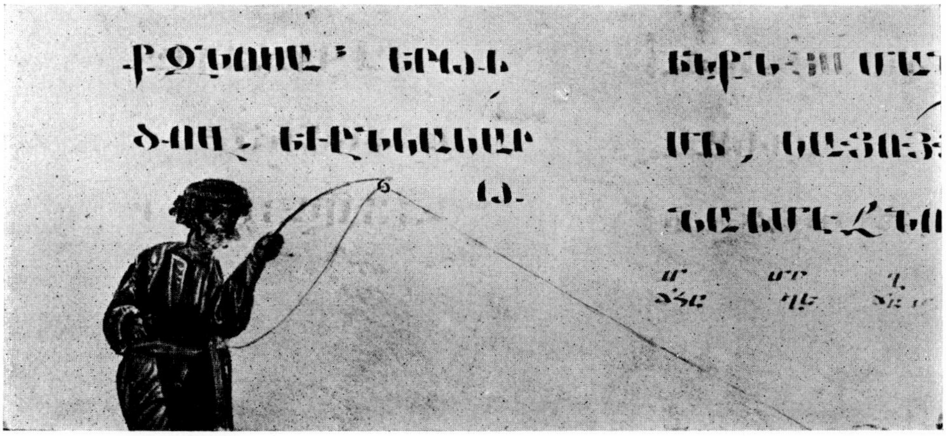

FIG. 6. Fishing rod with reel in an Armenian Gospel (thirteenth century). Courtesy of Freer Gallery, Washington.

tury.[59] In Marco Polo's time it was already very popular in China, yet the Venetian traveler did not refer to it. The first European account we owe to the Franciscan Odorico da Pordenone.

Inasmuch as Fra Odorico's cormorants have taken us to China, we may pause a moment there and examine the paintings of Wu Chên (1280–1354). One of them, a makimono (that is, a horizontal scroll) bearing the general title "Fishermen," represents various types of fishermen, each accompanied by a short poem —a practice for which Wu Chên was noted. Now, two of those men are holding rods with reels. Did the Chinese invent the fishing reel? Remember my remarks above concerning the impossibility of dating technical discoveries, especially simple ones, however important they may be. It is possible that the Chinese had known that trick for centuries before Wu Chên gave us a graphic representation of it. Moreover, the idea occurred to other people as well as to them, for we find a fishing reel in an Armenian parchment Gospel of the thirteenth century, illustrated in the style of T'oros Roslin. In this case, the reel is independent of the rod. The Armenian fisherman is Peter casting an hook in the sea (Matthew 17:27).

My information on these Chinese and Armenian reels was obtained exclusively from John Ellerton Lodge (d. 1942), curator of the Freer Gallery in Washington (letters and interview January 1941), who had these two monuments in his keeping. Wu Chên's makimono (no. 37.12) is 5.622 m. long and 0.325 wide, and the detail which we reproduce is taken from its fourth section. The Armenian figure occurs on page 107 of no. 32.18. We are able to reproduce these two figures, hitherto unpublished, thanks to the courtesy of the Freer Gallery and of its learned curator.

These illustrations of fishing reels are the earliest on record. According to Radcliffe (p. 8, 1921), the earliest description of a reel occurs in The art of angling of Thomas Barker (London 1651), but the same author suggests that Egyptians may have used them when spearing hippopotami (p. 238, 311).

All these, the reader, especially one who does not fish or angle, may think are trifles. They are not. The lives of many men depended on fishing, and the reel was a material improvement.

An invention of far greater scope, however, was being made about the same time in Western Europe, that is, the invention of new ways of preserving and packing herrings. It is ascribed to the Dutchman Willem Beukels, and though I have devoted a longish note to him, I am not certain that he deserves all the credit. It is not even certain that the invention was first made in Dutch Zeeland, or in Holland, or that it was not made more or less simultaneously elsewhere, e.g., in Scandinavian fishing harbors. Moreover, that invention, like any other, might be made and was made in many steps, hence the credit for it should be shared by many ingenious men engaged in that profession, able to understand its needs and to help in their fulfilment. What is certain is that that invention, making it possible to distribute fish to distant places by land and water, had far-reaching economic consequences; it is equally clear that Holland was its main beneficiary.

[59] The earliest Chinese mention of cormorants trained for fishing is in the Ch'ing i lu written by T'ao Ku (902–70; Giles no. 1898). Text given by Berthold Laufer: Domestication of the cormorant (p. 221, Chicago 1931; Isis 24, 254). Chinese have known cormorants from very early times, witness the representation of one on a piece of jade of the Chou dynasty. B. Laufer: Archaic Chinese jades collected in China by A. W. Bahr now in Field Museum (pl. xxvi, no. 7, New York 1927); Domestication (p. 205, 1931). James Lee Peters, Harvard ornithologist, tells me that it is a fair representation. It is possible after all that cormorant fishing developed independently in China and Japan; there are material differences between the Chinese and Japanese methods.

Though I am not by any means convinced that Beukels was the first or the main inventor, he is the only fourteenth-century man named in connection with it, and he may be allowed to stand as the symbol of it. It is the invention itself that matters—not the man who made it, but the millions of men whose life was made a little sweeter because of it.

13. *Special animals*

We have already spoken of falcons, cormorants, and herrings, but these were not the only animals to draw more particularly the attention of fourteenth-century writers.

Silkworms and bees are naturally discussed in some of the agricultural books, in the cosmographies and encyclopaedias, but I do not know of special treatises of this period devoted to sericulture or apiculture. Strangely enough, the earliest mention of glowworms in Western belles lettres is in Dante's Inferno. How is it that the poets of Greece, Rome, and mediaeval Europe—those who lived in the southern regions where fireflies often illuminate the summer nights—never referred to them? The only explanation of their silence is that references to such eerie creatures were tabooed. Even after Dante's time the taboo was but seldom broken, and fireflies are still waiting for a poet worthy of them.

Insects have always challenged men, and they have often had the best of them. Even today, in spite of all our knowledge and all our resources, the fight against them is not by any means an easy one, and it can never be relaxed without danger. They can still jeopardize our farmers, and they occasionally starve them, but in earlier times they could drive them out completely. They have been held responsible for the ruin of ancient civilizations, e.g., in Greece and Rome by W. H. S. Jones,[60] and in Central America.[61] In the Middle Ages, there was no knowledge of the real nature of various insect menaces, or of insect tactics, and even if such knowledge had been available, the means of coping with them would have been utterly insufficient. No wonder, then, that refuge was taken in fantastic theories and superstitious methods.

The idea of deprecatory offices or prayers against insects and other pests is very ancient and as widespread as religion itself. It will suffice to mention the Roman festival of Robigalia, celebrated on April 25 to preserve the fields from mildew. In the course of time the Robigalia were Christianized and became the Litania maior,[62] celebrated on the same day, which was the day of the evangelist St. Mark. A litany is exactly the same as a rogation, but it was often, as in the case of crops, a prayer against (a deprecation) as well a positive entreaty. In addition, criminal proceedings were sometimes instituted against animals, perhaps in obedience to the Biblical injunction (Exodus 21:28). For example, a pig which had devoured a baby was condemned and burned to death in Fontenay-aux-Roses, near Paris, in 1266. Such judgments continued to be rendered in France until the end of the seventeenth century. Proceedings were instituted against cockchafers (Melolontha vulgaris, hanneton) by the ecclesiastical court of Avignon 1320, and according to Bodenheimer (1, 239, 1928) this is the earliest process of that kind on record.

[60] William Henry Samuel Jones: Malaria, a neglected factor in the history of Greece and Rome (114 p., Cambridge 1907); Malaria and Greek history (184 p., Manchester 1909; Isis 6, 48).

[61] This has been denied by Sylvanus G. Morley: Guide book to the ruins of Quirigua (Washington 1935; Isis 25, 511–13). Morley ascribes the decadence of Maya civilization to extremely wasteful agricultural methods, the practice of milpa.

[62] It is often ascribed to Gregory I (VI-2), but may date back to Liberius (pope 352–66).

It has been said[63] that insects were "excommunicated." The idea is not incorrect, but the term is certainly wrong, for one can excommunicate only communicants. The church did not stop at deprecations and admonitions, however, it promulgated curses, exorcisms, anathemas. St. Bernard (XII-1) anathematized flies in Foigny abbey, Laon, 1121. Locusts were formally exiled by the priest in the pulpit of Bolzano (Bozen, southern Tirol) in 1338. The next process against insects (cockchafers) mentioned by Bodenheimer did not occur until 1497, in Lausanne. These events were thus very rare, but it is well to bear them in mind in order to appreciate a curious aspect of mediaeval entomology.

Information concerning insect plagues is found in many chronicles, too many to be listed. Consider, for example, the locusts; invasions of them were recorded in Hungary 1338–40; Italy 1339, 1341; Germany 1333–41, 1338; France 1337; Eastern Europe 1334–35. The years 1337–39 were "locust years" over a great part of Europe. A summary of these matters with bibliography will be found in Bodenheimer (2, 26–48, 1929).

Invasions by birds are also occasionally recorded, but these were much rarer. Matthew Paris (XIII-2) spoke of an invasion of England by crossbills in 1251.[64] I do not know of any similar event in our period.

The most curious ornithological document of this period, as far as it can be dated, is the Byzantine poem Pulologos. The spirit of this work is comparable to that of the bestiaries (Introd. 2, 57), that is, animal lore applied to Christian edification, but we find in it also the satirical intentions characteristic of the cycle of animal stories, Reynard the Fox (XII-2), and its equivalent in almost every European vernacular. Some of the bestiaries were restricted to birds, being then called volucraries. I cannot insist upon the volucraries any more than upon the bestiaries, all of which concern the historian of comparative literature and mediaeval manners rather than the historian of science. The most that the historian of ornithology could hope to glean in them would be lists of bird names, and again this would interest the philologist more than the ornithologist.

Other writings in vulgar Greek were devoted to animals, for example, "The children's story of the four-footed animals" and "The ritual of the honorable ass." Georgios Pachymeres (XIII-2, Introd. 2, 972) described a giraffe, and Manuel Philes, an elephant (in verse!). No doubt many more such items might be mentioned, but the aggregate would not amount to much as compared with the mass of similar information available in the contemporary Arabic writings. Indeed, the Arabic cosmographies contain zoological information too abundant and too detailed to be analyzed here, but attention must be drawn to another class of books which gave a new prestige to Arabic literature, namely, the treatises in hippology. At least five authors distinguished themselves in that field, and, but for one who was an Arab of Yaman, all were Mamlūk subjects. The Arabic love and care of horses reached a climax under Mamlūk patronage.

'Abd al-Mu'min al-Dimyāṭī (XIII-2) compiled a collection of traditions concerning horses. Lājīn ibn 'Abdallāh of Tripolis (of Syria) and Ibn Qayyim al-Jawzīya wrote treatises on chivalry and cavalry tactics. All these works are far less important than the two which remain to be named. The first was written

[63] Alexandre Sorel: Procès contre des animaux et insectes suivis au Moyen âge dans la Picardie et le Valois (46 p., Compiègne 1877; p. 33). Henry Charles Lea: Studies in church history (p. 409–15, Philadelphia 1869). Edward Clodd (ERE 5, 628–29, 1912).

[64] Cronica maiora (ed. H. R. Luard, 5, 254–55).

by a ruler of the Rasūlī dynasty of Yaman, al-Mujāhid 'Alī al-Rasūlī. His treatise deals with the breeding, upkeep, and training of domestic animals, chiefly horses, but also mules, camels, elephants, buffaloes, sheep, and cattle. In that respect it is outstanding, if not unique, in mediaeval literature. As far as the horses are concerned, the most elaborate mediaeval book was composed by Ibn al-Mundhir, master of the horse to the Mamlūk sulṭān al-Nāṣir Muḥammad ibn Qalā'ūn. We may well end our account of the main books on animals with this treatise by Ibn al-Mundhir, which had no equivalent in any other language or country until a much later period.

14. *Translations of books on natural history*

Strangely enough, the main translations which might interest the historian of natural history were made from Arabic into Hebrew, but this may be due to the fact that the books thus translated were already available in Latin. As has been explained before, the Hebrew translations were relatively late, because as long as the Jews knew Arabic as well as Hebrew they had no need of decanting knowledge from that language into their own.

In 1302 Jacob ben Maḥir ibn Tibbon (XIII-2) translated Ibn Rushd's commentary on Aristotelian zoology; two centuries later his Hebrew version was to be translated into Latin! Qalonymos ben Qalonymos translated Ibn Rushd's commentary on the De plantis. Thus before the middle of the century Peripatetic zoology and botany had become available in the Hebrew language, together with mediaeval accretions in Averroistic form.

XI. MEDICINE

The history of medicine at any period is almost hopelessly complicated, for it involves at least three very different things: (a) the history of medical knowledge (or science), (b) the history of the medical art (that is, the application of that knowledge), finally (c) the history of the medical profession (or the reactions between the people and the doctors). It is true one might claim that the historian of science can deal only with (a), but that is rather a narrow interpretation and it implies that (a) can always be clearly separated from (b) and (c). As a matter of fact, art and science are always blended, and the physician can never be considered apart from the patient.

Another difficulty meeting us in this section is that the number of distinguished physicians was exceedingly large. Medicine, we should remember, was in mediaeval times almost the only scientific profession; I added the word almost, because there were also a few alchemists and astrologers, but most of these were physicians, for physic was the only scientific profession which could feed a man and his family with sufficient regularity. By the beginning of the fourteenth century, the number of physicians must have been considerable, because every town had at least one, and doctors were attached to every court, whether lay or ecclesiastical, of any pretension. Many of these physicians were doctors, having received their M.D. from one or another of the medical schools flourishing in various countries. In addition there were quite a number of surgeons, herbalists, apothecaries, midwives, wandering leeches of many kinds, the whole gamut from honest if irregular healers down to quacks and swindlers.

Some of the most successful physicians among town or court doctors, such as the archiaters of popes and kings, are almost completely forgotten today. This is due to the simple fact that they left no writings recommending them to posterity, but were satisfied with their contemporary fame. In what follows we shall naturally devote our attention mostly to the physicians who transmitted their knowledge to us rather than to those who preferred to cash in on it and left us no means of judging whether their popularity was really deserved. One should always bear in mind that the success of a doctor is due not only, nor even primarily, to his superior knowledge, but rather to his entregent and to his ability in winning his patients' confidence. The best healer is often the one whom the sick trust most. However, the best healer is not necessarily the most successful doctor in a worldly sense, for worldly success depends on the possession of various qualities and vices, the analysis of which would take us too far away from medicine.

Scholars interested in the "successful" doctors of each place or country are invited to refer to the accounts to be found in the local chronicles, or in the publications of local antiquarians. In particular there are memoirs listing and discussing the physicians of the popes or of definite royal or princely courts.[1] These lists of royal physicians include illustrious names well known to the historian of medicine, together with many others which are meaningless to him. Some of the royal physicians were so famous and influential in their time that they have been immortalized by painters and scholars, but that is another story.[2]

To return to medicine, the best way to explain its state in the first half of the fourteenth century will be to give a brief account of the main physicians country by country, and then to deal with a few special topics.

Our geographical survey will be subdivided into nine parts, to wit, (A) Latin Christendom, (B) Christian East, (C) Western Jews, (D) Eastern Jews, (E) Western Muslims, (F) Eastern Muslims, (G) India and Tibet, (H) China, (J) Japan.

Geographical survey

A. *Latin Christendom*

The number of physicians in the Latin West deserving mention is so large that we must separate them into six groups: (1) Italy (by far the largest one), (2) Hispanic peninsula, (3) France, (4) England, (5) Belgium, (6) Germany. It is remarkable that Scandinavia is not represented.

A1. *Italy*

The Italian group is so imposing (over forty members) that it might serve to illustrate by itself all the medical peculiarities of Western Christendom, and hence

[1] E.g., for the papal physicians, see Prospero Mandosio: Θέατρον in quo maximorum Christiani orbis pontificarum archiatros spectandos exhibet (156 p., Roma 1784). This was considerably amplified by Gaetano Marini (1742–1815): Degli archiatri pontificj (2 vols., Roma 1784). Pierre Pansier: Les médecins des papes d'Avignon, 1308–1403 (Janus 14, 405–34, 1909), derived from Marini but from other sources as well.

[2] I cannot cite any fourteenth-century example, genuine portraits being rare in that century. But the reader will probably remember the magnificent portrait of Dr. Demetrio Cavenari by Van Dyck, now in the Frick collection in New York. Cavenari was famous in the early seventeenth century for his bibliomania, for his greed, and for having been the physician of Urban VII. He was immortalized not by his own pen, but by Van Dyck's brush. In an article on Demetrio Canevari (thus far unpublished) I prove that that portrait cannot be Demetrio's or else was not painted by Van Dyck. The case of Sir Theodore Turquet de Mayerne (1573–1655) is not so clear, for he was a distinguished physician, some of whose scientific writings and achievements are memorable; yet his portrait would not have been painted as often as it was if he had not been attached to the court of James I. Arnold C. Klebs: L'iconographie de Turquet de Mayerne (Genava 16, 173–76, 1 pl., 1938). Thomas Gibson: The iconography of Turquet de Mayerne (Annals of medical history 3, 288–96, 1941).

it is worth while to describe it with special care. As we divide these Italian doctors into various groups according to the outstanding peculiarities of each, the reader will bear in mind that these new classifications are somewhat artificial. It is easy enough to separate a Muslim doctor from a Christian one; it is fairly easy also to separate an Italian physician from a German one;[3] but when we begin to distinguish between the philosophically minded, the professors, the anatomists, etc., we walk on dangerous ground. The one classified as an anatomist was also very likely a "professor," and he may even have been a philosopher, and so forth. The reader should go through the whole list and consider my groupings as tentative, to be discarded and reshuffled if necessary.

Let us begin at the margin of the field with a few men who were not physicians, yet dabbled in medicine. The best example is the Augustinian Giles of Rome (XIII-2), who composed a treatise on embryology, De formatione corporis humani in utero, which was brought later to the attention of Leonardo da Vinci. It was largely derived from Ibn Rushd (XII-2). Dante also was interested in embryology, but only from the psychological angle. Christians pondering on the mysteries involved in the creation of a new man were necessarily fascinated by the greatest mystery of all: When and how is the new creature besouled? These questions are susceptible of many answers, which are briefly described in my Dante article. It will suffice to say here that Dante, following St. Augustine and Ibn Rushd, was apparently a "traducianist," i.e., he believed that the soul is generated together with the body, though it may appear only at a certain stage of the fetal development (in the second month of pregnancy according to St. Augustine). Of course, one can find many other allusions of medical interest in the Divina commedia or in other Dante writings, but none deserves to stop us in this rapid survey. The letters of Petrarca concern the medical historian more directly. In two of them, addressed to Giovanni de' Dondi (XIV-2), he strongly criticized all forms of medical superstition as well as the unbearable pedantism of many of the physicians of his day. These letters are a real treatise on the subject; they form the whole of book XII of the Epistolae rerum senilium.[4] As they were written in Petrarca's old age, they belong to the second half of the century, but I speak of them now because the main part of Petrarca's life was spent in the first half of the century and there are many medical references also in his earlier letters. Indeed, the Petrarca letters constitute the richest source for the study of the social background of medical thought in those days.

A second group is that of the translators, that is, of the physicians whose main title to medical immortality lies in their translations. Pietro d'Abano was no mean physician; the treatise on physiognomy which he composed in 1295 and the treatise on poisons written somewhat later enjoyed much popularity; to be sure, they were full of astrology and other nonsense, but that was the medical taste of the time as Petrarca bitterly described it. Our gratitude to him, however, is based not on these writings, but on his translations from the Greek into Latin. Some of them were nonmedical, Pietro being very much interested in the so-called Problems of Aristotle and other Problemata ascribed to Alexander of Aphrodisias and Cassios the Iatrosophist, but we speak of him here because of his Galenic translations. While Pietro was thus engaged in Padua, a similar task was being performed on a larger scale in south Italy by Niccolò da Reggio as "translator regius" for the

[3] Though there are difficult cases; where shall we place the Spanish physician, educated in Montpellier and practicing in Germany? or the Italian practicing in Avignon?

[4] They can be easily read in the Italian translation of Giuseppe Fracassetti: Lettere senili (2, 207–68, Firenze 1870).

Angevine kings. He translated from Greek into Latin a good many Galenic (or pseudo-Galenic) texts and a few Hippocratic (or pseudo-Hippocratic) ones; the most important text which we owe him is the De usu partium, dedicated to king Robert in 1322. Niccolò's activity in giving us a more direct knowledge of Greek medicine than was then available through Arabic channels is a very important landmark in the history of medical tradition.

In addition to Pietro d'Abano, there were many physicians in the astrological group. In fact, almost every physician having scientific pretensions, whether justified or not, was somewhat of an astrologer. Some, however, did not simply practice astrology, they tried to refine or improve it, they taught it, they wrote learned or childish books about it. We need not tarry very long with them. Niccolò di Paganica and Ugo de Castello, both Dominicans, wrote textbooks of medical astrology, and Andalò di Negro composed a whole series of astrological books, some of which were definitely medical in purpose. Still other medico-astrological treatises were produced by the Augustinian Augustine of Trent, by Paolo Dagomari (Paolo dell' Abbaco), and Maino de Maineri. The last named was the most medical-minded of them all. He was a kind of royal physician, being entrusted with the medical and astrological service (the two could hardly be separated) of the Visconti family of Milano. His treatise on the plague was full of astrology, but other treatises of his, e.g. one on medicinal waters, were apparently more strictly medical. There were probably few treatises of this time absolutely free of astrology, for astrological conceptions permeated everything.

We now come to what I am tempted to call the group of the "professors," that is, physicians who, whether they actually occupied a university chair or not, published dogmatic treatises. The first exemplar is Taddeo Alderotti (XIII-2), who taught in Bologna and wrote abundant commentaries on the Greek and Arabic classics. He was somewhat of a humanist, and as he tried to imitate the style of his colleagues of the law school, he tended to develop his arguments in a legal or scholastic form. His qualities and defects influenced more or less many medical writers of the fourteenth century, especially the "professors." Among the latter we might cite again Pietro d'Abano, or Petrus Conciliator as he was appropriately nicknamed after his magnum opus (note the title), Conciliator differentiarum philosophorum *et praecipue medicorum*. The purpose of that famous book was to reconcile all difficulties and contradictions of medicine in the same way that, say, Peter the Lombard (XII-2) had resolved theological puzzles in the Libri sententiarum. By the way, the Conciliator contains plenty of astrology; that was really unavoidable. The same scholastic tone was given by Francesco di Piedimonte to his Complementum, a continuation of the Grabadin of Mesuë the Younger (XI-1). Then we have the Aggregator or Aggregator brixiensis of William Corvi of Brescia (XIII-2), who lived until c. 1326. Dino del Garbo, nicknamed Expositor (Avicennae), continued and aggravated the tendencies of his master, Taddeo Alderotti, in his commentaries and his Dilucidatorium. Another one of Taddeo's pupils, Guglielmo da Varignana, carried these mannerisms to the banat of Croatia. Both he and Dino taught in Bologna. Niccolò da Santa Sofia, whose writings are lost, taught in Padua. The best disciple of Taddeo was Pietro Torrigiano, named the Plusquam commentator, on account of his scholastic commentary on Galen's Microtegni called Plusquam commentum. Note all these musty titles, Conciliator, Complementum, Aggregator, Expositor, Dilucidatorium, Plusquam commentum, which are typical of a definite stage in the development of medicine, medical scholasticism.

The books on materia medica lent themselves naturally enough to scholastic methods; we have already mentioned the Complementum of Francesco di Piedimonte. Consider also the Synonyma medicinae (or Clavis sanationis) of Simon of Genoa (XIII-2), though in this case the dominating idea was philological rather than scholastic (this is a real distinction, the hairsplitting being of a different kind). Simon's Synonyma was abbreviated (but in some parts expanded) by Mondino Friulano. Finally we have the Pandectae of Matthaeus Sylvaticus. More than enough to enlighten or to confuse the poor practitioner.

Italian surgeons had been since the time of Roger of Salerno (XII-2) the leaders of Christendom. At the beginning of our period the leader was still an Italian, Lanfranchi (XIII-2), but established in Paris. As we shall see later on, the most illustrious surgeons of the first half of the fourteenth century were not Italian, but French (Lanfranchi's pupils) or Flemish.

Anatomy, however, continued to be the exclusive glory of Italy. Apropos of this we may remark that the earliest autopsy of which we have a formal record was made in Bologna in February 1302 by Bartolommeo da Varignana assisted by another physician and three surgeons, but many other autopsies had certainly been carried out before that date (Introd. 2, 1081–83). Human dissections were repeatedly made by the "restorer of anatomy," Mondino de' Luzzi. The Anatomia Mundini (1316) was the most popular treatise of its kind in pre-Vesalian times; it is a practical textbook arranged like a manual of dissection. The Anatomia of Guido da Vigevano (1345) was derived partly from Mondino's, partly from his own dissections. Mondino was probably the first teacher to make demonstrative dissections in the presence of the students, and furthermore he made them with his own hands. That useful practice was continued in the same university (Bologna) by Niccolò Bertruccio, Alberto de' Zancari, and Pietro Torrigiano, and in Padua by Gentile da Foligno. In short, anatomical research and teaching were placed by these Italian physicians on a sound basis; if the fruits of their studies were still insignificant, it was because of their inherent difficulty, and the greater difficulty of overcoming deep-rooted prejudices.

Many doctors are known to us because of regimina bearing their names, that is, little treatises containing rules of health either for healthy people or for people obliged to change or restrict their habits in various ways. Taddeo Alderotti (XIII-2) wrote the De conservanda sanitate, Magnino of Milan prepared a new edition of the Regimen sanitatis, Guido da Vigevano compiled sanitary regulations for elderly pilgrims to the Holy Land, Barnabas of Reggio wrote treatises on health and on diet, Albino da Montecaliero wrote an elaborate regimen for the prince of Acaia. The regimina are sometimes difficult to separate from consilia written for definite patients, as was often done by Taddeo Alderotti and by Gentile da Foligno. We shall come back to the consilia farther down.

Then we have the eye doctors, who are beginning to challenge the supremacy of their Muslim or Jewish colleagues: Guido of Arezzo, who flourished in south Italy c. 1326; Giovanni de Casso, who wrote in 1346 a Tractatus de conservatione visus; and Barnabas of Reggio, who composed in 1340 the De conservanda sanitate oculorum.

These treatises on the eyes are concerned with prophylaxis as well as with therapeutics and thus might have been placed in the previous category. Another subject close to hygiene which was beginning—very imperfectly—to take shape in those days was what we now call balneology. Gentile da Foligno explained the value of hot baths and of mineral waters, and in his De balneis spoke of the baths of Lucca. The first part of the Liber medicinalis of Maino de Maineri dealt with medicinal waters. Bonaventura de' Castelli wrote a book on the waters of Porretta (between Pistoia and Florence) which enjoyed some popularity and thus helped to direct medical thought in the balneological direction. It is interesting to note that at least two of these early balneological treatises, Castelli's and Maineri's, were translated into Hebrew.

Veterinary medicine is represented by the treatises of Uberto di Cortenova, Lorenzo Rusio, Maurus and Marcus, but the date of the first of these is uncertain as well as the identity of the two last named. According to legends, Maurus was a German and Marcus a Cypriote; it is probable that these two names relate to but a single author, and it is possible that Marcus was an Italian. We do not need him, however, for Cortenova and Rusio suffice to illustrate the Italian veterinary art of those days.

The class of "royal physicians" has already been introduced by Giovanni da Procida (XIII-2), physician to Frederick II and to Manfred, who may have witnessed the dawn of the new century, and by Maino de Maineri, who was in attendance on the Visconti. Galvano de Levanto was in the service of Philippe le Bel, Giacomo Pipino was physician to the Angevine court, Giovanni da Genoa, surgeon and physician to the pope Clement VI.

Treatises on the plague were written by Gentile da Foligno and Giovanni della Penna. It will be better to discuss them together with the other plague treatises in the book devoted to the second half of the fourteenth century.

Jejune as it is, my enumeration is sufficient to give one an idea of the amount and diversity of medical work accomplished in Italy. The preponderance of Italy in the second half of the thirteenth century (Introd. 2, 793) continued in the first half of the fourteenth, and Bologna remained the leading medical school of Christendom, though Montpellier was a close rival.

A2. *Hispanic peninsula*

Among the medical translators I can think of only two who originated in the peninsula. The first is Arnold of Villanova (XIII-2), who translated from Arabic into Latin treatises of Galen, al-Kindī, Qusṭā ibn Lūqā, Ibn Sīnā, etc.; and the second one, Stephanus Arnoldi, said to have come from Barcelona. Stephanus' translations, also from Arabic into Latin, are unimportant. The only one which may concern us here is that of a "dietarium" by Qusṭā ibn Lūqā, and that one is uncertain and as little known as the translator himself.

The medical fame of the peninsula was sustained primarily by two men whom one cannot help encountering over and over again in every field of endeavor, because they were among the outstanding personalities of the new century: Arnold of Villanova (XIII-2), who died in 1311, and Ramon Lull (XIII-2), who died four years later. Arnold's medical translations have just been recalled. He was a regular physician who had received in Naples the Salernitan traditions, and later had obtained more knowledge in the medical circles of Paris, Montpellier, and other places. He wrote a great many medical works (49 are enumerated in Introd. 2, 895–98), the most famous being his edition of the Regimen sanitatis dedicated to the king of Aragon in 1307. Ramon Lull, on the other hand, was not a physician, but since he was a philosophical touche-à-tout, his lack of technical preparation did not prevent him from writing half a dozen medical treatises and did not prevent the public from giving them a better reception than they deserved; one of those treatises was even translated into Hebrew.

The other peninsular physicians were decidedly second-raters. Alexander of

Spain wrote a book of home medicine arranged in monthly order, and other simple medical texts. Peter Figarola's activity was of the same kind. Alfonso of Cordova and Jacme d'Agramont were among the first to discuss the plague; in fact, Jacme's treatise is the earliest dated one (April 24, 1348); we shall come back to that later on. Another treatise on the plague has been ascribed to the apostate Abner of Burgos.

Three Spanish writers on the veterinary art were listed in my volume 2 (p. 1091), though I was unable to determine their floruit: Jacme de Castro, Juan Alvarez Salamiellas, Fray Bernardo Portuguès. From the name of the last named we can conclude that he was a Portuguese established in Spain. We have more definite knowledge about another Portuguese, master Giraldes, who was physician to the good king Dinis. He wrote in Lisbon 1318 a veterinary textbook in Portuguese.

Note that with the exception of the Portuguese Giraldes, and of the Spaniards Alexander, Alfonso of Cordova, and Abner of Burgos (assuming that Abner belongs here at all), all the medical writers mentioned above were Catalan or Valencian (Figarola?). This was the golden age of Catalonia. Other Catalan writers, Christian and Jewish, will appear in some of the following sections, that is, if we understand Catalan in a cultural or a linguistic sense (a form of langue d'oc) rather than in a strictly regional one.

A collection of Catalan recipes was compiled by one Bernat de Pujol in 1347; that is the Receptari de Manresa, so called because the MS is kept in the municipal archives of Manresa (30 miles from Barcelona). It was edited by Luis Comenge y Ferrer (72 p., Barcelona 1899).[5]

To gain an understanding of medical folklore and of the diffusion of medical ideas outside of professional circles, one of the best ways is to analyze contemporary belles lettres. This has been done, e.g., with regard to the foremost Castilian author of this period, Don Juan Manuel. Out of the fifty stories of El conde Lucanor, six contain items of medical interest, none of which is very significant.[6]

A3. *France*

Let us now pass to France; we cross the Pyrénées, but we do not cross the linguistic frontier between the "langue d'oc" and the "langue d'oïl," hence some ambiguities which the reader can easily remedy by considering together the two sections A2 and A3 and reshuffling some elements, should he deem it necessary.

Beginning as usual with the translators, we find in southern France a curious situation. John de Planis was translating Ibn Rushd's treatise on laxatives from Hebrew into Latin; of course, he could do that only with the help of a Jew, and he found one named Maynus ready to help him. Another southern doctor, educated in Montpellier, one Berenger, translated Abū-l-Qāsim's tract on diet from Catalan into Latin (the Catalan text in this case was simply an intermediary step between Arabic and Latin). This Berenger or Berengarius may be identical with a Berenger of Thumba (?), who wrote medical treatises in Montpellier c. 1334.

In the meanwhile, a northern clerk, Jean de Prouville, wrote a medical poem in Latin and translated the surgical treatise of the unknown abbé Poutrel from Latin into French. This is very interesting, as it points to the existence of a growing class of surgeons who do not know Latin and are ipso facto outside the regular medical profession. And yet by this time the surgeons were beginning to be aware

[5] Not available to me on account of the war. No copy in the United States. Quoted by Canibell (no. 776, 1918).

[6] V. Bugiel: La médecine et les médecins dans les récits de Jean Manuel (Bull. Société française d'histoire de la médecine 16, 293–303, 1922).

of themselves as a separate professional group. This was due partly to the fact that higher surgical standards had been introduced into Paris by Guido Lanfranchi (XIII-2) and perhaps by the Quattuor magistri (XIII-2) or whoever impersonated them. A surgical guild was soon established, and became known, we do not know exactly when, as the college or brotherhood of St. Cosmas. The guild existed before 1268, and the earliest Frenchman to obtain fame as a surgeon, Jean Pitart, was associated with it; it was thanks to him that Philippe le Bel promulgated in 1311 an edict protecting and delimiting the surgical profession. Thus began the endless fight of the surgeons against the doctors on the one side and the barbers on the other.

Regulations are necessary to establish a group, that is, to give it a legal existence and sufficient protection against outsiders, but no amount of regulations can create the social recognition which the members of any profession desire. Recognition and prestige are obtainable only by the achievements of distinguished individuals. The surgeons of Paris were fortunate in having among them not only a Pitart, whose fame was as evanescent as that of a tenor (such is the fame of most surgeons of all times, a life annuity), but also a great teacher called Henri de Mondeville. Mondeville wrote in Latin, but part of his Cyrurgia was translated into French within his own lifetime. His treatise was not restricted to surgery; it was really a medical encyclopaedia for the surgeon's use. This is very important from the social as well as from the purely scientific point of view. The surgeon could only emulate the doctor if he became a doctor himself, if he had a sound medical preparation, not only a purely surgical one. In order to appreciate what this means, it suffices to realize that the same progress has been accomplished with regard to another branch of medicine (dentistry) only within our own days.

The main center of medical teaching in France was not in Paris, that is, in the north, but in Languedoc, in the Mediterranean city of Montpellier. The University of Montpellier can be traced back to the twelfth century (Introd. 2, 352–53); the medical school was probably an offshoot from Salerno and was at first stimulated by Jewish and Arabic influences, yet it was strongly Catholic in the midst of a country famous for its heretical tendencies. The main composition of its student body is illustrated by its division into three nations, Provence, Burgundy, and Catalonia. Using modern political terms, the medical school of Montpellier was Hispano-French. During the Babylonian captivity (1309–76), Montpellier must have derived not a few advantages and not a little prestige from its proximity to the comtat d'Avignon and the comtat Venaissin (Vaucluse), which were papal territories. The presence of the curia in Avignon attracted there the faithful from the whole Catholic world, and Montpellier tended to become the medical center of all these people, from the popes down. In fact, the popes took a deep interest in their medical faculty, and thanks to that we are exceptionally well informed on the course of studies followed in Montpellier. Says Rashdall (2, 127–28, 1936):

"In 1309 Pope Clement V, by the advice of his Montpellier physicians, Arnald of Villanova and others, prescribed the following as the books which candidates for the licence must possess—Galen, De complexionibus, De malicia complexionis diverse, De simplici medicina, De morbo et accidente, De crisi et criticis diebus, De ingenio sanitatis, together with either the books of Avicenna or those of Razes, Constantinus Africanus, and Isaac, with commentaries thereon. He must further have 'read' as a bachelor three books, one with and one without comments, selected from the following list—the Tegni of Galen, the Prognostics and Aphorisms of

Hippocrates, the De regimine acutorum of Johannicius, the liber febrium of Isaac, the Antidotarium, the De morbo et accidente of Galen, and the De ingenio sanitatis of the same writer.

"It may be well to add the list of books appointed as subjects for lectures in 1340, arranged in courses, each of which was to be taken by one doctor: (1) Primus Canonis (Avicenna), (2) Liber de morbo et accidente (Galen) and de differentiis febrium (Galen), (3) Liber de crisi et criticis diebus and de malicia complexionis diverse (Galen), (4) Liber de simplicibus medicinis and de complexionibus (Galen), (5) Liber de iuvamentis membrorum and de interioribus (Galen), (6) Liber Amphorismi (Hippocrates) with de regimine acutorum (Hippocrates) or de prognosticis, (7) Liber de ingenio (sanitatis) and ad Glauconem (Galen), (8) Quartus Canonis (Avicenna), 'quoad duas primas seu cum Iohannicio de pulsibus et urinis Theophili,' (9) Tegni (Galen) with de prognosticis and de regimine acutorum, (10) Liber de regimine sanitatis and de virtutibus naturalibus (Bartholomew the Englishman).

"Upon these books there were always to be lectures; if the number of doctors sufficed, there might be lectures on other parts of the canon, other books of Galen, or the de febribus and de dietis universalibus of the Jew Isaac."[7]

This program is interesting, because it was typical not only of Montpellier, but of every medical faculty in Latin Christendom, and gives us a definite idea of the "library" which a learned physician of 1340 was supposed to draw upon if not to read or master completely.

The most famous professors of Montpellier at this time were Bernard of Gordon (fl. c. 1283–1308), Jordanes de Turre (fl. 1313–35), Gerald de Solo (fl. 1335 sq.). The first and third were French, the second may have been French, Italian, or Spanish. Bernard was the author of one of the most successful medical books of mediaeval times, the Lilium medicinae (1304), the popularity of which is proved by the abundance of MSS, the number of editions (down to 1617!), and translations into Irish, Hebrew, French, and Spanish. This was Bernard's main book, but he wrote many others. Gerald was a great textbook writer, and his Introductorium juvenum was also translated into Hebrew. This is very significant. It means that Jewish doctors, far from being ahead of the Christians because of a greater ability to drink at the Arabic sources, had lost that ability altogether and were now reduced to borrowing from Christian Latin sources; the tradition was reversed. Jordanes, sandwiched between Bernard and Gerald, is relatively unimportant. He composed a dozen medical tracts, but none attracted much attention.

While Bernard, Jordanes, and Gerald were thus teaching in Montpellier, a similar task was performed in Paris by Pierre de Saint Flour, who compiled a medical anthology entitled Colliget florum medicine, the flowers being culled mainly in the gardens of Galen and Ibn Sīnā.

Peter of Capestang, brother Vital du Four, and Raymond of Molières wrote regimina; Pierre Chauchat, a commentary on Galen; Pierre de Damouzy and Geoffroy de Meaux, plague treatises.

The writings of what might be called the French school of medicine were almost exclusively in Latin, but Mondeville's Cyrurgia was promptly translated into French. Of course, many documents of medical interest may be found in contemporary French writings. For example, there is a description of scurvy in the Histoire de Saint Louis of Joinville. Then we have an abundance of recipes in

[7] The Jew Isaac is Isḥāq al-Isrā'īlī (X-1), Johannitius is Ḥunain ibn Isḥāq (IX-2). The other names quoted by Rashdall are easily identified.

langue d'oc as well as in langue d'oïl. Some taken from a MS of the beginning of the fourteenth century have been excellently edited by Paul Meyer: Recettes médicales en français publiées d'après le MS. B.N. Lat. 8654 B (Romania 37, 358–77, 1908), with a glossary and references to other publications of the same kind which have been investigated mainly for philological purposes. Popular medicine was practiced by surgeons and herbalists; we have already spoken of the former; as to the latter, they could not sell their herbs without a good patter. A fine example of such "sales talk" has been preserved for us in Li diz de l'erberie of Rutebeuf (Oeuvres complètes, edited by Achille Jubinal, 1, 250–59, Paris 1839). Rutebeuf was the greatest French poet of his time next to or ex aequo with Jean de Meung (XIII-2), but the latter lived until 1305, whereas Rutebeuf died c. 1285; both flourished mainly in Paris. The herbalists satirized by Rutebeuf must have been fairly common during the first half of the fourteenth century, witness severe ordonnances decreed against them by Philippe le Bel in 1311, and by Jean le Bon in 1352 (Jusserand p. 105–8, 1884). These ordonnances are interesting prototypes of our regulations against various forms of illegal medicine; they were probably inspired and motivated by the medical schools.

Various other studies. Louis Bossu: Médecins experts et médecine légale au XIVe siècle (40 p., reprinted from Droit médical, Paris 1908), based on Parisian archives. Ernest Wickersheimer: Les médecins de la nation anglaise (ou allemande) de l'Université de Paris aux XIVe et XVe siècles (Bull. Société française d'histoire de la médecine 12, 285–344, 537–38, 1913). Pierre Pansier: Les prétendus statuts de la reine Jeanne réglementant la prostitution à Avignon en 1347 (ibid. 17, 157–75, 1923). Georges d'Avenel: Revenus d'un intellectuel de 1200 à 1913 (p. 168–212, Paris 1922), very interesting details on medical economics. Karl Sudhoff: Eine Diätregel für einen Bischof aufgestellt von vier Professoren in der Mitte des 14. Jahrh. (AGM 14, 184–86, 1923). Pierre Galland: L'église et l'hygiène au Moyen-âge (thesis, 220 p., Paris 1933), exclusively derived from Latin and French sources, one-sided pleading for the church (Isis 32).

A4. *England*

The accounts of Spanish and French medicine took less space together than that of Italian medicine alone. The remaining sections, to be devoted to English, Belgian, and German medicine, will be even shorter.

As to England, only three names occur to me, and the first of these is doubtful. The John of Bassoles who was teaching in the faculty of Paris c. 1325, was he English, French, or Catalan? The two other Johns are each immortalized by an outstanding book. The Summa anglicana of John of Ashendon might serve as a type of the astrological treatise of its time, encyclopaedic in purpose because astrology was supposed to be the "master" science, without which a deep understanding of the rest was impossible. Thus John's Summa contains not only astronomy, physics, meteorology, but also medicine. It was completed in 1348, hence its influence was felt only after the middle of the century, but then it continued to grow for two or three centuries, and Ashendon could still be spoken of at the end of the seventeenth century as one of the greatest scientists of England.

The Rosa medicinae of John of Gaddesden (c. 1314) is a work of a much humbler kind, but, in spite of many superstitions, more directly in the line of medical progress. It includes many valuable clinical observations and must have been really helpful to contemporary physicians. It is the finest symbol of the English medicine of its time, medicine derived from Italy or southern France, but with original additions doing credit to the author's clinical experience and power of observation. The Rosa was appreciated in England and on the Continent, and also in Ireland, being promptly translated into Goidelic.

There are a number of anonymous treatises and recipes in Latin and English (Wells p. 428 ff.), but as most of them seem to belong to the end of the century or are of uncertain date, I shall deal with them in chapter XXV. The medical folklore which can be extracted from contemporary English literature has been gathered by Ida B. Jones (Bull. Institute of the History of Medicine 5, 405–51, 538–88, Baltimore 1937).

A5. *Belgium*

The term "Belgium" is somewhat anachronistic (both backward and forward!), but is used here for the sake of convenience, to indicate that the physicians to be considered were not all Flemings; two came from the Walloon districts of modern Belgium. The territory covered in this section corresponds roughly to the whole of modern Belgium; it is different on the one hand from Flanders, and on the other hand from that of the "fortissimi Belgae" of Julius Caesar or from ancient Belgium (which was equal to the Low Countries largo sensu, i.e., modern Belgium plus the modern Netherlands).[8]

The Flemish group is small but extremely distinguished. It includes two of the greatest surgeons of the century, both writing in Flemish (or Dutch). It is remarkable that two Flemings, Jan Yperman (meaning, of Ypres) and Thomas Scellinck of Tirlemont, addressed themselves to the same task at about the same time, Jan before 1331 and Thomas in 1343. The coincidence may be due to the frequency of wars in Flanders, increasing surgical needs. Apparently they worked independently, yet their works have very much in common, because they were largely derived from the same sources. Jan was perhaps a little more up-to-date with regard to the abundant surgical experience which had been accumulated just before his time in Italy and France. Thomas was perhaps less of a surgeon, but more of a physician. The extrinsic importance of these two treatises is small, for only four MSS of the first and two MSS of the second have survived, and neither text was printed for practical (vs. archaeological) purposes. They appeared in printed form, the first in 1867, the second not until 1928.

The third Fleming, Bartholomew of Bruges, was of a very different class, not a lowly surgeon, but a Montpellier doctor who gave Aristotelian lectures in Paris, wrote medical as well as philosophical commentaries, and wound up as a princely physician. Needless to say, he wrote in Latin, not in Dutch, and the greater part of his life was spent in foreign pastures.

The two men remaining to be dealt with came from the Walloon country, John of Saint Amand (XIII-2) from Tournai (or Valenciennes? in which case he should be counted as a Fleming), and Simon from Couvin. John of Saint Amand was a medical erudite to whom we owe two compilations, the Expositio super antidotarium Nicolai and the Revocativum memoriae; Simon of Couvin is of the type with which we are already very familiar, the medical astrologer. John was probably, and Simon certainly, a graduate of the Paris, not of the Montpellier, school of medicine.

[8] See Ferrari and Baudrand (p. 96, 1697). Albert Tiberghien: Lingua belgica (Isis 23, 445, 1935). These remarks will give scientists, not trained in historical methods, an inkling of the endless difficulties of historical geography.

Additional information on Belgian medicine will be found in the following publications: A. Geyl: Un traité de médecine du XIVe siècle (Janus 14, 354–89, 1909); Dutch text from the Royal Library, The Hague (73 J.8), edited with French translation, dealing mainly with uroscopy, bloodletting, diet. J. Verdam: Quelques observations littéraires sur le MS. (Janus 14, 390–92, 1909); philological notes concluding that the text might come not from Flanders, but from the northeastern provinces (Holland, Utrecht, Gelderland).

J. Munk: Een vlaamsche leringe van orinen uit de veertiende eeuw (Diss. Leiden 1917; Janus 17, 415–16, 1917); two Dutch treatises on urine taken from MS 15624/41, Royal Library, Brussels; MS on parchment, written in 1351 by Johannes de Altre. The second treatise is simply an extract from the former; both are derived from earlier Dutch texts. The main sources are Theophilos Protospatharios (VII-1), Isḥāq al-Isrā'īlī (X-1), and Giles of Corbeil (XII-2). Munk has examined a similar treatise on uroscopy, also in Dutch, preserved in a Leiden MS (B.P.L. cod. 1905).

Oscar van Schoor: La plus ancienne législation médico-pharmaceutique de Belgique. La keure d'Ypres, XIIIe–XIVe siècles (Vorträge 1934, 22–28, Gesellschaft für Geschichte der Pharmazie; Isis 24, 480); medical regulations taken from a book of ordinances of Ypres with a French title, from 1281, 1292, to 1310.

Medical information may be deduced from the Livre des métiers (Isis 19, 261), a book of French-Flemish conversation to which we shall come back in chapter XIV. Paul Dorveaux: Note sur la médecine en Flandre au XIVe siècle (Janus 7, 197–98, 1902). Jean Gessler: Médecins et chirurgiens d'après les manuels de conversation du XIVe et XVe siècles (Janus 36, 311–17, 1932).

A6. *Germany*

German medicine was apparently the poorest of Western Christendom, with the exception of Scandinavia's, about which we know nothing for this period.

The encyclopaedically minded writers dealt naturally with medical subjects. That is the case for the Spiegel der Natur written in Low German by Eberhard von Wampen, and the Buch der Natur composed in Bavarian by Conrad von Megenberg. In both works the fundamental theories of medicine are set forth, relatively more space being devoted to them and their applications in Eberhard's work than in Conrad's. John of Saxony and Conrad wrote about the plague; John, being an astrologer, gave an astrological account of it, whereas Conrad, the naturalist, connected it with earthquakes.

The internationalism of mediaeval medicine is illustrated by Johann Hake of Göttingen, who studied in Montpellier and practiced in Avignon as well as in his own country; and by Eberhard von Wampen, who flourished in Sweden; or, inversely, by the Italian doctor Albert of Parma, who was one of the outstanding physicians in Strassburg. These examples might be multiplied without too much trouble, but they suffice.

More details concerning the practice of medicine in Germany will be found in the following papers:

Karl Sudhoff: Zwei deutsche Rezepte aus dem 14. Jahrhundert (AGM 8, 449–50, 1915), recipes in German of the lower Rhine in University of Leipzig MS 1118; Rezepte des Arztes Magister Heinrich, genannt Vrigedanch (Freidank) für den Abt des Klosters zu Deutz [bei Köln] und seine Schwester (AGM 11, 231–32, 1919), Latin text of c. 1320–40 in Erfurt, Amploniana 288 in folio last page; Deutsche Rezepte im Leipziger Cod. 1146 der Universitätsbibliothek aus der Mitte des 14. Jahrh. (AGM 11, 216–17, 1919).

Hermann Schöppler: Über Regensburger Ärzte (AGM 15, 105–11, 1923), physicians of Ratisbon in fourteenth and fifteenth centuries, the first named being Conrad of Ascania (= Eichstädt) (1325/26) and one Meister Heinrich der Wundarzt (1326–55).

Joseph Klapper: Schlesische Volkskunde auf kulturgeschichtlicher Grundlage (384 p., ill., Breslau 1925), including notices not only on folk medicine, but also on folklore concerning plants, animals, agriculture. This book is cited here as a specimen of a very large class of books on the folklore of every German district. It is particularly rich, being based on the extensive collections of the Schlesische Gesellschaft für Volkskunde (Silesian Folklore Society). I must warn the reader, however, that he will seldom find grist to his mill in ethnological collections, the reason being that folklore is generally undatable and is not special to any period. It is easy to describe German folklore, but hardly possible to determine the specific lore of the fourteenth century.

Rudolf Kaiser: Deutsche und lateinische Texte des 14. und 15. Jahrh. über die Heilwirkungen des Weingeistes (Diss., 23 p., Leipzig 1925).

Karl Heinrich Schäfer: Das Testament eines Würzburger Arztes an der päpstlichen Kurie vom Jahre 1348 (AGM 30, 295–300, 1937). Ex Arch. Vat. instr. misc. 1753, testament of Albert of Würzburg, Avignon 1348.

B. *Christian East*

B1. *Byzantium*

Two courtiers in the service of the Palaeologoi emperors in the first quarter of the century, Nicephoros Chumnos and his son Joannes, were distinguished men of letters. Joannes was somewhat of a physician and wrote a regimen for podagrics. It is probable that his views on the subject did not differ materially from those of Demetrios Pepagomenos (XIII-2). Apparently gout was not an uncommon affliction among the Byzantine upper classes.[9] It is clear that neither Demetrios nor Joannes Chumnos knew much about it, but are we much wiser? Both recognized the need of unloading the tissues as much as possible, and the methods ad hoc of their time were frugality, which was all right, plus purgation and bloodletting.[10]

The outstanding doctor of the age of the Palaeologoi was the court physician Joannes Actuarios. He closes the series of the great Byzantine physicians. His works were used considerably not only in the Christian East but also in the West, being read in Latin translations until the middle of the sixteenth century and even later.

Even as the Chumnoi, other Byzantine literati liked to discuss medical subjects. Here are three examples: Maximos Planudes (XIII-2) wrote a treatise on one of the most popular methods of the Middle Ages, uroscopy. Georgios Choniates translated a book on antidotes from Persian into Greek (my dating of his activity is tentative). The mathematician Joannes Pediasimos wrote a very curious treatise on the viability of seven-month and nine-month foetuses, and discussed the old superstition with regard to the nonviability of the eight-month ones. We should not judge these fancies too severely, bearing in mind that they continued to be entertained not only by uneducated people, but by learned doctors for centuries afterward. Ideas concerning the length of human pregnancy were especially

[9] E. Jeanselme: La goutte à Byzance (Bull. Société d'histoire de la médecine 14, 137–64, 1920). See my note on Anna Comnena (XII-1).

[10] To appreciate Chumnos' studies on gout, remember that the first satisfactory description of that disease was given more than three centuries and a half later by Thomas Sydenham: Tractatus de podagra et hydrope (London 1683), himself a hopeless victim of it. We know the disease pretty well, but can do little if anything to cure or alleviate it.

vague; it was (and still is) very difficult if not impossible to determine exactly the beginning of each pregnancy, hence its duration was necessarily ambiguous. The Romans spoke of ten (lunar) months,[11] we speak of nine (solar) ones. Even as late as Louis XIV, "le roi soleil," one was still considering viability possible between the limits of 210 and 390 days, i.e., one could argue the legitimacy of a child born thirteen months after the death of his putative father.[12]

Of course, the theory that eight-month children were not viable was particularly fantastic and far less excusable than ignorance of the exact length of normal pregnancy, and yet it was blindly accepted by the majority of physicians and lawyers until the middle of the seventeenth century! One of the first to fight it was the papal archiater Paolo Zacchia in his Quaestiones medico-legales (book 1, 1621), the first great work on legal medicine.[13] Zacchia discusses it in liber 1, titulus II (De partu legitimo et vitali), quaestio IV; he reviews the fantastic arguments which were used to prove that eight-month foetuses could not possibly live—it would be difficult to find a more perfect example of solemn and pretentious unreality[14] (see Locard, p. 383–85). The papal doctor brushed all that nonsense aside and concluded that eight-month children have a better chance to survive than the seven-month ones; one should not pay too much attention to certain numbers, he remarked: "Res non sunt propter numerum, sed numerus propter res."[15] If it was necessary to make such statements in a book addressed to the intellectual elite of the seventeenth century, we should not look down on Pediasimos for discussing them three centuries earlier. Before abandoning that question, let me add that though Zacchia considered nine months the normal length of pregnancy, he did not reject completely the possibility of longer pregnancies, up to more than ten (solar) months.

B2. *Armenia*

There is nothing to report about the medical activities of other Christians of the Near East, except perhaps a book on the warm springs of Cilicia ascribed to Nerses Balì. That book is lost, however, its existence and ascription are uncertain. Moreover, Nerses was a Catholic and flourished at least for a time in Avignon; thus he is not a good representative of the Christian East.

[11] Virgil: Bucolica, end of eclogue IV. Similarly, Jesus Christ and the Virgin Mary are often spoken of as having been born at ten months. According to the church calendar, however, there are exactly nine (solar) months between the Annunciation and Christmas, if one accepts the date March 25 for the former. That date has not been accepted always and everywhere; see Frederick G. Holweck (CE 1, 541–43, 1907), Ginzel (3, 161–63, 1914).

[12] Léon Bouchacourt: La grossesse. Etude de sa durée et ses variations (524 p., Paris 1901). Edmond Locard: Le XVIIe siècle médico-judiciaire (p. 378–90, Paris 1902).

[13] For Paolo Zacchia (1584–1659), see BL (5, 1020). His work, which remained the medico-legal canon until the end of the eighteenth century, was entitled Quaestiones medico-legales in quibus omnes eae materiae medicae, quae ad legales facultates videntur pertinere proponuntur, pertractantur, resolvuntur, opus juris peritis apprime necessarium, medicis, etc. libri VII (1st ed. in 7 vols., Rome 1621–50). Often reprinted, e.g., in one large folio, 1200 p. (Amsterdam 1651). Zacchia's pre-eminence in the field of legal medicine was consecrated by the creation of a journal called "Zacchia," Rassegna di studi medico-legali (Roma 1921–33, Torino 1937 f.).

[14] It is easy enough to make jokes about this, but we should not forget that examples of similar unreality can be found every day in our newspapers. For an elementary but excellent discussion, see Samuel Ichiyé Hayakawa: Language in action (254 p., New York 1941; Isis 34, 84). As to the reproach of unreality made against primitive people by the late Lucien Lévy-Bruhl (1857–1939), see Isis 12, 343–47; 30, 306–10.

[15] See edition of Amsterdam 1651 (p. 43) in the Summarium quaestionis IV; see also sectio 28 eiusdem quaestionis (p. 46).

C. *Western Jews*

In spite of persecutions, the Jews of Western Europe continued their efforts to transmit medical knowledge and even to improve it. This is particularly true of the Jews of southern France and of the Hispanic peninsula.

C1. *Southern France*

In the Jewish colonies of Languedoc and Provence, medical work was largely in the nature of translations. It is possible that the rabbinical habits acquired in the bait midrash or the yeshivah caused that kind of activity to be more congenial to the Jewish doctor. It is certain that medical books originally written in Hebrew were utterly insufficient. We must remember that by far the best medical books of Jewish origin, those of Maimonides (XII-2),[16] were written in Arabic and had to be translated into Hebrew to become available to the Transpyrenean Jews, and even to a growing number of Spanish ones.

The great majority of these scholars were translating into Hebrew, but we find at least one at the beginning of the century, Armengaud son of Blaise (XIII-2), who was working not for his brethren but for the Christians, translating medical books from Arabic not into Hebrew but into Latin. With the help of Hebrew versions he Latinized various texts of Galen, Ibn Sīnā, and Maimonides.

In earlier days the translations into Hebrew were primarily if not exclusively from the Arabic. This was still the case for two translators, Samson ben Solomon and Qalonymos ben Qalonymos. Samson translated the "sixteen books of Galen" (that is, the Byzantine Galenic canon) from the Arabic under the title Sefer ha-qibuẓim; Qalonymos rendered greater services as a translator of mathematical and astronomical works, but we owe him also Hebrew versions of medical treatises by Galen (two small texts), Ḥunain ibn Isḥāq, and 'Alī ibn Riḍwān.

Most of the translators were now studying the medical literature available in Latin and putting it in Hebrew in order that Jewish doctors might be able to compete with their Christian colleagues. Alas! they were now running a losing race. In the not distant past the Jewish doctor had had better means of information than the Christian, for the whole of Greek and Arabic medicine was open to him. Now, not only was that corpus largely available in Latin, but the Jews had lost their Arabic sources of supply without having gained the ability to tap easily the Latin ones. Moreover, regulations discriminating against them made it more and more difficult for them, if not impossible, to practice medicine except among their own people. Happily these "racial" laws were never applied with as much savagery and efficiency as in modern Germany, and the reputation of Jewish doctors (especially eye doctors) was so high that kings and even popes were the first to overlook anti-Jewish regulations when their own health was in danger.

To return to the translators, Jacob ben Joseph ha-Levi translated from Latin into Hebrew treatises by Arnold of Villanova, Mesuë the Third, and Agilinus; an original Latin treatise by Armengaud son of Blaise (XIII-2) was Hebraicized in Barcelona c. 1306 by the topographer Estori Farḥi. Israel ben Joseph Caslari and Hezekiah ha-Miliabi translated writings of Arnold of Villanova. It is clear that the latter was popular in Jewish circles.

[16] Introd. 2, 371–73. For additional information on Maimonides as a physician, see Max Meyerhof: Un glossaire de matière médicale de Maimonide édité et traduit (Cairo 1940; Isis 33, 523–25). For the Hebrew edition of Maimonides' medical works by Suessman Muntner, Jerusalem 1940 f., see Isis 33, 92; 34, 243.

Outside of these translations, the Hebrew medical literature is not brilliant, nor do we obtain from the medical practice of Jewish doctors an impression which justifies their prestige. Some of them were very superstitious, even as many of their Christian colleagues. For example, we know that Isaac ben Judah Lattes, established in Perpignan, used talismans to effect his cures. This suggests that the recriminations and discriminations against Jewish doctors may have increased superstitious belief in their medical power. Feeble-minded Christians may have thought that if talismans were good, Jewish talismans would be especially good.

Hezekiah ha-Miliabi and Abraham ben David Caslari wrote tracts on fevers and bloodletting; Jedaiah ben Abraham ha-Bedersi,[17] a commentary in the form of a catechism on the Qānūn of Ibn Sīnā; and Moses ben Joshua of Narbonne, a collection of remedies for various diseases, Oraḥ ḥayyim.

C2. *Hispanic peninsula*

Conditions south of the Pyrénées were not very different from those obtaining north of them. Rabbis and their flocks, frightened by growing persecutions and by the irrepressible development of rationalism and liberalism among Averroists and Maimonideans, tried to offset these dangers with increasing piety and more rigid orthodoxy. El Rab d'España (as Solomon ben Adret, XIII-2, was affectionately called) took a leading part in that reaction, and in 1305 he excommunicated the men who dared study "philosophy" (physics and metaphysics) before having completed their twenty-fifth year. It is significant, however, that physicians and medical students were excepted from that excommunication. This shows that the intellectual needs of the medical profession were appreciated then better than they are in the poorer medical schools of our own days! It is not enough to learn tricks and recipes, the good physician must have a sound philosophical training. Solomon ben Adret saw that clearly, in spite of his obscurantism and timidity.

The Hispanic doctors, like their Provençal colleagues, were busy most of them with translations. Some were even beginning to translate from the Latin into Hebrew. The Portuguese David ben Yom-ṭob ben Bila translated that wretched tract Salus vitae, on the virtues of pulverized snakeskin, while on the opposite side of the peninsula Samuel Benveniste, physician to the court of Aragon, was translating a medical treatise of Maimonides (on asthma). The astounding fact is that that treatise was translated not from the original Arabic, but rather from a Latin version. Thus were medical ideas conveyed from one Jew to another via Arabic and Latin!

In the meanwhile, one Joseph ibn Waqar (who may be identical with the Talmudist Joseph ben Abraham ibn Waqar) translated from Arabic into Hebrew the great surgical treatise of Abū-l-Qāsim (that translation, however, was a work of superfetation, for the Kitāb al-taṣrīf was already available in Hebrew as well as in Latin). The Galenic book de crisibus was translated from Arabic into Hebrew by Solomon Bonirac, and another medical treatise was translated from Arabic into Catalan by Judah Bonsenyor.

Please note that the translating activities of Jewish physicians occur in the main sectors of the peninsula, Portuguese, Castilian, and Catalan. However, with the

[17] It is better not to call him Bedersi, as is sometimes done, except in an unambiguous context, for that word, meaning "he of Béziers," is a bit vague. Béziers was an important Jewish center and there were thus many Jewish "Biterrois." The name Bedersi (or Bedaresi) suggests the poet Abraham ben Isaac, who flourished c. 1273–85 (EJ 3, 1210–12), as well as the philosopher Jedaiah ben Abraham and others.

exception of the last-named one, who wrote in Catalan, they all wrote in Hebrew. It is true Joseph ben Abraham ibn Waqar may have written his qabbalistic treatises in Arabic as well as in Hebrew, but the translation of Abū-l-Qāsim, assuming it to be his, was made into Hebrew. Two other Jewish physicians wrote in Arabic. The "Royal Castilian book of medicine" was composed in that language by a Toledan Jew, who may probably be identified with Samuel ben Waqar. Solomon ibn Ya'īsh, who flourished in Seville, wrote an extensive Arabic commentary on the Qānūn of Ibn Sīnā.

If one wishes to measure the complexity of Hispanic medicine in its fullness, one ought to bring together the Christian and Jewish sections (A2 and C2) of my account. The peninsula was subdivided not only by its sierras, some of which were formidable enough, but also by many human differences—(a) Portuguese, (b) Castilian, (c) Andalusian, (d) Catalan (to name only the main Christian varieties); (α) Christian, (β) Jewish, (γ) Muslim (or at least Arabic-speaking). These groups might be combined in various ways, forming subgroups, as aβ, cγ, bα; the subgroups were isolated but not completely so, hence all kinds of mutual influences were conceivable and actually took place, as aα vs. dβ.

C3. *Italy*

The only Jewish physician who distinguished himself at that time in Italy was Samuel ben Solomon ha-Me'ati, who translated treatises of Galen and Ibn Zuhr from Arabic into Hebrew.

This completes our picture of Jewish medicine in the West in the first half of the fourteenth century. The reader will easily recognize its common characteristics. The Western Jews were mainly engaged in transmitting medical ideas from Arabic or from Latin into Hebrew; some of them re-expressed the same ideas in Latin or vernaculars. There was not among them a single original and creative physician.

D. *Eastern Jews*

There is very little to say about the Eastern Jews, at least about those writing in Hebrew. We have already mentioned Estori Farḥi among the Western Jews, for he came from the south of France and spent in Egypt and Palestine only ten years (1313–22) at the end of his life; though his most important work, the topographical work which immortalized his name, was done in Palestine, his medical activities had apparently come to an end before his migration to the East. The only other man I can think of is Aaron ben Joseph the Qaraite (XIII-2); he was a real Easterner who was born in the Crimea and spent most of his life in Istanbul; he was still living c. 1320. He was called physician, but we have only indirect proofs of his medical training; his famous commentary on the Torah, entitled Mibḥar, gives the reader a few glimpses of a scientific point of view, but many more of Aaron's fundamentalism mixed with superstitions.

In great contrast with the second half of the thirteenth century, when some of the most important medical works in Arabic were written by Jews, the first half of the fourteenth century finds no Jewish physician mixed with the Muslims. Was this due to a new wave of anti-Semitism in Islām? I am tempted to think that it was, for in this very period (1318–36 to be exact), Rashīd al-dīn and two of his sons were persecuted and put to death; these crimes were partly explained and condoned by accusations of Judaism.

E. *Western Muslims*

This group is small but interesting. To the Tunisian al-Tijānī, author of a famous Riḥla (travel book), we owe also an erotic work which contains many items of medical interest. Passing to Andalusia, we find there two very distinguished physicians, Muḥammad al-Shafra and Ibn Khātimah. The first was a herbalist and the creator of one of the earliest botanic gardens, which was of course a medical garden; moreover, he wrote a surgical treatise recording many original observations. Ibn Khātimah was a poet as well as a physician; he composed one of the earliest treatises (not only in Arabic but in any language) devoted to the Black Death.

F. *Eastern Muslims*

For the sake of variety we shall consider this time all the Easterners together, except the Persians writing in Persian, who constitute too natural a group to be disturbed. Leaving purely national distinctions for the time being out of account, the most notable group perhaps is that of what might be called the commentators (somewhat similar to the groups of "professors" in Italy and France).

'Abdallāh ibn 'Abd al-'Azīz of Sīwās and Aḥmad ibn Muḥammad al-Kīlānī wrote commentaries on the aphorisms of Hippocrates. Quṭb al-dīn al-Shīrāzī (XIII-2) is so famous as a physicist that one does not think of him as a physician, yet we owe him commentaries on Ibn Sīnā as well as treatises on medical deontology and on leprosy. Other commentaries on Ibn Sīnā were produced by Muḥammad ibn Muḥammad al-Khujandī and by Maḥmūd ibn Muḥammad al-Jaghmīnī. The relative value of such works, some of which are bulky, cannot be determined until we have patient analyses of each of them, none of which is available. In the meanwhile we must take refuge in vague statements.

Other physicians are more difficult to classify. For example, we have two al-Ṣafadī (there is no reason why they should be related except by their connection to the important Palestinian city Ṣafad, whence their common nisba was derived). The first, Khalīl ibn Aibak, might properly be called al-Ṣafadī (tout court), for he is perhaps the most illustrious Safadian; he composed an immense biographical dictionary, to which we shall come back later on; we mention him now not for his contribution to the literature of homosexuality, but for a treatise on physiognomy dealing particularly with "moles" or "beauty spots." The second al-Ṣafadī, named Aḥmad ibn Yūsuf, composed a medical dialogue in rhymed prose between a sulṭān and a philosopher.

A treatise bearing the equivocal title Medicine of the Prophet (Al-ṭibb al-nabawī) is ascribed to the historian al-Dhahabī. The treatise I have in mind (translated by Perron in 1860) is not a collection of medical traditions concerning the Prophet, but a general treatise on hygiene and medicine camouflaged under that alluring title. Criticism of such a text is difficult; I am not even prepared to say that it belongs to the fourteenth century, or at any rate that it belongs to it in the form in which it is best known to us. The ascription to al-Dhahabī may be as fictitious as the prophetic association. Ibn al-Wardī composed a poem on the plague, and devoted some attention to the interpretation of dreams.

Treatises on materia medica were compiled by Ibn al-Kutubī and by Maḥmūd ibn Ilyās al-Shīrāzī.

Books on veterinary medicine have been discussed in the previous section; the two most important were written by al-Mujāhid 'Alī al-Rasūlī and by Ibn al-Mundhir. These were the outstanding treatises, not only in Arabic but in any language. Horses were much loved by the Arabic-speaking peoples, and Arabic treatises explaining the breeding, care, and treatment of horses were naturally popular among them. Thus, even theologians like 'Alī al-Subkī would be tempted to write books on that subject. By the way, it is curious that among Christians we found as many books dealing with the treatment of dogs and falcons as with the treatment of horses.

Another "medical" subject enjoying some popularity in those days was physiognomy. We have already referred to the treatise on beauty spots by Khalīl ibn Aibak al-Ṣafadī. Physiognomy, like astrology, might be applied to all kinds of problems, e.g., government. The expert physiognomist might help the sulṭān to select his wuzarā' (ministers) and the members of his dawāwīn (councils). The famous cosmographer al-Dimashqī wrote a treatise on physiognomy in relation to government, and there are many data ad hoc in his other writings. For another application of that art we are indebted to the oculist Ibn al-Akfānī. He explained the value of physiognomy for the buying of slaves. Indeed, one of the tenets of physiognomists was that, the dimensions of different parts of the body being related (a fact amply confirmed by modern anthropometrists), it is possible to deduce the qualities of hidden parts from those of visible ones. They went farther and claimed, e.g., that the sexual aptitudes of a female slave could be read in the lineaments of her face and body. Other treatises on physiognomy were composed by this same Ibn al-Akfānī, by Ibn Qayyim al-Jawzīya, and very probably by others. The scholar wishing to write the history of that art would discover many more treatises than I did, for I did not look for them and only mention those which I came across unintentionally in the course of my general survey. To put it otherwise, I might say, "Physiognomy must have been an important part of the folklore and even of the scientific lore of those days, because I could not help finding many treatises ad hoc while I was searching for other books."

Note the national diversity of all these Eastern doctors. There is but one Arab of Arabia among them, the sulṭān al-Mujāhid 'Alī al-Rasūlī. Going to the other extreme, the largest national group is, as always, the Mamlūk one: al-Dimashqī, Ibn al-Mundhir, Aḥmad ibn Yūsuf al-Ṣafadī, Ibn al-Wardī, Ibn Qayyim al-Jawzīya, 'Alī al-Subkī, Khalīl ibn Aibak al-Ṣafadī. Two Iraqians, Ibn al-Kutubī and Ibn al-Akfānī. Three Turks, 'Abdallāh ibn 'Abd al-'Azīz of Sīwās, al-Dhahabī, Aḥmad ibn Muḥammad al-Kīlānī. Four Persians, Quṭb al-dīn al-Shīrāzī, Maḥmud ibn Ilyās al-Shīrāzī, Maḥmūd ibn Muḥammad al-Jaghmīnī, and Muḥammad ibn Muḥammad al-Khujandī. Al-Jaghmīnī came from Khwārizm and al-Khujandī from Transoxiana; were they Iranians or Turanians, Persians or Turks? God knows. The point to remember is that the Arabic-speaking doctors were scattered from Spain to Central Asia, and belonged to a great variety of national and ethnical groups.

We still have to speak of the few Persians who wrote in Persian, undoubtedly the most Persian of the Persians, though even in their case one could not say that each of them was a pure and unadulterated Persian. Such statements are made only by the ignorant and fanatical.

None of these Persian writers was a professional physician; or, more exactly, every one of them is better known for something else. The most illustrious of them was Rashīd al-dīn, who was primarily a historian and humanist, yet whose medical activities are in some respects the most interesting of the Middle Ages. I am not referring now to his medical practice, to his activity as a founder and patron of hospitals, to his efforts in procuring the best drugs from everywhere, though all that is remarkable enough in itself. He took pains to obtain and publish all available knowledge on Chinese and Mongolian medicine, and thus he built a bridge—the only one I know of—between the medicine of China on the one side and that of Islām and the West on the other. It so happened that the bridge was not used as it might have been, but the builder of it deserves our admiration.

The Nuzhat al-qulūb of Ḥamdallāh Mustawfī includes a large amount of medical information, especially in the first part, dealing with natural history somewhat in the spirit of a herbal, the main consideration being always the medical or magical virtue of each item, whether it be a plant, an animal, or a stone. Al-Nakhshabī, whose main significance in our eyes lies in his attempt to connect the Sanskrit and Persian literatures, wrote a strange anatomical treatise.

The outstanding medical writer in Persian was Muḥammad ibn Maḥmūd al-Āmilī, who wrote commentaries on the Qānūn of Ibn Sīnā, comparable to those in Arabic previously mentioned. Commentaries on the Qānūn were general medical treatises, even as commentaries on, say, Aristotle's Physics were physical treatises. The Qānūn provided a convenient frame of reference of which medical writers availed themselves for centuries.

G. *India and Tibet*

There is nothing to report in India, except perhaps the commentary on the Ashṭāṅgahṛidayasaṃhitā of Vāgbhaṭa (VII-1)[18] which was compiled by Hemādri (XIII-2) in Ḥaidarābād. It is possible that Hemādri was still engaged in that work at the beginning of the fourteenth century.

Though Vāgbhaṭa's saṃhitā was essentially a treatise of Āyurveda (i.e., of ancient Hindu medicine, Vedic, Brahmanic), it contains many traces of Buddhism, and these traces have probably persisted in the commentary, in spite of the fact that by this time Buddhism had long vanished from India proper.

Buddhism continued in a special form in Tibet, and the Hindu medical ideas, whether Āyurvedic or Buddhist, were extensively developed in many of the treatises which constitute the Tibetan Kanjur and Tanjur (Introd. 1, 467-69). For a discussion of Tibetan medicine, see Heinrich Laufer: Beiträge zur Kenntnis der tibetischen Medizin (90 p., Berlin 1900), a classic paper not yet superseded, though valuable additions to it will be found in Wilhelm Filchner: Kumbum Dschamba Ling (p. 362-75, 519-28, Leipzig 1933).

More information on Buddhist medicine is given below in the Chinese and Japanese sections.

H. *China*

There is no country where the state organization of medicine began more early than in China. State medical examinations may be dated back to the Chou dynasty (1123-255 B.C.). According to the Chou rituals (Chou li t'ien kuan), "At the end of the year the work of the doctors is examined and the salary of each fixed according to the results shown. If the statistics show that out of ten cases treated all get well, every satisfaction may be felt. If, however, one out of ten dies, the results may be regarded as good; if two out of ten die, the results are only fair; if three out of ten die, they are poor; if four out of ten, they are bad" (as quoted by Wong and Wu p. 94, 1936). In the course of time the teaching and practice of medicine were repeatedly regulated. According to the institutes of the

[18] A complete German translation of that treatise by Luise Hilgenberg and Willibald Kirfel was published in Leiden 1941 (Isis 34, 174-77).

Yüan dynasty (Yüan tien chang), ten medical fields were recognized and the books relative to each determined. Alas! the books recommended were not new ones, but such immemorial classics as the Su-wên (Introd. 1, 310, 539; also 2, 478) and the Shên-nung pên-ts'ao (Introd. 1, 122, 436; 2, 247). Thus the medical regulations were used to insure respect for traditions and make novelty and progress impossible! The ten recognized fields were: diseases of adults, children's diseases, diseases due to wind, obstetrics and gynaecology, eye diseases, diseases of mouth, teeth, and throat, fractures and wounds, swellings and sores, acupuncture and moxa, charms and incantations (faith healing). According to a decree of 1305/6, teachers were held responsible for the students and punished for the latter's offenses as well as for their own.

Medical schools had declined toward the end of the Sung dynasty, but the Yüan revived them, and by decree of 1317/18 state medical examinations, which had been interrupted since the Sung decadence, were revived.[19] This is so remarkable for the time (nothing comparable existed anywhere else) that I beg leave to reproduce the information taken from the Chang an keh hua as Englished by Wong and Wu (p. 97, 1936).

The state medical examinations "were conducted somewhat like the ordinary competitive government examinations of former times, i.e., once every three years. Those who passed the medical examinations were given appointments; those who failed were referred to the examining board for decision to suspend practice. The first examinations were held in autumn in the provincial towns and were open to all comers able to comply with the following requirements: Candidates were to be above thirty years of age, of good medical knowledge, high moral character, and esteemed by their friends. Out of the candidates one hundred were selected from each place. The following autumn the examinations were held in the Capital and only thirty candidates were chosen. In the final tests each candidate was examined twice. At the first sitting two essays, one on the principles of medicine and one on therapeutics, were required. At the second sitting two further essays were required, one on the principles of medicine and one on materia medica. The thirty successful candidates were again classified into grades. Those in the first grade were appointed court physicians, those in the second grade as assistant examiners, and those in the third grade as teachers. In the same dynasty, women doctors were for the first time given official recognition. They were first selected by the Government Office in the country, then brought to the Imperial Chamberlain, and lastly examined by the court physicians. The successful ones were allowed to have their names recorded in the book and wait for appointments."

Another branch of state medicine which developed earlier in China than in other parts of the world is what we call forensic medicine (or medical jurisprudence). Aside from criminal codes (1507 etc.) and a few unimportant tracts, the first treatise in Europe was that of Paolo Zacchia (1650) referred to above. By that time forensic medicine was very old in China. The first Chinese treatise, not comparable of course with Zacchia's immense encyclopaedia, was the Instructions to coroners (Hsi yüan lu) put together by Sung Tz'ŭ (XIII-1) four centuries before Zacchia. The Hsi yüan lu was periodically revised, for example by Wang Yü in 1308.

Passing from state to individual medicine, our first observation is that there

[19] For information on Sung conditions see Ilsa Veith: Government control and medicine in eleventh century China (Bull. history of medicine 14, 159–72, 1943). Translated from Wang An-shih (XI-2).

were at this time in China a number of professional physicians (we deal separately with nine of them) who were physicians and little if anything else; remember, by contrast, that the majority of Christian, Jewish, and Muslim writers on medical subjects were not professional physicians, but philosophers, theologians, cosmographers, etc. It is possible, however, that a deeper knowledge of Chinese literature, revealing the existence of medical items in other than purely medical books, would modify that impression.

Another observation is that Chinese medicine was purely Chinese, and apparently unaffected by Muslim or Nestorian medicine, though there were Muslim and Christian officers in the Mongol court. The only exception (a partial one) is that of 'Īsā tarjamān (XIII-2), a Nestorian, who was said to be a physician as well as an astronomer; he and his sons were in attendance at the imperial court. There is no trace of their medical activities, however, and I do not know of any Chinese medical book including non-Chinese ideas; the influences were in the other direction, as was explained above apropos of Rashīd al-dīn's translations of Chinese medicine into Persian and Arabic.

Before speaking of the eight leading physicians, it would be well to say a few words about another one, Wang Hao-ku, who was omitted from volume 2 because I thought that his floruit occurred c. 1308. He really belongs to the middle of the preceding century. He elaborated the old pulse theory and was one of the most prolific medical writers of his time.

Tsou Hsüan wrote in 1307 a book on the diet and hygiene of old people. In the following year Wang Yü revised the standard book on forensic medicine. In 1323 Wên-jên Kuei wrote a treatise on smallpox, thus continuing a very old Chinese or Asiatic tradition; not only was smallpox recognized in China before it was recognized in the Mediterranean world, but variolation was practiced in Asia from time immemorial. Hu Ssŭ-hui wrote a treatise on the principles of correct diet, which evidenced some empirical understanding of deficiency diseases and of their cure by proper diet. That knowledge was part and parcel of ancient Chinese folk medicine and could probably be detected in many earlier treatises on nutrition, a subject on which the Chinese produced a fairly abundant literature. They did not discuss simply the diet of people in good health, but also that appropriate to various illnesses, and the diet appropriate to various age groups, to pregnant and nursing women, etc. (see Tsou Hsüan above). Chinese interest in diet was a part of their deep concern for hygiene and prophylaxy. We are given an amusing illustration of that concern in one of their old proverbs, "The superior doctor prevents sickness; the mediocre doctor attends to impending sickness; the inferior doctor treats actual sickness" (Isis 33, 277).

Wei I-lin compiled in 1328–37 a collection of prescriptions summarizing his own and his ancestral experience, five generations back! Ch'i Tê-chih contributed during the same period a treatise on surgery. Hua Shou published in 1341 a treatise on anatomy and medicine, dealing especially with blood vessels; his book obtained much favor all over the Far East. Chu Tan-ch'i revised the materia medica, developed the theoretical basis of therapeutics; he was the first to mention the use of chaulmoogra oil for the cure of leprosy (the use itself is probably much older, being, like variolation, an undatable tradition of folk medicine).

This Chu Tan-ch'i was said to be a Taoist, but I cannot find him in the Taoist patrology. On the other hand, that enormous collection may contain medical writings of this time (dated or more probably undated) which ought to be considered in a review of contemporary Chinese medicine. This would require long preparatory investigations, for which I am not qualified, even if it were possible to interrupt my own synthesis long enough for them. See Wieger's index (1911) sub vocibus diet and hygiene, aero- and phototherapy, medicine and physiology; see also Maspero (1937). The latter has remarked that Taoist views on anatomy and physiology are often retrograde as compared with non-Taoist ones; that is possible, but the investigation of many more dated or datable texts is needed before such a statement can be accepted.

Medical facts and theories are scattered also through the Buddhist Chinese literature, but the Buddhist ideas are as difficult to date as the Taoist ones. The best general account of Buddhist medicine will be found under the Japanese heading byō (in Chinese ping, meaning disease) in Hōbōgirin (part 3, 224–65, 1937). When I remarked above that Chinese medicine was purely Chinese, I was thinking only of the possibility of Christian and Muslim influences, which the Chinese had eschewed; I did not think of Buddhism, which of course introduced Hindu elements. Yet Buddhism had become such an integral part of Chinese thought that it is difficult to consider foreign any one of the many wares which had been imported into China, whether in the lesser vehicle (hīnayāna) or in the larger one (mahāyāna). That is so true that Buddhist medical ideas are found not only in Buddhist books, but also in Taoist ones. For example, in the Sun-chên-jên ch'ien-chin-fang of Sun Ssŭ-mo (VII-2), a work duly included in the Tao-tsang (Wieger no. 1149, 1911), it is explained that to be a good physician it is not enough to be versed in Confucian and Taoist letters, for he who has not read the Buddhist books will lack kindness, compassion, and the joy of renunciation, he will not approach his patients in the proper spirit, and hence will not be able to cure them (Hōbōgirin p. 263). As to theories, one might say that the Chinese books illustrate in various degrees a perennial conflict and readjustment between the Buddhist theory of four elements (earth, water, fire, and air)—diseases are due to the disequilibrium of these elements; each element may cause 101 ailments, and together they can cause 404—the Āyurvedic theories[20] of tridoṣa (three humors) and pañcabhūta (five elements, earth, water, fire, air, and aether), and their own conceptions of yin and yang, etc. It is probable that the only Hindu ideas (whether Buddhist or Āyurvedic) which permeated Chinese medical thought were not technical ideas, but general ones (like the theories referred to) and, alas! superstitions. It is difficult to say whether more superstitions originated from Taoist circles or from Buddhist ones; it is certain that in spite of Confucian[21] rationalism (or perhaps because of the spiritual vacuum which that rationalism created), Chinese medicine was impregnated and polluted with an abundance of fantasies and absurdities.[22]

[20] For the Āyurvedic theories, see Dhirendra Nath Ray: The principle of tridoṣa (Calcutta 1937; Isis 34, 174–77).

[21] The old Confucianism is meant, not the neo-Confucianism (hsing li) of the Sung dynasty, which contained many Buddhist and Taoist ingredients (Introd. 2, 397) and was more capable of nourishing the mind and soul of the average man.

[22] Many books have been devoted to them, partly because Western observers have often seemed to be more eager to discover the seamy and irrational side of Chinese culture than the fair and rational side. The Recherches sur les superstitions en Chine of the late Jesuit father Henri Doré (1859–1931), 18 vols., published in the Variétés sinologiques (Shanghai 1911–1938), contain hardly anything of medical interest, but see Eugène Vincent: La médecine en Chine (316 p., Paris 1915). Jean Jacques Matignon: La Chine hermétique. Superstitions, crime et misère, Souvenirs de biologie sociale (420 p., 42 pl., Paris 1936), first published under its subtitle Superstitions etc. (Paris 1899, reprinted 1900, 1902). Wong and Wu (p. 67–73, 1936).

J. *Japan*

Much of what has just been said concerning Chinese medicine applies mutatis mutandis to Japanese medicine. Indeed, the two are essentially identical; the ideological background is the same. The differences due to nationality and language are not greater than those which might obtain at the same time between distant parts of China, or, let us say, between distinguished and strongly individualized physicians. The Japanese doctor was building almost exclusively on a Chinese foundation, or, in the sense explained above apropos of the influence of Buddhism on Chinese medicine, he was building on a Hindu-Chinese foundation. He was less independent of that foundation than his English or French contemporaries were of their Greek-Arabic one.

In Japan and in China the Buddhist leaders and monks influenced the medical art not only by their philosophy, but more by their merciful and loving spirit. Hospitals and other institutions of medical assistance were organized by them (Hōbōgirin p. 245–59), even as European hospitals were organized by Christian orders. Thus we hear of a monk called Ninsei (d. 1303) who founded refuges for lepers and other patients.

As against the eight Chinese doctors, I can only cite two Japanese ones, Kajiwara Shōzen and Aki Morisada. Kajiwara wrote two elaborate treatises covering the medical field in its entirety; Aki was an obstetrician.

Topical survey

Having obtained a general view of the medical contributions of each national or ethnical group, we shall complete our survey by asking ourselves how much progress was made or what was done in each branch of medicine. Let us first consider the ideological background (§1–3).

1. *Medical astrology* (Introd. 2, 91–93, 790)[23]

It is no exaggeration to say that the physician's philosophy was astrological, as far as his theology and church discipline permitted it, rather more than less. The Catholic church tried to repress astrological superstitions, but it could only succeed in circumscribing them. In fact, every man, from the pope down, accepted as a fundamental postulate the existence of correlations between the microcosmos (the patient) and the macrocosmos (the outside world). The postulate seemed sufficiently established by a number of experimental facts or pseudofacts, e.g., the rich folklore concerning the moon (tides, farmer rules, menstruation). Though astrology was universally acquiesced in, the acquiescence varied considerably in kind and degree from man to man, from physician to physician; it might be a vague idea somewhat neutralized by the Christian belief in freedom; at the other extreme it might be applied to every physiological or pathological detail with pedantic precision.

To the many medico-astrological treatises which had been written in the thirteenth century or before, quite a few were added by authors of many Western European nationalities. There is no point in enumerating them again, but it is interesting to note that all of them were written in the Latin language (not in Greek or Arabic). Though most of the Western astrologers had received their initiation in

[23] These references added to subtitles of the topical survey will help the reader to find rapidly the most pertinent parts of previous volumes; for deeper study he is invited to use the indexes of volumes 1 and 2.

Arabic treatises (or their Latin versions), in this period astrology was far less preponderant in the Arabic Muslim world than it was in the Latin Christian one.[24]

2. *Translations and commentaries* (Introd. 2, 64–67, 790–91)

At the beginning of the fourteenth century the main classics of Greek and Arabic medicine were available to Latin readers. Yet there was still plenty of work left for translators, translating from Greek, Arabic, or Hebrew into Latin, or in some cases from Latin into French. The number of books available in Hebrew was much smaller, but now that Western Jews had lost their Arabic contacts, more translations had to be made for them from Arabic into Hebrew. One of the most significant developments was the increase of medical books translated from Latin into Hebrew.

Among the texts newly translated into Latin were small Galenic and Hippocratic treatises (genuine or apocryphal) and some secondary treatises by al-Kindī, Qusṭā ibn Lūqā, Abū-l-Qāsim, Ibn Rushd, and Maimonides; the texts translated from Arabic into Hebrew were relatively more important, and included many parts of the Galenic canon, Ḥunain ibn Isḥāq, Abū-l-Qāsim, 'Alī ibn Riḍwān; the texts translated from Latin into Hebrew were secondary ones by Agilinus, Mesuë the Third, and Arnold of Villanova. These translations give us some idea of the medical tastes of Dante's contemporaries; other glimpses are occasionally afforded by literary allusions or catalogues of books.[25] The best information of that kind, however, is revealed by the commentaries. Translations might be and often were accidental, but when a text was not simply translated, but commented upon time after time, we may be sure that that text was deemed especially important. Outside of Galen and Hippocrates, the author most often discussed, not only in Latin and Hebrew, but even more in Arabic, was Ibn Sīnā. By the middle of the fourteenth century, his Qānūn was well on its way to becoming the medical bible.

By far the most remarkable body of medical translations of this period is the one which was accomplished in Tabrīz at the behest of Rashīd al-dīn. It included Chinese medicine, theory and practice, Chinese materia medica, and Mongolian materia medica. The translations were made from Chinese into Persian and Arabic. Unfortunately, when Rashīd al-dīn was executed, in 1318, they shared his disgrace and fell into oblivion.

3. *Literary and scholastic background* (Introd. 2, 67–71, 90–91, 792)

The juxtaposition of the words literary and scholastic may shock fastidious readers, for schoolmen were never credited with a feeling for bonae litterae even by their most uncritical admirers. The most important literary writings of medical interest were those of Petrarca, who despised the schoolmen because of their pedantism and their lack of letters. However, what I mean is this. In addition to the commentaries, we have a good many general medical treatises (in Arabic, Latin, Greek, etc.) which fall under the heading of medical literature "faute de mieux," and are written in the style made popular by the theologians and the jurists. The latter were now almost as influential in this respect as the former, and many a physician found his "literary" inspiration almost as frequently in the books of civil or canon law as in the Books of sentences or the summae of the

[24] This impression is derived not only from my own investigations, but also from those of Dr. Aydin Sayili, carried out under my direction.

[25] E.g., Karl Sudhoff: Ein kleines Verzeichnis medizinischer Handschriften aus der ersten Hälfte des 14. Jahrh. (AGM 11, 213–15, 1919).

theologians. In spite of the growth of medical experience, to be illustrated by and by, many doctors were hypnotized by their colleagues of the faculties of law or theology, and their ideal was to explain medicine in the scholastic manner, with as much erudition and logical order as they could muster. We should not blame them too hastily, remembering, in the first place, that their experimental knowledge was at best very limited, disjecta membra unconnected by verifiable explanations, and, in the second place, that medical teaching was still very largely deductive as late as the second half of the seventeenth century.[26]

The authors of the main treatises on general medicine can be easily found in the preceding pages. Instead of enumerating them, it is more interesting to remark that by this time the medical traditions were to a large extent amalgamated in the Greco-Arabic-Latin world—our world—and that it did not make much difference, except for the doxologies and other religious allusions, whether a medical book was written by a Jew, a Christian, or a Muslim. By this time, indeed, Jewish, Christian, and Muslim physicians, especially the learned ones, the authors of ambitious text-books or encyclopaedias, were equally saturated with the teachings of Hippocrates, Galen, and Ibn Sīnā; hence their descriptions and explanations were essentially the same irrespective of religion, nationality, and language.

The unification was not so complete in the Far East, in spite of the ubiquity of Buddhism, as it was in the Mediterranean world, divided between three religions.[27] It is true Buddhism had carried some of the theories of Āyurvedic medicine to China, yet Chinese medicine accepted those theories only as accretions, and did not allow them to supersede its own tenets or to modify essentially its own structure. In the end Āyurvedic medicine remained supreme in non-Muslim India, while Chinese medicine conquered the Far East.

Having obtained some knowledge of the leading ideas which dominated medical knowledge, we may now consider more technical questions, concerning which general ideas lose more or less their supremacy.

4. *Anatomy* (Introd. 2, 71–73, 1081–83)

To our previous discussion of human dissections (Introd. 2, 1081) this may be added. The first dissections were more probably autopsies made for legal purposes —to discover the cause of death when murder was suspected. That was certainly the case for the autopsy carried out in Bologna 1302 by Bartolommeo da Varignana (text ad hoc in Wolff p. 254). Dissections had already been made in the thirteenth century, however, for purely anatomical purposes. In 1308, the grand council of Venice ordered the arrangement of a dissection every year (Wolff p. 256). In 1315 Mondino de' Luzzi dissected two female bodies; he was probably the first to dissect publicly, and he did the work himself. In 1319 there was a scandal in Bologna when four medical students were arrested for having disinterred the corpse of a criminal and taken it to the house of one magister Albertus for the purpose of anatomical study; however, the prosecution was dropped. Public dissections began in Padua in 1341 (Wolff p. 258). In short, dissections, even public ones, were

[26] See chapter 1 of Edmond Locard: Le XVIIIe siècle médico-judiciaire (Paris 1902). A fine example is the purely deductive refutation of the theory of circulation of the blood as late as 1672 by one Fr. Bazin in his doctor's thesis before the Parisian faculty (ibid. p. 27).

[27] Perhaps one should say five, for the Catholic Christian was deeply separated from the Orthodox, and the Shī'a Muslim from the Sunnī. "Mediterranean" is taken here in a very broad sense, to include Europe, North Africa, the Near East; the main domain of Christendom and Islām.

certainly made in the first half of the fourteenth century, and their frequency increased, but very very slowly; they remained exceptional, say, single annual events in the leading medical schools. The lay and church authorities frowned upon them, tolerating them only on rare specified occasions.

Giuseppe Portigliotti: Dissections clandestines au XIVe siècle (Aesculape, Dec. 1923, 284–86; Isis 7, 194). Gerhard Wolff: Leichen-Besichtigung und Untersuchung bis zur Carolina[28] als Vorstufe gerichtlicher Sektion (Janus 42, 225–86, 1938). Walter Artelt: Die ältesten Nachrichten über die Sektion menschlicher Leichen im mittelalterlichen Abendland (Abhandlungen zur Geschichte der Medizin, Heft 34, 25 p., 1940), not seen (Mitt. p. 135, 1940; Lychnos p. 417, 1941). Mary Niven Alston: Attitude of the Church toward dissection before 1500 (Bulletin of the history of medicine 16, 221–38, 1944; Isis 36, 57).

Of course, many anatomical facts could be demonstrated on the bodies of animals (e.g., pigs), as was done in Salerno. It is possible even that a certain amount of vivisection took place, though we have no definite evidence of this, except an earlier story told by Guibert of Nogent (XII-1) in his Gesta Dei per Francos.[29] Baldwin (afterward king of Jerusalem) having been grievously wounded, the leech who had been summoned suggested making a similar wound on a Muslim prisoner, who would be slain afterward; the leech could then study the matter experimentally and treat his lord better. This Baldwin refused, but agreed that the experiment be made on a bear.

The bull Detestandae feritatis issued by Boniface VIII in 1299 did not prohibit dissections, but the cutting up of corpses and their boiling in order to separate the bones from the flesh. That practice had originated during the Crusades to make possible the repatriation of at least one part of the body. This was done also for the body of St. Thomas Aquinas, in this case lest it be too difficult to transport it and to protect it from relic robbers. Boniface VIII's prohibition was frequently lifted in favor of powerful people who were able to pay for the necessary indult or license. Thus bodies could be, and were actually, divided for simultaneous burial in many places. Coulton gives a long list of examples (3, 48, 62, 617–19, 1936). As to the superstitions connected with relics, the stealing of them, and the relic market, see ibidem (3, 87–129). Relics are anatomical fragments but have nothing to do with the history of anatomy.

Ad maiora redeamus. In spite of the fact that anatomical progress had been somewhat jeopardized in the West in the thirteenth century by the growth of Aristotelianism (Aristotle vs. Galen!), it made great steps forward in the fourteenth century, especially in Italy. The reader will have observed that the examples of dissections quoted above were all Italian. This is not arbitrary; I do not know of non-Italian cases.[30] We shall discuss later, in chapter XI, the activities of five Italian doctors who were primarily anatomists, to wit, Mondino de' Luzzi, the restorer of anatomy, Guido da Vigevano, Niccolò Bertruccio, Gentile da Foligno, and Alberto de' Zancari. To be sure, these men were physicians, having many other interests than the purely anatomical, but on the other hand we must assume that many other doctors not named took part occasionally in dissections or made anatomical observations. The five are a fine group of pioneers.

[28] That is, the Carolina constitutio criminalis promulgated by the emperor Charles Quint in 1532. I have used the German text printed in Mainz 1533 (folio, xlii p.).

[29] Gesta Dei (PL 156, col. 798). English version in Coulton (2, 7–8, 1930).

[30] I am thinking only of formal dissections, not the informal ones which a surgeon might be obliged to make or which, being made accidentally, could be observed and completed by him.

The greatest of them all was Mondino, whose Anatomia (1316) enjoyed two centuries of popularity. It was largely, though, alas! not exclusively, based on his own autopsies. Singer calls it (p. 75, 1926) "the first modern work on the subject." In a way its very success was prejudicial, for it gave a new lease on life to the many old errors which Mondino had been too timid to challenge. The Liber notabilium a libris Galieni extractus which Guido da Vigevano compiled in 1345 contained a new Anatomia, derived partly from Mondino's and partly from his own dissections. Guido was probably a pupil of Mondino, but he practiced in Pavia; another pupil, Niccolò Bertruccio, continued the tradition of public dissections in his master's own university, Bologna; he was himself the teacher of Guy de Chauliac. In Padua the dissections were conducted by Gentile da Foligno, who discovered a gallstone in the course of one of them. Other dissections were made publicly by Alberto de' Zancari in Bologna or in Ravenna.

Everything hinged on the dissections, especially on the academic ones. As soon as these were properly made, they were bound to increase interest in anatomy and to rectify errors. The fact that some obviously erroneous theories continued to be accepted as correct proves that "authorities" may be too well established and prejudices too strong even for the best of men. Each age can shake off only a limited amount of its intellectual shackles and not more. Therefore, the anatomical revival of the fourteenth century did not produce the fruits which one might have expected from it, and which remained in abeyance two centuries longer, until the times of Leonardo da Vinci and Vesalius.

That premature revival was restricted to the Latin West and more especially to Italy. Of course, most of the encyclopaedias in Arabic and other languages contained anatomical and physiological data, but nothing new, and in the absence of dissections no novelties could be expected. The most curious anatomical book (if it may be so called) in contemporary Oriental literature, the Chil nāmūs, was written in Persian by al-Nakhshabī. It describes or rather alludes to various parts of the body, their mutual convenience, their pre-established harmonies and occasional disharmonies.

5. *Physiology* (Introd. 2, 72)

Mediaeval anatomy cannot be dissociated from physiology. Some progress in the latter was bound to follow progress in the former, though the discovery of functions was incomparably more difficult than that of organs. In spite of the backwardness of Muslim as compared with contemporary Italian anatomy, the outstanding physiological discovery was made not by a Christian but by a Muslim, Ibn al-Nafīs (XIII-2), and not in Italy but in Syria or Egypt. It was made just a little before our time (Ibn al-Nafīs died in Cairo in 1288), but I speak of it now because it was omitted from my summary of anatomy in volume 2.[31] Ibn al-Nafīs discovered the lesser circulation of the blood before 1288, anticipating the Spaniard Miguel Servet (1511–53) by more than 265 years. Unlike Servet, who hid his discovery in a theological treatise (Christianismi restitutio, Vienne, Dauphiné 1553), Ibn al-Nafīs published his right where it belonged, in a commentary on Ibn Sīnā's anatomy. It was perfectly proper to discuss the pulmonary circulation apropos of the anatomy of pulmonary vessels. Unfortunately, the Sharḥ tashrīḥ al-Qānūn was discouragingly voluminous and appeared too late to be appreciated by the

[31] I spoke of it in the text (Introd. 2, 1099–1101), but left it deliberately out of the summary, because I was not sufficiently sure of it. Since then it has been amply confirmed by Max Meyerhof (Isis 23, 100–20, 1935).

decadent Muslims or to be translated into Latin. At any rate, Ibn al-Nafīs was allowed to live to a ripe old age, whereas poor Servet was burned at the stake in Geneva 1553 by order of Calvin.[32]

The Chinese had had for centuries some empirical knowledge of what we call deficiency diseases and of their cure by means of a proper diet. Such knowledge is implied in a treatise written about 1330 by Hu Ssŭ-hui. Of course, they had no idea of vitamins, but they knew that some foods were better than others for the re-establishment and the preservation of health.

6. *Embryology and obstetrics* (Introd. 2, 80)

The strange unreality of much anatomical work is well illustrated by the special case of the womb. Mondino had dissected that organ many times and had been able to examine it under various circumstances (normal, after menstruation, during and after parturition), and yet he continues to describe it, after Aristotle and Michael Scot and in spite of Galen, as divided into seven chambers, three to the right, three to the left, and one in the middle![33] The marvelous facts of impregnation and pregnancy were eagerly discussed in all kinds of books, not only in the encyclopaedias and medical treatises meant for learned people, but also in such books as the Physionomia of Michael Scot (XIII-1) and the Secreta mulierum ascribed to Albert the Great (XIII-2) but of uncertain date and origin. The Secreta mulierum appealed to a relatively large public and was one of the mediaeval best sellers (Sarton, Osiris 5, 189–91, 1938). These momentous and disturbing questions were treated also by philosophers and theologians such as Giles of Rome (XIII-2), or whoever was the author of the De formatione corporis humani in utero ascribed to brother Giles. The psychological problems connected with pregnancy (when is the embryo an individual? when is it besouled?) were no less absorbing; Dante pondered on them, and we may be sure many other laymen and clerics pondered with him. There were also legal matters involved. What was the length of human pregnancy? Ten lunar months (or nine-twelfths of a year) was the accepted duration, yet that duration might be shortened or lengthened, might it not? The famous lawyer Cino da Pistoia having consulted the physician Gentile da Foligno, the latter wrote a very elaborate treatise exhibiting many strange perplexities. We have already spoken of the Greek treatise of Joannes Pediasimos on the viability of seven-month and nine-month foetuses and the non-viability of the eight-month ones.

Such questions were cogitated not only in Christendom, but also in Islām and the Far East, wherever thinking men existed. A Japanese treatise on obstetrics was written by Aki Morisada, but we do not know whether similar questions were reviewed in it.

Another set of problems which has always exercised the minds of men and women is the determination of conception. When does a woman know that she is pregnant, and how?[34] Is it possible to guess, or better still to predetermine, the sex of the unborn child? Is the child influenced in any way by the mother's diet and conduct, by her deeds or dreams? These were secrets indeed, tantalizing ones,

[32] One might object that neither Ibn al-Nafīs nor Servet really understood the pulmonary circulation, and that the first to understand it was William Harvey (Sarton, Isis 34, 29, 1942; 35, 186, 1944).

[33] Felice La Torre: L'utero attraverso i secoli da Erofilo ai giorni nostri (p. 79, Città di Castello 1917; Isis 5, 279).

[34] Of course, the discontinuance of the periods was known, but the uncertainty of that test was realized.

and secrets call for magic. They offered a standing invitation for astrologers and all kinds of soothsayers and charlatans.

It would take too long to follow that obstetrical folklore in all its ramifications and in all its connections with other kinds of knowledge and superstition. The following example should suffice. One of the oldest methods of diagnosis was the examination of urine (Introd. 2, 75). A Greek canon of uroscopy was composed at the beginning of our period by Maximos Planudes (XIII-2), and many other treatises were available in every scientific language; indeed, every general medical treatise gave some place to that method. It was thus natural enough to apply it to the diagnosis of pregnancy. According to the Secreta mulierum, it was possible to find out from her urine whether a woman was pregnant or not, and also to determine from his (or her) urine whether a man or woman had generative faculties.[35] The author of the Secreta realized in some obscure fashion that the conception and the development which follows is a conservative, constructive process, opposed to the destructive process called putrefaction. These were intelligent queries and musings, even if they led but too often in those days to fantastic conclusions. William Harvey was still asking himself, how is it that an unfertile egg will soon rot while a fertilized one remains sweet? We have not yet succeeded in answering that question completely. It is curious that in very recent years (1930 ff.) it has been definitely established that the urine of a pregnant female contains oestrogenic hormones which can incite ovulation in animals and hasten germination processes in plants. Hence it has become possible to diagnose pregnancy from the urine and, what is more, to use the hormones for various biological purposes.[36]

7. *Anatomical (and medical) iconography*

The crudities rather than the merits of the new anatomy appear in MS illustrations, which are relatively abundant East and West. It is not convenient to analyze these illustrations without an atlas of reproductions at hand, and it would be an endless task to examine them from every point of view. It is generally more instructive to compare all the mediaeval illustrations relative to a special organ or set of organs, such as the womb or the eye. Some of the monographs devoted to special organs and including sets of illustrations are quoted in other sections of this volume; iconographic monographs relative to, say, Mondino or Guido da Vigevano will be found in the notes on those men.

General iconographic surveys have been published by Karl Sudhoff and Ernst Seidel in AGM (vols. 1–9, 1907–16); by Weindler (1908), Sudhoff (1908b), Choulant-Frank (1920), Sudhoff-Singer (1924), Singer (vol. 1, 1925).

Karl Sudhoff: Tradition und Naturbeobachtung in den Illustrationen medizinischer Handschriften und Frühdrucke vornehmlich des XV. Jahrh. (92 p., Leipzig 1907). Antonio Muñoz: Un Theatrum sanitatis con miniature veronesi del sec.

[35] A related problem which agitated the mediaeval mind is the question of male or female impotence. As male impotence is often due to psychological inhibitions, it opened a tempting field to magical practices. Gerda Hoffmann: Beiträge zur Lehre von der durch Zauber verursachten Krankheit und ihrer Behandlung in der Medizin des Mittelalters (Janus vol. 37, reprint 37 p., Leiden 1933; Isis 21, 425). Henry E. Sigerist: Impotence as a result of witchcraft (Essays in biology in honor of Herbert M. Evans, p. 541–46, Berkeley 1943).

[36] These reflections are borrowed from H. P. Bayon: Ancient pregnancy tests in the light of contemporary knowledge (Proceedings of the Royal Society of Medicine, historical section, 32, 1527–38, 1939). Udall J. Salmon, Samuel H. Geist, A. Austin Salmon, and Irving L. Frank: A six-hour pregnancy test, chorionic gonadotropin (Journal of clinical endocrinology 2, 167–70, 1942).

XIV nella Biblioteca casanatense (Verona 1908). William A. Locy: Anatomical illustration before Vesalius (Journal of morphology 22, 945–88, 23 fig., 1911). Gerard van Rijnberk: Le dessin anatomique avant Vésale et de son temps (Archives néerlandaises 3, 176–94, 11 fig., La Haye 1916; Mitt. 16, 398–99), beginning with the Fasciculus medicinae. Charles Singer: A study in early Renaissance anatomy (Studies in the history and method of science 1, 79–97, Oxford 1917). Giovanni Carbonelli e R. Ravasini: Commenti sopra alcune miniature e pitture italiane a soggetto medico specialmente dell'arte d'illustrare il Tacuinum sanitatis nei secoli XIV e XV colle referenze ad alcune pitture murali (80 p., 52 pl., Roma 1918).

8. *Physiognomy*

The art of physiognomy was an integral part of medicine. At its best it was a natural development of physiology. Indeed, the main physiological theory, inherited from Greek antiquity, was the doctrine of temperaments, and were not the various temperaments (sanguine, phlegmatic, choleric or bilious, melancholic) easily recognizable even by laymen?[37] Like astrology, physiognomy was justified by common sense as a first approximation. Every intelligent man judges other men on the basis of their features, especially their face, and their behavior; that is, every man practices physiognomy to some extent. Some learned specialists, however, refined the art and rationalized it. This had been done from early days, witness the pseudo-Aristotelian φυσιογνωμονικά (Introd. 1, 135) and the treatise bearing the same title by Polemon of Laodicea (II-1). The physiognomic tradition can be followed throughout the centuries in many languages: Apuleius (II-2), Adamantios Sophista (IV-1), Sirr al-asrār (IX-1), al-Rāzī (IX-2), Giles of Corbeil (XII-2), Fakhr al-dīn al-Rāzī (XII-2),[38] Michael Scot (XIII-1). Coming closer to our period, Bartholomew of Messina (XIII-2) translated the pseudo-Aristotelian treatise into Latin, a new one was ascribed to Albert the Great, and a French summary was included in the Régime du corps by Aldobrandin of Siena (XIII-2). A very remarkable physiognomic text was recently analyzed by Lynn Thorndike (Speculum 18, 99–103, 1943). It is a series of questions on the pseudo-Aristotelian treatise by no less a person than the philosopher Jean Buridan. Buridan does not deal only with the usual physiognomical diagnoses, such as "whether the method of physiognomy by facial characteristics is a good one; whether soft hair signifies timidity and hard hair bravery; whether a deep voice is a sign of fortitude; whether slow movement signifies a soft intellect, weakness and timidity, while swift movement indicates the opposite; whether a large forehead signifies a slow and lazy nature; whether large projecting eyes indicate stolidity; whether small deep-set eyes are a sign of sharp-sightedness; whether large ears show stolidity; a big nose, irascibility; and a big mouth, voracity," but discusses the more general problems concerning the relation of physiognomy to astrology, and the reconciliation of both with freedom. His own solution was to assume that man's constitution (complexio) is partly determined by his nativity, partly acquired. This may be considered the mediaeval equivalent of the modern problem, nature vs. nurture. The fate of each man is largely determined by the circumstances of his birth; mediaeval and modern men agree thus far, but they interpret those circumstances differently. From the mediaeval point of view, the circumstances were set forth

[37] Sarton: Remarks on the theory of temperaments. With a German "temperament" text of c. 1480 edited by Erika von Erhardt-Siebold (Isis 34, 205–8, 1943).

[38] My note on Fakhr al-dīn (Introd. 2, 364) was far too short, and I did not speak of his Kitāb al-firāsa, recently edited in Arabic and French with a study on Arabic physiognomy by Mourad (1939).

in the man's horoscope; from the modern point of view, they are represented by the sets of chromosomes and genes which he has inherited from his parents.

The list of texts concerning physiognomy which we have given could be considerably extended. As it is, it amply suffices to show that many books were available to the fourteenth-century physician, whatever might be his language, and that he could not escape physiognomic doctrines even if he tried. The fate of physiognomy was similar to that of astrology. Around a nucleus of true or plausible facts accumulated gradually a mass of fantasies and stupidities. The physiognomist was soon tired of reading a man's character in his face, he claimed to be able to predict his future. Physiognomic fancies were inextricably entangled with astrological ones. The Arabic writers went especially far in that direction. Some of them claimed that their art (qiyāfa they called it, or firāsa) enabled them to deduce all kinds of hidden qualities from external appearances. The boundaries of the art were extended so much that finally some mystics boasted the ability to see occult realities far beyond the limitations of time and space (Isis 33, 248; EI 2, 108, 1047).

Even as the astrologer, the physiognomist (both were often combined in a single person) tended to apply his art or his science (fann or 'ilm) to every problem of life. He would diagnose the hidden diseases of one man as well as the hidden moral defects of another. Al-Dimashqī and later Mūsā ibn Ziyān applied physiognomy to the art of government, Ibn al-Akfānī applied it to the buying of slaves. Or else the physiognomist might restrict his attention to special features and refine his analysis of them to any extent. Khalīl ibn Aibak al-Ṣafadī wrote a treatise interpreting the meaning of naevi or beauty spots; Arabic treatises on horses, e.g. the one by 'Abd al-Mu'min al-Dimyāṭī (XIII-2), attached various significations to colors and to markings of good or evil omen. One such specialty, the reading of lines and marks in the palm of the hand (palmistry, chiromancy, chirognomy), was exceedingly popular East and West,[39] and, alas! is exploited to this day even in the most "civilized" communities.[40]

9. *Surgery* (Introd. 2, 73–75)

Surgery might have been discussed immediately after anatomy if my attention had not been diverted in other directions. In particular, the same prejudices which impeded dissections tended to discredit surgery. The church discouraged clerics from practicing medicine because that was an officium saeculare, the exercise of which was not always compatible with their spiritual duties; as to surgery, it was completely forbidden, and that prohibition was not due only to the church's abhorrence of blood.[41] I have found only one cleric among the early surgeons, that was Teodorico Borgognoni (XIII-1), who assumed the Dominican habit and became a bishop; he is supposed to have written his Cyrurgia while he was penitentiary to Innocent IV. He may have obtained the necessary indult through the pope's favor. The pontiffs could afford to be more compliant than other bishops; for example, the

[39] A book of palmistry ascribed to Maino de Maineri is available to us only in an early French translation. Books on the subject were among the incunabula best sellers. Klebs (no. 272, 1938). Sarton (p. 182, 191, 194, 1938).

[40] On the other hand, the study of fingerprints, which goes back to very early days (Introd. 1, 571), is not a genuine part of physiognomy, for its purpose was simply the identification of individuals (e.g., in the form of signatures to contracts), not the deduction of their character or of their fate.

[41] Nec ullam chirurgiae artem subdiaconus, diaconus vel sacerdos exerceat quae adustionem vel incisionem inducat. Third Lateran council, 1179 (DTC 2, 2392–94, 1923).

teaching and practice of surgery was permitted to the faculty of Montpellier during the Babylonian captivity, but forbidden immediately afterward.[42]

Though dissections could easily be stopped, there was no way of stopping the accidents of war and peace. Men would break their legs or cut one another's throats, and surgeons had to be summoned. Natural experiments were being made all the time, and the good surgeon could not help learning from them. Therefore, not only did surgery exist in spite of the prejudices and contumely from which it suffered, but it was the most progressive branch of medicine. It is curious, however, that its center of progress was shifting almost continuously northward.

The high water of Muslim surgery had been reached in Cordova thanks to Abū-l-Qāsim al-Zahrāwī (X-2). Christian surgery had begun a little higher up (in latitude) and two centuries later with Roger of Salerno (XII-2). A little later it was carried to Lombardy by Roland of Parma (XIII-1) and by the two Borgognoni (XIII-1), and to Montpellier by William of Congenis (XIII-1). At the end of the thirteenth century Lanfranchi took it to Paris. It is possible that the foundation of the Guild and College of St. Cosmas in that city helped to establish the surgical profession on a better footing. At any rate, the greatest surgeon of our time, Henri de Mondeville, was a Frenchman who had studied in Bologna and Montpellier and joined the royal armies. He was a learned man as well as an experienced one, and his great treatise Cyrurgia did not deal only with surgery; it was a general treatise on medicine adapted to the needs of the surgeon, beginning with an anatomy and ending with an antidotary. Such a book would have increased the prestige of the profession and put some surgeons at least on the same level as physicians, if it had been possible to dispose of vested prejudices as easily as that. The better-educated surgeons were impressed, but the M.D.'s were not, and they continued to treat their surgical rivals in a high and mighty way. The fight of the surgeons against physicians on one side and barbers on the other was to be dragged on for centuries.[43]

The northward march of surgery did not stop in Paris. The greatest surgeons of that time next to Mondeville were two Flemings, Jan Yperman and Thomas Scellinck. Mondeville's treatise was written in Latin, but promptly translated into French and Provençal; Yperman's and Scellinck's books were written in Flemish. It is clear that surgical literature was meant to be read chiefly in the vernacular and that the social cleavage between physicians and surgeons was to a large extent linguistic. The M.D.'s were trained in Latin, they wrote in Latin and taught in Latin, they used Latin in their formal meetings and even informally among themselves or to give the patients a higher idea of their importance.[44] The surgeons spoke and wrote the vernacular. The physicians were bookmen, the surgeons craftsmen. Experience, wisdom, and even learning, however, are not found only or exclusively in books. Bookish knowledge was useful, but it might be deadly; it often was.

The books of Mondeville, Yperman, and Scellinck were the outstanding medical books of their time, but not by any means the most influential.

Though mediaeval surgery, as distinguished from Greek and Byzantine, was initiated by Abū-l-Qāsim (X-2) of Cordova, the Muslims did not maintain their supremacy in that field. The mysterious Mesuë the Third (XIII-1) may have

[42] Emile Forgue in Laignel-Lavastine (2, 392, 1938).

[43] For a summary of this see Garrison (p. 294–96, 393–95, 1929), or Emile Forgue's article on surgery in Laignel-Lavastine (vol. 2, 1938).

[44] This continued until modern times. Remember the ridicule which Molière (d. 1673) cast on their ignorant and pretentious jargon.

composed his treatise in Arabic, but he was probably a Christian; its translator (if it was translated), Faraj ben Salīm (XIII-2), was a Sicilian Jew. The Syrian Ibn al-Quff (XIII-2), who wrote a surgical treatise in Arabic before 1286, was certainly a Christian. I imagine that religious prejudice against surgery had become even stronger in Islām than in Christendom, in spite of the fact that Muslim surgeons had been trained to avoid effusions of blood as much as possible by the use of cauterization. A distinguished surgical book was composed, however, probably in Cadiz c. 1314–22, by Muḥammad al-Shafra. It is possible that that Muslim treatise would challenge comparison with the Christian treatises just mentioned, but at any rate it would be only one against many. The surgical leadership had definitely passed from Muslim to Catholic hands.

For the study of contemporary Chinese surgery the best plan would be to read and analyze the treatise of Ch'i Tê-chih (c. 1332), but that is not at all easy.

10. *Eye diseases* (Introd. 2, 82–84)

The thirteenth century was the third golden age of Muslim ophthalmology. The eye doctors of Cairo and Damascus were then the world leaders of their profession. Though the outstanding treatises of that century were in Arabic, a few others appeared in Hebrew and Latin. The superiority of Jewish oculists in the Latin West was undermined by anti-Semitic regulations and by the growing expertness of their Christian rivals.

Eye diseases were often discussed in general medical treatises. Much of the eye doctor's work was surgical, and surgical treatises did generally contain a section devoted to the operation of the cataract.

The trained eye doctor, as contrasted with the "rusticus" and charlatan, was likely to call himself or be called chirurgus (or chirurgicus) with perhaps the specification "expertus in oculis." We hear of such a chirurgus, Guido Aretino, receiving a reward in Salerno 1326 from king Robert because of his expertness. Latin treatises were written in 1308 by Arnold of Villanova (XIII-2), De confortatione visus (Introd. 2, 895, no. 43); in Venice 1340 by Barnabas of Reggio, De conservanda sanitate oculorum; in Florence (?) 1346 by Johannes de Casso, De conservatione visus. Though largely derived from Arabic sources, these treatises were behind the times from the Arabic point of view. Indeed, they were derived from the Latin translations of early writers such as Ḥunain ibn Isḥāq (IX-2), Māsawaih al-Mārdīnī (XI-1), and Ibn Sīnā (XI-1); the Arabic treatises of the thirteenth century were not at all available to the Christian oculists, and hardly to the Western Jewish ones.

Eye troubles were then (and remained for many centuries afterward) one of the favorite fields for all kinds of amateurs and quacks, ranging all the way from innocents trying to heal complaints with holy waters and benedictions to predatory charlatans selling unguents and elixirs for as much money as they could extract from their patients. According to Mondeville, who has bitter words to say on the subject, kings and prelates had more confidence in charlatans than in medical experts. This was partly justified by the circumstance that in many cases the experts did not know much more than the quacks; indeed, the intuition of an experienced quack might be of greater value than the academical diagnosis of a licensed dullard. The case of the most famous patient of that time, king John of Bohemia, is an interesting illustration. His eyesight was always weak; as it got worse, he called a French doctor, who failed to cure him. The French doctor was sewn in a bag and thrown into the river Oder. A "paganus de Arabia veniens" was then called in, but did not venture to come until he was promised a safe-conduct whether he succeeded in curing the royal patient or not; he caused the king much suffering but did not improve his condition. John then went himself to Montpellier and was treated by Guy de Chauliac; being dissatisfied with Guy, he put himself into the hands of a Jewish practitioner in Montpellier. By 1339 his eyesight was all but gone; at the time of his gallant death at the battle of Crécy, in 1346, he was completely blind. It is probable that John's trouble was too much for any doctor of his time, whether licensed or not; it is not certain that he could have been cured in our own days.

Many early anatomical or ophthalmological treatises contain diagrammatic sections of the eye. See the writings on anatomic iconography listed above. Also Karl Sudhoff: Augendurchschnittsbilder aus Abendland und Morgenland (AGM 8, 1–21, 2 pl., 1914; Isis 3, 327). Stephen L. Polyak: The retina (617 p., 100 pl., University of Chicago 1941; Isis 34, 234), including some new illustrations obtained from Istanbul. For comparison, Julius Hirschberg: Zum Leipziger Augendurchschnittsbilde aus dem Ende des 15. Jahrh. (AGM 1, 316, 1 pl., 1908).

11. *Various diseases* (Introd. 2, 84–88)

As one would naturally expect treatises devoted to special diseases to be richer in content than the corresponding sections of medical encyclopaedias, it is worth while to examine these special treatises. They are fewer in our time than in the centuries immediately preceding it. For example, I found nothing comparable to the Arabic treatise on haemorrhoids by Maimonides (XII-2) or to the Hebrew one written by Solomon ibn Ayyub (XIII-2) in Béziers 1265, though the subject is naturally dealt with in the general treatises of Bruno da Longoburgo (XIII-2), Lanfranchi (XIII-2), etc. Nor did I find anything comparable to Maimonides' Arabic book on asthma, or to the Greek treatise on gout by Demetrios Pepagomenos (XIII-2).

The first "fever" to be identified as a special disease was probably smallpox, by al-Rāzī (IX-2); then measles, by Ibn al-Jazzār (X-2). Ibn Rushd (XII-2) was the first to recognize the immunization conferred by an attack of smallpox against further attacks, and Gilbert the Englishman (XIII-1) was fully aware of the contagious nature of that "fever."[45] Similar discoveries were not made in the first half of the fourteenth century, which must be considered from that point of view as a period of stagnation.

The main epidemic disease was the Black Death, whose outbreak was an international disaster of unparalleled magnitude, but as this happened at the very end of this period, in 1348, it is perhaps more appropriate to discuss the calamity itself and its widespread consequences in part II.

As to syphilis, I have been thus far unable to discover a single description of it anterior to those which appeared in quick succession in 1495 and following years.[46] In spite of frequent reaffirmations in recent years of the pre-Columbian antiquity

[45] This brief account leaves out the Oriental history, which did not influence our traditions. According to Chinese scholars, the earliest description of smallpox was given by Ko Hung (IV-1), text given by Wong and Wu (p. 82, 274, 1936), and the first inoculation was made during the reign of Chên Tsung (997–1022) to save the sons of the prime minister Wang Tan (957–1017; Giles no. 2230), thus before 1017. The practice of inoculation was immemorial in Asia (Wong and Wu p. 215–16, 269, 273–74, 1936).

[46] Charles Sudhoff and Charles Singer: The earliest printed literature on syphilis 1495–98. In complete facsimile with introduction (Florence 1925; Isis 8, 351–54).

of European syphilis, I remain unconvinced. The explosive development of syphilis toward the end of the fifteenth century is easy to explain if Spirochaeta pallida was then a newcomer against whom Europeans were entirely unprepared; it is difficult if not impossible to explain otherwise (Isis 29, 406–7, 1938).

The following papers may suggest lines of investigation which cannot be followed here and now.

Ludwig Schirow: Zahntexte in zwei italienischen Handschriften (Diss., 48 p., Leipzig 1924; Isis 7, 194). Elise Seidler: Über das Konsilium eines Ungenannten aus dem 14. Jahrhundert betreffend Heilung des Gesichtsausschlages einer Dame (Diss., 7 p., Leipzig 1925). Kurt Hänel: Eine Gesundheitsregel für Brustkranke aus dem 14. Jahrhundert (Diss., 9 p., Leipzig 1925).

12. *Lepers and cagots*

Aside from the plague, the main epidemic disease was still leprosy, but the history of leprosy is full of incertitudes from the beginning to recent times. To put it more bluntly, it is full of the worst kind of incertitudes, for we do not always know what we are talking about—whether the disease we are dealing with is what *we* call leprosy, and whether it is always the same disease or not. Was the disease against which the Babylonians took a series of prophylactic measures our leprosy? Was the ẓara'at many times mentioned in the Old Testament our leprosy or something else like psoriasis? Did our leprosy exist in ancient Egypt?[47] Is the λέπρα of the New Testament our leprosy? It is the same word, of course, but is it the same thing? Such queries are insolvable. What is certain is that the early Babylonians and Hebrews had a definite knowledge of the transmissibility of certain diseases such as ẓara'at and invented elaborate means of preventing their transmission from ill people to healthy ones.

It is clear also that the notion of illness was promptly associated with the idea of uncleanliness, which was all right, and even equated with it, which was dangerous. The evil consequences are already obvious in the regulations against lepers ordered by the council of Ancyra (modern Ankara) in 314. In those regulations the words λεπροί and λεπρώσαντες are already taken metaphorically, as we might say "unclean" people—people whom we consider unclean bodily or morally.[48] This meant that the word might be used to designate heretics, and it was thus used, as we shall see later on.

Such terrible misunderstandings could be cleared only when the disease itself was clearly defined, and the definition remained very insufficient for centuries. We might almost say that our definition of it was not completed until 1871–74, when the Norwegian Armauer Hansen (1841–1912) discovered the specific bacteria. Clinical descriptions were gradually improved from the tenth century to the nineteenth; successful therapeutics date only from our own days!

It would seem that the first valuable descriptions since the time of Aretaeos (II-2) were made by Arabic physicians. The first to note definite symptoms—prickling or tingling sensations over the whole body (totius corporis titillatio) and relative insensibility—was Abū-l-Qāsim (X-2), but his translators do not seem to

[47] A. Bloom: La lèpre dans l'ancienne Egypte et chez les anciens Hébreux. La lèpre dans la Bible (82 p., Le Caire 1938; Isis 29, 511). Maurice Bear Gordon: Medicine among the ancient Hebrews (Isis 33, 454–85, 1941) avoids the question.

[48] A scholiast explains λεπρός as ἀκάθαρτος καὶ μεμολυσμένος and λεπρώσας as μιάνας. Karl Sudhoff: Hat das Konzil von Ankyra Absonderungsvorschriften für Leprakranke erlassen? (AGM 4, 379–83, 1911).

have appreciated their semeiological value. The disease, however—which from Abū-l-Qāsim's description and from later Latin descriptions, e.g. that of Gilbert the Englishman (XIII-1), was probably identical in most cases with one of the forms of modern leprosy—spread enormously all over Europe in the twelfth and thirteenth centuries. It is possible that the diffusion was helped by the Crusades and by the large migrations produced thereby. In any case, a great many special houses were established all over Europe, including Iceland, to segregate the lepers.[49] These houses were called maladreries, lazaretti, leper or lazar houses, Gutleuthäuser, etc. A complete account of them is impossible, for in addition to the thousands which can be definitely located there must have been many more, small and informal village houses without archives which have disappeared without leaving any traces; we are aware of their existence only through casual references, items in accounts, etc. Moreover, lepers of the upper classes were often secluded by special permission or without permission in their own homes. The leper houses were always established extra muros, for their purpose was not to cure the patients, but to isolate them from the rest of the community.

After the thirteenth century the number of lepers began to diminish rapidly, and within a few centuries lepers almost ceased to exist in Europe except in a few places. It is true many leper houses continued to exist, partly because they were endowed and partly because they could be used for other patients. For example, the house of Terzieken (near Antwerp), founded c. 1231, continued in operation for six centuries (Van Schevensteen 1930).

The eradication of leprosy from Western Europe was due first of all to the prophylaxy which was applied almost everywhere with extreme severity and unusual constancy; it was due also to the general improvement of public and private hygiene and to the higher standards of living, e.g., better housing, the use of shirts, bed linen, etc. Nevertheless, it remains somewhat mysterious. The ebb and flood of an epidemic can never be completely explained. The gradual disappearance of leprosy was strange, but much less so than its quick and enormous flood across Europe. This was the more mysterious because leprosy, though contagious, is not very contagious (Introd. 2, 95), and because communications with some countries where it flourished, say, Iceland, were relatively uncommon.[50]

The isolation of a leper from his community, being a matter of the utmost gravity, was not done without a definite procedure ("ad examen leprosorum"). For some reason, probably Biblical, that procedure originated with the clergy in most places and remained for many centuries within its jurisdiction.[51] The decisions were taken by the "official" of the church or by the bishop; in some towns, however, that tremendous power was taken over by town authorities, that is, by laymen. The examiners included generally the official or his representatives, expert lepers,

[49] It is probable that the mediaeval renascence of bathing in its Oriental form (see my note in Introd. 2, 631) was considerably stimulated by the fear of leprosy and of other skin troubles. Eventually the ḥammāmāt contributed to the diffusion of those very troubles.

[50] Leprosy exists to this day in many tropical and subtropical countries; it is generally regressing, but there are places, like New Caledonia, where it is actually increasing. After this war, it will probably reappear in many places.

[51] The government of the lepers was discussed and regulated by many councils. Reference has already been made to Ancyra (314). The third Lateran council (1179) paid much attention to them. It divided the lepers into two classes, those who were secluded in leper houses and had to remain continent, and those who enjoyed some freedom and were permitted to marry. As far as the lepers of southern France were concerned, decisions were taken by the synods of Morcenx (Landes, Gascony) in 1326 and Lavaur (Tarn, Languedoc) in 1368.

barbers, and, later, surgeons or physicians; the intervention of medical experts must have been very exceptional before the fourteenth century. There was a preconceived idea, but slowly dislodged, and in some places impossible to eradicate, that the determination of leprosy was a priestly rather than a medical business. A complete history of leprosy and of the care of it, or rather of the disposal of its sufferers, cannot be summarized here, because the regulations varied widely from place to place and from time to time, and might be applied very differently by all kinds of individuals, whose characters ranged all the way from sainthood to criminality or from high intelligence to a bestial one.

The procedure of examination for leprosy is well known through a number of archival documents. See, for example, a case in Nîmes 1327 reported by Jeanselme (p. 51, 1931), or the "Lepraschaubriefe," the medicolegal conclusions of the jury, published by Ernest Wickersheimer (AGM 2, 434, 1909), this being the earliest of its kind, Cologne 1357, and by Karl Sudhoff (AGM 4, 370–77, 1911), Vienna 1380, Constance 1397, etc. The great majority of these documents are posterior to the fourteenth century; it is to be feared that the early inspections (let us say, those anterior to the fifteenth century) were less formal and less technical, and the judgments arbitrary to a degree.

The jury had to decide whether the accused was a leper, and if so, whether his case required segregation. It might decide that the accused (1) was clean and innocent, or (2) should be warned to mind his way of life lest he become a leper, or (3) should be warned more severely, or (4) should be ordered to be segregated (Jeanselme p. 51).

How was the diagnosis made? It was not difficult in extreme cases, when the "signa infallibilia" were visible, the leonine face and the "corruptio figurae et formae." But how was it made when these signs were not yet available? Alas, the diagnosis was largely based on fantastic experiments made with the patient's blood and urine;[52] but as time went on it was based also on real symptoms, those already known to Abū-l-Qāsim (X-2), to wit, general formication and local anaesthesia. Some symptoms apparently irrational may be justified by later knowledge; for example, one threw water on the patient's skin, and if it did not cling to it the probability of leprosy was increased.[53] It is a fact that lepers suffer from hypersecretion of the sebaceous glands, and hence that their skin is more greasy than that of normal people. This was already known to Chauliac (XIV-2).

If the verdict was leprosy in its dangerous phase, the patient was as it were condemned to death, at least, to civil death. He was excommunicated, if not from the church, at least from the congregation. We are very well informed about this because of special chapters to be found in almost every mediaeval code, civil or ecclesiastical, and of endless regulations. Special rituals (varying somewhat from one diocese to another) were used to solemnize the segregation of the patients;[54] these rituals were comparable to funerals, sometimes with gruesome realism. The treatment of lepers varied from evangelical charity to cruel persecution (especially in times of panic). The leper was an outcast, and vice versa the best way to make

[52] E.g., Karl Sudhoff: Neue Aussatzproben aus dem Anfang des 14. Jahrhunderts (AGM 8, 71, 1915).

[53] Karl Sudhoff: Mittelalterliche Aussatz-Proben (AGM 3, 80, 1909), from fourteenth-century MS in Trinity, Cambridge.

[54] Reims: De separatione leprosorum; Treves: Modus ejiciendi seu separandi leprosos a sanis; etc. (Jeanselme p. 64–65, 1931). For the office of the exclusion of a leper according to the Sarum use see Clay (p. 273–76, 1909).

an outcast of a man was to declare him a leper. As long as the expertises of leprosy were conducted by the official without medical guidance, the definition of leprosy was certainly colored by the Biblical or canonical identification of it with other forms of uncleanliness, whether physical or moral (heresy).

To prove the possibility of such confusion, consider Hildegard (XII-2), Causae et curae, including many descriptions of and references to lepra; it is clear that what she called lepra was a mixture of indefinite skin troubles, ulcers, and immorality.[55]

Yet some of the best symptoms (local anaesthesia) had been described by Arabic physicians long before Hildegard's time. These symptoms were also explained with increasing detail by Theodoric Borgognoni (XIII-1), Gilbert the Englishman (XIII-1)—his description of leprosy in the Lilium medicinae is considered the best Latin one down to his time—Lanfranchi (XIII-2), Arnold of Villanova (XIII-2), who introduced new experiments to check on the anaesthesia, Bernard of Gordon, Henri de Mondeville, Jan Yperman, Vital Du Four, John of Gaddesden, etc. It would be interesting to find out when these symptoms were first used in the medicolegal examination of people accused of leprosy; I should not be surprised if a long interval elapsed between that particular nosological description and its legal application, and if the delay varied considerably from place to place. It is highly probable that not only in the fourteenth century, but also in the fifteenth and sixteenth centuries many people were declared to be lepers who were not.

Leprosy was largely but not by any means exclusively a disease of poor men. Many important people (abbots, bishops, lords, kings) are said to have died as lepers. It will suffice to name two illustrious lepers of the period to which this book is devoted: Robert de Bruce VIII, king and liberator of Scotland, who died of leprosy in 1329 at the age of 55; and Richard Wallingford, one of the greatest mathematicians of the Middle Ages, who died of leprosy in 1335 at the age of c. 43. Some leper houses were restricted to the aristocracy, such as one in Noyon (Picardy) and the St. Lawrence house in Canterbury. Not a few rich lepers were probably hidden away in their own homes. Statistics are impossible because of such circumstances added to uncertain diagnosis.

This leads us to the consideration of the cagots[56] of southern France, the Basque country on both sides of the Pyrénées, and Brittany. They were a people of outcasts obliged to separate themselves completely from others in their own houses or villages, and submitted to all manner of restrictions; they remained faithful members of the church, but pariah members. They were baptized in separate fonts, entered the church through a side door, were divided by a rail from the rest of the congregation, took holy water from separate bénitiers, were buried in separate plots. In some places they were obliged to wear distinctive garments or insignia; the trades and crafts except woodcrafts (pit sawing, carpentry), and professions except a little healing among themselves,[57] were forbidden to them; they were placed under the church's immediate control.

[55] See edition of the Causae et curae by Paul Kaiser (Leipzig 1903), the main quotations being on p. 161, 211–13.

[56] Cagot was the most common name in Gascony, but there are many variants of it, not only in Gascony, but in other parts of southern France (caffot, gahet, gabet, etc.). Fay discusses that matter at great length (p. 277–334, 1910), and gives a table of 54 variants (p. 296). The terminology of leprosy itself is equally luxuriant and bewildering, all of which makes it more difficult for the historian to know what he is talking about.

[57] Fay (p. 62, 1910) mentions four cagot "physicians," flourishing respectively in 1374, 1384, 1434, 1472. That is very little, of course, considering the large number of cagots distributed among some 600 localities in southern France alone.

Who were these cagots? And where did they come from? They begin to appear in documents in the eleventh century, and their earliest name perhaps was crestiaa (= christianus), which is read for the first time in a charter of A.D. 1000 of the abbey of Lucq in Béarn (Fay, doc. no. 1, p. 338). In a document of 1291 (Fay no. 3, p. 339), the words christiana and leprosia are equated.[58] There is very little information about these people before the fourteenth century. In 1320, cagots and Jews were accused together of having poisoned springs. The first scientific discussion occurs in the Grande chirurgie of Guy de Chauliac (XIV-2), traité VI, doct. 1, ch. II de ladrerie (1383). According to Chauliac the cagots were afflicted with some kind of larvate leprosy, what has since been called small leprosy or white leprosy, as opposed to the great or red leprosy (was that white leprosy leucodermia?). The first medical report on them was made in 1439 by order of the dauphin Louis, son of Charles VII (Fay p. 40). Further medical descriptions of them were given by Laurent Joubert (1563) and Ambroise Paré (1568). Throughout the sixteenth century one continues to consider the cagots as some kind of free lepers.[59] The first doubts are expressed by Guillaume Bouchet (Troisième livre de sérées, Paris 1598). After that the doubts increase and many new hypotheses are presented. The cagots are said to be descendants of the Phoenicians, Visigoths, Vandals, Arians, Sarrazins or Saracens, Jews, Gypsies or Gitanos,[60] Albigenses, witches, or other heretics. One Basque curate, Dom Martin de Vizcay, writing about them in 1621, says they were treated "como si fuessen leprosos." In his Histoire de Béarn (Paris 1640), the archbishop Pierre de Marca concludes that they were of Sarrazin origin. In the Observations faites dans les Pyrénées (Paris 1789) Ramond de Carbonnières identifies cagots with cretins; this particular hypothesis was accepted by the great medical historian Emile Littré (1872). Victor de Rochas in 1876 returned to the idea that cagots were lepers.

Assuming the plausibility of a medical hypothesis, how does it happen that there was so little agreement about the disease and that at least three different ones were suggested by competent men, leucodermia, cretinism, and leprosy? And if it was leprosy, how is it that these lepers were treated so differently from others? Mind you, the ostracism existed in full force until the French Revolution, and it continued in mitigated forms almost until yesterday. The English physician Daniel Hack Tuke (1827–95) visited colonies of Pyrenean cagots in 1879, examined many individuals, and found no difference between them and their non-cagot neighbors. He did not even observe among them an abnormal number of so-called "cagot ears."[61] I must add that in spite of that he leaned toward Rochas' views.

Bearing in mind the ambiguities of the name leper (or its equivalents) and the fact that it was used from ancient times to designate heretics as well as people suffering from a physical infection, it is not at all improbable that the cagots were originally cast out for religious (or political) reasons. We understand this better in the light of the terrible events which happened in Germany. The Nazis were trying to cast out the Jews, they did not hesitate to call them by any evil name they

58 The names crestiaa, christianus have been explained by the defenders of the leprosy hypothesis on the ground that lepers were sometimes called pauperes Christi (or pauperes sancti Lazari). Fay (p. 322–28, 1910).

59 As distinguished from the lepers shut up in lazar houses. The number of lazar houses was relatively small in the south.

60 In the Basque country, e.g. in and around St. Jean de Luz, the cagots (or cascarots) are distinctly of the gitano type.

61 The cagots were supposed to have a degenerated kind of ear without pendulous lobule and were sometimes called on that account "esaurillés" or "courte oreille."

could think of, say, Aussätziger, to claim that Jewish blood is a kind of racial poison, etc. Imagine a similar propaganda directed against heretics of southern France and northern Spain for centuries, without scientific correction. If the orthodox Catholics of southern France did what the Nazis of Germany did yesterday, i.e., considered any quality of any persecuted individual as an exception, and ascribed every taint, physical or moral, to the whole group, then obviously the group would soon be slandered beyond redress and proved to be as unclean and wicked as one chose. The fact that the Catholic authors of today accept the leprosy theory as correct is not altogether surprising, for the church was largely responsible for the outcasting which it sanctioned and solemnized, and the outcasting which may be justified on medical grounds is odious on any other.

Leprosy in Asia. The Arabic writers were the first to give useful clinical descriptions of leprosy. One of the first, it is true, was Abū-l-Qāsim (X-2), who lived in Andalusia, that is, in the West, but the Eastern Muslims paid much attention to leprosy and continued to do so throughout the centuries. Quṭb al-dīn of Shīrāz (XIII-2) wrote a Risāla fī-l-baraṣ (epistle on leprosy).

Various forms of leprosy have existed immemorially in India and exist there in many places to this day. For a discussion of this see, e.g., Paramananda Mariadassou: Médecine traditionnelle de l'Inde (2, 255–70, Pondichéry 1934); Luise Hilgenberg and Willibald Kirfel: Vāgbhaṭa's Aṣṭāṅgahṛdayasaṃhitā (Leiden 1941, passim; Isis 34, 174–77). In my note on Fa-hsien (V-1) my interpretation of chaṇḍālas as lepers (it is true, with a question mark) was misleading. Fa-hsien speaks of them in the Fo kuo chi (ch. 16, James Legge's ed., p. 43, Oxford 1886). The chaṇḍālas were outcasts; possibly some of them were lepers, even as the poor cagots. The words "leper" and "outcast" were often interchangeable in the past; either condition might entail the other, and thus was the ambiguous terminology apparently justified.

Chinese traditions push the history of leprosy back to the sixth century B.C. They say that one of Confucius' disciples died of it, but the passage ad hoc in the Lun yü is as vague as can be. Descriptions in medical books are equally inconclusive to me, and the Chinese terminology of leprosy—ta fêng, ma fêng; li fêng (this fêng is different from the two others); etc.—is even less definite than the European (see Wong and Wu p. 209–11, 1936).

The Chinese were the first to use what is now known as the best remedy, chaulmoogra oil; they used it from time immemorial. Chu Tan-ch'i was the first to write about it, however, and he remarked how difficult it was to retain it in the stomach, for it is strongly emetic. It was only within the twentieth century that a method was found of administering chaulmoogra to patients in a bearable way, and this marks the beginning of a new hope for the remaining lepers of the world.

Leprosy existed also in Japan (always with the same restriction as to the uncertain identity of the disease). We hear of a Buddhist priest Ninsei, who founded leper houses and died in 1303.

Select bibliography on leprosy. Jón Jónsson Hjaltelín: Spedalskheden eller Leproserne, med specielt Hensyn til deres Forekomst i Island (137 p., Copenhagen 1843). Rudolf Virchow: Zur Geschichte des Aussatzes und der Spitäler (Virchows Archiv für pathologische Anatomie vols. 18–20, Berlin 1860–61). Léon Le Grand: Statuts d'hôtels-Dieu et de léproseries: Recueil de textes du XIIe au XIVe siècle (Collection de textes pour servir à l'étude et à l'enseignement de l'histoire, 316 p., Paris 1901), precious collection well edited and well indexed. Clay (p. 35–69, 273–76, 1909). Charles Arthur Mercier: Leper-houses and mediaeval hospitals (Fitz-Patrick lecture, 1914, 47 p., London 1915). Georg Sticker: Lepra, in Carl Mense's

Handbuch der Tropenkrankheiten (vol. 2, 3d ed., 119 p., 45 ill., 6 pl., Leipzig 1924). A. F. C. Van Schevensteen: La lèpre dans le marquisat d'Anvers aux temps passés (Recueil de mémoires couronnés . . . de l'Académie royale de médecine de Belgique, vol. 24, 129 p., 4 pl., Bruxelles 1930; Isis 22, 315–17). Edouard Jeanselme: Comment l'Europe au Moyen âge se protégea contre la lèpre (Bull. Société d'histoire de la médecine, 155 p., Paris 1931), carelessly written yet valuable. Demetrius Alexandre Zambaco (d. 1913): La lèpre à travers les siècles et les contrées (857 p., Paris 1914), with a list of the many writings of Zambaco pacha on leprosy.

Many documents concerning mediaeval leprosy have been edited by Karl Sudhoff in AGM. A few have been quoted in the footnotes; though the following refer to fifteenth-century documents, they may be of help in explaining earlier facts, and are listed here for the sake of comparison.

K. Sudhoff: Lepraschaubriefe aus dem 15. Jahrh. (AGM 4, 370–78, 1911), referring also to similar documents of Cologne 1357, Vienna 1380, Constanz 1397 declaring people to be free of leprosy; Was geschah mit den (nach erneuter Schau) als "leprafrei" Erklärten und aus den Leprosorien wieder Entlassenen, von behördlicher und ärztlicher Seite? (AGM 6, 149–54, 1912); Eine Blutprobe zur Erkennung der Lepra (AGM 6, 159, 1912); Vier Schemata für Lepraschau-Atteste der Wiener medizinischen Fakultät (AGM 6, 392–93, 1913).

As to literary works inspired by leprosy, it will suffice to recall Hartmann von Aue (c. 1165–1210): Der arme Heinrich, and six centuries later the Lépreux de la cité d'Aoste, written in 1811 by François Xavier de Maistre (1763–1852), one of the classics of romantic literature. This means that the horrors of leprosy segregation were still a matter of actuality to the French people of a little more than a century ago.

Bibliography on cagots. Francisque Michel: Histoire des races maudites de la France et de l'Espagne (2 vols., Paris 1847). Victor de Rochas: Les parias de France et d'Espagne, cagots et bohémiens (309 p., Paris 1876). D. Hack Tuke: The cagots (Journal of the Anthropological Institute of Great Britain 9, 376–85, 1880). H. Marcel Fay: Lépreux et cagots du Sud-ouest (Histoire de la lèpre en France, vol. 1 [the only one published], 810 p., ill., Paris 1910), very elaborate study tending to show that some cagots were lepers; includes a long bibliography, topographical index, index of cagot names, maps (p. 132, 450), and many illustrations. A. H. Keane (ERE 3, 56, 1911).

Walter Cranston Larned (1850–1914) of Chicago: Arnaud's masterpiece. A romance of the Pyrenees (New York 1897). A novel on the cagots.

13. *Famines*

The discussion of famines at this place may seem inappropriate, for famine, one might argue, is not a disease. It is impossible, however, to disentangle famines from plagues, and there was always a high correlation between these two kinds of calamities. For example, Loveday remarks (p. 14, 1914) that there is but a single instance recorded of an outbreak of plague (in India) between 1033 and 1683 in which there is no evidence of famine conditions. In ancient and mediaeval times famines were very frequent; we might almost say that they never ceased to exist in one place or another. Ancient chroniclers often use such a sentence as "There was a famine in the land . . . ," simple words which I cannot read without the appalling vision of starving children, of frantic mothers, of men ghastly or rebellious, without feeling myself surrounded by all the ghosts of human misery in all its forms, physical and mental. The causes of famines, functioning separately or jointly, were bad crops, epizootics, war, revolts, plagues. The crops might be annihilated or jeopardized by climatic changes (such as drought in tropical countries), floods, tempests or hurricanes, locusts or other pests, plant diseases, etc.

Statistics of ancient and mediaeval famines are necessarily very vague, and it is even difficult to compile simple enumerations of them, in the first place because it is hardly possible to draw the line between scarcity and actual famine, and in the second place because different writers do not agree on the minimum territories justifying enumerations. In mediaeval times communications were often so precarious, especially in mountainous districts, that famine conditions might obtain in small localities without being remedied from the outside. How large should a district be to be counted in a list of famines? Moreover, we might say that the outstanding disease of the Middle Ages, East and West, was poverty, the poor constituting the vast majority of the population. Thus in periods of scarcity the cornering of food and the increase of prices would create famine conditions for the masses.

We are witnessing today the gradual starvation of large countries because of war, and it does not require much imagination to evoke the calamities which must have occurred in the past when the four horsemen of Revelation were let loose across the land. There was little then, if anything, to restrain them. Even in peacetime, the balance between comfort and scarcity was so precarious that a single year of drought might suffice to reverse it. Consider Egypt, which was one of the most fertile countries of antiquity, the granary of the Mediterranean world, and remember the story of Joseph. When the Nile did not rise high enough, famine would promptly follow.[62] Similar disasters recurred periodically during the mediaeval period, witness those of the year 1181 or 1200 described so vividly by 'Abd al-Laṭīf.[63] This description is one of the most terrible known to me. A history of Egyptian famines and discussion of their causes was written by the great Egyptian historian Aḥmad ibn 'Alī al-Maqrīzī (1364–1442) under the title Ighāthat al-umma bi kashf al-ghumma, recently edited by M. M. Ziyāda and J. M. al-Shayyāl (102 p., 1 pl., Cairo 1940; Bull. School of Oriental Studies 10, 798; Journal of the Royal Asiatic Society, 1941, p. 262). For al-Maqrīzī the causes of famines were largely economic and financial—the sale of offices, the increase in the price and rent of land, the debasement of the currency. He was moved to write this tract by the occurrence of a famine; he wanted to show that, bad as conditions were in his days, they had been worse in earlier times.

In Western Europe famines were equally frequent. Curschmann's account (1900) is unfortunately restricted to the Germanic countries and to the period extending from the eighth to the thirteenth century, but his chronological summary is continued to 1317. For the period 1300 to 1317, which is of special interest to us, it is easier to cite the years when no famines were reported; there are only two such years, 1301 and 1307!

William Farr has compiled a list of the famines recorded in the English chronicles from 822 to 1545. For the fourteenth century he listed famines in 1315, 1316, 1341, 1369, 1390, 1392. He concluded (p. 163): "In the 11th and 12th centuries a famine is recorded every 14 years on an average, and the people suffered 20 years

[62] Jacques Vandier: La famine dans l'Egypte ancienne (Recherches d'archéologie, de philologie et d'histoire, vol. 7, 192 p., Le Caire 1936). Account of all the famines reported in Egyptian documents from the ancient empire down to Hellenistic times.

[63] See Silvestre de Sacy's translation (p. 360–76, Paris 1810). 'Abd al-Laṭīf's account can be read also in prince Omar Toussoun (= 'Umar Ṭūsūn): Mémoire sur l'histoire du Nil (quarto, 3 vols., Mémoires présentés à l'Institut d'Egypte, vols. 8–10, Cairo 1925; 2, 458–74). Prince Ṭūsūn puts that famine under the date 577 = 1181/82, which is puzzling, for in that year the maximum level of the Nile was 17.52 m., 17.94 m., whereas in 1200 it was 15.70 (average maximum for the period 1122–1221, 17.69 m.). For the annals of the Nile in the fourteenth century, see same work (2, 475–80).

of famine in 200 years. In the 13th century, my list exhibits the same proportion of famines, and nearly the same number of years of famine; the addition of five years of high prices makes the proportion greater: upon the whole, the scarcities decrease during the three following centuries; but the average from 1201 to 1600 is the same,—namely, 7 famines, and 10 years of famine to a century. This is the law regulating scarcities in England."

In spite of the number of famines in Western lands, these calamities were even more frequent, and when they occurred more terrible, in the vast territories of central and eastern Asia. In these countries the equilibrium between subsistence and scarcity was always unstable; its precariousness was often aggravated by overpopulation. This, by the way, introduces religion as a major cause of famine, a cause which functioned with special rigor in China. Every Chinese must have at least one male survivor of his own blood to fulfill the requirements of ancestor worship, and no one could be sure of that without having many sons, nor could he have many sons without the risk of having many daughters as well. Thus the population always tended to increase beyond its food possibilities, and famine became a certainty.

The outstanding famines of the century occurred in India, and they happened there toward the end of each half of the fourteenth century, in 1342–44 and again in 1396 and following years. The famine of 1342 was precipitated by the southern march of Muḥammad ibn Taghlaq, sulṭān of Delhi (1325–51). An epidemic of cholera broke out in his camp and an awful famine destroyed people and cattle throughout Mālwā, being especially severe in and around the capital, Delhi. The famine lasted for many years. See Ibn Baṭṭūṭa's account of it (Defrémery's ed., 3, 372).

Chinese chronicles contain abundant information on the famines which desolated the land with such frequency and regularity that one cannot help feeling they were the physical consequences of chronic overpopulation. According to an investigation made by the department of agriculture of the University of Nanking, between the years 108 B.C. and A.D. 1911 there were 1828 famines in China, or nearly one a year in some part or other of the country.[64]

Chronic overpopulation was one of the causes of recurrent famines. Another cause almost equally important was the wild unruliness of the great rivers, which flooded the country repeatedly. The crops saved from the floods were often destroyed by droughts. The two causes combined, overpopulation and crop failure, were overpowering. Yao Shan-yu: The chronological and seasonal distribution of floods and droughts in Chinese history 206 B.C.–1911 A.D. (Harvard journal of Asiatic studies 6, 273–312, 1942); The geographical distribution of floods and droughts in Chinese history 206 B.C.–A.D. 1911 (Far Eastern quarterly 2, 357–78, 1943).

Bibliography. William Farr: The influence of scarcities and of the high prices of wheat on the mortality of the people of England (Journal of the Statistical Society 9, 158–74, 1846). Fritz Curschmann: Hungersnöte im Mittelalter. Ein Beitrag zur deutschen Wirtschaftsgeschichte des 8. bis 13. Jahrhunderts (225 p., Leipzig 1900). There is no account completing Curschmann's for the fourteenth century, but my Harvard colleague Professor N. S. B. Gras kindly wrote me (Dec. 24, 1941) that indirect information on fourteenth-century European famines may

[64] "Numbers of famines during the last 2000 years," article in Chinese in Nung lin hsin pao (vol. 6, no. 4, Nanking, March 1924). Thanks to Dr. A. K. Chiu, librarian of the Chinese-Japanese library in Harvard.

be deduced from the study of prices, e.g., from James Edwin Thorold Rogers: History of agriculture and prices in England from 1259 to 1793 (6 vols., Oxford 1866-87; vols. 1, 2) and Georges d'Avenel: Histoire économique de la propriété, des salaires, des denrées et de tous les prix en général de 1200 à 1800 (4 vols., Paris 1894-98).

Alexander Loveday: The history and economics of Indian famines (175 p., London 1914).

Walter Hampton Mallory: China, land of famine (American Geographical Society, no. 6, 216 p., ill., New York 1926; Isis 11, 508), describing only modern conditions, without historical introduction to them.

14. *Veterinary medicine* (Introd. 2, 89-90)

The pathology of animal diseases and their treatment is dealt with in a number of books devoted mainly to other subjects, such as husbandry, hunting, and falconry. As to the books specifically devoted to the veterinary art, we noticed that those of the thirteenth century were written mostly in Sicily. The only possible exceptions noted in volume 2 (p. 1091) were three Spanish treatises the dates of which are uncertain. One of them, El libro menescaleia e de albeyteria et fisica de las bestias, composed by Juan Alvarez Salamiellas, exists in a fifteenth-century MS of the Bibliothèque nationale, Paris (no. 214). The text, divided into 96 chapters, is written in Spanish, and each chapter ends with a colored image illustrating the mode of treatment; in addition, 28 smaller drawings in the text represent 14 different types of instruments.[65] That little treatise will give us a good idea of the veterinary art in the fourteenth century, even if it be itself a little earlier or later; its illustrations might be compared with those found in many MSS of the treatise on horse medicine of Bonifazio da Gerace (XIII-2);[66] in fact, the Bonifazio illustrations might help us in dating more exactly the Salamiellas MS. Another standard is afforded by the veterinary book written in Portuguese in Lisbon 1318 by mestre Giraldes, physician to king Dinis o Lavrador.

Similar treatises were written in Latin by the Italians Uberto di Cortenova and Lorenzo Rusio, and by the mysterious "Maurus and Marcus," who claimed to be marshals, the first to the Roman emperor and the second to the Byzantine one! We have also some German texts; at least two of them are known to me, both very short. The first is a fourteenth-century text in the University of Leipzig (MS 1244), the second is a German poem of 273 lines (many MSS) to which the name of a master Albrecht (or Alebrand) is attached.[67]

Thus, in spite of the fact that various veterinary works were already available at the beginning of the fourteenth century, not only in Latin but in sundry vernaculars, many new ones were composed in Latin, Spanish (?), Portuguese, German, and this proves sufficiently that the subject was a popular one. No wonder, for horses were precious, and some knowledge of their proper care was an essential part of a gentleman's education. Farriers were called in case of illness, but the first problem was to avoid illness and to treat the horses so well that they would remain strong and active as long as possible; that was obviously their owner's business.

[65] The text is analyzed chapter by chapter, and many illustrations are reproduced, in Wilhelm Rieck: Das Veterinär-Instrumentarium im Wandel der Zeiten (Berlin 1932; Isis 28, 294).

[66] One such Bonifazio MS, written in southern Italy c. 1345, is kept in the Pierpont Morgan Library, New York, together with photographs of the illustrations of the other Bonifazio MSS (Isis 27, 362). Ricci and Wilson (2, 1492, 1937).

[67] Karl Sudhoff: Deutsche Rossarzneibücher des Mittelalters (AGM 6, 223-30, 1913). Richard Schmutzer: Die Schrift des Meisters Albrecht über Pferdekrankheiten (Quellen und Studien zur Geschichte der Naturwissenschaften vol. 4, no. 1, p. 11-36, 1933; Isis 22, 339).

The Western books were as much surpassed by the Eastern ones, however, as the love and lore of horses in the West were surpassed by Eastern love and knowledge of the same animals. The Latin treatises do not begin to compare with the leading Arabic ones, namely those of al-Mujāhid 'Alī al-Rasūlī and Ibn al-Mundhir, which represent the climax of mediaeval hippology and hippiatry and remained unsurpassed for centuries.

15. *Regimina et consilia* (Introd. 2, 88–89, 93–94)

A good many medical texts of this period are in the form of regimina, that is, of directions for the ordering of one's life in order to avoid disease and remain in good health as long as possible. These directions might be of a very general nature, as in the Tadbīr al-ṣiḥḥa of Maimonides (XII-2) and in the series of texts entitled Regimen sanitatis, of which the best-known edition was composed for the king of Aragon in Barcelona 1307 by Arnold of Villanova (XIII-2), and another popular edition was prepared at about the same time by Magnino of Milano. The same directions might be arranged according to the almanac, as in the Regimen salutis per omnes menses ascribed to Peter of Spain (XIII-2), in the first chapter of the Melleus liquor of Alexander of Spain, or in the anonymous Liber de minucione et medicina secundum variationes lunarum.[68] Some of these health books are of a wider scope; for example, the De sanitatis custodia written by Albino de Montecaliero for a prince of Acaia is a regular medical treatise, and the Pro conservanda sanitate tuendaque prospera valetudine of Vital Du Four is a dictionary of materia medica. Sometimes the regimina are restricted to more special needs, as in the many Regimina acutorum derived from Galen's commentary on the Hippocratic treatise ad hoc, the Regimen castra sequentium (military hygiene) of Arnold of Villanova, the Regimen iter agentium vel peregrinantium (hygiene of travelers and pilgrims) of Adam of Cremona (XIII-1), the Liber conservacionis sanitatis senis written chiefly for older pilgrims by Guido da Vigevano, the Regimina de confortatione visus, etc.

Some regimina might be even more restricted. Instead of being written for all men, or for large groups of men, they would be prepared at the request of a definite patron.[69] The doctor would consider the latter's temperament and condition and draw up special regulations to fit them. If the patron was in good health, the regimen prepared for him would not be very different from the regimina sanitatis, except perhaps for a few rules corresponding to his horoscope, his age or sex, or the manner of life determined by his profession. In other cases, the patron might be in trouble and request special guidance for the alleviation of it; he might be asthmatic, apoplectic, podagrous,[70] suffer from megrim or piles, and the regimina drawn for his particular needs might come very close to other compositions called consilia. Indeed, between such special regimina as the Regimen curativum et praeservativum contra catarrhum (Introd. 2, 895) and the consilia the difference exists only in the title. Many consilia were drafted by Taddeo Alderotti (XIII-2), Guglielmo Corvi (XIII-2), Gentile da Foligno, and contain the best evidences we have of clinical

[68] Edited by Karl Sudhoff: Medizinische Monatsregeln für Aderlass, Schröpfen, Baden, Arzneigebrauch und Auswahl der Speisen und Getränke aus einer Pariser Handschrift des 14. Jahrhunderts (AGM 2, 136–40, 1908). Minutio means bloodletting.

[69] In addition to other examples given in this volume, see Christoph Ferckel: Ein Gesundheitsregiment für Herzog Albrecht von Österreich aus dem 14. Jahrhundert (AGM 11, 1–21, 1918), regimen probably composed for Albert I, duke 1282–1308 and king of Germany 1298–1308.

[70] See, e.g., the regimen written by Peter of Capestang (XIII-2) as to how to avoid paralysis, and the one addressed to a sufferer from the gout by Joannes Chumnos.

observations, though we should not take an exaggerated view of this (as I did perhaps in Introd. 2, 93-94). A safe judgment will not be possible until most of these consilia have been edited or at least analyzed. It is probable that most of them, even those dealing with very special conditions, lay more emphasis on diet and manner of life than on special therapeutics. That was wise, especially in view of the fact that the therapeutic methods then available were so limited and uncertain. Moreover, the means of objective diagnosis were very few and the doctor was largely dependent on the information given to him by the patient; as the means of transportation were difficult and painful for sick people, the consultation of a famous doctor often took place in writing or indirectly through a third person, and the doctor was always ready to give medical guidance without having examined the patient. This helps to explain the existence of so many written consilia and regimina, though some may have been written after due examination to refresh the patient's memory. The practice of writing medical directions for unseen patients was continued for centuries, until the beginning of modern times. For example, the famous Genevese doctor Théodore Tronchin (1709-81), Boerhaave's best disciple, often gave "consilia" but seldom expressed the wish to see the patient with his own eyes; he was satisfied with the information given by the patient and by the latter's family physician.[71]

Additional references. Karl Sudhoff: Zur korrektiven weiblichen Genitaltoilette im Mittelalter (AGM 12, 82-83, 1920). Hans Scheffer: Ein therapeutischer Thesaurus pauperum des 14. Jahrh. in lateinischen Versen (Diss., 31 p., Leipzig 1921; Isis 4, 407). Alfons Fischer: Gesundheitsfürsorge im 14. Jahrhundert (Schering-Kahlbaum med. Mitt. 4, 192-99, 2 fig., 1 pl., 1932).

The reader should bear in mind that the word regimen often occurs in the titles of nonmedical books. Indeed, the word "regimen" simply means direction, guidance, government, and may be used for any purpose where guidance is needed. We have a whole series of books entitled Regimen principum (or bearing equivalent titles) dealing with royal ethics and politics, the Regimen Judaeorum of St. Thomas (XIII-2), the Regimen et modus studendi of Martino da Fano (XIII-2), the Regimen solitarii of Ibn Bājja (XII-1), etc. The last-named one is a philosophical treatise, and the two preceding ones deal respectively with politics (how to deal with the Jews) and with methods of study.

To return to the medical regimina and treatises on health, the fact that I have spoken only of Latin and Greek ones should not suggest that they did not occur in other languages. That would be very unlikely, for health is equally precious and the means of preserving it equally interesting to all people. Indeed, the Regimen sanitatis has an Arabic prototype, the Sirr al-asrār, itself partly derived from Greek exemplars, and one of the main hygienic treatises of mediaeval times is the Tadbīr al-ṣiḥḥa of Maimonides. It would not be difficult to find in my preceding volumes other similar treatises in Arabic and Hebrew (Introd. 2, 88). As to the health guides written in any vernacular, the best known is the Régime du corps which Aldobrandino da Siena (XIII-2) dedicated to Beatrice of Savoy. Passing to Chinese literature, it will suffice to mention that a treatise dealing with the care and feeding of old people was completed in 1307 by Tsou Hsüan.

16. *Balneology* (Introd. 2, 96)

The field of balneology is strangely complex, for it includes not only ordinary bathing in all its forms and with its various auxiliaries such as massage, anointing,

[71] Henry Tronchin: Un médecin du XVIIIe siècle Théodore Tronchin (p. 300, Genève 1906).

and epilation, but as well the therapeutic use, external or internal, of water, especially spring waters, thermal or mineral. Thus when we take our morning dip or shower, or when we drink a glass of Poland or Vichy, we are indulging in balneotherapy! All the activities enumerated above have been practiced from time immemorial. Fine balneological traditions were developed in Rome and extended to the limits of the Roman Empire. One may find vestiges of balneae or thermae in every country which the Romans colonized, from Rome down to North Africa, Syria, or Arabia.[72] Under the influence of Christianity the habit of bathing was discountenanced in the Latin West and was revived only after a long interval, during the Crusading age, most probably under the influence of the Muslim ḥammāmāt (Introd. 2, 631), with which so many Christians became acquainted in the East. Ecclesiastical opposition to bathing was not as complete as anticlerical writers have maintained, and such as it was, it was amply justified on moral grounds. It is clear enough that the promiscuous bathing which existed in many mediaeval towns was physically and morally dangerous. Indeed, the main accessory to public bathing in the Middle Ages was not massage but prostitution.

As to the use of thermal or mineral waters, we may assume that it was never interrupted, though in this case also it is probable that the Romans carried it to a climax which was not attained again until more than a thousand years later. The Romans had a singular flair for valuable springs, and many of the modern spas located within the limits of the "imperium romanum" were actually discovered and exploited in Roman days.[73]

The balneological literature of the Middle Ages is meager. To be sure, there are chapters on bathing in many medical treatises, e.g., in the Fuṣūl Mūsā of Maimonides (XII-2) and the Expositio of John of Saint Amand (XIII-2), and Maino de Maineri discusses medicinal waters in his Liber medicinalis, but separate treatises are rare. One of the earliest balneological texts is the De balneolis puteolis ascribed to Peter of Eboli (XII-2) and also to Alcadino of Syracuse;[74] Roger Bacon (XIII-2) wrote a tract De balneis senum et seniorum; Gentile da Foligno explained the value of hot baths and mineral waters and discussed the baths of Lucca; Bonaventura de' Castelli wrote about the waters of Porretta. It is remarkable that all these writings refer to Italian springs—in Puteoli (near Naples), Lucca (near Pisa), and Porretta (near Florence); of course, many other springs had been used since Roman times and are referred to occasionally in mediaeval writings.[75]

The revival of medical interest in baths and springs does not appear only in Latin writings. We have already referred to the Fuṣūl Mūsā of Maimonides. Previous to him another Spaniard, Ibn Wāfid[76] (XI-1), had written in Arabic, and the Latin

[72] These balneological traditions were not initiated by the Romans, but are in most cases much earlier. In a letter addressed to the members of the American School of Oriental Research (dated Hakima, Transjordan, Aug. 22, 1942), Nelson Glueck refers many times to the fact that he always expects to find early Bronze Age sites in the neighborhood of strong springs, and vice versa. Our prehistoric ancestors were always on the lookout for springs (waters for drinking, bathing, and healing) and thus found them.

[73] On the other hand, the comparative neglect of our abundant thermal resources may be ascribed to the fact that America was never colonized by the Romans! Henry E. Sigerist: American spas in historical perspective (Bull. history of medicine 11, 133–147, 1942). Or to the fact that the Amerindians were not as intelligent as the Mediterranean populations of the Bronze Age.

[74] Alcadinus Siculus, son of Gersinus. Born in Syracuse, died at the age of 52. Studied in Salerno, physician to the emperors Henry VI and Frederick II (Choulant p. 313, 1841).

[75] See, e.g., the splendid volume of Antonio Cocchi: Dei bagni di Pisa (Firenze 1750). Many mediaeval references (p. 353 ff.).

[76] H. P. J. Renaud: Ibn Wāfid not Ibn al-Wāfid (Isis 35, 29, 1944).

version of his text was integrated in the balneological literature of the West. Then we have the περὶ λουτροῦ of Psellos (XI-2). Various treatises were available in Hebrew, the Fuṣūl had been translated in 1277, and the texts of Maino de Maineri and Bonaventura de' Castelli were soon Hebraicized. An Armenian book on the springs of Cilicia was ascribed to Nerses Balì.

Massage. From ancient times on, massage (i.e., friction or rubbing of the body, stroking, kneading, tapping, etc., either with the hand or with instruments, with or without ointment) was associated with bathing. Hippocrates explains in the περὶ ἄρθρων (ch. 9; Littré 4, 102) that the physician should be well acquainted with massage (ἀνάτριψις), and he announces his intentions of devoting a book to the subject. Oribasios (IV-2) discusses lengthily various kinds of friction (τρῖψις) in his book VI (Bussemaker and Daremberg vol. 1). That tradition was passed on to the Arabs, who may have received parts of it also from India. We gather from the Arabian nights and from other writings that various forms of massage were an essential part of the ḥammām ritual; some of the ḥammām servants were specialists in ṭaqṭaqa (or ṭarṭaqa, cracking the joints), kayyasa (Egyptian word for rubbing), dallaka, massada (other words for rubbing). Such practices were popular also in Ḥijjāz and Tihāma; their origin may be Greek or may be independent. The history of bathing and massage in the Arabic world has not yet been written.[77]

Short bibliography. Julian Marcuse: Bäder und Badewesen in Vergangenheit und Gegenwart (167 p., 22 fig., Stuttgart 1903). Eduard Bäumer: Die Geschichte des Badewesens (83 p., 13 fig., Abhandlungen zur Geschichte der Medizin, part 7, Breslau 1903). Karl Sudhoff: Aus dem antiken Badewesen (2 parts, Berlin 1910). Paul Négrier: Les bains à travers les âges (345 p., ill., Paris 1925). HDA (1, 796–852, 1927), for Germanic folklore.

There are many monographs devoted to the balneological history of regions rich in thermal and mineral waters, or to the history of particular spas.

17. *Pharmacy*

Mediaeval pharmacy was centered upon the study of herbs and other simples, and the results were published mainly in the form of herbals. These have been discussed above in section X.

The physician and druggist or pharmacist of the fourteenth century had at their disposal a rich collection of books on materia medica. Not to speak of old classics like Dioscorides (I-2), the Grabadin of Mesuë the Younger (XI-1), the Antidotarium parvum of Nicholas of Salerno (XII-1), and special parts in almost every medical encyclopaedia, they might have on their shelves more recent publications such as the Clavis sanationis of Simon of Genoa (XIII-2) or its abbreviation by Mondino Friulano, the Complementum of Francesco di Piedimonte, the Pandectae of Matthaeus Sylvaticus, the Dispensarium ad aromatorios of Niccolò da Reggio. The Greek druggists had the Greek text of Dioscorides and the Byzantine medical encyclopaedists, plus the Dynameron of Nicholaos Myrepsos (XIII-2) and the last books of the Methodus medendi of Joannes Actuarios. The Arabic ones had Dioscorides and their own encyclopaedias, chiefly the Kitāb al-ḥāwī of al-Rāzī (IX-2), the Kitāb al-malikī of 'Alī ibn 'Abbās (X-2), and the Qānūn of Ibn Sīnā (XI-1). They had also special treatises such as the Jāmi' al-mufradāt of Aḥmad

[77] For general information, see Edward William Lane: Manners and customs of the modern Egyptians (2 vols., London 1836; ch. 16). At the time of Lane's observations (1825–35), Egyptian manners were still mediaeval to a large extent, hence his careful descriptions have a great historical value; they have often been reprinted.

ibn Muḥammad al-Ghāfiqī (XII-2) abridged by Abū-l-Faraj Bar-Hebraeus (XIII-2),[78] or the more famous Jāmi' fī-l-adwiya al-mufrada of Ibn al-Baiṭār (XIII-1), or the more recent volumes of Ibn al-Kutubī and Maḥmūd ibn Ilyās al-Shīrāzī. The relative value of all these books is difficult to determine, for each of them was naturally derived from its predecessors. No literature lends itself more readily to endless borrowings and interpolations.

Finally, the Chinese had a whole series of pên ts'ao reaching back to immemorial days,[79] and in addition there were pharmaceutical chapters or digressions in their medical treatises. The only drug which we can ascribe to this period (XIV-1), chaulmoogra oil, was first discussed by a Chinese doctor, Chu Tan-ch'i. This is one of the most precious drugs ever discovered, being practically the only means of curing leprosy, but we must credit it as well to the Chinese empiricists who used it for centuries before Chu Tan-ch'i wrote about it as to Chu himself. Chaulmoogra is an undatable Chinese (or Hindu? or Burmese?) discovery, even as cinchona (hence quinine) is an undatable Peruvian one. The first entered into literature in the first half of the fourteenth century, whereas the second had to wait three centuries longer; the second, however, was internationally appreciated as soon as it was published, whereas chaulmoogra obtained international recognition only within our own days.

The remembrance of these astounding folk discoveries, the use of chaulmoogra, cinchona, and the practice of variolation (going back in China at least to Sung times)[80] should sober our thoughts when we criticize too freely the old pharmacopoeias. It is easy enough to make fun of mediaeval recipes; it is more difficult and may be wiser to investigate them. Instead of assuming that the mediaeval pharmacist was a benighted fool, we might wonder whether there was not sometimes a justification for his strange procedure. For example, the frequent use of urine in his recipes is disgusting, but the therapeutic value of urea is now recognized. Not only is urea used for diuretic action,[81] it has been proved to be good medicine for slow-healing wounds.[82]

The number of mineral drugs was small as compared with the large number of "herbs," but that smallness has been exaggerated by scholars who would have iatrochemistry begin with Paracelsus. As a matter of fact, some minerals, such as sulphur, arsenic, antimony,[83] mercury, had been experimented with not only by the Arabs but by the Greeks. It is impossible to go into the detail of this, for the story of each element (at least those known before 1800) is a very long one, and the earliest steps of man's acquaintance with them were naturally very obscure.[84] Frequent references have been made to mercury and its medical uses in volumes 1 and 2 (chiefly 2, 84, 667). Mercurial ointments were applied to the cure of various skin troubles, and the salivation caused by excessive use had already been noticed

[78] Edited by Max Meyerhof and Georgy Sobhy (Cairo 1932–40), not completed (Isis 20, 454–57; 33, 359).

[79] Not only in MS, but printed copies from 973 on (Isis 33, 439).

[80] Wong and Wu (p. 215, 1936).

[81] Louis Goodman and Alfred Gilman: Pharmacological basis of therapeutics (p. 631, New York 1941).

[82] William Robinson: Use of urea to stimulate healing in chronic purulent wounds (American Journal of Surgery 33, 192–97, 1936); The healing properties of allantoin and urea discovered through the use of maggots in human wounds (Smithsonian Report for 1937, p. 451–61).

[83] The ancients did not know pure arsenic and antimony, but their sulfides; this, however, does not affect the argument.

[84] Very valuable summary by Mary Elvira Weeks (1933; Isis 21, 455; 35, 264).

by Teodorico Borgognoni (XIII-1). The peculiar properties of mercury caused it to be very popular with alchemists all over the world; its antiseptic powers could not remain very long unobserved by people handling it, and were confirmed by many trials. It was one of the most powerful drugs in the mediaeval pharmacopoeia, and it was as natural to apply it to the cure of syphilis at the end of the fifteenth century as it is natural for us to experiment with sulfanilamides in our pathological difficulties.

One might expect to obtain some information on the practice of pharmacy from the rules regulating the profession and from archaeological relics concerning it. For example, apothecaries were first mentioned in French records in 1178, and before the end of the century there existed in London the guild of pepperers, including druggists, and in Florence the guild of physicians and apothecaries. The first apothecary shop recorded in Germany was in Cologne 1225; in 1271 herborists and apothecaries were forbidden to practice medicine in Paris; in 1297 a guild of pharmacists was organized in Bruges. The first recorded apothecary shop in London dates from 1345. In 1353 "master" apothecaries were mentioned in a Parisian ordinance concerning the inspection of apothecary shops.[85] Archaeological data, such as the remains of apothecary shops, registers, pots and pans, mortars, pestles, and other tools are rare for this period; they do not begin to appear in sufficient numbers before the sixteenth century.

For the drug jars see Georg Urdang: Kunst- und Kulturgeschichtliches aus alten Apotheken. Ausstellung im Schlossmuseum, Berlin, Mai 1939 (20 p., ill., Gesellschaft für Geschichte der Pharmazie 1929). Josef Anton Häfliger: Pharmazeutische Altertumskunde und die Schweizerische Sammlung für historisches Apothekenwesen an der Universität Basel (204 p., 53 fig., Zürich 1931), largely based upon the very rich Swiss collections preserved in Basel. Geoffrey Eliot Howard: Early English drug jars (quarto, 50 p., 22 pl., Medici Society, London 1931). Bernard Rackham: Catalogue of Italian maiolica (vol. 1, 510 p.; vol. 2, 222 pl., Victoria and Albert Museum, London 1940). George Urdang and Ferdinand William Nitardy: The Squibb ancient pharmacy (190 p., ill., New York 1940; Isis 32). There are no Italian drug jars anterior to the fifteenth century, nor English ones (in Howard's book) anterior to the seventeenth century. Both Rackham and Howard give interpretations of the inscriptions found on many jars.

There is a lengthy chapter on pharmacy in the fourteenth century in Louis Reutter de Rosemont: Histoire de la pharmacie à travers les âges (2 vols., Paris 1931; 1, 183–253).

18. *Medical teaching and profession* (Introd. 2, 96–97)

By the beginning of the fourteenth century medical teaching was well organized in a number of places East and West, and no essential novelties were introduced during that century. Some idea of the medical teaching in one of the leading schools of Western Europe has been given above apropos of Montpellier. In addition, there was some kind of state supervision, at least in Naples, for we hear of a doctor Giacomo Pipino, in the service of the Angevine court, who examined medical and surgical candidates and gave them, or not, the license to practice. Whether medical degrees and licenses were granted by a medical school or by a state inspector, their need and meaning were now well understood. Yet the number of

[85] The data of this paragraph are taken without verification from Edward Kremers and George Urdang: History of pharmacy (p. 389, Philadelphia 1940; Isis 33, 307–8). See also Pietro Sella and Emilio Paolo Vicini: Inventari di farmazie Modenesi del secolo XIV (Boll. Istituto storico italiano dell' arte sanitaria 12, 143–64, 1932).

medical graduates was probably very small as compared with the number of practitioners. It was possible for an intelligent man to learn more as an apprentice to a doctor than could be learned in the best schools of the day; it was easy enough for any kind of empiric or charlatan to take advantage of the people's credulity. From the professional point of view, the main event of the century was the establishment, or, let us say, the growth to maturity, of the College of St. Cosmas in Paris, and the gradual recognition of a class of surgeons standing halfway between the barbers on the one side and the doctors on the other. That three-cornered fight was only beginning, however, and would have to continue for centuries.

The medical profession was organizing itself in guilds and binding as well as protecting itself with various regulations. See, e.g., Giorgio del Guerra: Gli "ordinamenta medicorum" Pisani del secolo XIV (Boll. Istituto storico italiano dell' arte sanitaria 11, 171–77, 1931).

Some information on medical practice may be obtained from the biographies and letters of contemporary physicians. We know that Taddeo Alderotti (XIII-2), who died in 1303, was able to command enormous fees, e.g., from the pope Honorius IV. Doctors in royal or princely service were often members of the royal domesticity and received annual salaries, which varied considerably from country to country and from one palace to another. As the financial data are not understandable without explanations as to the value of money in the corresponding times and places, it is simpler to refer the reader to other publications, e.g., those of vicomte Georges d'Avenel (Isis 8, 640): Les riches depuis sept cents ans (p. 167–212, Paris 1909); Revenus d'un intellectuel (p. 168–212, Paris 1922).

For medical education and the organization of state and forensic medicine in China, see the remarks printed above.

19. *Faith healing* (Introd. 2, 85)[86]

Faith healing is probably as old as mankind, but we need not go back to the intangible beginnings. The transition from deontology to it is a most natural one. The very Hippocratic writings which constitute the foundation of medical deontology explain repeatedly (e.g., Παραγγελίαι, IX) that one of the physician's duties is to soothe the patient's mind. That is, the Hippocratic doctors understood already that faith healing is an essential part of scientific therapeutics.

It is true when we speak today of faith healing we are not thinking of it as associated with scientific methods, but as independent and exclusive of the latter. Exclusive dependence on faith for the cure of illness was almost universal[87] in mediaeval times, though the object and nature of the faith might vary considerably. Buddhist medicine was largely faith healing (see article byō in Hōbōgirin 1937), and the same can be said of Christian medicine, though in those days it was not yet called Christian Science. The tradition of faith healing had been strongly established in the New Testament, and every revival of it in Christian lands was naturally based on Biblical precedents. In both the Latin and the Greek world sainthood was very soon associated with healing power; in fact, that power as exercised in life or death (by means of relics) was soon recognized as one of the decisive proofs (though insufficient by itself) of a man's sanctity. Accounts of miraculous cures constitute to this day one of the main features in the processes of beatification or canonization directed by the Congregation of Rites of the Catholic

[86] For a general statement, see W. F. Cobb (ERE 5, 697–701, 1912).
[87] Meaning that in every country a good many people shared that attitude.

church.[88] When the Jesuit father Heribert Rosweyde (d. 1629) drew the first outline of the Acta sanctorum, he planned a final volume including tables, and one of these tables was to be a classification of saints in the alphabetic order of the diseases cured by the intercession of each of them.[89] It is highly probable that such lists enabling one to find the saint to propitiate or the best pilgrimage to make in any medical emergency are available (and even published) today, but I have no time to hunt for them.[90] All over Christendom, East and West, diseases were treated and are still treated by the application of relics, holy water, sacred medals, or ceremonies of exorcism.

For the medical virtues of the Agnus Dei see Curt F. Bühler: Notes on a MS of the Virtutes Agnus Dei (Bull. history of medicine 15, 220–24, 1944; Isis 35, 226).

The same conditions obtained in the Muslim world, where the majority of people had probably far more confidence in various talismans and the barakāt of saints[91] than in the remedies of doctors. The superstitious (vs. religious) nature of most of these procedures is apparent in countries of the Near East, where three religions (Judaism, Christianity, Islām) have been for centuries in close contact, for there are endless examples of superstitions shared by Jews, Christians, and Muslims alike which bring them all to the same shrines, to ask for the same blessings, according to their several rites and languages.[92]

Muslim physicians give many illustrations of healing by spiritual means, by suggestion, and many Arabic books deal with "spiritual medicine," but we have to bear in mind that Arabic titles are more often than not metaphorical. Such a title as al-ṭibb al-rūḥānī may refer to some kind of psychotherapy, as I said before (Introd. 2, 86), or to ethical philosophy. This is the case, e.g., for a treatise by al-Rāzī (IX-2) recently edited by Paul Kraus (Cairo 1939; Isis 33, 246).

I have already referred to Buddhist medicine, which attached considerable importance to prayers, incantations, and other religious or superstitious practices. The same belief in faith healing existed in non-Buddhist circles all over the Far East and even in purely medical circles. Indeed, faith healing was one of the nine (or ten) medical branches officially recognized during the Sung and Yüan dynasties (Wong and Wu p. 95–96, 1936). The unanimity of Chinese belief in various forms of faith healing may have been due to religious syncretism; it was more probably the result of cultural convergence. Indeed, that belief is not simply Chinese, but human. It is nothing but the excessive generalization of experimental facts which may be observed by intelligent men anywhere and everywhere.

20. *Medical deontology* (Introd. 2, 95)

Inasmuch as the fourteenth century witnessed the growth to maturity of the medical profession and to a humbler degree of the surgical one, it is not surprising to observe a revival of medical deontology, the most notable perhaps since Hip-

[88] CE (13, 144–45, 1912).

[89] Hippolyte Delehaye: L'oeuvre des Bollandistes 1615–1915 (p. 12, Bruxelles 1920). Isis (28, 10).

[90] A few indications may be obtained in Heinrich Samson: Die Schutzheiligen (349 p., Paderborn 1889), and in Clay (p. 244–71, 1909). For the Orthodox church, see Mary Hamilton: Greek saints and their festivals (p. 38–72, Edinburgh 1910).

[91] For Muslim saints, see Hughes (p. 555, 1885) and the words walī, pīr, etc. in EI.

[92] Sarton: The unity and diversity of the Mediterranean world (Osiris 2, 457–60, 1936). I have given a curious example of religious syncretism apropos of terra sigillata in my article on Busbecq (Isis 33, 571, 1942).

pocratic times. A most interesting treatise on the subject, De cautelis medicorum, was written by the Bolognese doctor Alberto de' Zancari. Moreover, special chapters are devoted to it in the treatises of Henri de Mondeville and Jan Yperman, as well as in those (a little later) of Guy de Chauliac (XIV-2) and John Arderne (XIV-2). Chauliac's conclusion may be quoted:

"The doctor should be of good character [bien morigeré]. He should be bold in matters which are certain, fearful in danger, and avoid false cures or practices. He should be gracious to the sick, kind-hearted to his companions, wise in his forecasts. He should be chaste, sober, compassionate, and merciful; he should not be covetous nor extort money before he is due to receive a moderate salary according to the patient's ability [to pay], to his own labor, the degree of success of his treatment, and his dignity."[93]

It is interesting to note that all these men showing a particular interest in medical manners and etiquette were, with the exception of the first named, Zancari, surgeons. It is probable that the very fact of being surgeons put them, as it were, on their ethical mettle. It was essential for surgeons to prove that they were gentlemen just as much as the highbrow and Latin-speaking doctors.

21. *Hospitals* (Introd. 2, 245–57, 95)

There is not much to add to what has been said in volume 2, for though many new hospitals and lazaretti were established in the fourteenth century, these do not seem to have been essentially different from those of earlier centuries. Indeed, by 1300 the hospital movement was well under way.

A history of Muslim hospitals has been written by Ahmed Issa bey (French ed., Cairo 1929, Isis 14, 535; Arabic enlarged ed., Damascus 1939, Isis 31, 225). Much additional information has been collected by Aydin Mehmed Sayili in his Harvard thesis: The institutions of science and learning in the mediaeval Moslem world (Cambridge, Mass. 1941); this includes an impressive list of about a hundred mediaeval Islamic hospitals (p. 164–73). Many were created in the fourteenth century, especially thanks to Turkish initiative.

Passing from Islām to Buddhist Asia, there were probably small infirmaries in Hīnayāna monasteries restricted to the monks; Mahāyāna generosity extended them to laymen, but our knowledge of them is very meager. Japanese hospitals were derived from the Chinese models. It is probable that these establishments were purely charitable ones (like the European leper houses, hôtels-Dieu, and hospices) rather than medical. They generally included a dispensary, however. The Japanese dispensary or seyakuin was a part of the Buddhist hospital, where herbs were cultivated and drugs prepared. Such a seyakuin was founded by Kōmyō-kōgō (701–60), widow of the emperor Shōmu, who had shaven her head at the time of the latter's abdication (758) and taken the religious name Mampuku; she gave to the hospital sixty kinds of drugs packed in twenty-one lacquered boxes bequeathed by Shōmu.[94] Similar dispensaries are mentioned in Japanese documents of the eighth and ninth centuries; they seem to have disappeared in the tenth century (Hōbōgirin p. 245–49). However, Ninsei (d. 1303) is said to have founded refuges for lepers and other patients.

[93] Translated from the Grande chirurgie (Nicaise ed., p. 19, 1890). Other extracts may be found in Mary Catherine Welborn: The long tradition (Medieval and historiographical essays in honor of James Westfall Thompson p. 344–57, Chicago 1938; Isis 29, 142, 213).

[94] The inventory still exists in the Shōsōin of Nara. The drugs have been identified by Keizo Dōhi: Medicine in ancient Japan (The young East 2, 151–57, 185–95, 1926). Jiro Harada: A glimpse of Japanese ideals (p. 100, Tokyo 1938; Isis 35, 256).

As to Indo-China, our knowledge is still very rudimentary. The following item is quoted simply to illustrate the fact that hospitals existed in Buddhist Cambogia; other similar items would probably be found if one hunted for them. In the temple Tà-prohm built by king Jayavarman VII there is a long inscription (290 Sanskrit lines) of that king dated 1108 śaka = A.D. 1186, mentioning pious foundations, among which are 102 hospitals; the locations of 15 of those hospitals have been identified thanks to the discovery of foundation stones. George Coedès: La stèle de Tà-prohm (Bull. Ecole française d'Extrême Orient 6, 44–85, 1906); Les hôpitaux de Jayavarman VII (ibid. 40, 344–47, 1941).

In the Christian world many hospitals had been established before the fourteenth century, but the early history of the most ancient is as dark as that of the earliest universities, and for the same reasons (one does not realize the existence of a new thing until it has grown somewhat; the origins are only known retroactively, that is, very imperfectly). It is thus difficult, if not impossible, to put them in an unobjectionable chronological order.

Here are a few data by way of illustration: Many hospitals were created by hospital orders, not simply the Hospitalers proper, or Knights of St. John of Jerusalem (XII-1), but other hospitalers. The most important of these orders, as far as hospitals were concerned, was the one led by Guy of Montpellier (d. 1208), who dedicated a hospital to the Holy Ghost in Montpellier c. 1145. The brethren in charge of it were submitted to the Augustinian rule. That organization was sanctioned in 1198 by Innocent III (pope 1198–1216). Now a xenodochium[95] had been founded in Rome near the Vatican by Offa, king of the Mercians (d. 796), who also dedicated a church to the Holy Ghost. In 1204, Innocent III called Guido of Montpellier to Rome and entrusted to him the reorganization of Offa's foundation under the name of Santa Maria in Sassia (= in Saxony, with reference to Offa's old foundation).[96] Guy soon gave it the new name Santo Spirito in Sassia, under which it was destined to become one of the most famous hospitals in the world. San Spirito was enlarged by other popes and has continued to be to this day the outstanding hospital of Rome. Was San Spirito thus called because of the early foundation by an English king, or because of the Montpellier hospitalers? Was it founded at the end of the eighth century or at the beginning of the thirteenth?

San Spirito was not by any means the first hospital of Rome, but it completely eclipsed its predecessors, and became a model for the whole of Europe. Hospitals bearing the Holy Ghost's name appeared everywhere.

[95] The Greek name is not unusual; the early hospitals and hospices of the West were often given Greek names in the charters and other documents. Thus we come across the words nosocomium (νοσοκομεῖον), a house for the sick, and gerontocomium (γεροντοκομεῖον), one for the aged; orphanotrophium (ὀρφανοτροφεῖον) for orphans, brephotrophium (βρεφοτροφεῖον) for foundlings, ptochium (πτωχεῖον) for the poor, xenodochium (ξενοδοχεῖον) for pilgrims or strangers. This series of Greek names proves the Byzantine origin (Introd. 2, 245) of Christian hospitals. H. Bolkestein: Ξενών. Gastverblijf, pelgrimsherberg, armhuis (Mededeeling der K. Akademie van Wetenschappen, 84 B, no. 3, 107–46, Amsterdam 1937).

[96] The xenodochium was presumably a part of the Schola Anglorum (or Saxonum) founded not by Offa but by Ina, West Saxon king from 688 to 726; he abdicated in 726, pilgrimed to Rome, and died there in the same year (DNB 28, 428). Thus the name of Offa in my text should be replaced by that of Ina, but the question is full of obscurity. Offa endowed the Schola Anglorum but did not create it. A hospice (that is, a hotel) for English travelers existed in Rome in 1362.

Cardinal Gasquet: History of the Venerable English College, Rome (p. 8–10, London 1920). W. J. Moore: The Saxon pilgrims to Rome and the Schola Saxonum (thesis, Fribourg, Switzerland 1937; p. 62), with a chronological list of English pilgrims to Rome from 653 to 798. Vincent Joseph Flynn: Englishmen in Rome during the Renaissance (Modern philology 36, 121–38, 1938).

Ferdinand Gregorovius: History of the city of Rome in the Middle Ages (8 vols. in 13, London 1894–1902; 2, 427; 5, 635; 7, 682, 719, 731). James J. Walsh (CE 7, 480–88, 1910). Enciclopedia italiana (25, 673–87, 1935).

Of equal importance was the Hôtel-Dieu of Paris, which remained for centuries the outstanding hospital not only of Paris, but of France. Its history has been traced back to the ninth century and even to the seventh, but its earliest charter extant dates from 1157. It was rebuilt at the end of the twelfth century. Other hospitals and hospices were created in the thirteenth to fourteenth centuries, notably the Quinze-vingt established by St. Louis in 1260 for three hundred blind men, and the first Parisian great house for orphans, the Hospice des enfants bleus, founded in 1326.

Léon Brièle: Collection de documents pour servir à l'histoire des hôpitaux de Paris commencée sous les auspices de Michel Möring, continuée par Charles Quentin et F. Peyron (4 vols., Paris 1881–87). Ernest Coyecque: L'Hôtel-Dieu au Moyen âge (Société de l'histoire de Paris, Documents, vols. 10, 11, Paris 1891, 1889). Léon Brièle: Archives de l'Hôtel-Dieu, 1157–1300, avec notices, appendice et table par E. Coyecque (Documents sur l'histoire de France, 695 p., Paris 1894).

Various hospitals were established in England in 1084 and following years. A tabulated list of mediaeval hospitals in England, unfortunately not in chronological order but by counties and for each county in alphabetical order of places, is appended to Clay (p. 277–337, 1909). The main foundation was that of St. Bartholomew in London by Rahere (d. 1144), prebendary of St. Paul's. The building was begun in 1123 and the first charter given by Henry I in 1133. Norman Moore: History of St. Bartholomew's Hospital (2 large vols., ill., London 1918). St. Bartholomew, familiarly called Barts by its friends, servants, and alumni, is one of the leading hospitals of the world today.

The hospitalers of the Holy Ghost were very active in German lands, and a good many hospitals were established by them in those countries. Virchow gave in 1877 a long list of these Heiliggeistspitäler, ranging from the thirteenth to the sixteenth centuries. The earliest are those of Brandenburg (1204), Zürich (1207), and Wien (1209). He lists 28 hospitals for XIII-1, 56 for XIII-2, 21 for XIV-1, 37 for XIV-2; or 84 for XIII, 58 for XIV, 7 for XV, 6 for XVI; that is a total of 155, most of which (142) were founded in the thirteenth and fourteenth centuries.

Rudolf Virchow: Der Hospital-Orden vom heiligen Geist, zumal in Deutschland (Monatsberichte der K. preussischen Akademie der Wissenschaften zu Berlin, 1877), reprinted together with many other papers on the history of hospitals in his Gesammelte Abhandlungen aus dem Gebiete der öffentlichen Medizin und Seuchenlehre (2 vols., Berlin 1879; 2, 1–127).

The monographs concerning the Hôtel-Dieu, Barts, etc. will give the historian very definite ideas about mediaeval hospitals in Christendom. It is probable that many more monographs devoted to other European hospitals might be found in the archives or journals of regional antiquarian societies. A synthesis of our knowledge of mediaeval hospitals and hospices remains to be written.

Most of these institutions were philanthropic rather than scientific. It is impossible to say when hospitals began to be the medical laboratories which they are today; the transition from blind charity to scientific charity was very gradual; it varied considerably from place to place, and must have been much influenced in each place by the presence (or absence) of doctors taking a deeper interest in scientific problems.

22. *Erotics*

It is proper to end our review of the main medical topics of mediaeval literature with erotics, though it is unnecessary to repeat the generalities set forth in volume 2 (p. 79). Mediaeval interest in erotics is best illustrated by the need of aphrodisiacs, such as cantharides (Lytta vesicatoria, "Spanish flies," "Russian flies"; in Arabic dhurrāḥ, dharārīḥ, etc., also dhubbān al-hind or dhubāb hindī, both meaning "Hindu flies"), which were abused for venereal purposes and must have caused considerable damage to men's bodies. All the pharmacopoeias and especially the Eastern ones contain such drugs, and also sometimes their opposites (anaphrodisiacs). In addition to physical aphrodisiacs, there was also some need of literary ones, less pernicious to the body but more dangerous to the mind.

As such erotica do not concern the historian of science except indirectly, I have not hunted for them and shall mention only two characteristic ones which I came across incidentally. They represent respectively the Western and Eastern wings of the Islamic world.

The first is the "Gift of the bride," written in Arabic by the Tunisian geographer al-Tijānī. It is an erotic anthology derived from the writings of Arabic poets and theologians. The second, written in Persian by al-Nakhshabī, was an adaptation of the rich erotic lore (kāmaśāstra) available in Sanskrit. It would be interesting to compare these two forms of ars amatoria, and to compare both with the classical and Latin mediaeval, but this cannot be done here and now.

My main point is that the medical historian of the Middle Ages should not neglect erotics, though this will give him a poor impression of mediaeval psychology and a poorer one of mediaeval pharmacodynamics.

XII. HISTORIOGRAPHY

The history of men's efforts to record, as well as they conceived it and knew how to do it, the events of their past is definitely a part, and an important part, of the history of science. The fact that the accounts of the past were often incorrect and falsified and that every nation tended to mythologize its beginnings increases the difficulty of our task, but does not make it less necessary. After all, mythological and superstitious tendencies existed (and still exist) in every field of knowledge, not simply in historiography. Generally speaking, we may expect historians and chroniclers to be more accurate when dealing with events closer to them in space and time than when they deal with events more distant; on the other hand, in the case of contemporary events the accounts may be (and often are) tampered with or colored (by suppression, addition, emphasis, or twisting) because of religious, national, political, or social prejudices. In other words, whereas superstitions tend to increase with the temporal or spatial distance, various prejudices become stronger in inverse proportion to that distance. That is as true of the fourteenth century as it is of today.

Though the mythological inclination was stronger in the Middle Ages than it is now, a few bolder minds tried to escape it and to give a rational account of the past, even as they tried to give a rational account of nature. They were sustained in this endeavor by the example of the great historians of antiquity, and perhaps by a trickle of the Euhemerist[1] tradition which had been kept alive by the fathers of the church in their struggle against paganism. It required considerably more courage to analyze, discuss, and discount historical traditions in the fourteenth century

[1] See the notes on Euhemeros (IV-2 B.C.) and Ennius (II-1 B.C.).

than now, but that makes it the more necessary to commemorate the noble men who gave us even then examples of criticism and freedom of thought.

For the historian of today whose purpose is to resurrect as exactly as possible the days of the fourteenth century, every chronicle of that time, however humble, is precious. Every such chronicle, if it be honest and genuine, is a positive contribution to our knowledge. As it would be impossible to mention them all, a few will have to represent the others, many of which are anonymous or written by men otherwise unknown. All that I can hope for in this survey is to give a general idea of the work done in many countries by chroniclers, historians, critics, and humanists. It is thanks to the work of such men that we are able to know what little we know of the past, and that earlier traditions have been handed down to our ancestors and finally to ourselves.

The best classification is by cultural types. We shall consider in turn: (A) Western Christendom, (B) Eastern Christendom, (C) Western Islām, (D) Eastern Islām, (E) Ceylon, (F) China and Korea, (G) Japan.

A. *Western Christendom*

A1. *Italy*

The Italians were the leaders in the Latin world, so much so that an analysis of Italian activities would suffice to exemplify almost every aspect of Latin historiography. We shall divide the Italian scholars into five groups: (a) chroniclers, (b) missionaries and diplomats, (c) historians, (d) historians of science and culture, (e) archaeologists and humanists. As usual these groups are tentative, not mutually exclusive.

a. *Chroniclers.* The Pomerium of the church of Ravenna, which Riccobaldo da Ferrara completed in 1312, is a mixture of history, chronological summary, and chronicle. It is not by any means restricted to the diocese of Ravenna, but relates the main deeds of the emperors and popes as introduction to a general chronology. Dino Compagni wrote a chronicle of Florence from 1280 to 1312 which is one of the most important works of its kind in mediaeval times, though it has not come down to us in its original form. The Florentine chronicle of Giovanni Villani is even more important. The scope is larger, for it deals with the history of Florence from the origins to 1346, and is not restricted to Florence; it is rather, especially the final part, a picture of the Western world as seen through a Florentine window. Giovanni's chronicle was continued by his brother Matteo, and later by his nephew Filippo. It is of special interest to the student of economic history, but it contains valuable grist for the mill of every historian of the fourteenth century. Passing to Venice, materials for its history were assembled by Andrea Dandolo, who was at one time, as three of his ancestors had been before him, the doge (that is, the dux, duce, ruler) of that city.

Opicinus de Canistris composed a little book in praise of his native city, Pavia. Niccolò Speciale compiled a chronicle of Sicily (1282–1327), and Giovanni de' Marignolli, a chronicle of Bohemia.

b. *Missionaries and diplomats.* Marignolli's chronicle of Bohemia, which has just been mentioned, would have been doomed to oblivion but for the Oriental interpolations which it contained. His reminiscences of India and China have already been recalled in the geographical section, and so have the accounts of other Italian travelers to the East. Whether that be geography or history is a matter of taste; at any rate, there is no point in speaking twice of the same achievements. Reread the beginning of the geographical summary. Perhaps the most valuable of these travel accounts for the historian (vs. the geographer) is that of Odorico da Pordenone, to whom we owe the best contemporary history of the Catholic missions in China.

The Catholic missions to the Far East were diplomatic as well as religious ventures. The purpose was not simply to convert the people of the East (and more particularly the Nestorian communities which had been there for many centuries),[2] but to obtain eventually allies against the Muslim or the "Turcs." The "propaganda" crusading literature which has been discussed in section II contains an abundance of historical facts, selected with a definite anti-Muslim bias; that bias, however, is so well known that it can easily be discounted. The outstanding work of that kind from the purely historical point of view is the Liber secretorum of the Venetian statesman and diplomat Marino Sanudo il Vecchio.

c. *Historians.* One of St. Thomas' disciples, Ptolemy of Lucques (XIII-2), wrote annals and an ecclesiastical history from Jesus Christ to 1312. Albertino Mussato of Padova, trained as a diplomat and humanist (for a few centuries diplomats had to be humanists, but happily it was not necessary for humanists to be diplomats, and most of them were as undiplomatic and indiscreet as it is possible to be), was the first of mediaeval historians who ventured to write books in the classical tradition, the model par excellence being Livy. Like Dante, he was a moderate Guelf (see below). He wrote histories of the Holy Roman emperors of his own time. He tried to explain events as well as to narrate them, and if that characteristic is used to define the historian (vs. the mere annalist), then Dino Compagni and the Villani were historians too. Another history of contemporary Italy as viewed from the imperial and classical angle was composed by Ferreto de' Ferreti of Vicenza, and an attempt to survey imperial history from Augustus to Charlemagne (as if that were a continuous whole)[3] was made by Giovanni de Matociis of Verona.

d. *Historians of science and culture.* It is worth while to group separately three scholars who adumbrate new historical conceptions, and might be considered humble forerunners of the "historians of thought" of today. The Dominican Giovanni da San Gimignano compiled a kind of encyclopaedia for the preachers of his order, the idea being to give them all the information which they might need for the redaction of masterly and overpowering sermons. Alas! I am afraid that the Summa de exemplis et rerum similitudinibus (note the title) was responsible for the perpetration of dull and soporific discourses rather than for the creation of inspired ones, but that is another question. One of the ten books of that Summa was devoted to a history of inventions and inventors, conceived, it must be admitted, in a very strange manner. A similar task was accomplished by Guglielmo da Pastrengo of Verona, who wrote an account of illustrious men including inventors. We must also mention in this connection the Expositio theorice planetarum of Thaddeus of Parma, one of the features of which is a classification of the occult sciences, the main inventor of each being named. This was an erratic form of a sound idea, and as such may be rescued from oblivion.

e. *Archaeologists and humanists.* The historians of group (c) who derived their inspiration from such Roman writers as Livy, Sallust, and the Plinii were humanists,

[2] Moule (1930). P. Yoshio Saeki: The Nestorian documents and relics in China (654 p., ill., Tokyo 1937).

[3] It was typical of the humanists to assume the continuity of Latin traditions, as if the invasion of the Barbarians, the fall of the Western Empire, the development of Romance languages, etc., did not constitute essential discontinuities. Their tendency, whether expressed or not, was to disregard and forget those discontinuities.

but different from those who will now be named. The leader and master of these was Dante, who wrote no historical books, yet stirred up the past as no one had done before, resurrected glorious and evil memories, and created a new historical consciousness. Even to this day many personalities and events of the distant past exist in men's minds only because of his magical evocation of them. No writer or poet of his time can stand up against him, except the young Petrarca. The latter was more of a humanist in the new sense which he did so much himself to introduce. Like the historians dealt with above, he was interested in classical antiquities and was hoping to bring them back to life. He wanted to resurrect Latin letters, that is, to dig out forgotten MSS, to vivify the old classics, and to create new ones in the old language. He found two lost speeches of Cicero, and hunted not only for MSS, but for inscriptions and coins. He caused indirectly the creation of the Renaissance medals. Dante has assumed the proportions of a kind of archangel standing between two worlds; Petrarca is more definitely the father of the Renaissance, the grandfather of the modern age.

Petrarca's love of antiquity and his archaeological curiosity were shared by many of his contemporaries, at least in Italy, where the Roman past was still tangible enough. I have already spoken of the historians and the Latinists. Of course, one could not read intelligently the books of Virgil or Livy, amid the ruins and relics of the Roman past, without discovering that past again in all its splendor and complexity, and no man of imagination and sensitivity could read them long and deeply without being intoxicated. They needed more MSS, more coins, more inscriptions, more monuments, and they found them in abundance. A new fire had been lighted by Dante and was kept burning with increasing intensity by Petrarca and their followers. This was the literary beginning of what was called later the Renaissance. It is not surprising, after all, to come across a historian and humanist like Benzo of Alexandria, who began the archaeological exploration of Italy; it is perhaps a little more astonishing to witness the archaeological passion of the famous "duce" of that time, Cola di Rienzo, yet that helps us more than anything else to realize that a new wind was blowing.

A2. *Hispanic peninsula*

Criticism of the chronicles of Spain is made very difficult because of the multitude of variants found in the texts, summaries, amplifications, and translations. For example, the Chronica Hispaniae ab origine prima ad a. D. 1243 by Rodrigo Jiménez de Rada (XIII-1) was soon translated into Catalan by Pedro Ribera de Perpeja, and in the following century it was put into Castilian by Gonzalo de Hinojosa, bishop of Burgos, who continued it to the time of his death.[4] As Don Gonzalo was sent to Paris on a diplomatic errand in 1319, it is not surprising that his chronicle, the so-called Burgos chronicle, was soon known in France, and that it was eventually translated into French for Charles V the Wise by Jean Golein (XIV-2). I do not think that a comparative study of these Latin, Catalan, Castilian, and French texts has yet been made, and in the meanwhile we are obliged to consider these chronicles as a whole without being able to determine the merits of each contributor.

In great contrast with these official chronicles were the works of two historians

[4] Text edited, together with another (anonymous) continuation to 1454, by the Marqués de la Fuensanta del Valle: Colécción de documentos inéditos para la historia de España (vols. 105, 509 p., and 106, p. 1–141, Madrid 1893), without notes and indexes. Don Gonzalo was born c. 1260, elected bishop of Burgos in 1313, and died in that city 1327 (Enciclopedia universal illustrada europeo-americana 27, 1657, 1925).

remarkable for their strong individuality, the one Castilian, the other Catalan. The first was a prince of royal blood, Don Juan Manuel, the outstanding Spanish author of his time. He continued the tradition of Alfonso el Sabio (XIII-2), was well acquainted with Moorish manners and letters, and was influenced by Ramon Lull (XIII-2) as well as by his Castilian predecessors. His main historical work is a Cronica abreviada. His Catalan contemporary, Ramón Muntaner, though less known as a writer, is far more important as a historian. His chronicle, which is to a large extent an autobiography, is one of the essential sources for the study of the almost incredible deeds of the Catalan Company in the Near East.[5] He himself took a large part in those achievements as a soldier, administrator, and diplomat, yet his account is not at all as biased as one might expect; it shows a good deal of moderation and humor and is beautifully written. In the magnificent series of Catalan chronicles written by James the Conqueror (XIII-2), Bernat Desclot (XIII-2), Muntaner, and Peter the Ceremonious (XIV-2), Muntaner's is perhaps the most admirable. It is one of the peaks of mediaeval Christian historiography.

A3. *France*

The chronicle of France compiled in Latin by Guillaume of Nangis (XIII-2) was continued by divers hands to 1303 and 1340[6] and translated into French under the name Les grandes chroniques de France (or Les chroniques de St. Denis, because Guillaume and other authors, possibly all, were monks in the abbey and royal basilica of St. Denis near Paris). The Grandes chroniques were continued in French for the period 1340–1461, but by laymen and in different style; further continuations carried them eventually to 1516.

The Chroniques de France were first printed in an Italian version, Croniche di Francia e Cronica di San Dionigio (3 vols., Paris 1475). The first French edition, that is, the real princeps, appeared in Paris 1477 (Jan. 16, 1476 = N.S. 1477), being one of the first French books printed in France.[7] Other editions, often with continuations bringing them up to date, Paris 1493, 1514, 1517–18, 1533. Critical edition by Paulin Paris (6 vols., Paris 1836–40).

These "great chronicles" represent the official views as censored by the historiographers of the royal abbey of St. Denis. Happily we are able to complete and correct them with other documents, such as the chronicles in French verse composed by Geoffroy of Paris and Guillaume Guiard.

All these men were professional chroniclers or "novelists," but the best historical works were written by other men whose primary mission was different, men who, like the Catalan Muntaner, were primarily doers, participants not spectators, makers not simply writers of history. I am now referring to two remarkable men,

[5] Gustave Schlumberger: Le sceau de la compagnie des routiers catalans à Gallipoli 1305 (Académie des inscriptions, Comptes rendus, 1925, p. 131–37). Antonio Rubio i Lluch: La poblacio de la Grecia catalana en el XIV° segle (60 p., Institut d'estudis catalans, Memories de la seccio historico 4, Barcelone 1933).

[6] The chronicle of Jean de Venette (XIV-2) is not a true continuation; its spirit is very different from that of St. Denis.

[7] Not the first as is often said (e.g., Potthast p. 316, 1895). The first book printed in France was the Epistolarum liber of Gasparino da Barzizza (Gasparinus Pergamensis, c. 1370–1431), printed in Paris (Sorbonne 1470). The first two French books printed in France were Les merveilles du monde (Lyon 1475?) and La légende dorée (Lyon 18 avril 1476). The princeps of Chroniques de France was the first French book printed in Paris, but the third printed in France. See Claudin (1, 173; also 1, 151; 3, 5, 33).

the sire de Joinville, who crusaded with St. Louis against the Muslims, and the Dominican Bernard Gui, who spent his life fighting the heretics. The history of St. Louis which Joinville completed in 1309 is one of the masterpieces of mediaeval historiography as well as one of the classics of early French literature. As Joinville wrote it when he was in his eighties, he must be added to the list of men who did some of their best work and conquered immortality in their old age.[8] Bernard Gui wrote various books dealing with the history of the popes, the counts of Toulouse, the dioceses of Limoges and Toulouse, but he is known chiefly because of his treatise on inquisitorial practice, which is one of the most valuable documents for the history of the Inquisition. It includes much first-hand information on many forms of heresy, with which he was as well acquainted as is possible for a prejudiced but intelligent judge. He was obliged to condemn almost a thousand people, most of whom were probably as well-meaning and innocent as himself, yet less fanatical. His candid revelations help us to understand the growth of the aberration which led in less than two centuries to such criminal deeds as the bull Summis desiderantes affectibus of Innocent VIII (1484) and the Malleus maleficarum (Isis 25, 147–52), and they help us also to appreciate the demoniacal atmosphere, the mass psychoses which those deeds consecrated. In that sense it is correct, terribly so, to say that Gui was not simply a writer of history, but a maker. It is tragic to realize that this man, honest and pious, convinced deep in his heart of his love for God and his fellow men, was one of the creators of the inquisitorial traditions which caused more evil and suffering than any other until our own days.

A historian of French historiography would be entitled to add to the men already quoted three others, whom I have classified otherwise yet who might be considered members of the French group because of their use of the French language, to wit, Peter of Langtoft, who wrote a chronicle of England in French verse; Nicholas Trevet, whose history of the world was first written in French; and Hayton the Monk, author of the Fleur des histoires de la terre d'Orient. We shall come back to them presently.

A4. *Germanic countries*

There are a number of chronicles dealing with Germany and Austria, but none comparable to the best ones written in French or Catalan. All these chronicles except one were written in Latin. The exception is the Reimchronik from 1250 to 1309, composed in German by Ottokar of Styria. This is an enormous compilation, extending to some 100,000 lines and including a large amount of information drawn rather promiscuously but honestly from many sources.

The annals of Bavaria, Austria, and Bohemia compiled by Hermann of Nieder-Altaich (XIII-2) were continued by others until 1303. Peter of Dusburg wrote a history of Prussia and of the Teutonic Order to 1326. The Austrian Benedictine Engelbert of Admont was more of a philosopher than a chronicler; among his abundant writings there is a history of Rome, but, what is far more remarkable, we owe to him one of the few mediaeval autobiographies and autobibliographies, the De studiis et scriptis suis, dated c. 1320. The history of Austria and Carinthia from 1217 to 1342 written by John of Victring shows that he was not a mere chronicler, but a humanist and critical historian. A chronicle of Germany from 1273 to

[8] Think of Cato the Censor (II-1 B.C.), Pietro dei Crescenzi, Luigi Cornaro (1475?–1566), Bernardino Ramazzini (1633–1714), Fontenelle (1657–1757), Manuel Garcia (1805–1906), Eugène Chevreul (1786–1889). For the first two see my Introduction; for Ramazzini see Isis (33, 260–61); for the others, Bull. history of medicine (8, 419–45, 1940).

1350 is now generally ascribed to Matthias of Neuenburg, and there are continuations of it down to 1378. Hugo Spechtshart, best known for his Flores musice, wrote a kind of cram book in Latin verse summarizing the story of the emperors from Augustus to Charles IV of Luxemburg. Various historical books bear the name of the great naturalist Conrad of Megenberg.[9] A chronicle of southern Germany from 1198 to 1348 was composed by John of Winterthur.

In addition to their local value, all these German chronicles contain information on the main ideological conflict of that age, the rivalry between popes and emperors. Some of them, especially the last named, are of interest to the historian of culture. The writers were seldom impartial, but as their prejudices were different, their chronicles correct one another. Ottokar was a layman; Matthias of Neuenburg, a master of canon law and advocate; Peter of Dusburg, Conrad of Megenberg, and Hugo Spechtshart, secular priests; Engelbert of Admont, a Benedictine; John of Victring, a Cistercian; John of Winterthur, a Franciscan. Moreover, they lived in different countries, Ottokar and Engelbert in Styria, John of Victring in Carinthia; Peter of Dusburg came from the duchy of Cleves, Hugo Spechtshart from Württemberg, Conrad of Megenberg was a Bavarian. Matthias of Neuenburg came from the neighborhood of Basel (but on the German side), and John of Winterthur was a real Swiss of the canton of Zürich.

A5. *Low Countries*

In spite of their relatively small size, the Low Countries have produced a number of historical works.

Considering first the Walloon districts, we may recall the treatise on chronology De concordia temporum, by Giles of Lessines (XIII-2), who lived at least until 1304. Giles' preoccupation, the determination of historical dates by means of eclipses and other scientific methods, was unique in his time, at least in Christendom. Canon Jean de Hocsem wrote in Latin a chronicle of the prince-bishops of Liége from 1247 to 1348.

The Dutch historians wrote in their own language, which had been raised to a very high level by the genius of Jacob van Maerlant (XIII-2). Only one of these historians, Stoke, was a Hollander, the three others were Flemings.

Melis Stoke wrote a chronicle of Holland and neighboring countries from 694 to 1305 in Dutch verse. The Spieghel historiael of Maerlant was completed by Lodewijk van Velthem and Philip Utenbroeke. A chronicle of Brabant to 1350 and other chronicles were written in Flemish verse by Jan van Boendale.

A6. *Bohemia*

The chronicle of Dalimil is a rhymed chronicle of Bohemia from Adam to 1310, which is not only an indispensable document for the correction of the German chronicles, but also one of the earliest monuments of Czech literature. It was twice translated into German before the middle of the century.

A7. *England*

It is convenient to divide the English historiographers into two groups.

We place in the first group the scholars who wrote chronicles of England. One of these was composed in French verse by Peter of Langtoft, but was translated into English verse by Robert Mannyng before the middle of the century. Two

[9] Potthast (p. 343, 1896).

other chronicles of England were written in Latin by Nicholas Trevet and Walter de Hemingburgh. A third Latin chronicle, the Flores historiarum, is a mixed composition the first part of which, to 1259, is derived from Matthew Paris (XIII-2), the rest being added by various chroniclers, chiefly Robert de Reading, whose name is given somewhat arbitrarily to the whole.

The other group gathers three or four men whose interests were a little broader. Walter Burley, who was primarily a philosopher, compiled a collection of biographies of ancient philosophers and scholars down to the sixth century. Adam Murimuth wrote a chronicle of England from 1303 to 1347 which is different from the other chronicles in that the author, canon of Hereford, paid special attention to ecclesiastical affairs. The most ambitious as well as the most popular of all these men was the Benedictine Ranulf Higden, whose Polychronicon was a universal chronicle from Adam to 1327, later continued by himself and by others. The first book of that "polychronicle," called Mappa mundi, was a geographical introduction, illustrating the encyclopaedic scope of the undertaking which Ranulf was able to conceive if not to realize. Nicholas Trevet, quoted in the first group, had also conceived a history of the world, which he first wrote in French but translated himself into English.

A8. *Ireland*

John Clyn, Franciscan of Kilkenny, wrote annals of Ireland from Adam to 1349.

A9. *Scandinavia*

By this time the golden age of Icelandic literature was passed, and there was nobody to emulate Sturla Thórdarson (XIII-2), thanks to whose genius Icelandic historiography had been raised to as high a level as was reached anywhere else in the Christian West during mediaeval times. Judge Haukr Erlendsson was a distinguished epigonus, who prepared a new edition of the Landnámabók of Ari Fróthi Thorgilsson (XII-1) and gathered historical facts together with other kinds of knowledge in his Hauksbók.

B. *Eastern Christendom*

B1. *Byzantine historiography*

Two historians of the previous period, Georgios Pachymeres (XIII-2, Introd. 2, 972) and Maximos Planudes (XIII-2), lived until 1310 and hence belong to this period also. Pachymeres continued the chronicle of Nicetas Acominatos (XIII-1) and Georgios Acropolites (XIII-2), down to 1308. Planudes wrote a biography of Ptolemy, compiled a historical anthology, and translated into Greek the De bello Gallico of Julius Caesar.

Xanthopulos continued the ancient Byzantine tradition of ecclesiastical history, but his work, extending only to 610, is nothing but a rehash of earlier ones.

We have spoken above of the Catalan chronicle of Ramón Muntaner. Other accounts of the same events are to be found in the Latin work of Marino Sanudo il Vecchio, in the Greek writings of Thomas Magister, and in the so-called Chronicle of Morea. The latter was astonishingly popular, being published in Greek, Italian, French, and Catalan versions. The multiplicity of these versions is characteristic of the international chaos which then obtained in Greece. Note that the original text was anterior to 1326, that three versions were available before the middle of the century, and that the last one (in Catalan) was made in 1393. Thus by the end of the century the events of Morea could be read in four languages as explained by spokesmen of many factions; this, however, was not as helpful as it may seem, for most people could read only one version, and then as now they would not have chosen to read another one encountering their prejudices, or at any rate if they had read it they would have refused to believe in it.

The greatest Byzantine historian of the age was Nicephoros Gregoras, to whom we owe a very elaborate chronicle from 1204 to 1359, the greater part of which deals with his own times.

The school of Trebizond is represented by the "periegetic" history of Andreas Libadenos, which contains interesting historical facts completing or correcting those given in other sources.

B2. *Armenian historiography*

The Armenian chronicles of this time do not compare favorably with those of the thirteenth century, but one of the historians of that century, Stephen Orbelian (XIII-2), lived until 1304. In spite of increasing Catholic pressure he remained loyal to the faith of his fathers.

The two other Armenian historians succumbed to the Catholic propaganda which had received the official sanction of the kings of New Armenia (Cilicia). Nerses Balì flourished in Avignon under Clement VI (pope 1342–52) and translated the chronicle of Martin of Troppau (XIII-2) from Latin into Armenian. Martin's chronicle was the most mediocre and the most popular, and Nerses' choice of it was as natural as it was unfortunate. On the other hand, the other Catholic Armenian, Hayton the Monk, was one of the greatest mediaeval chroniclers. He belonged to the royal Armenian family, but assumed the Praemonstratensian habit in Cyprus, which under the Lusignan dynasty was even more completely under French tutelage than Armenia itself. His Fleur des histoires de la terre d'Orient was dictated in French in 1307, but translated into Latin within the same year. The great success of that chronicle was well deserved, for it included considerable first-hand information hitherto unavailable in the West.

Note that both Nerses and Hayton did their work in France, the former in Avignon, the latter in Poitiers; but whereas Nerses transmitted a third-rate Latin chronicle to the Armenian Catholics, Hayton brought to the West new and valuable knowledge concerning the Near East. Nerses jeopardized Armenian historiography as well as Armenian traditions, but Hayton increased the prestige of his people and materially improved Western knowledge and understanding of the Near East.

B3. *Georgian (or Iberian) historiography*

References to Georgian literature have been thus far very rare, partly because most of it, being ecclesiastical and hagiographic, is irrelevant to our purpose, partly because of chronological uncertainties. In the note on St. Mesrop (V-1) the invention of the "older" Georgian alphabet was ascribed to him.[10] The Georgian

[10] That was misleading. There were two Georgian alphabets, the mkhedruli (civil) and the khutzuri (ecclesiastical). The first of these has so many analogies with the Zend alphabet that it may have been derived from it; that would put it back at least to the fourth century B.C.; the second is in all probability Christian. Mesrop may have introduced it, but it is very different from the Armenian alphabet. In any case, the khutzuri, whether it was Mesrop who introduced it or not, was not the older script, but rather a new, Christian one. According to tradition, the Iberians were evangelized in the fourth century by a woman, St. Nino, the "Illuminator of Georgia," but the first great teacher was St. Mesrop (V-1).

language was spoken in western and central Transcaucasia, in the country called by the Greeks 'Ἰβηρία; by the Persians, Arabs, and Turks, Gurjistān; by the Russians, Gruziya; by the natives, Sakharthvelo; by Europeans, Georgia. Its main cultural center was and is Tiflis, and to this day the richest collection of MSS is in Tiflis. A translation of the Bible into Georgian was (wrongly) ascribed to St. Mesrop; it is largely derived from the Septuagint, but also from Hebrew traditions (Introd. 1, 381). The early literature was largely if not exclusively Christian.[11] It was developed in monasteries established in Georgia, but also abroad, e.g., the laura of Mār Sābā near Jerusalem, and the Iviron on Mount Athos, dating back to the end of the tenth century. One of the earliest Georgian texts is the translation of Epiphanios (IV-2), De gemmis, the Greek original of which, written in 394, is lost.[12] The chronicle of Georgios Monachos (IX-1) was translated into Georgian, and Georgian chronicles began to be written. The golden age of Georgian secular literature, much influenced by Greek and Persian models, extends from the middle of the eleventh to the middle of the thirteenth century. Not only were chronicles written under Byzantine influence, but also romances derived from the Alexander cycle, Lailā wa Majnūn (EI 3, 96), Kalīla wa Dimna (Introd. 1, 540), Firdawsī (XI-1), etc.

One of the earliest chroniclers included in the Georgian annals (Kartlis tzkhovreba) is Leonti Mroveli, who flourished about the end of the eleventh century. More chronicles were written during the twelfth century, for example under the prosperous rule of queen Tamara (1184–1212), but soon afterward (1220) the Mongol invasions put an end to such activities for a full century. The Dzegli Eristavta (Monument of the eristavni),[13] a sort of family history of the eristavni of the Ksani district including an account of the Ossetians, was probably written in the fourteenth century. The mediaeval chronicle included in the Kartlis tzkhovreba[14] ends with the death of king Giorgi V Brtsqinwalé (= the brilliant) in 1346. Thus this period (XIV-1) may be said to have witnessed the end of mediaeval Georgian historiography.

Criticism. Franz Carl Alter: Über georgianische Litteratur (286 p., Wien 1798). This is, I believe, the earliest Western account. Marie Félicité Brosset (1802–80): Histoire de la Géorgie (2 vols., St. Pétersbourg 1849–57). A. Dirr: Georgia (EI 2, 131, 1914). Kornéli S. Kekelídze: History of Georgian literature (2 vols., Tiflis 1923–24), in Georgian. First history based on the MSS, though restricted to the Tiflis ones. Robert Pierpont Blake: Georgian theological literature (Journal of theological studies 26, 50–64, Oxford 1925); Georgian secular literature (Harvard studies and notes in philology 15, 25–48, 1933). Though largely derived from Kekelídze, it refers to other Georgian and Russian sources. W. E. D. Allen: History of the Georgian people (p. 314, London 1932). Josef Karst: Littérature géorgienne chrétienne (p. 104–8, Paris 1934).

Thanks to Professor Blake's interest, there is a good collection of Georgian texts in the Harvard library. A letter of his (Cambridge, Mass., Feb. 3, 1942) enables

[11] The Georgian church obtained its independence from the Byzantine at the sixth council, Constantinople, 680–81.

[12] Robert Pierpont Blake and Henri De Vis: Epiphanius de Gemmis. The old Georgian version, the fragments of the Armenian version, and the Coptic-Sahidic fragments (509 p., London 1934; Isis 24, 127–29).

[13] The word eristavi is the Georgian equivalent of στρατηγός, but the office became hereditary, and the eristavi himself, a kind of feudal lord. Full discussion by Allen (p. 237–49, 1932).

[14] That is, the collection of chronicles, entitled Life of Georgia, edited at the beginning of the eighteenth century by king Wakhtang VI (Ḥusain Qulī Khān).

me to add the following facts. The Oxford collection of Georgian texts is richer than the Harvard one. Most of the MSS are in Tiflis; some or all of the Leningrad MSS were moved to Tiflis. There are smaller collections of Georgian MSS in St. Catherine's monastery, Sinai (c. 100), the Iviron, Mount Athos (84), the Greek Patriarchate, Jerusalem (161), Vatican (c. 40), Paris (20), England (3 or 4). There are four Gospels in the United States, in Andover Newton Theological School; Walters collection, Baltimore; Public Library, Utica, N. Y.; Blake's own library.

B4. *Monophysite and Nestorian historiography*

The Majmū' mubārak of Jirjīs al-Makīn (XIII-2) was continued for the period 1260–1348 by another Egyptian Christian, Mufaḍḍal ibn abī-l-Faḍā'il (XIV-2). That continuation is valuable for the history of the Coptic church.

The chronicle of the Nestorian patriarchs down to 1147, written in Arabic by Mārī ibn Sulaimān, was completed to c. 1317 by two other Nestorians, 'Amr ibn Mattā and Ṣalībā ibn Yūḥanna. 'Amr came from Ṭīrhān and Ṣalībā from Mūṣul, both towns on the Tigris River.

All the chronicles mentioned in this section were in Arabic; the section might have been entitled Arabic Christian historiography.

B5. *Abyssinian historiography*

The rule of 'Amda Ṣion (1314–44) is important from the cultural point of view, for that king encouraged the writing in the Ge'ez language of chronicles covering the years 1270 to 1344. It was probably at this time too that the Sefer Yosippon was translated from Arabic into Ge'ez.

C. *Western Islām*

It is remarkable that we have no Jewish chronicles of this time, but Jewish doctors would naturally discuss chronological questions. This was done best by Isaac Israeli the Younger in the fourth part of his Yesod 'olam.

As compared with that poverty, or rather with the complete absence of Jewish chronicles, the abundance of Muslim ones is startling. Before recapitulating the main historiographical achievements of Western Islām dealt with in this volume, it is proper to say something of a chronicle which is not so well known, yet is important because it was used repeatedly by later historians such as al-Qalqashandī (XIV-2) in his Subḥ al-a'shā, al-Maqrīzī (d. 1442), and al-Maqqarī (d. 1632). I am referring to the Kitāb al-rawḍ al-mi'ṭār fī khabar al-aqṭār (The perfumed garden concerning the stories of the countries), written by Abū 'Abdallāh Muḥammad ibn 'Abd al-Mun'im al-Ṣinhājī al-Ḥimyarī, generally called Ibn 'Abd al-Mun'im, who flourished probably at the end of the thirteenth or the beginning of the fourteenth century. His Rawḍ mi'ṭār was rewritten by a descendant who died in 1494. The MSS confirm that late date, yet the original Rawḍ must be much earlier, for otherwise Qalqashandī and Maqrīzī would not have been able to use it. In the form in which it has come to us, the Rawḍ mi'ṭār is a dictionary of geography and history in alphabetical order of place names. In addition to geographical, archaeological, and historical data (the latter extending for Spain from 708 to 1287), it includes information concerning mines and minerals, thermal springs, trees, culture of cereals, fruit trees, sugar cane, vines, olive trees, cotton, flax, mulberry trees (and sericulture), safflower (Carthamus tinctorius), woad (Isatis tinctoria), saffron, irrigation, stock farming, apiculture, fisheries, all kinds of industries, taxes, etc. The notes cover not only the Western countries, but also the Eastern ones (e.g., for the letter alif 95 articles deal with the East, 79 with the West).[15]

Ibn al-Khaṭīb tells us in his Iḥāṭa fī ta'rīkh Gharnāṭa that Ibn 'Abd al-Mun'im lived in Ceuta. His Moroccan origin or residence is somewhat confirmed by the fact that out of four MSS of Al-rawḍ al-mi'ṭār, three are in Moroccan libraries, and the fourth (the only complete one) came from Timbuktu.

Other works of historical interest were composed by Moroccans; for example, Ibn abī Zar' wrote a chronicle of North Africa from 788 to 1325; Muḥammad ibn Rushaid (XIII-2), who was born in Ceuta and died in Fez 1321, compiled collections of Western and Eastern biographies. The Riḥla of the Tunisian al-Tijānī contains valuable historical information on the Ḥafṣī kingdom. Al-Balawī and Abū Ḥaiyān came from Granada but spent a good part of their life in the East. Al-Balawī wrote an account of his travels and especially of the men whom he came across. To Abū Ḥaiyān is ascribed a history of Spain, which is lost, but he established himself in Cairo, where he died.

Out of the six Moors mentioned in this section, four lived part of the time in the East or devoted as much attention to Eastern as to Western matters. This shows the futility of trying to separate the Maghrib from the Mashriq, except in the way I am doing it, the two groups being kept so close together that the reader has no trouble in passing from the one to the other and back again.

D. *Eastern Islām*

The Eastern Muslim historians are so numerous that for the sake of clearness it is well to divide them into four groups: (1) Arabia, (2) Mamlūk, (3) 'Irāq, (4) Persia. The historians of the first three groups wrote in Arabic, those of the fourth in Persian.

D1. *Arabia*

A political and literary history of Yaman to 1323 was written by al-Janadī. It was continued to 1335 by another hand.

D2. *Mamlūk*

As usual, the Mamlūk group is the most important; it includes more men than the three other Eastern groups put together. That is natural enough, for many of the cultural centers of Islām, Cairo, Alexandria, Jerusalem, Damascus, Aleppo, were under Mamlūk control.

Local histories were compiled by the famous lexicographer Ibn Manẓūr (XIII-2) and by al-Birzālī. The former wrote chronicles of Damascus and Baghdād; the Damascus one was an abridgment of that composed by Ibn 'Asākir (XII-2); al-Birzālī continued the chronicle of Damascus of Abū Shāma (XIII-2). These chronicles were largely collections of biographies of the learned men, thanks to whose devotion Damascus and Baghdād had become the civilized cities which they were, magnets and maḥārīb to other learned men, theologians, poets, artists, and scholars.

Al-Adfuwī gathered biographies of the men of Upper Egypt and also biographies

[15] Ḥājjī Khalīfa (3, 490, 1842). Evariste Lévi-Provençal: La péninsule ibérique au Moyen-âge (quarto, 344 p., 1 map, Leiden 1938; 236 p. in Arabic, Cairo 1937), elaborate edition of the Rawḍ mi'ṭār with French translations and elaborate notes, indexes, glossary, but unfortunately restricted to Spain, Portugal, and southwestern France. Brockelmann (2, 41, 1902; suppt. 2, 38, 1938).

of men of the seventh century (i.e., the thirteenth century). The great collection, Wafayāt al-a'yān, completed by Ibn Khallikān (XIII-2) in 1274 was twice continued, by al-Muwaffaq Faḍlallāh ibn abī Muḥammad, writing biographies of Mamlūk subjects who died between 1261 and 1325, and by Muḥammad ibn Shākir al-Kutubī, who added a series of omitted biographies (Fawāt al-wafayāt) and died in 1363. All these efforts were dwarfed by al-Ṣafadī, whose Wāfī bi-l-wafayāt put together the biographies of some fourteen thousand men of all kinds and classes.[16] It might be called a "national biography of Islām." The undertaking was so ambitious that it jeopardized its own existence. Indeed, there is no complete MS of it anywhere, and it is not yet certain that it will ever be possible to reconstruct the whole collection. Al-Ṣafadī was not simply a compiler, but a methodical historian who took considerable pains to insure the accuracy of his notices. The introduction to the Kitāb al-wāfī is devoted to the explanation of a number of historical difficulties.

After the chroniclers and the biographers, going a step higher still, we should consider the historians. There is Baibars al-Manṣūrī, who wrote a general history of Islām to 1324 and a history of the Baḥrī Mamlūk rulers from 1250 to 1321. For the first work, which was of considerable size, he was assisted by his Coptic secretary Abū-l-Barakāt. Then Abū-l-Fidā', perhaps, all considered, the greatest historiogeographer of the period irrespective of nationality or religion, composed the Mukhtaṣar ta'rīkh al-bashar, a universal history from pre-Islamic times down to 1329. Abū-l-Fidā's work was soon appreciated, witness a number of summaries, abstracts, continuations. The first continuation, to 1348, was prepared by Ibn al-Wardī, not long after Abū-l-Fidā's death. The encyclopaedist al-Dhahabī compiled an enormous history of Islām down to 1340; it was so large that it discouraged the copyists and baffled the librarians; out of an abundance of MSS there is not a single complete one, nor is it possible to reconstruct the complete text. This compilation includes many biographies but much else; though it is not exclusively a collection of biographies, modern editors have extracted such collections from it. Al-Dhahabī's work was continued, extracted, summarized by other writers, and there are Persian and Turkish translations of the text itself or of these various adaptations of it. The encyclopaedias of al-Nuwairī and Ibn Faḍlallāh al-'Umarī are also rich treasures of historical data. Both works give us a very high idea of the Mamlūk government, for they were expressly composed for the education of administrators and chancellors. The Mamlūk rulers, or at any rate their chief advisers, had realized that good government and efficient government required first of all sound knowledge of all the elements involved, the countries, the peoples, their physical and spiritual needs; it required just as imperiously good manners, humanities. The Nihāyat al-arab fī funūn al-adab was compiled by al-Nuwairī to collect all the knowledge and the humanities which a civil servant must have in order to serve the king and the people well. The Masālik al-abṣār fi mamālik al-amṣār was produced by Ibn Faḍlallāh al-'Umarī for the same purpose. These two works being of enormous size, it is almost impossible to compare them, except with regard to this or that item. We have not yet a complete edition of either, though complete photographic MSS of both have been assembled in Cairo thanks to the zeal and devotion of the late Aḥmad Zakī pāshā (1867–1934).[17] When both works are properly edited and indexed it will become possible to compare them with regard

[16] The DNB to 1900 contains 30,378 biographies.

[17] Biography with portraits by Bichr Farès (Revue des études islamiques p. 382–92, Paris 1934).

to particulars and, gradually, to compare them in toto. Assuming that the two compilers worked independently, they could not help using to a large extent the same sources, and their points of view were somewhat identified by their having received the same kind of training,[18] followed the same professions, and been exposed throughout to similar influences. The main difference between them was that of age. Al-Nuwairī died in 1332, Ibn Faḍlallāh died seventeen years later; on the other hand, Ibn Faḍlallāh's life was five years shorter, being abruptly terminated in its maturity by the plague.

It is clear that the first half of the fourteenth century was a golden age of historiography in the Mamlūk empire. Where else could one have found such a galaxy of historians as al-Ṣafadī, Abū-l-Fidā', al-Dhahabī, al-Nuwairī, and Ibn Faḍlallāh al-'Umarī? It was a period not only of great activity, but of distinguished and thoughtful activity. Let me recall once more that the muqaddama to al-Ṣafadī's immense collection of biographies was already a kind of manual of historical method, the first of its kind produced anywhere in the world.

D3. *'Irāq*

Two distinguished historians can be definitely associated with 'Irāq, though it is well to bear in mind that there were always close relations between Baghdād and her sister cities of the Mamlūk empire, Damascus and Cairo. It is possible that men already named not only visited Baghdād, but spent a few years in that city. Baghdād, called even on coins Dār al-salām (the abode of peace, Εἰρηνόπολις), always exerted a very strong attraction on every Muslim, especially on the men of letters.

Ibn al-Ṭiqṭaqā wrote a very distinguished book, the Fakhrī, the second half of which is a history of the Muslim dynasties from 656 to 1258. It is remarkable because of its moderation and its relative impartiality, unequaled, I believe, in the works of contemporary Latin or Greek authors. 'Abd al-Razzāq al-Shaibānī, librarian of the observatory of Marāgha, wrote a chronicle of the last 'Abbāsī caliphs and of the Mongol rulers to 1300; he compiled a large biographical dictionary (almost completely lost) and a collection of historical anecdotes.

One of the characteristics of 'Irāq is illustrated by the fact that one at least of these two men, Ibn al-Ṭiqṭaqā, was a Shī'a. Though Shiites were always a small minority in the Near East except during the Fāṭimī interlude (909–1171), in 'Irāq they were far more numerous. In 'Irāq and only there could the two great divisions of Islām meet on anything like equal terms; the Shī'a group, in spite of its numbers,[19] never obtained an overwhelming importance nor seceded too completely, because it continued to speak and write Arabic instead of Persian. Ibn al-Ṭiqṭaqā was a Shī'a but also an Arabic author, able to commune with the Arabic-speaking Sunnites.

D4. *Persians (writing in Persian)*

The Persian group is small but extremely distinguished.

Two of the Persians, Rashīd al-dīn and al-Banākatī, wrote universal histories which are unparalleled in scope, for they were derived not only from Arabic and Persian documents, but also from Uighūr, Mongol, and Chinese ones! These men

[18] From childhood on and even from before, for both belonged to prominent and well educated families.

[19] In 1935, the proportion of the Sunnī to the Shī'a population of 'Irāq was 5 to 8 (Whitaker's Almanack 1941).

were thus able to build up a synthesis of Asiatic history never attempted before and hardly since. Rashīd al-dīn was the older man, and it is probable that al-Banākatī's work was largely derived from his. It is impossible to settle that question until we have a joint critical edition of both histories. In the meanwhile, we should speak of both men together ex aequo.

Al-Waṣṣāf of Shīrāz wrote a continuation of al-Juwainī's (XIII-2) history of the Mongols from 1257 to 1328. Unfortunately, he wrote it in an extremely rhetorical style, overloaded with metaphors and hyperboles, a kind of euphuism which exerted a most pernicious influence on Persian literature.

The fourth and last member of the group is Ḥamdallāh Mustawfī, better known as the author of the encyclopaedia Nuzhat al-qulūb. He wrote a short history of Persia ending with a special account of his home town Qazwīn, and a continuation of the Shāh-nāma of Firdawsī (XI-1). That continuation, entitled Ẓafar-nāma (Book of victory), is an enormous poem, one-quarter longer than Firdawsī's. It tells the history of Persia under Arabic, Persian, and Mongol rulers until Ḥamdallāh's own days (c. 1331).

E. *Ceylon*

It is debatable whether the Buddhist stories written in Pāli by the monk Vedeha may be counted as "history," though they were history to him and his brethren.

True chronicles, however, were produced in Ceylon (although we have practically none in India proper). An important section of the great chronicle Mahāvaṃsa was completed in or soon after 1333 by Dhammakitti. It is written in Pāli verse.

F. *China and Korea*

The Chinese have always been the most historically minded people of Asia, and they were certainly the most historically minded people of the Middle Ages. Hence we should not be surprised to find among them a number of scholars engaged in historical work of one kind or another.

Let us begin with the official historiographers, who continued imperturbably the task begun by their predecessors in office more than fourteen hundred years before, irrespective of dynastic changes and other vicissitudes. The first of the "dynastic histories" (chêng shih) is the Shih chi of Ssŭ-ma Ch'ien (II-2 B.C.). For a list of them, see Introd. 1, 797, to which add: 20, Sung shih; 21, Liao shih; 22, Chin shih; 23, Yüan shih; 24, Ming shih; 25, Hsin Yüan shih (see my note on Sung Lien, XIV-2); 26, Ch'ing shih kao (Isis 33, 389). During the first half of the fourteenth century no new dynastic history was completed, but Chang Chu contributed to the Sung, Liao, and Chin histories (nos. 20 to 22).

For additional information on Chinese historiography and especially on the chêng shih see Wylie (p. 15 f., 1867, ed. of 1922), Couling (p. 232-33, 1917). Arthur William Hummel: The autobiography of a Chinese historian, being the preface to a symposium on ancient Chinese history (242 p., Leyden 1931; Isis 33, 132). Mlle Lo Tchen-ying [= Lo Chên-ying]: Les formes et les méthodes historiques en Chine. Une famille d'historiens et son oeuvre (Lyon thesis, 117 p., Paris 1931), chiefly apropos of Pan Ku (I-2) and the Han shu. Gardner (1938).

Korean ideas on historiography were the same as the Chinese. No new Korean dynastic history was produced in the first half of the fourteenth century, because for the Koreans as well as the Chinese it was tabu to write the history of a dynasty while it was in power. (The Koryo dynasty was not replaced by the Yi until 1392.) That attitude is highly typical of the Chinese spirit. The active rulers not only foresaw the eventuality of their dynasty's downfall, but appointed historiographers charged to put together and keep safe all necessary documents for the writing of its history when a new dynasty should be in power.[20] These documents were not available to the ruling kings (Trollope p. 23 f., 1932).

To return to China, much historical work was done in addition to the preparation of correct and reliable archives for the future historian of the Yüan dynasty. The work was not only abundant but very diversified. Thus, Li Tsê wrote a history of Annam, modeled upon the chêng shih. Li Tsê was an Annamite, but thoroughly familiar with Chinese culture. His history of Annam, composed in Chinese in the same way as the Chinese annals and in the same spirit, was the main contribution of that Oriental quisling to the Sinification of his native country. Ch'ên Li wrote a short history of China to 1279 and a commentary on the Shu ching of Confucius. The censor Su T'ien-chio compiled biographies of civil servants of the Yüan dynasty. Such collections were not as usual in China, except among Buddhists, as they were in the Dār al-Islām; that is, they were not as frequently published in separate form, but we must not forget that biographies were an essential feature of every chêng shih. The same Su T'ien-chio gathered materials for histories of the Liao and Chin dynasties and of the Yellow River.

The historical spirit of Chinese scholars is revealed also in investigations of a more special nature. Wu-ch'iu Yen was a student of epigraphy and sphragistics. T'ang Hou composed a history of painting, discussing the characteristics of various schools from the third century down to the Yüan artists. Lu Yu wrote the history of ink manufacturers, which, as has been explained above, was a contribution to the study of Chinese letters (even as a study of English publishers might be a contribution to the history of English literature). Finally, we owe to Nien ch'ang a history of Buddhism to 1344, largely focused on the development of the Ch'an-tsung (Zen-shū).

Please note that these historians did not come from a single province, but, as far as can be ascertained, from many, as distant and different from one another as can be. Traveling from north to south, Su T'ien-chio was a son of Chihli; Ch'ên Li, of Anhui; Wu-ch'iu Yen, of Chehkiang; Chang Chu, of Yünnan; Li Tsê, of Annam.

G. *Japan*

Though Japanese culture was almost entirely derivative from Chinese culture, the Japanese chronicles have a flavor of their own distinguishing them from the Chinese ones or any others. Two celebrated chronicles or "mirrors"[21] cover this period (XIV-1), the Masu-kagami, extending from 1184 to 1333, and the Taihei-ki, from 1318 to 1368 and 1382.

Like their brethren in China, the Japanese Buddhists were anxious to preserve from oblivion the deeds of their saints. One of the most elaborate and best Buddhist biographies, that of Hōnen-Shōnin (1133–1212) or Genkū, founder of the Jōdo-

[20] Compare with our own archivists, whose duty and pride is to preserve every document entrusted to them, even those which will eventually incriminate their employers. That, however, is rather a novelty with us, whereas it is a millennial tradition in China.

[21] This metaphor for historical works is universal, cf. kagami, speculum, Spiegel, miroir du monde (myrrour of the worlde), etc.

shū, or Pure Land sect,[22] which introduced Amidaism to the Japanese people (Introd. 2, 282, 336), was written at the beginning of the fourteenth century by Shunjō Hōin.

The "Correct genealogy of the divine emperor" of Kitabatake Chikafusa includes a history of Japan from the beginning to 1335. We remarked at the beginning of this section that every nation tends to mythologize its beginnings. None did that more thoroughly than the Japanese, nor did any succeed as completely in hypnotizing itself with its own fantasies. Kitabatake's book was largely responsible for this, though the evil was already ancient in his own days; he did not invent it, but crystallized it.[23]

XIII. LAW AND SOCIOLOGY

It should be clearly understood at the threshold of the two remaining sections of this chapter that the author is not a jurist, nor a sociologist, nor even a philologist in the technical sense. He did not try to write a complete survey of legal and social views, nor of grammatical efforts, but in the course of his inquiries he could not help coming across repeatedly the mention of writings and achievements in those fields. Thus he accumulated nolens volens a fair amount of materials which he is now classifying according to his usual method. The reader will thus be given unusual cross sections of those fields which may facilitate deeper explorations of them.

The notes on legal writings would have been much richer if those writings had been more fully exploited by historians of science, but thus far relatively few (e.g., Thorndike) have done so. Such exploitation could be best done by a scholar as familiar with the legal collections and the legal forms of thought as with mediaeval science.

[22] As I have spoken repeatedly in volume 2 of the "originality" of the Jōdo-shū and other twelfth-century sects, I am glad to be able to introduce the following correction. These sects were original Japanese sects, as contrasted with the eight preceding ones, but only in a superficial way. Their founders were Japanese and they had naturally many characteristic Japanese features, but the doctrines were Chinese or rather Hindu. The Chinese founder of the Amidaist school, Ching-t'u tsung, was Hui Yüan (IV-2). The favorite scriptures of the Japanese Amidaist sects are (1) Daimuryōjukyō, (2) Amidakyō, (3) Kwammuryōjukyō, (4) Myōhō-renge-kyō or Hokkekyō, to which might be added (5) Kishinron. Now the first two are the large and small Sukhāvatīviyūhasūtra (in Chinese Wu-liang shou ching and O-mi-t'o ching, the Book of the eternal life and the Book of Amida); (3) is the Amitāyurdhyānasūtra (Kuan-wu-liang shou ching, the Great book of eternal life); (4) is the Saddharmapuṇḍarīka (Fa hua ching, Lotus sūtra); (5) is the Mahāyānaśraddhotpāda (Ch'i hsin lun), the Awakening of the faith ascribed to Aśvaghosha (II-1). In short, the fundamental Amidaist texts were Sanskrit and Chinese before being adopted by Japanese Buddhists. Of course, I realize that there are many variants in the Chinese translations (each text having been translated more than once), and there may be additional ones in the Japanese versions, each sectarian introducing his own bias (cf. Catholic vs. Protestant versions of the Bible). Amidaism was as successful in China as in Japan; the most popular sects in both countries are Amidaist. The popular success of Amidaism is due to the same psychological reasons as the popularity of the Roman Catholic and the Orthodox churches. Nanjio (1883). August Karl Reischauer: Studies in Japanese Buddhism (New York 1917). Winternitz (vol. 2, 1920). Tokiwa and Ogiwara (1930), for Japanese transcriptions. Karl Ludvig Reichelt: Truth and tradition in Chinese Buddhism (Shanghai 1934). Nanjio, Tokiwa, and Reichelt include Chinese characters.

[23] For a summary of Japanese mythology and of the so-called "age of the gods," kami-yo, see Brinkley and Kikuchi (p. 8–27, 1914).

The notes on law and sociology are divided into seven sections: (A) Christian West, (B) Christian East, (C) Jewish West, (D) Muslim East (note the absence of sections on Jewish East and Muslim West), (E) India and Burma, (F) China, (G) Japan.

A. *Christian West*

This is by far the largest of the seven sections, as large, if not as important, as the other six together. It is well to divide it into six subsections dealing respectively with (1) Italy, (2) Spain and Catalonia, (3) France, (4) Germanic countries, (5) England, (6) Pays de Liége. The first of these subsections is again almost as large as all the rest, and may serve to exemplify almost every tendency.

A1. *Italy*

Let us first consider the authors of outstanding legal books. Oldrado da Ponte, who taught law in various Italian schools and in Montpellier and was finally attached to the curia in Avignon, wrote commentaries on the Pandects and issued a large number of consilia. Cino da Pistcia, who was Oldrado's almost exact contemporary (they died within a year of each other, 1335/6), obtained greater fame as a jurist and remained a pure civilian unwilling to compromise with the canonists or to subordinate his law to theirs. He was one of the first "commentatores" of the civil law (as contrasted with "glossatores," who were more literal), and his humanity is sufficiently illustrated by the fact that he was not only a lawyer but a distinguished poet; he earned the friendship of Dante and Petrarca, and is immortalized by the gracious tomb built in the cathedral of Pistoia, soon after his death, by Cellino di Nese, or under Cellino's direction. It is a good thing to be remembered by lawyers and litigants; it is a better one to be remembered by poets and lovers.

In the meanwhile, Giovanni d'Andrea was teaching canon law in Bologna and leading the canonists of his time. Alberico da Rosciate did not restrict himself to civil law like his master Oldrado, nor to canon law like Giovanni, but wrote dictionaries for each field. His double dictionary enjoyed some popularity and is still useful today to orient oneself with regard to moot questions; for example, if one wants to find out what was the contemporary legal attitude, whether civilian or canonic, with regard to alchemy or the practice of dissections. Alberico was not a professor of law like Oldrado and Giovanni, but spent his life in the legal and diplomatic service of Bergamo.

Materials of very different kinds are scattered in the writings of the two Venetian statesmen Marino Sanudo il Vecchio and Andrea Dandolo. Sanudo's writings are very valuable for the student of economic history; they contain crude statistical data. Dandolo edited collections of diplomatic agreements in two volumes, the Liber blancus and the Liber albus,[1] dealing respectively with the Western and the Eastern powers. His chronicle is full of information on Venetian trade. Similar remarks would apply to the contemporary Florentine chronicles of Dino Compagni and of Giovanni Villani. These Venetian and Florentine chroniclers were business-minded; they were too keenly aware of the importance of economic factors ever to overlook them.

We have already drawn the reader's attention to a class of books which ob-

[1] Are these the earliest examples of the use of colors, "white book," "blue book," etc., to designate collections of diplomatic documents?

tained a place of honor in the manorial libraries, the Regimina principum.[1a] The three outstanding books of the kind at the beginning of the fourteenth century were the De eruditione filiorum nobilium[2] written by Vincent of Beauvais (XIII-2) about the middle of the thirteenth century for Marguerite of Provence, wife of St. Louis; the De regimine principum begun by St. Thomas Aquinas for Hugh II of Lusignan, king of Cyprus, and completed c. 1274–82 by his pupil Bartolommeo da Lucca; and the treatise bearing the same title written by Giles of Rome (XIII-2) for his pupil Philippe IV le Bel, not long before the latter's accession to the throne of France in 1285. Vincent and Thomas were Dominicans, Giles an Augustinian, but in such matters as these they were very much in agreement. The three treatises were informed with the Thomist spirit of moderation and sweet reasonableness. St. Thomas' idea of sovereignty was very similar to that of the limited or constitutional monarchy of our own times (Hyma p. 36–41, 1938). Another type of Regimen principum was written for the same king of France in 1295 by Galvano de Levanto, the advice being cleverly camouflaged in the form of discussion of chess games.

The Summa of the Dominican Giovanni da San Gimignano contains "exempla" of legal or social interest.

So much for legal and political education. The main political issue of the day in Europe was the conflict between pope and emperor, a conflict which had been protracted for centuries and had not become sweeter in the meanwhile. Peaceful people, of whom there were many, claimed that the pope and emperor were the two pillars of the world—equal pillars, of course, or else the world would slide off to its destruction. That metaphor was enticing but all wrong, for the pope and emperor were as unlike static pillars as could be; they could not help making decisions at every moment, changing things, appointing some people and disappointing others, making friends and enemies. When their decisions conflicted, which was to be the ruling one?

Some publicists claimed that the pope was the supreme lord from whom the emperor derived his own authority. The pope crowned the emperor and claimed the right to uncrown him as well—could he not anathematize and excommunicate him? The best spokesman of that party was the Augustinian brother Agostino Trionfo; a humbler one, the priest Opicinus de Canistris.

The opposite party was much stronger and gained more strength every day, especially when the Avignonese popes (from 1309 on) committed so many blunders that they discouraged their best friends everywhere except in France. Thus the most eloquent voices of the century spoke for the emperor against the pope. Their theory was simple and convincing. The pope and emperor are the pillars not of one world, but of two, the spiritual world and the temporal one. Each is the supreme authority in his own world. That would have been easy enough but for the fact that the Avignonese popes were extremely interested in the temporal world, and to leave them nothing but the spiritual one was rather a bad joke.

My account of the quarrel is oversimplified. As usual in politics, the main issue

[1a] The prototype in Western literature was the Cyropaedia of Xenophon (IV-1 B.C.), especially the first book, dealing with the education of Cyrus. Earlier examples in Egyptian literature may be traced back to the Fifth Dynasty and perhaps even to the Third Dynasty (i.e., the beginning of the third millennium). Alan H. Gardiner: Egyptian grammar (p. 23, Oxford 1927).

[2] Since the printing of our volume 2 (p. 931) a new edition has been published by Arpad Steiner: De eruditione filiorum nobilium (Mediaeval Academy, no. 32, 268 p., Cambridge, Mass. 1938). For the Eruditio principum of Guillaume Pérault, c. 1260 or 1265, see Introd. 2, 925 and Steiner's paper in Speculum (8, 51–58, 1933; Isis 20, 523).

was inextricably mixed with innumerable side issues varying in each country and in each locality. In Italian politics, the conflict between papists and imperialists was largely identical with the conflict between Guelfs (tradesmen and bankers, the new burgher class, the city people) and Ghibellines (feudal and county people), yet crisscrossed with other rivalries and jealousies which would lead one city to reject certain views simply because they were accepted by a "sister" city. Dante, educated as a Guelf, was turned by such circumstances into a Ghibelline. When he wrote the De monarchia (c. 1311?) he restricted the pope's supremacy to spiritual matters; from the extreme papal point of view that was hardly better than to deny it altogether. The same attitude was assumed by the civilian Cino da Pistoia, by the historian Mussato, and by Petrarca. The latter's reasons were somewhat different. He was largely inspired by his love for Latin (pagan) letters and the old Roman Empire; this helps to explain also his sympathy for Cola di Rienzo. In their instinctive opposition to the temporal claims of the papacy, Dante, Cino, and Petrarca were harbingers of modern Italy. The opposition of these four humanists, Dante and Petrarca, Cino and Mussato, firm as it was, was gentleness itself as compared with the uncompromising and violent treatise issued in 1324 by Marsiglio of Padua. That treatise, the Defensor pacis, written by him with the assistance of one of the leading French philosophers, John of Jandun, is one of the outstanding political books of the Middle Ages. It includes a complete theory of the state, of sovereignty, of government, defending, apropos of almost every issue, lay rights against ecclesiastical ones. Thus it was not simply a defense of Ludwig IV against John XXII; but also of laity in lay matters against the clerks. So bold was the Defensor pacis that the author has been called a forerunner of the French Revolution as well as of the Reformation. Marsiglio continued his fight in other books, but none obtained the same popularity nor caused as great a scandal as the Defensor pacis. Out of that earnest "defense of peace" grew a war of pamphlets and increasing hostilities between the two parties, the painful travail and preparation of a new world.

The antipapal literature of this time, it should be noted, was not irreligious, and with the exception of some bold sayings of Marsiglio's it was not even anticlerical. Nevertheless, as the conflict which it stirred up became hotter and harder, the complaints against the temporal usurpations of the pope changed gradually into anticlericalism, anti-Catholicism, and sometimes (very rarely) into antireligion.

A2. *Spain and Catalonia*

Any history of ideas in Italy after 1300 begins with Dante; even so, as soon as we have crossed the Pyrénées every history of ideas begins with Arnold of Villanova and Raymond Lull. Both were visionaries who added more fuel to the fire than meat to the pot. Neither seems to have taken sides in the conflict between the empire and the papacy, a conflict which was far less intense in the Hispanic peninsula than it was in the rest of Western Europe.

A third Catalan, Guiu Terrena, was of a very different kidney. A Carmelite to begin with, and a defender of orthodoxy and of the status quo, he compiled an Expositorium decreti, wherein the intricacies of canon law were explained to theologians.

To these three men should be added the anonymous author of the first code of maritime commercial law, the Llibre del consolat de mar.

As against these four Catalans I can think of only two Spaniards, Alvaro Pelayo and Don Juan Manuel. The first, a Franciscan of Galicia, wrote a Regimen principum for the king of Castile, whom he praised for being independent of the emperor. Fra Alvaro was a strong defender of the pope, not only against the emperor but against the more liberal members and the general of his own order. It has been remarked above that Spaniards did not worry as much as other Catholics about the great conflict concerning the temporal government of the world. Fra Alvaro was an exception because he was a member of the curia in Avignon, being for a time one of John XXII's penitentiaries.

Don Juan was a man of letters and a moralist. He had been influenced not only by the stern annals of his own people, but also by the prophetic and didactic books of Ramon Lull, and even by Arabic exemplars. As his own books were widely read, he must be counted as one of the political educators of Spain.

A3. *France*

French contributions to legal and political thought were almost as varied as those of Italy; the Italians were more numerous, but two or three of the Frenchmen were men of very great distinction, second to none.

Peter of Auvergne (XIII-2), who lived until 1304, completed the Politics of his master St. Thomas Aquinas. The fundamental importance of that work has been so heavily underlined in volume 2 that I may now take it for granted.

Two important law schools had developed in France, Montpellier in the south and Orléans in the north. The law school of Montpellier was started a little ahead of the medical school by a transfuge from Bologna, Peter of Piacenza (Placentinus) (XII-2), c. 1166; the law school grew slowly in the thirteenth century, but we know nothing definite about its organization before 1339 (Rashdall 2, 128–33, 1936). The law school of Orléans was more ancient, but it began a new life in the thirteenth century and it did not assume much importance before 1320 (Rashdall 2, 149). It should be noted that both schools taught canon as well as civil law; however, the leading French representatives of these two kinds of law were not teachers in either school. The civilian was Jean Faure, author of two popular handbooks, the Breviarium and the Lectura, which were praised not only in his own country but also in Bologna, where the revival of civil law had originated and where the traditions ad hoc were the strongest and most brilliant (Bologna remained throughout the Middle Ages the leading school of law in Catholic Europe). Guillaume de Montlauzun, the canonist, was a member of Cluny. He wrote commentaries on canon law, but his fame rests mainly on the Sacramentale, a discussion of the sacraments wherein theological difficulties are revealed to lawyers. He did the opposite of what was done by his Catalan contemporary Guiu Terrena. The latter had tried to explain canon law to the theologians, Montlauzun explained theology to the canonists. The two disciplines, theology and canon law, were closely related. According to legend, Peter the Lombard (XII-2) and Gratian (XII-1) were brothers, yet both subjects had developed in such a luxuriant manner that either required five or six years of study before graduation. And yet both were needed, and they were intertwined in a number of ways. The modern reader would perhaps be shocked if I were to compare their twin growth to the growth of chemistry and physics today, and yet the comparison is not irrelevant, because theology and law were two of the main subjects of the fourteenth century. It was hardly possible for any thinker to escape both or either. Even so chemistry and physics dominate modern life (in peace and war); though each field is so enormous that no single man can master it, yet he is perplexed at every turn with difficulties belonging to the other field as well as to his own. Faure came from Angoumois and Montlauzun from Quercy, two "pays" of middle western France not so far distant from each other as to be very different.

In the Italian subsection above, reference was made to the Regimen principum composed for Philippe le Bel by Galvano de Levanto with illustrations taken from the game of chess. The same conceit was adopted by the French (or Lombard?) Dominican Jacques de Cessoles in his Ludus scacchorum. Jacques and Galvano seem to have been almost exact contemporaries, flourishing about the end of the thirteenth century. They both wrote in Latin, but Jacques' book, which was probably the earlier by a few years and was certainly the more popular, was promptly translated into French by the Dominican Jean Ferron (or Le Ferron) of Paris, chaplain to Bertrand Auberi of Tarascon (May 1347), and by Jean de Vignai (c. 1332-50). Thus it belongs to French literature. It was translated almost as rapidly into Italian, German, and Dutch; in the fifteenth century more translations of it appeared in Catalan, English, Swedish, and Czech; it thus obtained before the end of the Middle Ages an international importance. The English translation was made by William Caxton from the French one of Jean de Vignai. The Latin princeps appeared in Utrecht 1473; the first Caxton (English) edition was printed in Bruges c. 1476 and reprinted in Westminster 1483. There are many incunabula editions (13 to 16) in five or six languages. Félix Lajard (HL 25, 9-41, 1869).

These two treatises are analyzed by Murray (p. 537-45, 1913), who gives much information on other "chess moralities." According to Murray, the prototype of that mediaeval genre was a short Latin tract, Moralitas de scaccario (text in Murray p. 560-61), the authorship of which has been variously ascribed to Innocent III (pope 1198-1216) and to the Franciscan John of Waleys.[3] The second ascription is more plausible, for the tract is curiously anticlerical, and such outspoken attacks as it contains on the dignitaries of the church would be more likely in the mouth of a Welsh Franciscan than in that of a pope! However, the "Innocent morality" (as Murray persists in calling that text) was completely overshadowed by the book of Jacques de Cessoles, which was more ambitious, written on a higher level, yet popular. Cessoles had received his inspiration and much information from the Polycratus of John of Salisbury (XII-2). His great success has already been indicated. Thanks to him, "moralized chess" became a commonplace of mediaeval thinking. That influence was transmitted by innumerable MSS in Latin and vernaculars plus the many incunabula editions already mentioned. It was transmitted also indirectly by that strange collection entitled Gesta Romanorum, dating probably from the first third of the fourteenth century. Murray gives the relevant extracts from the Gesta, in Latin (p. 562-63) and in Middle English (p. 551). The Gesta Romanorum was itself one of the most popular of mediaeval books (many incunabula, the first being Utrecht 1473).

This kind of treatise seems to have been a specialty of the Latin West. I do not know its equivalent in other parts of the world. In particular, the anonymous Arabic treatise on chess, Kitāb fīl-shaṭrang wa manṣūbātihi wa mulaḥihi (Book of chess, its problems and subtleties), British Museum MS dated 1257, is purely technical. See edition and Spanish translation of it with introduction by Félix M. Pareja Casañas: Libro del ajedrez, de sus problemas y sutilezas (2 vols., Madrid 1935; Isis 25, 199).

[3] The name Waleys suggests a Welsh origin. This John was D.D. in Oxford 1260, regent master of the Oxford Franciscan college, lecturer in theology in Paris 1262. He was sent by Edward I on an embassy to Wales in 1282, and was in Paris again in 1283. His main work is the Communiloquium sive Summa collectionum (collationum).

I hope that the reader will forgive us this digression on "moralized chess" because of its quaintness. It certainly reveals a curious and pleasant aspect of mediaeval life. It does not require much imagination to conjure a group of knights playing chess together. While they watch the game or meditate a move, the older or more serious-minded may remember the moral analogies. There are fundamental differences between real men as between chessmen, and every move, whether right or false, is pregnant with consequences which can no longer be eschewed once the move is made. Every life is like a game of chess in which we play against one another, or against the Devil, or against Death. In any case Death says the final checkmate.

To return to more weighty matters, there were of necessity many conflicts between canon law and civil law, because both claimed jurisdiction over the same questions. It was difficult to say where each law began or ended, because it all depended on whether you considered each problem from a lay angle or a religious one. It is certain that the church's irresistible tendency to interfere in every activity caused a corresponding inflation of canon law. Moreover, canonists and civilians (but chiefly the former) were dominated and led astray by theological prejudices. This is especially true with regard to the inquisitorial procedure so well illustrated by Bernard Gui. Similar perversions appear in the legal treatment meted out to the unfortunate lepers and cagots, and in the controversies against Muslims which formed a part of the crusading propaganda. Consider the legal aspects of the writings of, say, Guillaume Adam and Brocard.

By far the outstanding legal conflict of the time was the contest for supremacy between pope and emperor. That might be considered a particular case of the conflict between canon and civil law. The French looked at it from a new angle. They were willing enough to acknowledge the pope's priority over the emperor, but introduced a new claimant to temporal supremacy, the king of France. John of Paris, Dominican and Thomist as he was, did not hesitate to take sides with Philippe le Bel against Boniface VIII. The defense of royal politics was conducted by the ablest publicist of the time, the lawyer Pierre Dubois. It is possible that if Philippe le Bel had understood all the implications of Dubois' championship he would have been frightened. Dubois indeed was a radical who pursued his thoughts on the need of reform of church and state to the very limit bearable in his days, or rather quite a little beyond. Combined with this radicalism, and camouflaging it to the royal eyes, was a well thought-out but frightening program of French imperialism. Dubois was one of the boldest spirits of the Middle Ages, but his liberalism came sometimes too close to the strange liberalism advocated by dictators to be attractive to the common people. For example, he was one of the first defenders of women's rights; that is, he defended their right to be subordinated to the state as completely as the men would be.

The danger of money depreciation and inflation was then being rapidly increased by the royal government, and Dubois was one of the first to describe it and give necessary warnings. This task of special urgency and difficulty was continued by the philosopher Jean Buridan and a little later by Nicole Oresme (XIV-2); it implied the creation of a theory of money, which is not yet satisfactorily completed to this day. Moreover, Buridan was led to the discussion of many other social questions in his commentaries on the Ethics and Politics of Aristotle. These pregnant writings of the second half of the fourth century B.C., we should remember, remained the framework of political discussion for more than two millennia.

A4. *Germanic countries*

The codification of German law was continued by Ruprecht of Freising, who put together Bavarian laws in his Rechtsbuch. In the meanwhile the Sachsenspiegel was being discussed by Johann von Buch, who helped to introduce Roman ideas into the German codes.

To Engelbert of Admont we owe treatises on the education of princes, such as have been discussed in the previous subsections. Conrad of Megenberg defended the pope's prerogatives against the emperor's.

A5. *England*

A similar work of legal unification had been accomplished in 1250–56 by Henry de Bracton (XIII-2) in his Leges et consuetudines Angliae, which was very influential in itself and also through two summaries compiled during the reign of Edward I (1272–1307), the one "Fleta," in Latin, the other "Britton," in French. These were collections of English laws and customs, more or less rationalized, and harmonized to some extent with the teachings of Azo (XIII-1) and his disciples in Bologna. Much of that English law was exceedingly brutal and cruel, especially with regard to people who had been declared outlaws and had lost every right (Jusserand p. 141–61, 1884).

The main contributions of England were not in the field of civil or criminal law, but in that of constitutional theory and practice. Much progress had been made since the days of the Magna carta (1215); see Introd. 2, 691. Recall Simon de Montfort's Parliament (1265), two knights from each shire and two burgesses from every borough being summoned—the first summons to burgesses in parliamentary history (outside Iceland). Then the Model Parliament (1295), in the writ of summons of which Edward I made the statement, "Sicut lex justissima, provida circumspectione sacrorum principum stabilita, hortatur et statuit ut quod omnes tangit ab omnibus approbetur, sic et nimis evidenter, ut communis periculis per remedia provisa communiter obvietur." The Parliament of Westminster (1327) was strong enough to force Edward II to abdicate. A statute of 1340 recognized the Parliament's right to control taxation. In addition there were also meetings of merchants. These began in 1275 but did not take shape until the beginning of the fourteenth century. Seven such meetings were held between 1300 and 1335 (Eileen Power p. 68, 1941).

This parliamentary development was characteristic of England, but constitutional efforts were made in other countries. The democratic tendencies of this period are remarkable. They appear in the writings of civilians and in the laws due to the latter's initiative. Unfortunately the enforcement of those laws was generally weak, and bullies (whether they were kings, or lay or ecclesiastical lords) had great opportunities which they improved. This led to chaos and eventually to the tyrannies of the Renaissance.[4]

As contrasted with these public achievements which do so much credit to the English nation, those of individuals are relatively few. I can name but one Englishman in this chapter, the Franciscan William of Occam, but it is true that he was one of the greatest and most influential thinkers of his time. Occam was a strong defender of imperial against papal claims, and in addition he was one of the early

[4] C. H. McIlwain: Mediaeval institutions in the modern world (Speculum 16, 275–83, 1941).

advocates of what was to be called later the conciliar theory, the view that even in spiritual matters the pope's authority should be subordinated to that of a council. Moreover, according to him, the council should represent the laity as well as the clergy, and women as well as men!

One is very much tempted to compare William of Occam with his brother Franciscan and his brother Englishman of the preceding period, Roger Bacon. Both were what would be called today "radicals," that is, people who had the courage to think deeply on controversial issues and blurt out their conclusions without fear of consequences. Neither sought notoriety; their main concern was truth—truth and justice.

A6. *Pays de Liége*

A legal dictionary, Digitus florum utriusque juris, was compiled by Jean de Hocsem in 1341. In his chronicle of the prince-bishops of Liége from 1247 to 1348 the same author reveals frequently his interest in Aristotelian politics and his awareness of political problems and difficulties.

B. *Christian East*

B1. *Byzantine law*

The legal writings of Orthodox Europe were not essentially different from those of Catholic Europe. To begin with, some doctors compiled the legal dictionaries and compendia which are indispensable in everyday life. Thus, Matthew Blastares compiled a dictionary of canon and civil law, the two kinds of law being even more closely interrelated in the theocratic Byzantine state than in the Catholic world. That dictionary of his, or Syntagma, is of great traditional importance because it influenced not only the Greek people but also the Slavs, witness a number of Slavonic translations. The Hexabiblos, composed at about the same time by Constantine Armenopulos, shared a similar popularity which continued until last century.

Thomas Magister wrote treatises on the duties of kings and the duties of citizens which are the Greek counterparts of the Latin regimina principum. In fact, a similar treatise was written by another Byzantine scholar, Theodoros Palaeologos, not in Greek but in Latin, and it was promptly translated into French. The subject had become a commonplace of education. It is remarkable that political education was deemed more essential then than it is now, but was restricted to a very small group of people. Though the authors insisted on the duties of rulers as well as on their rights and privileges, it is clear that their main interest was the art of government from the point of view of the governors.

B2. *Abyssinian law*

A kind of government or court manual was compiled on Byzantine models by order of 'Amda Ṣion, king of Abyssinia from 1314 to 1344. The text which has come down to us was probably written after his rule, but it reflects his personality and his legendary power.

C. *Western Israel*

The main addition to Jewish law was the Arba' ṭurim of Jacob ben Asher, which superseded to some extent the Mishneh Torah of Maimonides and remained authoritative until it was itself abrogated by the Shulḥan 'aruk two centuries later.

D. *Eastern Islām*

The legal and sociological activities of Islām were restricted to the Eastern countries, yet they are sufficiently abundant to require subdivision into two groups: (1) Mamlūk (i.e., Syria and Egypt), (2) 'Irāq and farther East. This classification leaves out Anatolia, but none of the activities which probably occurred in that country arrested my attention. It should be remembered that I am not writing the history of administration and government, but rather an account of the theoretical contributions (chiefly in written form) to those arts. We are dealing with the theory, rather than with the practice.

D1. *Mamlūk*

It would be proper to speak of the theological treatises representing the various schools of Muslim law (Ḥanafī, Shāfi'ī, Ḥanbalī, Mālikī; Shī'a), just as we spoke of the Arba' ṭurim in the preceding paragraphs. This, however, would take us too long without helping us much. It is better to restrict our synthesis to works which are more characteristic.

The class of treatises called "regimina principum" is a rich one in Arabic literature. The best book of this age was the one written by a Shāfi'ī theologian, Ibn Jamā'a, wherein the duties and rights of Islamic rulers were clearly explained. Another theologian, this one of the Ḥanbalī rite, Ibn Qayyim al-Jawzīya, and the encyclopaedist al-Dimashqī wrote treatises on physiognomy in relation to government. This is, I believe, an original feature of Arabic literature. At any rate, I am not aware that any Latin regimen devoted much space, if any, to physiognomic considerations. And yet if physiognomy was a reliable art derived from sound principles, as the Muslim doctors believed, did anybody need some knowledge and experience of it more keenly than the men whose main business it was to rule and use other men?

Another originality of Islām was the class of books dealing with ḥisba, and a very remarkable example of it was given at this time by Ibn al-Ukhuwwa. Ḥisba in this sense is much more than accounting, it is the function of the muḥtasib, the inspector of markets, the man in charge of weights and measures and more generally of fair trade, a kind of municipal judge. Ibn al-Ukhuwwa's guide for the muḥtasib gives information on all the arts and crafts and regulations to which they were submitted. Such regulations existed in the West, but nothing exactly comparable to the office of muḥtasib or to the books on ḥisba. These books are especially valuable for the economic historian, but sociologists will find in them much grist for their own mill.

An abundance of facts illustrating various aspects of Muslim society will be found in the Nukhbat al-dahr of al-Dimashqī, the Nihāyat al-arab of al-Nuwairī, and best of all in the Masālik al-abṣār of Ibn Faḍlallāh al-'Umarī. Indeed, the last-named work, being composed for the special use of chancellors and civil servants, contains detailed information on Mamlūk administration.

D2. *'Irāq and farther east in the Dār al-Islām*

Leaving out the Ḥanafī treatises which al-Nasafī (XIII-2) wrote in Samarqand, all the work to be reviewed in this paragraph was done in 'Irāq and belonged to the class "regimina principum." A fine example of it had been produced in 1237 by an earlier 'Irāqī of Turkish family, Yūsuf ibn Qiz-ughli (XIII-1). Two more books of the same kind were written by Ibn al-Ṭiqṭaqā and Ibn Nubāta. The first of these writers was a Shī'a, and his book, the first part of the Kitāb al-fakhrī, is one of the best. Ibn Nubāta was an 'Irāqī, but he had been educated in Egypt and spent most of his life in the Mamlūk empire (hence he might have been included in the previous section, D1). His administrative duties had given him an especially good knowledge of the Christian residents in and pilgrims to the Holy Land. His treatise on the duties of princes seems very comprehensive, but it is unknown to me.

Many of the men quoted in the D sections were Shāfi'ī doctors, Ibn Jamā'a, Ibn al-Ukhuwwa, al-Nuwairī, Ibn Faḍlallāh al-'Umarī. Ibn Qayyim was a Ḥanbalī; al-Nasafī, a Ḥanafī; Ibn al-Ṭiqṭāqa, a Shī'a; al-Dimashqī, a ṣūfī.

E. *India and Burma*

A collection of laws and customs was compiled by Hemādri (XIII-2), who was minister to kings of the Yādava dynasty in Ḥaidarābād. A similar work was produced a few years later by Caṇḍeśvara, who was minister to a king of Mithilā (modern Tirhut, in Bihar, north of the Ganges).

A Buddhist code of laws was introduced into lower Burma by its ruler Wagaru (XIII-2).

F. *China*

The standard textbook of medical jurisprudence (forensic medicine, instructions to coroners) was revised by Wang Yü in 1308.[5] Su T'ien-chio wrote a short treatise on the art of government.

G. *Japan*

A new code, Kemmu shikimoku, was promulgated in 1337. It is important because it remained in force until the end of the Ashikaga shōgunate, in 1573. More important still for the future of the country was the treatise Jingō shōtō-ki, written a few years later (1340–43) by Kitabatake Chikafusa. It was an application of the Chinese theory of government to Japan, and its harmonization with Shintō mythology. Kitabatake was one of the first to suggest that Shintō, Buddhism, and Confucianism could be amalgamated. Of course, one can amalgamate everything, if there is a sufficient desire to do so and if one be willing to replace inconvenient realities by formulas.[6]

Additional Notes

The two following notes are restricted to conditions obtaining in the Latin West. The subjects were not selected arbitrarily, but empirically. The author did not choose them, it is rather they who sought him out and teased him. His account of them may be helpful to other historians of science.

1. *Internationalism of trade*

The internationalism of mediaeval universities and of learning has already been pointed out (p. 78). It was natural enough, because the main controlling factor, the Catholic church, was itself international, or, more exactly, supernational.

[5] The first edition of that work, Hsi-yüan lu, was compiled about the middle of the thirteenth century by Sung Tz'ŭ (XIII-1). For this and later editions, see Introd. 2, 668 and Report of the Librarian of Congress (p. 272, 1941).

[6] The Japanese have always been very able to do that. E.g., they can carry on on foreign soil a war causing the death of millions of people, yet refuse to recognize a state of war. Such tricks may satisfy legal minds; to the scientific-minded man they are nothing but lies.

Students, teachers, architects, and other artists passed with ease from one country to another (similar remarks would apply to the Dār al-Islām). On the other hand, economists often speak of the economic self-sufficiency of manors, communities, or relatively small districts throughout the Middle Ages. A large measure of self-sufficiency undoubtedly existed, especially if one compares mediaeval conditions with modern ones. At present it is probable or possible that the majority of the materials or fabricated items which we buy come from other districts than our own, or even from other, distant, countries; in the Middle Ages the great majority came from one's own demesne, village, or county. The self-sufficiency, however, has been much exaggerated.

The existence of small industries (the best example being cloth manufacturing in England) created the need of exporting surpluses. Foreign demand for English cloth increased the manufacture and the exportation. Exportation created importation, and vice versa. The development of towns was another factor (very important in our period) which made self-sufficiency more and more difficult, for as the town grew it sooner or later outgrew the victualing possibilities of its own district, and it tended also to produce more special goods than it could consume. Even in the field of husbandry certain cultures made international trade almost inevitable. Not to speak of rare products (such as spices, perfumes, precious furs) which could be obtained only in definite regions and nowhere else except by importation, there were certain cultures which led unavoidably to overproduction and hence to the search for outside markets. That was definitely the case for pastures and vineyards, for the producer could consume only a small fraction of his wine, hides, or wool. Other crops like flax, woad, and madder were also sufficiently localized to create outside demands for them and thus an outgoing flow of merchandise. The most important materials, coal and ores, have not yet been mentioned because their importance did not yet appear at this time. They are of course the best examples of localized materials, which can be found only in relatively rare and small localities and must be exported to be available anywhere else.

In short, an abundance of goods was already traveling in many directions, as much of them as the traffic could bear. International trade was in evidence in every commercial city of fourteenth-century Europe. Its reality was especially tangible in the cities of the Hanseatic League (Introd. 2, 1063), because there would be a house serving as headquarters for international trade. Such a house was founded in Bergen, Norway, 1350, and memories of it are preserved in the Hanseatic museum of that city. The Hanseatic League was not the only one of its kind. An association of fifteen Flemish towns called the Hanse of London had been organized as early as the twelfth century to manage the wool trade with England. The leader of these towns was Bruges, but in the following century Douai, Ypres, and Ghent started a rival organization with the same purpose. The welfare of these commercial leagues was often subordinated to political considerations, and it was always jeopardized by the vicissitudes of war.

The relations of English towns with Continental ones belonging to the same leagues were sometimes closer than their relations with other towns or demesnes in their own shires. From that point of view one might say that international commercial ties were relatively stronger in the fourteenth century than they were during the Renaissance or later, when they were frustrated by national jealousies.

Of course, in some cases the government of each nation tried to control the international transactions of its own merchants. The trade became then public instead of private, but it remained international. Some merchants, known as merchants of the staple, enjoyed monopolies of staple commodities (such as wool, leather, tin, lead), which would be stored for them in staples, and their contentions would be heard before special courts (staple courts). It was a difficult question for merchants to decide where the king's staple should be located. At an assembly of English merchants held in 1328 to discuss the location of the staple, it appeared that some merchants favored home staples, whereas the wool dealers wanted a foreign one. In 1343, the English merchants were ordered to take their wool to the staple of Bruges (Power p. 89, 92, 1941).

By the twelfth and thirteenth centuries the international trade was already sufficient to bring to life a substantial amount of international banking (Introd. 2, 38, 317). Italians were the leaders in this, partly because, as they visited other countries, such as England, in order to receive papal taxes, it was natural enough to invest that money in commercial transactions. The receipt of papal taxes enabled them to capture a fair amount of the international wool trade of England; it enabled them also to make loans to the monasteries and thus to obtain commercial privileges. Wool customs were farmed out to Italian firms or syndicates of firms which were acting at the same time as royal bankers—the Riccardi of Lucca, the Frescobaldi, the Bardi and Peruzzi of Florence. From the time of Edward I on, all these firms played a leading role in the wool trade (Power p. 54, 1941). That Italian predominance, however, lasted only until c. 1320 or c. 1330, and the trade fell gradually into the hands of a company of English merchants, the Fellowship of the Staple. The history of these rivalries is too complicated to be told, for it involved many more interests than can be indicated here.

One of the most tangible forms of international trade, insurance, dates back to the end of the twelfth century. It began with marine insurance (for the sea risks were more obvious and more frequent) in Lombardy c. 1182. It functioned in Barcelona in the thirteenth century, in Bruges at the beginning of the fourteenth century. A large amount of commercial insurance was already underwritten before the middle of that century.[7] On the other hand, it is misleading to speak of life insurance, which did not exist until much later, except perhaps in the form of individual gambling. The earliest known life policy was issued by the Royal Exchange in London on June 18, 1583, but there were probably earlier ones, the records of which have been destroyed either during the great Fire (1666) or otherwise. Tables of mortality did not appear until a century later, the first being Edmund Halley's (1693), a facsimile of which was published in Isis (vol. 23, p. 13, 16, 1935).[8]

[7] For the practice of maritime assurance in the fourteenth century, see the Llibre del consolat de mar and similar documents edited and Englished by Sir Travers Twiss: The Black Book of the Admiralty. Appendix, part III (p. 275, 277, 299, 361, London 1874).

[8] Dr. William A. Berridge, of the Metropolitan Life Insurance Co., kindly sent me the following correction (letter dated New York, Feb. 26, 1942): "According to some reputable writers, life insurance began as an accompaniment of marine insurance. Prior to 1400, so-called respondentia and bottomry loans were known, and performed an economic function closely related to present-day insurance. As you recall, these loans—the former on goods and the latter on a ship—were made on the security of a venture. If the voyage was successfully completed, the loans were repayable with generous interest; but if the ship was lost they were canceled. Viewed in this narrow form, it was a logical step forward to provide protection against loss resulting from the deaths of the traveler-venturers themselves. There is also some evidence to indicate that, as early as the thirteenth and fourteenth centuries, means for burial were included among the benefits provided by guilds. In this respect, of course, they performed a service very roughly analogous to one of the purposes of modern life insur-

As international trade increased in volume and variety, there was more and more need of laws and regulations. The international guilds of towns and merchants hastened their formulation and codification. The leading commercial cities, such as Bruges, Florence, Genoa, Venice, Barcelona, appointed representatives to watch over their interests abroad. The best example of such organization is given us by Catalonia. The establishment of "sea consulates," mercantile courts, etc. for the protection of Catalan merchants goes back to the rule of Jacme lo Conqueridor (XIII-2). We know the Catalan regulations exceedingly well because they were codified in the Llibre del consolat de mar, which has been transmitted to us in many editions. In the form in which it has come to us it dates probably from the middle of the fourteenth century, but it is derived from earlier "costums de la mer" which had developed and crystallized in Barcelona, Valencia, and Majorca. The oldest MS is of the end of the fourteenth century, called the St. Peter MS because it was edited by Pere de Sant Pere (Peter, notary of St. Peter in Majorca). There are six other MSS, all in Catalan; this Catalan exclusiveness is significant.

This collection of commercial and maritime law was the most important one of mediaeval times; it was authoritative not only in Catalan places and colonies, but also to some extent all over the Mediterranean world. In Catalonia itself it remained valid until 1829, when it was replaced by a Spanish code of French inspiration.

The editio princeps was prepared by Francesch Celelles (Barcelona 1484) and was often reprinted, Barcelona 1494, 1502, 1518 (twice), 1523, 1540, 1592, 1645, 1791; Paris 1831, London 1874. Spanish translation, Valencia 1538, Barcelona 1732, Madrid 1791. French translation, Aix en Provence 1577, Paris 1808, 1831. The second of these translations, by Pierre B. Boucher: Consulat de la mer, Pandectes du droit commercial et maritime (2 vols., Paris 1808), was very pretentious but bad. The third, by Jean Marie Pardessus, is good. Italian translations, Rome 1519, Venice 1539, 1544, 1549, 1564, 1567, 1576, and many more. Dutch translations, Leyden 1704, Amsterdam 1723. English translation by Sir Travers Twiss in Rerum Britannicarum medii aevi scriptores, Monumenta juridica (vol. 3, London 1874), with Catalan text.

I have used the admirable Catalan edition of Ernest Moliné y Brasés: Les costums maritimes de Barcelona universalment conegudes per Llibre del consolat de mar (folio, 480 p., ill., Barcelona 1914), critical edition reproducing the text of the princeps with variants, bibliographic and historical notes, glossary, and 13 appendixes.

2. *Economic power of the church*

An institution as powerful and ubiquitous as the church was bound to influence economic relations in many ways. It is not necessary to believe in the economic theory of history in order to realize that every human activity has of necessity economic aspects, and thus that an institution controlling to some extent all the

---

ance. Nevertheless, it seems clear that life insurance as now regarded did not become common until after 1700.

"Several known facts concerning the early history of insurance have been summarized by Dr. C. L. Parry of my staff under the topic 'insurance' in the current edition of the Encyclopedia Americana. Other useful references, heavily documented, are the following:

"Amrhein, George L., The liberalization of the life insurance contract, Philadelphia 1933. Magee, John H., General insurance, Chicago 1942. Magee, John H., Life insurance, Chicago 1939. Vance, W. R., Handbook of the law of insurance, 2d ed., St. Paul 1930."

activities must have a multitude of economic bearings. Everything economic touches it, and in turn it cannot help influencing every transaction. Let us consider two aspects only, the church's teachings concerning interest, and the situation created by ecclesiastical taxation and mortmain.

In volume 2, the political and economic views of St. Thomas were discussed at least twice (p. 798–800, 915–16). St. Thomas' prophetic views on sovereignty, on the subordination of the state to the individual, made a strong contrast with his backward views on serfdom and on commerce. In spite of the tremendous economic development which he could not help witnessing, for it occurred with special vigor and brilliancy in some Italian cities, he continued to hold the Biblical and Aristotelian views concerning the evil of "usury," that is, the taking of interest on a loan of money.[9] It is strange that with all his genius St. Thomas did not see that leasing a house or a field was not essentially different from leasing money, yet the latter was condemned and the former was not. One consequence of this was that the money market was abandoned to the Jews. Christian merchants, however, especially the great merchants of northern Italy, could not always share such fantastic views, and gradually assumed a number of functions which were canonically wrong yet unavoidable if they were to stay in business at all. Banking and insurance transactions were not by any means monopolized by Jews; they were made in increasing quantity by Christian merchants, especially Genoese, Florentine, Venetian, Lombard ones.[10] Moreover, it was always possible to lend money without interest yet profitably, and that was done. In spite of these exceptions and subterfuges, it is certain that ecclesiastic objections to usury slowed up the development of trade, and indirectly of arts and crafts. To be sure, the church's emphasis on otherworldliness and on the notion that man can own nothing in full property, but only as a kind of usufruct (real property, even as full sovereignty, rests only in God), discouraged temporal activities of any kind, but the laws against usury and the contempt in which any business was held paralyzed commercial efforts more completely. The fact that merchants continued to prosper and to increase in number in spite of the disapproval which they received from their own venerated church simply proves that economic developments cannot be stopped artificially.

Money might be needed by a merchant for business purposes, or it might be needed by a poor man to buy bread. These were two very different problems. The second could be solved by charity, the first not. As individual wealth and poverty increased and poor people became more numerous and troublesome in the growing cities, charitable duties were more complex and more difficult. The creation of monti di pietà (that is, pawnbroking offices run on a charitable basis) was one of the methods used to help the poor; that method did not originate in the fourteenth century, however, but only in the second half of the fifteenth.[11]

[9] The word usura (or faenus) was used throughout the Middle Ages not for excessive interest, but for any interest. See article usurare, etc., in Ducange's Glossarium. In classical Latin, however, faenus did not always have that pejorative meaning, for Cicero had to qualify it, "magnum s. grave faenus." A glimpse into ancient practice is given us by Diogenes Laërtios (III-1), who speaks (6, 99–100) of an ἡμεροδανειστής, a man lending money on daily interest. The words ἀνατοκισμός (used twice by Cicero) and τόκος τόκου, referring to compound interest, τόκος ἐπίτριτος, τόκος πεντώβολος, etc., are other illustrations of existing usages. There are many references to interest, rates of interest, etc., in the Greek papyri (from the third century B.C. to the eighth after Christ).

[10] The word Lombard came to mean in English (as early as the fourteenth century) a banker, money-changer, pawnbroker (OED).

[11] See my note on Durand de Saint Pourçain.

Though the church did its best to handicap commerce, it did nothing to prevent the accumulation of landed property, and, in fact, it became itself the largest landowner of Europe. This was partly because of its own immortality. Private estates changed hands as often as their owners or "usufructuaries" needed money[12] or died. The serfs and villains were generally sold with the estates, but sometimes they were manumitted. In the meanwhile, the estates and the serfs of the church accumulated, and the mortmain became heavier and heavier.[13] In our time (XIV-1), after a thousand years of accumulation, the church was exceedingly wealthy, and its landholdings all over Western Europe are variously estimated, from country to country, at from one-fifth to one-third of the total.

In addition, the popes derived a considerable income from every diocese in the form of various kinds of taxes, donations, and sales of indulgences (Introd. 2, 34, 823). Collections of taxes of whatever kind have always aroused resentment, and they were probably far more disliked in the past, when the determination of the taxes was or seemed more arbitrary than it is today. We are very well informed on these matters today, because the curia (e.g., the curia of Avignon) kept all accounts in a very businesslike manner, and since 1881 the archives ad hoc in the Vatican library have been opened to competent scholars.

My remarks on the church's existing and accruing wealth are not written in a critical or unfriendly spirit. That wealth, excessive as it certainly was, had not been deliberately obtained, its growth had been to a large extent automatic. The fact that it was impersonal and therefore escaped the precariousness of personal fortunes and could accumulate endlessly was not the church's fault. Nor could the church be blamed because so many estates were bequeathed to her by old sinners who were anxious in extremis to be saved from hell or to decrease their stay in purgatory.[14] These fears of course could be and often were abused by greedy churchmen, but my point is that even if there had never been instances of greed, generous bequests and donations would still have been made to the church and would have accumulated with less speed but with equal steadfastness. It was largely the Church's otherworldliness, or rather her unconscious exploitation of the otherworldliness of her saints, that caused her financial success.[15]

If, however, one could make a statistical investigation of all the cardinals, bishops, canons, prebendaries, abbots, in short of all the officers of the church who were most often accused of graft and greed, and if one could plot, let us say, their goodness along the abscissa and their numbers along the ordinate, one would probably obtain the normal distribution curve. The vast majority would be found to be moderately good, not more greedy than other men, doing their best according to their lights. Two small minorities would be represented by the flat ends of the curve, a small group of saints to the right and an equally small group of rascals to the left. Anticlerical writers try to focus our attention on the left side of the curve, whereas apologists speak as if the right side were the only one.

It is probable that the growing discontent of a growing mass of people with the

[12] A great many were sold by Crusaders who needed money for the equipment of their men and for their own adventures.

[13] See a correction to this below in ch. XV.

[14] I have already spoken of oblates, that is, children offered to a monastery by their parents. There were also older oblates who offered themselves to the church. We find a formula ad hoc in the Formularium notariorum curie (c. 1327) edited by Geoffrey Barraclough (no. 428, p. 244, London 1934): "Quando homo offert se et bona sua monasterio."

[15] A valuable analysis of the situation may be read in John Moffatt Mecklin: The passing of the saint, study of a cultural type (214 p., University of Chicago 1941).

church's fiscality was not due so much to the means of obtaining money as to the means of distributing it. When benefices were given to foreigners without regard to provincial feelings some resentment was necessarily created, and if those foreigners were really greedy, remained absent, collected their tithes but abandoned their duties to others, the resentment was bound to increase, sometimes beyond bounds. Such abuses would be remembered against the church and would eventually cause in some countries a violent reaction against her.

Flick (1, 88–169, 1930), summary of the Avignon financial system. Geoffrey Barraclough: Papal provisions. Aspects of church history, constitutional, legal and administrative in the later Middle Ages (204 p., Oxford 1935). William Edward Lunt: Papal revenues in the Middle Ages (2 vols., Columbia University 1934); Financial relations of the papacy with England to 1327 (775 p., Mediaeval Academy 1939).

Henry Charles Lea: The ecclesiastical treatment of usury (Yale review 2, 356–65, 1894); Lea (p. 129–51, 1942). Terence Patrick McLaughlin (C.S.B.): The teaching of canonists on usury, XIIth to XIVth cent. (Mediaeval studies of Toronto, vol. 1, 81–147, 1939; 2, 1–22, 1940). Carl F. Taeusch: History of the concept of usury (Journal of the history of ideas 3, 291–318, 1942).

For comparative views on usury, Babylonian, Christian, Hebrew, and Jewish, see ERE (12, 548–58, 1922).

XIV. PHILOLOGY

1. *The Linguistic Situation*

Before trying to analyze, however briefly, the main philological achievements of many nations, let us take a bird's-eye view of the linguistic situation in the first half of the fourteenth century. The texts which have been dealt with in this book were written in some thirty languages. How were those languages distributed, and what was their relative importance? In order to answer these very natural and legitimate questions, I made a rough statistical survey of all my notes. Counting the authors using a definite language involved ambiguities and difficulties. Some authors using two languages were counted twice; anonymous works of enormous size (e.g., the Mongolian translation of the Tripiṭaka) were counted as one unit though there was probably a legion of collaborators. As to the men who did not write or whose books are unknown (chiefly explorers, sailors), I assumed that they wrote or would have written in their mother tongue (as far as I remember, this rule was applied almost exclusively to Italians). Any attempt to refine the counting would have increased considerably the difficulty of the census without profit, for the outstanding cause of confusion is the fact that the author of a single tract and the author of a great many books are each counted as one. However, from the point of view of the man who wants to know how much a definite language was used by scholars, ten men writing one book each are more important than one man writing ten books. We are counting men, not books, and for the sake of simplicity all these men are considered equal.

Moreover, as I am far more familiar with Latin and Arabic writings than, say, with Armenian or Chinese ones, it is highly probable that my Latin and Arabic notes are more complete than the Armenian and Chinese ones. Bearing in mind these causes of error, my little census may still be of some value as a first approximation.

The language most frequently represented is Latin (223),[1] and the number of Latin authors is more than twice larger than that of authors of the language second in importance, Arabic (104). We may thus say without fear of error that Latin was by far the most important scientific language in the first half of the fourteenth century.

Consider now nine European vernaculars. In order of decreasing popularity they are Italian (24),[2] French (22), German (12), Catalan (7), Flemish (6), English (4), Spanish (4), Portuguese (2), Icelandic (1). The grand total of these vernaculars is 82, against 223 for Latin alone. This is just what we should expect, for Latin was the learned language for all the people using those vernaculars; however, the relatively large number of scientific books written in the vernaculars shows that there was a growing interest in science and knowledge among people, for example women, who were not learned.

In Eastern Christendom,[3] the outstanding language was Greek (32). Armenian (8) follows after a long distance, and farther still Russian (1), Polish (1), and Czech (1). To complete the account of Indo-European languages, we must also mention Persian (11).

The Caucasian languages are represented only by my note on Georgian historiography, and Coptic by a single note also.

Let us now take the four Semitic languages (166), the leading one being Arabic (104), then Hebrew (59), Aethiopian (2), and Syriac (1).

Finally, we have a few (5) Turkish writers and one Mongolian. That single one, however, stands for all the anonymous translators of the Tripiṭaka.

Having reached this point, it is interesting to ask oneself how these authors were distributed among the three great Western religions. The following table will answer the question.

Israel	*W. Christendom*	*E. Christendom*	*Islām*
Hebrew.....59	Latin............223	Greek........32	Arabic....104
	W. vernaculars... 82	Slavonic...... 3	Persian.... 11
		Armenian.... 8	Turkish... 5
		Georgian..... 1	
		Coptic....... 1	
		Aethiopian... 2	
		Syriac........ 1	
	305	48	
59	353		120

The Jewish total is certainly too small, for there should be added to it a few Jews writing in Arabic. That would not affect the conclusion—the overwhelming pre-

[1] The numbers written between parentheses in this section are the numbers of authors for each language as roughly counted by me.

[2] My Italian counting, however, included various sailors or explorers who were probably Italian-writing but did not write. If these were taken out, French would come ahead of Italian, but only in rough numbers, not in real importance.

[3] "Eastern Christendom" is used here in a purely geographical sense. Of course, neither the Poles nor the Czechs were Orthodox; the Armenians dealt with belonged to their own church or were under Roman influence. I could not say "Eastern Europe," for the Armenians were not in Europe.

ponderance of Christian authors, a preponderance which would not be jeopardized even if all the Eastern Christians were left out.

To return to the general census, the languages of India are represented by writers in Sanskrit (3), Pāli (3), Telugu (2), Canarese (2). The first two of these languages are Aryan (6), the last two, non-Aryan (4).

As to the Far East, we dealt with writers in Chinese (40), Mongolian (1 whose name is legion), Japanese (12).

The totals (including a few duplications) are:

Israel		59
W. Christendom	305	
E. Christendom	48	353
Islām		120
India		10
Far East		53
Grand total		595

The most important individual languages were: 1, Latin (223); 2, Arabic (104); 3, Hebrew (59); 4, Chinese (40); 5, Greek (32).

6, Italian (24); 7, French (22); 8, German (12); 9, Japanese (12); 10, Persian (11).[4]

2. *Latin*

We may now examine the situation and circumstances of each language and—"à tout seigneur tout honneur"—we must begin with Latin. Latin was used by so many authors (I counted 223) that a detailed analysis of their works would take too long. It will suffice to remark that the domain of Latin was coextensive with that of the Roman church. That domain was international, and Latin was thus the international language of Catholic Christendom.[5] Theoretically, it extended as far as missionaries of the church would go. Franciscan and Dominican friars of various nationalities carried Latin as well as the cross to the ends of the known world. Their ritual was in Latin, their reading was exclusively Latin (Vulgate, breviary, hagiography, fathers of the church, etc.), and their common speech while in foreign parts was often Latin. In spite of the fact that their holiest books had been revealed not in Latin, but in Hebrew or Greek, Latin had become for them a sacred language.[6]

[4] If Castilian and Catalan were lumped together (a very questionable procedure), they might be listed here, their total being 11.

[5] Franz Cumont: Pourquoi le latin fut la seule langue liturgique de l'Occident (Mélanges Paul Frédericq p. 63-66, Bruxelles 1904), explaining the monoglottism of Western Christendom in contrast with the polyglottism of Eastern Christendom.

[6] The case of the Vulgate is sufficiently interesting to be explained in a footnote. The Vulgate (as the official Latin version of the Bible is called) was derived by St. Jerome (IV-2) from old Latin versions of the Septuagint Greek, corrected with reference to the Hebrew text. This Hieronymite edition was declared by the council of Trent (1545-63) to be the authentic version, and a standard text was published by order of Clement VIII in 1592. In 1907 Pius X ordered the revision of that text and entrusted the task to the Benedictine order. Thus far three large volumes have appeared, containing the Pentateuch, Biblia sacra iuxta latinam Vulgatam versionem . . . iussu Pii PP. XI cura et studio monachorum S. Benedicti . . . praeside Aidano Gasquet (3 vols., Vatican 1926, 1929, 1936). See article by cardinal Gasquet (CE 15, 515-20, 1912). The average Catholic layman or even cleric tends to consider the Vulgate as literally inspired, which of course it is not. The Vulgate is a sacred text and hence Latin is raised, by the Catholic church at least, to the same level as Hebrew and Greek.

The exaltation of Latin among other languages was not restricted to religious writings, for scholars in Catholic Europe had been trained, because of their clerical affiliation, to read their philosophical and scientific standard books exclusively in Latin.[7] Thus to every scholar of Western Europe Latin was the language not only of religion and theology, but also of science and learning; Latin was to them exactly what Arabic was to the Muslims.

We should expect a language of such importance and sacredness to be the subject of analysis, and we are not disappointed. In fact the study of grammar, and this meant almost exclusively Latin grammar, was one of the favorite studies of this time. The old grammar of Donatus (IV-1) and Priscian (VI-1) was still holding its ground, being revived periodically by commentaries, e.g., the poems of Eberhard of Bethune (XIII-1), Alexander of Villedieu (XIII-1), and Hugo Spechtshart, or the treatises of the English Dominican Robert Kilwardby (XIII-2) or the Frenchman Yon. Probably for most practical purposes the old-fashioned grammar was *the* grammar. From the thirteenth century on, however, some philosophers had become dissatisfied with it. They wanted something deeper, or, to change the metaphor, something higher. They wanted to establish closer links between grammar and logic, and even between grammar and philosophy, grammar and life. Their main sources were the περὶ ἑρμηνείας of Aristotle and commentaries upon it, chiefly the one by Boetius (VI-1). Whether they were conscious of it or not, they were also reviving some of the Stoic ideas on language as explained by Zeno the Cypriot (IV-2 B.C.) and Diogenes the Babylonian (II-1 B.C.). One of the first books dealing with that speculative grammar (grammatica speculativa) was the De modis significandi ascribed to the Englishman John of Garland (XIII-1). This John labored for a time in Paris, and other "modistae," such as Boetius of Dacia (XIII-2), probably obtained their inspiration ad hoc in the same university. The "modistae," as the grammarian-philosophers were called, were investigating the connection between words (or other symbols) and ideas. Their name, modistae, was derived from one of their favorite terms, modi significandi; they were interested in significatio, meaning—the meaning of meaning. They were in a humble and obscure way the precursors of our "semanticists"[8] of today, but they never thought—and that was their mistake—of "basic Latin."

The new grammar was connected with the new logic (logical terminism, Occamism). That connection was suggestive and useful up to a certain point; it was dangerous to extend it too far. Linguistic knowledge was so undeveloped in those days that the empiricism and erraticness of grammar could not be sufficiently appreciated. Grammar and logic do sometimes agree, but more often they do not. Grammar is largely dependent on psychological, sociological, and accidental factors, and cannot be accounted for, except inductively, on a natural-historical basis.

In the first half of the fourteenth century, "speculative grammar" was in full

[7] For a list of them, see Sarton (1938); the easiest way is to examine the facsimiles, p. 125-56.

[8] Charles Kay Ogden and Ivor Armstrong Richards: The meaning of meaning (London 1923). The first of these authors, Ogden, is the inventor of "basic English," which he first explained in "Basic English" and in "The basic vocabulary" (Psyche, London 1930), then in three little books, The ABC of basic English, The basic words, The basic dictionary (London 1932), and in many more. Count Alfred Korzybski: Science and sanity. An introduction to non-Aristotelian systems and general semantics (Lancaster, Penna. 1933; 2d ed. 1941).

More popular books by Samuel Ichiyé Hayakawa: Language in action (Madison, Wis. 1939; Isis 34, 84), Hugh R. Walpole: Semantics. The nature of words and their meanings (New York 1941), Rudolf Carnap: Introduction to semantics (275 p., Harvard University Press 1942; Isis 34, 229).

swing, and we witness scholars of many nations devoting themselves to it: in Belgium, Siger of Courtrai; in England, William of Occam; in Germany, Thomas of Erfurt.[9]

Latin lexicography seems to have attracted less attention, and "dictionaries" were still a kind of novelty in Western Europe. Vocabularies had been compiled by Alexander Neckam (XII-2) and by John of Garland (XIII-1). The latter's was more elaborate and was actually called Dictionarius (this being the first example of that word!), but in spite of that it was still a vocabulary rather than a dictionary. The second use of the word Dictionarius or rather Dictionarium (morale utriusque Testamenti) was apropos of the Biblical encyclopaedia compiled c. 1328-42 by Pierre Bersuire. In the meanwhile a real Latin dictionary had been published by Giovanni Balbi of Genoa (XIII-2) under the name Catholicon, and the usefulness of that work was so obvious that it enjoyed considerable popularity.[10] The Catholicon was frequently copied, and served as the basis of bilingual dictionaries such as the Latin-French dictionaries studied by Mario Roques (1936-38).

Other vocabularies were compiled, such as the Latin-German one, Vocabularius rerum, by Conrad of Heinrichau, and the Synonyma medicine of Simon of Genoa (XIII-2). Various herbals or pharmacopoeias, being arranged in alphabetical order, might be called dictionaries of botany or medicine. The word dictionary in the modern sense (book of words in one or more languages in alphabetic order) does not appear before the sixteenth century.[11]

The first meaning of "dictionarius" was, of course, a book of "dictiones," concerning not so much words as such, as their literary use, or modes of expression. The point of view was rhetorical rather than philological or utilitarian. This introduces the subject of "dictamen," which was given considerable importance in mediaeval times not only in the Latin world but also in the Arabic one.[11a] The chanceries of popes, emperors, kings, lords, bishops, towns, etc. needed secretaries and notaries able to write official documents in proper style. Theirs was a difficult task, because the proper style was determined by many traditions, varying from country to country, from chancery to chancery, from occasion to occasion. Thus it was found necessary to compile collections of examples of private or official letters, bearing such titles as Summa dictaminis, or Formularium pro notariis, or Formularium audientie contradictarum (a formulary of the papal chancery which had the widest circulation), or Formularium instrumentorum notariorum, or Formularium notariorum curie, etc. Every ancient library contains MSS of this type. Their study is interesting to the linguist, but much more so to the student of constitutional and administrative history. The dry formulas of the chancellors record

[9] This Thomas conducted a school of grammar and logic in Erfurt before 1350. He is the author of the Grammatica speculativa wrongly ascribed to Duns Scot (XIII-2). Martin Grabmann: De Thoma Erfordiensi auctore grammaticae quae Ioanni Duns Scoto adscribitur speculativae (Archivum franciscanum historicum 15, 273-77, 1922).

[10] Another kind of dictionary may here be mentioned: Vocabularium difficiliorum vocum Bibliorum or Liber Britonis, ascribed to a Franciscan brother Guillaume le Breton, who wrote it after 1248 and died before 1285 (thus in HL 29, 584-92, 1885). This seems more correct than what is said in the article in DNB (6, 359, 1886), apropos of William Briton (or Breton), Franciscan or Cistercian, who wrote the Vocabularium Bibliae and died in 1356. The same work is meant in both articles.

[11] Sir Thomas Elyot (1490?-1546): [Latin-English] Dictionary (London 1538). Robert Estienne (1503-59): Dictionarium latinogallicum (Paris 1543). After that the word dictionary (and its variants in other languages) became fairly common.

[11a] And in the Chinese world as well, as is explained below in the section devoted to the Chinese language.

administrative realities. Such a collection, the Formularium notariorum curie romane sub Iohanne papa XXII compositum (completed c. 1327), has been edited for the British School at Rome by Geoffrey Barraclough: Public notaries and the papal curia (293 p., London 1934). See also Ludwig Rockinger: Briefsteller und Formelbücher des XI. bis XIV. Jahrhunderts (Quellen und Erörterungen zur bayerischen und deutschen Geschichte, vol. 9; 2 vols., München 1863-64). Helene Wieruszowski: Ars dictaminis in the time of Dante (Medievalia et humanistica p. 95-108, 1943).

Though these summae dictaminis were compiled and handed down by each notary to his successor, and though the old chancellors would insist on literal correction of the documents drafted by their young assistants, a revolt was growing against them, the eternal revolt of the men of ideas against the men of formulas, the revolt of the humanists against the bureaucrats. And as the pedantic observation of formulas had been spreading everywhere because of the ubiquity of papal agents and the prestige enjoyed by jurists and schoolmen, the revolt spread everywhere also. We find it expressed in the writings of a physician like Taddeo Alderotti (XIII-2), of a historian like Albertino Mussato, and even of a poor amateur like Opicinus de Canistris. These humanistic tendencies were roused by the discovery of ancient MSS or monuments; Petrarca found the Pro Archia of Cicero (I-1 B.C.) in 1333 and his letters to T. Pomponius Atticus (109-32 B.C.) in 1345; the tribune Cola di Rienzo felt exalted by the ruins and inscriptions of ancient Rome. Latin humanism was stimulated by Italian literature and vice versa. Dante and Petrarca revived Latin as well as Italian letters.

This early wave of humanism was thus far restricted almost exclusively to Italy. For the only exemplar of it that I can think of in another country, we have to travel all the way from Italy to England, even to the north of it, as far as Durham, and there we meet the Benedictine Richard de Bury, father of bibliophiles.

The presence of that humanist in northern England is the more remarkable because Latin was less known in that country than in Southern Europe. Nowhere is the artificiality of that language already more in evidence. A man's natural language is the one he obtains without effort and without thought from his mother's lips. In that sense Latin had ceased for many centuries to be a natural language; even Italians did not obtain it intuitively from their mothers. Some children might get it from their preceptors, or oblates from older monks, and this would be as natural a transmission as one could imagine next to that from mother to child, but such cases were exceptional. In England the difficulties were increased, because the native language was so utterly different from Latin and because the children were obliged to acquire not one but two artificial languages, French and Latin.

The educational dangers of such a system have been well illustrated by G. G. Coulton in a delightful little book, Europe's apprenticeship (London 1940), whence the facts of this paragraph are largely derived.[12] Before considering English conditions, we may recall that even in Gaul, Latin was already an artificial language in the seventh century. Some people wrote it but hardly spoke it, and those who got words by ear did not know how to spell them because nobody pronounced them correctly. Later on, as scholarship improved, great efforts were made to learn Latin, but its knowledge remained self-conscious. It has remained self-conscious (vs. instinctive) and thus secondary ever since. In 1119 Philip of Thaon (XII-1)

[12] See, for example (p. 234-40), his extract from the Gemma ecclesiastica, wherein Gerald the Welshman (XII-2) tells ludicrous stories of priests misunderstanding the Gospels because of their abysmal ignorance of Latin.

was obliged to translate the compotus into Anglo-Norman verse, yet the compotus was the business of clerks. In 1235 Gregory IX (pope 1227–41) decreed that when the monastic rule was read in chapter it should be explained in the vernacular. Similar decrees often occur throughout the thirteenth and fourteenth centuries, and they prove that many monks (not only nuns) did not understand Latin. Even the Dominicans, perhaps the most learned of them, did not understand it well enough, for their general, sending a circular letter to the order in 1254, requested that it be expounded in the vulgar tongue. About 1270 Robert of Greatham found it necessary to translate the Gospels of the mass into French. At the beginning of the fourteenth century an English manual for the use of the laity at mass was adapted for the Cistercians of Rievaulx[13] "to make it useful for both those monks who could read and those who could not." Monastic cartularies are full of documents written in the vernacular and signed by ecclesiastics, sometimes eminent ones (Coulton p. 89 ff., 1940). Other documents are in Latin but reveal the growing ignorance of that language. Thus, Meister Eckhart uses the French definite article for the sake of increasing the clearness of his Latin; this was done by many other schoolmen. In English monasteries French was often allowed as a substitute for Latin, as a lesser evil than English—but the English would not be repressed, witness many condemnations of its use by monks (e.g., Augustinian order, provincial chapter of England, 1343).

Some clerks learned Latin very well, so well that they almost forgot their own native tongue. Yet the latter remained dominant in their subconsciousness. Indeed, though they might manage to write much in Latin, and write it with relative correctness and elegance, yet occasional sentences must be mentally retranslated into the vernacular to be intelligible. However well a man may know a language, he cannot keep it pure in the midst of a different linguistic environment. Moreover, he cannot think freely in a language as long as he remains conscious of its difficulties. We might even say that as long as his knowledge of it is self-conscious it is essentially imperfect.

Latin was an international language but an artificial one, and therefore a very defective tool for creative thought. The ubiquity of Latin was an advantage on the lower level of communication, but a terrible handicap on the higher level. In a sense Latin was everywhere, in a deeper sense it was nowhere. The Latin talkers were like people wearing a mask in a comedy, not quite themselves; their better self was kept in bondage, betrayed, or lost. As Coulton puts it (p. 79, 1940), "I feel more and more strongly that mediaeval education did a great deal for many centuries to divorce men from their mother tongue; and thereby, from a good deal of common sense. . . . The use of Latin as a world language did indeed extend knowledge, but it diminished its intensity." We may be sure that it was because of that inherent weakness of Latin that it finally lost the ground to the vernaculars. The very pedants who defended it and expressed their contempt of the common tongue, like the French clerk who wrote, "Lingua romana coram clericis saporem suavitatis non habet,"[14] expressed at the same time the insipidity of their Latin and the mediocrity of their minds. Original thinkers wrote more and more in their own tongue, as they got tired of translating their thoughts into another; Latin was gradually left to the pedants and dunces, whose own knowledge of it became thinner and thinner, and hence it was bound to die.

[13] Or Rivaulx in the North Riding of Yorkshire.

[14] Petit de Julleville (2, 228, 1896).

d'Alembert: Sur l'harmonie des langues et en particulier sur celle qu'on croit sentir dans les langues mortes, et à cette occasion sur la latinité des modernes (Oeuvres 3, 107–46, 1805). Sarton: Lagrange's personality (Proceedings American Philosophical Society 88, 457–96, 1944; p. 461).

3. *Italian*

The most important vernacular, qualitatively as well as quantitatively, was Italian. It ennobled itself not in one way, but in many, which we shall briefly describe.

Let us begin with the bonae litterae. At the threshold of the century stands the gigantic figure of Dante. About 1302 he wrote, but unfortunately did not complete, the De vulgari eloquentia, which was a defense of the Italian language, one of the earliest books of its kind on any vernacular, one of the earliest European contributions to general philology (there are many earlier ones concerning Semitic, Chinese, or Sanskrit philology). This unfinished treatise would already suffice to place Dante among the fathers of Italian letters, but he did infinitely more twelve years later when he began the edification of the Divina commedia (completed toward the end of his life; he died in 1321). It is hardly necessary to insist on this, for the Divina commedia is one of the international classics of Christendom which everybody has read or is supposed to have read. Its canonization began very early, and various commentaries had already been composed before the middle of the century, notably those of Ser Graziolo, Guido da Pisa, and the poet's son Jacopo Alighieri. In the meanwhile, a pure spring of lyrical poetry had been opened by the Laude of Jacopone da Todi (d. 1306; Introd. 2, 822), and the "dolce stil nuovo" (that is, the sweet new style of Italian vs. Latin poetry) was cultivated not only by Christians like Cino da Pistoia, but even by a Jew like Manoello (Immanuel ben Solomon). Manoello adapted a part of the Commedia to Hebrew verse, and he even introduced some peculiarities of Italian prosody into his own language. Finally, we have another giant, Petrarca, who completed the enthronization of the Italian language.

Petrarca was a younger contemporary of Dante's, and to some extent a continuer. Both ennobled themselves with Latin writings as well as with Italian ones, and were humanists in the deepest sense, lovers of style and beauty, irrespective of language. Yet forty years separated them, forty momentous years, and in spite of his prophetic gifts Dante was essentially mediaeval whereas Petrarca is often unexpectedly modern. Dante seems to close one age and Petrarca to open another. Think of the latter's Trionfi, a noble series of twelve pöems written in terza rima like the Commedia, yet far less symmetrical, and inwardly very different. In a way, Petrarca begins where Dante left off, for the last lines of the Paradiso celebrate the supremacy of love. The first of the triumphs is the triumph of love over mankind, the second that of chastity over love, the third that of death over chastity, the fourth that of fame over death, the fifth that of time over fame, the sixth that of divinity (eternity) over time. The classification is sometimes a little artificial, but the general progression is very clear. The five canti of the first two triumphs were written to the glory of Laura, who had inspired his youth; in the following canti there appear gradually a number of men who had obtained power, riches, fame, all of which turned to ashes. He himself had savored his greatest triumph on Easter 1341, when he had been crowned poet laureate on the Capitol, but, intelligent and sensitive as he was, he must have soon realized the vanity of even the purest kind of fame. Time destroys everything, or at least it destroys everything which has no inherent permanence. The last canto reiterates the same ideas in apocalyptic fashion; the world as we see it is doomed to pass, but eternity remains. Eternity, and this means the very goal of religion, triumphs over everything else. Much of that thinking is assuredly mediaeval, and not only Christian but Jewish and Muslim, but the tone is surprisingly modern. The Trionfi introduced a new kind of poetry. One might object that these poems do not really belong to our period because Petrarca did not begin them until 1352, when the failure of his Latin epic Africa or other motives had brought him back to Italian letters; but that would be a little pedantic. Petrarca was forty-six years of age at the middle of the century, a man who had already known fame and discovered, as every sensible man must sooner or later, that it was not what it was cracked up to be. Moreover, the germ of his Trionfi may be discovered in the Africa (II, 428–65)—completed, as far as it was completed, about 1340—the idea of the three deaths (of the body, of memorials, of fame) finally overcome by the triumph of eternity. In any case, Petrarca had written enough poetry before 1350 to be counted forever as one of the immortal creators of Italian literature.

Some of the other lyrics of Petrarca may be even more modern than the Trionfi, but I selected the latter for special consideration because of their great influence upon the arts and letters,[15] upon the sensibility of many generations of men. The six progressive triumphs were a challenge to artists, which they took up eagerly and which led them to the creation of things of beauty.[16] Few poets have succeeded in challenging artistic imagination with as much vigor or in introducing as many iconographic traditions as Petrarca.

To sum up, just visualize that group of poets—Jacopone da Todi, Dante, Cino da Pistoia, Manoello Giudeo, and finally Petrarca! Put Dante and Petrarca in the center and the others around them. When and where did one ever meet a finer group? Italian poetry began triumphantly.

Next to these poets, we might perhaps introduce a few men who also wrote in verse, though their compositions were didactic rather than lyrical, and pedestrian rather than poetical. No less than three memorable didactic poems were written in Italian within half a century, the Intelligenza by Dino Compagni, the Acerba by Cecco d'Ascoli, and the Dottrinale by Jacopo Alighieri. To these compositions might be added the prose writings of Zucchero Bencivenni; this would complete what might be called the didactic group.

[15] For that influence, in addition to the references given at the end of my note on Petrarca, see: Prince d'Essling and Eugène Müntz: Pétrarque, ses études d'art, son influence sur les artistes, ses portraits et ceux de Laure. L'illustration de ses écrits (folio, 298 p., 21 pl., 191 fig., Paris 1902). Giulio Bertoni: Per la fortuna dei Trionfi in Francia (62 p., Modena 1904). Renato Serra (1884–1915): Dei Trionfi (La Romagna vol. 16; reprint 95 p., Bologna 1929), with author's biography and portraits.

[16] Each reader will conjure his own favorite examples among a great many, for the Trionfi inspired painters, sculptors, engravers, and the makers of many kinds of art objects in ivory, wood (Italian marriage chests), etc. I am remembering with special pleasure the fine sets of Flemish tapestries of the sixteenth century to be found in many places—South Kensington, Hampton Court, Royal Palace of Madrid, Vienna, Metropolitan. The Vienna set is complete (six tapestries); the two magnificent tapestries bequeathed to the Metropolitan by George D. Pratt are nos. 4 and 5 of a similar set.

Reproductions in Prince d'Essling's book of 1902. Ludwig Baldass: Die Wiener Gobelinsammlung (nos. 1–6, Wien 1920). James J. Rorimer: The triumphs of fame and time (Bull. Metropolitan Museum 35, 242–44, 1940). The courtesy of Francis Henry Taylor, director of the Metropolitan Museum of New York, is appreciated.

It has been claimed that the prototype of the chronicle of Morea was written in the Venetian dialect. In this field (historiography) as in others, however, it was the Florentine dialect which won out and thus assured the establishment of the new language. The Florentine chroniclers, Dino Compagni and even more so Giovanni Villani, were literary craftsmen of such vigor that they must be counted among the founders of Italian prose. And the same can be said of the great travelers, Marco Polo, Odoric of Pordenone, and Niccolò da Poggibonsi. The original text of Marco's narrative was written in French, but the Italian version was established within his lifetime (i.e., before 1324), and that version, whoever wrote it, was as vigorous as can be. Niccolò's Libro d'oltramare and Odoric's De rebus incognitis[17] were monumental additions to the literary language. On the other hand, the activities of other travelers like Sorleone Vivaldo, Andalò da Savignone, and Nicoloso da Recco, or of cartographers like Pietro Vesconte and Giovanni di Carignano, might help to diffuse the Italian tongue but not to establish it.

One of the most remarkable monuments of the early Italian language is the Libro di divisamenti di paesi completed c. 1340 by the Florentine Francesco Balducci Pegolotti—a curious combination of commercial geography and arithmetic, typical of its time and place.

Scientific writings stricto sensu are few: a few lost translations by Zucchero Bencivenni (the man who is said to have been the first to distinguish the vocalized v from the consonantal one), an anonymous text on commercial arithmetic, the Tractatus algorismi of Jacob of Florence, and the Trattato d'abbaco of Paolo Dagomari. That is not much, but hardly less than we expected, for the position of Latin as a learned language was as secure as its sacredness. However much one might admire the new language, there was no reason for adapting it to purely scientific purposes, for scientific readers were too few and Latin-minded.

The main conditions for the creation of a new language are, first, the supremacy of one dialect among others competing with it; second, the existence of masterpieces consecrating its dignity. These conditions were fulfilled for the Italian language. For a time a southern dialect had been favored thanks to the influence of Frederick II and his court, but after Frederick's death, in 1250, the Tuscan dialect began to predominate, and by the end of the century the toscaneggiamento was well under way (Introd. 2, 577). The Divina commedia was the necessary masterpiece which exalted Tuscan high enough for security and permanence. The establishment was completed by a number of other writings, excellent among their own kind, but the Commedia and Petrarca's poems were the primary factors.

HISPANIC LANGUAGES (4 TO 7)

4. *Castilian* (*Spanish*)

The linguistic unification was not so successful in the Hispanic peninsula as it was in the Italic one, and this cannot be explained simply in political terms, for the lack of political unity was almost equal in both cases. That the differences between, say, Castilian and Portuguese were not insuperable is illustrated by the fact that Alfonso X el Sabio (XIII-2), one of the masters of Castilian prose, wrote his poems in the Galician dialect, closer to Portuguese than to modern Spanish. Thus Alfonso is a founder of both the Spanish and the Portuguese languages and

[17] The title is Latin but the text Italian. This procedure was not uncommon and has continued to our own days, cf. "Areopagitica," "In memoriam," "Quo vadis?," "Arabia deserta." In a similar way Persian and Turkish books received Arabic titles.

literatures. We must assume that the centrifugal forces, whichever their origin, social or purely linguistic, were much stronger in the Hispanic peninsula than in Italy.

The outstanding Castilian author of our period was a royal prince, Don Juan Manuel. He was a writer of distinction, but so much inferior to Dante and Petrarca that it is silly to compare him to them. The inferiority of Castilian to contemporary Tuscan appears in every field. Strangely enough, among the few Castilian writings I came across were those of two Jews. The first, Isaac ben Joseph ben Pulqar, wrote a refutation of astrology in Castilian as well as in Hebrew; he also wrote a defense of his religion in Hebrew. On the other hand, the second, Abner of Burgos, was a renegade who made use of the Castilian language to vituperate his own brethren. Thus was the new language used not only for cultural but also for anti-Semitic purposes.

The most remarkable Castilian document of this time is a compendium of geographical knowledge, Libro del conosçimiento, composed in 1348 by a Franciscan who flourished in Seville.

5. *Provençal*

Though the references to Provençal are relatively few in this book, many more were made in the previous ones, and a survey of that language and literature is desirable now that we approach the time of its gradual suppression by the people speaking the "langue d'oïl." The case of Provençal illustrates tragically the decisive part which wars and politics can play in linguistics. Provençal was linguistically as promising as any other Romance language, but it was brutally suppressed about the middle of the fourteenth century, and it would have died out completely if it were possible to kill a whole people and uproot its aspirations.

The term Provençal is taken here broadly to signify the dialects of "langue d'oc" grouped around one of them, separately from the Catalan group to be considered later. The dialects called broadly Provençal were spoken not only in Provence, but also in Languedoc, Auvergne, Périgord, Limousin, Gascogne.

Provençal literature began very early. Its two earliest monuments, two religious poems, Boèce and the Chanson de Sainte Foy, may be anterior to the eleventh century. Boèce (257 decasyllabic lines) tells the story of Boetius (VI-1); the Chanson (593 octosyllabic lines), the life of Sainte Foy of Agen (on the Garonne), virgin and martyr. After this, for more than two centuries the Provençal language was illustrated by a series of lyrical poets, the Troubadours (XII-2), whose success and influence were considerable. As some of the most prominent Troubadours came from Limousin, their language was often called lenga lemosina. The Troubadours, however, flourished not only in Limousin but in other parts of the Provençal linguistic territory (as defined above), in the other països d'oc (Catalan territory), and even in other countries where they found patrons, Aquitania (where they were welcomed by Henry II and Richard Lionheart), Castile, Italy. It was truly an international movement, for the Troubadours inspired the Trouvères (XII-2), speaking the langue d'oïl, and even the Minnesänger (XII-2) and the Meistersänger in Germanic countries. It is no exaggeration to say that the Troubadours opened a new spring of poetry in Europe. Had they themselves drunk at Arabic sources? Their origins are obscure, but their influence is obvious. In particular, they originated the dolce stil nuovo which prepared the masterpieces of Dante and Petrarca.

Before the thirteenth century, there was hardly any prose literature and the poetry was almost exclusively lyrical. The prose texts were: a part of St. John (end of eleventh century), a number of sermons and religious precepts (twelfth), and the Codi (c. 1149; Introd. 2, 267), earliest code of law in a vernacular. A new note was struck in the Chanson d'Antioche, a true chanson de geste dealing with the First Crusade (Introd. 2, 252). Some 700 alexandrine lines of the Provençal text are extant, which may have been composed c. 1135 by the Limousin poet Grégoire Bechada. This inspired the Chanson de la croisade, relating events of the Albigensian persecution, written by Guilhem of Tudela (XIII-1) and by an unknown continuer. Guilhem dealt with the period 1207–13 (2,768 alex.), his continuer with the years 1213–18 (6,810 alex.). Guilhem expressed moderately the crusader's point of view; his continuer was a defender of the oppressed people.

In the thirteenth century the Troubadours continued to sing their songs, and in addition various didactic poems were written: (1) Adaptation (1,571 alex.) of the Practica chirurgiae of Roger of Salerno (XII-2) by Raimon d'Avignon c. 1200. (2) Daude de Pradas (beginning of XIII; Introd. 2, 648): Romans dels auzels cassadors, on falconry.[18] (3) Tezaur (Treasure), over 500 alex., by Peire de Corbian. History of Christ and information on astronomy and history. (4) Treatise on health derived from the Secretum secretorum (448 octosyll.). See Introd. 1, 556; 2, passim. (5) Treatises on astrology (1,550 lines) and geomancy (3,700 lines) written somewhat later, c. 1332.

During the same century prose work was restricted to various translations of the Gospels, in spite of the fact that the Provençal version made by Estève or Estienne d'Anse for Peter Waldo (Introd. 2, 331) was condemned by the council of Toulouse in 1229 and the reading of the Bible in the vernacular was forbidden by the same council. Translations continued to be made, however, one of which, of Albigensian inspiration, is followed by a Catharic ritual (for the Cathari see Introd. 2, 157–59); MS dates from 1250–80. There were also written a few biographies of Troubadours. The most important prose work of the thirteenth century is the so-called Enfant sage, a dialogue between Hadrian (emp. 117–38) and Epictetos (II-1) on religion and morality, which had an enormous success during the Middle Ages. Walther Suchier: L'enfant sage (das Gespräch des Kaisers Hadrian mit dem klugen Kinde Epitus). Die erhaltenen Versionen hrsg. (626 p., Dresden 1910). According to Suchier, the vernacular Urtext was written in Provençal about the middle of the thirteenth century, being derived from Latin texts of the ninth to twelfth centuries. There are 16 vernacular texts of the Enfant sage, representing 11 different versions, of which 2 are in Provençal, 1 in Catalan, 4 in French, 3 in Castilian, and 1 in English, called Ypotis (Wells p. 425).

This golden age of Provençal poetry was already over by the end of the thirteenth century, but much was written in prose during the fourteenth century. In fact, most of the prose work is posterior to 1300. As to poetry of the fourteenth century, there are translations of an Infancy gospel of Christ and of the Gospel of Nicodemus (there is also a prose version of the latter), and an enormous composition, the Breviari d'amor (34,597 octosyll.), by Matfre Ermengaut of Béziers (d. 1322). The Breviari d'amor, begun in 1288, is an encyclopaedic poem of theological, ethical purpose, including a little natural history derived from the Speculum naturale of Vincent of Beauvais (XIII-2). Much attention is paid to the defense of pure and noble love, hence the title.[19]

[18] A new edition and translation of the Auzels cassadors, prepared by Alexander Herman Schutz, has been published by the Ohio State University (234 p., Columbus, Ohio 1945).

[19] Gabriel Azaïs: Le Breviari d'amor de Matfre Ermengaud, suivi de sa lettre à sa soeur (2 vols., Société archéologique de Béziers 1862–81), with glossary.

The main prose texts are (they are enumerated in rough chronological order of the original texts from which they are derived): (1) Barlaam and Ioasaph (Introd. 1, 507). (2) Surgery of Abū-l-Qāsim (X-2). (3) Lapidary of Marbode (XI-2). (4) Circa instans of Matthaeus Platearius (XII-1). (5) Elucidarium of Honorius of Autun (XII-1). (6) Disciplina clericalis of Peter Alfonso (XII-1). (7) Practica oculorum of Benevenutus Grassus (XII-1). (8) Mulomedicina of Teodorico Borgognoni (XIII-1). (9) Romance of Sidrach (XIII-1). The Provençal text is seemingly older than the French one. (10) De proprietatibus rerum of Bartholomew the Englishman (XIII-1). Elucidari de las proprietats de totas res naturals, translated for Gaston II count of Foix (1315–43), with a prologue in verse, Palais de savieza (description of the palace of wisdom). MS in Ste Geneviève, Paris, illustrated with drawings of animals and birds. (11) Contemplation of the life and miracles of Jesus Christ, by St. Bonaventure (XIII-2). (12) Somme le Roi (or Livre des vices et des vertus), written in 1279 by the Dominican Laurent, for whom see my note on Michael of Northgate. (13) Régime du corps of Aldobrandin of Siena (XIII-2). (14) Liber marescalchiae of Jordan Ruffo (XIII-2). (15) Small anatomy of Henry de Mondeville, the lessons given by him in Montpellier 1304. (16) Nicolai Antidotarium (Introd. 2, 239).

To these should be added archives and documents which are without literary pretensions, but which may be of great linguistic importance, especially when they are exactly dated, as they often are. For example, the documents edited by Marie Zéphirin Isnard: Livre des privilèges de Manosque.[20] Cartulaire municipal latin-provençal, 1169–1315. Suivi de remarques philologiques sur le texte provençal par Camille Chabaneau (quarto, 336 p., Digne 1894), with glossary.

There are also various anonymous treatises on algorism, anatomy, urine, bloodletting, botany, alchemy, conservation of wines, miniature painting; bestiaries, table of coins, medical recipes and aphorisms, etc. Some of these texts may be a little anterior to 1300, or, and this is more likely, a little posterior to 1350. One of the bestiaries is a moralized one of Waldensian inspiration. Edited by Alfons Mayer: Der waldensische Physiologus (Romanische Forschungen 5, 392–418, 1890).

This enumeration, incomplete as it is, is more than sufficient to illustrate the encyclopaedic curiosity of the Provençal-speaking peoples. It suggests that the Provençal language had attained a high degree of maturity, not only in verse but also in prose. The maturity is proved by the existence of grammatical writings such as did not yet exist in other Romance languages. Let us now consider these.

a. Razós de trobar, grammar and prosody of the lenga lemosina by the troubadour Ramon Vidal of Besalù (XII/XIII).[21]

b. Donatz proensals, another grammar with special emphasis on the forms of conjugation, a glossary of the main verbs, and a dictionary of rhymes, composed by Uc Faidit for two Italian lords c. 1240.

c. Leys d'amors. Edited by Joseph Anglade (4 vols., Toulouse 1919–20). This is the largest treatise on grammar and poetry; like the two preceding ones, it was written in prose, but it is more elaborate. It was probably composed in the second quarter of the fourteenth century, for it is connected with the creation in Toulouse 1323 of the Consistory of gay knowledge (Consistori de la gaya sciensa, or del gay saber). This was an academy of letters, organizing poetical competitions, jeux floraux, the first of which occurred in Toulouse on May 1, 1324. The chancellor of the Consistori, Guilhem Molinier, was ordered to compile a code of the Pro-

[20] Manosque is in the district of Forcalquier (Basses-Alpes, Provence).

[21] In the province of Gerona, hence in the Catalan rather than the Provençal district.

vençal language for the guidance of the new poets. There are two different redactions of the Leys d'amors. The first is divided into three books, of which the first tells the history of the Consistori and deals with ethics, philosophy, and theology. That book is derived from the Ars loquendi and the Liber consolationis of Albertano of Brescia (XIII-1), the Tresor of Brunetto Latini (XIII-2), and the Compendium theologicae veritatis wrongly ascribed to Albert the Great (Introd. 2, 941).

The second redaction does not contain that book one, and the two others are developed into five, treating the following subjects: I, Correct pronounciation and phonetics; II, Prosody, definition of lyrical forms; III, Morphology; IV, Rhetoric; V, Technical and moral precepts. Note the comprehensiveness of that plan; there was nothing comparable in any other literature. The moral and religious considerations set forth in part I of the first redaction and part V of the second are typical of the Provençal Consistori, the aims of which were religious as well as literary.

All these books were written in prose, but the Leys d'amors were summarized in verse (7,615 octosyll. lines) by Guilhem Molinier under the title Flors del gay saber. The Leys d'amors being too long and detailed for the average reader, another summary was composed in prose by Joan de Castelnou of Toulouse (c. 1341). Castelnou's Compendi was the source of the Catalan prosody Mirall de trobar, by Berenguier of Noya. The influence of the Leys d'amors and of the Floral games was considerable throughout the països d'oc and even in the other Romance countries.

Unfortunately, while a few men of exceptional literary genius were thus making their own language illustrious above others, political events were destroying the ground under their feet. The crusade against the Albigenses (1209–18) had become, under the leadership of Simon IV of Montfort, earl of Leicester (c. 1165–1218), a means of conquering the lands of the southern lords. The South never recovered from that crusade. Moreover, in 1246, Charles d'Anjou (Charles I of Naples), brother of St. Louis, married Béatrice, daughter of Raymond Bérenger IV count of Provence; Béatrice brought her husband Provence as her dowry. Another brother of St. Louis, Alphonse of Poitiers, married Jeanne, daughter of Raymond VII count of Toulouse; in 1271 the county of Toulouse (the old kingdom of Aquitaine) was inherited by Philippe III le Hardi, king of France. Philippe le Bel established a parliament in Toulouse in 1302 and an archbishopric in 1317, and thus that county was brought almost completely within the sphere of French influence, for cultural as well as for political purposes. The county of Toulouse was formally united to the crown in 1361. In 1349, Montpellier was added to the French dominions, but a few years later Charles V (king 1264–80) ceded it to the king of Navarre; it was retaken in 1382 by Charles VI.[22] In 1360, John II the Good made a duchy of Auvergne in favor of his son. Thus was the linguistic Provençal territory gradually added to the linguistic French one. Everything concurred to its destruction, church, state, and women. Though the "langue d'oc" was then far superior from the point of view of culture and humanities to the "langue d'oïl," it was branded as the language of rebels, heretics, and boors.

By the middle of the fourteenth century, the South was largely conquered and its rich culture driven underground. In spite of its maturity and nobility, the Provençal language was degraded into popular, unofficial dialects. Thus was

[22] These vicissitudes of Montpellier are often forgotten when one speaks of its famous university. Montpellier was a part of Aragon from 1204 to 1349, then French except for a brief Navarrese interlude; completely French since 1382.

Provençal literature smothered by the French even as Catalan was to be smothered later by the Spaniards. The coup de grâce was given by Francis I in the edict of Villers-Cotterets 1539, forbidding the use of Provençal in official acts.

6. *Catalan*

The other dialects of "langue d'oc" may be grouped under the term Catalan. Their territory includes not only Catalonia proper, but also Cerdagne, Roussillon, Valencia, the Balearic Islands, and even a part of the northwest coast of Sardinia near Alghero (colonized by Catalans from 1353 to 1391). Sometimes the territories of both Provençal and Catalan groups are shown together under the title "Els països d'oc" (I have such a map, printed in Barcelona, undated, before my eyes as I write). The Catalan group seems to have developed a little later than the Provençal one; the earliest document in Catalan is one of 1171 from the Roda monastery (Meillet and Cohen p. 57–58, 1924). Of course, earlier documents may have disappeared, and the language had been preserved by centuries of oral tradition before being written down. The literature which has come to us is hardly anterior to the thirteenth century. The earliest writings extant are lyrical poetry and a few sermons or religious texts in prose. The Troubadours were as popular in the Catalan district as in the Provençal. In fact, the Catalan lords welcomed not only their own Troubadours but also Provençal ones, who sang in Provençal or in Catalan, or mixed the two languages (this could hardly be helped on account of their close relationship). Catalan and "Limousin" texts occur sometimes in the same MSS (Anglade p. 169, 1921).

One of the earliest Catalan datable texts is the collection of proverbs, Proverbis rimats, some 1,200 sayings taken out of Biblical and patristic writings by Guillem de Cervera, lord of Juneda and monk in Poblet (d. 1245). The Catalan language was finally established by the king of Aragon, Jaume I lo Conqueridor (XIII-2), who lived and ruled until 1276. Jaume ordered the official use of Catalan instead of "lemosina." He may not be the author of the Llibre de saviesa (Book of wisdom) indirectly derived from Arabic lore through the Poridad de poridades (Introd. 2, 834), but he caused its compilation even as Alfonso el Sabio (XIII-2) caused the publication of the Poridad. In 1235 Jaume convoked a synod of bishops in Tarragona; that synod prohibited the translation of the Bible into Catalan, and this would seem to prove that such translations were then already in circulation; in fact, early Biblical texts in Catalan are extant.

Jaume's greatest contribution is the chronicle of his own deeds. This was the beginning of a series of Catalan chronicles, which are among the masterpieces of mediaeval historiography. Jaume's great example was followed by Bernat Desclot (XIII-2) and best of all by Ramón Muntaner. Moreover, the Chronica Hispaniae of Rodrigo Jiménez de Rada (XIII-1) was put into Catalan by Pere Ribera de Parpejà c. 1267.

The outstanding writer was Ramon Llull (XIII-2), who produced from 1272 to 1315 a long series of Catalan writings in verse and prose. Llull was one of the most original minds of the Middle Ages, and his works, eventually published in many languages, exerted considerable influence all over Europe. He gave to Catalan the masterpieces which placed it on the same level as French or Italian.

There is not much scientific literature; a treatise on falconry has already been mentioned (Introd. 2, 648), as well as versions of the Mulomedicina and of the Cyrurgia of Teodorico Borgognoni (XIII-1); a collection of medical aphorisms is difficult to date. Translations from Arabic into "romancio" were made for Jaume

II el Just (king of Aragon 1291–1327) by Judah Bonsenyor. Judah translated a collection of proverbs and a medical treatise. Jacme d'Agramont wrote on April 24, 1348 in Catalan what is probably the earliest treatise on the plague. Finally, the most important code of commercial regulations published in the Middle Ages, the Llibre del consolat de mar, was written in the Catalan language.

We should expect a language which was the vehicle of many fundamental works to have attained some degree of grammatical consciousness, and our expectation is not deceived, though the initiative in grammatical efforts seems to have been taken north of the Pyrénées. I say "seems," because I am not sure whether the Razós de trobar of Ramon Vidal should be counted as Provençal (as the Provençaux do) or as Catalan; Ramon came from Besalù, which is in the Gerona province of Spain, south of the Pyrénées. At any rate, the Razós de trobar were followed by texts which are indisputably Catalan, as the Doctrina de compondre dictats, anonymous treatise on prosody, and the Regles de trobar composed by Jofre de Foixà, who was a Franciscan from 1267 to 1275 and later a Benedictine. He composed the Regles in Sicily between 1286 and 1291. Later still came the Doctrinal de trobar dedicated by Ramon Cornet in 1324 to the child Pere son of Jaume II el Just, and a Glossa or correction to the Doctrinal dedicated in 1341 to the same prince by Joan de Castelnou. The outstanding grammatical work of the "langue d'oc," however, was the Provençal Las leys d'amors, which exerted as strong an influence on Catalan letters as on Provençal.

All in all, the early Catalan writings are less numerous and less varied than the Provençal ones, but some of the Catalan authors were without peers north of the Pyrénées. The Provençaux had the initiative and kept the leadership in lyrical poetry and in grammar, but they had no writer comparable to Ramon Llull, and no historians of the stature and prestige of Jaume I, Desclot, or Muntaner.

Moreover, the Catalan efforts were not thwarted as soon as the Provençal ones, they were privileged to continue almost a century longer, though with decreasing vigor, until the union of Aragon with Castile (1479) put an end to them.

7. *Portuguese*

The earliest documents in Portuguese date from the end of the twelfth century (poems of 1189, 1199, charter of 1192); thus Portuguese would seem to have reached the written stage later than Provençal and perhaps a little ahead of Catalan. The earliest literary texts are poems of a very original kind, the cossantes, strikingly different from Troubadour poetry. The first example of this form (1199) is ascribed to king Sancho I o Povoador (ruled 1185–1211). The cossantes now and then suggest comparison with the short Japanese poems. Their mood is one of wistful sadness (saudade; Isis 22, 451). Later the cossantes were replaced by Troubadour poetry, but all the early poems were written in Galician dialect, not necessarily in Galicia. Early Portuguese poetry originated in that province (in northwestern Spain), where the shrine of Santiago de Compostela (Introd. 1, 774), second only in the people's veneration to the shrines of the Holy Land, had created an international center of Christian culture; foreign pilgrims were streaming to Santiago from the coast or else came from the east along the "camino francés." From Galicia, the new poetry, whether of the Troubadour kind[23] or more popular

[23] The Troubadour kind of poetry became more prevalent during and after the rule of Afonso III o Bolonhès, the fifth king of Portugal (ruled 1248–79), who completed the liberation of his country by the conquest of Algarve (in southern Portugal) from the Moors and its revendication from the Castilians.

like the cossantes, spread all over the peninsula. In the cancioneiros which have come down to us from the twelfth to the fourteenth centuries are gathered some 2,000 poems[24] by two hundred poets, the most important collection (c. 450 poems) being the Cantigas de Santa Maria by Alfonso X el Sabio (XIII-2). Thus was the great Spanish king a founder of Portuguese poetry as well as of Castilian prose. By the way, the modern Galician dialect is still much closer to Portuguese than to Spanish.[25]

Portuguese poetry, born in Galicia, flowered all over Portugal and Spain, and the Portuguese poets competed with their Provençal and Catalan brethren. The example of Alfonso el Sabio was followed by his grandson Dinis o Lavrador (XIII-2), sixth king of Portugal (1279–1325). Dinis encouraged the translation of many books into Portuguese, and because of his enlightened patronage deserves to be called the founder of Portuguese prose, just as his grandsire was one of the founders of Castilian prose. Both distinguished themselves as Portuguese poets. Before abandoning the subject of poetry, I would remark that we have an old Portuguese poetica dating probably from Dinis' time, and an epic poem, Poema da batalha do Salado,[26] by Afonso Giraldez, who took part in that famous battle.

Portuguese prose works were very few in the fourteenth century. In addition to the translations made by order of king Dinis, especially that of his grandfather's Cronica general and of the Spanish chronicle of Abū Bakr Aḥmad ibn Muḥammad al-Rāzī (X-1),[27] there is very little to quote.

Biblical translations are scanty and almost negligible; there are some Biblical stories, lives of saints, chivalresque romances. The criticism and dating of these wretched texts are full of difficulties; it is probable that the majority are later than 1350 and even 1400. There are no scientific writings except the Libro de alveitaria and the Arte de volateria (treatises on farriery and poultry) by one master Giraldes, Dinis' personal leech. As to original historiography, we have only the Livro de linhagens (Book of descent, genealogy) written by one of Dinis' illegitimate sons, Dom Pedro conde de Barcellos (1289–1354). There are other books of the same kind though probably of later date. For noblemen the history of their house was more interesting than the history of their country, they would have said without hesitation "L'Etat c'est nous"; the canaille did not count, they did not even think of it.

For bibliographical information see my notes on Alfonso el Sabio, Dinis, and Giraldes, and Bell's excellent history (1922).

8. *French*

French was the first Romance language which emancipated itself from Latin. The oldest document in langue d'oïl is the oath of Strassburg, dated 842. In that year Charles the Bald and Louis the German, grandsons of Charlemagne, formed an alliance against their brother Lothair. They and their soldiers swore the oaths of

[24] Most of them were published only after 1846.

[25] A Galician literary revival began in the middle of the nineteenth century, and floral games (juegos florales, xogos froraes) were instituted at La Coruña in 1861 (Bell p. 347–57, 1922). This movement was contemporary with the Provençal and Catalan revivals.

[26] About the battle of Salado, near Gibraltar (1340), wherein Alfonso XI of Castile and Afonso IV of Portugal defeated Abū-l-Ḥasan 'Alī al-Marīnī. Moroccan rulers did not invade Spain any more after that disastrous reverse.

[27] This Arabic chronicle has come down to us in a Spanish version, Cronica del Moro Rasis, made from the Portuguese. The Arabic and Portuguese texts are lost. Brockelmann (1, 150, 1898). Hurtado and González Palencia (p. 30, 216, 1932).

Strassburg in their (Romance and German) vernaculars. The language of Charles's oath was definitely langue d'oïl; and the emancipation of that language had been possible only because Latin had reached an advanced stage of disintegration. If the Latin language had remained alive, the Romance dialects would have had as much chance of developing as maggots on a living body.

By the end of the eleventh century, the maturity of the langue d'oïl was already consecrated by the creation of a masterpiece, the Chanson de Roland (XI-2), the noblest epic poem of mediaeval Europe. The Albigensian war a century later gave the French language an opportunity of extending its sphere of influence at the cost of the langue d'oc. A Provençal writer like William of Tudela (XIII-1) trying to write in "langue d'oc" was already using many "langue d'oïl" phrases and turns. Moreover, French was written by the Italian Daniel of Cremona for Enzio, the natural son of Frederick II (Introd. 2, 648), by the Englishman Walter of Henley (XIII-1), by the Jew Joseph ben Samson (XIII-1). The latter compiled a Hebrew-French glossary for the Old Testament, explaining the la'azim which had gradually found their way into the Hebrew speech of French Jews. French was spreading all over Western Europe including Scandinavia, not as common speech, but as a sort of court language succeeding Latin. This movement gained strength in the second half of the thirteenth century. Out of thirty-seven accounts of pilgrimages to the Holy Land of that period, about twenty-eight were in Latin and eight in French. Books of various kinds were composed in French by Villard de Honnecourt, Richard de Fournival, Etienne Boileau, Pierre de Fontaines, Philippe Beaumanoir, Jean de Meung; and at least three Italians wrote in French, Aldobrandin of Siena (1256), Brunetto Latini (1266), and Rustichello of Pisa (1298). All that under the growing shadow of Dante!

This success of French as a literary language is the more remarkable when we realize how inadequate the writing was as compared with the spoken reality. Many French phonemes were entirely new and could not be reproduced with the alphabet inherited from Latin.[28] In great contrast with the Sanskrit, Greek, and even Latin scripts, which were phonetically correct, the French was very incorrect, for the simple reason that it was written by means of a script adapted to the phonetic requirements of another language. This must have been a cause of great difficulty to foreigners then as it is today. The difficulties of a language, however, do not handicap its diffusion, nor do the facilities of another favor it, as much as one would expect. A language is popular not because it is easy but because people want it, and if they want it badly enough they are willing to pay a high price for it.

The Hebrew-French glossary of Joseph ben Samson has already been alluded to; other French glossaries were gradually accumulated in the form of marginal glosses to Biblical MSS and to other treatises, or of systematic collections (often bilingual, Latin-French) putting together the words relative to the parts of the body, domestic utensils, plants, etc., and even of collections in alphabetic order.[29] This method was stimulated by the Catholicon, the Latin dictionary completed in 1286 by Giovanni Balbi (XIII-2) of Genoa, which obtained considerable success. There are a great many MSS of it, and it was finally adapted to the French language, but we must not anticipate. Thus lexicographical consciousness was slowly maturing; on

[28] Ferdinand Brunot: Histoire de la langue française (1, 483–85, Paris 1905). To be sure, defective writing did not disturb oral traditions, which were predominant at least for poetry.

[29] Mario Roques: Lexiques alphabétiques français (2 vols., Paris 1936–38).

the other hand, I am not acquainted with any grammatical efforts worth mentioning anterior to the sixteenth century.

Turning to poetry, enough of it was written in the first half of the fourteenth century to ennoble the French language and to place it above every other vernacular, except Italian, which the genius of Dante and Petrarca was putting out of reach. Jean de Meung (XIII-2) had completed the Roman de la rose before the end of his century, but he lived until 1305. Chrétien Legouais's Ovide moralisé was composed about the same time, being dedicated to queen Jeanne (queen 1284–1305). Jean Pitart, more famous as a surgeon, rhymed the Dit de bigamie. Geoffroy of Paris and Guillaume Guiard versified chronicles. Guillaume Deguilleville wrote his Pélérinages, three religious poems which served to edify many generations not only of Frenchmen but also of Englishmen, Spaniards, and even Germans. The greatest of these poets, Guillaume de Machaut, the French Petrarca, being secretary to John of Luxemburg, king of Bohemia, traveled with him and thus encouraged the expansion of French poetry across Europe. He was a musician as well as a poet, and, together with Philippe de Vitry, the main promoter of the ars nova in France and wherever the French influence was strong enough.

In the meanwhile philosophical reflections on many subjects were made available to French readers by the priest Jean Bonnet or whoever else was the author of the scientific dialogue Placides et Timéo ou Livre des secrets aux philosophes. This was rather naïve, but it set people thinking. It was a popular introduction to scientific consciousness.

Many works were being translated from Latin into French, a fact which proves that there existed a growing public for serious reading in the vernacular. Jean de Prouville translated the surgical treatise of the abbé Poutrel (?); the south Italian Bartolommeo Siginulfo, the letters to Lucilius for Charles II of Anjou; Arnaud de Quinquempoix, astrological treatises; Pierre Bersuire, Livy's Decades; and Jean de Vignai, various historical texts. The last named revised the French version of the Gospels of the Day. His was only one Biblical version among a good many, the earliest of which date back to the beginning of the twelfth century. All these French versions, including Vignai's, were made from the Latin without reference to the Hebrew and Greek originals.[30] The non-Biblical versions from the Latin form an imposing group which was destined to be considerably increased in the second half of the century, thanks to royal patronage.

The main scientific book written in French was the anonymous translation of Henri de Mondeville's Surgery. In spite of many crudities and imperfections, it is an important landmark in the history of French scientific terminology, the cradle of many medical terms which have endured.

The geographical and historical literature is very rich. Not to speak of Marco Polo's reminiscences, written down by Rustichello of Pisa at the very end of the thirteenth century, we have the Livre de l'Estat du grant Caan of John of Cora (it was written in Latin but we know it only through an almost contemporary French version), the Fleur des histoires de la terre d'Orient by the Armenian monk Hayton, the French version of the Chronicle of Morea, the rhymed chronicles of France by Guillaume Guiard, and of Paris by Geoffroy of Paris. The outstanding book of that group, and one of the greatest of the Christian Middle Ages, was the

[30] An elaborate study of them was made by Samuel Berger: La Bible française au Moyen âge. Etude sur les plus anciennes versions de la Bible écrites en prose de langue d'oïl (466 p., Paris 1884).

history of St. Louis, the composition of which occupied and solaced Joinville's old age.

We have already spoken of the Latin-French glossaries which were the natural by-products of translating activities, and were used mainly by Frenchmen. As the French language was diffused in higher circles abroad, there was a growing need of "helps" for its study. A most interesting group of conversation manuals has come down to us.[31] These manuals were called "livres benoîts" because they began with an invocation to the Holy Trinity and the "benoîte" (i.e., blessed) Virgin; they were also called "Livres des métiers" because the earliest of their kind was the Livre des mestiers composed by a schoolmaster of Bruges c. 1340. The title was due to the importance of the métiers (the arts and their guilds) in Bruges; it may have been a conscious or unconscious imitation of the title used by Etienne Boileau (XIII-2) or Stephanus Bibens aquam for his collection of the guild usages of Paris. The composition of this French-Flemish manual of conversation was natural enough in Bruges, where the French language was becoming more and more necessary at least in court circles. Three languages were thus used in the great commercial city: Flemish was the language of common intercourse; French, that of the counts of Flanders of the house of Dampierre (1278–1384), aping their liege lords, the kings of France; Latin, that of the church. The Livre des métiers was used to bridge the gap Flemish-French (Picard dialect). It is a document of great interest not only from the linguistic point of view, but also for the study of manners and folklore. There is but a single MS of it, in the Dutch collection of the Bibliothèque nationale, Paris. It was edited by Henri Michelant (Paris 1875), and by Jean Gessler (1931).

The Livre des métiers was found so useful and attractive that various imitations of it were soon produced. The first, called Gesprächbüchlein, was probably composed in the third quarter of the fourteenth century; and the unique MS of it in Cologne dates c. 1420. It was edited by A. H. Hoffmann von Fallersleben: Horae belgicae (pars IX, Hannover 1854) and by Gessler (1931). Another imitation, Franco-English, entitled Ryght good lernyng, was prepared by William Caxton, who resided some time in Bruges (c. 1441–70), and printed by him in Westminster c. 1483. New editions by Henry Bradley: Dialogues in French and English by William Caxton (Early English Text Society, London 1900) and by Gessler (1931). An adaptation of the original French-Flemish text, Vocabulair pour aprendre Romain et Flameng, was printed in Antwerp by Roland Van den Dorpe before 1501, and reprinted by Gessler (1931).

Paul Dorveaux: Note sur la médecine en Flandre au XIVe siècle (Janus 7, 197–98, 1902). Coulton (p. 326, 1938b).

French in England. The French language had a privileged position in England; it was the noble tongue next to Latin, and thus English boys of the upper classes were obliged to be trilingual.[32] They learned English from their mothers, and from the peasants and the servants, and as time went on used it more and more among themselves, but for the church they had to know Latin, and for the law, for society, for higher educational purposes they had to know French. The result can readily be imagined. Most of them did not know well either Latin or French, and they

[31] The information which follows is taken from the excellent edition of the Livre des mestiers de Bruges et ses dérivés by Jean Gessler (6 fascicles in a box, Bruges 1931; Isis 19, 261).

[32] The origins of that situation have been discussed, and some prejudices relative to it corrected, by Percy Van Dyke Shelly: English and French in England 1066–1100 (thesis, 98 p., Philadelphia 1921).

spoke English roughly as one speaks a dialect. The requirements were too high even for the average run of clerks, and bishops were annoyed and had to be constantly on the alert because so many of the priests did not know enough Latin to read the Bible or the Offices without occasional misunderstandings (Coulton 1940).

Hence we have also a trilingual literature in England. The most important books appeared in Latin because of the ecclesiastical prestige of that language; those second in importance were published in French because of its social glamour; to the English speech were left the needs of the hearth and of the heart. This seemed little, but happily it was very much.

To illustrate the services which were expected in England from the French language, it will suffice to recall the Britton, a French abridgment of the De legibus of Henry de Bracton (XIII-2), written about the end of the thirteenth century. This suggests that French was then beginning to replace Latin, and that there was a group of people to whom French, legal French, was clearer and more agreeable than either Latin or English. Peter of Langtoft wrote an English chronicle in French verse, and Nicholas Trevet composed his chronicle of the world in French before translating it into Latin. A treatise on hunting was composed by William Twici and John Gyfford for Edward II. Curious information on the teaching of French from the cradle on is given by Ranulf Higden in his Polychronicon. Some attention was paid to the study of French in Oxford and Cambridge. In Queen's College, founded in Oxford 1341, scholars were allowed to talk French instead of Latin at table; English of course was out of the question. In Pembroke, founded in Cambridge 1347, students of French birth were accorded preference over others. This may have been due to the fact that the founder of Pembroke was a French woman, Marie, daughter of the count of Saint Pol (at that time widow of the earl of Pembroke), or to the desire for improving French scholarship. Leach (p. 195, 1916); Rashdall (3, 162, 208, 305, 1936).

English students would need glossaries to help them accumulate and retain the French vocables, and such glossaries (English-French or English-French-Latin) were provided from the twelfth century on and even more early. For example:

1. English-French legal gloss (c. 1130–50), represented by some 40 MSS.
2. MS Digby 172 (c. 1150–1200). Anglo-French-English glosses.
3. MS Stowe 57 (c. 1200). French and English equivalents of Latin names of animals.
4. MS Harvey 978 (c. 1265). French and English equivalents of plant names. For plant names, see John Earle: English plant names from the tenth to the fifteenth century (234 p., Oxford 1880); George Henslow: Medical works of the fourteenth century, together with a list of plants (293 p., London 1899).
5. Cambridge-Arundel gloss. Two MSS of the first quarter of the fourteenth century. English-French glossary.
6. Cambridge E E gloss, Nominale sive verbale in gallicis cum expositione eiusdem in anglicis. French-English glossary of words arranged by topics—parts of the body, utensils, winds and storms, etc., 888 verses.

Wells (p. 430–31, 1926) and supplements.

The Volume of vocabularies published by Thomas Wright (Liverpool 1857) contains a number of French glosses and a French didactic poem (p. 142–74), La doctrine (The teaching), written by Walter de Biblesworth for the lady Dionysia de Monchensi, who died in 1313. The purpose of Walter's Doctrine was to provide his gentle readers with an abundant French vocabulary suitable to their needs.

9. *English*

In addition to being subordinated to Latin and French for the higher purposes of life, English was handicapped by dialectal rivalries. Three dialects were competing for supremacy, a southern one (south of the Thames), a northern one, and a Midland one (around London). This last named finally won, partly because it was used in the metropolis (even as the Ile-de-France dialect dominated the other langue-d'oïl ones), partly because of the literary genius of Chaucer and Wycliffe; but we must not anticipate.

In the time of Higden, the situation of the English language was pretty bad, yet it was beginning to improve about the middle of the century. English was hardly used for any scientific purpose. We have a geometrical treatise, but it may be later than 1350 and is very short. Happily, it was felt that devotion and morality did not concern gentlemen only and that it was necessary to teach them to the people, and thus we have a series of very remarkable didactic treatises. To begin with, Robert Mannyng in his Handlyng synne translated a treatise on sins which had been written in French in the previous century by another Englishman; he also wrote a rhymed chronicle of England from Noah to 1307. Then another treatise on sins and virtues, a more famous one, the Somme le roi of the Dominican Laurent, was put into English by Michael of Northgate under the excellent title The ayenbite of inwyt. Finally we have the writings of Richard Rolle, which are not inconsiderable even if the Pricke of conscience is taken away from him. Rolle was equally familiar with English and with Latin, and some of his works exist in both languages; it is not easy to say whether he wrote them himself in either language, or in which first.

It is noteworthy that the main, if not the only, English prose writings of this period worth mentioning are books of moral and religious edification. It was felt that the common people had souls, souls which were worth saving, and that could be done only by means of the English language.

10. *Dutch*

The word Dutch is here used to designate both Dutch (Hollandsch) and Flemish, in spite of the fact that these two words are now used to designate respectively the northern and southern dialects of a single literary language, the official designation of which is Netherlandish.[33] The reasons for keeping the designation Dutch for the literary language are, first, that that was the mediaeval term. Thus the literary founder of the language, Jacob van Maerlant (XIII-2), was called "die vader der dietscher dichtren algader" (father of all the Dutch poets). The word Dietsch (and its variants Dutch, Duitsch, Deutsch) is derived from diet (meaning people, populus). The Dietsch language was the language of the people as opposed to that of learned men, Latin. The term Dietsch was replaced by Nederlandsch only about the middle of the sixteenth century.[34] In the second place, Dutch is the term most familiar to English readers.

Unfortunately, Dutch may be confused with Deutsch (as in the phrase Pennsylvania Dutch), but the confusion rests on historical reality. The Dutch dialects

[33] The excellent grammar by Jozef Vercoullie which the author studied as a child was entitled Nederlandsche spraakkunst (150 p., Gent 1894). He is still treasuring his annotated copy of it.

[34] Joos Lambrecht of Ghent (d. c. 1556) published in 1549 a book entitled Nederlandsche spellinghe, of which a facsimile was produced in 1882 by the Society of Flemish Bibliophiles. It deals not only with grammar, but with orthography and phonetics. This Lambrecht was one of the forerunners of scientific phonetics.

indeed are very close to the Low German ones (Plattdeutsch), of which the earliest monument is the Heliand (The Saviour), a poem in "old Saxon" on the life of Christ composed c. 835.

The Dutch language had been raised to a very high level by Jacob van Maerlant, who died c. 1299, that is, just when our period opens. Thanks to Maerlant, Dutch was then as respectable a vernacular as any other in Europe. His example was followed by many writers, most of whom were like himself Flemings, not Hollanders.

In fact, the only Hollander we came across is Melis Stoke, who wrote a chronicle in verse to 1305. All others are Flemings. Lodewijk van Velthem continued the Historical mirror of Maerlant to 1316 and translated books from Latin and French. French was the court language in Flanders (but not the administrative or legal language, as in England) because of the Francophilism of the house of Dampierre,[35] which was then ruling the county; moreover, the literary prestige of French romances and chansons was considerable. Jan van Boendale composed a rhymed chronicle of Brabant to 1350. These works, however valuable for the determination of historical facts, are not extraordinary. We expect local chronicles to be written in the local idiom. The remaining works to be quoted are more startling.

Two important surgical treatises were written in Dutch, by Jan Yperman and by Thomas Scellinck. Yperman also wrote a treatise on practical medicine in the same language. A number of books on theology and mystical philosophy were produced by Jan van Ruysbroeck, who may be called the founder of the Dutch philosophical language.

By the middle of the fourteenth century, Dutch had established itself as the vehicle not only of common life and poetry, but of science and philosophy. Moreover, "common life" as Ruysbroeck interpreted it was something sacred; he brought out the nobility and beauty of it, its grandeur and servitude, and prepared the way for the Brethren of "Common life" and the Christian renaissance which blossomed out in the Dutch country soon after his death.

11. *German*

The earliest documents in the German language date from the eighth century, but there was no literature for centuries, and the dialectal differences were many and deep. Did Charlemagne (VIII-2) and his advisers take much interest in the language? Certainly not enough to standardize it. The earliest glossary is the Glossaria latina-theodisca of Hrabanus Maurus (IX-1), but grammatical consciousness was very slow in developing. Learned men knew Latin grammar; they studied it in the catechism of Donatus (IV-1), in Priscianus (VI-1), or in later writings derived from these, e.g., Hrabanus wrote an abridgment of Priscianus which enjoyed some popularity. Strangely enough, these people did not think of applying Latin grammar to their own vernacular (the statement is true not only for German but for other vernaculars), or they did not consider it worth while. The Germans were especially slow in this respect. Their first grammars did not appear until the fifteenth century; they published in that century a German version of Donatus wherein the Latin paradigms were naturally translated in the form of German paradigms, but the latter were given only to explain the Latin rules, not the German! The earliest German grammar is the Tractatulus dans modum teutonisandi casus

[35] The family originated in Dampierre (dépt. Aube) in Champagne pouilleuse.

et tempora written by one "doctor decretorum" Henricus in Münster i.W. 1451. The title of that book is dog Latin, but the text itself, German.[36]

To return to the language, the earliest monument is the Nibelungenlied (XII-2), a cycle of folk epics which was unified about the beginning of the thirteenth century. There are a few medical texts which may date back to the beginning of the thirteenth century (Introd. 2, 659), and the Sächsische Weltchronik ascribed to Eike von Repgow (XIII-1).

By the beginning of the fourteenth century the language was fully ready for all kinds of intellectual purposes in spite of its lack of grammatical consciousness. Didactic poems were written in Low German by Eberhard von Wampen and in Swiss German by Ulrich Boner. Toward the end of our period (1349), the Bavarian Conrad von Megenberg composed his natural history, Das Buch der Natur, and before that he had already written his astronomy, the Deutsche Sphaera. He may be called the founder of the German scientific language, even as his younger contemporary Nicole Oresme (XIV-2) would be a little later the founder of the French scientific language.

The philosophic terminology was created by a number of mystics who were the banner bearers of German culture in those days and have remained until now among the most lovable representatives of it, Meister Eckhart, Johann Tauler, Suso, and the unknown author of the Theologia Deutsch.

Contemporary medicine is represented, strangely enough, by an Italian, Albert of Parma, established in Strassburg. Ottokar of Styria compiled an immense rhymed chronicle (almost four times longer than the Iliad and the Odyssey put together, but doggerel rhymes, not poetry), and Ludolf of Sudheim wrote an account of his travels to the Holy Land.

The most efficient workshops for the new language were provided by lawyers, who were constantly obliged to adapt it to the needs of life. The Sachsenspiegel (XIII-1) and the Schwabenspiegel (XIII-2) have been discussed in volume 2. To these were added the Rechtsbuch compiled by the Bavarian jurist Ruprecht von Freising, the Landrechtsbuch, and the commentaries of Johann von Buch.

12. *Scandinavian*

The oldest Germanic texts which have come down to us are Scandinavian inscriptions in runic alphabet dating back to the third century. These inscriptions are older even than the Gothic translation of the Bible by Ulfilas (IV-1), though they are comparatively insignificant. Moreover, after a while these runic texts stopped, and there is a gap of a few centuries before other Scandinavian texts made their appearance.

The earliest texts of the new series date from the eighth century and are in Norwegian, a language which spread as far as Scotland, Ireland, and even Iceland. It shared in the great cultural awakening of the last-named country and developed there into a separate language, Icelandic, to which so much prestige was given by outstanding literary creations that it became one of the most important languages of the Middle Ages.

[36] The Tractatulus has been reprinted in Jahrbuch des Vereins für niederdeutsche Sprachforschung (p. 36-56, 1877). Max Hermann Jellinek: Geschichte der neuhochdeutschen Grammatik von den Anfängen bis auf Johann Christoph Adelung, gest. 1806 (2 vols., Heidelberg 1913-14).

The value of Icelandic literature, with regard to substance as well as to form, has been made abundantly clear to our readers. See the articles on the Edda (XII-1), on the mathematician Stjörnu Oddi (XII-1), above all on the famous historians Ari Fródi Thorgilsson (XII-1), Snorri Sturluson (XIII-1), and Sturla Thórdarson (XIII-2); then think of the anonymous authors of sagas (epic stories partly legendary, partly historical) and compilers of gragas[37] (legal texts). Surely that was a great wealth for the culture which originated in a small island reaching the Arctic Circle; it would be great wealth for any country, even those which enjoy perfect climates. By the fourteenth century the golden age of Icelandic was over, and we had to deal with but a single author, Haukr Erlendsson.

In the meanwhile, Norwegian culture (as distinguished from its Icelandic offshoot) had progressed. The Norwegian spirit of adventure is illustrated by the royal pilgrim Sigurd of Norway (XII-1) and the sailor Skopti Ogmundson (beginning of XII; Introd. 2, 224); the intensity of its scientific spirit is proved by the Konungs skuggsjá (XIII-1), one of the most original encyclopaedias of mediaeval times. Yet the Norwegian language in which it was written did not survive mediaeval conditions.

From the thirteenth century on, Scandinavian letters were represented mostly by Icelandic writings, and by Danish and Swedish, which now began to appear. The interrelations between these three languages are too complex to be set forth here. For example, the writings of the leading Danish scientist, Henrik Harpestraeng (XIII-1), have come down to us in a number of MSS, most of them in Icelandic, others in Swedish,[38] Norwegian, Danish, not to speak of Latin versions. We cannot enter into the intricate discussions caused by the simultaneous use of four Scandinavian languages. It will suffice to have proved the great importance of these languages as a whole, and, above all, of Icelandic.

Should we try to evaluate the maturity of Icelandic, as we have done for other languages, by the investigation of its grammatical consciousness, we should find treatises on prosody in the so-called Edda Snorra Sturlusonar, which dates back to the middle of the twelfth century, and grammatical treatises in other Eddas (Introd. 2, 202, 678).[39] Thus Icelandic was one of the earliest European vernaculars which became for intrinsic and extrinsic reasons a scientific, full-fledged language. It is possible that its remoteness from Latin invited and facilitated its early grammatical development.

13. *Greek*

We need not deal with Greek as we have done with many vernaculars whose graduation to the level of formal languages had to be proved. Greek had reached that level many centuries before those vernaculars were born. The Homeric poems are the earliest literary monuments of Europe, and they are among the earliest for the whole world. Their maturity and their beauty imply centuries of preparation. From that time on, that is, from pre-Homeric days, the Greek language has never interrupted its development for very long; it has known periods of exhaustion and sleep, but it has never died.

[37] On gragas (Swedish, grågås) see Nordisk Familjebok (10, 454–55, Stockholm 1909).

[38] The Swedish philologist Johan Erik Rydquist (1800–77) placed the classical age of the Swedish language about the year 1300. According to Michel Bréal: Essai de sémantique (p. 296, Paris 1897).

[39] The first grammatical treatise of the Snorra Edda dates from the middle or second half of the twelfth century. It was edited by Finnur Jónsson and Verner Dahlerup (Copenhagen 1886). Anne Holtsmark: En islandsk scholasticus fra det 12. århundre (121 p., Oslo 1936; Isis 29, 110).

Its prestige was established by Homer and other poets, by a long series of masterpieces in every field of literature, science, and philosophy, and finally by the Septuagint (III-1 B.C.) and the New Testament. The Septuagint, it is true, was a translation, but much closer to the inspired original than the Vulgate. The New Testament was the original text of a new revelation, the Christian revelation. Thus Greek was not only a language of immemorial fame in the world of letters, it was also a sacred language, comparable in this respect to Hebrew; to the faithful it was the language of God, the language of heaven.

This does not mean that Greek had remained what it was in Homer's days. On the contrary, it had changed very much, for it had remained alive. As for every other organism, there are but two alternatives for languages, to change or to die. Greek, unlike Latin, never died; it never ceased to be spoken by women and children as well as by men, and thus it never created opportunities for new languages to develop at its own expense. Its wide diffusion exposed it to the competition of many tongues and to the danger of contamination by them, but its vitality was always sufficient to overcome those perils. The persistence of the Greek language was due to its vitality, but also to the fact that the changes which befell it were not simply centrifugal, but quite as often centripetal. For example, the many dialects of ancient Greek were harmonized and disappeared in the common tongue of Hellenistic times, *ἡ κοινὴ διάλεκτος* (or simply the *κοινή*). As that *κοινή* was spoken in many localities (Greece proper, Constantinople, mountain districts, islands, Asia Minor, Egypt, southern Italy, Corsica, coasts of the Black Sea, etc.), widely separated and very different from one another, it might have disintegrated; its unity was preserved by its literary heritage on the one hand, and by the administrative unity and prestige of the Byzantine Empire. It may be that the main explanation is political; Latin broke into fragments and Greek did not, because the Eastern Empire lasted a thousand years longer than the Western one.

The unifying function of a great literature is well illustrated in the case of Greek. The Homeric poems were kept alive by rhapsodists or reciters throughout the Hellenic, Hellenistic, and Byzantine ages; thanks to these reciters, the poems were brought continually to the attention not of scholars only, but of all kinds of people. References to them are preserved in literature and in everyday documents (papyri).[40]

There never was a time when an educated Greek could not read the masterpieces of his ancestors, though there were times when he read them less, and also periods of revival and "Atticism," e.g., under Photios (IX-2), Michael Psellos (XI-2), Anna Comnena (XII-1), Demetrios Triclinios. It may have been sometimes difficult for him to understand the best works of the golden age because of their grammatical, rhetorical, and intellectual subtleties, but he never could have any difficulty whatsoever in reading the Septuagint, the Gospels, the church rituals, or the innumerable lives of saints.[41]

[40] A. S. Hunt and C. C. Edgar: Select papyri (2, 439, 1934). No. 359, engagement of performers, including a Homeric reciter (*ὁμηριστής*), for a feast in Arsinoe, Fayum (late third century). According to Athenaeos (III-1), *ὁμηρισταί* were first called to the stage by Demetrios Phalereus (Dipnosophists XIV, 620b), that is, in the last quarter of the fourth century, B.C., but they functioned more informally before that time and later.

[41] For these see Bibliotheca hagiographica graeca, ediderunt socii bollandiani. Editio altera emendatior, accedit synopsis metaphrastica (316 p., Bruxelles 1909). The "synopsis metaphrastica" is the menology compiled by Symeon Metaphrastes (X-2), which had as much success in the Orthodox church as the Legenda aurea of James of Voragine (XIII-2) in the Catholic one. By the way, when I spoke of Symeon Metaphastes in Introd. 1, 686, I did not explain the meaning of his name. *Μεταφράζειν* generally means to paraphrase, to translate, but here the connotation is to express in good Greek as opposed to the vulgar.

The Greek language changed considerably throughout the centuries, but retained its integrity. There never was a solution of continuity. In spite of many grammatical simplifications and of vocabulary additions and subtractions, the language has remained essentially the same language from Homer down to our own days. Instead of being disintegrated into other languages, its inherent difficulties caused it to undergo a double development on two levels of refinement, on the one hand the purer kind of language (ἡ καθαρεύουσα), restricted to the belles lettres and more formal uses, on the other hand the vulgar language (γλῶσσα δημώδης, ἁπλῆ, ἁπλοελληνική, καθημαξευμένη, καθωμιλημένη, Ῥωμαιïκή, δημοτική) spoken by everybody. It may be observed that a similar duplication of language, the pure or more sophisticated versus the informal, has occurred in every European vernacular without jeopardizing in the least its literary integrity.[42] The Greek schism was much deeper than the one obtaining in, say, French or English, but not essentially different.

In the case of these vernaculars as in the case of Greek, the integrity of the purer language was preserved by the combined strength of literary tradition and administrative unity. The European vernaculars developed, in spite of the prestige of Latin literature, because the very leaders of the new European countries ceased to understand Latin; neither literary prestige nor ecclesiastical ritual suffices to preserve a language if it be not buttressed by administrative procedure and sanctioned by the best people ("le bon usage").

The Greek language was submitted to unusual dangers when Constantinople was taken by the crusaders in 1204 and the Greek world was dominated by Western rulers (1204–61). The Latin domination was extended to Greece, e.g., the "Duchy of Athens," ruled successively by the La Roche and the Brienne families, then by Catalans, Sicilians, Florentines, and Venetians! Each of these predatory nations brought its own language and usages, favored its own courtiers and merchants, etc., and yet the Greek language emerged from that long ordeal, tainted with foreign idioms to be sure, yet essentially unchanged. Those vicissitudes are well illustrated by the Chronicle of Morea, wherein they were told in Greek, French, Italian, and Catalan. The three last-named languages were actually spoken in the Greek peninsula with various degrees of success; the salvation of Greek may be partly ascribed to the competition of its rivals among themselves; it was due primarily to its own vigor and dignity.

That vigor is proved by the contemporary writings. It would take too long to discuss all of these, for I deal with more than thirty Greek authors in the first half of the fourteenth century. It will suffice to consider the "grammarians," the men who took special pride in their own language and were anxious to understand its structure and to analyze its wealth. These grammarians were not by any means professionals, except perhaps two of them, Triclinios and Thomas Magister; the others were mathematicians, historians, jurists, theologians.

Grammatical treatises were composed by Maximos Planudes (XIII-2), Manuel Moschopulos, Nicolaos Rhabdas, Matthaios Blastares, Nicephoros Gregoras. The grammatical questions of Moschopulos are of special importance in the history of classical philology, because they were among the first to be printed and were much used by the early students of Greek in the West. Collections of words and phrases

[42] Literate Germans, Frenchmen, Flemings, e.g. country physicians, can and do speak correctly on formal occasions, but enjoy dialectical speech in their intimate circle, this being a form of relaxation or a means of proving their good nature and comradeship. According to G. L. Kittredge (Webster's), "Every educated person speaks his mother tongue in at least two ways, and the difference between the dignified and the colloquial style is considerable." Other differences exist between the written and the spoken style of even the most fastidious people.

were compiled by Moschopulos, Thomas Magister, and Constantinos Armenopulos. It is hardly necessary to recall Planudes' share in the reconstitution of the "Greek anthology," but he compiled two other anthologies. We owe an abundant collection of scholia on the ancient classics to Moschopulos and Demetrios Triclinios; Gregoras explained Odysseus' wanderings. Finally, Barlaam was one of the earliest transmitters of Greek scholarship to the West.

This introduces the question of Greek learning in the West. That learning had gradually, though very slowly, increased throughout the centuries. The time when a scholar like John Scot Erigena (IX-2) stood almost alone[43] because of his knowledge of Greek, that time was long past. I have described in volume 2 the long series of translations from the Greek into Latin which were made in the twelfth and thirteenth centuries by a fine series of scholars culminating in the Flemish Dominican Willem of Moerbeke (XIII-2).[44] It is probable that some teaching of Greek was organized at the short-lived College of Constantinople established in Paris shortly after the Latin conquest (1204).[45] A century later at the council of Vienne in Dauphiné (1311–12) it was decided to establish chairs of Greek, Hebrew, Arabic, and Chaldaean in five universities, Rome, Paris, Oxford, Bologna, and Salamanca. It is true little was done, and the purpose was not so much learning as missionary propaganda. The visits of Barlaam to the court of Naples and his interviews with Boccaccio and Petrarca were probably more influential. Barlaam planted living seeds which would germinate in due time. The translations occupied a few scholars but made Greek learning less necessary for the others. The tradition of Greek teaching did not begin until a generation later, and did not really flourish until the fifteenth and sixteenth centuries.

14. *Slavonic Languages*

The Slavonic languages appear very seldom in our survey. Let us consider first the Western forms, Czech and Polish. The earliest Czech texts go back to the thirteenth century, and by the beginning of the fourteenth century (c. 1312) we have already a literary monument of great merit, the rhymed chronicle of Dalimil. Polish was less advanced; we came across a few botanical glosses which establish its existence, hardly more.

The southern form was the earliest Slavonic dialect to attain maturity, for St. Cyril (IX-2) used it for his translation of the Septuagint, and "old Slavonic," as that language came to be called, remained the vehicle of Russian orthodoxy. The early translators could not help making grammatical remarks suggested by the differences between their language and the Greek originals; e.g., differences in the gender of certain nouns caused the Slavonic word to be a poor substitute for the Greek one. The earliest Slavonic grammar, entitled O vosmi chastyakh slova (On the eight parts of speech), reproducing the Byzantine model *περὶ τῶν ὀκτὼ μερῶν τοῦ*

[43] Henry Bett began his study of Erigena (Cambridge 1925) with the statement, "He is the loneliest figure in the history of European thought." Erigena owed his extraordinary knowledge of Greek to his education in an Irish monastery, Ireland being the only country of Western Europe where the teaching of Greek had survived.

[44] Those translations are enumerated in Introd. vol. 2: for XII-1, p. 115; for XII-2, p. 283; for XIII-1, p. 493; for XIII-2, p. 716.

[45] Rashdall (1, 505, 1936). Abel Lefranc: Histoire du Collège de France (p. 3–5, 17, Paris 1893). The oldest charter concerning the College of Constantinople is a bull of Innocent IV, c. 1243–48. The purpose was to teach and Westernize Oriental scholars; there were 20 Oriental scholars in Paris 1286. In 1362, there remained only one student, and the building of that college, located "in vico Sine capite, prope plateam Mauberti" (= place Maubert), was given up.

λόγου, seems to have been composed in Serbia in the first half of the fourteenth century. Bulgarian and Russian versions appeared only later.

The main eastern form, or (Great) Russian, is represented in our book only by the account of a pilgrimage made by Stephen of Novgorod to Constantinople and beyond.

15. *Armenian*

The Armenian language is very ancient, but its earliest monuments date only from the fifth century. St. Mesrop (V-1), who invented a special alphabet for it,[46] began a translation of the Bible which was completed by Moses of Chorene (V-1). That translation was derived from the Septuagint, but took into account the investigations of Origen (III-1), partly based on Hebrew traditions. Armenian chronicles were written by Stephen Asolik (XI-1) and Matthew of Edessa (XII-1). The new golden age of Armenian literature in the twelfth century was linguistically different from the earlier, fifth-century, one because it took place not in Greater Armenia (Anatolia), but in Lesser Armenia (Cilicia); it originated the western tradition and language, as against the older and eastern one.

Aristaces the Grammarian (XIII-1) compiled an Armenian dictionary, and the grammar was codified by Vardan the Great (XIII-2). On the basis of Vardan's work and other Armenian treatises and of the Greek grammar of Dionysios Thrax (II-2 B.C.), John of Erzinjān (XIII-2) composed a new grammar. This takes us well into the fourteenth century, for John lived until 1326.

John of Erzinjān translated a treatise of St. Thomas into Armenian. Many other scholars were enrolled by the Catholic church to put Latin theology into Armenian shape: Zacharias of Dsordsor, bishop of Ardaz and abbot of Arzakh (thirteenth century, according to Chevalier), Bartholomew of Bologna, Jacob the Dragoman, John of Karīn, Nerses Balì. All these men were Armenians except the Italian Dominican Bartholomew, who may be called the first Western Armenologist.

The greatest Armenian writer of the period was Stephen Orbelian (XIII-2), who remained faithful to his church and his people, but by 1304 he was dead and the field was open to Dominican missionaries and their converts. The naturalist Thomas of Cilicia may have flourished at this time. Hayton the Monk, who became famous because of his French chronicle of the Near East (c. 1307), may have written a chronography and other books in Armenian before 1299.

16. *Georgian*

The only Caucasic language which was written in mediaeval times was Georgian or Iberian. See the articles by prince N. Troubetzkoy and A. Meillet in Meillet and Cohen (p. 327–44, 1924), and my note on Georgian historiography in section XII above.

17. *Syriac*

The ancient form of Syriac called Aramaic[47] dates back at least to the eighth century B.C. Aramaic dialects were spoken all over the Persian and Macedonian

[46] The oldest specimen of Armenian script is an Armenian-Greek papyrus, containing a kind of conversation manual, dating from before the Muslim conquest of Egypt (640). Maurice Leroy: Un papyrus arméno-grec (Byzantion 13, 513–37, 1938). The oldest Armenian MS is a tetraevangel in Moscow, copied in 887.

[47] The ancient name of Syria was Aram, occurring many times in the Old Testament. The name Syria is derived from Suri, denoting in Assyrian inscriptions a district of the upper Euphrates. Greek usage (ἡ Συρία), from Herodotos down, caused the word Syria to supersede Aram.

empires by peoples of many races, nationalities, and religions.[48] There are a few Aramaic fragments in the Old Testament. In Roman times, Aramaic had almost completely superseded Hebrew in Palestine, and Christ spoke no other language, witness familiar sayings in the Gospels, especially Mark's.[49] It was given wide currency by the early Christians, especially those established around Edessa (Urfa in the upper Euphrates district, the ancient Osroëne) or those for whom Edessa had become (in the second century) the religious and spiritual center, the new Athens.

About the middle of the second century, if not before, the Old Testament was translated into Aramaic or Syriac (from now on I shall use the latter word). That translation, called Pĕshīṭtā (Introd. 1, 291), was made probably in Edessa, from the Hebrew but with due reference to the Septuagint. The first Syriac New Testament dates also from the second century, being derived from the Diatessaron.[50] These versions of the Old and New Testaments were followed by various others which need not be enumerated here. The point is that by the end of the second century the Syriac language was solidly established by the existence of these two Biblical monuments.

A little later a new center of Syriac learning was established much farther East, by Nestorians and other refugees, in Jundīshāpūr (not far from Susa). This second center was far more cosmopolitan; the mixture of Greek, Iranian, Hindu, and Syriac ideas favored the development there of a famous medical school (Introd. 1, 435; Isis 16, 480). It may be that there was already some rudimentary medical teaching in Edessa (second and third centuries); the school of Jundīshāpūr began later, perhaps much later (fourth or fifth century?); it was flourishing in the sixth century. The Syriac anatomical and medical texts edited by E. Wallis Budge (1913; Introd. 1, 309) may date back to the second century, but they are possibly much later, even posterior to Sergios of Resaina (VI-1), who translated many philosophical, scientific, and medical books from Greek into Syriac.

Syriac continued to be spoken by Eastern Jews. The Gemārā, a part of the Talmud, completing the Mishnāh, was written in Syriac. As late as the tenth century Sherira Gaon (X-2) was writing consilia in Syriac as well as in Hebrew.

To return to the Christians, from the middle of the fifth century on, the Syriac-speaking people were hopelessly divided into two opposite heresies, the Nestorians, according to whom there are two natures and two persons in Christ, and the Eutychians or Monophysites, according to whom there is but one nature and one person.[51] Hence in any study of the Syriac language and literature one is obliged to take into account two separate traditions, the Nestorian and the Monophysitic.

The break between the two sects was so complete that they could not be satisfied

[48] Aramaic was the international language of the Achaemenian empire (558–330 B.C.), which at its height extended from Egypt to India. At the time of Alexander's conquests (334–23 B.C.), the two outstanding languages of Western Asia were Aramaic and Greek.

[49] Mark 5:41, ταλιθά, κοῦμι; 7:34, ἐφφαθά; 14:36, ἀββᾶ; 15:34, Ἐλωΐ, λαμὰ σαβαχθανί.

[50] To my note ad hoc (Introd. 1, 292) should be added the new, excellent edition by A. S. Marmardji (Dominican of the Ecole biblique of Jerusalem): Diatessaron de Tatien. Texte arabe établi, traduit en français, collationné avec les anciennes versions syriaques . . . (760 p., Beyrouth 1935).

[51] The orthodox view is that there are two natures and one person. The Nestorians were finally condemned at the council of Ephesos in 435; the Monophysites at the council of Chalcedon in 451. The battles of the church on two opposite fronts caused infinite pains, the memory of which is still alive in the East today. One of the best early treatises on the subject, sufficiently near in time for direct information and sufficiently distant in space for relative objectivity, is the Liber contra Eutychen et Nestorium written by Boetius (VI-1) in 512.

with the same Biblical texts. The Nestorians[52] remained faithful to the old Pĕshīṭtā; the Monophysites favored later versions, like the Philoxenian of 505–8 or the Hexapla of 615–17 (Introd. 1, 291). Then the labor of translating Greek writings into Syriac was performed for the Nestorians by Probos of Antioch (V-2) and for the Monophysites on a larger scale by Sergios of Resaina (VI-1).

The Monophysitic church was established so vigorously by Jacob Zanzalus or Burdeana,[53] bishop of Edessa (d. 578), that it was thenceforth called by outsiders after him, Jacobite (Ἰακωβίτης). The following outstanding Syriac writers were Jacobites: Severus Sēbōkht of Qen-neshrē (VII-2, Introd. 1, 493), Aristotelian and scientist, and his disciple Jacob of Edessa (VII-2), author of the first Syriac grammar; Michael the Elder (XII-2), historian; Jacob bar Shakkō (XIII-1), theologian and grammarian; and above all, Abū-l-Faraj or Barhebraeus (XIII-2), one of the greatest scholars of the Middle Ages, who reorganized Syriac grammar on the basis of the Arabic grammar of al-Zamakhsharī (XII-1).

The Nestorian tradition was hardly less remarkable. After the work of Probos (V-2) and of the school of Jundīshāpūr, it reached a first climax under Ḥunain ibn Isḥāq (IX-2), who was not simply one of the greatest translators of all times, responsible for the transmission to the Arabic world of a whole library of Greek masterpieces, but also a very active Syriac writer, author of a Syriac grammar and of the first Greek-Syriac dictionary. Ḥunain's lexicographical efforts were completed by Bar Bahlūl (X-2), author of the most elaborate Syriac dictionary of mediaeval times. Another grammar and another dictionary (in topical order) were composed by Elias bar Shīnāyā (XI-1), and still another grammar by Elias of Ṭīrhān (XI-1). The Nestorians had spread over southern India and Central and Eastern Asia and obtained considerable influence in China.[54] This was made clear to Western people when Bar Ṣauma (XIII-2) visited Europe (1287), he being the first identified Chinese to do so. The last great writer was Abhd-Īshō' bar Bĕrīkhā (XIII-2), who did for the Nestorians what Barhebraeus had done for the Jacobites. The latter died in 1286, Abhd-Īshō' in 1318. They were the last outstanding writers of their nation. After them Syriac ceased to be a living language, being completely superseded by Arabic. The cause of its death will be discussed below in the section devoted to Coptic.

[52] When the Nestorians broke away from the Orthodox church at their council of Selaucia 498, they called themselves Chaldaean Christians, and their chief was entitled patriarch of Babylon (resident in Seleucia-Ctesiphon, and from 762 on in Baghdād). When a uniate church was constituted in 1552, however, it was deceivingly called and is called to this day the Chaldaean church, and its patriarch was called the patriarch of Babylon! It is thus better to call the original body Nestorian in order to avoid confusion.

[53] Alias Jacob Baradai (he of the horsecloth, barda'thā, Βαραδαῖος). W. Wright (p. 85–88, 1894), Duval (p. 360, 1907), Baumstark (p. 174, 1922). Articles on Monophysitism by G. Krüger (ERE 8, 811–17, 1916) and M. Jugie (DTC 10, 2216–51, 1929).

[54] The Nestorian settlement in southern India hardly began before the sixth century. The Nestorian patriarchate of Babylon continued the tradition of St. Thomas (just as the patriarchate of Antioch continued the tradition of St. Peter). The so-called Christians of St. Thomas (or "Syrians") were established on both the southern Malabar and the southern Coromandel coasts. The first account of them was given by Cosmas Indicopleustes (VI-1); later ones by Giovanni di Montecorvino (XIII-2), Jordan Catala (1321, 1324), and Giovanni de' Marignolli (1347). For their history see George Milne Rae: The Syrian church in India (402 p., 7 ill., Edinburgh 1892). T. K. Joseph, of Travancore: Malabar Christians and their ancient documents (52 p., Trivandrum 1929); The Syrian Christian copper plates at Tiruvalla (20 p., Kottayam 1933).

For the Nestorian monument of 781 in Hsi-an fu, see Introd. 1, 526. For Chinese Nestorians in general see Moule (1930); P. Yoshio Saeki: The Nestorian documents and relics in China (Tokyo 1937).

The preceding sketch does not attempt to give an idea of the great wealth of Syriac literature, but simply to indicate its evolution in two parallel streams. For example, there is an abundant religious literature which I have not touched, as it lies outside our own field; it includes treatises on apologetics, polemics, irenics, paraenesis, homiletics, canon law, ritual, hymnology, exegesis and hermeneutics, the lives and acts of the martyrs and of the saints. Syriac has the same importance for Christian Asia that Greek and Latin have for Christian Europe, and we may say, roughly, that Syriac, Greek, and Latin are the vehicles of three different branches of Christianity. In addition to the Nestorians and Jacobites there were also Orthodox writers, but these were far less important, at least from the Syriac (linguistic) point of view, for any inclination to Greek orthodoxy implied a preference for the Greek language, and any inclination to Roman orthodoxy implied a preference for Latin. There were also orthodox saints, separate from the Nestorian or Jacobite ones. It should be noted that the Bibliotheca hagiographica orientalis put in order by the learned Bollandists (Subsidia hagiographica no. 10, 312 p., Brussels 1910) refers only to the orthodox saints, leaving out the others irrespective of their saintliness or martyrdom. Of course, we cannot blame the Jesuit fathers for being consistent, but we are utterly unable to share their exclusiveness. Christian love and saintliness mean infinitely more to us than dogmatic subtleties.

In addition to the Jewish or rabbinical form of Aramaic and to the Christian one, there developed also in lower Mesopotamia the Mandaean form. For the Mandaeans, see W. Brandt (ERE 8, 380–93, 1916).

Syriac script. One is often obliged to transliterate other languages into one's own script, either because one is not able or one does not wish to use the foreign script. Thus in antiquity hieroglyphics and cuneiform[55] were repeatedly used for the transcription of foreign languages, or else Sumerian or Assyrian was written in Greek characters. A minor deviation consisted in using a foreign script but treating it as one's own, e.g., Aramaic-speaking people minted coins bearing Greek inscriptions spelled from right to left.[56] In the East these tendencies were aggravated by the sacredness attached to script (vs. language). That is, script often meant more than language as a means of national or religious affirmation. Thus the Samaritan script was used successively to transliterate Hebrew, Aramaic, and Arabic; the languages were allowed to change, but the nation and its peculiar script remained (Introd. 1, 152).

This Oriental characteristic is most beautifully illustrated in the case of Syriac. The antagonism between Nestorians and Jacobites revealed itself not only in ideas and language, but also, more tangibly, in script. In this matter as in Biblical traditions, the Nestorians proved to be the more conservative, for they stuck to the older esṭrangelā script of their language even as they remained faithful to their Pĕshīṭtā. About the eighth or ninth century, the Nestorians wrote in a kind of esṭrangelā with vowel points as in Arabic, while the Jacobites used a more divergent script called serṭō, including symbols derived from the Greek vowels. Thus it is possible to tell at a glance whether a given document is Nestorian or Jacobite and to discount immediately the prejudices implied.

On account of the extraordinary diffusion of Nestorians across Asia, their script was very influential. It was used to write the Uighūr (old Turkish) language, and

[55] There is at least one Aramaic document in cuneiform. It is an incantation written on both sides of a clay tablet, found at Uruk in Babylonia (east of lower Euphrates), Louvre. Photographs of both sides in Cyrus H. Gordon: The living past (p. 198–99, New York 1941; Isis 34, 444, 1943).

[56] Jacques de Morgan: Manuel de numismatique orientale (1, 197, fig. 222, Paris 1923–36).

the Uighūr script in its turn was appropriated by the Manchus (in 1119, c. 1140) for the transcription of their own language (Introd. 2, 273). That attempt, however, was not successful. The present Manchu writing was established only in 1632, being derived from the Mongol script, itself derived from the Uighūr.

When the Syriac language succumbed to the pressure of the Arabic, the Syriac script (serṭō) continued a vigorous resistance. The language died, but the script lived, and was used (and is used to this day) to transliterate Arabic writings. Such writing, Arabic in Syriac serṭō script, is called Karshūnī or better Garshūnī;[57] it is to be found in thousands of MSS (not only Jacobite, but also Maronite and Melkite). There are also Garshūnī MSS in esṭrangelā (Nestorian script), but they are exceptional.[58]

In order to round out my remarks on script vs. language, let me recall that Mānī (III-2) had devised a special script for his own religion, and one has found in Central Asia Manichaean writings in Sogdian (a kind of middle Persian) and Turkish, but in Manichaean script (Introd. 1, 333).

There is an abundance of Persian and Arabic MSS written by Jews in Hebrew script. The script consecrated a kind of adaptation and assimilation, it caused the text to become secret to non-Jews. On the other hand, there are Hebrew books in Arabic script. Armenians, Syrians, and Greeks living in Turkey wrote Turkish in Armenian, Syriac, or Greek alphabet.[59] Moors wrote Spanish in Arabic script (aljamiadas).[60] There are Greek documents in Hebrew, Syriac, and Roman characters.

In southern India the application of the word "Nestorian" to the Syriac language was a new cause of confusion. The early Syriac books were all destroyed by the Portuguese at the time of the synod held at Diamper or Udayamperur in 1599 by the archbishop of Goa. The Syriac language is now printed in Malayalam script. For an example, the fate book (sortes) of Napolean (Palpushtakam), see L. K. Anantakrishna Ayyar: Anthropology of the Syrian Christians (p. 23, 136–46, Ernakulam 1926).[61]

18. *Coptic*

The Coptic language is simply a modern form of the old Egyptian, the name itself meaning 'gyptian (the Arabs derived Copt[62] from Αἴγυπτος, or rather from Αἰγύπτιος). Jean Jacques Champollion succeeded in deciphering the hieroglyphics because of his knowledge of Coptic; he could not have succeeded otherwise.[63] The

57 According to Hartwig Derenbourg (1, xli, 1884), the word is derived from Karshĕnā (near Edessa), where there was a famous monastery (?). For another derivation see C. Brockelmann (EI 2, 775, 1925). According to A. Mingana, the form Garshūnī is more correct (Journal of the Royal Asiatic Society, 1928, 891–93); this is confirmed by professor Philip Hitti (letter dated Princeton, N. J., Mar. 23, 1942).

58 The only example known to me was brought to my attention by professor Hitti. It is a MS of a sermon on pilgrim life by Ephraim the Syrian (d. 373), the "prophet of the Syrians." August Haffner: Die Homilie des heiligen Ephräm über das Pilgerleben (Sitzungsberichte der Kais. Akademie der Wissenschaften, philos. Klasse, 135, Abh. IX, p. 7–12, Wien 1897).

59 Turkish versions of the Bible have been printed not only in Arabic script, but also in Roman, Armenian, Greek, Russian, Cyrillic, and Hebrew characters! Facsimiles may be seen in Eric M. North: The book of a thousand tongues (New York 1938).

60 See aljamiadas glossary in González Palencia (vol. prel., 136–40, 1930).

61 Book brought to the author's attention by Dr. Horace I. Poleman, director of Indic studies, Library of Congress (letter of Apr. 16, 1942).

62 The Arabic form is really qibṭ (EI 2, 990–1003, 1927).

63 See his own explanation in his Lettre à M. Dacier relative à l'alphabet des hiéroglyphes

first monument of the Coptic language was the translation of the Bible, completed before the end of the second century, not only in the Boḥairī dialect but also in the Ṣa'īdī one. These were the two main Coptic dialects, the first being spoken in Lower Egypt (i.e., the maritime provinces, the Delta; baḥr means sea in Arabic), the second in the Ṣa'īd or Upper Egypt. The first dialect gradually obtained the supremacy, and from the eleventh century on was the liturgical language of all Copts.[64]

The date of these Biblical translations shows that the Copts became Christians very early. They adopted the Eutychian views on the nature of Christ and have remained loyal Monophysites ever since.[65] The word Coptic soon had a religious meaning as well as a racial one. If a Copt was Islamized he ceased to be a Copt. For religious reasons the Coptic language was much influenced by the Greek; it is written with an alphabet composed of 24 Greek letters plus 7 Demotic ones, the vowels being indicated as in Greek by seven letters (alpha, e psilon, ita, iota, o micron, y psilon, o mega). In spite of periods of merciless persecution, the great majority of Copts have remained faithful to their religion; they have been frequently employed by the Muslim rulers of Egypt as notaries, treasurers, administrators, and have occupied positions of high trust and responsibility.

Coptic literature is almost exclusively religious, the only exceptions noted by me being the following: Horapollon (IV-1) wrote a book on hieroglyphics which has come down to us in a poor Greek version. A medical papyrus of the ninth or tenth century contains a collection of recipes in the Ṣa'īdī dialect, derived from Egyptian, Greek, and Arabic sources (Introd. 1, 614; Isis 7, 184). Finally, we have a whole series of grammatical writings dating from the eleventh century on, when the language was already succumbing to Arabic pressure. The climax of that grammatical and lexicographic work was reached by Abū-l-Barakāt, who died in 1324. These grammatical works were written in Arabic, chiefly for the benefit of the Coptic deacons and priests, who had to learn their ecclesiastical language in an artificial way even as English or French priests had to learn Latin.

The decline and fall of Coptic are very similar to the decline and fall of Syriac. Coptic resisted Arabic pressure a little longer than Syriac, but with far less distinction. Both languages died because they allowed themselves to be replaced by Arabic in daily life. The Copts and Syrians may have imagined that it was enough to preserve their own language for religious and liturgical purposes, and that any other language was good enough for other purposes. They were sadly mistaken. When a language is no longer used for common life and poetry, when women and children cease to speak it and prospective clerics have to learn it in school, the language is dying; very soon it is a dead language. By the middle of the fourteenth century Syriac was dead; Coptic lasted a century or two longer. As far as Syriac is concerned, its artificiality is illustrated by the fact that even the priests know it so badly that they need Arabic translations of their liturgical books! I obtained a few years ago in Beirūt a Syriac liturgy with Arabic version in parallel columns, the shame being hidden to outsiders by the use of Syriac script for both texts. Even so, missals, breviaries, and rituals are printed in Coptic and Arabic, but in this case there is no means of hiding the translation, for the two scripts are very

phonétiques (52 p., 4 pl., Paris 1822). Centenarian facsimile reprint with introduction by Henri Sottas (Paris 1922).

[64] At present, parts of the ritual are read in Arabic, but the Gospels are read in Boḥairī.

[65] A uniate Coptic church was formed in 1732, headed by a patriarch whose see is in Alexandria. It has remained very small.

different.[66] To appreciate the situation, just imagine a Catholic priest who could not read his breviary without a French or English translation printed on the same page.

When I applied to professor W. H. Worrell for information concerning the possible existence of Coptic documents in other scripts, he kindly wrote me (letter dated Ann Arbor, Michigan, Mar. 23, 1942):

"Among the Arabized Copts Arabic is always represented by Arabic letters and Coptic by Coptic letters in official, standard, or dignified usage. There are a number of specimens, however, of Coptic in Arabic letters and Arabic in Coptic letters. You will find these fully described in my Coptic sounds (Ann Arbor 1934, p. 5 ff., 134 ff.).

"W. E. Crum, 'Coptic documents in Greek script,' in the Proceedings of the British Academy, vol. 25, London, of recent date, describes some specimens of Coptic in Greek letters. He thinks these are the work of a colony of Orthodox Greek Christians whose language was the contemporary late Egyptian (i.e., essentially Coptic) but who would not know the Coptic alphabet, and were untouched by the Coptic literary movement.

"You may safely assume that your bilingual manuscripts in Coptic and Arabic are written respectively in the Coptic and Arabic alphabets."

19. *Aethiopic*

Aethiopic[67] and Coptic belong to the large group of Hamitic-Semitic languages, but whereas the latter is a member of the Hamitic (North African) group, Aethiopic is more definitely on the Semitic side. The ancient language, Ge'ez, in which the Biblical translations were written and which has remained in use for liturgical purposes, is relatively close to Arabic. The Abyssinian church was founded in the fourth century and has been ever since under the control of the Coptic (Monophysitic) patriarch of Alexandria. The Aethiopic script dates probably from about that time. Its syllabary consists of 26 consonants, each of which exists in seven vocalized varieties.

The Ge'ez translation of the Bible dates probably from the fifth or sixth century. In the course of time other dialects made their appearance, the most important being Amharic, which was spoken in the central highlands and became the royal language. It contains many more non-Semitic (Hamitic and even Kushitic, i.e., East African) elements than Ge'ez (Meillet et Cohen p. 122-27, 142, 1924). It is the official language today,[68] Ge'ez remaining the ecclesiastical one.

A literary revival occurred in Aethiopia in the first half of the fourteenth century under the influence of the powerful king 'Amda Ṣion (ruled 1314-44) and of the metropolitan Salāmā. The latter, who, like every other church dignitary, came

[66] A set of ritual books Coptic-Arabic was prepared in the second half of the eighteenth century by Raphaele Tuki, bishop of Arsinoe, and published by the S. Congregatio de propaganda fide in Rome. I do not know whether the non-uniate Copts are linguistically as weak as their uniate brethren.

[67] The name Aethiopic is of Greek origin (Αἰϑίοψ). The national name is derived from the Semitic root ḥ b sh (ḥabasha in Arabic, hence the corrupted European forms, Abyssinia, etc.). I. Guidi (EI 1, 119-21, 1908).

[68] For recent books printed in that language (Amharic), notably the arithmetic of St. Takla Hāmānot (Addis Ababa 1921), see Isis (7, 314, 1925; facsim. opp. p. 171). On the other hand, the Italians favored another dialect, Tigrigna, spoken in the region around Axum in the north, not far from the Eritrean border. A manual of obstetrics was recently translated from Swedish into Tigrigna by Teresa de Pertis (Asmara, Eritrea 1928; Isis 34, 279).

from Egypt, revised the Biblical translations or caused them to be revised by others on the basis of Arabic models. He also initiated a school of translation from Arabic (and Coptic?) into Ge'ez which continued until the beginning of the fifteenth century, and included liturgical and monastic books, lives of saints, apocryphal acts of the apostles. As to 'Amda Ṣion, he ordered the writing of new chronicles, of a treatise on government methods and curial rites, and of more translations from the Arabic. The translations of the Sefer Yosippon and of the Majmū' al-mubārak of al-Makīn (XIII-2) may date from his time, but they are more probably later.

Knowledge of Aethiopia and of Aethiopic was very limited, if not nonexistent, in other countries. The earliest account was written by Cosmas Indicopleustes (VI-1). The legends concerning "Prester John" (XII-2) included Aethiopic elements unfortunately not differentiated from others. There are a few Aethiopic references in Blanquerna, which Ramon Lull (XIII-2) composed c. 1283, and also in the accounts of Giovanni di Montecorvino (XIII-2) and Marco Polo (XIII-2). According to Georgios Pachymeres (XIII-2, Introd. 2, 972), Michael Palaeologos received a giraffe from the king of Aethiopia. Much information must have been available to the Coptic patriarchate, and some of it appears in the chronicles of al-Makīn (XIII-2) and Mufaḍḍal ibn abī-l-Faḍā'il. The only man to show some interest in the language was the great philologist Abū Ḥaiyān, but his book on the subject has not yet been recovered.

20. *Hebrew*

Hebrew was one of the most important languages of the fourteenth century, not only because it was used by a good many scholars, but also because its sacredness was fully realized. Nor were the persecuted Jews alone in realizing it; the Christians were fully aware of it, and so were the Muslims, who found in their Qur'ān many references to the Old Testament (Hughes p. 439, 1885). Its antiquity was also realized, the general tendency everywhere being to magnify it rather than the opposite.

It certainly is a very ancient language, and the collection of books which forms the Old Testament represents a very long linguistic evolution. From the earliest texts in it, such as the Song of Deborah (Judges ch. 5), to the latest ones, such as Ecclesiastes, there elapsed at least eight centuries. The word Hebrew, by the way, was at first a national designation; the Jews did not use it to designate their language much before the second century B.C., and later they preferred to call it loshon haqodesh (the holy language). The word ἑβραϊστί (= Hebraice) occurs in the version of the Septuagint and in John 19:20.

To the Christians as well as to the Jews it was a divine language, the original language (linguarum mater), and its ancient script (the square characters) was supposed to be the original script of the sons of man. Thus it is not surprising that some scribes took extraordinary pains to insure the proper writing and ornamentation of the divine letters, as explained, e.g., by Abraham ben Ḥayyim (Introd. 2, 1041), or that an endless line of scholars ascribed magical virtues to them. Considerations on the symbolic meanings of letters, taken one by one or in combinations, or their arithmetic values are found in mystical writings such as the Sefer yeẓirah (Introd. 2, 367), the Bahir ascribed to Isaac the Blind (XII-2), the Zohar ascribed to Moses of León (XIII-2), and their innumerable commentaries. The follies of gematria (Introd. 2, 881; 367, 608, 879, 888) were periodically repeated throughout the course of Hebrew literature, and they were applied from time to time to other alphabets. Indeed, Jewish superstitions concerning their script were shared by almost every Christian scholar having obtained some knowledge of it. Their tenacious hold on Christian minds is illustrated by the fact that as late as 1687 Harvard students were still discussing whether the Hebrew vowel points were of divine origin as well as the letters themselves.[69] Apparently the divine nature of the latter was above discussion!

The vowel points, by the way, were relatively late additions to the script. The text of the Old Testament edited by the ancient scribes (sopherim) was purely consonantal. As the masoretes (that is, the rabbis striving to establish the masora, the textual tradition of the Old Testament) wanted to indicate the correct pronunciation of the sacred text, they were obliged to borrow from the Nestorians (say, in the sixth to seventh century) signs to represent the vowels. Before that time only long vowels were indicated, and that by means of some quiescent consonants (matres lectionis). As the writing of the square letters took too long, it was gradually replaced by cursive scripts, called rabbinic, the best known of which is named after the great exegete Rashi (XI-2). On the other hand, calligraphy was practiced by artists, to whom the rigor of Jewish religion left but little scope outside of pure ornamentation. The fact that the Hebrew letters had magical properties raised the calligraphic art to the level of a hieratic function, a level which the Arabic and even the Chinese calligraphists could never reach in spite of the greater artistic possibilities of their own scripts.

For more information on the Hebrew alphabet, script, methods of writing, and customs ad hoc, see JE (1, 439–54, 1901; 8, 303–15, 1904), EJ (1, 400–51, 1928; 7, 936–47, 1931), and Samuel Krauss: Talmudische Archäologie (3, 131–98, 1912).

In spite of general beliefs to the contrary, the Hebrew language and script were not the most ancient, and they were neither original nor pure, let alone divine. They were simply ancient means of expression, unstable and imperfect, the changes of which could never be stopped except by death. No language can coexist with another one in the same territory without mutual borrowings and contaminations. The authors or editors of the Old Testament were not alone in the world, nor was their language the only one spoken in their time, not even in their own country. This can be deduced from the Old Testament itself, which, far from being pure Hebrew, contains a number of vocables derived from a dozen other languages, to wit (1) the Arabic or Midianitic dialect spoken by Moses (pesaḥ, passover), (2) Philistine, (3) Sumerian (through Akkadian), (4) Assyrian-Babylonian (Akkadian), (5) Anatolian (?), (6) Egyptian, (7) Aethiopic, (8) Arabic, (9) Ḥittite, (10) Aramaic, (11) Persian, (12) Greek.[70] The number of Egyptian borrowings may have been exaggerated by Yahuda, but they cannot be altogether denied, and the less so as they were literary as well as linguistic, extending to the content as well as to the form. Some Greek borrowings may have occurred early, most of them date from Hellenistic times. Aramaic was the main language spoken in the Holy Land for many centuries before Christ (and in Christ's own time; he spoke Aramaic). There are two Aramaic words in Genesis 31:47 (jegar shahadutha, the heap of witness), and the following sections are entirely written in Aramaic: Ezra 4:8–6:18; 7:12–26, dating from III-1 B.C.; and Daniel 2:4b–7:28, dating from II-1 B.C. (Introd. 1, 163, 180).

[69] In 1687 Gurdon Saltonstall (later governor of Connecticut) defended the affirmative on the Harvard question "An puncta hebraea sint divinae originis" (Isis 25, 515, 1936).

[70] Information kindly given to me by my Harvard colleague Robert H. Pfeiffer (letter dated Mar. 26, 1942). His Introduction to the Old Testament (932 p., New York 1941; Isis 34, 38) is a rich treasure of knowledge, well indexed.

T. Eric Peet: A comparative study of the literatures of Egypt, Palestine and Mesopotamia (144 p., London 1931; Isis 21, 305–16). Abraham Shalom Yahuda: The language of the Pentateuch in its relation to Egyptian (vol. 1, 366 p., London 1933).

Aramaic words are listed separately in the Gesenius-Robinson Hebrew lexicon of the Old Testament (Clarendon Press, Oxford 1906; reprinted 1929, p. 1078–1118).

If Biblical Hebrew already contained so many foreign elements and such a variety of them, we can imagine the situation with regard to Talmudic and mediaeval Hebrew. In particular, when Jewish scholars began to translate into their own language a large number of texts originally written in Greek, Arabic, Persian, Latin, etc. they could not help introducing alien words.

Considering the sacredness ascribed to Hebrew and the need of interpreting the Scriptures with the utmost precision, it is surprising that formal grammar took so long in shaping itself. Of course, the efforts made to establish the divine text and later to vocalize it implied grammatical analysis. The oldest grammatical writing is probably the Sefer ha-niqqud by Ashi (V-1), an amora of the fourth generation, first editor of the Babylonian Talmud; and there was produced c. 600 in Palestine a tract Sopherim, explaining in twenty-one chapters how to write the rolls of the Torah. The gigantic labor of the masoretes was completed many centuries later, early in the tenth century, by Ben Asher of Tiberias for the Palestinian (or western) tradition (which has been followed in the printed texts), and by Ben Naphtali for the Babylonian (or eastern) one (Introd. 1, 624).

In spite of all that immense travail, the scientific analysis of the Hebrew language was not achieved nor even started in the right way until Jewish scholars had obtained sufficient experience from the Arabic grammarians. As soon as they understood the logical and lexicographical points of view of the latter, they made rapid progress. The potential maturity of Hebrew grammar, which required only a certain amount of outside stimulation to become real, is proved by the circumstance that the new grammatical developments occurred independently in two parallel streams, the rabbinical (or orthodox) and the Qaraite.

As the latter was apparently a little ahead of the other and on the whole less important, let us describe it first. Qaraism was founded by Anan ben David (VIII-2), and the movement was hardly started when the first Qaraite grammarian appeared, Nissi ben Noah, who lived in Baṣra and later in Jerusalem about the eighth/ninth century (JE 9, 314, 1905). He was soon followed by Joseph al-Baḥtawi the Babylonian, called ha-medaqdeq (the grammarian), and by al-Qirqisānī (X-1), encyclopaedist and theologian rather than philologist, but ready to apply his keen mind to every problem.[71] Before the end of the same century the philological efforts of the Qaraites had blossomed out in the grammar and the Hebrew lexicon of Sahl ben Maẓliaḥ (X-2) and the dictionary of David ben Abraham of Fez (X-2). We shall come back to the Qaraites a little later.

The orthodox Jews began their new philological efforts in the Babylonian academy of Sura, under the leadership of Saadia Gaon (X-1), often called (not quite correctly) the founder of scientific Hebrew philology. We have just seen that Saadia had been preceded by two Qaraite grammarians. It may be true, however, that his Hebrew grammar and dictionary were the first systematic books of their kind

[71] In his code of Qaraite law, Kitāb al-anwār wal-marāqib, which Leon Nemoy has edited 1939–43 (Isis 33, 89, 357; 35, 57), there are many philological remarks, e.g., on the permutation of consonants, the influence of the article on the noun, tenses, interpretation of Hebrew words and Biblical verses, criticism of other people's opinions on the ground that they are philologically unsound (mā lā taḥmaluhu al-lugha).

(his Agron was completed in 913). Saadia was followed by a long procession of rabbinic philologists, most of whom have been dealt with in volumes 1 and 2. A rapid enumeration will suffice. Please note that after Saadia's death, in 942, though the academies of Sura and Pumbedita continued for another century (until 1034 and 1038 respectively), most of the work was done in the West. Dunash ben Labraṭ (X-2) was a Moroccan, who had come to Sura to sit at Saadia's feet, then had returned to Fez and Cordova. His great rival in the latter city was Menahem ben Saruq (X-2), and their quarrels, duly intensified by their disciples, accelerated philological progress. Menahem wrote the first complete dictionary of the Old Testament. Then came the great master Ḥayyuj (X-2), also in Cordova. Note that the latter's famous grammar was written in Arabic. Then Samuel ha-Levi (XI-1), Ibn Janāḥ (XI-1), the greatest Hebrew philologist of the Middle Ages, still writing in Arabic, Abū Zakarīyā Yaḥyā Ibn Bala'm (JE 6, 519, 1904), Nathan ben Jehiel (XI-2), author of the Talmudic dictionary 'Aruk. The first three were Spaniards, but Nathan was a Roman.

With the twelfth century things take a new turn. Abraham ben Ezra (XII-1) translated Ḥayyuj's treatises into Hebrew; he also wrote other grammatical treatises directly in Hebrew, and so did Joseph Qimḥi (XII-2), followed by his two sons Moses ben Joseph (XII-2) and David ben Joseph (XII-2). In the meanwhile Abraham bar Ḥiyya (XII-1) was beginning to create a new scientific terminology, and Berakya ha-Naqdan (XII-2) was adding his own contributions to it. The greater task of re-creating the language for scientific and philosophic purposes, however, was initiated by Judah ibn Tibbon (XII-2), the "father of Jewish translators," and continued by his son, Samuel ben Judah (XIII-1), and the latter's son-in-law, Jacob Anaṭoli (XIII-1). Jewish grammarians were working in England, witness Moses ben Isaac ha-Nessiah of London (fl. XII/XIII), alias Moses ha-Naqdan (Neubauer-Renan p. 484–87, 1877), and in France, to wit, Joseph ben Samson (XIII-1), who compiled a Hebrew-French glossary, Solomon ibn Ayyub of Béziers (XIII-2), who translated Ibn Janāḥ's grammatical book into Hebrew, and the poet Abraham ben Isaac Bedersi, who flourished in Perpignan about the end of the thirteenth century and compiled a list of Hebrew homonyms (Ḥotam toknit) in alphabetic order.[72]

Very little work was done at this period by Eastern Jews. The Samaritan scholar Abū-l-Isḥāq Ibrāhīm (XII-2) and Tanḥūm ben Joseph of Jerusalem (XIII-1) wrote their grammatical works in Arabic, and the latter compiled a Hebrew-Arabic dictionary. Of course, they had to use the Arabic language, because the Eastern Jews were living in an Arabic environment and were themselves so deeply Arabicized that they could learn their own sacred language only by means of that other one.

Inasmuch as the Jews learned grammatical methods from the Muslims and even wrote the first Hebrew grammars not in Hebrew but in Arabic, that is, inasmuch as they knew Arabic as well as Hebrew, we are not surprised that a by-product of their grammatical efforts was the adumbration of comparative Semitic philology. The earliest contribution to that subject was made by Judah ben Quraish (IX-1)[73]

[72] He was a friend of David Caslari (XIII-2). M. Zobel (EJ 3, 1210–12, 1929). The Ḥotam toknit was edited by Gabriel ben Isaac Polak and Joseph Ẓebi Dünner (Amsterdam 1865).

[73] My dating of his activities in Introd. 1, 581 was too early. Instead of (IX-1) it should have been (IX-2) or (X-1), as given in EJ 8, 1006, 1931. Judah ben Quraish (or Qarīsh) was acquainted with the famous traveler Eldad ha-Dani, who flourished in Tahort and Qairawān c. 880 (EJ 6, 393–99, 1930).

of Tahort (near Tlemcen). In his Arabic risāla to the Jewish community of Fez he exhorted them not to neglect the study of the Aramaic Targūm (Introd. 1, 151, 402), and discussed (1) Hebrew and Aramaic in the Bible, (2) Hebrew and Aramaic in the Mishna and Talmud, (3) Hebrew vs. Arabic. He was aware of the affinities of these three languages, and had some knowledge of Berber. The next steps were taken by Saadia Gaon (X-1), by the Qaraites al-Qirqisānī (X-1)[74] and Abū-l-Ḥasan of Jerusalem (XII-1), by Isḥāq ibn Barūn (XII-1) of Lucena (Andalusia), who wrote an Arabic treatise on the "balance" (al-mīzān) between Arabic and Hebrew. It is proper to add at this place that at least one Christian doctor, Roger Bacon (XIII-2), was realizing the affinities between Hebrew, Aramaic, and Arabic.

Jewish people throughout the ages tended to be polyglot. In Biblical times many of them spoke Persian, Aramaic, or Greek; later they learned Arabic and various other languages; their knowledge of Arabic was so deep that they could and did take a large part in the development of Muslim culture, as administrators, philosophers, and scientists. Moreover, some of the masterpieces of Jewish thought were written in foreign languages; it will suffice to recall the Greek books of Philon (I-1) and Flavius Josephus (I-2), and the Arabic ones of Ibn Gabirol (XI-1) and Maimonides (XII-2). For many centuries the philosophic and scientific education of every Jew was received by him in the Arabic language. How is it, then, that Hebrew did not share the fate of Syriac and Coptic? It is clear that literary masterpieces are in themselves unable to save a language, though they may help to preserve it. Abū-l-Faraj (XIII-2) had raised the Syriac language and culture to a very high level indeed, but that was insufficient if the people themselves relinquished their language to the priests. Syriac and Coptic, we have shown above, were permitted to die because they were considered too holy for everyday use. A similar feeling existed among the Jews, and it was almost strong enough to inhibit the astounding Hebrew renaissance of our own days (Osiris 2, 448). Hebrew was saved, however, because of the energy and individualism of the Jewish people. Those people were never satisfied to abandon their religion to the mercy of a kind of clergy; it was always the duty of an educated Jew to know his language well enough to read the Scriptures. The ceremony which solemnizes the puberty of a Jewish boy, his admission to the duties of manhood, includes an examination of his knowledge of the sacred language, for he must read aloud the portion (the weekly selection of the Torah) and the haphṭarah (lesson taken from the Prophets). To faithful parents and friends this is the most touching part of the festivity.[75]

To be sure, the Bar miẓwah examination did not prove then any more than now that the young man who passed it successfully had a deep knowledge of the language. The examination was often insufficient, if not perfunctory, yet matters would have been irremediably worse without it. An elementary knowledge of Hebrew obtained in boyhood would enable any man to get as much additional knowledge as he wanted later on with relative ease; it was like an open door, without that elementary knowledge the door was shut. To read any Hebrew text offhand required a fair amount of knowledge; so much so that even in early days the ḥazzan (JE 6, 284–

[74] In his Kitāb al-anwār, we find remarks on the various pronunciations of Hebrew by Jews of ʿIrāq and Persia, on the common roots of Hebrew and Arabic, etc. Information kindly given me by Leon Nemoy in a letter dated New Haven, Mar. 26, 1942.

[75] The ceremony is very ancient, but its name, bar miẓwah (son of commandment, man of duty), cannot be traced, as such, earlier than the fourteenth century. The ceremony takes place when the boy has completed his thirteenth year, average time of male puberty in the Near East (JE 2, 509–10, 1902; EJ 3, 1034–37, 1929).

87), overseer and official reader of the synagogue, always helped in the reading whether the individual were learned or not, in order to avoid putting the unlearned to the blush (Abrahams p. 18, 1896).

The differences between languages are ultimately differences between the people speaking them. The Hebrew language suffered terrible vicissitudes, the worst of which was its abandonment by the leading thinkers in favor of other languages, but in spite of all that it survived because the Jewish people loved it too deeply to let it die, because their faith was not passive, but strong and tenacious. Thus the language, after being betrayed and almost forgotten, was resurrected time after time, by Rashi (XI-2), by Abraham ben Ezra (XII-1), by Judah ibn Tibbon (XII-2) and his followers, by Levi ben Gerson, and finally within our own lifetime by Eliezer ben Judah (1857–1922).

To return to the fourteenth century, this is a time when Hebrew was still very much alive in Spain, yet competing with Arabic. To illustrate the situation, the great astronomical work of Isaac Israeli of Toledo was written in Arabic, but an abbreviated Hebrew translation (Qiẓẓur yesod 'olam) was soon published by a member of his family. The members of that family wrote in both languages. An Italian dealer in MSS, called Aaron the Bookseller (JE 1, 7, 1901), spent seven years in Toledo at the beginning of the century collating Arabic and Hebrew books, and was able to circulate a catalogue listing some seventy of them among the students of Perugia. This Aaron was a member of the circle of literati who gathered around Immanuel ben Solomon ha-Romi. The outstanding philologist of the time was Joseph Kaspi, who wrote at least two treatises on grammar and a book wherein he discussed the roots of the Hebrew words (Sefer ha-shoreshim). Joseph was primarily a Biblical scholar, and grammar was of deep concern to him as a necessary tool for scientific exegesis. In one of his many books dealing with Biblical subjects, the Shulḥan kesef, he defended the Hebrew language, explaining the necessity of reading the Scriptures in Hebrew, not in Arabic or Latin. This suggests that some of his contemporaries could not read the original text any more, at least not without the help of translations or living interpreters. It is interesting to note that for Joseph Kaspi, living in Tarascon, Arabic and Latin were considered as it were on the same footing. It is possible that some of the Provençal communities were sufficiently Hebraicized to resist the competition of foreign languages, but that was certainly not true when one went away from them, nor was it necessary to go very far. In northern France and Germany Hebrew existed only as a learned language, just as artificial as Latin was in the Christian world. When Asher ben Jehiel (XIII-2) came from Germany to Toledo c. 1303, his Hebrew was at first so weak that he could not teach the Bible to the Spanish Jews (Abrahams p. 358, 364, 1896). Happily, he had time enough to obtain a full mastery of it, for he lived until 1327. This was a paradoxical situation; the best Talmudic work of that time was done in France and Germany, yet for a fluent knowledge of Hebrew one still had to go close to the Pyrénées or beyond them. The situation is not uncommon, for the scientific use of a language and the practical use of it are not always combined as they should be; as we have explained apropos of Latin, such a situation is full of dangers which are the more insidious because the scholars using a learned language are generally too complacent to realize their fundamental ignorance of it.

The Qaraites were also very active. Aaron ben Joseph (XIII-2), who came from the Crimea but flourished in Constantinople until c. 1320, wrote a Hebrew grammar, and much philological work was done by his younger contemporary Aaron ben Elijah, who flourished in the same city until 1369. This second Aaron, often called

Aaron the Younger to distinguish him from the other, was the greatest as well as the last philosopher of his sect, the Maimonides of Qaraism.

Two other Oriental Jews should be named, the Greek Joseph ben David ha-Yewani, who compiled a Hebrew grammar followed by an incomplete dictionary; and the Persian Solomon ben Samuel, to whom we owe an elaborate Hebrew-Persian dictionary. Unfortunately, this work is not yet available in print; the analysis of it suggests that it will be of great value not simply on philological grounds, but also as a historical document concerning Asiatic life and manners.

Hebrew studies in the West. It only remains to say a few words about the knowledge of Hebrew among Christian scholars. That knowledge remained very superficial, the main reason being that Western Christians regarded the Latin Vulgate as if it were itself sacred and perfect, and hence did not realize the need of referring again and again to the original Hebrew text, and did not even begin to imagine the difficulties implied. To be sure, St. Jerome (IV-2) had obtained a good knowledge of Hebrew in Palestine, if not before, and the Vulgate was not composed without reference to the Hebrew text, but that was not enough; the Vulgate did not have by any means the finality superstitiously ascribed to it.[76] After St. Jerome, knowledge of Hebrew dwindles almost to zero. Some familiarity with the Hebrew alphabet and the ability to spell out a few words were rare enough to be looked upon as remarkable achievements. However, a few, very few, Christian scholars were more ambitious. We may mention Venerable Bede (VIII-1), Hrabanus Maurus (IX-1), and the mysterious Alchandrus (X-2). In the twelfth century matters improve a little. St. Stephen Harding (d. 1134; Introd. 2, 154), the third abbot and real founder of Cîteaux, besought Jewish help for his revision of the Latin Old Testament; Peter the Venerable (XII-1) examined the Talmud under the guidance of Jewish converts; Plato of Tivoli (XII-1) translated a mathematical treatise from Hebrew into Latin; Godfrey of Viterbo (XII-2) had some knowledge of Hebrew.

In the following century, an unknown converted Jew, probably of French origin, prepared a Hebrew copy of the whole Old Testament, writing above each Hebrew word in Hebrew script its Latin translation in Roman script. Robert Grosseteste (XIII-1) owned a copy of that work. A little later Hermann the German (XIII-2) translated the Psalter into Castilian, this being the first attempt to translate the Old Testament from Hebrew into a vernacular. Robert's famous pupil Roger Bacon (XIII-2) was keenly aware of the need of Hebrew studies and began the composition of a Hebrew grammar. He understood that the best way of studying the language was with Jewish help.

The English Franciscans were stimulated by their desire to convert the Jews; unfortunately, that innocent desire in other hearts and in a different climate was perverted into a drive to persecute. The renegade Nicholas Donin of La Rochelle (XIII-1) denounced the iniquities which he claimed were contained in the Talmud, and caused the persecution of the Jews and of their sacred writings to be organized; he debated publicly on these matters with four rabbis. The Catalan Dominicans Ramon de Peñafort (XIII-1) and Ramon Martí (XIII-2) distinguished themselves in similar debates, polemics, and persecutions. They did not want simply to con-

[76] This was realized by the Catholic church only within our own days, in 1907. See footnote 6 in Latin section above. As late as 1534 the Sorbonne tried to stop the teaching of Hebrew and Greek interpreters of the Bible at the Collège de France, because those interpreters were undermining, or might undermine, the authority of the Vulgate. Abel Lefranc: Histoire du Collège de France (p. 145–48, Paris 1893).

vert the Jews, but to silence and crush them by fair means or foul, to censor and suppress the Talmud, to destroy, not to build. However evil these thoughts were, they tended to increase Hebrew knowledge among Christians, chiefly Dominicans. Thus the fourteenth century began with a keener appreciation of the need of Hebrew scholarship.

Happily, there were not only Dominicans moved by hatred, but other men moved by love. For example, let us take the greatest exemplar of that century, Dante Alighieri. Being a poet, not a persecutor, he thought of Hebrew primarily as the sacred tongue. His genius enabled him to understand intuitively the problems of comparative philology. He knew that languages, being human, were imperfect and changeable, the only exception perhaps being the "original" language, Hebrew. Yet it would have been impossible for him to make at the beginning of the fourteenth century the provincial blunders repeatedly perpetrated by scholars who fondly imagined that the language of their mothers was the mother language.[77]

Some other Hebraists of the fourteenth century were as gentle as Dante. John de Planis translated a medical work from Hebrew into Latin with the assistance of a converted Jew. Judah ben Moses (Leone Romano), who compiled a Hebrew-Italian glossary of philosophical terms, helped king Robert of Anjou to read the Hebrew Bible. The greatest Christian Hebraist of the age was undoubtedly the French Franciscan Nicholas of Lyra, who knew Hebrew well enough to read not only the Bible, but rabbinical commentaries as well, especially those of Rashi (XI-2), and used the information thus obtained in his own exegesis.

About 1319 a converted Jew, Jean Salvati of Villeneuve-le-Roi (diocese of Beauvais), was teaching Hebrew and Chaldaean in Paris. Indeed, John XXII wrote at that date to Guillaume d'Auvergne, bishop of Paris, enjoining him to provide for the support of the new teacher. Abel Lefranc: Histoire du Collège de France (p. 16, Paris 1893).

21. *Arabic*

The importance of Arabic has been so often emphasized in this Introduction that it is hardly necessary to insist on it again. Moreover, so many of the authors who flourished in the first half of the fourteenth century used the Arabic language that it would take too much space to consider them one by one. It will suffice to remark that they were more than a hundred in number, men representing a great diversity of races, nationalities, regions, and religions. We shall speak only of the philologists, but before doing so it is well to examine the causes of the Arabic success.

Though its complicated structure suggests high antiquity, the literary monuments of the Arabic language were relatively late in appearing. As compared with the earliest Hebrew texts they were very late indeed. Between the Song of Deborah and the earliest Arabic poems there elapsed at least a thousand years and probably as much as fifteen hundred. Those earliest poems, however, were but the latest representatives of an immemorial tradition. The first monument in Arabic prose is the Qur'ān, which, being inspired by God, was presumably perfect. Hence

[77] The queerest examples of such provincialism were given by Swedish scholars, Olof Rudbeck (1630–1702) in his monumental Atlantica (Upsala 1679–1702; reprinted Uppsala 1937–39; Isis 30, 114–19; 33, 71), and the less known mystic and alchemist Anders Kempe of Västergöthland (1622–89). In Kempe's book Die Sprachen des Paradieses (1688), it was claimed that God in Paradise spoke Swedish, Adam answered in Danish, and the Serpent addressed Eve in French!

the language was immediately established on the firmest foundation. Since Arabic was the vehicle of the latest revelation, one meant to complete or abrogate previous ones, its expansion was naturally coextensive with that of Islām. The enormous success of Muslim invasions caused an equal success of their sacred language. The religious ban against translating the Qur'ān into other languages insured at one and the same time a greater purity of the faith and the supremacy of its own language. The Arabic script was even more successful, for it overflowed the boundaries of the Arabic territory, large as the latter was, and was extensively used for the spelling of other languages such as Persian and Turkish.

The success of Arabic cannot be completely explained in Muslim terms. Indeed, the language found ready acceptance among Jews and Christians, so much so that the former abandoned Hebrew and Aramaic, and the latter Aramaic and Coptic, in its favor. The religious feelings which prospered Arabic among Muslims could not but prejudice non-Muslims against it, and yet every resistance fell before it. Believers accepted it because of its religious implications, and "infidels" in spite of them.

The intrinsic causes of the supremacy of a language in its struggle with others are too subtle for complete analysis; we can only guess. It is certain that many reasons which would appeal to poets or philologists, such as beauty, richness of vocabulary, are irrelevant as far as popular success is concerned; indeed, these titles to the approval of a relatively small group of people are also causes of difficulty, and one would expect a language to be less popular if it were too difficult. Arabic, however (like English), is very easy to approach; it is easy to obtain a little knowledge of it and make that little go a surprisingly long way.

Though the Qur'ān caused it to be from the beginning a sacred and learned language, the literary Arabic is associated with and buttressed by a number of homely dialects. Not only that, but, Arabic texts being unvocalized, it is possible to read them aloud in a simplified and dialectal form, if only by leaving out the vowels which do not belong to the words themselves but are only grammatical accretions.[78] Thus a single text, written by a well educated person, can be read in as highbrow or lowbrow a manner as the reader chooses or the audience demands. Such flexibility must gain friends for any language endowed with it.

During the Middle Ages, Arabic and Latin were the outstanding learned tongues. The former outlived the latter, because it was not exclusively a learned language spoken only by men, but a homely one, used by women as well. When women use a language, you may depend on it that they will use it abundantly. It runs out of their mouths like a life-giving river; children get it from them without effort, and the language increases naturally with the people who speak it. Thus Arabic lived and prospered while Latin died.

The situation of Arabic is comparable in many ways to that of Greek (Isis 28, 573). The popularity and vitality of each language was insured by the parallel development of many easy-going dialects, its beauty and dignity were maintained by the existence of a purer form, sanctified by religion and ennobled by literary masterpieces. Though uneducated people are unable to speak the purer language, they can more or less understand it, and they do revere it as an ideal which their

[78] Comparable to the Latin inflections which disappeared in the Romance languages. The Arabic dialects, however, were never new languages (like French) succeeding to an old one, but simplifications of the older language, which continued vigorously alongside them. Thus the conflict between them and Arabic was never a conflict between youth and senility, in which youth is sure to win, but rather a conflict between equal partners.

children if not themselves may possibly attain. Thus do the literary language and its dialectical forms help one another; the former contributes a nobility which all share to some extent, the latter give life.

It was because of its dialectical exuberance that Arabic was able to overflow its religious boundaries. Whereas Latin remained essentially the language of Catholicism, Arabic was used by Christians and Jews as well as by Moslems. The Qur'ānic language was the Muslim heritage, but the living Arabic outgrew Islām even as it had outgrown Arabia or the early Arabic-speaking tribes.

The cooperative partnership between a literary language which is used only by few people on ceremonial occasions, and various dialects which everybody speaks with more or less abandon, is bound to be linguistically profitable. For the dialects facilitate all kinds of experiments and novelties, while the purer language exerts a conservative influence; the one makes for progress and the other for sufficient inertia and stability, without which progress becomes futile.

The development of Arabic philology was exceptionally rapid, for it began very shortly after the publication of the Qur'ān. The Arabs, however, deserve very little credit for it. For one thing, the spread of Islām was so wide and sudden that large numbers of foreigners were impelled to learn Arabic, and they could learn it only in an artificial way; these people needed grammars and dictionaries, and the need was such a crying one that it created its own fulfillment. Moreover, the Arabs did not have to invent grammar, they received it from other people and had only to apply Greek and Syriac patterns to their own language. These patterns were properly explained to them by their Syrian tutors. The Arabic people, however, had a special genius for grammar and lexicography; they were able to use the Syriac models to such good purpose that three centuries later the situation was reversed, and Syriac grammar was improved on the basis of the Arabic (Introd. 1, 701).

Arabic grammar was born and spent its youth in Baṣra. Its discovery is traditionally ascribed to Abū-l-Aswad al-Du'alī (VII-2) of that city, but the gestation lasted almost a century. The first grammarians were Khalīl ibn Aḥmad (VIII-2) and Sībawaihi (VIII-2). Khalīl is said to have "invented" prosody, and Sībawaihi, a Persian be it noted, wrote the first elaborate grammar, the Kitāb, i.e., the Book par excellence. Khalīl had begun a dictionary, but the first complete one we owe to Ibn Duraid (X-1). All these men flourished for a time at least in Baṣra.

By the second half of the tenth century, philological work was being done all over the Dār al-Islām. The Spaniard Ibn al-Qūṭīya (X-2) wrote the first treatise on conjugations; Ibn Jinnī (X-2), of Greek ancestry, discussed the philosophy of grammar; dictionaries of increasing fullness were compiled by Ismā'īl ibn 'Abbād (X-2), al-Jauharī (X-2), and Ibrāhīm ibn Ṣāliḥ. The first of these was the author of the Kitāb al-muḥīṭ and the two others wrote the Ṣiḥāḥ; these two names, the first of which, muḥīṭ, implies comprehensiveness, and the second, ṣiḥāḥ, correctness, have remained associated to this day with Arabic dictionaries. It is possible that the earliest Latin-Arabic glossary dates from this time; it was compiled by a Spaniard.[79] Another Spaniard, Ibn Sīda (XI-2), compiled a new dictionary. Lexicographical efforts were unavoidably duplicated in various places and times, because a living language is always calling for new dictionaries, and attentive scholars are bound to discover omissions which have to be remedied.

[79] See note in Introd. 1, 782, where it is placed under (XI-2), but it is possibly earlier. Walter Muir Whitehill: The date of the earliest Latin-Arabic glossary, Leiden, Cod. 231 Scal. (Isis 26, 370-72, 1937).

Further efforts may be listed in the briefest manner. Grammatical treatises were contributed by al-Ḥarīrī (XII-1), Ibn al-Jawālīqī (XII-1), Ibn al-Anbārī (XII-2), Ibn al-Ḥājib (XIII-1), al-Sakkākī (XIII-1), and Ṣafī al-dīn (XIII-2). Arabic-Persian dictionaries were compiled by al-Maidānī and al-Zamakhsharī (XII-1), and we owe an immense Arabic one, the Lisān al-'arab, to Ibn Manẓūr (XIII-2). The Lisān was the greatest lexicographical monument of the Middle Ages in any language; there was nothing in the West which deserves to be compared with it. All the scholars mentioned in this paragraph were Easterners, and curiously enough four of them, to wit al-Ḥarīrī, Ibn al-Jawālīqī, Ibn al-Anbārī, and the famous musician Ṣafī al-dīn, came from 'Irāq. Al-Maidānī and al-Zamakhsharī were Persians, Ibn al-Ḥājib and Ibn Manẓūr, Egyptians. Al-Sakkākī, the "Arabic Quintilian," was a Turk.

It is thus clear that the Arabic philologists of the fourteenth century inherited magnificent tools for the study of their language. This was in a way a great privilege, but it was also a loss, for the age of discovery and invention was decidedly over. Most of the fourteenth-century work is repetitious, yet many of the grammars which were then published East and West enjoyed considerable popularity for centuries to come.

Beginning with grammatical work, it is surprising that so little of it was done in Spain, where the Arabic language remained very important, if not predominant. To be sure, Muslim Spain was now reduced to the Naṣrī kingdom of Granada, but Arabic continued to be spoken in Christian Spain, by Jews, Mudejars, and Mozarabs. For example, Israel ben Joseph of Toledo (brother of the better-known Isaac Israeli) used the Arabic language even for the composition of a Jewish liturgical treatise! As to the Mozarabs, it will suffice to consult the archives of Toledo analyzed by González Palencia (1926–30). In spite of that, I can think only of one Spanish grammarian, Abū Ḥaiyān, who, however, spent so much of his life in Cairo that it is more legitimate to consider him with the other Mamlūk scholars. There was a contemporary grammarian in Morocco, Ibn Ājurrūm, who sojourned a few years in the East when he performed the Pilgrimage, but there is no evidence that he lived in Spain. His grammatical books were very popular. Ere betaking ourselves to the East, it is worth while to consider an agricultural poem written by Ibn Luyūn of Granada, for it includes a number of Latin-Spanish terms. This is more interesting, however, for the study of the language than for the study of philology, which is our concern.

Under the Mamlūk there flourished three famous grammarians: Abū Ḥaiyān, who hailed from Granada and in the cosmopolitan atmosphere of Cairo became one of the outstanding polyglots of the Middle Ages; Ibn al-Wardī, and Ibn Hishām. The last named wrote a good many treatises and was considered by Ibn Khaldūn the foremost grammarian of his time.

Other Arabic grammars were composed by two Persians, Niẓām al-a'raj and al-Jārabardī.

The rhetorical tradition so brilliantly begun by the Turk al-Sakkākī (XIII-1) was continued by his countryman Khaṭīb Dimashq and by the Persian Ya'qūb ibn Aḥmad al-Kāshānī. Mention should be made here of the manuals of administrative and diplomatic redaction which were compiled for the use of Mamlūk chancellors; they form the Arabic equivalent of the Western ars dictaminis.

Arabic lexicography was brought to a climax by the Lisān al-'arab of Ibn Manẓūr (XIII-2), who lived in Egypt until 1311. Al-Multānī wrote in Persian explanations of selected Qur'ānic terms. In his Taqwīm al-buldān, Abū-l-Fidā' took special pains to establish the correct orthography and orthophony of proper names; I must say that Arabic geographers, historians, and biographers were very careful in that respect; the fact that their script was not vocalized or that vowel signs if added could easily be misread or mistaken obliged them to indicate in full words the correct vocalization of any unfamiliar name, and they generally did so. Thus there is no ambiguity concerning the thousands of place names given by Abū-l-Fidā' in his geography.

A special form of lexicography was illustrated during this period by 'Abd al-Razzāq al-Kāshānī, who compiled a lexicon of the technical terms used by mystical philosophers, the Kitāb al-iṣṭilāḥāt al-ṣūfīya. This was not the first philosophical dictionary; at least two others have already been mentioned by me, the Kitāb al-ḥudūd wal-rusūm of Isḥāq al-Isrā'īlī (X-1) and the Mafātīḥ al-'ulūm of Muḥammad ibn Aḥmad al-Khwārizmī (X-2); nor was it to be the last one, for Arabic philosophers have always insisted on correct definitions of their terms.[80]

Arabic studies in the West. Reference has already been made to the earliest Latin-Arabic glossary, the unique MS of which is preserved in Leiden. Whether we assign it to the tenth century or to the eleventh, it is the earliest document proving the scientific study of Arabic by a Latin scholar; not only is it the earliest document of its kind, but it remained exceptional for a long time. The second and third Latin-Arabic vocabularies which have come down to us are much later, being ascribed to Ramon Martí (XIII-2) and to Pedro de Alcalá (fl. 1505), whose work was the first to be printed (Granada 1505). This is rather puzzling, for as soon as books began to be translated from Arabic into Latin we should expect Arabic-Latin vocabularies (and Latin-Arabic ones) to appear as by-products. The first important translator was Constantine the African (XI-2). The earliest glossary due to a translator is the so-called "Stephen's synonyms," compiled by Stephen of Antioch (XII-1), giving the Greek and Latin equivalents of Arabic terms.

One of the earliest champions of Arabic studies in the West was the emperor Frederick II (XIII-1), who has well deserved in many ways his nickname stupor mundi. Having chartered the University of Naples in 1224, he ordered for it a large collection of Arabic MSS. Maybe Frederick II meant it to be a bilingual institution? This was certainly the case for the studium generale established at Seville in 1254 by Alfonso el Sabio (XIII-2). Both Frederick II and Alfonso needed officers conversant with Arabic, and their schools were to a large extent seminaries for political and administrative purposes.[81]

In the meanwhile, Arabic schools had been established by Dominicans, who felt it their special duty to make themselves intelligible to the Muslim infidels, as well as to the Greeks and Jews. They established studia arabica, graeca, hebraica in Paris soon after 1217. We know from a letter of Innocent IV (1248) and from bulls of Alexander IV (1258) and Honorius IV (1285) that some Oriental students received fellowships, to be educated in Paris (possibly in the College of Constantinople, founded there after 1204).[82] This seems to have been a means of using Arabic (or other Oriental) people for Catholic purposes rather than of teaching Arabic to Europeans; however, the bringing together of Western and Eastern students would make it easier for the former to study Arabic (or other Oriental languages). The

[80] Sarton: Mlle. Goichon's studies in Avicennian metaphysics (Isis 33, 326–29, 1941).

[81] Rashdall (vol. 2, 1936). For Naples, p. 21–26; for Seville, p. 90–91.

[82] Charles Jourdain: Un collège oriental à Paris au XIIIe siècle (Revue des sociétés savantes 6, 66–73, Paris 1861). Reprinted in his posthumous Excursions historiques à travers le Moyen âge (Paris 1888). Contains Latin text of the letter and bulls.

Dominicans soon realized that seminaries for the study of Arabic would be far more efficient if located in Arabic-speaking countries, and they had two such seminaries, in Murcia and Tunis, before 1265.[83]

In the second half of the thirteenth century a number of eminent scholars realized the need of Arabic studies, chiefly for missionary purposes. They were the Catalans Ramon Martí (XIII-2), Arnold de Villanova (XIII-2), Ramon Lull (XIII-2), the Valencian St. Peter Paschal (XIII-2), the Italian Ricoldo di Monte Croce (XIII-2), even an Englishman, Roger Bacon (XIII-2). Bacon's knowledge of Arabic was rudimentary, but the others were probably as good Arabists as some who are permitted to teach in Western universities today. Ricoldo was able to preach in that language, and Ramon Lull could speak and write it. He actually composed one or two of his books in Arabic! It was because of Ramon's entreaties that James II of Majorca and pope John XXI founded a Franciscan school of Arabic at Miramar (Majorca) in 1276 (it lasted only 16 years). Other colleges of Arabic were established in Valencia 1281, and Játiva 1291 (Introd. 2, 911). The climax of Ramon's efforts was his petition to the council of Vienne in Dauphiné (1311–12), which was favorably accepted. In order to implement the wishes of that council, Clement V ordered in 1312 the organization of the teaching of Arabic (as well as Hebrew, Chaldaean, and Greek) in five universities, Rome, Paris, Oxford, Bologna, Salamanca.[84] Professors were actually appointed in Rome, but otherwise the order remained a dead letter. The "trilingual colleges" established in various universities two centuries later were not concerned with Arabic—the "three languages" were Hebrew, Greek, and Latin.[85] The scientific teaching of Arabic began only later; for example, at San Pietro in Montorio in 1610.

To complete this picture of Arabic teaching we may also evoke the clever but somewhat repelling figure of the lawyer Pierre Dubois, who thought of educating French girls for exportation to the Orient; they would be expected to Frenchify their husbands and thus increase French power in the Levant. Don Juan Manuel, who exerted a deep influence on Spanish letters, had a very good knowledge of Arabic.

The outstanding representatives of Arabic scholarship in the West were Ramon Lull and Ricoldo di Monte Croce, who died within a few years of each other, in 1315 and 1320. Ricoldo's influence lasted much longer, but it was not wholesome, for it tended to perpetuate errors. Ramon Lull's plans miscarried, yet it is fair to call him the founder of Western Orientalism. The scholars mentioned in this section were interested in Arabic primarily if not exclusively for missionary purposes. To learn Arabic was for them simply a means of fighting Islām. Their hopes were squashed, and genuine Arabic studies made for the love of Arabic, not for the hatred of something else, were postponed for centuries.

22. *Persian*

The fact that the Iranian threads are thinner and less numerous than others in my Introduction should not deceive the reader. Many had to be left out, because they were outside our frame of reference or because of chronological uncertainties;

[83] Murcia surrendered to the Christians in 1243, but Don Jaime of Aragon took definite possession of it only in 1266 (EI 3, 735, 1933).

[84] The text of the decree of Vienne is printed in appendix to Arduinus Kleinhans: Historia studii linguae arabicae et collegii O.F.M. in conventu ad S. Petrum in Monte Aureo Romae erecti (Firenze 1930; Isis 29, 189–91).

[85] Percy Stafford Allen: The trilingual colleges of the early sixteenth century, in his Erasmus, Lectures and wayfaring sketches (p. 138–63, Oxford 1934).

the ancient and pre-Islamic history of Iran is full of holes and doubtful matters. Yet definite continuities enable one to pass from the Zend religious writings (Avesta)[86] to the Pahlawī, and finally to modern Persian. Pahlawī was the official language of the Sasanian (Sāsānī) state and church (227–641). It was used not only by Iranians, but also by Greek and Syrian refugees at the Sāsānī court, e.g. the physician Theodoros (IV-2) or Theodosios, who flourished under Shāpūr II (king 309–79), and the physicians at the school of Jundīshāpūr (Introd. 1, 435). Its golden age was during the rule of Khusraw I = Nūshīrwān the Just (531–79), when many works were translated from Greek and Sanskrit. The main translator from Sanskrit into Pahlawī was Burzūya (VI-2). The Muslim conquest did not completely stop Pahlawī literature, witness the annals Khudhāy-nāmak (VII-1), the Zoroastrian encyclopaedia Dīnkart (IX-2), and the philosophical treatise Shikand-gūmānīg vījār (IX-2), which is known to us only through a Pāzand-Sanskrit[87] version made by Nēryōsang about the end of the twelfth century (see Introd. 1, 482, 540, 591).

The great majority of Persians, however, became Islamized and to some extent Arabicized. They continued to use their own Persian speech,[88] but Arabic was to them what Latin was to their contemporaries of Western Europe, their sacred and learned language. Many, though using the Arabic language and using it in a masterly way, resented Arabic predominance and defended the cultural dignity of non-Arabs, especially Iranians. This movement, called shu'ūbīya,[89] flared up in the eighth century, its main representatives being Abū 'Ubaida (VIII-2) and Ḥamza (X-2); the leading defenders of Arabic superiority were al-Aṣma'ī (VIII-2) and Ibn Duraid (X-1).

During the second half of the tenth century, the status of the Persian language was heightened, because it began to be used for scientific purposes, e.g. in the materia medica of Abū Manṣūr Muwaffak (X-2), but considerably more so because it was the vehicle of the gigantic Iranian epos, the Shāhnāma of Firdawsī (XI-1), begun c. 975 and completed in 1010. The Persians could lift their heads up, their language was fully equal to Arabic, except for the Qur'ān. A number of important books were written in Persian in the second half of the eleventh century, books which a century or two earlier would have been published more probably in Arabic—the travel account or Safar-nāma of Nāṣir-i-Khusraw (XI-2), the treatise on eye diseases Nūr al-'uyūn of Zarrīn Dast (XI-2), the treatise on government Siyāsat-nāma of Niẓām al-Mulk (XI-2, Introd. 1, 780; Nidhām is incorrect), and the Persian dictionary Lughat-i-Furs of Asadī of Ṭūs (XI-2). The Persian language

[86] For the early history of our Avestan knowledge, see my articles on Zoroaster (Introd. 1, 60) and Anquetil-Duperron (Osiris 3, 193–223, 1937). Joseph Bidez and Franz Cumont: Les mages hellénisés. Zoroastre, Ostanès et Hystaspe d'après la tradition grecque (2 vols., Paris 1938; Isis 31, 458–62). For the classification of Iranian languages, see Meillet et Cohen (p. 34–44, 1924).

[87] Pāzand is the transcription of Pahlawī into Avestan characters, Aramaic words being replaced by Persian ones. Zoroastrian refugees in India (mostly Bombay) wrote their own dialect (Pārsi) in Arabic script (like modern Persian). Jensen (p. 204, 1925).

[88] The number of original early documents in modern Persian is curiously small. V. Minorsky: Some early documents in Persian (Journal of the Royal Asiatic Society, 1942, 181–94), enumerating only seven documents from the end of the eighth century to 1217, and editing two new ones dated 1107 and 1211.

[89] Qur'ān 49, 13. God said, we created you "shu'ūban wa qabā'ila." In this phrase, shu'ūb is understood as equal to 'ajam and opposed to qabā'il (Arab tribes). Thus those who were anti-Arab for nationalistic, religious, or linguistic reasons called themselves shu'ūbī (D. B. Macdonald, EI 4, 395, 1927).

was now established on as solid a foundation as was possible, short of a divine revelation. It spread extensively, but only toward the east, where competition with colloquial Arabic did not block its path. It was taken to Delhi by the Ghaznawī rulers, became one of the main languages of the northern part of India, and showed its influence in the Urdū dialect (the Persianized form of Hindūstānī[90]). In the second half of the thirteenth century, it flourished as a scientific language during the revival initiated by Nāṣir al-dīn al-Ṭūsī (XIII-2) in the Marāgha observatory, and Persian technicians in the Mongol service, like Jamāl al-dīn = Cha-ma-li-ting (XIII-2), carried it as far as China.

Abū Ḥaiyān wrote a book on Persian grammar which is unfortunately lost, and thus we know next to nothing concerning the beginnings of that grammar. It is possible that the formulation of Persian grammar was impeded by the success of Arabic grammar, even as the formulation of French grammar was hindered by the Latin? The comparison is inadequate because the structure of the Persian language is very different from that of the Arabic; Persian is one of the Indo-Aryan languages, whereas Arabic is a Semitic one. In both cases, however (Persian and French), grammar may have been associated with the learned language and considered unnecessary for the colloquial. The Ḥanafī doctor al-Multānī, who lived in the Punjab, wrote in 1317 Persian explanations of Qur'ānic terms; this confirms our impression that Arabic was a difficult language even for the clerks.

The Persian-speaking people occupied a strategic position in Asia, for every communication between the Arabic and Western world on one hand and the Hindu and Eastern world on the other hand had to pass through them. Hence their cosmopolitanism and polyglottism, which became second nature to them, are not surprising. Some very striking information on that subject was given us by al-Bīrūnī (XI-1) in the introduction to his materia medica.[91] In Khwārizm, he had met people of many kinds, including Greeks. They needed polyglot dictionaries, some of which extended to ten languages; Nestorians used Greek-Syriac-Arabic-Persian glossaries! .Unfortunately, none of these books have come down to us; it is probable that they were worn out by their users, as dictionaries often are, as well as portolani and technical guides of every sort. There has come to us, however, a Hebrew-Persian dictionary completed in Khwārizm in 1339 by Solomon ben Samuel. The polyglottism of the Persians is revealed also in the historical writings of Rashīd al-dīn and al-Banākatī and the encyclopaedia Nuzhat al-qulūb of Ḥamdallāh Mustawfī al-Qazwīnī. The latter had the boldness to continue the Shāhnāma of Firdawsī, writing a new epos, the Ẓafarnāma, even larger than the former! The two poems together contain 60,000 plus 75,000, 135,000 couplets! (the Iliad and Odyssey together, less than 28,000 lines). Rashīd al-dīn and al-Banākatī consulted not only Persian and Arabic documents, but also Uighūr, Mongolian, and Chinese ones; their writings teem with Chinese words. Ḥamdallāh, writing like them in Persian, gives the names of animals in Arabic, Turkish, Mongolian! Sanskrit books were translated into Persian by al-Nakhshabī.

[90] As distinguished from Hindī, which is the Sanskritized form of the same language. It is a thousand pities that the growing nationalism of the Muslims and of the Hindus aggravated the differences between Urdū and Hindi instead of improving the Hindūstānī synthesis, which would have been to the advantage of all concerned. Valuable remarks ad hoc in Halidé Edib: Inside India (p. 342–43, London 1937). Mulk Raj Anand: Some observations on the Hindustani language (Indian arts and letters 17, 114–20, 1943).

[91] Max Meyerhof: Das Vorwort zur Drogenkunde des Bīrūnī (Berlin 1932; Isis 20, 451–54).

23. *Turkish*

The Turkish people were first brought to our readers' attention in the chapter dealing with the second half of the sixth century. Zemarchos the Cilician (VI-2) was sent in 568 by Justinos II (emp. 565–78) to Samarkand to form an alliance with the Turkish khān against Persia, and thus oblige the latter to resume the silk trade. A few years later, we hear of Jinagupta (VI-2),[92] one of the translators of Buddhist books from Sanskrit into Chinese, who resided from 575 to 585 at the court of the Turkish khān T'o-po and of the latter's successor; at least one sūtra was translated into Turkish for T'o-po.

A large number of Uighūr (a Turkish tribe) were established in eastern Turkistān, their capital being Turfan (Ṭurfān).[93] Their state religion was Manichaeism (see Introd. 1, 333). Turkish Manichaean writings, notably the Khuastuanift (Confession), were discovered by Sir Aurel Stein in 1907 and Paul Pelliot in 1908 in Tun-huang, Kansu (Introd. 1, 604). The Uighūr culture flourished in eastern Turkistān in the eighth to twelfth centuries. In the meanwhile, the Turks had been submitted to Buddhist influences, and various sūtra had been translated into their language from Chinese (and Tibetan?). They were submitted also to Islamic and probably Nestorian influences. Throughout Central Asia there was a welter of tribes, some of which were likely to move in and out with incredible rapidity, causing a rare confusion of races, languages, religions. The caves of Tun-huang contained books written in six languages, Tibetan, Sanskrit, Sogdian,[94] eastern Iranian, Uighūr (Turkish), and Hebrew!

The proof of Islamic influence is given by a poem, the Kudatku bilik (The knowledge that brings happiness), developing the Aristotelian theory of government as transmitted by Arabic authors. This was composed c. 1069–70 by a follower of Ibn Sīnā (XI-1);[95] the author was then 51 years of age and Ibn Sīnā had been dead for 32 years, yet the former may well have been an immediate disciple of the latter. A few years later, in 1073–74, one Maḥmūd of Kāshghar (in eastern Turkistān) published the Dīwān lughat al-Turk, a vocabulary of eastern Turkish including grammatical remarks and comparisons with other Turkish dialects.[96]

The so-called Uighūr script was obviously derived from the Manichaean script, which was itself a variety of the Syriac (Nestorian) esṭrangelā. The name Uighūr is also applied to a mediaeval eastern Turkish dialect; the fact that the same word is applied to a definite dialect and to a script, which may have been used for the transcription of other dialects, is a cause of confusion. It would perhaps be better to use the term Uighūr only for the script and to describe the dialect otherwise (mediaeval eastern Turkish).

There seem to have been two climaxes in the evolution of the Turkish language and literature, the first in the eleventh century, the second in the fourteenth, with a fallow period in between. A Turkish-Arabic glossary was compiled in 1245/6, however, and a Persian-Turkish-Mongol one sometime later. In 1313, the first

[92] Nanjio (app. II, nos. 125, 129, 1883).

[93] W. Barthold (EI 4, 893–94, 1931).

[94] Sogdian was a kind of middle Persian, different from Pahlawī, but derived like the latter from Zend. The name refers to the district Sogdiana (= Sughd, part of Turkistān and Bukhārā). See article Soghd, by W. Barthold (EI 4, 473, 1927).

[95] Otto Alberts: Aristotelische Philosophie in der türkischen Litteratur des 11. Jahrh. (Halle a.S. 1900); Der Dichter des Kudatku-bilik (Archiv für Geschichte der Philosophie 14, 319–36, 1901).

[96] For modern views on these dialectical differences, see the clear account by Jean Deny in Meillet and Cohen (p. 185–218, 1924). The subject is extremely difficult.

systematic Turkish grammar was written by the great Spanish scholar Abū Ḥaiyān, who had spent the best part of his life in Cairo and had found there good opportunities for learning Turkish.[97] His grammar is a landmark in the history of the Turkish language, but it does not belong to Turkish literature. It is a foreign work, written in Arabic.

The Turkish books thus far mentioned, the Khuastuanift, the Kudatku bilik, and the Dīwān lughat al-Turk, were the fruits of eastern Turkish culture and all anterior to the twelfth century. The Saljūq domination of Anatolia (except small Armenian states in Cilicia) which began in the eleventh century came to an end in 1300. The fall of the Saljūq and the Mongol invasions created a state of chaos in Anatolia; in addition to the relatively small 'Uthmānlī territory in the north, there were nine Turkish states competing with one another. The fourteenth century was a period of political stress and spiritual fermentation; it witnessed the beginning of Turkish literature, and that literature was chiefly western Turkish.[98]

The earliest western Turkish monument was the Rabābnāma of Bahā' al-dīn Sulṭān Walad, a son of Jalāl al-dīn-i-Rūmī (XIII-2), composed in 1301. It was soon followed by the Gharīb nāma of 'Āshiq pāshā, and the poems of Yūnus Emre and of Gülshehrī. It is remarkable that all these early Turkish poets devoted themselves to the inculcation of ṣūfī doctrine. The last named, Gülshehri, composed a translation of the Manṭiq al-ṭayr, the mystical allegory written in Persian by Fārid al-dīn 'Aṭṭār (XIII-1). Thus the early western Turkish literature was essentially philosophical and religious. The early ṣūfī poets came from different parts of Anatolia—Sulṭān Walad, 'Āshiq pāshā, and Gülshehri from Qarāmān, Yūnus Emre from Isfandiyār. This is a further illustration of the fact that ṣūfī aspirations were widely diffused in the world of Islām, East and West.

The study of the Turkish language and of Turkish matters in general was then a foreign concern rather than a national one. We have already mentioned the first Turkish grammar, composed by a Spanish Muslim. An earlier document is the Codex Cumanicus (begun in 1303), containing a Latin-Persian-Coman dictionary, plus various Coman texts. The Coman dialect was spoken by Tatars established in southern Russia. A comparative study of Chinese and Uighūr chronology had been made in Marāgha by Muḥyī al-dīn al-Maghribī (XIII-2). Thus we owe some of the earliest investigations of the Turkish language and antiquities to Western Muslims and Western Christians.

24. *Mongolian*

The Mongolian dialects are closely connected with the Turkish ones, especially with those spoken by Tatars. In spite of the fact that the Mongol invasions covered immense territories in Asia and Europe, the Mongolian dialects are less dispersed than the Turkish ones. For many centuries they have been restricted to Mongolia itself, with relatively few overflowings outside of the borders. The people speaking Mongolian dialects are ten times less numerous than those speaking

[97] Egypt was "invaded" by Turks, mostly Qipchaq, during the Mamlūk regime. A good many Mongols were also added to the Egyptian population. The sulṭān Baibars had received three large groups of them in Cairo, October 1263; they all embraced Islām. In 1296, under the rule of Zain al-din Kitbughā, a whole Mongol tribe, composed of 10,000 tents, led by Taraghay, son-in-law of Hūlāgū, was received with great honors. Gaston Wiet: L'Egypte arabe (p. 388–91, Paris 1937).

[98] For political or ethnical background, see Richard N. Frye and Aydin M. Sayili: Turks in the Middle East before the Saljuqs (Journal of the American Oriental Society 63, 194–207, 1943).

Turkish ones. The dialectical differences are smaller in the Mongolian family than in the Turkish; this may be due to their smaller geographical dispersion.

The early Mongolian people are far better known than the Turkish. They are repeatedly dealt with in the Chinese annals, beginning with the T'ang shu. As the Mongol invasions affected the whole world, and their great conquerors Chingiz Khān (XIII-1), Hūlāgū, Kublai Khān (XIII-2) created universal fears, it is not surprising that we find an account of them not only in Chinese books, but also in Persian, Arabic, Armenian, Georgian, Syriac, Greek, and Latin ones. Remember, e.g., the Historia Mongolorum of Pian del Càrpine (XIII-1) and the great work of Rashīd al-dīn. Rubruquis (XIII-2) learned Mongolian, Marco Polo (XIII-2) made many remarks about it, Giovanni de Montecorvino (XIII-2) translated the Psalms and New Testament into it. The Mongol invasions of the thirteenth century were followed by a period of relative quietness, the Pax mongolica, which was finally broken by another Mongolian or Turkish world conqueror, the worst of them all, Tīmūr Lang (XIV-2).

Chingiz Khān (XIII-1) never knew any other language than Mongolian. After his conquest of the western Mongols, in 1204, one of them called Tatatonga introduced Uighūr writing. Later still, in 1219, Chingiz favored the use of Chinese characters; the latter, however, did not supersede the Uighūr script. Chingiz was not simply a conqueror, but the first teacher of his own people. His educational efforts were continued on a larger scale by his grandson Kublai Khān (XIII-2), who ordered the translation into Mongolian of the Chinese annals of Ssŭ-ma Kuang (XI-2) as revised by Chu Hsi (XII-2), and of the Tibetan Kanjur. The first task was very large, the second was gigantic. Kublai had charged a group of 29 Tibetan, Sanskrit, Turkish, and Chinese scholars with its fulfillment, but the Kanjur was not completely put into Mongolian until after his death (1294), c. 1310. Kublai's main adviser was the lama Phagspa (XIII-2),[99] who introduced in 1269 a new method of transcribing Mongolian by means of an alphabet derived from Tibetan and written vertically.[100] Before the end of the Yüan dynasty that script was again replaced by a Uighūr script not essentially different from the older one, except with regard to ductus; it is always written from top to bottom and left to right. The Uighūr script has continued to be used for the Mongolian language, but it has been modified from time to time. At the beginning of the fourteenth century the Galik alphabet was introduced, i.e., the Uighūr alphabet plus five new characters derived from Sanskrit for the transcriptions of Sanskrit terms. Other characters were introduced to reproduce Tibetan sounds. In 1648 the Kalmuk (a Tatar tribe established since the beginning of the seventeenth century along the lower Volga) added seven more characters by means of diacritical signs in order to improve the phonetic accuracy of the transcription.

In 1293 Kublai Khān ordered the printing of books in Mongolian as well as in Chinese (Introd. 2, 981).

Various Oriental texts of the thirteenth and fourteenth centuries contain, implicitly or explicitly, Mongolian glossaries. A good example is the Nuzhat al-qulūb

[99] Nanjio (II no. 169, III no. 74, 1883). In the Sakya monastery lying to the southwest of Shigatze (Tibet) there is preserved a sinistral chank shell said to have been presented to Phagspa by Kublai. The rare sinistral form of that shell (Xancus pyrum L.) is supposed to have magical virtues and is the object of a cult in Tibet and India. James Hornell: The chank shell cult of India (Antiquity 16, 113–33, ill., 1942).

[100] It was called Phagspa after its inventor, or dürbäldzin (square) after its shape. It was an alphabet of 32 consonants and 9 vowels, the latter being represented with remarkable precision.

of Ḥamdallāh Mustawfī al-Qazwīnī. In my note on Abū Ḥaiyān reference is made to a Persian-Mongol glossary of c. 1245, and to a Persian-Turkish-Mongol dictionary of a somewhat later date.

For more information see Józef Szczepan Kowalewski: Dictionnaire mongol-russe-français (3 vols., Kasan 1844–49). Berthold Laufer: Skizze der mongolischen Literatur (Revue orientale 1907, 165–261). Jean Deny in Meillet et Cohen (p. 219–33, 1924). Jensen (1925). A. Neville John Whymant: Mongolian grammar (82 p., London 1926).

For the Mongolian grammars and dictionary published in Russian (Leningrad 1931–38) by Nikolai Nikolayevich Poppe, see K. H. Monges: Recent studies in the field of Mongolian studies (Journal of the American Oriental Society 63, 17–24, 1943).

25. *Manchu*

The Manchu language, as well as the Tunguz languages of eastern Siberia, is related to Mongolian. As most people think of the Manchu only with reference to the latest Chinese dynasty (the Ch'ing, ruling from 1644 to 1912), they may wonder why they are dealt with here. The Ch'ing dynasty, however, had been preceded by another Manchu dynasty, the Chin dynasty of the Nü-chên Tatars, ruling from 1115 to 1260 (Introd. 2, 144, 273). Their first ruler, Akuta (in Chinese T'ai Tsu), tried to reduce their language to writing in 1119; his tentative was renewed by a later Chin ruler in 1135 or 1145. Some 18 books written in the Nü-chên characters, derived from the Chinese, were preserved in the Imperial Library of Peking. All these efforts were frustrated when the Chin dynasty came to an end, in 1260, and was soon afterward succeeded by the Yüan dynasty (1280–1368).

The Manchu literary revival began many years before their new political triumph. Their great leader Nurhachu[101] decided in 1599 to adapt the Mongolian (Uighūr) script to the Manchu language. The Manchu emperors took considerable pains to promote the study of the Manchu (and accessorily of the Mongolian) language, patronizing the creation of a considerable literature. Two hundred fifty works, some of them of considerable length, were gradually translated from Chinese into Manchu. The earliest printed Manchu text (forbidding the culture and smoking of tobacco) was published in 1639 (Isis 33, 130). In 1708 appeared the "Mirror of the Manchu and Mongolian languages," in 21 volumes; later, two elaborate dictionaries in four and five languages, Chinese-Manchu-Mongolian-Tibetan plus (or not) Turkish. From 1728 on, Russians began to study Manchu and to use it as a diplomatic language in their relations with the Manchu court; an American commissioner in China proposed in 1844 to do the same, it being much easier to learn Manchu than Chinese.

In spite of all the imperial efforts to preserve it, that language was too artificial to resist the growing pressure of Chinese; the cultural superiority of the Chinese was too great and the Manchus were too few. After 1760, Manchu examinations were abandoned and the language went down rapidly.

Joseph Marie Amiot: Dictionnaire tartare mantchou français (3 vols., Paris 1789–90). Lucien Adam: Grammaire mandchou (137 p., Paris 1873). Berthold Laufer: Skizze der manjurischen Literatur (Revue orientale, 1908, 1–53). Couling (p. 323–25, 1917). Jean Deny in Meillet et Cohen (p. 234–43, 1924). Jensen (p. 216, 1925). Walter Fuchs: Beiträge zur mandjurischen Bibliographie (Tokyo 1936; Isis 33, 130).

[101] Nurhachu (1559–1626), who ruled under the name T'ien ming (1616–26), was the real founder of the Manchu dynasty (Giles no. 1580; Hummel p. 594–99, 1943).

26. *Sanskrit and Pāli*

Sanskrit may be one of the most ancient literary languages. Its Vedic form is undoubtedly of high antiquity, yet it is not absolutely pure; that is, it is not derived exclusively from one kind of dialect, a Panjabī one, but also subsidiarily from other dialects spoken in countries east of the Panjab. It soon became a learned language like Latin in the West, while various spoken dialects (Prākrit) diverged more or less from it. One of these dialects, Pāli, became, before our era, the religious language of Buddhism.

If Sanskrit is not the most ancient literary language, it certainly is the first which reached the level of grammatical consciousness. The Brāhmi alphabet[102] used for the transcription of Sanskrit existed already in the fifth century B.C.; it is a model from the phonetic point of view, far superior to our own. As to grammar, there was already plenty of it in the Nirukta, a commentary on the Veda by Yāska (V B.C.), but the real founder of Sanskrit grammar was Pāṇini (IV-1 B.C.), a contemporary of Plato. The development of lexicography was much slower. The first great Sanskrit dictionary was compiled by Amara (VI-2). The international progress of Buddhism caused the creation of bilingual dictionaries needed for the translation of the Buddhist scriptures—the Three baskets, Tripiṭaka—into Chinese, Tibetan, Korean, Mongolian, Japanese. Thus a Sanskrit-Tibetan dictionary is included in the Tanjur (Introd. 1, 468), and Sanskrit-Chinese dictionaries were compiled by I-ching (VII-2), Li Yen (d. c. 792),[103] and Fa Yün (XII-2). The greatest Sanskrit lexicographer of the Middle Ages was Hemacandra (XII-2). A new type of Sanskrit grammar was composed by Vopadeva (XIII-2).

The most important Sanskrit works of this period are the code of Hindu laws and customs compiled by Hemādri (XIII-2) and the code of Burmese laws compiled by Wagaru (XIII-2). Other Brahmanical codes were published c. 1320 by Caṇḍeśvara. It is quite possible that other works of this period would have deserved mention and even discussion if one could be sure of their date, but unfortunately the majority of early Sanskrit books are undated and undatable.

Pāli is almost exclusively a Buddhist language, and so close to Sanskrit that the need of an explicit grammar was not felt for a relatively long time. Sanskrit grammar satisfied the needs of Pāli scholars, even as Latin grammar satisfied those of French-speaking ones. When the famous Buddhist scholiasts Buddhadatta, Buddhaghosha (V-1), and Dhammapāla[104] wrote their commentaries, they simply applied the rules of Pāṇini (IV-1 B.C.) to the Pāli phrases. The earliest Pāli grammarians were Kaccāyana (of unknown date), Aggavaṃsa (XII-2), and Moggallāna (XII-2). Aggavaṃsa was a Burmese, Moggallāna a Singhalese; they initiated rival schools. Both wrote Pāli grammars, and the second was the author of the first Pāli dictionary. For more information on Pāli grammar and lexicography see B. C. Law (2, 630–41, 1933).

[102] Derived from the Semitic alphabet but considerably enriched (46 letters instead of 22), it gave birth to the Devanāgarī alphabet, various forms (Nāgarī) of which are used to this day not only for Sanskrit, but for other Hindu languages, even non-Aryan ones. The Tibetan script is also derived from Nāgarī.

[103] The dictionaries of I-ching and Li Yen have been edited by Prabodh Chandra Bagchi (Paris 1929–37; Isis 33, 356). Fa Yün's dictionary was not by any means the last; it was followed by a whole series of similar works published in China, Japan, and Western countries. The latest is William Edward Soothill and Lewis Hodous: Dictionary of Chinese Buddhist terms (quarto, 530 p., London 1937), with Sanskrit and Pāli index.

[104] Buddhadatta was a contemporary of Buddhaghosha; Dhammapāla came later but before Hsüan Tsang (VII-1).

The main Pāli authors of our period were Vedeha and the anonymous redactor of the Singhalese chronicle in Ceylon, and Medhaṃkara in Burma.

27. *Dravidian Languages*

We have come across a few of the non-Aryan languages of India, all of them belonging to the Dravidian group. To speak of them as non-Aryan would be unnecessarily vague, for there are other non-Aryan languages used in India, to wit the Muṇḍā, related to Indo-Chinese, near the northeast coast; Himalayan Tibeto-Burman dialects, etc. Dravidian languages are spoken not only in southern India, but also (one of them at least, Brahui) in Balūchistān.

We did not come across writings in Tamil, though that is by far the most important Dravidian language of India and its literature is the richest next to that of Sanskrit itself. At the present time Tamil is spoken by some eighteen million people along the south Coromandel coast (the eastern coast of Hindūstān). A dialect of it, Malayalam, is spoken along the south Malabar coast (the western coast) by seven more millions.

Between them Tamil and Malayalam constitute the language of southern India. If one goes farther north, above the latitude of Madras, the main languages are Canarese in the west and Telugu in the east.

Canarese (or more correctly Kannaḍa, Karṇāṭaka) is spoken today by more than ten million people. It is the most ancient Dravidian language as far as texts are concerned, being introduced by a short inscription as early as the fifth century. Its beginnings, even as those of Tamil, seem to have been due to the initiative of the Jaina sect (Introd. 1, 69). The oldest text is a prosody, the Kavirájamárga (Royal road of the poets), composed c. 850 and referring to earlier poets. Canarese was much influenced by Sanskrit grammarians and Sanskrit literature;[105] most of the abstract terms are derived from Sanskrit (being either unchanged, tatsama, or somewhat modified, tadbhava); the alphabet follows the order of the Sanskrit one. The script common to Canarese and Telugu is derived from northern Hindu ones, chiefly from the so-called southern Aśoka or brāhmī lipi, which changed into draviḍa brāhmī, finally into andhra lipi, and crystallized into its present shape about the thirteenth century.[106]

The Canarese people are divided religiously into two main communities, the Jaina, for which see my note on Mahāvīra (VI B.C.), and the Liṅgayat (or Śivāchār or Vīraśaiva), members of a Śaiva sect who always carry a small liṅga (phallus) on their person.

About the beginning of the fourteenth century, the Jaina Nāchirāja wrote a Canarese commentary on the great Sanskrit dictionary compiled by Amarasiṃha (VI-2). See my note on Abhinava Maṅgarāja (XIV-2). Another Jaina, who flourished at the same time as Nāchirāja, Raṭṭa-kavi, wrote a sort of popular encyclopaedia, the Raṭṭa-mata, in Canarese.

Telugu is the Dravidian language spoken by the largest number of people, some

[105] Even as Persian was deeply influenced by Arabic in spite of its belonging to a very different linguistic group.

[106] An ancient Canarese dictionary has recently been edited by A. Venkata Rao and H. Sesha Ayyangar. It is the Abhidhānaratnamālā of Halāyudha with the Kannaḍa Ṭīke of Nāgavarma (174 p., Madras University 1940). The Sanskrit lexicographer Halāyudha flourished about the middle of the tenth century (Winternitz 3, 413, 1922), the Canarese one Nāgavarma II, c. 1145. Edward P. Rice: History of Kanarese literature (2d ed., Calcutta 1921; p. 111). This Nāgavarma II is quoted by Rice as being the author of the oldest Sanskrit-Canarese dictionary, Vastu kōśa.

twenty-four millions at least. Like Canarese, it was deeply influenced by Sanskrit. The oldest Telugu writers flourished about the eleventh century. A Telugu version of the Mahābhārata[107] was begun in that century and completed by Errāpragaḍa before 1350. That version is naturally the outstanding monument of Telugu letters. The Raṭṭa-mata, originally written in Canarese, was translated into Telugu by Bhāskara within the same century.

The indebtedness of all these Dravidian languages to Sanskrit is well appreciated when one consults their dictionaries. In fact, as Sanskrit words are assimilated in various degrees, one of the main difficulties of the lexicographer is to know just how many Sanskrit words he should include.[108] For the interrelations of these languages see Meillet et Cohen (p. 345–59, 1924). Robert Caldwell: Comparative grammar of the Dravidian or South Indian family of languages (London 1856; new ed. 1875, reprinted 1913). Sten Konow in Linguistic survey of India (4, 277–681, Calcutta 1906). Catalogues of books in the British Museum, edited by Lionel David Barnett, Tamil (2 vols., 1909–1931), Canarese (1910), Telugu (1912).

Edward P. Rice: History of Kanarese literature (Heritage of India series, Calcutta 1915; reprinted 1921). P. Chenchiah and Raja M. Bhujanga Rao Bahadur: History of Telugu literature (same series, Calcutta 1928).

28. *Tibetan*

No Tibetan writings were considered in this volume, but the great Buddhist collections Kanjur and Tanjur, briefly discussed in volume 1 (p. 467–69), remained very much in evidence in the background. Tibetan was reduced to writing in the seventh century, the script being derived from the Sanskrit Devanāgarī. A Tibetan-Chinese treaty is inscribed in Tibetan and Chinese script on a pillar in Lhasa, the inscription being dated 822.

Practically all the Tibetan writings which concern us are included in the Kanjur (the Tibetan Tripiṭaka) and the Tanjur (commentaries on the Kanjur), the two collections filling respectively 100 (or 108) and 225 large volumes. The dates of the individual parts are difficult if not impossible to determine; the minimum date is seventh century; it is probable that the Kanjur was almost completed before the tenth century. The Tanjur includes a Tibetan-Sanskrit dictionary. An anatomical and medical text of some importance, the "Four tantras," written c. VIII-2 (Introd. 1, 538), remained outside these Buddhist collections.

Under the patronage of Kublai Khān (XIII-2) and the direction of Phagspa (XIII-2), Tibetan literature was investigated and parts of it were translated into Mongolian. An effort was even made to reduce Mongolian to a kind of Tibetan script, but within a century that script was superseded by a Uighūr one. A few

[107] One of the two epics of India, the other being the Rāmāyaṇa. The Mahābhārata is an immense compilation (c. 220,000 lines), badly unified, including elements of many epochs (even Vedic), largely completed within the period fourth century B.C. to fourth century after Christ. The most attractive and popular part of it, Bhagavadgītā (Song of the blessed one), is relatively late, post-Christian. See Introd. 1, 561, 707, 754. The Rāmāyaṇa is shorter (c. 48,000 lines) than the Mahābhārata and better integrated; it was probably edited before our era, but may not have reached its present shape before the second century after Christ. These two poems represent a thousand years of Hindu culture; they were the main vehicles of Hindu and Sanskrit influences in India, Indo-China, and Malaya, among nations of various races and languages. See Winternitz (vol. 1, 1907).

[108] See preface of the Rev. Hermann Gundert: Malayalam and English dictionary (1134 p., Mangalore 1872).

Westerners obtained some vague knowledge of Tibet and the Tibetan language, to wit, William of Rubruquis (XIII-2), Marco Polo (XIII-2), and Odorico da Pordenone.

29. *Chinese*

Chinese philology is at least as ancient as the Sanskrit, but it was restricted to calligraphy and lexicography, instead of being primarily grammatical. Orthography was naturally inseparable from lexicography, and calligraphy was an art as well as a science.

The earliest Chinese dictionary, called Ērh ya, was probably compiled by a disciple of Confucius, Tzŭ Hsia, who was born in 507 B.C. (Introd. 1, 110). It was frequently revived by editors, commentators, illustrators. Under the rule of the "First Emperor," Shih Huang-ti (III-2 B.C.), the art of writing is said to have received various improvements; Mêng T'ien (III-2 B.C.) introduced the use of brushes and of silk rolls, and Ch'êng Mo invented the "lesser seal" (hsiao chuan) and the li script. The first dictionary wherein the words were arranged by radicals[109] was the Shuo wên, by Hsü Shên (II-1). The system fan ch'ieh indicating the pronunciation of characters was introduced by Sun Yen (III-2), and the ssŭ shêng (four tones) by Shên Yo (V-2). These phonetic improvements were due to contacts with Sanskrit and possibly to the needs of Sanskrit scholars. Lu Tê-ming (VI-2) wrote a glossary of the Chinese classics, and Hsüan Ying (VII-1) a Buddhist one. The earliest extant phonetic dictionary (the words being classified according to rhyme) was compiled by Yen Chih-t'ui (VI-2) and Lu Fa-yen (VII-1); their work was continued and revised by Ch'ên Pêng-nien (XI-1), Sung Ch'i (XI-1), and Ting Tu (XI-1).

A very elaborate dictionary, the Lei p'ien, was put together by the historian Ssŭ-ma Kuang (XI-2); it included over 31,000 words.[110] This illustrates the enormous amount of lexicographical work which had been accumulated by Chinese scholars. It is not surprising that they were tempted to extend their philological inquiries in other directions. Tai T'ung (XIII-2) tried to classify characters in a more general way (than by radicals), according to their graphic origins, and Chou Po-ch'i wrote treatises wherein he discussed the etymology of the characters given in the Shuo wên, and their orthography. Wu-ch'iu Yen composed the earliest treatise in any language on sphragistics.

Another aspect of mediaeval Chinese philology is given us by their epigraphic treatises, written at a time when no other people paid any attention to the problems involved, or, more exactly, when no other people had recognized the existence of such problems. The earliest treatise on epigraphy was composed by Ou-yang Hsiu (XI-2); a century later Hung Kua (XII-2) published a large collection of Han inscriptions. Before the very recent discovery of "oracle bones" (in 1899),[111] the

[109] That is, according to some of their structural (graphical) elements. In the Ērh ya the words were arranged by subjects. In the Shuo wên they were classified under 540 radicals (tzŭ pu). In the imperial dictionary, K'ang-Hsi tzŭ tien (1716), the number of radicals was reduced to the present number, 214.

[110] There are some 40,000 in the K'ang-Hsi tzŭ tien.

[111] Examples of very early writing on fragments of bones. An abundant literature in Chinese and Japanese is devoted to them, with all necessary illustrations. Western readers may refer to Tchang Fong: Recherches sur les os du Ho-nan et quelques caractères de l'écriture ancienne (84 p., lithographed, Paris 1925). W. Percival Yetts: The Shang-Yin dynasty and the An-yang finds (Journal of the Royal Asiatic Society, July 1933, 657–85, 4 pl.). James M. Menzies: Old bones of the Shang dynasty (Bull. Rotary Club of Tsinan, Shantung 1933). Harry E. Gibson: Animals and agriculture in the Shang pictographs, in Arthur de Carle

main problem of Chinese epigraphy concerned the so-called "stone drums," enormous drums bearing long inscriptions and supposed to date from the Chou dynasty (c. 1027–256 B.C.). As early as the twelfth century the epigraphist Chêng Ch'iao (XII-2) dared to suggest that the stone drums were posterior to the Chou! These moot questions have been agitated periodically by many generations of Chinese scholars. I have referred many times to the interest shown by Mongol rulers, especially Kublai Khān (XIII-2), in Chinese letters and archaeology. The stone drums by this time had suffered many vicissitudes. One of Kublai's successors, Ayuli Palpata (ruled 1311–20; canonized as Jên Tsung; Giles no. 13), ordered the stone drums to be placed in the gateway of the Confucian temple, Peking, where they have remained ever since.

The teaching of the Chinese language and script being the basis of Chinese education, many books were provided for the purpose, not only editions of the Classics and the Four Books, commentaries and glossaries, but smaller books for children, like our abecedaries though incomparably more difficult. The most popular of these Chinese primers are the Ch'ien tzŭ wên (Thousand character essay) ascribed to Chou Hsing-ssŭ (VI-1) and the San tzŭ ching (Three character classic) ascribed to Wang Ying-lin (XIII-2), which was honored with many imitations. Kublai Khān proved his interest in Chinese literature by his reorganization of the Han-lin yüan and its integration with the government printing press. In 1315, the first list of Mongol chin shih was published by order of Jên Tsung.

The authenticity of the classics and the constitution of the Confucian canon were discussed by many Sung scholars, such as Ou-yang Hsiu (XI-2) and Ssŭ-ma Kuang (XI-2), already mentioned, and Ch'êng I, one of the Five philosophers (wu tzŭ) who were responsible for the great Confucian revival and reformation of the eleventh and twelfth centuries. For a summary of these discussions and of later ones on the same subject see Leonard Shih-lien Hsü: The political philosophy of Confucianism (p. 14–25, London 1932; Isis 30, 316. Synoptic table on p. 18). During the Sung dynasty the number of accepted classics had grown to thirteen, plus the four books (ssŭ shu). The number generally accepted at present is five classics and four books (wu ching ssŭ shu). List in Introd. 1, 797.

Emphasis on rites, forms, etiquette being an essential feature of Confucianism, it is not surprising that there developed early among official classes the Chinese equivalent of the Western ars dictaminis. Chinese officials attached an immense importance to the correct wording of dispatches or letters of homage; in fact, incorrect wording might be a serious cause of friction or hostility. For example, see L. Carrington Goodrich: Sino-Korean relations at the end of the fourteenth century (Transactions of the Korea Branch of the Royal Asiatic Society, 30, 33–45, Seoul 1940).

To return to the mediaeval study of Chinese, we should bear in mind that the language used in the classics was extremely different from the spoken one. In fact, that cleavage had existed and kept on increasing for centuries. As early as

---

Sowerby: Nature in Chinese art (p. 169–89, passim, New York 1940; Isis 34, 68). For the stone drums bearing inscriptions of the early part of the Chou dynasty (c. 1027–256 B.C.), see Couling (p. 149, 1917).

The first to recognize the significance of the oracle bone inscriptions and to investigate them, in 1899, were Liu Ê (1857–1909) and Wang I-jung (1845–1900), see Hummel (p. 517, 827, 1943–44). The oracle bones are often called Yin bones, Yin being the name given to the Shang dynasty (c. 1523—c. 1027 B.C.) after the removal of its capital to Yin, Honan. Later still (twelfth or eleventh century B.C.), the capital was moved to An-yang, Honan, where a great many inscribed fragments of tortoise shells and bones, as well as other antiquities, have been found.

the second century B.C. the classical language was already unintelligible to the people. In 124 B.C. the privy councillor Kung-sun Hung[112] memorialized the emperor Wu Ti, saying, "The imperial edicts and laws that have been proclaimed . . . while they are most elegantly worded and contain benevolent instructions, are not generally understood by the public officers, who are too inadequately educated to explain these to the people."[113] Not only was the classical language established in the Confucian age very different from the language commonly spoken centuries later, it was so terse and elliptic that it was impossible to understand it unless one could actually see the characters and knew the context by rote. It was because of these increasing difficulties that it soon became necessary to organize a special training in the classics and examinations ad hoc for every candidate to public office. The situation was comparable to that in Western Europe, for classical Chinese was as artificial a language to the Chinese people as Latin was to Frenchmen or Englishmen.

However, the colloquial language (pai hua) was irrepressible. It was spoken not only by illiterate people, but by literate ones as well. It received some additional dignity from the monks of the Ch'an tsung (Zen shū), originated by Bodhidharma (VI-1). As centuries passed, the Ch'an Buddhists liked to record the familiar sayings of their teachers, and they recorded them in the plain language in which they were uttered.[114] The practice was continued by the wu tzŭ of the Neo-Confucian school and their followers. It was developed also by the storytellers, whose spoken text (hua pên) was the origin of the Chinese novels. To be sure, the latter were despised by literati and were completely left out of the literary histories and bibliographies, yet they existed, grew, won the people's approval and their love. Pai hua has finally triumphed in China for the same reason that French superseded Latin in France. This was very fortunate, for China needed to express itself, and "no dead language can produce a living literature."[115]

As to Chinese learning outside of China, a fair amount was taken westward by the Mongols, but did not go much farther than Persia. At any rate, men like Rashīd al-dīn and al-Banākatī either had a sufficient knowledge of Chinese or could command the services of Chinese scholars. A few Christians like Marco Polo (XIII-2) had learned a little Chinese, not to speak of missionaries who were conversant with the language but did nothing to transmit their knowledge. A language is kept alive by the people who speak it, but it cannot be transmitted across time and space except by writers. There were in the fourteenth century plenty of Westerners in China, not only Catholic missionaries, merchants, and agents, but the very guard of the great khān, recruited from the Caucasus, the A su or Alains (Introd. 2, 982). In 1336–38, the Alains sent to Benedict XII an embassy headed by Andrew and William de Nassio. We must assume that these Alains knew Chinese, but there were no Western Sinologists in the fourteenth century.

30. *Korean*

Korean is dealt with here only pro memoria. Indeed, our work contains frequent references to Korea and the Korean people, but none to the Korean language.

[112] Died 121 B.C. (Giles no. 1030).

[113] Quoted by Hu Shih in Zen (p. 154, 1931).

[114] For the influence of Buddhist monks and other influences on popular literature see Jaroslav Průšek: The narrators of Buddhist scriptures and religious tales in the Sung period (Archiv Orientální 10, 375–89, 5 pl., Prague 1938); Researches into the beginnings of the Chinese popular novel (ibid. 11, 91–132, 10 pl., 1939); to be continued.

[115] Hu Shih: The literary renaissance, in Zen (p. 150–64, 1931).

The Chinese were in contact with their Korean neighbors during the Han dynasty, if not before. The historian Pan Ku (I-2) gives much information about them. Buddhism is said to have been introduced into Korea in 372, and together with it writing, that is, Chinese writing. In the early accounts it is not always clear whether "Chinese writing" refers to a transcription of the Korean language by means of Chinese characters, or to Chinese writing pure and simple. It is certain that Chinese characters were used to reproduce Korean sounds; it is equally certain that Korean scholars and the Korean aristocracy wrote preferably in Chinese because of their Confucian training. The Chinese language was used in Korea for all the higher purposes of life, just like Latin in the West, the native Korean language being reserved for domestic and popular use.

Korea was the main bridge for the introduction of Chinese culture into Japan. The art of (Chinese) writing was probably brought over from Korea into Japan in 405 (not in 285 as some Japanese scholars claim). Korean physicians were called to Japan in 414, and again c. 468 (Introd. 1, 393). More of them arrived in 554 (Introd. 1, 454), and Korean influence increased considerably from that time on.

The earliest Korean book is dated 950; it is a sūtra, not translated from the Sanskrit but originally written in Chinese. Printing with movable type did not begin in Korea until 1403. This refers to Chinese type.

In the seventh century a system of interlinear script derived from Chinese had been introduced by a Korean called Sŏl Ch'ong (the Chinese characters are read in Chinese Hsüeh ts'ung), to help his people pronounce the Chinese characters representing their own language. That auxiliary script, called in Korean ido (Japanese, rito; Chinese, li tou), meaning "official reading" or "clerk method," was an anticipation of the Japanese kana, or, more exactly, of the manyōgana used in the "Kana" Nihongi in 714 (Introd. 1, 516).

A Korean alphabet of 28 letters was invented in 1443 by the king of that time, who drew up instructions for their use, entitled "True sound characters for the instruction of the people," and explained the advantage of alphabetic writing.[116] That alphabet was derived from Sanskrit (the king did not refer to its origin, probably because Buddhism and hence Sanskrit were then in disfavor), but the grouping of the letters into syllables followed the Chinese pattern (left to right and top to bottom), and the syllables followed one another also in the Chinese way (top to bottom, right to left). This Korean alphabet, used to this day, is called ŏnmun (the Chinese pronunciation of these characters is yen wên). In spite of its simplicity, it obtained but little success in mediaeval times, for the literate people preferred to use the Chinese characters, with which they were thoroughly familiar, or even to use the Chinese language.

In the fourteenth century and before, every book of interest to us was written in the Chinese language and of course in Chinese script. There were steady relations between China and Korea, witness the Chinese map of Korea made about 1043 and engraved on a stone slab in 1137 (Introd. 2, 225); the elaborate description of Korea, its customs and institutions, by Hsü Ching (XII-1); and the account of Ma Tuan-lin (XIII-2). In 1314 a Korean emissary was sent to China to obtain books; he brought back 10,800 volumes, and in the same year the emperor of China made a present to the king of Korea of 4,371 volumes.

The first European to speak of Korea was William of Rubruquis (XIII-2).

116 The text is summarized in the Korean annals of the latest dynasty, Kuo chao pao chien, under the year 1446. Translated by W. G. Aston: Writing, printing and the alphabet in Corea (Journal of the Royal Asiatic Society, 1895, 505–11, 2 pl.).

W. G. Aston: The önmun, when invented? (Transactions of the Asiatic Society of Japan 23, 1–4, Yokohama 1895). Maurice Courant: Note sur les différents systèmes d'écriture employés en Corée (ibid. 5–23, 1895). Courant (1894–1901). Serge Elisséev in Meillet et Cohen (p. 255–61, 1924). Youn (1939). G. M. McCune and E. O. Reischauer: Romanization of the Korean language based upon its phonetic structure (Transactions of the Korea Branch of the Royal Asiatic Society vol. 29, 55 p., Seoul 1939), discussing the ŏnmun and Chinese scripts.

31. *Japanese*

Even as Japanese culture is to a very large extent derivative from Chinese culture, Confucian or Buddhist, even so the Japanese language, though essentially different from the Chinese, received its philological guidance from China. For example, the first Japanese lexicographer, Sakaibe Iwazumi (VII-2), traveled to China in 653, and after his return compiled a collection of Japanese words written in Chinese characters. The earliest Japanese chronicles (Introd. 1, 516), the Kojiki of 712 and the Nihongi of 714, were written partly in Chinese, partly in Japanese; the early Shintō prayers norito (or noritogoto), the early anthology entitled Man-yō-shū[117] were written entirely in Japanese, but as there was as yet no Japanese script, the Japanese sounds were represented by Chinese characters written in full. Sometimes homonym characters were used for the sake of variety to represent the same Japanese sounds, but in the course of time a limited number of Chinese characters, constituting the manyōgana, were selected to serve the needs of Japanese script. Such a kind of rebus writing was not very convenient, and as the same characters had to be written repeatedly, they were gradually abbreviated. Thus originated simplified forms of syllabic writing, or kana. The first to be invented, namely the katakana, was ascribed to Kibi Makibi (VIII-1); the second, hiragana, to Kōbō daishi (IX-1). From that time on, Japanese was written by means of Chinese characters connected and grammatically articulated with the help of the syllabic script.

The first Sino-Japanese dictionary, the Wamyōshō, was compiled by Minamoto no Shitagau (X-2), the words being arranged as in the Ērh ya, in order of subjects.

Perhaps nothing contributed more to the establishment of the Japanese language and of the new Japanese script, composed of a mixture of Chinese characters and Japanese kana, than the great romances, Taketori monogatari and Ise monogatari, written at the end of the ninth century and the beginning of the tenth, and the chronicle of two centuries ending in 1092, entitled Eigwa monogatari (XI-2). The code of laws Jōei-shikimoku, promulgated in 1232, and various Japanese chronicles or mirrors (kagami), such as the Ō-kagami of Fujiwara Tamenari (XII-1) and the Masu-kagami, were also written in the new way; the Azuma-kagami (XIII-2), however, was written in Chinese. This proves that the Chinese influence was still strong enough at the end of the thirteenth century to outclass, as it were, the national script.

From the ninth century on, the spoken language began to diverge from the written one, but that does not concern us. Such divergence is a characteristic of every living language, the written form being generally more conservative, and the spoken one more adventurous. The spoken language, and more so the spoken dialects or lingoes, constitute the living and growing edges of every language. If their development is stopped or stunted, the language itself is bound to die.

[117] A collection of some 4,000 poems, mostly tanka (including 31 syllables only), put together c. 750 by Tachibana no Moroe.

The growth of Japanese as well as Chinese scholarship was favored by the existence of the great library Kanazawa-bunko (XIII-2), the first period of which extended from 1270 to 1333. The most influential classic of the period was the Tsure-zure-gusa, written by Yoshida Kenkō before 1350.

Final Remarks

The notes to which this final section of chapter I is devoted concern the evolution of the languages which were used in the first half of the fourteenth century and the explanation of their status at that time. Our interest being restricted to scientific and philosophic writings, our notes do not refer as a rule to the bonae litterae. No attempt was made to evaluate these several languages from a purely literary point of view. Some emphasis was laid on the grammatical development of each language, that is, on the conscious analysis of its grammatical form and lexicographical possibilities. Such consciousness was stimulated in most cases by the needs of translators and their efforts to find in their own language expressions equivalent to foreign ones. Linguistic creations are more willful than is generally realized;[118] those due to translators are not only willful but deliberate.

Chapters II to XIV contain amplifications of chapter I and a large amount of detailed information which is not meant to be read consecutively. Readers may thus jump from this chapter to chapter XV, and are invited to do so.

118 Excellent remarks on this subject were made by Michel Bréal in his Essais de sémantique (Paris 1877).

CHAPTER II

RELIGIOUS BACKGROUND

(First Half of the Fourteenth Century)

N.B. For a general survey of the religious background in the first half of the fourteenth century, see section II of chapter I. In this chapter, we deal only with the main events; many other events are referred to in other chapters, and information relative to them can easily be found by means of the survey and the index.

A. WESTERN CHRISTENDOM

2. Propaganda for the Crusades

PSEUDO BROCARD

Burcardus, Brochard. A French Dominican living in Avignon about 1332, who in that year dedicated a work entitled Directorium ad passagium faciendum ad Terram Sanctam to Philip VI (king of France 1328–1350). The author's real name is not known, since it does not appear on any of the MSS of his work, in the reports concerning it, nor in the French translation of 1333 made by Jean de Vignai. In 1455 Jean Mielot, canon of Lille, translated the Directorium into French and added the name Brocard, thinking the work had been written by Burchard of Mount Sion (XIII-2). Pseudo Brocard and Burchard of Mount Sion cannot have been the same, since the latter, who was in Palestine c. 1275–85, was then an elderly person, whereas the Directorium was written in 1332. Also Burchard of Mount Sion was a German, and the pseudo Brocard was probably a Frenchman, since he himself says that he was a subject of Philip VI. Professor Kohler, in his new edition of the Latin text of the Directorium, has pointed out the possibility that pseudo Brocard and William Adam are the same. There are striking resemblances between Adam's De modo Sarracenos extirpandi and the Directorium; the same style of writing, knowledge of the same events, the same conclusions on historical events, they traveled at the same time in the same places, etc. There are, however, some divergences in the two works which leave some doubt on the question of authorship.

From the text itself we learn that the author spent at least 24 years preaching the gospel in Eastern Europe and the Near East. In 1307 he was in Constantinople and in different parts of the Greek peninsula, and he gives us valuable information on their economic and commercial life. He was in Persia after 1312. Like William Adam, he visited Socotra, an island at the entrance to the Gulf of Aden, and went so far south of the equator that he considered the belief in the antipodes neither false nor frivolous. Pseudo Brocard explains his reasons for believing he had gone south of the equator; he observed that the lengths of the days and nights at the equator were equal at all times of the year, that the stars were in different positions in the southern regions, and that the north star was no longer visible. He also concluded from his own travels and from statements made by other travelers that the size of the inhabited part of the earth is larger than had been indicated in the earlier works on geography. He says that the mistake was probably due to the fact that at the time these first estimates were made, either the other parts of the earth were not inhabited or these outlying places had not yet been discovered by the Western peoples. About 1317–18 pseudo Brocard was sent by John XXII to Lesser Armenia to open schools for teaching Latin, and to negotiate a union of the Armenian church with that of Rome—a reconciliation which was finally consummated in 1318.

The main thesis of his Directorium is a plan for a crusade, in fact it was probably written at the instigation of John XXII, who was trying to persuade the king to lead a new crusade. The preparations for it had been started in 1330, and in July 1332 the king took the cross. Although Philip continued to plan for the crusade, it never started because of the growing troubles with England which developed into the Hundred Years' War.

There are two central ideas in the Directorium: to fight the Saracens and to force the members of the Greek church to acknowledge obedience to Rome; throughout the entire work he shows intense hatred of the Greeks. The work is divided into two parts. The first part deals with the reasons for a new crusade, details concerning the preparations of ships, food, men, etc., and detailed information on the various routes to the East. Pseudo Brocard favored the land route through Hungary to Constantinople. In the second part there are discussions of the peoples of the Near East and the various ways in which they could be bribed or forced to help the French. He also discusses at some length the geography of the Near East and the routes for the army to follow.

Text. L'advis directif pour faire le passage d'oultremer, French translation made by Jean Mielot in 1455, edited by Baron de Reiffenberg: Documents relatifs aux croisades (Monuments pour servir a l'histoire des provinces de Namur, de Hainaut et de Luxembourg 4, 227–312, Brussels 1846).

Critical edition of the Latin text, Directorium ad passagium faciendum ad Terram Sanctam, made by Charles Kohler (Recueil des historiens des croisades, documents arméniens, 2, 367–517, Paris 1906). The French translation of Jean Mielot is included on the lower half of each page of the Latin text.

Fragment of Latin text printed by Quétif and Echard (1, 571–74, 1719).

Criticism. Victor LeClerc: Brocard, Dominicain, auteur d'une description de la Terre Sainte (HL 21, 180–215, 1847). J. Delaville le Roulx: La France en Orient au XIVe siècle (p. 89–98, Paris 1886). Röhricht (p. 74–76, 1890). Charles Kohler: Pseudo-Brocardus (Recueil des historiens des croisades, documents arméniens, 2, cxliii–clxxvi, Paris 1906). Beazley (3, 210–12, 1906). Charles Kohler: Quel est l'auteur du Directorium ad passagium faciendum? (Revue de l'Orient latin 12, 104–11, 1909). Hennig (3, 144–47, 1938). Atiya (p. 95–113, 1938).

For another contemporary Brocard, Dominican and canonist, see Barthélemy Hauréau (HL 26, 567–71, 1873).

GALVANO DE LEVANTO

Genoese physician and religious writer who flourished in the time of Boniface VIII (1294–1303) and Philippe IV le Bel (1285–1314). His own birth and death dates are unknown. I suspect that his main activities took place rather before 1301 than after, but since I overlooked him in my volume 2[1] it is not too late to devote a note to him in this volume.

He wrote in 1295 for Philippe le Bel a treatise on the recovery of the Holy Land, Liber sancti passagii Christicolarum contra Saracenos pro recuperatione Terrae Sanctae Galvani de Levanto Januensis. It is divided into two parts, the first of

[1] I had accepted Thorndike's dating (fl. 1338) in Isis 13, 72.

which, divided into 59 (really 58) chapters, is a treatise on government as illustrated by the game of chess (without any reference to the Holy Land); the second part deals with the subject indicated in the title, but only (so far as can be judged from 6 chapters extant out of 16) in a rhetorical and unprofitable manner. The book included originally a map of Palestine which is lost.

The first part of this treatise, entitled De regimine principum atropologice [tropologice?, allegorically] educto de ludo scacchorum, belongs to a kind of literature, "chess moralities," which enjoyed much popularity in mediaeval times. For a more famous example, the De ludo scacchorum of Jacques de Cessoles, see my note on Jean de Vignai, who translated it from Latin into French. For a general survey of moralizing chess works, see Murray (p. 529–63, 1913).

Galvano's Liber Paleofilon curativus languoris articulorum multiplicis dolorosi was dedicated to Albert or Albertin de Fiesque, archdeacon of Reims (fl. 1298–1303). He wrote other medical tracts: Remedium salutare contra catarum; Liber contra calculosum languorem (dedicated to Boniface VIII; lost).

Most of his writings were theological or religious, as the Liber neophytus spiritualis thesauri indulgentiarum (written for two cardinals, probably apropos of the Jubilee of 1300), the Liber fabrice corporis mistici et regiminis ejus (written for Boniface VIII), Contemplatio de gratia Dei, Thesaurus religiose paupertatis, Ars navigativa spiritualis, Neophyta doctrina de inferno purgatorio et paradiso (dedicated to Albanese gentlemen recently converted to the Catholic faith), etc.

Criticism. Charles Kohler: Traité du recouvrement de la Terre sainte par Galvano de Levanto médecin génois (Revue de l'Orient latin 6, 340 ff., 1898; reprinted in Kohler's Mélanges pour servir à l'histoire de l'Orient latin p. 213–40, Paris 1900), including analysis of and extracts from that treatise. Lynn Thorndike: Vatican Latin MSS (Isis 13, 53–102, 1929; no. 40). Wickersheimer (p. 164, 1936). Atiya (p. 71–72, 1938).

3. The Trial of the Templars

The history of the foundation of the order of the Knights Templars (XII-1) and of their main vicissitudes has been told before (Introd. 2, 160), but their end less than two centuries later was so dramatic and so pregnant with mischief that a brief account of it is an essential part of any history of thought in the fourteenth century.

The order had prospered tremendously in the twelfth and thirteenth centuries and had obtained considerable political and economic power; consequently many of its leaders had become inordinately greedy, insolent, and jealous of their civil and religious prerogatives. They were exempt from outside jurisdiction, episcopal and secular, from tithes, and from the consequences of interdicts. Their wealth was enormous; they acted as international bankers for princes and merchants; they owned thousands of estates in many countries and astounding[2] strongholds in the Holy Land. No wonder they excited considerable distrust and jealousy, and when the Holy Land was finally lost, with the surrender of Acre (1291), the blame fell largely on their shoulders. They had failed in their main purpose.

Yet crusading activities continued, and the rivalry between the Knights Templars and the Knights of St. John (Hospitalers) appeared more and more as a fundamental cause of weakness which should be removed. The amalgamation of the two

[2] Astounding to this day. I visited one of them, Karak or Krak, Le Crac (east of the Dead Sea), on my way to Petra in the spring of 1932.

orders had already been discussed by Gregory X (1274), Nicholas IV (1292), and Boniface VIII, but without success. Hence the growing impatience with the Templars felt by Philip the Fair (king of France 1285–1314) and, under the latter's instigation, by Clement V (pope 1305–14).

After a secret investigation, Philip ordered all the Templars of France to be arrested on October 13, 1307. They were examined under torture, or more "freely" under menace of torture, and they naturally produced the incriminating confessions which the king needed. Seventy-two selected Templars were duly coached to repeat their confessions before Clement at Poitiers (June 1308), and thereupon the pope started an inquiry of his own, not restricted to France, but of international scope.

In spite of the evidence thus obtained, the council of Vienne (October 1311) did not formally condemn the Templars; neither did the pope condemn them, but he dissolved the order (bull of March 22, 1312). Their property was given to the Hospitalers, except in Portugal and Aragon, where it was handed over to the new orders of Christ (1319) and of Our Lady of Montesa (1316). A large part of the property of the French Templars remained temporarily or permanently in the king's power, and similar spoliations occurred in other countries. Indeed, the Templars' wealth was one of the main causes of their fall, for Philip and others needed it.

It should be noted that many Templars recanted the confessions which had been wrung out of them. Thus 54 were condemned as relapsed (according to inquisitorial procedure) and burned to death in 1310. The last grand master, the noble Jurassien Jacques de Molay, imitated their example, recanted and proclaimed the innocence of the Templars on a ceremonial platform in front of Notre Dame of Paris in 1314, and was immediately burned at the stake. His heroic death, soon followed by the deaths of Philip and Clement, impressed the people profoundly and caused a popular reaction in favor of the Templars.

The procedure of that trial was so irregular that the complete truth will never be known. It is certain that the order as a whole had been gradually corrupted by its wealth and autarchy, and it is probable that individual members were guilty of various sins or crimes.[3] Its financial and political power had become a danger to church and state, especially the French state. Philip's confiscation of their property was not very unlike the evil perpetrated two centuries later by Henry VIII against the English monasteries (1536–39). It was a tragic episode in the growing conflict between the state or growing nationalism on the one side, and the church or papal power on the other.

Whatever was the guilt of the order, it is equally certain that the odious accusations leveled against it by its enemies (heresy, antinomianism, blasphemy, idolatry or devil worship, bestiality) were unfounded. The trial was the grossest miscarriage of justice as well as the largest, and the most complete denial of justice, ever recorded until that time. It prepared the way for a number of inquisitorial trials in cases of heresy or witchcraft.

Apropos of the Templars and Hospitalers, we may remark that other military orders were created or developed during this century, partly to reawaken or strengthen the crusading spirit, but they are of no importance. See Charles Moeller: Military orders (CE 10, 304–7, 1911). Atiya (p. 305, 320, 1938).

[3] The Templars' bad reputation is borne out by the popular expression "boire comme un Templier."

Criticism. There is an abundant literature on the trial (some early items of which are quoted in other articles of this book), but in proportion as the original documents are exhumed and published, the general conclusions tend to absolve the order rather than incriminate it. To the books quoted before (Introd. 2, 161) add Konrad Schottmüller: Der Untergang des Templer-Ordens (2 vols., Berlin 1887; Lea p. 381–87, 1942). H. C. Lea: The absolution formula of the Templars (Papers of the American Church History Society 5, 37–58, 1892; Lea p. 97–112, 1942). Julius Gmelin: Schuld oder Unschuld des Templerordens (546 p., 20 tables, Stuttgart 1893; Lea p. 387–91, 1942); much of the evidence is presented synoptically in the form of 20 extensive tables. Charles Moeller: Templars (CE 14, 493–95, 1912). Jules Piquet: Des banquiers au Moyen âge, les Templiers (284 p., Paris 1939), study of mediaeval banking and accounting. Georges Lizerand's little book: Le dossier de l'affaire des Templiers (Classiques de l'histoire de France au Moyen âge, 254 p., Paris 1923) is an excellent introduction to the subject, especially valuable for methodological purposes, e.g., for use in a historical seminar. Mrs. Agnes Moncrieff Leys (Sandys): The forfeiture of the lands of the Templars in England (Oxford essays in medieval history presented to Herbert Edward Salter p. 155–63, Oxford 1934).

4. Religious Orders

THE OLIVETANS

The origin and development of the Benedictine order has been discussed apropos of St. Benedict (VI-1), of the reform of Cluny (X-1), and of the reform of Cîteaux (XII-1). The Cistercians assumed in 1127 a white cowl instead of the original black one, and hence were sometimes called the White Monks.

A new reform of the white Benedictines was accomplished in 1313–19 by the Sienese patrician Giovanni di Mino Tolomei, who was born in 1272, and studied law and theology, but withdrew from the world with two friends in 1313. He assumed the name Bernard in honor of St. Bernard of Clairvaux (XII-1), and in 1319 founded a new religious house on Monte Oliveto[4] (near Asciano, prov. Siena). The Benedictine rule was given to him by his bishop in 1319, and the order was sanctioned by John XXII in 1324, and consecrated by Clement VI in 1344. Bernardo Tolomei (Bernardus Ptolomaeus) nursed plague-stricken people and died of the plague in 1348. He was canonized in 1634.

His reform was in the direction of greater solitude and austerity. It was partly inspired by the Camaldulian reform of St. Romuald (c. 950–1027) (Introd. 2, 154). It implied a special devotion to Our Lady, and tried to combine Benedictine with Franciscan ideals.

By the end of the fourteenth century, there were some 300 Olivetan houses, and by 1524 almost 1,200. The order is still widespread, but relatively small in numbers; it includes nuns as well as monks, and oblates of both sexes. It exerted a great influence upon Italian monasticism in the fourteenth century; some Olivetan brethren were even called in 1369 to Monte Cassino (the mother house of Benedictines) in order to help in reviving the regular observances. The Olivetans developed a school of limning, woodwork, etc.

J. C. Almond (CE 11, 244, 1911). Placido Lugano (Enciclopedia italiana 25, 285, 1935).

[4] So named of course after the Mount of Olives near Jerusalem.

THE SPIRITUALS

Religious orders tend to develop very much along the same general pattern. The enthusiasm of the saintly founders cannot be maintained indefinitely; sooner or later it cools down and the rule is gradually relaxed. After a while, this arouses discontent and fresh enthusiasm for reform. Then there is a protracted fight between the reformers and the conservatives, which may end in many ways. The order may be reformed or not, or a number of the brethren may swarm off to another monastery, a new branch or a new order may be created. We have sketched some such stories in the previous volumes, and there is no reason for us to explain the evolution of every religious foundation.

We must make an exception, however, for the Franciscan order, in the first place because of its great importance in the history of mediaeval science, in the second place because the quarrel of which we are going to speak made a considerable stir in the fourteenth century. We shall have many opportunities for referring to it in this volume.

For the early history see my notes on Joachim of Floris (XII-2), St. Francis of Assisi (XIII-1), and the Eternal Evangel (XIII-2). From the middle of the thirteenth century on, there appeared among the Friars Minor an increasing number who longed for greater austerity. They were called Spirituals,[5] and were strongly influenced by Joachimist and millenarian ideas. They wanted a return to evangelical purity and poverty, and did not hesitate to criticize the governments of their order and of the church.

The first group of Spirituals was led by Angelo da Clareno (or da Cingoli) of the March of Ancona, who was condemned as early as c. 1278 and exiled to Armenia, and after his return (1293) continued his fight for reform. He was excommunicated by John XXII in 1317 and died in 1337, but his brethren Fraticelli did not lose courage. One of them, Fra Michele Berti, died a martyr of his faith in Florence 1389, maintaining to the end that John XXII (pope 1316–34), chief adversary of the Spirituals, was a heretic.

Another group of Spirituals was led by Peter Olivi (XIII-2), and supported by such men as Arnold of Villanova (XIII-2). It is interesting but not surprising that many of these reformers were also men of science, the greatest being William of Occam; many references to them will occur in this volume (see index).

The history of the Spirituals and Fraticelli is extremely complicated; it involves not only quarrels within the order, but also quarrels between the whole order and the curia. Indeed, at the Franciscan chapter of Perugia 1322, under the presidency of Michele da Cesena, general of the order, a decision was taken in favor of the absolute poverty of Christ. John XXII immediately attacked the order, and trouble increased. Franciscan leaders took refuge with the emperor, etc.

The details of these quarrels, of the bulls and excommunications, counter-condemnations, are not very edifying; it will suffice to remember that throughout the century there was a growing movement of criticism and dissatisfaction against the religious and social conditions of the time, not only among the laymen and the seculars, but even within the religious orders, especially within one of the most important, the order of St. Francis.

We must still note the steady growth (from at least 1334 on) of a movement of

[5] Or Zelanti (vs. Relaxati). Also Fraticelli. Fraticellus is equivalent to Frater Minor, but the term soon acquired a different meaning, and was extended to designate radical friars of various kinds.

compromise or moderate reform which was called the Observance (regularis observantia). The Observants (as they were named later)[6] had taken to heart the words of John XXII in his bull of 1317 (Quorumdam exigit), "great is poverty but greater is obedience." Their organization was completed in the fifteenth century under the influence of such men as St. Bernardino of Siena (1380–1444) and St. Giovanni da Capistrano (in Calabria, 1386–1456), and they gradually dominated the order. At the general chapter of 1517 summoned by Leo X, the Observants were declared to constitute (as against the older Conventuals) the true order of St. Francis; their general is the general of the whole order (minister generalis totius ordinis Fratrum Minorum) and they take precedence of the Conventuals.

For further orientation, see the articles by Michael Bihl: Fraticelli (CE 6, 244–49, 1909), Friars Minor (ibid. p. 281–98), and by Livarius Oliger: Spirituals (CE 14, 230–32, 1912). Of course, other religious encyclopaedias and histories of the church might or should be consulted, but for questions concerning the mediaeval church it is always better to begin with the study of scholarly Catholic conclusions.

6. Biblical and Homiletic Writings

NICHOLAS OF LYRA

Nicholas de Lyre. French Biblical scholar and Hebraist. Born at Lyre near Evreux, Normandy, c. 1270; he assumed the Franciscan habit in 1300 or 1301 at the monastery of Verneuil near by; he was soon sent to Paris to complete his theological studies and was a doctor of theology of that university before 1309; he became an important officer in his order, being provincial of France from 1319 at least and provincial of Burgundy from 1324 or 1325; in 1322 he attended the general chapter of Perugia. As one of the executors of Joan of Burgundy (d. 1330), widow of Philip V the Tall, he founded in 1332, together with cardinal Pierre Bertrand, the College of Burgundy in Paris; the statutes, presumably drawn by Nicholas, were approved by pope Benedict XII in 1335. He died in Paris in October 1349 (not 1340).

He was not by any means a great Hebraist, but he was easily the greatest and almost the only one among mediaeval Christians. So rare was this accomplishment that there grew a legend according to which he was of Jewish origin (like his follower Paul of Burgos, XIV-2). He was certainly of Christian birth, but had the genius to realize ahead of others the necessity of going beyond the Vulgate and of referring to Hebrew sources for the correct understanding of the Old Testament. He was probably influenced by the Oxford Franciscans, such as Roger Bacon and William de la Mare (XIII-2), and may have been helped by a Jewish tutor, such as the apostate John Salvatus (fl. Paris 1319). He obtained information also from Franciscans and others who had traveled in the Near East.

His knowledge of Hebrew sources was amazing for his time. His main authority was Rashi (XI-2), whom he followed so closely in most cases (though occasionally he would differ from him and criticize him) that he was nicknamed "simius Solomonis" (Rashi's ape). His general attitude was very similar to Rashi's and he even imitated some particularities of the latter's style (simplicity, homely illustrations, insertion of French words in the Latin text like Rashi's la'azim). In addition to Rashi, he quoted the Talmud, the tosafot of Joseph ben Simon Qara (d. c.

[6] In the fourteenth century they were called Zoccolanti or Lignipedes, because they wore wooden clogs (zoccoli).

1135) and Samuel ben Meïr (XII-1), and the Moreh nebukim. His Arabic information was derived from the Jewish sources and from Raymond Martin (XIII-2). As to Western authorities, he quoted Aristotle, Boetius, Hugh of Saint Victor (XII-1), William of Tyre (XII-2), James of Vitry and Alexander of Hales (XIII-1), William of Nangis, John Peckham, and Thomas Aquinas (XIII-2), etc. These Latin sources were not inconsiderable, but the value of his work was chiefly due to his extensive use, for the first time in Christendom, of rabbinical knowledge, and to his integration of it into Christian exegesis.

His main work is a commentary on the Bible, the Postilla litteralis super Biblia, which he began in 1322 and completed about ten years later. In the introduction he explains the difference between the literal interpretation and the mystical, of which he distinguishes three kinds (allegoric, ethical, anagogic),[7] and concludes that the literal interpretation is fundamental (a sensu litterali est incipiendum). Unfortunately the letter has been corrupted by translators and thus it is necessary to return to the Hebrew letter for the Old Testament, and the Greek letter for the New. The Postilla is divided into two main parts, dealing respectively with canonical books, and with apocrypha. The apostate Paul of Burgos (XIV-2) wrote "additiones" to the Postilla.

Nicholas' fame is based almost exclusively on his Postilla. It will suffice to mention briefly some of his other writings.

The Differentia nostrae translationis ab hebraica littera Veteris Testamenti (Liber differentiarum) is a summary of the Postilla for the use of students, written in 1333. This was praised by Richard Simon (1638–1712).

Probatio adventus Christi contra Judeos (1309, 1331–34); also known under other titles, such as De Messia ejusque adventu praeterito. Discussing the question, How can intelligent Jews refuse to acknowledge Christian truths clearly announced in the Old Testament? This anti-Jewish pamphlet was refuted in 1456 by Ḥayyim ben Judah Ibn Musa in his book Magen wa-romaḥ (Shield and spear). Nicholas' views were also discussed by Isaac Abarvanel (1437–1508) in his commentary on Daniel, Ma'yene ha-yeshu'ah.

Responsio ad quemdam Judeum ex verbis Evangelii secundum Matheum contra Christum nequiter arguentem (1334).

Postilla moralis. Written in 1339 to complete the Postilla litteralis in the same sense that the midrash is needed to complete the peshaṭ.

Commentary on the Book of sentences of Peter the Lombard (lost).

Two apocryphal works (among many others) may be mentioned for the sake of curiosity: Questiones de quolibet Henrici de Gandavo abbreviate, summary of the questions of Henry of Ghent (XIII-2); Questiones magistri Nicolai de Lyra ad Scotum super lapide philosophico. Other alchemical treatises are ascribed to him, as well as an alchemical correspondence with Bernard of Verdun (XIII-2). There is hardly any trace of astrology, and none of alchemy, in Nicholas' authentic works.

Nicholas' popularity was considerable almost until the middle of the seventeenth century; there are more than 1,200 MSS of his works (chiefly the Postilla), and more than a hundred printed editions since 1471. In addition, translations and adaptations of the Postilla litteralis were soon made in French, Dutch, German, and Italian, also indexes, summaries, and extracts of various kinds. That popularity is not surprising if one bears in mind that he was the main, if not the only,

[7] Cf. Jewish distinction between peshaṭ on the one hand, derash and midrash on the other, as formulated, e.g., by Abraham ben Ezra (XII-1).

Christian interpreter of rabbinical knowledge almost until the time of Richard Simon (1638–1712). Jewish rabbis read his books, but chiefly to refute them. As to Nicholas' influence on Luther, it is well expressed by the saying "Si Lyra non lyrasset, Lutherus non saltasset."

Commentaries on Genesis naturally involve scientific discussions. For example, according to Francesco Giuntini of Florence (1523–90) in his commentary on the Sphaera of Sacrobosco (Lyon 1578), Nicholas de Lyra assumed that the earth and water spheres were not concentric with each other and with the world, and thus explained the fact that the waters do not cover the whole earth. In order to solve the same difficulty, Albert of Saxony assumed a little later that the centers of gravity of the earth and of the water sphere coincide with the center of the world, but that the geometrical center of the earth is somewhat different. In other words, Nicholas of Lyra solved the problem (emergence of some lands from the ocean) by assuming the excentricity of the earth; Albert of Saxony, by assuming imperfect sphericity. Nicholas' theory is possibly older; it has been credited to Giovanni Campano da Novara (XIII-2) in the commentary on Aristotle's Meteorology formerly ascribed to Duns Scot (see my note on Tunsted, XIV-2).

Text. Nicholas' main work, the Postilla litteralis, was first edited by John Andrew, bishop of Aleria (Corsica), and printed by Conrad Sweynheim and Arnold Pannartz under the title Glossae seu Postillae perpetuae in universa Biblia (folio, 5 vols., Rome 1471–72).[8] There are about 26 incunabula editions, which appeared in Nuremberg, Venice, Strasbourg, Rome, Basel, Lyon, and Cologne. An elaborate bibliography is given by H. Labrosse (Etudes franciscaines, 1908). It will suffice to mention the main editions.

Edition prepared carelessly from Nicholas' autograph MSS (?) by François Feuardent, Jean Dadré, and Jacques de Cuilly (folio, 6 vols., Paris, Lyon 1588–90).

Edition prepared by Douai theologians, Léandre de Saint Martin, Jean Gallemart, D. Gaugericus, and Aug. Lenglet (folio, 6 vols., Douai 1617). Reprinted Antwerp 1634.

Large extracts were also reprinted in the Biblia maxima of Jean de la Haye (folio, 19 vols., Paris 1660).

Postilla moralis. First printed in Strasbourg (n.d., before 1478). Generally printed with the other Postilla.

Tractatus de differentia nostrae translationis ab hebraica littera Veteris Testamenti. At least two incunabula editions, both undated, one of them printed in Rouen.

Probatio adventus Christi. First edition, Strasbourg 1470. Often printed with the Postilla. Latest editions, Antwerp 1634, London 1888. Also reprinted "ad calcem" of Hieronymus de Sancta Fide (i.e., Joshua ben Joseph ha-Lorqi, XIV-2): Hebraeomastix, vindex impietatis ac perfidiae judaicae (Francfort a.M. 1602).

[8] The last volume of this work printed by Sweynheym and Pannartz "contains a prefatory letter written by Joannes Andreae de Bussi, Bishop of Aleria, who had for many years served as an editor for these earliest Italian printers. In this letter, addressed to Pope Sixtus IV on behalf of the printers, he appeals for financial help on the grounds of their great service to scholarship, asserting that the volumes unsold by the press were overburdening the shelves of the establishment. The appeal provides a list of the books produced by the press and records the number of copies each edition contained, a most useful aid for determining the output of this particular press, and an addition to our knowledge of the early methods of book-production. It is pleasant to note that this appeal was not unsuccessful. The generosity of the Pope enabled the printers to weather their difficulties, brought about by the excessive competition which overwhelmed the printing trade throughout Italy in 1472" (The Pierpont Morgan Library, New York 1941; p. 75, 90).

Responsio ad Judaeum. Always printed together with and after the Probatio.

Criticism. The main source is a series of elaborate biographical and bibliographical studies by Henri Labrosse in Etudes franciscaines (16, 383–404, 1906; 17, 489–505, 593–608, 1907; 19, 41–52, 153–75, 1908; 35, 171–87, 400–32, 1923).

J. Neumann: Influence de Rashi et d'autres commentateurs juifs sur les Postillae perpetuae (Revue des études juives 26, 172–82, 1893; 27, 250–62, 1893). Gotthold Weil (JE 8, 231, 1904). Duhem (vol. 2, passim, 1906). Savage (p. 56, 134, 1911). Rubió i Lluch (by index, 1908–21). There are many mentions of Nicholas in Catalan documents, not important but proving Catalan interest in him. Charles Victor Langlois: "Quidam libellus hebraice scriptus" (Comptes rendus de l'Académie des inscriptions p. 71–79, 1925); (HL 36, 355–400, 1927). B. Suler (EJ 10, 1263, 1934). Williams (p. 408–15, 1935). Herman Hailperin: Nicholas de Lyra and Rashi. The minor prophets, in Rashi anniversary volume (p. 115–47, American Academy for Jewish Research, New York 1941; Isis 34, 44).

Iconography. Henri Labrosse (Etudes franciscaines 17, 606, 1907), refers to various portraits, one of them in a fifteenth-cent. MS of Nicholas' Commentary on St. Matthew and St. Mark (Laurentiana, Florence), "auctor ipse ad vivum delineatus in sella sedens plumam ad scribendum acuens," but he adds "sans doute hypothèse toute gratuite." Another portrait (?) of Nicholas writing is in a MS of the Postilla written in 1402 at the Franciscan monastery of Pesaro by Ugolino Marini Gibertuzzi; it is reproduced by Charles and Dorothea Singer: Legacy of Israel (p. 282, Oxford 1927).

7. Apologetic Writings, Especially Those Directed against Heresies

GUIU TERRENA

Catalan Carmelite, philosopher (d. 1342).

Guiu Terrena (Gui Terrien, Guido Terreni, Guido de Perpiniano). Guy Terré or Terrien of Perpignan (during Guy's life Perpignan and the whole county of Roussillon, of which it was the main city, were part of the kingdom of Majorca). His birth date is unknown, but he was old (in senectute bona) at the time of his death in 1342. He studied in Paris, and was there a disciple of Godfrey of Fontaines (XIII-2), who died after 1303, and later the teacher of John Baconthorpe. He obtained his doctorate in theology in 1313 or not long before; he was a master regent from 1313 to 1317/18. We do not know when he assumed the Carmelite habit (in Perpignan, c. 1290), but he became provincial of Provence in 1318 and prior general of the whole order in the same year. In 1321 John XXII elevated him to the bishopric of Majorca, and in 1332 the bishops of Majorca and Elne (near Perpignan) were permitted to exchange their sees. Guy died in Avignon on August 24, 1342.

He wrote commentaries on the Books of sentences, on various Aristotelian works (De anima, Physics, Metaphysics, Ethics, Politics), quodlibeta, quaestiones ordinariae, quaestiones disputatae. He wrote with Pierre de la Palu for John XXII the Reprobatio operis catalonici, that is, a report against a Catalan treatise De statibus ecclesiae secundum expositionem Apocalypsis, expanding the Joachimist views of Peter Olivi (XIII-2). He composed various other treatises, the most important of which are the De perfectione vitae dedicated to John XXII in 1323 (against the Spirituals); a defense of that treatise, written c. 1329–32; the Expositorium Decreti (1339), that is, a commentary on the Discordantium canonum concordia which Gratian (XII-1) had compiled two centuries earlier and which has remained ever since the basis of canon law; the Summa de haeresibus (c. 1338–42).

This last named was by far the best known of his works. It is devoted to the definition, refutation, and history of heresies. It deals with the Jews, Greeks, Armenians, Jacobites, Monophysites, Arians, Nestorians, Eutychians, Cathari, Waldenses, Beguines, Apostolics, etc., and ends with a very long chapter concerning the author's special "bête noire," Peter Olivi. He made use of St. Augustine's De haeresibus, the Etymologiae of Isidore of Seville, and the Practica inquisitionis of Bernard Gui (1323). Guiu's Summa was much used in the fifteenth and sixteenth centuries and very strongly criticized in the sixteenth and seventeenth centuries. Obviously Guiu was ill prepared for a work of that kind.

As to the Expositorium Decreti, it is to some extent the counterpart of the Sacramentale of Guillaume de Montlauzun. The purpose of the Sacramentale was to explain theology to canonists; that of the Expositorium, to explain canon law to theologians.

Guiu's philosophy was eclectic, with Thomist tendencies such as appear in the thought of his master Godfrey. He recognizes no real distinction between essence and existence, rejects the formalitates of Duns Scot and the modi reales of Durand of Saint Pourçain, etc. We quote him here mainly as a distinguished representative of Catalonia and of the Carmelites.

Text. The Summa de haeresibus was printed in Paris 1528, Cologne 1631, 1655.

Criticism. Bartolomeu F. M. Xiberta (O.C.): Guiu Terrena, carmelita de Perpinyà (Estudis universitaris catalans, sèrie monografica, 2, 338 p., Barcelona 1932); elaborate study containing many texts (p. 265–322). The same author has written 9 shorter studies on Guiu Terrena, see list on p. 337 of his book. De Wulf (2, 218–19, 1926). Paul Fournier: Gui Terré (HL 36, 432–73, 1927).

PELAYO

Alvaro Pelayo. Spanish Franciscan and theologian (d. 1352).

Alvaro Pelayo, or Alvarez Paëz, Alvarus Pelagius, was born out of wedlock at San Payo (now Aranga) in Galicia, c. 1280. His early education was looked after by Sancho IV (king of Castile 1284–95). He continued his studies in Bologna, under the canonist Guido Baisio (of Reggio nell' Emilia; appointed archdeacon of Bologna and chancellor of the university in 1296), one of his schoolmates being the famous canonist Giovanni d'Andrea (q.v.). In 1304 he attended the general Franciscan chapter in Assisi. In spite of being a Franciscan, he taught canon law for a time in the Dominican house of Perugia. He probably remained in Italy until 1329.

In 1328 he was terribly shocked by two sets of revolutionary events. John XXII having excommunicated the emperor Ludwig of Bavaria, the latter created at Rome in 1328 the antipope Nicholas V, who crowned him and excommunicated John XXII (Nicholas V made his submission to John XXII in 1330, and died a prisoner in Avignon in 1336). Alvaro was very bitter against the emperor and the antipope. His feelings were still embittered when the general of his order, Michele of Cesena, and William of Occam fled from Avignon in 1328 and took refuge at the imperial court.

In 1329 Alvaro was appointed penitentiary by John XXII, and took up his residence in Avignon. In 1333, he was ordained bishop of Silves in Algarve (Portugal). He was removed from his see in 1346, and died in Seville on January 25, 1352. He was buried in the Clarist monastery of that city.

During his stay in Avignon, Alvaro took part in the many polemics which were dividing his order, and in the discussion concerning John XXII's views on visio beatifica (i.e., the immediate sight of God as enjoyed by the blessed in heaven).

Alvaro and the Franciscan general Geraldus Odonis were among the few who defended the pope's views. He recanted later, however, when those views had been declared erroneous by Benedict XII in 1336.

His main writings are the De planctu ecclesiae, written in Avignon 1330–32; revised in Silves 1335 and in Santiago de Compostela 1340; the Speculum regum (1341–44), dedicated to Alfonso XI (king of Castile 1312–50); and the Collyrium adversus haereses, completed after 1344.

The Lament of the church contains criticisms of the ecclesiastic and monastic organizations and habits which are impressive because the author, papal penitentiary and bishop, was well acquainted with the realities of the matter as they could be witnessed from privileged inside positions, and because he was a staunch curialist and conservative. His criticisms are not those of a disgruntled outsider, but of a highly favored insider. Yet his account of the church is as black as any moderate reformer could have wished it to be.

The Planctus ecclesiae is divided into two books, of respectively 70 and 93 chapters; the second book is more than twice as long as the first. The first book is largely a defense of papal authority in general, and of John XXII's authority in particular. Popes enjoy the plenitudo potestatis, against every other man, emperors not excluded. Their powers of dispensation are indicated, as well as the powers of dispensation of other churchmen. The heretical views ascribed to John XXII are justified; moreover, God alone can judge a pope. The subject "church vs. state" is fully discussed (chs. 30–40). Chs. 51–63 include the De regimine principum of James of Viterbo.[9] Chs. 64–67 tell the history of the church, the vicissitudes of which are ascribed to schismatics of various kinds. Salvation may be expected from the friars. In conclusion (chs. 68–70) Alvaro recommends absolute loyalty to the pope, deprecates erroneous theories such as are found in the Defensor pacis of Marsiglio of Padua, and ascribes the loss of prestige of the church largely to the scandalous life of prelates.

This leads naturally to the second book, which is the real Planctus, according to Job (30:31). In chs. 2–9, Alvaro discusses the moral decline of the church, largely due to its wealth and to the scramble for benefices. In chs. 10–45 he describes the vices of the church a capite (the pope) ad calcem (the laity). The many shortcomings of monastic life are dealt with in chs. 48–67, and the rest of the book is devoted to the consideration of various monastic vices from the points of view of ethics and theology. The whole work is dedicated to John XXII, who encouraged the author in writing it.

The Speculum regum was completed at Tavira (Algarve) in 1344. It is also called collyrium (an eyesalve which would enable Alfonso XI to see his duties better). It is full of flattery for the king of Castile, the only king not subordinated to the emperor. He recommends that the king should extend his conquests to Africa, which rightly belongs to him. His knowledge of classical writers, chiefly Cicero and the Spaniard Seneca, is remarkably extensive.

The Collyrium adversus haereses was not begun before 1344. The purpose is to attack old and new heresies which may jeopardize the faith of Spaniards. The Collyrium is divided into six parts: (I) 65 errors which menace the unity of the church and the papal primacy. Jewish and Muslim superstitions. Pantheism of Amaury of Bêne (XIII-1). (II) 77 errors concerning canon law. (III) 17

[9] Jacopo Capocci, Augustinian Hermit, who taught at the University of Paris in 1293. Disciple of his religious brother Giles of Rome (XIII-2). Archbishop of Benevento 1302, of Naples 1303; died 1308.

heretical usages explained in the Decretum of Gratian (XII-1). Judicial trials by water, or red-hot fire, or duel. (IV) 32 errors explained in the Liber sextus and the Clementine Decretals. Errors of the Beghards, condemned at the council of Vienne (1311–12). (V) Contemporary errors of Marsiglio of Padua and of the Franciscan Thomas Scotus (?).[10] (VI) 41 dogmatic errors of the Greeks (i.e., of the Orthodox church), some of which were condemned at the council of Lyon (1274).

Text. The only treatise thus far printed is the De planctu ecclesiae, first published in Ulm 1474, with an index compiled by the Augustinian Hermit Petrus Dominici for Gregory XI (pope 1370–78). That edition is poor. The second edition (Lyon 1517) is much better. The third edition (Venice 1560) was the only one available to me.

Criticism. Heinrich Baylaender: Alvaro Pelayo (Diss., 58 p., Aschaffenburg 1910). Coulton (2, 179, 391, passim, 1927). Flick (1, 180, 206–7; 2, 441, 1930).

GUI

Bernard Gui, Bernardus Guidonis. French (Limousin) Dominican, theologian, historian, theorician of the Inquisition (c. 1261–1331).

Bernard Gui was born at Royère, Limousin, in 1261 or 1262; he assumed the Dominican habit in 1280; he was inquisitor in the region of Toulouse from 1307 to 1324. John XXII sent him on pacificatory missions to Italy (1317–18) and to Flanders (1318). In 1323 he was appointed bishop of Tuy in Galicia, and in 1324 was transferred to the see of Lodève in Languedoc (dépt. Hérault). He died in the castle of Lauroux, Lodève, on December 30, 1331.

He wrote many theological, hagiographic, and historical treatises. The latter include a catalogue of the popes, chronicles of the counts of Toulouse, of the bishops of Limoges and Toulouse, of the Dominicans of Provence, of the Roman emperors; a description of Gaul and history of the Franks. The most important of his hagiographic writings is the Speculum sanctorale, composed while he was inquisitor in Toulouse; it was dedicated to John XXII in 1324. It is one of the most important mediaeval compilations of its kind, answering the same need as the Βίοι ἐν συντόμῳ and the Συναξάρια in the Greek and Oriental churches, and comparable to the Legenda aurea of Giacomo da Varaggio (XIII-2), though it did not obtain the immense success of the latter.

He is chiefly remembered, however, because of another work of his, a treatise on inquisitorial practice, to which may be added a register of the inquisitorial sentences delivered by him in Toulouse (1307–23), recording the trials and condemnations of no less than 930 prisoners.

The treatise, Practica officii inquisitionis heretice pravitatis, was completed by Gui in 1323. There are six MSS of it. It was written as a guidebook for inquisitors, especially for those working in southern France. It is divided into five parts: (I) 38 formulas for the citation and arrest of heretics, subpoena of witnesses; (II) 56 acts of grace and commutation; (III) 47 formulas of sentences of condemnation; (IV) powers and virtues of inquisitors, written in scholastic style, with an abundance of quotations from imperial edicts, juridical consultations, and apostolic constitutions

[10] Alvaro had known him personally. He calls him "summus hereticus hereticorum." According to brother Thomas, there had been three great impostors, Moses, Christ, and Muḥammad! He taught the eternity of the world and denied the immortality of the soul. Faith is justified by philosophy better than by Scriptures, Decretum, and Decretales. In the All Saints Church of Lisbon he declared publicly that the miraculous power which Christ had given to his apostles had not been transmitted to their followers.

included or not in the Corpus iuris canonici. (V) The fifth and most important part is entitled De modo, arte et ingenio inquirendi et examinandi hereticos, credentes et complices eorumdem. When we speak of Gui's treatise, we generally think of that part, constituting a guide of inquisitorial procedure and one of the outstanding documents for the history of the Inquisition. It also contains abundant and detailed information on the heretics with whom Gui had to deal. In spite of the terrible crusade against the Albigenses and their extermination in 1244—or perhaps because of that crusade—heresies of many kinds were rife in Provence in Gui's time. Witness the fact that he had to condemn almost a thousand people in fifteen years! His book gives information on the Poor Men of Lyon, the pseudo Apostles, the Beguins and Fraticelli, the converted and relapsing Jews, above all on the Cathari and the Waldensians.[11] It helps one to appreciate the atrocious denial and perversion of justice which was implied in good faith, and this is the more impressive because Gui not only was a man of great experience, erudite and precise, but was conscientious and even kind, as kind as his deep-rooted prejudices allowed him to be.

The sources of his book are mainly his own experience and the original documents recording his activity or connected with it, but also for parts IV and V earlier compilations of a similar kind. His main outside source in part V is the De inquisitione hereticorum by the German Franciscan David of Augsburg (d. 1272),[12] from which long extracts are quoted almost verbatim.

Part V is divided as follows: General information; (1) the new Manichaeans (i.e., the Cathari); (2) Waldensians; (3) pseudo Apostles; (4) Beguins; (5) Jews; (6) sorcerers and witches (De sortilegis et divinis et invocatoribus demonum); (7) manners of abjuring heresy; special procedures being used for various kinds of heretics.

On December 29, 1319, Gui ordered an auto-da-fé of copies of the Talmud in Toulouse.

Text. The Liber sententiarum inquisitionis Tolosanae was edited by Philipp van Limborch: Historia inquisitionis (Amsterdam 1692); the Liber sententiarum is paginated separately, 397 p., at the end of this work.

Practica officii inquisitionis heretice pravitatis. First edited by the late Mgr. Célestin Douais (1848–1915) (392 p., Paris 1886). New edition with French translation, by the abbé Guillaume Mollat and Georges Drioux: Manuel de l'inquisiteur (Classiques de l'histoire de France au Moyen âge, 2 vols., Paris 1926–27). I have not seen Douais' edition; the Mollat-Drioux edition is restricted to part V, plus a few extracts from part III and additional documents on the sect of the pseudo Apostles and on the inquisitorial office. It is a very convenient edition, and is published with Catholic imprimatur.

For other texts see Potthast (p. 150–52, 1896).

Criticism. Dietrich König: Ptolomaeus von Lucca und die Flores chronicorum des Bernardus Guidonis (72 p., Würzburg 1875). Neubauer-Renan (p. 450, 1893). Célestin Douais: Documents pour servir à l'histoire de l'inquisition dans le Languedoc (2 vols., Paris 1900). Antoine Thomas (HL 35, 139–232, 1921).

Of course, every history of, or treatise on, the Inquisition deals with Bernard Gui. General bibliography ad hoc in Introd. 2, 553. I recommend a recent volume of George Gordon Coulton: Inquisition and liberty (London 1938; Isis 30, 558–60), because of its brevity, generosity, and timeliness; see also his Medieval panorama (p. 473, 1938).

[11] For the Cathari (XII-1) see Introd. 2, 157–59, and for the Waldensians (XII-2), Introd. 2, 331 and passim by index.

[12] Preger (ADB 4, 782–84, 1876).

WITCHCRAFT

Gui's Practica, completed in 1323, is a date in the history of witchcraft and of the Inquisition, for it afforded for the first time complete definitions and procedure. Witchcraft itself was very old. There are many references to it in the Old Testament (kashaf, keshafim), and to divination (qesem), the main texts (Exodus 22:18; Leviticus 20:27) having proved to be sources of infinite evil. The first of these texts, brief enough to be quoted, "Thou shalt not suffer a witch to live," caused the lynching or legalized murder of thousands of men and women. According to the early church, a witch was a person who was in league with a demon (or with demons); at the synod of Elvira,[13] witchcraft was declared to be one of the three canonical sins, apostasy. Yet for all that, until about the beginning of the thirteenth century the attitude of the majority of people, lay or clerical, with regard to witchcraft was one of skepticism and indifference.

Some heresies, it is true, changed their mood; there were violent reactions against the Manichaeans and later against the Albigenses. Innocent III took extreme measures against the latter in 1198 and again in 1207 (Introd. 2, 552 and by index); Gregory IX entrusted the discovery and repression of heresy to the Dominicans in 1233; Innocent IV in his bull Ad extirpanda (1252) approved the use of torture to obtain confessions. In the meanwhile demonology had been systematized by theologians (including as a climax St. Thomas), and popular preachers, playing upon the fears of their audiences, had often focused their imaginations upon all the devilries and tortures of hell to a dangerous extent.[14] Conceptions of personal devils of many kinds became more and more prominent and obsessive; the idea of witchcraft became correspondingly more familiar and more definite. It was gradually taken for granted that many people, especially women, had made a compact with the devil. They were of course the kind of unbalanced and hysterical people which would now be submitted to the care of physicians or interned in a hospital.[15] The mediaeval point of view was: Witches are the instruments of the devil against all that is good. Such a definition explained and justified every persecution. If witches were such absolute and irreconcilable enemies of God and man, they were obviously beyond the pale and deserved neither mercy nor justice. Moreover, one of the results of inquisitorial activity was to insist upon the heretical nature of witchcraft as well as upon the demonic nature of heresy; thus the two issues were confused and each crime arbitrarily added to the other!

By the beginning of the fourteenth century the situation was ugly enough. Michelet, speaking of France (Histoire de France, book 5, ch. 5), remarked: "The early years of the fourteenth century are nothing but a long criminal trial. There was an epidemic of crimes. Accusations came crowding,—poisonings, adulteries, falsifications, above all witchcraft. The last was mixed with everything, adding the necessary touch of allurement and horror." We have already dealt with the most sensational and the most horrible of these crimes, the trial of the Templars, the victims being, as usual in such cases, on both sides of the bar. There was the

[13] The first council held in Spain; in Elliberis or Illiberis, near Granada, early in the fourth century.

[14] The reader who is not acquainted with those hell-fire sermons may know or find their equivalent in the paintings of the Dutch artist Hieronymus Bosch (c. 1450–1516) in the Escorial and elsewhere.

[15] For the medical aspect of that question, see Gregory Zilboorg: The medical man and the witch during the Renaissance (225 p., Baltimore 1935; Isis 25, 147–52). It should be noted that though the disease existed in the fourteenth century and before, it did not assume the proportions and features of an epidemic until the last quarter of the fifteenth century.

extended trial of Boniface VIII (d. 1303); the burning of Marguerite Porrette[16] at the stake in the "place de Grève" (Paris) 1310, etc. Let me cite two more trials which caused considerable stir and thus helped in increasing the public hysteria.

Guichard, bishop of Troyes, was accused of having tried to hoodoo (envoûter) the queen, Jeanne of Navarre (wife of Philip IV), and of having encompassed her death soon afterward, in 1305. His trial, lasting six years (1308–13), ended in his acquittal, but not without having revealed numberless abuses and a nauseating amount of turpitude. The other case is that of Hugues Géraud, bishop of Cahors, accused of having poisoned the pope, John XXII. The bishop was condemned in 1317 and probably put to death. These two trials are known to us in considerable detail, the available documents having been carefully published. In both cases, all kinds of political intrigues were mixed with the accusations. The accounts of the trials are interesting for the study of the lay and ecclesiastical politics of those days, as well as from the points of view of criminal procedure, toxicology, and witchcraft.

Conditions were not better in Italy. Superstitions of every kind, from the most innocent to the most loathsome, were rife all over the country. The favorite haunts of witches, however, were the Apennines of Norcia (St. Benedict's birthplace!) and the Lombard valleys of the Alps. Apparently witchcraft grew more formidable the closer it approached the German frontier. There were plenty of women practicing all manner of black magic, or simply feeble-minded women taken for witches or streghe because of their queerness. There were also male witches, named stregoni, negromanti, or alchimista. The Italian earth, land, and water were teeming with sprites even as the Arabian countries with jinn; and even as the jinn were divided into various categories, Muslim or infidel, good or bad, so were the sprites, some being fiends from hell, others, less dangerous, spiriti folletti. Italian literature is full of them.

Here too witchcraft, heresy, and politics were all mixed up, but accusations of witchcraft were the best means of getting rid of adversaries or independent thinkers. We shall come back to that when we discuss the cases of Pietro d'Abano, who died c. 1316, and of Cecco d'Ascoli, who was burned at the stake in Florence 1327.

Criticism. Symonds (5, 302–6). Rigault: Le procès de Guichard, évêque de Troyes, 1308–1313 (Mémoires et documents publiés par la société de l'Ecole des chartes vol. 1, 327 p., Paris 1896). Edmond Albé: Autour de Jean XXII. Hugues Géraud, évêque de Cahors. L'affaire des poisons et envoûtements en 1317 (200 p., Bull. Société des études littéraires du Lot vol. 29, Cahors 1904). Rigault's and Albé's monographs constitute two excellent case studies. Both were discussed from the medical angle by P. Pansier (Mitt. 5, 512–14, 1906); interesting but very careless. For witchcraft in general, see bibliography given in chapter XV.

8. Criticism of the Church. Early Reformers vs. Conservatives

NEWCASTLE

Hugh of Newcastle. English Franciscan, religious reformer (fl. 1319–22).

Hugo de Novocastro (or Castronovo) was probably born at Newcastle-on-Tyne, or he assumed the Franciscan habit in that city. He studied at the University of Paris, where he became doctor in theology (before 1322) and licentiate in canon law; he spent the greater part of his life in Paris and died there. He shared with

[16] She was a kind of Beghard, loving God too much. Barthélemy Hauréau (HL 27, 70–74, 1877).

John of Wales and Nicholas de Lyra the honor of being buried in the Franciscan church of Paris. In spite of that, we do not know the date of his death. The only datable facts of his life are a writing of his in 1319 and his presence at the Franciscan chapter of Perugia in 1322, led by Michele da Cesena; he was then already a doctor in theology, and a man of importance in his order; he was one of those who approved the declaration on apostolic poverty which was then sent to the pope.

He wrote a very long commentary on the four books of Sentences before 1322. It shows him to have been a disciple of Duns Scot, whose lectures he may have attended in Paris before 1308. In 1319 he composed a treatise De victoria Christi contra Antichristum, but his most important work is a memorial on the sale of indulgences, wherein he castigated the abuses witnessed by himself in the dioceses of Paris and Reims, and indicated remedies. In this he anticipated the criticisms made by Chaucer in the Pardoner's tale, and even by the Reformers of a later time. The ascription of this writing to him is not certain, but very probable.

Text. De victoria Christi, printed at Nuremberg 1471.

The commentary on the Sentences is unpublished.

The memorial on the sale of indulgences, beginning Quia circa spiritualia magis vertitur, was edited by Barthélemy Hauréau: Notice sur le no. 16089 des MSS latins de la Bibliothèque nationale (Notices et extraits 35, 232–38, Paris 1896).

Criticism. A. G. Little (DNB 40, 317, 1894). Ch. V. Langlois: Hugo de Novocastro, frater minor, in Essays in medieval history presented to Thomas Frederick Tout (p. 269–75, Manchester 1925); (HL 36, 342–49, 1927).

PIERRE DUBOIS

French publicist and reformer (c. 1250–c. 1321).

Contents: (1) Life. (2) Main writings. (3) Political views. (4) Reformation of the church. (5) Organization of peace. (6) Education. (7) Economics. (8) Originality and style. (9) Influence.
(10) Text. (11) Criticism.

1. *Life*

Pierre Dubois or du Bois, Petrus de Bosco. Born in Normandy, perhaps in or near Coutances, between 1250 and 1260. He attended the University of Paris, where he listened to lectures of Thomas Aquinas (XIII-2; d. 1274) and Siger of Brabant (XIII-2). He established himself as a lawyer in Coutances. He was not a university man, nor a member of a monastic order, nor a high officer of the crown, but simply a lawyer, a very successful one, who enriched himself and enjoyed the king's confidence. His deep knowledge of French and European politics, unavailable in his day except to a few, proves that he had access to at least some of the leading men of the kingdom. He was an "advocatus causarum regalium" in Coutances and also a "procurator universitatis eiusdem loci," viz., an advocate of that community. In 1302 and again in 1308 he represented Coutances at the States-general. He gave legal advice on important political matters to Philippe IV le Bel (king of France 1285–1314), and also to Edward I Longshanks (king of England 1272–1307) in Guyenne. He died c. 1321.

2. *Main writings*

A rapid examination of his writings will complete our account of his political activities, for every one of his books or "pamphlets" was like a lawyer's brief written for a definite practical purpose.

1. Summaria brevis et compendiosa doctrina felicis expeditionis et abbreviationis guerrarum ac litium regni Francorum (et de reformatione status universalis reipublicae christicolarum). Written in 1300 for Philippe le Bel. Though not as bold as later writings, this first one already contains the germs of many of his political ideas. He explains the means of pacifying Europe under French suzerainty and denounces the abuses and usurpations of clerical courts.

2, 3, 4. Pamphlets written against Boniface VIII (pope 1294–1303), in defense of Philippe le Bel:

2. Deliberatio super agendis a Philippo IV contra epistolam Bonifacii papae VIII inter cetera continentem haec verba, Scire te volumus. Boniface VIII had issued on December 5, 1301 a bull Ausculta, fili. A false bull Scire te volumus, wherein the papal arguments were maliciously aggravated and distorted, was written in France soon afterward, possibly by the king's chancellor Pierre Flotte (died at the battle of Courtrai, Groeningen 1302), and circulated as the original one. Whether Dubois knew this or not, he answered the false bull as if it were genuine, concluding that Boniface VIII was heretical and Philippe the real defender of the faith. Dubois' answer was written in 1302. It is the only one of his writings to bear his name, and it made possible the attribution to him of the others.

3. Quaestio de potestate papae. Written c. 1302.

4. La supplication du pueble [sic, peuple] de France au roy contre le pape Boniface VIII. Written in French after Boniface's death (1303), probably not long afterward (September 1304). Treating the same subject with greater violence. The vernacular was obviously used for publicity purposes.

5. De recuperatione Terrae Sanctae. This is Dubois' longest and main work. His defense of a new crusade seems to be largely a pretext for the justification of a long series of reforms, political, ecclesiastical, judiciary, military, educational, which we shall outline presently. It was written in 1306 and, strangely enough, dedicated to Edward I Longshanks, though it was far more likely to please the king of France than the king of England.

6, 7, 8. Pamphlets against the Knights Templars, urging the king of France to suppress their order and confiscate their estates:

6. Request written in French supposedly by the people of France to their king, asking him to oblige Clement V (pope 1305–14) to suppress the Templars.

7. Quaedam proposita papae a rege super facto Templariorum. Draft of the letter to be addressed by the king to the pope.

8. New request of the people to the king, this time in Latin, Cum instancia devote supplicat. . . . More violent than the previous one.

We may recall that the French Templars were arrested on October 13, 1307, and their wealth appropriated by the king, who was greatly in need of it. The Templars were finally suppressed by Clement V in 1312. Their trial is one of the most atrocious on record. Much could be said against them, but it is clear that their power and wealth constituted their main guilt. The atrociousness of this affair does not lie in the murder, spoliation, and suppression of the Templars, but in the legal hypocrisy of the murderers and their agents. Pierre Dubois has a large share of responsibility in this.

9. Pro facto Terrae Sanctae. Brief written in 1308 after the murder of the emperor Albert I of Habsburg (1308), advising the king, as descendant of Charlemagne, to have himself elected emperor! The reconquest of the Holy Land and European peace are dependent on the unification of Europe under French suzerainty and on the transfer of the pope's temporal power to the king of France.

10. Brief written in 1308 advising the king to establish a kingdom in the Near East for his second son, Philippe le Long, the Templars' estates to be used as a financial prop for that kingdom.

3. *Political views*

Dubois' fundamental idea was the need of increasing the power of France and the royal power in that kingdom. That is the dominant motive of all his writings, the ostensible purpose of which may be different. The monarchy he conceives of is not absolute, yet is far more powerful than older legists, dominated by the concept of subordination of king to church and pope, would have thought possible. In order to increase the king's power, he advocates a whole series of military and legal reforms. Above all, the relation between the king and pope must be radically changed. The pope's power for peace and unity would be enhanced if he surrendered his temporal power to the king of France and devoted himself exclusively to his religious duties. The pope is the lord of the emperor, whom he confirms and crowns, but not of the king, descendant of Charlemagne. Dubois' naïve Gallocentrism in civil and canon law was supported by the University of Paris.

The conflict concerning sovereignty and pervading every political issue, whether lay or ecclesiastic, is now a three-cornered one, as it involves not only the pope and the emperor, but also, with increasing strength, the king of France.

4. *Reformation of the church*

Dubois has been described as one of the outstanding reformers before Luther. It is true he denounced the avarice, simony, nepotism of the clergy, and advocated repeatedly the secularization of church property, the abolition of clerical celibacy, a reduction in the number of cloisters, and modifications in their rules. It should be remembered, however, that his main purpose was always the defense of lay against ecclesiastical administration and justice. That is, his purpose was always political rather than religious. It must be conceded that the modern monarchy (in the manner of Louis XIV) could not emerge from the mediaeval monarchy (in the manner of St. Louis) without considerable weakening of ecclesiastical interference in nonreligious matters. Canonists had been extending the relevancy of canon law to an ever widening field; it was the business of lay advocates like Dubois to resist their encroachments. If not, the king could never be master in his own kingdom.

5. *Organization of peace*

Nowhere does Dubois' Gallocentrism reveal itself better than here. Universal peace he can conceive only as under French domination, and he uses the need of it as an argument to justify such domination. Moreover, the king of France should be born and bred in France, where the astrological conditions are the best. Dubois' program of "peace" includes the destruction of the Italian republics, the conquest of the Holy Land, etc. It is simply a program of French imperialism. The pope, shorn of material power and under French tutelage, might occasionally devote his spiritual influence to the adjustment of international difficulties. A court of arbitration would judge such difficulties and the recalcitrant princes would be excommunicated.

Dubois' plans for a new crusade and for a new colonization of the East are all subordinated to the same purpose: French hegemony. Some of his ideas of colonization are curious; e.g., to favor marriages between French people and the highest classes of Orientals.

6. *Education*

His most original ideas concern education. For example, his colonial politics led him to recommend the practical study of Oriental languages; in this, however, he was anticipated by the church, which had recommended similar studies for the needs of Christian propaganda in the previous century (see my note on Ramon Lull, Introd. 2, chiefly p. 911). In his main work, De recuperatione Terrae Sanctae, he develops an elaborate program of public education, including the study not only of grammar and Latin, using Donatus (IV-1), the Doctrinale of Alexandre de Villedieu (XIII-1), and the Graecismus of Eberhard of Bethune (XIII-1), but logic, Greek, or Arabic or other languages ad libitum, natural sciences (Albert the Great, Thomas Aquinas, Siger), mathematical sciences (Roger Bacon), ethics, politics, the Bible, etc. He advocated a simplification of legal procedure and teaching and the publication of smaller and cheaper books (libri portativi pauperum). Girls should be educated with special care, especially those who were to be given in marriage to members of the Orthodox clergy and to Oriental princes, and whose special business it would be to convert and Frenchify their husbands. These girls should be admitted to professional training, chiefly in medicine and surgery, in order that they might better fulfill their special mission.

It is clear that Dubois' educational ideas, like all his others, were essentially political. He was a kind of fourteenth-century "totalitarian," dreaming of educating boys and girls for the service of the state. The educational sphere and program were determined by the needs of the state and by nothing else.

His scientific interests were on a very low level, because the scientific needs of the state were still undeveloped and because of his own unscrupulous materialism. In spite of some contact with Averroism, it is probable that his own scientific curiosity did not extend beyond the calendar, medicine, and judicial astrology.

7. *Economics*

He realized the political dangers involved in the depreciation of money, and drew for the king a tragic picture of them. This may have influenced Oresme.

8. *Originality and style*

Even if it could be proved that most if not all of his ideas had already been expressed by others—and this could probably be done—he should still be regarded as one of the most original thinkers of the fourteenth century. New ideas are exceedingly rare in politics; whatever novelty there is lies generally in a reassortment of old elements. No other thinker of the Middle Ages presented such a curious and original assortment as his, one which was in many respects prophetic.

He was a typical "remueur d'idées," expert in combining as persuasively as possible all the notions, however strange they might seem, which would serve his purpose; he was probably able to do so without being restrained by any feeling of dishonesty, because his vigorous common sense was combined with a lack of imagination. His naïve radicalism, his Gallocentric provincialism, and his unscrupulousness can all be explained in the same manner, and not otherwise.

At its best his style was as original as his system of thought. It is neither scholastic nor pure; it is vivacious, loose, strong, with a modern accent, all this being partly due to the fact that he was neither a schoolman nor a philosopher, but simply a practical lawyer.

9. *Influence*

The best proof of Dubois' global originality is his lack of contemporary influence. That lack was due to the fact that his ideas were so much ahead of his time that they seemed visionary; also to their being subordinated to a political purpose which debased and sterilized them; finally, to their private nature, being in the form of documents prepared for his royal client, not for the general public, nor even for a group of scholars. His main work, and the first to be printed, appeared only in 1611. Many writings of his remained unidentified until 1846.

10. *Text*

De recuperatione Terre Sancte, edited by Bongars: Gesta Dei per Francos (2, 316-61, Hanover 1611), and by Charles V. Langlois (168 p., Paris 1891).

Summaria brevis et compendiosa doctrina felicis expeditionis et abbreviationis guerrarum ac litium regni Francorum, written c. 1300, analyzed and parts of it translated into French by Natalis de Wailly (Bibliothèque de l'Ecole des chartes 8, 273-315, Paris 1846). New edition by Hellmut Kämpf (61 p., Leipzig 1936).

Deliberatio super agendis a Philippo IV . . . contra epistolam Bonifacii Papae VIII inter cetera continentem haec verba: Scire te volumus, edited by P. Dupuy: Preuves, in Simon Vigor: Histoire du différend d'entre le Pape Boniface VIII et Philippe le Bel (p. 44-47, Paris 1655).

Quaestio de potestate papae (Recueil des actes de Boniface VIII et de Philippe le Bel p. 58-93, 1614), and in Dupuy: Preuves (p. 663-83, Paris 1655).

La supplication du pueble de France au roy contre le pape Boniface le VIIIe, in Simon Vigor: Acta inter Bonifacium VIII (p. 36-44, Paris 1613), and by Dupuy: Preuves (p. 214-19).

De facto Templariorum (1308), printed by Boutaric (Notices et extraits des MSS 20, 175-79, Paris 1865).

De facto Templariorum (1308), a different work under the same title, printed by Boutaric (ibid. p. 180-81).

Quedam proposita pape a rege super facto Templariorum (1308), printed by Boutaric (ibid. p. 182-86).

Pro facto Terre Sancte (1308), printed by Boutaric (ibid. p. 186-89).

11. *Criticism*

Ernest Renan: Pierre Du Bois, légiste (HL 26, 471-536, 1873); Etudes sur la politique religieuse du règne de Philippe le Bel (485 p., Paris 1899).

Adolphe Vuitry: Les monnaies sous Philippe le Bel et ses trois fils (Journal des économistes p. 447-59, 1880). Reginald Lane Poole: Illustrations of the history of medieval thought and learning (London 1884; revised ed. 1920, p. 224-28). Molinier (3, 196-97, 1903). Emile Bridrey: Nicole Oresme (p. 435, Paris 1906). F. M. Powicke: Pierre Dubois, a mediaeval radical (Historical essays, edited by T. F. Tout and J. Tait, p. 169-91, Manchester 1907). Ernest Zeck: Der Publizist Pierre Dubois (238 p., Berlin 1911). Giuseppina Bientinesi: Vincenzo di Beauvais e Dubois considerati come pedagogisti (Atti dell' Accad. di Torino 51, 1411-30; 52, 191-207, 1915/16). C. Delisle Burns: A medieval internationalist (Monist 27, 105-13, 1917). Eileen Power: Pierre Du Bois and the domination of France (Social and political ideas of some great medieval thinkers, edited by F. J. C. Hearnshaw, p. 139-66, New York 1923). Bede Jarrett: Social theories of the Middle Ages, 1200-1500 (p. 92 f., London 1926). Walther I. Brandt: Pierre Dubois; modern or

medieval? (American historical review 35, 507–21, 1930). Flick (vol. 1, 1930). Hellmut Kämpf: Pierre Dubois und die geistigen Grundlagen des französischen Nationalbewusstseins um 1300 (122 p., Leipzig 1935). Atiya (p. 47–73, 1938).

DÉLICIEUX

Bernard Délicieux. French (Languedocian) Franciscan. Resolute enemy of the Inquisition (died in prison in 1320).

Bernardus Deliciosus. Born in Montpellier, which was then under Majorcan, i.e. Aragonese, control; assumed the Franciscan habit at Carcassonne 1284; reader in the convents of Carcassonne and Narbonne; friend of Raymond Lull and Arnold of Villanova. He was eloquent and persuasive and undertook to deliver the Languedoc and especially the Albigeois from inquisitorial violence. At the beginning this was probably a phase of the fierce rivalry and growing hatred between the Franciscans on the one side, and on the other side the Dominicans who controlled the Inquisition. Bernard was not only a Franciscan, but a Spiritual, i.e., one of the "radicals" of his order, believing in apostolic poverty, in the urgent need of ecclesiastical reforms, and in the equal need of a monkish change of heart.

In 1300 the Dominican inquisitors of Carcassonne started a post-mortem trial against Castel Fabri, a rich man, who had died with Franciscan blessings and been buried in the Franciscan cemetery. They were about to condemn him and seize his property when Bernard began to defend him; in spite of that, Castel Fabri was duly condemned and his wealth confiscated. This increased Bernard's hatred of the Inquisition. In 1304 Benedict XI issued an order for his arrest, but died before it could be executed. During the papal interregnum which followed (1304–5), Bernard caused the people and the clergy of Albi and of the neighboring villages to petition the college of cardinals and the king against the excesses of the inquisitors. Obtaining no redress, he committed the error of negotiating with a son of the king of Majorca (Jayme II) for Aragonese help against the French oppressors of his country. This was treason. Bernard owed his life for many years to the protection of Philippe le Bel and the mercy of Clement V, who tried vainly to repress the inquisitors. After the election of John XXII in 1316, his fate was sealed. He was accused, among other things, of having killed Benedict XI (d. 1304) by poison or sorcery. Bernard was thrown into prison, formally tried, twice tortured. In the depositions against him it was reported that he asserted publicly in Toulouse that "Saints Peter and Paul would not be able to defend themselves from heresy if they were now alive and if they were examined in the fashion followed by the inquisitors." At the end of 1319 the judges concluded that Bernard was an enemy of the Inquisition, a traitor against the king, and a sorcerer, and he was condemned to abjuration, degradation, and lifelong imprisonment in chains; he died a few months later.

Bernard should not be thought of as a defender of free thought. He was simply a denouncer of inquisitorial arbitrariness, injustice, and cruelty. He was orthodox, except in so far as he favored the intransigeance and disobedience of the Spiritual party of his order.

Barthélemy Hauréau: Bernard Délicieux et l'inquisition albigeoise, 1300–1320 (219 p., Paris 1877). I have read this book with deep interest. It has been criticized by Franz Ehrle, "freilich ein gut Theil Roman," in his study on Die Spiritualen, ihr Verhältniss zum Franciscanerorden und zu den Fraticellen (Archiv für Litteratur- und Kirchengeschichte 2, 145, 1886). And yet! See the "pièces justificatives" edited by Hauréau (p. 167–218 of his book). Coulton (1938a).

GUILLAUME DURANT LE JEUNE

Languedocian theologian and publicist (d. 1330).

Guilelmus Durantus ep. mimatensis. He was born in the diocese of Béziers (dépt. Hérault; Languedoc), and was a nephew of William Durant (or Durand), bishop of Mende (in Gévaudan; dépt. Lozère), called "Speculator" (XIII-2; d. 1295 or 1296). At the time of his uncle's death, the younger William was archdeacon in Mende; he was elected to the bishopric in 1296 in succession to his uncle. The story of his life is very complicated because of endless administrative and financial difficulties with his flock, his clergy, his chapter, the king, and the pope. He managed to work out agreements with the king and pope against the feudal lords of Gévaudan. Clement V appointed him his legate in Italy (1305-6); later (1307) William was sent to England to investigate the canonization of Thomas de Cantelupe (1218?-82), bishop of Hereford (the canonization was effected by John XXII in 1320). He attended the council of Vienne (1311-12). He was employed on many other missions, the last one being in 1329, when he was sent by John XXII and Philippe de Valois to the Near East to negotiate in regard to a new crusade. He traveled in great state, accompanying Marie de Bourbonnais, engaged to Gui de Lusignan, heir of Cyprus. Pierre de la Palu, new patriarch of Jerusalem, was also in the company. William negotiated with the sulṭān of Egypt. He died in Cyprus, July 1330 (not 1328), and was buried in Ste. Marie de Beaulieu, the Cistercian church of Nicosia.

William wrote many papers and letters relative to his various missions to Italy, England, and the Near East, and to the affairs of his bishopric, but his main work and title to remembrance is a Tractatus de modo celebrandi concilii (et de corruptelis in Ecclesia reformandis), wherein the conciliar theory is developed with great vigor. It was written hastily before the council of Vienne, i.e. before 1311, and is sometimes a little incoherent, but is full of practical wisdom. The sovereign power, claimed William, is vested not in the pope (who is simply the bishop of the first see, primus inter pares), but in the general council of bishops, which should meet periodically. He denounced all the vices of the church, which should be reformed "tam in capite quam in membris." He condemned not only institutional errors, but also moral vices, e.g., the existence of brothels near the doors of the pope's palace, other scandals of the Avignonese court, the frequent incontinence of the clergy, and the abuse of indulgences. In spite of these fearless denunciations, William remained on good terms with Clement V, and even, to some extent, with John XXII. He defended the special rights of the French state and people. He forged excellent weapons for the use not only of gentle critics like Pierre d'Ailly (1350-1420), Jean Gerson (1363-1429), and Nicholas of Cues (1401-64), but also of the Gallicans and of the Reformers.

On account of the fact that William Durant, uncle and nephew, were both bishops of Mende, the De modo celebrandi concilii was often ascribed (e.g., by Bossuet, who admired it) to the elder instead of to the younger. See also my notes on two other Durands, contemporaries of William Durant, Jr.: two Dominicans, the nominalist Durand of Saint Pourçain (d. 1334), and the Thomist Durand d'Aurillac (fl. 1330-34). Durand, it should be remembered, is a very common name in France, almost like Smith in England.

Text. Tractatus de modo celebrandi concilii. First edition, Lyon 1531. Many later editions: Lyon 1534, Paris 1545, 1561, 1617, 1635, 1671. It is also included in the Tractatus illustrium in utraque tum pontificii tum caesarei juris facultate jurisconsultorum (13, 154–82, Venice 1584). The third edition (or second, for the second Lyonese edition may be only a "title" edition) was published by Philip Probus of Bourges and dedicated to Paul III (pope 1534–49) in view of the council of Trent (1545–63).

Criticism. Paul Viollet (HL 35, 1-139, 1921); elaborate study, including a long analysis of the De modo celebrandi concilii (p. 79–129). Atiya (1938).

B. BYZANTINE CHURCH

10. Defense of the Orthodox Faith

ANDRONICOS OF CONSTANTINOPLE

Unknown Byzantine theologian who composed about 1310 an apology for Christianity against the Jews. It was written for Christians rather than for Jews. The author had met some of the latter and had discussions with them in Constantinople, also in Macedonia and Thessaly; his knowledge of Judaism, however, was poor. The apology is written in the form of a dialogue, and discusses such topics as the Holy Trinity, why did Christ desire to be born of a virgin?, worship of images, circumcision.

This text has been known for centuries, but was wrongly ascribed to the autocrator Andronicos I Comnenos (Ἀνδρόνικος Α' Κομνηνός), emperor from 1183 to 1185. The date of the work, however, is given in chapter 41 as 6818 (era of Constantinople, according to which the Creation occurred in 5508 B.C.), which is equivalent to 1310 A.D.

Text. The Greek text has never been published, though there are many MSS of it.

A Latin translation was first edited by the Belgian priest Pierre Stevart of Liége (1547–1624) in his Tomus singularis (Ingolstadt 1616), which was a kind of supplement to the Antiquae lectionis tomi I–VI edited by the Dutch theologian Henricus Canisius (d. 1610) in Ingolstadt 1601–8. That Latin text was reprinted in the augmented re-edition of the Lectiones antiquae prepared by Jacques Basnage (1653–1725) under the title Thesaurus monumentorum ecclesiasticorum et historicum (folio, 7 vols., Antwerp 1725; 4, 255–330). Second reprint in PG (133, 797–924, 1864).

Criticism. Krumbacher (p. 91, 1897). Williams (p. 181–87, 1935).

C. OTHER EASTERN CHRISTIAN CHURCHES

11. Missionary Efforts

WILLIAM ADAM

Guillaume Adam, also called Gérard, Georges, and Gaspard. Dominican traveler, probably French (d. 1341).

William was born about 1275, probably in France, although he may have been born in Antivari, which was then in Serbia. He was one of the early members of the Christian mission to Persia established by pope John XXII at the beginning of his pontificate. He traveled as a missionary across Asia Minor, Syria, Palestine; in 1313–14, he was in Persia; he visited the Mongol Empire, India, and the Aethiopian regions of East Africa. He returned to France in 1316–17. In 1318 he was one of six Dominicans sent back to Persia to carry the pallium to the first archbishop of Sulṭānīyah (in Jibāl); he was back at Avignon in 1322, and then he himself was appointed archbishop of Sulṭānīyah, and was instructed to Christianize the pagans of his diocese, and to reunite with the Catholic church the Armenian communicants who were scattered around in the empire of the Mongols of Persia. In 1323 he was sent by the pope to Leo IV, king of Armenia. On his return to Avignon, in 1324, he was appointed archbishop of Antivari. He spent most of his time in Avignon and Narbonne; he died in Antivari, however, about 1341.

About 1317, after a sojourn of many years in Asia, he began to write his De modo Sarracenos extirpandi, also called Tractatus quomodo Sarraceni sunt expugnandi, which was completed by 1328. It was dedicated to cardinal Raymond de Farges (d. 1346), nephew of Clement V.

This treatise is an argument for another crusade, and tells with minute detail how to prepare the way for a successful one: "Primo per mercatores subditos Romane Ecclesie; secundo per peregrinos nostre Ecclesie; tercio per imperatorem Constantinopolitanum; quarto per imperatorem Tartarorum aquilonis; quinto per mercatores maris Indie."

William, unlike his contemporaries, realized that the chief cause for the failure of the proposed crusade lay in the West itself, and was due to the indifference of the Christian leaders, and to love of gain on the part of the traders who were willing to supply the agents of the sulṭān with food, weapons, and materials of all sorts. He discusses at great length the native products of the countries under the control of the sulṭān and the goods that were imported into them from Europe and India. In order to stop all trade with Egypt, an international fleet should be established to police the Mediterranean; this idea was also found in the writings of others, for instance Jacques de Molay and Marino Sanudo, but the latter failed to realize that blockading the port of Alexandria would not stop all trade with Egypt; he ignored the Indian trade.

All pilgrims should be forbidden to go to the Holy Land, because the sulṭān was gaining too much money from the tax he collected from them.

In the third place, it would be necessary to capture Constantinople and substitute Latin control in the East for Greek. William gives many reasons why this should be done: (1) In order to carry the war through Asia Minor as well as Syria; and there should be an attack on the Saracens of Egypt also. (2) In order to have a well protected place to use as a base of operations against both these places. (3) So that the crusaders might approach the Holy Land by a land route, through Hungary, and along the Danube. (4) To gain control of the Turks living near Constantinople. (5) The Greeks had always been against the Christians of the West, therefore should be subdued. (6) The Greeks had caused the Schism, therefore should be punished. (7) The Greeks had been too friendly with the sulṭān; had sent him food in times of famine, and young men and girls as slaves. This part of his work, concerning Constantinople, is by far the most original and interesting, and occupies the greater part of his book; he was the first to develop this idea to any great extent.

Not only were the Greeks to be conquered, but also the khān of the Tatars of Gazaria[17] must be kept from taking aid to the sulṭān; and an alliance with the khān of the Mongols of Persia should be made. This idea of an alliance between the Christians and the Mongols in Persia appears in practically all the memoirs dealing with the Crusades, especially in that of Hayton. William gives a favorable account of the īl-khān's court and also of that of Ūzbeg (khān of the Golden Horde 1312–40),

[17] The name Gazaria (or Khazaria) designated the Crimea region, the land of the Khazars (see Introd. 1, 680).

which, although not true, was one of the main causes of the establishment of the new Persian sees, and was all-important in the creation of those which lay within the realm of the Golden Horde, especially Caffa and Sarai.

There was to be a fleet in the Arabian Sea as well, cruising between the Gulf of Aden and the Persian Gulf to check all trade between Egypt and India. It is probable that William was the first to realize that a complete blockade of Egypt was not possible unless the trade through the Red Sea was stopped.

Adam's work shows a great understanding of men and of Eastern affairs. It also reveals his great missionary zeal. His work is less rich in historical material than the works of Hayton and Marino Sanudo; it is a treatise written with a single purpose, to interest the West in a new crusade.

According to Kohler, Adam was very possibly the author of the Directorium ad passagium faciendum, a work written some ten or twelve years later than the De modo Sarracenos extirpandi. Indeed, the Directorium, dedicated to Philippe VI of France, was written with the same purpose as the earlier work, and the author, whoever he was, was a Dominican living in Avignon at the same time as Adam. It has been ascribed also to Brocard; see the note devoted to pseudo Brocard.

Four liturgical works are sometimes ascribed to Adam: Officium sanctificationis B. V. Mariae, Officium undecim millium virginum, Officium B. Thomae de Aquino, and Officium D. Georgii Martyris.

Text. De modo sarracenos extirpandi, edited with a long introduction by C. Kohler (Recueil des historiens des croisades, documents arméniens, 2, clxxvii–ccvii, 521–55, Paris 1906). For the Directorium, see note on "Brocard."

Criticism. Daniele Farlati: Illyricum sacrum (7, 67–70, Venice 1817). Louis de Mas Latrie: L'officium robarie ou Office de la piraterie à Gênes au Moyen âge (Bibliothèque de l'Ecole des chartes vol. 53, 264–272, Paris 1892). Charles Kohler: Documents relatifs à Guillaume Adam archevêque de Sultanieh, puis d'Antivari, et son entourage, 1318–1346 (Mélanges de l'Orient latin et des croisades p. 475–515, Paris 1900), letters of John XXII relative to William Adam. Henri Omont: Guillaume Adam, missionnaire (HL 35, 277–84, 1921). Gabriel Ferrand: Une navigation européenne dans l'Océan indien au XIVᵉ siècle (Journal asiatique 20, 307–9, 1922; Isis 7, 193).

D. ISRAEL

BAḤYA BEN ASHER

Baḥya ben Asher ben Halawa. Judeo-Aragonese exegete, theologian, and moralist. Born about the middle of the thirteenth century, flourished in Saragossa, died in 1340. Disciple of Solomon ben Adret (XIII-2), he represented the most conservative aspect of Judaism.

He wrote at least seven works, of which we shall mention only the two most famous:

1. Bi'ur 'al ha-Torah. A commentary on the Pentateuch, completed at Saragossa 1291. He often quoted Rashi (XI-2), Abraham bar Ḥiyya (XII-1), Solomon ben Adret and Moses ben Naḥman (XIII-2), and he occasionally mentioned al-Baṭalyūsī (XII-1) and others, even Maimonides. He was very conservative but catholic. He used four exegetical methods, all of which were in his opinion necessary, none sufficient, to wit: (a) the peshaṭ, or literal explanation, after Rashi; (b) the midrash, or haggadic illustrations; (c) the method of reason, or philosophical explanation, as prudently or timidly as one might expect from a pupil of Solomon ben Adret; (d) the mystical or qabbalistic method or "path of light,' mainly after

Moses ben Naḥman. The popularity of Baḥya's commentary is proved by the existence of at least ten supercommentaries; it was first printed at Naples in 1492. The most important supercommentaries are the Naftule elohim by Naphtali (Hirz) ben Eliezer Treves (sixteenth cent.), first printed at Heddernheim 1546 and often reprinted, and the Manoaḥ maẓa ḥen by Manoah ben Shemariah Hendel (d. 1612), incompletely printed at Prague 1611.

2. Kad ha-qemaḥ (Flour jar), also called Sefer (or Ḥibbur) ha derashot (Book of explanations). A treatise on ethics and practical religion written for a larger circle of readers than the Bi'ur. It was first printed in Constantinople 1515. It is of interest for the study of Hispano-Jewish society of that time. It includes many foreign words (Arabic, French, and Spanish).

According to Baḥya's computations, the year 1402/3 was the last possible date for the coming of the Messiah.

Text. The Bi'ur was first printed at Naples 1492. Many later editions: Pesaro 1507, 1514, 1517; Constantinople 1517; Rimini 1524–26; Venice 1544, 1546, 1566; Riva 1559; Cracow 1593, 1610; Amsterdam 1726.

The Venetian edition of 1546 and the Cracow edition of 1593 contain Naphtali Treves' commentary; the Cracow edition of 1610 contains Manoah Hendel's commentary.

First edition of the Kad qemaḥ, Constantinople 1515. Later editions Venice 1545–46, Lublin 1596. Modern edition with commentary by Ḥayyim ben David Breit (Lemberg 1880).

Criticism. Steinschneider (col. 777–80, 1860). Philipp Bloch and Kaufmann Kohler (JE 2, 446–47, 1902). S. A. Horodezky (EJ 3, 930–31, 1929). Solomon Gandz: Artificial fertilization of date palms (Isis 23, 245–50, 1935); refers on p. 246 to Baḥya's general conception of sexuality in plants.

ABUDRAHAM

David ben Joseph ben David Abudraham (or Abudarham, Abudrahim). The family name is a corruption of the Arabic name Abū dirham or Abu darāhim (father of the drachmas), borne by various Spanish Jews, to begin with, by one David, who was a tax collector in Tudela in the second half of the thirteenth century.

This David ben Joseph was a pupil of Jacob ben Asher and flourished in Seville c. 1340. He wrote a commentary on the liturgy and the prayer book, Sefer Abudraham, Ḥibbur perush ha-berakot we ha-tefillot, which includes an explanation of the Jewish calendar. This was completed at Seville in 1339–40. This humble but honest book enjoyed some popularity, being first printed in 1489, and at least eight more times.

Text. Princeps, Lisbon 1489. Second edition, Constantinople 1513. Third edition, Fez 1521, this being the first book printed in Africa (Adler collection; Portuguese type). Then Venice 1546, 1566; Amsterdam 1726; Prague 1784, 1817; Lemberg 1857; Warsaw 1877.

Criticism. M. Steinschneider: Die Mathematik bei den Juden (BM 12, 7, 1898). Kaufmann Kohler (JE 1, 139, 1901).

ABNER OF BURGOS

Rabbi Abner. Jewish apostate, who assumed at the time of his baptism (after 1320) the name of Alfonso. As he then flourished in Valladolid, he is often called Alfonso of Valladolid (as well as Alfonso of Burgos, Alfonso el Burgalés, Alfonso Converso). He died about the middle of the fourteenth century (c. 1348). The date of his birth is unknown, but he was already an elderly man or past middle age at the time of his baptism.

He was a physician and taught (?) medicine in Valladolid, and is said to have written a treatise on the plague (?). On the other hand, it is claimed that after his conversion he became sacristan in the cathedral of Valladolid.

His writings include:

1. A commentary on Abraham ben Ezra's commentary on the Decalogue, written before his conversion.

2. Concordia de las leyes. Attempt to harmonize the Old and the New Testaments.

3. Sefer milḥamot Adonai (Wars of the Lord). Translated by himself into Spanish, Libro de las batallas de Dios, by order of the infanta Doña Blanca, daughter of Alfonso III of Portugal. Now Doña Blanca, a Cistercian nun in the convent of Las Huelgas near Burgos (not abbess, but protectress of that convent),[18] died in 1321. Hence the Spanish text, not to speak of the Hebrew one, must have been written before that date. Yet it is strongly anti-Jewish. The Hebrew and Spanish texts are both lost, but extracts of the latter are preserved in the Fortalitium fidei of Alfonso de Spina.

4. Iggeret ha-gezerah (Letter on fate). Probably written soon after his conversion, which he tries to justify on astrological grounds: his conversion was caused by planetary influences. This was much resented by his Jewish contemporaries, notably by Isaac ben Pulqar and Moses ben Joshua of Narbonne, and the discussions which ensued became gradually embittered.

5. Moreh ẓedeq (Teacher of righteousness). Dialogue in ten chapters between the teacher (moreh) and a (Jewish) rebel (mamre). The teacher disproves the Jewish arguments against Christianity. This exists only in a Spanish version, Mostrador de justicia, the Hebrew origin of which is transparent in the Spanish style.

6. Las maliciones de los Judios (Jewish malices or blasphemies). This was perhaps the book wherein he accused the Jews of cursing the Christians and apostates in their prayers. Alfonso XI (king of Castile and León 1312–50) ordered in February 1336 that those curses should be omitted. See Alfonso de Spina in the book mentioned above.

7. Libro de las tres gracias. Christian edification, anti-Jewish.

8. Minḥat qinaot (Offering of jealousies). Defense of astrology against Isaac ben Pulqar.

9. He is probably the real author (or editor) of the translation into Latin of Samū'īl ibn 'Abbās' refutation of Judaism, Ifhām ṭā'ifat al-Yahūd. That book is said to have been translated into Latin in 1339 by Alfonsus Bonihominis. Are Alfonsus Bonihominis and Alfonso of Valladolid identical, or did the second Alfonso simply edit and publish the work of the former? In volume 2 (p. 402), I stated that the former was bishop of Morocco in 1346?

Text. None of these texts has been published except no. 9, the Epistola Samuelis Marocani, first printed in 1475 and often reprinted in Latin and other languages (Introd. 2, 402). Fragments of it are included in Alphonsus a Spina.

Criticism. Alphonsus a Spina: Fortalitium fidei contra Judeos, Sarracenos, aliosque Christianae fidei inimicos (first printed in Strasbourg 1471, often reprinted).

[18] She is called Señora de las Huelgas, not Señora abadesa. See Amancio Rodriguez López: El real monasterio de las Huelgas de Burgos (2 vols., Burgos 1907; vol. 1, ch. 9).

This is the Alfonso de Spina mentioned above; he was of Jewish origin, became a Minorite in Valladolid, bishop of Orense in 1466, died in 1469. Meyer Kayserling: Biblioteca española-portugueza-judaica (p. 114, Strasbourg 1890). Frederick de Sola Mendez (JE 1, 71–72, 1901). Fritz Baer (EJ 1, 339–40, 1928). Vera (1, 118, 1933). Williams (p. 259–60, 267–71, 1935). George Sarton: A plague treatise by Abner of Burgos (query no. 55, Isis 24, 430, 1936).

Alfonsus Bonihominis. Klebs mentions (no. 200, 1938) a Libellus arabicus in malos medicos ascribed to him, printed in Italy, Venice? c. 1500. There is a copy of that leaflet (6 printed leaves) in the Boston Medical Library. James F. Ballard: Catalogue (p. 70, Boston 1944; Isis 35, 218).

DAVID BEN SAMUEL KOKABI

David ben Samuel of Estella (in Hebrew kokab). Languedocian Talmudist who flourished in the beginning of the fourteenth century—he was in Avignon c. 1305—and died c. 1340. He came from a city called Estella, but that name is not uncommon in France.[19] The best-known Estella is Estella in Navarra, near Pamplona, but David ben Samuel may have come from another one.

He wrote two works completing each other, the Migdal David and the Qiryat sefer.

The Migdal David (Tower of David, allusion to Proverbs 18:10; Canticles 4:4) is divided into two parts: doctrine and precepts. The first part deals with the creation of the world, freedom of will, providence, revelation, eternal rewards and punishments, arrival of the Messiah, resurrection; the second, with practical theology. Each part is divided into doors (she'arim, cf. Arabic abwāb), and the doors into columns ('ammudim). The theoretical part is slavishly Maimonidean.

The Qiryat sefer (Kirjath-sepher in Joshua 15:15, the Book city) is divided into three parts, and the parts into chapters called baitim (houses), hence the work is also called Sefer baitim: (1) Unity and love of God, in 5 baitim; (2) precepts for the conservation of our body and salvation of our soul, in 5 baitim; (3) social relations, in 2 baitim. Each bait is divided into she'arim. In this work also Maimonides is the main authority, very few others being even mentioned. The preface contains an interesting history of oral tradition in Israel from the time of rabbi Judah ha-Nasi (II-2) on.

Text. Both works are still unpublished.

Criticism. Adolf Neubauer: David Kokhabi (Revue des études juives 9, 214–30, 1884). Includes long extracts, e.g., the passage relative to the history of Jewish tradition above mentioned, also extracts from his contemporary Isaac de Lattes. D. Kaufmann: Une liste d'anciens livres hébreux conservés dans un ms. de Paris (Revue des études juives 13, 300–4, 1886), apropos of Kokabi's library. Neubauer-Renan (p. 471–77, 1893). J. Heller (EJ 5, 870, 1930).

ISRAEL BEN SAMUEL MA'ARABI

Israel ben Samuel ha-Dayyan (the judge) Ma'arabi (al-Maghribi). Qaraite scholar, who lived in Cairo about the beginning of the fourteenth century. His name suggests that he was probably of Western origin. He was the teacher of the Qaraite physician Japheth ben Ẓaghir of Cairo.

He wrote in Arabic a treatise on religious laws, Kitāb al-farā'iḍ, of which only the part dealing with the calendar is extant, in Hebrew translation. This Qaraite

[19] See my note on Isaac of Stella (XII-2), abbot of Etoile in Poitou.

treatise on the calendar, dated 1313 (or 1323?), is entitled Ḥishbon 'ibbur ḥodshe ha-shanah (Calculation of the intercalation of the months of the year).

His other works, also in Arabic, do not concern us.

Text. The Hebrew version of the treatise on the calendar is included in the Tiqqun ha-Qara'im (Institution of the Qaraites) edited by Johann Christoff Wolf: Bibliotheca hebraea (4, 1077 f., Hamburg 1715–33).

In the great collection of Biagio Ugolini: Thesaurus antiquitatum sacrum (22, col. 531–52, Venice 1759), there is in the section "Institutio Karaeorum nunc primum a Blasio Ugolino ex hebraico latine reddita" a text entitled Supputatio intercalationis et mensis anni, Hebrew and Latin in parallel columns, which is possibly different, though the title is the same. It is dated 5171 = 1410/11.

Criticism. M. Steinschneider: Die Mathematik bei den Juden (BM 11, 73, 1897); (p. 243, 1902). Isaac Broydé (JE 8, 233, 1904).

E. ISLAM

MUSLIM MYSTICAL BROTHERHOODS

We have already spoken of the Muslim ṭuruq (pl. of ṭarīqa) or orders of darāwīsh (pl. of darwīsh), which are to some extent the equivalents of the Christian monastic orders. Many of these orders have mythological beginnings, but the earliest the history of which can be traced is:

1. The Qādirīya, named after its founder, 'Abd al-Qādir al-Jīlī (XII-1), who died in Baghdād 1165/6. Other orders can be traced back with sufficient confidence to the thirteenth century, to wit:

2. The Qalandarīya,[20] an order of wandering mendicant dervishes which originated in Central Asia, where they may have been influenced by Hinduism; they become tangible in Damietta c. 1213 (EI 2, 676).

3. The Suhrawardīya, founded in Baghdād by 'Umar al-Suhrawardī (XII-2), who died in 1234/5. The early history of the order is very obscure and mixed with that of similar orders, Nūrbakhshīya and Ishrāqīya, which are differentiated from it or not. The first al-Suhrawardī (from Suhraward in Jibāl) of that family is 'Abd al-Qāhir ibn 'Abdallāh al-Suhrawardī (d. 1167), author of Ādāb al-murīdīn (Manners of the disciples), and the history of the order is sometimes made to begin with him (Brown p. 158–61, 1927).

4. The Aḥmadīya, founded in Ṭanṭā by Aḥmad al-Badawī Sīdī (born Fez 1199, died Ṭanṭā 1276), who spent the last 41 years of his life in Ṭanṭā and is considered the greatest saint of Egypt; his order had definite yogi tendencies (EI 1, 192–95).

5. The Mawlawīya (the so-called dancing or whirling dervishes), founded by the great ṣūfī poet Jalāl al-dīn-i-Rūmī (XIII-2) in Qūniya, where he died in 1273 (EI 3, 418–19).

Two more orders date from the first half of the fourteenth century:

6. The Ṣafawīya, founded by the shaikh Ṣafī al-dīn (born in Ardabīl, Adharbāyjān; educated in Gīlān, southwest of Caspian Sea; died 1334). This may be considered a branch of the Suhrawardīya. In its turn, it gave rise to the Turkish Shī'a sect of Qizil-bāsh (red head), to other Turkish sects, and to the Ṣafawī dynasty which ruled Persia from 1502 to 1736 (EI 4, 54).

7. The Baktāshīya, a Turkish sect with Shī'a tendencies, the foundation of which is ascribed to Ḥājjī Baktāsh or Baqtāsh (died 1337). As this sect is of great

[20] Each darwīsh of that kind was called Qalandar, hence the English word calender, used since 1614 at least.

importance for the history of Turkish literature and civilization, I shall have many opportunities for referring to it. See EI (1, 691–92) and Birge (1937).

Two more orders will be dealt with in the second part of this volume.

These ṭuruq differ in many particularities, yet they have many elements in common. They are always real fraternities (in the Moroccan and Algerian ones the members are called ikhwān); they have strong mystical tendencies; they attach great importance to their peculiar traditions and rites, which may be strange, complicated, moving, beautiful. They manage to combine the most mulish obscurantism in certain matters with liberalism in others, or rather with receptiveness to erratic ideas, unpopular outside the ṭarīqa (e.g., Shī'a ideas in the midst of Sunnī Turkey). Like the monasteries of Christendom, they often obtained considerable popularity, influence, and power. Their power might become political, even military (as with the Baktāshīya).

Some of the darāwīsh live in monasteries, others are wanderers like the mendicant friars or tertiaries.

The darwīsh habit was as widespread in Islām as the monkish in Christendom. Observe that out of the seven ṭuruq selected by me in my summary, two, the Qādirīya and the Suhrawardīya, originated in Baghdād; two others, the Mawlawīya and Baktāshīya, in Anatolia; one each in Central Asia, the Qalandarīya; in Egypt, the Aḥmadīya; in Persia, the Ṣafawīya.

To the general references given in volume 2 (p. 164), and the special ones cited above, should be added the article faqīr in Hughes (p. 115–23, 1885), Edouard Montet (ERE 10, 719–26, 1919), D. S. Margoliouth: Dervish (ERE 4, 641–43, 1912), and Brown (1927). J. W. McPherson: The Moulids of Egypt (366 p., Cairo 1941; Isis 34, 267). Carlo Alfonso Nallino: Raccolta di scritti editi e inediti (vol. 2, Roma 1941; Isis 34, 177).

The religious orders of knighthood, chiefly the order of St. John of Jerusalem (XII-1), of which Eastern peoples obtained some knowledge during the Crusades, may have influenced some of the ṭuruq. At any rate, there were complex interrelations between the monastic orders and the order of St. John on the one side, and the ṭuruq, futūwa, aṣnāf (guilds), and taṣawwuf on the other. See these words in the index and the note on Islamic guilds in chapter I, section VII.

IBN TAIMĪYA

Taqī al-dīn Abū-l-'Abbās Aḥmad ibn 'Abd al-Ḥalīm Ibn Taimīya al-Ḥarrānī al-Ḥanbalī. Syrian Muslim theologian (1263–1328).

He was born at Ḥarrān, near Damascus, in January 1263; a few years later the family was obliged to move to Damascus to take refuge from the Mongols. His father was professor of Ḥanbalī law, and when he died, in 1282, Ibn Taimīya succeeded him. A good part of his life was spent in the jails of Damascus, Alexandria, and Cairo. He died in Damascus in September 1328.

Ibn Taimīya was an aggressive and popular preacher, a convincing and abundant writer, who revived the Ḥanbalī doctrine, representing the extreme right of Muslim orthodoxy. He was a fundamentalist and puritan who wanted to return to the early days of Islām, basing his theology upon a literal interpretation of the Qur'ān and ḥadīth, disregarding the ijmā' (agreement of the learned, one of the four sources of the faith), rejecting not only the heresies but all the novelties which the changing political and social circumstances of seven centuries had made necessary, criticizing violently the cult of the saints, pilgrimages to their tombs, and other "superstitions." He attacked almost everybody, especially the mystics and the followers of two great

Shāfi'ī doctors, al-Ash'arī (X-1), the founder of Muslim scholasticism, and al-Ghazzālī (XI-2), who might be called the St. Thomas as well as the St. Bonaventure of Islām. He assailed every school and sect except his own—the scholastics, the philosophers, the mystics, not to speak of Jews and Christians. Thus he made many enemies and was often thrown into prison, where he spent his time writing commentaries on the Qur'ān and all kinds of theological pamphlets, becoming more and more uncompromising and irreconcilable. His writings are distinguished by merciless logic, intolerance, aggressiveness. It would take too long to enumerate them, as more than 150 remain out of some 500 ascribed to him. I quote one title to illustrate his avenging spirit: Kitāb ṣārim al-maslūl 'alā shātim al-rasūl (The drawn sword against the insulter of the Prophet).

The Riḥla of Ibn Baṭṭūṭa testifies to Ibn Taimīya's popularity and crankiness (Defrémery's ed., 1, 215–18). His popularity was made manifest at the time of his funeral in the ṣūfī cemetery of Damascus, where he was buried among his enemies and where his tomb is visited by many pilgrims in spite of his lifelong opposition to such worship.

In spite, or rather because, of his fanaticism, Ibn Taimīya has profoundly influenced Islamic thought, in at least two directions. To begin with, he furnished the inspiration and doctrine of the Wahhābīya, the puritan reform of Islām accomplished by Muḥammad ibn 'Abd al-Wahhāb (1703–87), which is dominating the religious and social life of Sa'ūdī Arabia today. In the second place, his writings were read considerably by Muḥammad 'Abduh (1849–1905) and through him have influenced the new school of Islamic thought, a purely intellectual revolt against all the superstitious accretions which had gathered around the faith and contaminated it.

Text. For various small editions of many writings, see Brockelmann. The earliest is the tract which Ibn Taimīya composed to shame the Christians, Takhjīl ahl al-injīl, the substance of which was included by father Lodovico Marracci (1612–1700) of Lucca in the introduction to his Refutatio Alcorani (Padua 1698), which forms the second folio volume of his edition and translation of the Qur'ān.

Criticism. Wüstenfeld (part 2, 157–60, 1882). Brockelmann (2, 100–5, 1902; suppt. 2, 119–26, 1938). Macdonald (1903). Moh. ben Cheneb (EI 2, 421–23, 1918). Lammens (1926). Charles D. Matthews: A Muslim iconoclast on the "merits" of Jerusalem and Palestine (Journal of the American Oriental Society 56, 1–21, 1936). Farmer (no. 210, p. 50, 1940), apropos of a text of Ibn Taimīya condemning music, R. fī-l-samā' wal-raqṣ wal-ṣurākh (Concerning listening, dancing, shouting), printed Cairo 1905.

Every book on Islamic thought must deal with Ibn Taimīya. For the Wahhābī movement see D. S. Margoliouth (EI 4, 1086–90, 1933).

F. BUDDHISM

VEDEHA

Siṅhalese writer in Pāli (fl. c. 1325?).

Vedeha thera, born a Brāhmin, was a Buddhist monk, member of the Vanavāsī or Araññavāsī fraternity centered at the great minster (mahāvihāra) in Anurādhapura. Vedeha flourished probably during the rule of Parākramabāhu IV (often called paṇḍita Parākramabāhu), c. 1325.

Two or three Pāli works are ascribed to him:

1. Rasavāhinī. Collection of 103 Buddhist stories revised from an earlier Pāli

version by Raṭṭhapāla thera of the Siṅhalese text Taṅgutta-vaṅka pariveṇa of the Mahāvihāra. Of the 103 stories, 40 are of Hindu origin, the others Siṅhalese. This very beautifully written book is much used to this day as an elementary Pāli reader in temple schools of Ceylon, Burma, and Siam. A Siṅhalese adaptation was prepared by Dhammakitti V (XIV-2).

2. Samanta-kūṭa-vaṇṇanā. Pāli poem of 800 verses, describing the Adam's Peak, on which the Buddha left the imprint of his left foot on his third visit to Ceylon.[21] It includes a biography of the Buddha.

3. Sidat-saṅgarāva. Earliest grammar of Eḷu (or old Siṅhalese, a language closely akin to Vedic, the earliest form of Sanskrit). This grammar is anonymous, but it was written at this very time for Pratirājadeva paṇḍita, minister dispatched by Parākramabāhu to southern Ceylon to repair dilapidated temples; the author describes himself as head of the Pratirājapariveṇa in southern Ceylon, and Vedeha claims authorship of a Siṅhalese grammar in the colophon of the Rasavāhinī.

We may thus ascribe the Sidat-saṅgarāva to Vedeha or to a contemporary. It obtained considerable prestige in Ceylon, a prestige comparable to that of Pāṇini (IV-1 B.C.) for Sanskrit or of Kaccāyana for Pāli.[22]

Text. Rasavāhinī in Anecdota pālica, edited by Friedrich Spiegel (Leipzig 1845). Also edited by Dines Andersen (Copenhagen 1891). Englished by Lakshmaṇa Śāstrī (Journal of the Asiatic Society of Bengal p. 57–72, 1910). Other partial editions, Emeneau (3499, 3624–29, 1935).

The Sidat-saṅgarāva was first edited by J. d'Alwis: Grammar of the Singhalese language, translated with introduction and notes (Colombo 1852). Shrī Sumangala: Sinhala grammar or a commentary on the Sidat sangarāva (Colombo 1884), etc.

Samanta-kūṭa-vaṇṇanā, Māgadhī (= Pāli) text in Journal of the Buddhist Text Society of India (vol. 1, part 2, 11 p., Calcutta May 1893). Siṅhalese paraphrase by two monks, Dhammānanda and Ñāṇissara (Government Press, Colombo 1890).

Criticism. Wilhelm Geiger: Litteratur und Sprache der Singhalesen (Grundriss der indo-arischen Philologie vol. 1, part 10, Strassburg 1900; p. 8). H. W. Codrington: Short history of Ceylon (London 1926). G. P. Malalasekera: Pāli literature in Ceylon (London 1928; chiefly p. 210, 222). G. C. Mendis: Early history of Ceylon (Heritage of India, Calcutta 1932). Codrington and Mendis agree on the date for Parākramabāhu IV, to wit c. 1325.

For the Adam's Peak and Anurādhapura see T. W. Rhys Davids (ERE 1, 87–88, 599–601, 1908).

NIEN CH'ANG

Chinese historian of Buddhism (fl. c. 1344).

Nien ch'ang's original name was Huang mei wu; he wrote a history of Buddhism, from mythical times down to 1344, entitled Fo-tsu li-tai t'ung tsai, paying special attention to the development of the Ch'an tsung, the contemplative school[23] founded by Bodhidharma (VI-1).

[21] The imprint is seen to this day by countless pilgrims and other visitors. It is about 5½ feet long, 2¾ feet broad, and 3 to 5 inches deep.

[22] The date of the earliest Pāli grammar, Kaccāyanappakaraṇa, cannot be determined. It is later than Buddhaghosha (V-1) and earlier than the Burmese Aggavaṃsa (XII-2) and the Siṅhalese Moggallāna (XII-2), probably closer to the upper limit than to the lower.

[23] That is, the Dhyāna school, better known in the West under its later Japanese name, Zen. That school was exceedingly popular in China; it was introduced into Japan in 1191 and 1227.

Criticism. Wylie (p. 211, 1902), with references to other Chinese histories of Buddhism or fo-chiao. Wieger (p. 373, 492, 1920).

SHUNJŌ HŌIN

Buddhist priest and historian (fl. thirteenth and fourteenth cent.).

Shunjō was born in Shiga, province of Ōmi, and at the age of 12 his head was shaven by Ryūshin, a priest of Yokawa, a Tendai monastery on Hiei-zan. He became the abbot of another Tendai monastery, Kukokuin, on the same mount Hiei, and received from the imperial court the title Hōin.

Later he studied the Jōdo doctrine at the Chion-in temple in Kyōto, and became eventually chief priest of that temple. He was over 80 when he died.

The years of his birth and death are unknown, but we know that it was the retired emperor Go-Fushimi who ordered him to write the biography of Hōnen-Shōnin (1133-1212), founder of the Jōdo-shū (Introd. 2, 337). Now Go-Fushimi was emperor from 1299 to 1301 and lived until 1336; hence the order was given to Shunjō in or soon after 1301, and we may assume that Shunjō was then already an elderly man. Shunjō is said to have collected information for the biography of Hōnen from the latter's disciples and from the old men who had actually known him (Hōnen had died in 1212 at the Chion-in temple).

Shunjō's biography of Hōnen filled 48 volumes divided into 237 sections, with an illustration for each section prepared by the court artists. The final fair copy was engrossed by the retired emperor Go-Fushimi, by the bonze emperor Fushimi (d. 1317), by the emperor Go-Nijō (ruled 1302-8), and others. Then a second copy was made, being almost completely written by Go-Fushimi. The making of the double transcription lasted from 1307 to 1317; hence we may conclude that Shunjō's work was completed in 1307 or not long before. The original fair copy is still preserved in the Chion-in temple, Kyōto; the second imperial copy is in Ōjōin temple at Taima (prov. Yamato).

This biography of Hōnen is perhaps the most important work of its kind and time, and one of the most elaborate documents for the history of Japanese Buddhism. It is interesting to note that this biography of a Jōdo saint was written by a Tendai monk, or at least by a monk who had spent the greater part of his life in the Tendai fold and was for a time a Tendai abbot. It is true the Tendai-shū (founded in 805) was very syncretic and combined high metaphysics with humble Amidaism (Introd. 1, 552-53); in a sense it was already a partial forerunner of the Amidaism[24] which was triumphantly developed by the Jōdo-shū. Yet the Tendai and Jōdo sects were very different. Shunjō's activity in both sects is typical of the unity of Japanese Buddhism, overcoming sectarian differences. We should hardly expect a Dominican to write a most elaborate study of a Franciscan saint, but in Japan that sort of thing has been done more than once.

Text. The original MS and the imperial copy were frequently copied and also reproduced in many early printed editions. An edition in 24 volumes was printed by Unchiku in 1700, Chinese characters with hiragana, woodcuts by Kokan. The text of that edition had been carefully revised by Gizan (1648-1717) and Ninchō (1645-1711). Later editions by Sōbei Ōmura (24 vols., Tokyō 1881) and by Hōjun Kaji (1 vol., 1908).

Commentary by Enchi, continued by Gizan: Helps to the study of Hōnen's life (60 vols.). One-volume edition printed in modern type in 1910, forming vol. 16 of a series of Jōdo classics.

[24] Amidaism means that everything depends primarily upon the grace of God (Amida) and that the root of salvation is faith in him (Introd. 2, 337).

Harper Havelock Coates and Ryūgaku Ishizuka: Honen the Buddhist saint, his life and teaching (1050 p., many plates, Kyōto 1925). This includes an English translation of the biography (p. 85–788) prepared with the utmost care, together with abundant notes largely derived from Gizan's commentary, an elaborate English index, and an index of the Chinese characters (Isis 9, 365–67). This great work was published in commemoration of the 750th anniversary of the foundation of the Jōdō-shū, in 1175.

G. HINDUISM

RĀMĀNANDA

Hindu Vaishṇava reformer, born at Prayāga (= modern Allāhābād) of a Brāhmaṇa family in 1299; according to tradition he died in 1410; it is certain that he lived to a very old age.

The philosopher Rāmānuja (XI-2)[25] had founded a new church, the Srī Vaishṇava; his third successor was Rāghavānanda, who traveled all over India to spread his doctrines and finally settled in Benares. One day Rāghavānanda chanced to meet the boy Rāmadatta, who was so precocious that he had become a finished scholar or paṇḍita at the age of twelve. Rāghavānanda received him into his communion, that is, taught him the Srī Vaishṇava initiatory mantra, changed his name to Rāmānanda, and before dying accepted him as his successor. Thus Rāmānanda was the fourth successor of Rāmānuja. After a long pilgrimage to the holy places of India, he returned to Benares and settled at Pañchgangā ghāṭ, where his footprints can still be seen.

Rāmānanda, having been expelled from his own sect for real or imaginary impurities, founded a new sect, less ritualistic, more charitable, and humbler, named Rāmāwat. His philosophy was the same as Rāmānuja's, but he paid less attention to castes and rites, and based his religion on two broad principles: (1) bhakti, faith in God, (2) the brotherhood of man, irrespective of birth or condition. He would call a follower of his avadhūta (one who has "shaken off" worldly cares), but outsiders would call him Rāmānandī. His broad humanity appears in the choice of his twelve disciples, some of whom it is true were Brāhmaṇa, but among whom were also a Muslim, a soldier, a barber, a Jāṭ,[26] a chamār (leatherworker, very low caste), and even two women! Instead of using the noble Sanskrit language, he and his disciples spoke the vernaculars which the common people understood. The most illustrious of his disciples was Kabīr (c. 1440–1518), founder of the sect called Kabīrpanthī (R. Burn, ERE 7, 632–34, 1915); another almost equally famous was Tulasī-Dāsa or Tulsī Dās (c. 1532–1623), one of the greatest poets of India, whose main work, the epic Rāmacarita-mānasa (or the Tulasī kṛta Rāmāyaṇa), begun in 1574, has been described as the Bible of northern India (G. A. Grierson, ERE 12, 469–73, 1922).

For more information on Rāmānanda and bibliography, see George A. Grierson (ERE 10, 569–72, 1919).

[25] Introd. 1, 754; 2, 826.

[26] Group of tribes scattered all over northwestern India, H. A. Rose (ERE 7, 489–91, 1915).

CHAPTER III

THE TRANSLATORS

(First Half of the Fourteenth Century)

N.B. The reader should bear in mind that only the main translators, or rather the men whose main activity was translating, are dealt with in this chapter. For a general survey of all the translations, see section III of chapter I. More information on the additional translators and their translations may then be easily obtained by means of the index.

1a. TRANSLATIONS FROM ARABIC INTO LATIN

STEPHANUS ARLANDI

Stephanus Arnoldi, Arlandi (or Orlandi). The name Arlandi may have originated by mistake from Arnaldi or Arnoldi. Stephen the son of Arnold. Translator from Arabic into Latin, physician, and astronomer. He came from Barcelona (?) and flourished at the school of Montpellier in the first quarter of the fourteenth century.

At any rate, the records of Montpellier mention a magister Stephanus Arnaldi as vice-chancellor in 1319. A Stephanus Arnaldi is often mentioned by Guy de Chauliac and Valescus de Taranta. However, the magister Arnaldus who according to Chauliac (Chirurgie, tr. II, doct. II, c. 2) treated the eyes of John XXII (pope 1316–34) is not necessarily identical with Stephanus Arnaldi.

The study of his writings is difficult because of conflicting attributions of many of them. The following (1 to 4) are very probably his own works:

1. Translation of the Kitāb al-'amal bil-kurra al-fulkīya of Qusṭā ibn Lūqā (IX-2), De Sphaera solida (or volubili). In a Wolfenbüttel MS, this translation is ascribed to Stephanus Arlandi of Barchinon (Barcelona).

2. Dietarium, or Translatio dietarii a Costa ben Luca compositi. Probably a translation of Qusṭā's treatise fī tadbīr al-abdān. Or is the Dietarium an original treatise different from the Translatio dietarii?

3. Viridarium, id est expositio Antidotarii Nicolai Salernitani.

4. Experimenta.

Items 5 to 9 are uncertain:

5. De evacuatione (lost).

6. De febribus (lost). Nos. 5 and 6 may be two parts of a single treatise.

7. Prognosticationes (lost).

8. Regimen contra defectum coitus (not included in the list of Valescus de Taranta).

9. A treatise on cataract (not mentioned by Guy de Chauliac).

Items 10 to 14 are apocryphal:

10. Defensorium vitae, ascribed to Arnold of Villanova (XIII-2), his contemporary, also of Barcelona.

11. A treatise on bloodletting, ascribed to the same.

12. Annotationes in Anatomiam Mundini.

13. Isagoge in Hippocratis et Galeni physiologiae partem anatomicam, ascribed

to Alexander Arnauld and edited by Jacques Du Bois (printed Basel 1556, Paris 1561, 1587). I am not able to identify this Alexander Arnauld; the name Alexander may have been introduced mistakenly for Stephen?

14. Ars medicinarum laxativarum tam simplicium quam compositarum, written by Joannes Stephani, alias Pontii, of Narbonne, who died between 1420 and 1427 (Wickersheimer p. 793, 1936).

Criticism. M. Steinschneider: Übersetzer aus dem Arabischen (Serapeum 31, 292, Leipzig 1870); (p. 553, 691, 1893); (p. 77, 1904).

Ferdinand Wüstenfeld: Übersetzungen arabischer Werke (Abhandlungen der Kgl. Gesellschaft der Wissenschaften zu Göttingen 22, 121, 1877). Pierre Pansier: Les maitres de la faculté de médecine de Montpellier (Janus 10, 9, 1905). Zinner (p. 437, 1925). Lynn Thorndike: Vatican Latin manuscripts (Isis 13, 89, 1929). Wickersheimer (p. 135, 1936).

1c. TRANSLATIONS FROM ARABIC INTO CATALAN

JUDAH BONSENYOR

Judeo-Catalan physician and translator from Arabic into Catalan. Dates of birth and death unknown. Flourished in Barcelona c. 1287–1313; died before 1331.

Jahuda (or Jafuda, Jaffuda) Bonsenyor. Judah ben Astruc Bonsenior. Ben Astruc = En Astruc, Nastruch, Struch. The name Astruc is a good Jewish name of southern France and of Spain, which can be traced back to the first half of the eleventh century. The Provençal name Astruc means happy, born under a good star (Latin aster; cf. Provençal benastruc, malastruc).

The Bonsenyor family was a prominent Jewish family in the service of the court of Aragon as physicians and interpreters. Judah's father, Astruch Bonsenyor (d. 1280), had thus been employed by Jacme lo Conqueridor (XIII-2), who mentioned him many times in his Cronica, and entrusted to him delicate negotiations with the Moors of Murcia. Judah was employed as interpreter by Alfonso III in 1287 during the conquest of Minorca, but he was chiefly in the service of Jacme II el Just (king of Aragon 1291–1327), who appointed him Arabic notary in Barcelona in 1294 and gave him other privileges in 1305 and 1310. In 1305 Judah visited Provence. Judah's son Astruch (Astruc ben Judah Bonsenior) was physician to Alfonso IV (king 1327–36) c. 1331–34.

Judah Bonsenyor translated for Jacme II from the Arabic into Catalan a collection of proverbs entitled Llibre de paraules e dits de savis e filosofs. This work was begun before 1298. There are many points in common between it and Ibn Gabirol's Mukhtār al-jawāhir, which had been translated into Hebrew anonymously under the title Mibḥar ha-peninim, then again by Joseph Qimḥi (XII-2). Most of the proverbs are Oriental, a few may be traced back to Greek sources, very few to Latin and Christian ones. Judah's collection was translated from Limousinian (Catalan) into Castilian by Jacob Çadique in Velez 1402 under the title Libro de dichos de sabios é philosophos (Escorial MS). This Jacob Çadique (Ẓaddiq), born at Ucles, was physician to Lorenzo Suárez de Figueroa, maestre de Santiago (JE 7, 30), at whose request the translation was made.

Jaume II ordered in 1313 the payment of a thousand solidos to Jahuda for his translation "de arabico in romancio" of a book of medicine called "halçahahny" which I am not able to identify (Rubió i Lluch 2, 22, 1921).

Text. Partial edition in the Documentos ineditos de la corona de Aragon (Revista catalana vol. 13, 1889). Complete edition by Gabriel Llabrés y Quintana: Jahuda Bonsenyor. Llibre de paraules e dits de savis e filosofs (188 p., Palma de Mallorca 1889).

Criticism. The introduction to Llabrés' edition is still the best account. Steinschneider (p. 977–99, 1893) includes a brief analysis of the proverbs. Rubió i Lluch (1, 11, 40, 54, 1908; 2, xxix, 22, 1921); Notes sobre la ciencia oriental a Catalunya en el XIVen sigle (Estudis universitaris catalans 3, 389–98, 1909). Fritz Baer (EJ 4, 954, 1929), very short and careless. Garcia Silvestre (p. 50, 1932).

1d. TRANSLATIONS FROM ARABIC INTO HEBREW

MOSES BEN SOLOMON OF BEAUCAIRE

Judeo-Languedocian philosopher and translator from Arabic into Hebrew. Beaucaire is on the Rhône, not far from Nîmes. Moses flourished in Salon (halfway between Arles and Aix) in the first quarter of the fourteenth century. He was the teacher of Qalonymos ben Qalonymos.

He translated from Arabic into Hebrew Ibn Rushd's tafsīr on Aristotle's Metaphysics, Sefer mah sheaḥar ha-ṭeba'.[1] He wrote a Hebrew summary of Ibn Rushd's tafsīr or sharḥ on Aristotle's Physics. Whether Qalonymos ben Qalonymos translated that sharḥ or not (he had translated the talkhīṣ at Arles 1316), and whether Moses used Qalonymos' translation or not, are moot questions. Finally, Moses criticized the Ṭirat 'kesef (Sefer ha-sod) which Joseph Kaspi had composed at Arles in 1317.

Criticism. Neubauer-Renan (p. 412–16, 1893). Steinschneider (p. 123, 171, 1893). S. Kahn (JE 9, 93, 1905).

SAMSON BEN SOLOMON

Medical translator from Arabic into Hebrew who flourished c. 1322. The circumstances of his life are unknown except that he was called ha-qaẓin ben ha-qaẓin (a title of honor the meaning of which is somewhat like this: the learned one son of the learned one) and that he completed on August 8, 1322 a Hebrew translation, from the Arabic, of the Galenic canon, "the sixteen books of Galen." The general Hebrew title is Sefer ha-qibuẓim. For the Hebrew titles of the separate parts see Steinschneider. The list as given by him differs very little from the list of the Byzantine canon as given by me (Introd. 1, 480).

That Hebrew translation has been wrongly ascribed to Qalonymos ben Qalonymos.

Criticism. Steinschneider (p. 654–56, 1893). Neubauer-Renan (p. 456, 1893).

QALONYMOS BEN DAVID THE ELDER

Qalonymos ben David ben Ṭodros, or ha-Ṭodrosi. Judeo-Provençal translator from Arabic into Hebrew. He flourished at Arles and translated Ibn Rushd's treatise against al-Ghazzālī, the Tahāfut al-tahāfut, under the title Happalat ha-happala. This translation was probably made after 1318 and before 1328. In the preface Qalonymos refers to an earlier translation of the same work by one rabbi Isaac Denaḥna (?).

[1] This translation had been wrongly ascribed to his namesake Moses ben Solomon of Salerno, who flourished c. 1240–50, and wrote a commentary on the Moreh nebukim, annotated by the latter's son Isaiah (Steinschneider p. 433, 1893).

I call him Qalonymos ben David the Elder to distinguish him from a homonym, Qalonymos ben David the Younger (maestro Calo Calonymos), who was physician in Naples and Venice in the first half of the sixteenth century and translated various books from Hebrew into Latin, including the Happalat ha-happala above mentioned. The preface to his translation of the Happala is dated Brescia, November 27, 1526.

There are many other Qalonymos, as this was an important Jewish family, of Greek origin but scattered in France, Italy, and Germany (EJ 9, 836–38). I discussed the name in volume 2 (p. 103). My spelling agrees with the Hebrew script but disagrees with the Greek. The word is often spelled Calonymos or Kalonymos, or with the us ending instead of os.

Text. The Hebrew text, represented by many MSS, is unpublished. The Latin translation of it was printed in 1527, Subtilissimus liber qui dicitur Destructio destructionis Algazelis nuperrime traductus et suae integritati restitutus, adjunctis multibus Algazelis, cui additus est Libellus seu Epistola Averrois de connexione intellectus etc. doct. Calo Calonymos . . . atque praeclarum ejusdem volumen de mundi creatione physicis probata rationibus (Venice 1527).

Criticism. Neubauer-Renan (p. 461–62, 1893). Steinschneider (p. 332, 984, 1893). Isaac Broydé (JE 7, 426, 1904). M. Zobel (EJ 9, 838, 1932).

QALONYMOS BEN QALONYMOS

Qalonymos ben Qalonymos ben Meir ha-Nasi (the prince, a Jewish title of honor also given to his father), also called maestro Calo. Judeo-Provençal physician, mathematician, moralist. One of the greatest translators from Arabic into Hebrew; he also translated at least one work from Hebrew into Latin.

He was born at Arles in 1286/87; was educated at Salon[2] (near Aix-en-Provence), his two masters being Moses ben Solomon of Beaucaire and Sen Astruc de Noves; did most of his work at Arles (1307–17); in 1318 he was in Salon. After that he was for a time (c. 1318–28) in the service of Robert of Anjou, king of Naples and count of Provence; he met him probably in Avignon 1319, then worked for him in Rome, where he was in touch with the Jewish elite of that time (e.g., Immanuel ben Solomon, Judah ben Moses). C. 1322 we find him in Catalonia, in 1328 in Arles, then he is lost sight of.

Original works. His original works are far less important than his translations, and less numerous. Let us deal with them first:

1. Criticism of the Ṭirat kesef of Joseph Kaspi. The Ṭirat kesef was composed at Arles in 1317, and Qalonymos' criticism at Salon or Arles in 1318. These books deal with Biblical criticism.

Joseph Perles: Kalonymos ben Kalonymos' Sendschreiben an Joseph Kaspi (München 1879). See Neubauer-Renan (p. 441–45, 506–8, 1893).

2. Sefer melakim (Book of kings; Liber regum qui est geometricus et arithmeticus). Written c. 1320 for Robert of Anjou. Lost except probably for an anonymous fragment in Munich dealing with the properties of the first ten numbers, somewhat in the manner of Abraham ben Ezra in the Sefer ha-eḥad, and with amicable numbers. The treatise was said to be a summary of arithmetic, geometry, algebra, astrology. The author was well acquainted with the Arabic literature

[2] Not Salonica, as is said in JE!

(Steinschneider, Zeitschrift der Deutschen morgenländischen Gesellschaft 24, 369, 1870).

3. Eben boḥan (Touchstone). This is his best-known composition. It is an ethical and satirical work in cadenced prose, full of Biblical and Talmudic allusions, composed probably in 1322, and dedicated to ten learned Catalonian friends. Description of eleven kinds of vanity and snobbishness, including scientific snobbishness. Sarcastic condemnation of astrology. Description of the sufferings of his people: auto-da-fé of the Talmud, Toulouse 1319; persecution by the Pastoureaux 1320; persecution of the lepers 1321.

The Eben boḥan was first printed at Naples 1489. Second edition with Solomon ben Gabirol's Mibḥar ha-peninim (Selection of pearls), Venice 1546. Third edition, Cremona 1558. Fourth edition with Yiddish translation by Moses Eisenstadt ben Ḥayyim Katzenellenbogen, Sulzbach 1705. Fifth undated edition, Fürth. Sixth with index, Lemberg 1865. W. A. Meisel: Der Prüfstein metrisch übersetzt (Budapest 1878). For the condemnation of astrology, see Meisel's translation (p. 155–66).

4. Masseket purim. Parody of the Megilla treatise of the Talmud, composed in Rome. Satirical description of Italian rabbis, etc.

First edition, Pesaro 1507–22 (1513?), very rare. Second edition, Venice 1552. Later edition, Vienna 1871.

Criticism by M. Steinschneider: Purim und Parodie (Israelitische Letterbode vols. 7, 9, Amsterdam c. 1882).

Many other works are ascribed to Qalonymos either wrongly (e.g. by confusion with other Qalonymos) or on insufficient grounds.

4 bis. Let us mention only a recently discovered treatise wherein he describes his travels through Provence and Catalonia, mentioning the scholars he met. Dr. I. Sonne, of Jerusalem, promised an edition of it in 1936.

4 ter. Ethical will addressed to his son, written in Naples 1324. First printed in the Qobeẓ al-yad of the Meqiẓe nirdamim society of Berlin. Reprinted by I. Sonne (Jerusalem 1936).

Translations from Arabic into Hebrew. Quoted in the chronological order of authors translated; hence the Greek writings come first, then the purely Arabic.

5. Archimedes (III-2 B.C.): Treatise on the sphere and the cylinder, from the Arabic version by Qusṭā ibn Lūqā (IX-2). Completed probably c. 1311. Qalonymos translated this work twice. This Arabic version is otherwise unknown, but the same treatise was translated by Ḥunain ibn Isḥāq and Thābit ibn Qurra (IX-2).

6. Archimedes: The Κύκλου μέτρησις, translated into Arabic by Thābit ibn Qurra, and into Latin by Gerard of Cremona, De mensura circuli, was also translated into Hebrew, but the ascription to Qalonymos is uncertain. See also Eutocios, below.

7. Apollonios (III-2 B.C.): Possibly extracts from his geometry.

8. Hypsicles (II-1 B.C.): Book XIV of Euclid's Elements, together with the commentary of Simplicios (?). Completed at Arles in 1309.

9. Nicomachos of Gerasa (I-2): Translation of a summary of the Ἀριθμητικὴ εἰσαγωγή in two books, together with a commentary by Abū Sulaimān Rabī' ibn Yaḥyā, bishop of Elvira—possibly identical with Rabī' ibn Zaid (X-2). The Hebrew translation was made in 1316–17.

10. Ptolemy (II-1): Ὑποθέσεις τῶν πλανωμένων. Be-'inyane ha-kokabim ha-nebukim. 1317?

11. Pseudo Ptolemy: Καρπός (Centiloquium). Arabic translation and commentary by Aḥmad ibn Yūsuf al-Miṣrī (IX-2). Translated into Hebrew under the title Sefer ha-peri ha-niqra meah dibburim (combination of the Greek and Latin titles), in 1314.

12. Galen (II-2): De clysteribus et colica, from the Arabic translation by Ḥunain ibn Isḥāq (IX-2). That text, however, is not included in Ḥunain's list as published by G. Bergstraesser (1925; Isis 8, 685–724). The Hebrew version, Sefer Galinus beḥaqna ube-qulga, was completed in 1308. Latin translation from the Hebrew by Franciscus Raphelengius (Leiden 1591).

13. Galen: Περὶ φλεβοτομίας (no. 71 in Ḥunain's list). Be-haqqazah, Arles 1308.

14. Eutocios (VI-1): Commentary on Archimedes' Περὶ τῆς σφαίρας καὶ κυλίνδρου.

15. Jābir ibn Ḥaiyān (VIII-2): Fragments of his treatise on poisons, translated probably in Avignon 1319.

On that treatise, which I did not discuss in volume 1 (p. 532), see Julius Ruska: Das Giftbuch des Jābir (Orientalistische Literaturzeitung p. 453–56, 1928); Arabische Giftbücher (Fortschritte der Medizin vol. 50, 12 p., 1932; Isis 20, 587). Bettina Strauss: Das Giftbuch des Šānāq (Berlin 1934; Isis 23, 447).

16. Al-Kindī (IX-1): Igerret be-qiẓẓur ha-ma'amar be-moladot, short treatise on nativities (I do not know the Arabic title). Translation completed in 1314.

17. Al-Kindī: Iggeret be-'illot, etc. (On the causes in the higher spheres which determine rain), in 1314.

18. Al-Kindī: Iggeret be-laḥyit ube-maṭar, or Iggeret masfiqet (The sufficient treatise on dampness and rain). The undated Hebrew translation is more complete than the Latin one, Liber Alkindi de pluviis imbribus et ventis ac aeris mutatione (Venice 1507, Paris 1540).

19. Thābit ibn Qurra (IX-2): Kitāb fī shakl al-qaṭṭā', which had been put into Latin by Gerard of Cremona: De figura alchata, or De figura secante. The Hebrew version, Sefer ha-temunah ha-ḥittukit, was completed in 1311.

20. Ḥunain ibn Isḥāq (IX-2): Kitāb al-mudkhal fīl ṭibb (Introduction to medicine, i.e., introduction in catechismal form to Galen's Ars parva). Translated into Latin by Marc of Toledo: Isagoge ad tegni Galeni, Liber quaestionum medicinalium. The Hebrew version, Mabo' ha-gadol le refu'ah (Great introduction to medicine), is also ascribed, but it seems wrongly, to another Qalonymos.

21. Al-Fārābī (X-1): Kitāb fīl-'aql wal-ma'qūl (De intellectu et intelligibili). Hebrew version completed in 1314, Ma'amar be-sekel veha-muskal. There was another Hebrew version of the same work which was revised by Jedaiah ben Abraham Bedersi.

22. Al-Fārābī: Kitāb iḥṣā' al-'ulūm (Enumeration of the sciences). The Arabic text, long believed lost (Introd. 1, 628), was edited by Muḥammad Riḍa al-Shabībī (Ṣaida 1924), by 'Uthmān Muḥammad Amīn (Cairo 1931; Isis 19, 201–3), by Angel González Palencia with Latin and Spanish translations (Madrid 1932; Isis 20, 450–51). The work was twice translated into Latin, by Domingo Gundisalvo and by Gerard of Cremona. The abbreviated Hebrew version, Ma'amar be mispar ha-ḥokmot, was completed in 1314. This was really the second Hebrew translation of the Iḥṣā' al-'ulūm, for the second part of the Reshit ḥokmah of Shem-ṭob ben Joseph ibn Falaquera (XIII-2) is simply a complete and literal translation of al-Fārābī's work.

Israel Efros: Palquera's Reshit ḥokmah and Alfarabi's Iḥṣa al-'ulum (Jewish quarterly review 25, 227–35, 1935).

23. Al-Fārābī: Kitāb ,fīmā yanbaghī an yuqaddama qabla ta'līm al-falsafat. Iggeret be-siddur queri'at ha-ḥokmot. Undated. (On philosophical propaedeutics.)

24. Ikhwān al-ṣafā' (X-2): The twenty-first treatise of their rasā'il, in which various kinds of animals are compared with man, was translated into Hebrew, Iggeret ba'ale ḥayyim, in 1316.

The Hebrew version was printed at Mantua 1557, then at Frankfurt a.M. 1704. Yiddish translation by Enoch ben Ẓebi Hirsch (Hanau 1718). German translation by Julius Landsberger (Darmstadt 1882).

25. 'Alī ibn Riḍwān (XI-1): Kitāb al-'umūd fī uṣūl al-ṭibb. Twice translated by Qalonymos; his first translation (his first work) was lost in 1306 during his exile, the second was completed at Arles in October 1307. Sefer ha-'ammud be-shoroshe ha-refuah.

26. Ibn al-Samḥ (XI-1): Ma'amar be-iẓṭawwonot ube-ḥiddudim. Treatise on cylinders and cones, lost in Arabic (?). The Hebrew version was completed in 1312.

27. Jābir ibn Aflaḥ (XII-1): Ha-dibbur be temunah ha-ḥittukit. Commentary on the figura sectoris of Menelaos. Unknown in Arabic, unless it be simply an extract from the Iṣlāḥ al-majisṭī (Introd. 2, 206). See item 19 above.

28–37. Ibn Rushd (XII-2). Hebrew translation of Ibn Rushd commentaries:[3]

28. Priora analytica. Only an extract concerning ch. 16 of book I.

29. Posteriora analytica. Bi'ur le sefer ha-mofet. Translation of Ibn Rushd's sharḥ, completed at Avignon 1314.

30. Sophistici elenchi. Bi'ur sofisṭiqi. Translation of the talkhīṣ, 1313. The printed Latin translation by Abraham de Balmes was based upon Qalonymos' version.

31. Topica. Bi'ur ṭobiqi. Translation of the talkhīṣ, 1313. The printed Latin translations by Abraham de Balmes and Jacob Mantino are derived from this Hebrew version.

32, 33. Physica. Translation of the talkhīṣ, Arles 1316. Previously translated by Zeraḥiah Gracian, Sefer ha-ṭeba', in Rome 1284, but Qalonymos' translation was more popular and the printed Latin version by Jacob Mantino was derived from it. It would seem that Qalonymos translated also the sharḥ; though this may be due to a confusion with his teacher, Moses ben Solomon of Beaucaire.

34. De generatione et corruptione. Sefer ha-hawayh weha-hippased. Translation of the talkhīṣ, Arles 1316.

35. Meteorologica. Sefer otot ha-shamayim. Translation of the talkhīṣ, Arles 1316. The Latin version of it is incomplete.

36. Metaphysica. Sefer ma sheaḥar ha-ṭeba'. Translation of the talkhīṣ, 1317–18. Apparently independent of the previous translation by Zeraḥiah Gracian, Rome 1284. The Latin translation by Elijah del Medigo and the commentary by Abraham Bibago are based upon Qalonymos' version.

37. De plantis. Sefer ha-ẓemaḥim. The Greek text of this pseudo-Aristotelian treatise (ascribed to Nicholas of Damascus, I-2 B.C.) was translated into Arabic by

[3] I may recall that Ibn Rushd wrote three series of commentaries: the short ones, jāmi'; the intermediate, talkhīṣ; and the long, sharḥ or tafsīr (Introd. 2, 356).

Ḥunain ibn Isḥāq, and that translation revised by Thābit ibn Qurra. Qalonymos translated the Arabic text into Hebrew together with Ibn Rushd's commentary.

The translation of various other commentaries is ascribed to Qalonymos. For a list of these apocryphal translations, see Neubauer-Renan (p. 458, 1893).

38. Abū Sa'dān: Ha-dibbur ha-meshullash. Treatise on the triangle, 1311. The Arabic text is unknown, and I cannot identify the author. I give his name as transcribed from the Hebrew, which is ambiguous. In Arabic al-Sa'dān refers to the two lucky stars, Jupiter and Venus, but if the author's name were derived from that it would read Abū-l-Sa'dain.

39. Sefer meshalim be-tishboret. Translation, completed in 1311, of an anonymous and unknown Arabic treatise on geometry.

Translation from Hebrew into Latin. 40. Ibn Rushd: Tahafut al-tahafut, Destructio destructionis. Latin translation completed on April 18, 1328 for Robert of Anjou. That translation was revised and commented upon by Agostino Nifo (1473–1538): Destructiones destructionum Averroys cum Augustini Niphi de Suessa expositione (Venice 1497, reprinted 1517).

The translation by Qalonymos ben Qalonymos should not be confused with one made by another Qalonymos, Qalonymos ben David, physician in Naples and Venice in the first half of the sixteenth century. The confusion is increased by the fact that both men are occasionally called maestro Calo (JE 7, 426). The translation by Qalonymos ben David was published in Venice 1527. It is almost negligible for textual criticism. See Maurice Bouyges: Averroès, Tahafot al-tahafot (p. xxiii, Beyrouth 1930; Isis 19, 257).

To conclude, it is impossible in the absence of special investigations to appraise Qalonymos' value as a mathematician or as a physician. However, the fact that he was not afraid of tackling the Arabic versions of the most difficult remains of Greek mathematics (Archimedes, Apollonios, Hypsicles) speaks well for his mathematical training. It would be worth while to examine his translations of them, as well as of Ibn al-Samḥ's treatise lost in Arabic, of the treatise on the triangle by the mysterious Abu Sa'dān, and his Sefer meshalim be-tishboret. Of his medical translations, the most interesting perhaps are those of Ḥunain ibn Isḥāq's Isagoge and of Ibn Riḍwān's treatise. That also requires investigation. In the meanwhile it is clear that his main title to fame lies in his translation of Ibn Rushd's commentaries, and the more so because they are definite and important links in the transmission of Averroistic traditions to us.

Text. The texts already published have been indicated above.

Criticism. Special studies have been indicated above. M. Steinschneider (Ersch und Grubers Allgemeine Encyclopädie 32, 169–75; reprinted in Gesammelte Schriften 1, 194–215, 1925); (1893); Die Mathematik bei den Juden (BM 11, 75–82, 1897); (p. 53, 1904). Neubauer-Renan (p. 417–60, 1893), fundamental. Isaac Broydé (JE 7, 426–28, 1904). U. Cassuto (EJ 9, 841–43, 1932). Alexander Marx: Scientific work of some outstanding mediaeval Jewish scholars (Essays in memory of Linda R. Miller p. 150–53, New York 1938).

SAMUEL BEN JUDAH OF MARSEILLE

Samuel ben Judah ben Meshullam. Samuel of Marseille. Called in Provençal, Miles Benjudas (or Bongodos, meaning son of Judah), also Barbaveri, Barbavaire (gray beard?). The name Miles was not uncommon; its origin is uncertain (short for Samuel?). This Samuel ben Judah should not be confused with other Jews bearing the same names (a popular combination), notably Samuel ben Judah ibn Tibbon (XIII-1).

Judeo-Provençal translator from Arabic into Hebrew. Born at Marseille 1294. Studied astronomy at Salon under Sen Astruc de Noves (Abba Mari ben Eligdor); in 1321 he was put into prison at Beaucaire; then we find him in Murcia (1324), Tarascon (1329–31), Aix-en-Provence (1335–36), Montélimar (1340). Place and date of death unknown.

He was a very conscientious and excellent translator, who took special pains to obtain good texts and revised his work repeatedly. He often criticized his great contemporary Levi ben Gerson.

I shall list his translations in the chronological order of the works translated.

1. Plato's Republic, that is, Ibn Rushd's commentary on it. Translation completed at Aurès in 1320 and revised in the prison of Beaucaire in 1321. Again revised in 1322.

2. Aristotle's Organon. Translation of Ibn Rushd's jāmi', Tarascon 1329. This was a revision of a previous translation by Jacob ben Maḥir (1289).

3. Aristotle's Organon. Translation of questions concerning obscure points in Ibn Rushd's commentary. Completed in 1320 (his first dated work). Some of these questions are also found in a long Hebrew commentary by Samuel's pupil, Judah ben Isaac Kohen. The Hebrew text was translated into Latin by Abraham de Balmes (printed 1550, etc.).

4. Aristotle's Ethics. Translation of Ibn Rushd's talkhīṣ on the Nicomachean Ethics, completed in prison at Beaucaire 1321. Samuel was not pleased with the Arabic text available to him nor with his own translation, and was hoping to revise it out of prison.

Jewish commentators considered the Nicomachean Ethics to be the first part of the Politics, the second part being Plato's Republic.

5. Hypsicles (II-1 B.C.): Supplement to the translation by Qalonymos ben Qalonymos of book XIV of Euclid's Elements. This supplement, referring to figs. 30 and 31, lacking in Qalonymos, was written in 1335.

6. Ptolemy (II-1): Ibn Rushd's commentary on parts I–III of the Almagest, done in 1330–31, Tarascon.

7. Alexander of Aphrodisias (III-1): Book I of the treatise on the soul, translated into Arabic by Isḥāq ibn Ḥunain (IX-2), and from Arabic into Hebrew by Samuel at Murcia 1324. Samuel made his translation from an excellent Arabic text, revised it from another, and prepared a final revision at Montélimar 1340.

8, 9. Abū 'Abdallāh Muḥammad ibn Mu'ādh of Seville: Treatise on the total solar eclipse which occurred on Monday, the last day of the year 471 H. The last day of that year was Wednesday, July 3, 1079. There was a solar eclipse in Seville on July 1, 1079, which was a Monday. Schroeter (p. 109, Karte 57a, 1923).

Treatise on the dawn. The translator is not named but is probably Samuel (the two translations follow each other in the same MS). This Muḥammad ibn Mu'ādh was mentioned in my note on Gerard of Cremona (no. 50, Introd. 2, 342).

10. Al-Zarqālī (XI-2): Treatise on the movement of fixed stars. Lost in Arabic? There is but a single MS of the undated Hebrew translation (Paris, Bibliothèque nationale, 1036,3).

11. Jābir ibn Aflaḥ (XII-1): Iṣlāḥ al-majisṭī. Samuel studied Ibn Rushd's and Jābir's commentaries on the Almagest, together with his brother En Bondavi of Marseille, in Tarascon (c. 1331) and Trinquetailles (a suburb of Arles). Later Samuel obtained the autograph copy of Jacob ben Maḥir's translation of Jābir's

commentary and revised it, completing his task at Aix 1335. He knew of an earlier version by Moses ben Tibbon (1274) but failed to obtain it.

12. Ibn Rushd: For Ibn Rushd's commentaries see items concerning Plato, Aristotle, Ptolemy.

Criticism. Neubauer-Renan (p. 605, 724, 1877); (p. 553–67, 1893). The latter is the main study; it includes many extracts from Samuel's writings, in Hebrew. Ivo Bruns: Alexandri Aphrodisiensis praeter commentaria scripta minora. De anima cum mantissa (Supplementum aristotelicum vol. 2, part 1, Berlin 1887; p. xiv). Steinschneider (p. 152, 544, 55, 217, 98, 106, 574, 1893); Die Mathematik bei den Juden (BM 11, 108–10, 1897). Max Schlössinger (JE 3, 303, 1902), apropos of En Bondavi. Isaac Broydé (JE 8, 589, 1904, or 11, 20, 1905).

ṬODROS ṬODROSI

Ṭodros (Theodoros?) ben Meshullam ben David Ṭodrosi. Judeo-Provençal translator from Arabic into Hebrew. Born at Arles at the beginning of the fourteenth century, lived in the suburb of Trinquetailles on the other side of the Rhône; he lived at least until 1340. He translated the following works:

1. Al-Fārābī (X-1): Kitāb 'uyūn al-masā'il (Sources of the questions), including some 60 theses concerning Aristotelianism. Ṭodros made this translation at the age of 20 and entitled it 'Ain mishpaṭ ha-derushim (Source of the judgment of questions).

2. Ibn Sīnā (XI-1): Kitāb al-najāt (Salvation). A summary of Aristotelian philosophy. Hebraicized under the title Haẓẓalat ha-nefesh (Deliverance of the soul). The translation is incomplete; it includes the Physics and Metaphysics, not the Logic.

3. Ibn Rushd (XII-2): Translation of the talkhīṣ on Aristotle's Rhetorics, completed at Trinquetailles in 1337. He was able to use the Arabic dictionary Kitāb al 'ain of Khalīl ibn Aḥmad (VIII-2), which had not been available to Samuel ben Judah ibn Tibbon (XIII-1). Ṭodros' Hebrew version was Latinized by Abraham de Balmes (d. very old in 1523).

4. Ibn Rushd: Translation of the talkhīṣ on the Poetics, completed at Trinquetailles 1337.

5. Ibn Rushd: Three dissertations, the first two dealing with Ibn Sīnā's theory of the three modes of being, the third on prescience, Ma'amar be-da'at ha-qiddum. The translation of the three treatises was completed in 1340.

6. Ibn Rushd: Fragment of the treatise on the material (hylic) intellect, translated under the title Ma'amar be-sekel ha-hayulani. This includes a discussion of the views of Empedocles, Pythagoras, and Plato on the soul.

Text. 1. The Arabic text was edited by Friedrich Dieterici: Alfarabi's philosophische Abhandlungen (Leiden 1890). German translation by the same under the same title (Leiden 1892). Latin translation by August Schmoelders: Alfarabii fontes quaestionum, in his Documenta philosophiae Arabum (p. 43–56, Bonn 1863). Hebrew text unpublished.

2. The Kitāb al-najāt is printed at the end of the Qānūn (Rome 1593). Separate edition by Muḥyi al-dīn Ṣabrī al-Kurdī (527 p., Cairo 1913). Partial French translation by Pierre Vattier: La logique du fils de Sina (303 p., Paris 1658). Hebrew text unpublished.

3. Jacob Goldenthal: Averrois commentarius in Aristotelis de arte rhetorica hebraice versus a Todroso Todrosi arelatensi (Leipzig 1842). Hebrew text with copious introduction.

4. Fausto Lasinio: Il commento medio di Averroe alla Poetica di Aristotele (Annali delle università toscane, Pisa 1872). In two parts: part I, Arabic text; part II, Hebrew.

Criticism. Steinschneider (1893). Neubauer-Renan (p. 570–73, 1893). H. Gross (p. 247, 1897). Isaac Broydé (JE 12, 173, 1906).

SOLOMON BONIRAC

Judeo-Catalan translator from Arabic into Hebrew, who flourished in the first half of the fourteenth century, if not earlier, in Barcelona. The name Bonirac is perhaps Boniac, ben Isaac?

He translated Galen's περὶ κρίσεων (De crisibus) from the Arabic version of Ḥunain ibn Isḥāq (no. 18 in Ḥunain's own list, Isis 8, 692). This translation contains many Arabic words, or periphrastic renderings of Arabic terms into Hebrew. The title itself is half Arabic, Sefer buḥrân (from Kitāb fī-l-buḥrān).

Criticism. Steinschneider (p. 652, 1893). Very short notes by Isaac Broydé (JE 3, 308, 1902) and Irene Chanoch (EJ 4, 950, 1929).

SOLOMON BEN PAṬER

Solomon ben Paṭer ha-Kohen. Solomon of Burgos. Judeo-Castilian translator from Arabic into Hebrew who flourished in Burgos c. 1322.

In that year, 1322, he translated for the otherwise unknown Talmudist Jacob ben Meir the Kitāb fī hai'at al-'ālam (On the form of the universe) of Ibn al-Haitham (XI-1). This short astronomical treatise had been previously translated from Arabic into Spanish by Abraham of Toledo (XIII-2) for king Alfonso X, and from Arabic into Hebrew in 1271 (or 1275) by Jacob ben Maḥir ibn Tibbon. Later Jacob's Hebrew version was Latinized by Abraham de Balmes (d. 1523). These various translations illustrate the popularity of that little treatise in the Christian and Jewish worlds, in spite of its being almost completely forgotten in the Dār al-Islām.

Solomon of Burgos has been wrongly called Simeon of Baghdād.

Criticism. M. Steinschneider: Notice sur un ouvrage astronomique inédit d'Ibn Haitham (Bull. di bibliografia delle scienze matematiche 14, 721–40, Roma 1881); Supplément à la notice (ibid. 16, 505–13, 1883). The first article contains extracts from the Latin and Hebrew versions; the second, extracts from the Arabic text, rediscovered by the author in the library of the India Office, London. Steinschneider (p. 560, 1893); Die Mathematik bei den Juden (BM 11, 107, 1897).

ISAAC BEN NATHAN OF CORDOVA

Spanish translator from the Arabic into Hebrew. Born in Cordova (or Játiva), flourished in Majorca c. 1347.[4] Three (or four) important translations are ascribed to him:

1. Al-Ghazzālī (XI-2): Ma'amar bi-teshubot she'elot nisheal mehem (Treatise answering questions asked of him), translated while he was in Majorca in 1347. Arabic text lost or unidentified. Brief analysis in Steinschneider (p. 338–39, 1893).

2. Maimonides (XII-2): Maqāla fī-l-tawḥīd (On the unity of God), Ma'amar ha-yiḥud (Introd. 2, 370, 377).

3. Joseph ben Judah ibn 'Aqnīn (XII-2): Ma'amar bi-meḥuyab ha-meẓiut

[4] Twice mentioned in Introd. vol. 2, once as Isaac ben Nathan of Cordova (p. 871), once as Isaac ben Nathan of Majorca (p. 370). The same man is meant in both cases.

ve-ekut siddur ha-debarim mimenu (On the necessary existence and how things proceed from it). The ascription of the Hebrew text to Isaac ben Nathan is not certain (Introd. 2, 381). Steinschneider (p. 406–7, 1893). The original Arabic text, presumably written in Aleppo 1187, is lost.

4. Muḥammad ibn Muḥammad al-Tabrīzī (XIII-2): Commentary on Maimonides' introduction to the second part of the Dalālat al-ḥā'irīn. Text lost in Arabic but extant in two Hebrew translations, of which Isaac ben Nathan made one, the other being anonymous (Introd. 2, 871). Steinschneider (p. 362, 1893).

Text. 1. Heinrich Malter: Die Abhandlung des al-Ghazzālī, Antworten und Fragen, die an ihn gerichtet wurden (118 p., in 2 parts, Francfort a.M. 1896). Hebrew text, reconstruction of the Arabic one, German translation, and notes.

2. M. Steinschneider: Shene ha-me'orot (Berlin 1847). Contains no. 2 together with other texts by Abraham ben Ezra, German summary, and notes.

3. Ma'amar bi-meḥuyab ha-meẓyiut. Edited with German translation by Moritz Löwy (Diss. Berlin 1879). Judah Leon Magnes: A treatise as to necessary existence, the procedure of things from the necessary existence, the creation of the world (Heidelberg thesis, Hebrew and English, 46 p., Berlin 1904).

4. Saul ben Moses Kohen Ashkenazi: She'elot (Venice 1574).

Criticism. Steinschneider (1893) as indicated above. EJ (8, 539, 1931).

SAMUEL BEN SOLOMON HA-ME'ATI

Samuel ben Solomon ben Nathan ha-Me'ati. Last representative of a great family of Judeo-Italian translators from Arabic into Hebrew. For his father, Solomon ben Nathan, and his grandfather, Nathan ben Eliezer, the "Italian Tibbonid" (XIII-2), see volume 2 (p. 853). Samuel flourished sometime after 1306.

He completed the translation of Galen's commentary on Hippocrates' regimen in acute diseases (περὶ διαίτης ὀξέων, de diaeta acutorum) from the Arabic version, tafsīr li-kitāb tadbīr al-amrāḍ al-ḥādda (no. 92 in Ḥunain's list, Isis 8, 698). The translation had been begun by his father.

He translated also a medical work of Ibn Zuhr (XII-1) under the title Menorah ha-refu'ah (Lamp of healing). A translation of the same work had been made previously by Jacob ben Maḥir ibn Tibbon (XIII-2), but had been lost in the exodus from France (1306).

Criticism. Steinschneider (p. 663, 752, 1893). I. Broydé and Ismar Elbogen (JE 8, 398, 1904), only 6 lines.

1e. TRANSLATION FROM ARABIC INTO AETHIOPIAN

SALĀMĀ

Egyptian theologian who was appointed metropolitan of Abyssinia and became the leader of the revival of Aethiopic literature in the first half of the fourteenth century.

The Bible had been translated into Aethiopian in the fifth or sixth century (Introd. 1, 381); this text, which had gradually become corrupted, was revised by Salāmā. I do not know the extent of his revision; maybe he revised only the Gospels and the rest was done by others. It is probable that these revisions were made on the basis of Arabic models. It should be noted that the canons of the Aethiopic Old and New Testaments differ from every other Christian canon. Salāmā translated from the Arabic homilies, liturgical and monastic books, lives of saints and martyrs. Other books of the same kind were translated by other men; for example, the apocryphal acts of the apostles, Gadla ḥawāryāt, were translated from Arabic into Ge'ez in 1379. The lives of the saints, Gadla samā'etāt, were continued under the rule of David I (1382–1411).

Criticism. Littmann (p. 205, 207, 225, 1907). John Mason Harden: Introduction to Ethiopic Christian literature (120 p., London 1926).

2a. TRANSLATIONS FROM PERSIAN INTO GREEK

GREGORIOS CHIONIADES

Γρηγόριος ὁ Χιονιάδης. Byzantine physician born in Constantinople, at the end of the thirteenth century, flourished at the court of Trebizond during the rule of the emperor Alexios II (1297–1330).

He traveled to Persia by order of Alexios II, became familiar with the Persian language; was for a short time archbishop of Tabrīz, and returned to Trebizond with a number of Persian books. Some of these books were investigated by Georgios Chrysococces. He was thus the initiator of that short renaissance of Persian-Byzantine astronomy which lasted from c. 1323 to 1361. The first date, 1323, refers to an anonymous astronomical work which was freely translated from Persian into Greek by an unknown writer. See my note on Shams al-dīn Mīrak al-Bukhārī. The second date, 1361, refers to the floruit of Theodoros Meliteniotes (XIV-2). By that time the Byzantine scientists had already rediscovered the Greek originals corresponding to the Persian adaptations.

There are some 16 letters of his (Cod. Vindob. theol. gr. 203) addressed to the emperor Alexios; to Joannes XIII Glycys, patriarch from 1316 to 1320; and to Constantinos Lucytes (not Lycytes), protonotarios and protovestiarios at the court of Trebizond, and mathematician, who seems later to have inherited his library.

Text. Edition of the letters by Tryphon Euangelides: *Δύο βυζαντιακὰ κείμενα. α', Γρηγορίου Χιονιάδου ἐπιστολαὶ δεκαὲξ ἐκ κώδικος Βιενναίου. β', Βησσαρίωνος μονῳδία* (32 p., Hermoupolis [in Syra, one of the Cyclades] 1910; Byzantinische Zeitschrift 20, 285, 1911).

Criticism. Hermann Usener: Ad historiam astronomiae symbola (p. 23, Bonn 1876). Krumbacher (p. 478, 622, 1897). J. Papadopoulos: *Γρηγορίου Χιονιάδου τοῦ ἀστρονόμου ἐπιστολαί* (*'Επιστημονικὴ ἐπετηρὶς τῆς φιλοσοφικῆς σχολῆς, Πανεπιστήμιον Θεσσαλονίκης, ''Ετος* A', p. 153–206, 3 pl., Salonica 1927), includes by way of introduction an account of the academy of sciences of Trebizond (*ἡ ἀκαδημία θετικῶν ἐπιστημῶν τῆς Τραπεζοῦντος*). *'Εγκυκλοπαιδικὸν λεξικόν* (12, 899, 1931).

GEORGIOS CHONIATES

Γεώργιος ὁ Χωνιάτης. Byzantine physician of unknown date, who translated a treatise on antidotes from Persian into Greek, *'Αντίδοτοι ἐκ Περσίας κομισθεῖσαι καὶ ἐξελληνισθεῖσαι παρὰ τοῦ Χωνιάτου τοῦ Γεωργίου* (Escorial MS).

I place him here tentatively because his activity may easily have been a part of the Persian-Byzantine renaissance of this time. His work may have been a result of the Persian journey of Gregorios Chioniades.

Criticism. Krumbacher (p. 615, 1897).

3a. TRANSLATIONS FROM GREEK INTO LATIN

PIETRO D'ABANO

Peter of Abano or of Padua. Petrus de Apono, Aponensis, Paduanensis, "Conciliator." Italian philosopher, astrologer, physician, and translator from Greek and from French into Latin (c. 1250–c. 1316).

Contents: (1) Generalities. (2) Conciliator. (3) Lucidator. (4) Translations from the Greek. (5) Translation of Abraham ben Ezra's astrological treatises from the French. (6) Treatise on poisons. (7) Physiognomy. (8) Edition of the Latin Dioscorides. (9) Addition to Mesuë's Grabadin. (10) Apocryphal writings. (11) Pietro's astrological views and his "Averroism." (12) Astrolabium planum. (13) Pietro and the Inquisition. (14) Pietro's fame and influence.
(15) Text. (16) Criticism.

1. *Generalities*

Pietro was born in Abano near Padua c. 1250 (rather than 1257); he is said to have traveled considerably, and it is certain that he spent some time in Constantinople, probably before 1293, when he was established in Paris for the continuation of his studies. His residence in Paris may have lasted ten years or more. He then returned to Padua, where he taught in the university and spent the remainder of his life. He died, probably in that city, between 1315 and 1318 (c. 1316).

He talked with Marco Polo (c. 1295–1310) and spoke of him in his Conciliator (diff. 67), this being the only reference to Polo in a contemporary scientific work.

He was primarily an astrologer, but he had a good knowledge of astronomical theory, was genuinely interested in science and medicine, and was of the encyclopaedic type, anxious on the one hand to understand and interpret nature and man, and on the other hand to apply his knowledge to medical or other needs. According to Giovanni Pico della Mirandola (1463–94), he was a stupid compiler: "homo congerere plura natus quam digerere,"[5] but such a statement was hardly fair. He was a compiler, and on a large scale, but he had a good technical preparation and was not less intelligent, rather more intelligent, than the average of his kind. He was careful and kept his works many years on the stocks, with the result that his main productions, the Conciliator, the Lucidator, and the Expositio problematum Aristotelis, seem to have been completed (as far as they were completed) in the same year, 1310, and include mutual cross references.

His other dated works are anterior: translation of Abraham ben Ezra in 1293, treatise on physiognomy in 1295, translation of Alexander of Aphrodisias in 1300; but it is better to deal first with his main works.

2. *Conciliator*

The Conciliator differentiarum philosophorum et praecipue medicorum is Pietro's most famous book, witness the fact that he himself was nicknamed Petrus Conciliator. It was already well advanced c. 1303, but was not completed until 1310. It reminds one somewhat of earlier and humbler works such as the Quaestiones naturales of Adelard of Bath (XII-1) or the Dodi ve nekdi of Berakya ha-Naqdan (XII-2), but is done on a far larger scale and from a higher standpoint. The main purpose is the same: to settle as far as possible the moot questions of human knowledge. Pietro aims at reconciling conflicting opinions (Greek, Arabic, Jewish, Latin)

[5] Disputationes adversus astrologos (lib. III, cap. XIII, 1495), as quoted by Duhem (4, 229).

on more than two hundred questions (differentiae). For each of them the authorities are reviewed with tiresome fullness, a solution is offered, and objections are discussed. These questions concern science in general, medical philosophy, medical art, astrology, astrological medicine, astrological interpretation of history, magic. The central interests are medical and astrological. Pietro was often betrayed by his immense learning and his dialectical ability, and he allowed his experimental knowledge to be obscured by authorities. At his best he could be sound enough; too often his point of view is not the constructive criticism of the scientist, but rather the perverse subtlety of a schoolman and magician. In spite of its bulk, the Conciliator enjoyed some popularity; there are at least a dozen MSS, at least half a dozen incunabula, and thirteen sixteenth-century editions. It was sometimes quoted in Hebrew literature.[6]

The edition of Venice 1496 (and perhaps earlier ones) contains (f. 245v) a large woodcut illustrating the abdominal muscles. In the edition of Venice 1504 the same woodcut reappears at the same place (16.3 × 13 cm.). That illustration is very similar to one in the Commentaria . . . super anatomiam Mundini (Bologna 1521) of Jacopo Berengario da Carpi (d. 1550). It does not follow that Berengario took it from the Conciliator, for the Berengario illustrations have a MS tradition anterior to their publication. At any rate, that illustration does not belong to Pietro d'Abano; it is a fifteenth-century interpolation into the Conciliator. It does not occur in the princeps, 1472; it is inferior to the Berengario print.

3. *Lucidator*

The Lucidator astronomiae, dating from the same year, 1310, is the most important astronomical treatise written in this period in Italy. Its purpose is similar to that of the Conciliator, but it is restricted to astronomical and astrological topics, the fundamental questions of which are discussed. Pietro seems to have made astronomical observations, but his interests were primarily theoretical and astrological. According to the original plan, the Lucidator was divided into ten differentiae (I indicate the subject rather than the title of each): (1) Scientific value of astronomy. (2) Discussion of the motions of the stars, chiefly of the precession and the trepidation of the equinoxes; concluding against the existence of the trepidation and upholding the pure Ptolemaic doctrine. (3) Reality of the celestial spheres. (4, 5) Eccentrics and epicycles. This involves a very learned and detailed review of the three main planetary theories: the Aristotelian one of homocentric spheres, the Ptolemaic one of eccentrics and epicycles, and the Alpetragian (Introd. 2, 399); concluding against Aristotle and al-Biṭrūjī, in favor of Ptolemy. The author reveals incidentally his scientific philosophy: the purpose of science is to account for the facts (cf. σῴζειν τὰ φαινόμενα) as faithfully and as simply as possible. The Ptolemaic theory is to be preferred to the others, not only because of its greater accuracy, but also because of its greater economy. (6) Is the sun placed immediately above the moon or in the middle of the planets? (discussion of the geo-heliocentrical hypothesis). (7) Obliquity of the ecliptic. (8) Is the apogee of the sun mobile or not? (9) Whether the center of the sun's eccentric is distant from the earth 2°23′. (10) Whether the sun travels through its eccentric in 365 days and one-quarter.

Differentiae 1 to 6 are composed in the manner indicated above (arguments pro and con discussed, conclusions, objections, new conclusions). The seventh diffe-

[6] E.g., Steinschneider (p. 691, 734, 1893).

rentia is more like a regular treatise, repeating many statements already made in the previous differentiae (especially in the second); it devotes but little space to its professed subject, the obliquity of the ecliptic, but discusses very elaborately the theories concerning the eighth sphere. It is a second and final edition of the Tractatus de motu octavae sphaerae, on which Pietro was already working in 1303. Differentiae 8 to 10 remained unwritten.

The Lucidator astronomiae and the Tractatus de motu octavae spherae did not share the popularity of the Conciliator, which is hardly surprising in view of the fact that astronomical theories interest a far smaller number of people than medical ones. They were never published, and are represented by only a few MSS.

The main astrological ideas explained in the Conciliator and the Lucidator will be indicated presently.

4. *Translations from the Greek*

During his stay at Constantinople Pietro found a copy of the Problems of Aristotle. He translated them into Latin for the first time. He began a commentary on these problems while in Paris, and completed it at Padua in 1310. This commentary, Expositio problematum Aristotelis, enjoyed much popularity (about 20 MSS; first printed 1475; seven editions in less than half a century).

In 1300 he translated the Problemata ascribed to Alexander of Aphrodisias (III-1). He also translated the Problemata of Cassios the Iatrosophist (III-1). The first of these translations is preserved in an Escorial MS of the fourteenth century; the second is lost.

It is clear that Pietro had an unusually extensive knowledge of Greek literature—especially the Problemata literature, little known in the West—and that knowledge had probably been obtained, or his interest in it awakened, during his residence in the East. One would wish to know more about Pietro's experience and activities in Constantinople, for they represent a landmark in the history of scientific humanism.

He completed (Bologna, c. 1305) the translation of the fourteenth book of Galen's Methodus medendi ad Glauconem (Πρὸς Γλαύκωνα θεραπευτικά) left unfinished by Burgundio of Pisa (XII-2). That treatise was a part of the Arabic Galenic canon (no. 6 in Ḥunain's autobibliography; Isis 8, 691; 13, 87).

According to Steinschneider (p. 666, 1893), he translated the Galeni Prognostica de decubitu ex mathematica scientia (alias Astrologia Hippocratis,[7] or Hippocratis libellus de medicorum astrologia), an apocryphal text already translated by William of Moerbeke, and by one Gulideolus Mordicus (?).

Other Galenic translations ascribed to him: De optima nostri corporis compositione, De cholera nigra, De sectis, De ingenio sanitatis.

[7] With regard to Hippocrates' Astrologia sive liber astrologicus, see H. Diels: Die Handschriften der antiken Ärzte (Abhandlungen Preussischen Akad. 1, 50, 1905). This book, which has various titles, is once referred to as De luna in signis (Library of Padua). If this identification is correct, you will find all data concerning the book and its editions in Thorndike (2, 924, 1923); the article of Leo Norpoth (Kyklos 3, 305, 1930) gives some corrections to Thorndike. I did not find new material in Thorndike and Kibre (1937) s.v. "Hippocrates astrologia." There is, however, a pseudo-Hippocratic treatise, Prognostica secundum lunam, in the edition of the Articella printed in 1515; cf. Choulant (p. 309, 1841). Choulant himself refers (p. 217) to the pseudo-Hippocratic book which was translated by Peter of Abano. I am unable at the moment to decide whether these treatises are identical. Information kindly given to me by Ludwig Edelstein, of Baltimore (letter dated Mar. 21, 1939).

5. *Translation of Abraham ben Ezra's astrological treatises from the French*

Pietro translated Abraham's astrological treatises from the French version made in 1273 by Hagin Deulacres (Introd. 2, 188, 857). That French version had already been Latinized by Henry Bate (XIII-2) c. 1281–92; Pietro Latinized it in 1293, and a third Latin translation was made by Arnold of Quinqempoix at the beginning of the fourteenth century.

The treatises translated by Pietro are Liber principii sapientiae (Reshit ḥokma), Liber rationum or de rationibus (Ṭe'amim), Liber de revolutionibus et navitatibus (Moladot), Liber electionum (Mibḥarim), Liber de interrogationibus (She'elot), Liber luminarium (Meorot), Tractatus particulares.

There is nothing to show that Pietro knew Hebrew; on the other hand, one should not conclude from his knowledge of French that he had already spent by that time (1293) a few years in Paris or in France, for he could have learned French in other places, such as Padua or even Constantinople, the French language enjoying then an international diffusion second only to that of Latin (or Hebrew).

6. *Treatise on poisons*

The Tractatus de venenis eorumque remediis was written for a pope, possibly John XXII, who was elected on August 7, 1316 and ruled until 1334. If so, Pietro must have lived until after August 7, 1316. The De venenis is divided into 6 chapters, dealing with the classification of poisons, their action upon the body, how to protect oneself against them, the effects and antidotes of a number of particular poisons, and the general panacea or bezoar. Poisons are classified according to their origin and their form (forma specifica) or valence (meritum).[8] All this is mixed with astrology and superstitious ideas of various kinds. The De venenis was, as we might expect, very popular, judging by the large number of MSS, and the most popular of all of Pietro's writings.

7. *Physiognomy*

While he was in Paris in 1295, Pietro completed his Liber compilationis physiognomiae. His main authorities are the "founders" of the art, Philemon, Aristotle, Palemon (Polemon, II-1), and Loxius, and the Arabs al-Rāzī, Zacharias (?), and Ibn Sīnā. He develops considerably the astrological side of the subject.

8. *Edition of the Latin Dioscorides*

Leaving aside abbreviations and adaptations, there were two Latin translations of the περὶ ὕλης ἰατρικῆς: the one, literal and barbaric, was well known as early as the sixth century; the other, ascribed to Constantine the African (XI-2), is more polished, contains many interpolations, and is arranged alphabetically. This second version superseded the first and was immensely popular, in fact it was one of the most popular scientific books of the Middle Ages. Pietro's edition of it, Dyascorides quem Petrus Paduanensis legendo correxit et exponendo quae utiliora sunt in lucem deduxit, was printed in Colle 1478. Pietro had seen in Constantinople a Greek Dioscorides, also arranged in alphabetical order. Was this the famous Codex Aniciae Iulianae of 512 which the Flemish diplomat Busbecq rediscovered c. 1560?[9]

[8] To compare this notion with the chemical conception of valence as Thorndike does (2, 906, 1923) is highly arbitrary. There is nothing in common between them beyond the word itself.

[9] G. Sarton: Brave Busbecq (Isis 33, 557–75, 1942).

9. *Addition to Mesuë's Grabadin*

Pietro added a supplement, dealing with remedies for cardiac and digestive troubles, to the Antidotarium sive grabadin of Māsawaih al-Mārdīnī or Mesuë the Younger (XI-1).[10]

10. *Apocryphal writings*

Works on magic and geomancy are also ascribed to Pietro d'Abano: the Heptameron sive Elementa magica, often printed with the De cerimoniis magicis of H. C. Agrippa von Nettesheim (1486–1535), and the Geomantia.

11. *Pietro's astrological views and his "Averroism"*

Pietro's astrological views are explained or exemplified in the Conciliator, in the Lucidator, and passim in the rest of his writings. It is clear that he was first and last an astrologer, but this statement needs qualification. An "astrologer" then (somewhat like a "sociologist" today) might be almost anything from an austere scientist down to a quack.

He has also been called the father of the Averroistic school of Padua. Was he an Averroist? This term is also lacking in precision. It might be taken as a compliment or brandished like an insult (compare the term "philosophe" in eighteenth-century France or "bolshevik" today). He was well acquainted with the commentaries of Ibn Rushd, but was more interested in scientific than in theological problems. He had many opportunities for discussing the views of the Commentator (Ibn Rushd), but he was not an Averroist in the same sense as his disciple John of Jandun. Padua eventually became a stronghold of the new radicalism, but that is another story.

Pietro did not hesitate to defend the fundamental doctrine of astrology (that man's fate is controlled by planetary and stellar events), and its applications to medicine and to practical life in general. Everything, he holds, could eventually be explained in astrological terms. The factors to be considered are so numerous, however, that the problem is far too complex for human grasp. Disagreements between the facts and our astrological judgment are due to the endless difficulties of the problem and our insufficiency, not to any fault in the astrological principles. Such a defense leaves the astrologer in a position which is inexpugnable but hardly worth holding. Moreover, as experimental verification is evaded, the astrologer remains unprotected against his own fancies. This accounts for the contradictions in Pietro's thought: he tried, like other astrologers, to define a legitimate astrology against an illegitimate one, and denounced superstition, yet he himself indulged in various occult practices of the shadiest kind, e.g., the use of astrological images in order to capture and store up celestial influences (Conciliator, diff. 9, 10, 16, 64, 101, 113, after Thorndike 2, 899, 1923).

It would be easy to select enough passages in Pietro's writings to prove his relative rationalism, or on the contrary to evidence his irrational evasions and necromantic tendencies. He should be judged as a whole, and with proper indulgence.

He set forth repeatedly the astrological consequences of the precession of the equinoxes, giving to the Great Year (of 26,000 years) the meaning of a great astro-

[10] When pharmacists speak of Mesuë, this Mesuë is generally meant. The word grabadin is probably derived from γραφίδιον = libellus, via the Arabic aqrābādhīn (Introd. 1, 608, 729), or both forms are independent alterations of the same Greek word.

logical cycle.[11] This led him to the development of an astrological interpretation of history. The decadence of the world is explained by the precession of the equinoxes; it is thus periodic, not final. Conjunctions of planets are always ominous, and particularly those of Saturn and Jupiter. The latter may help to explain not only political catastrophes, but the creation of new religions such as Judaism, Christianity, and Islām (Conciliator, diff. 9).[12] As interpretations of historical events in stellar or solar terms are recurring periodically, even in our own days, Pietro should not be blamed too severely.

12. *Astrolabium planum*

Whether Pietro wrote a treatise on the astrolabe or not I do not know, but the Astrolabium planum composed by one of Regiomontanus' pupils, Johann Engel or Joannes Angeli (1463–1512), contains images which have been ascribed to Pietro. These images personify the 360 ascendants (παρανατέλλοντα). Scaliger gave a list of them in his edition of Manilius (ed. of 1600, p. 487–504) without indicating his source. There are many similarities between these illustrations and those in the Palazzo della Ragione (Salone) of Padua. Angelus' Astrolabium was first printed by Ratdolt (Augsburg 1488, 176 leaves, c. 443 woodcuts), then again in Venice 1494 and 1502. GW (2, 266, 1926). Boll (p. 434, 449, 455, 485, 1903). Saxl (2, 51–66, 1927).

13. *Pietro and the Inquisition*

In theory, astrology leaves no room for divine grace or human freedom. In practice, astrological determinism is tempered by man's ignorance and by his submission to the church. Astrology carried to the extreme was certainly heretical, but it never was carried so far, and on the other hand all the people shared astrological beliefs. Hence there is no special reason to think that Pietro, who bore witness to his orthodoxy on many occasions, would have fallen into trouble with the Inquisition on account of his astrology. He may, however, have been suspected of practicing black magic, and he is said to have denied the miracles of Christ. It is said that the Inquisition instituted proceedings against him twice, first in 1306 (or before 1303), when he was acquitted, and then in 1315, when he died during the trial. Thomas of Strasbourg, general of the Augustinian order from 1345 to his death in 1357, stated that he witnessed the burning of Pietro's bones in Padua, this being a posthumous punishment of Pietro's heresy. According to Giovanni Francesco Pico della Mirandola (nephew of the better-known Giovanni Pico della Mirandola), writing c. 1502 in his De rerum praenotione, Pietro's crime was rather that he denied the existence of demons and was not magical enough!! No certain conclusion can be reached.

This subject has been elaborately discussed by Lynn Thorndike on three occasions: History of magic (2, 938–47, 1923); Relations of the Inquisition to Peter of Abano and Cecco d'Ascoli (Speculum 1, 338–43, 1926); Peter and the Inquisition (Speculum 11, 132–33, 1936; Isis 25, 533).

[11] He spoke of a cycle of 36,000 years, because he did not know the correct value of the general precession; he thought that it amounted to one degree per century, instead of a little less than one degree and a half (50.″26 per year).

[12] This idea may be traced back at least to Abū Ma'shar (IX-1). There was no novelty in the principles of mediaeval astrology, and but little in the applications. It is for that reason that the history of astrology lacks real interest.

14. *Pietro's fame and influence*

These stories concerning the Inquisition are perhaps simply a part of Pietro's posthumous fame as a great magician. That fame was already well established within the time of Giovanni Micaele Savonarola (d. 1462), and it continued to grow throughout the sixteenth century. In the meanwhile, the many fifteenth- and sixteenth-century editions of his works are witnesses to his popularity as a medical astrologer. He was praised by many distinguished men, including Regiomontanus, the Savonarola already named (grandfather of the more famous one), Symphorien Champier (1472–1538), Gabriel Naudé (1600–1653). He was indeed one of the greatest representatives of medical astrology.

15. *Text*

Medical works. Conciliator differentiarum philosophorum et praecipue medicorum, Venice 1476, 1483, 1496 (two), 1504, and many later editions; Mantua 1472, Pavia 1490; and many others, three at least in the first half of the seventeenth century. The Quaestiones de febribus included in the collection De febribus (Venice 1576) are 9 differentiae taken from the Conciliator.

Tractatus de venenis eorumque remediis has often been printed with the Conciliator, beginning with the edition of 1476. There are many separate editions: Mantua 1473, Padua 1473, 1487, Rome 1475, 1484, 1490, Milan 1475, Leipzig 1498, 1500, etc.; it was translated into French by Lazare Boetus, Lyon 1593.

Liber compilationis physiognomiae, Padua 1474, Venice 1548.

Commentaries. Textus Mesuë noviter emendatus, Florence 1471, Venice 1484, 1485, 1489, 1491, 1495, etc., Pavia 1478, Naples 1475, 1478, Milan 1479, etc. (this work is found under varying titles).

Expositio in librum problematum Aristotelis cum textu eiusdem, Mantua 1475, Venice? 1482, Padua 1501, 1520, etc., Paris 1520.

Translations made by Pietro. Expositiones in Dioscoridem, Colle 1478, Lyon 1512; the first Latin edition of Dioscorides, i.e. the princeps edition in any language (Colle 1478), contains the text revised by Peter: Explicit Dyascorides quem Petrus Paduanensis legendo correxit et exponendo quae utiliora sunt in lucem deduxit. Peter is also named in the title of the second Latin edition.

Avenaris Judei [Abraham ben Ezra, XII-1] . . . in re judiciali opera . . . in Latinum traducta, Venice 1507; possibly Venice 1485.

Hippocratis [pseudo Hippocrates] de medicorum astrologia libellus ex Graeco in Latinum, Venice 1485, 1585, Leipzig 1505, Verona 1595.

Spurious works. Heptameron (or Elements of magic), Venice 1496, Paris 1565, in English 1600, 1655. In German, in Agrippa von Nettesheim: Magische Werke (3, 113–57, Berlin 1916). In English, in Henry Cornelius Agrippa's Fourth book of occult philosophy and geomancy (p. 126–72, London 1554). In Latin and French, in Les oeuvres magiques de Henri Corneille Agrippa (Liége 1547).

Geomantia, Italian translation, Venice 1541, 1544, etc.

16. *Criticism*

Prantl (3, 243–45, 1867). Renan: Averroes (p. 326–28, 1861). Cirillo Ronzoni: Della vita e delle opere di P. d'Abano (Atti dell'Accad. dei Lincei, memorie di classe di scienze morale, 2, 526–50, Roma 1878). M. Steinschneider: Abraham ibn Esra (Zeitschrift für Mathematik und Physik, suppt. vol. 25, 59–128, 1880; reprinted in Gesammelte Schriften 1, 407–506, 1925). Heinrich Suter: Die Mathematik auf den Universitäten des Mittelalters (Festschrift der Kantonsschule in Zürich p. 81, 1897). Werner (4, part 1, 139–40, 1887). Steinschneider (p. 666, 691, 734, 839, 973, 1893). Sante Ferrari: I tempi, la vita, le dottrine di Pietro d'Abano (506 p., Genoa 1900); completed in 1915 by a long memoir in Atti dell' Accad. dei Lincei, scienze morale (15, 629–727; Isis 5, 218). See also his study: Un ritratto di Pietro d'Abano e confronto fra due presunti ritratti di Dante in Padova (Atti dell' Accad. di Padova 35, 61–69, 1918). Duhem (p. 50–52, 1908). Neuburger (2, 404–11, 1911). Bruno Nardi: La teoria dell' anima e la generazione delle forme secondo Pietro d'Abano (Rivista di filosofia neo-scolastica 4, 723 ff., 1912). Duhem (3, 153–57, 1915), on the geoheliocentrical hypothesis (4, 229–63, 1916). Antonio Favaro: Pietro d'Abano ed il suo Lucidator astrologiae (Atti dell' Istituto veneto 75(2), 515–27, Venice 1916; Isis 4, 137). Choulant (p. 141–42, 1920). Adolf Dyroff: Dante und Pietro d'Abano (Philosophisches Jahrbuch der Görres-Gesellschaft 33, 253–71, 1920; Isis 4, 586). Thorndike (2, 874–947, 1923; with many critical appendixes, vol. 3, passim, vol. 4, passim, 1934). U. Cassuto: Peter of Abano (EJ 1, 124, 1928). Ueberweg (p. 613–15, 618, 777, 786, 1928). Lynn Thorndike: Vatican Latin manuscripts (Isis 13, 87, 1929). Leo Norpoth: Zur Bio-Bibliographie und Wissenschaftslehre des Pietro d'Abano (Kyklos 3, 292–353, Leipzig 1930; Isis 16, 487). Gustavo Tanfani: Pietro d'Abano nella evoluzione del pensiero scientifico medioevale (Boll. Istituto storico italiano dell' arte sanitaria 12, 65–91, 200–22, 17 fig., 1932). Wickersheimer (p. 608–10, 1936). Arturo Castiglioni: Abano (Minerva medica vol. 1, no. 2, 27, 1936). L. C. MacKinney: Medieval medical dictionaries and glossaries (Medieval essays in honor of J. W. Thompson p. 240–58, Chicago 1938, p. 254; Isis 29, 142). Lynn Thorndike: Translations of works of Galen from the Greek by Peter of Abano (Isis 33, 649–53, 1942); MSS of Peter's writings (Bull. history of medicine 15, 201–19, 1944; Isis 35, 227).

NICCOLÒ DA REGGIO

Niccolò de Deoprepio da Reggio. Nicolaus Rheginus, Reginus Calaber, de Regio, de Regio de Calabria, Nicolò Greco de Regio. Italian physician and translator of anatomical and medical works. Born in Reggio di Calabria c. 1280, died in Naples c. 1350.

He studied medicine and Greek in Reggio for some years, then went to Salerno c. 1300, where he studied and taught for a while. About 1308 he was invited to Naples by Charles II of Anjou, who, like other Angevin kings, was interested in promoting the knowledge of Greek works. In Naples Niccolò taught and practiced medicine, was given the post of Translator regius, and was commissioned to render Greek works into Latin. After the death of Charles (1309), Niccolò was under the patronage of Robert, king of Naples (ruled 1309–43); Philip of Tarent, brother of Robert, and Charles of Calabria, son of Robert, also gave him various commissions, and he made some translations for others besides the Angevins; for instance, the Latin rendering of the De tyriaca was made for Marcolconi de Mantua (Lo Parco p. 265, 1913). King Robert obtained Greek manuscripts for Niccolò from the emperor Andronicos II (ruled 1282–1328).

Wickersheimer refutes the statement of Neuburger that the Dispensarium ad aromatorios (also called the Antidotarium ad aromatorios) is the same as the Δυναμερόν ascribed to Nicholas Myrepsos, whose translation is often credited to Niccolò (Introd. 2, 1094). Wickersheimer says that the Dispensarium was written by Nicholas Prepositi in the second half of the fifteenth century. Lehmann goes still farther in this controversy and refutes the statement of Lo Parco that Niccolò da Reggio either translated the Δυναμερόν or abridged it.

Niccolò translated the Commemoratio ad labores, certamina et peregrinationes SS. Petri et Pauli, wrongly (?) ascribed to Sophronios (Σωφρόνιος Δαμασκηνός), Orthodox patriarch of Jerusalem from 629 to his death in 638.[13]

[13] PG (87, pars 3, 4011–14, 1860).

Between 1308 and 1345 he translated many works of Hippocrates and Galen. His translations were made directly and literally from Greek into Latin: de verbo ad verbum, nihil addens, minuens, vel permutans. This literalism was carried so far that his translations have often been used with advantage by modern editors of the Greek texts. He was the first to reveal Greek medicine without Muslim alterations.

His main translation was that of Galen's long treatise on the use of the parts of the human body, De usu partium, dedicated in 1322 to Robert d'Anjou, king of Naples. This publication is a very important landmark in the history of anatomy and medicine.

Text. Translations of Galenic writings. De victu attenuante (or De subtiliante dieta), Venice 1490, 1502; edited by K. Kalbfleisch: Galeni de victu attenuante (70 p., Leipzig 1898). (= Περὶ τῆς λεπτυνούσης διαίτης.)

De utilitate particularum (1317), Pavia 1515/16, Venice 1528. (= Περὶ χρείας μορίων.)

De passionibus uniuscuiusque particule (or Myamir) (1335), Pavia 1515/16, Venice 1528. (= Περὶ συνθέσεως φαρμάκων τῶν κατὰ τόπους.)

Subfiguratio empirica (1341), Pavia 1515/16, Venice 1528; edited by Max Bonnet: De Claudii Galeni subfiguratione empirica (80 p., Bonn 1872). (= Ὑποτύπωσις ἐμπειρική.)

De optima doctrinatione, Pavia 1515/16, Venice 1528. (= Περὶ τῆς ἀρίστης διδασκαλίας.)

De partibus artis medicative, Pavia 1515/16; edited by Diomedes Bonard, Venice 1490, 1502, also Venice 1528, 1541, 1576, Lyon 1550; edited by Chartier: Hippocratis et Galeni opera (2, 282–85, Paris 1679); by Hermann Schöne: Galenus de partibus artis medicativae (38 p., Greifswald 1911). (= Περὶ τῶν τῆς ἰατρικῆς μερῶν.)

De disnia (1345), Pavia 1515/16, Venice 1528. (= Περὶ δυσπνοίας.)

De constitutione artis medicative, Pavia 1515/16, Venice 1528. (= Πρὸς Πατρόφιλον περὶ συστάσεως ἰατρικῆς.)

De sequela operationum anime (or De substantia virtutum animalium, Quod animi mores corporis temperamenta sequantur), Pavia 1515/16, Venice 1528. (= Ὅτι τὰ τῆς ψυχῆς ἤθη ταῖς τοῦ σώματος κράσεσιν ἕπεται.)

De consuetudinibus, Pavia 1515/16, Venice 1528, Lyon 1550. (= Περὶ ἐθῶν.)

De causis procatarticis (sic), Pavia 1515/16, Venice 1528, 1576, Lyon 1550. (= Περὶ τῶν προκαταρκτικῶν αἰτίων.)

De tumoribus praeter naturam, Pavia 1515/16, Venice 1528. (= Περὶ τῶν παρὰ φύσιν ὄγκων.)

De typo, Pavia 1515/16, Venice 1528. (= Περὶ τύπων.)

De comate secundum Hippocratem, Pavia 1515/16, Venice 1490, 1528. (= Περὶ τοῦ παρ' Ἱπποκράτει κώματος.)

Liber pronosticorum sive de pronosticatione, Pavia 1515/16, Venice 1528. (= Περὶ τοῦ προγινώσκειν πρὸς Ἐπιγένην.)

De virtute simplicis medicine, Pavia 1515/16.

De flobotomia, Pavia 1515/16, Venice 1528. (Not the Περὶ φλεβοτομίας.)

De tyriaca, Pavia 1515/16, Venice 1528. (= Περὶ θηριακῆς πρὸς Παμφυλιανόν.)

De sanguisucis, Pavia 1515/16, Venice 1528.

De facile acquisibilibus ad Solonem Archimedicum, Pavia 1515/16, Venice 1528. (= book II of the Περὶ εὐπορίστων.)

De usu partium corporis humani, Paris 1528, 1531, 1538, Basel 1531, 1533, Lyon 1550, 1576. (= Περὶ χρείας μορίων.)

De causis continentibus libellus, edited by Karl Kalbfleisch (24 p., Marburg 1904). (= Περὶ τῶν συνεκτικῶν αἰτίων.)

De sectis ad eos qui introducuntur, Paris 1518, Basel 1529. (= Περὶ αἱρέσεων τοῖς εἰσαγομένοις.)

De optima secta ad Thrasybulum. (= Πρὸς Θρασύβουλον περὶ ἀρίστης αἱρέσεως.)

De morborum temporibus, Paris 1529. (= Περὶ τῶν ἐν ταῖς νόσοις καιρῶν.)

De totius morbi temporibus, Paris 1529. (= Περὶ τῶν ὅλου τοῦ νοσήματος καιρῶν.)

Spurious or doubtful works of Galen translated by Niccolò. De historia philosophorum (1341), Pavia 1515/16, Venice 1528. (= Περὶ φιλοσόφου ἱστορίας.)

De anatomia oculorum, Pavia 1515/16, Venice 1528, 1576, Lyon 1550, Paris 1536.

De virtutibus centauree, Pavia 1515/16, Venice 1528, 1576, Lyon 1550.

De gyneciis (or De passionibus mulierum), Pavia 1515/16, Venice 1528, 1576, Lyon 1550.

An omnes particulae animalis quod foetatur fiant simul, Venice 1528, 1545, 1576, Lyon 1550. (Not the same as Περὶ κυουμένων διαπλάσεως.)

De commoditatibus tyriace, Venice 1528.

In various libraries, particularly those of Paris, Dresden, the Vatican, Naples, and others, there are quite a few MSS of translations which are accredited to Niccolò. Some of these are translations of the works of Galen, but in other cases the authorship is doubtful.

Translations of works that are probably by Galen. De utilitate respirationis, De sanitate tuenda, De temporibus utilibus egenis, Hypocratis Aphorismi cum commento Galeni, De febribus ad Glauconem, De introductione medicorum, De substantia virtutum naturalium, Liber de regimine acutorum, De virtute consuetudinis.

Pseudo-Galenic. De simplicium farmacorum virtute, De clisteribus et colica, De nutrimento.

By unidentified authors. De vinis, De Zagonia, De temporibus periodorum, De cura icteri, De utilitate particularum, de utilitate digitorum et de motu eorum, De diamidiis, De passionibus uniuscuiusque particulae.

Hippocratic. Liber de regimine acutorum, Liber de lege, Liber juramentorum, Prognosticum.

Criticism. Renzi (1, 338–40, 1852; p. 520–23, 1857). Francesco Lo Parco: Niccolò da Reggio, grecista italiota del secolo XIV e la interpretazione dell' epigrafe greca del tempio dei Dioscuri di Napoli (Naples 1909). Ernest Wickersheimer: Nicolaus Prepositi, ein französischer Arzt ums Jahr 1500 (AGM 5, 302–10, 1911). Hermann Mutschmann: Zur Uebersetzertätigkeit des Nicolaus von Rhegium (Berliner philologische Wochenschrift 31, 691–93, 1911). Hermann Schöne: Galenus de partibus artis medicativae (38 p., Greifswald 1911). Francesco Lo Parco: Niccolò da Reggio antesignano del risorgimento dell' antichità ellenica nel secolo XIV (Atti della Reale accademia di archeologia, lettere e belle arti vol. 2, part 2, 243–317, Naples 1913), a very elaborate study. Hermann Lehmann: Zu Nicolaus Myrepsus (AGM 17, 299–306, 1925; Isis 11, 427). Wickersheimer (p. 576, 1936). Lynn Thorndike: Translations of works of Galen from the Greek by Niccolò da Reggio (to appear in Byzantion).

3b. TRANSLATIONS FROM GREEK INTO HEBREW

SHEMARIAH BEN ELIJAH HA-IQRIṬI

Greco-Jewish translator and exegete (d. in or after 1352).

He was born at the end of the thirteenth century in Negropont (i.e., Euboea) or more probably in Rome; the epithet "of Negropont" applied to him may refer to his parentage. He was called ha-Yewani (the Greek) and ha-Iqriṭi[14] (the Cre-

[14] The Arabic name of Crete is Iqrīṭ or Iqrīṭash; in Hebrew, however, one finds also the consonants k and t (Ikriti) instead of q and ṭ. Take your choice.

tan). Indeed, soon after his birth, his father was called as rabbi to Crete, where Shemariah probably spent his youth. According to his own testimony he translated various philosophical works which he used later for his Biblical commentaries, but he does not say which works, nor from which language he translated them: if it was from the Greek, this would be exceedingly interesting, because he would be the first mediaeval Jew to translate from Greek into Hebrew or to make direct use of Greek sources. In 1305 he undertook a Biblical commentary based upon the philosophical works he had translated, and later he obtained the patronage of Robert of Anjou (king of Naples 1310–43) and flourished at the latter's court at least until 1328. In 1352, being then an old man, he traveled to Spain to try to bring about a reconciliation between the Qaraites and the Rabbinists, but he failed, and was even thrown into prison, where he probably died.

In 1346 (?) he wrote the Sefer ha-mora to refute the philosophical views of creation; he composed a treatise on logic (higayon), and other works none of which have been published.

Criticism. Steinschneider (p. 498, 1893). Ismar Elbogen (JE 6, 559, 1904). U. Cassuto (EJ 8, 390, 1931). Mann (2, 295, 1935).

4a. TRANSLATIONS FROM LATIN INTO HEBREW

ISRAEL BEN JOSEPH CASLARI

Crescas Vidal Caslari. Israel ben Joseph ha-Caslari (cf. Caylar, Hérault), of the Yiẓhar family. Judeo-Languedocian physician and translator from Latin into Hebrew, who flourished at Avignon c. 1327.

In 1327–28 he translated the Regimen sanitatis of Arnold of Villanova (Introd. 2, 894), under the title Ma'amar be-hanhagat ha-beri'ut. In certain MSS the title is Arnavdina or Praṭiqa. He explains in a circuitous preface that he made this translation in spite of the availability of Maimonides' excellent treatise because (1) Arnold had composed the Regimen in 1307 for the king of Aragon (Jaime II), (2) the Regimen had been composed according to the Christian manner, and Jewish physicians obliged to live among Christians were expected to know Christian usages, (3) Arnold had surpassed all his predecessors in the medical art to the extent that the common people considered him a prophet.

Israel ben Joseph composed for the Purim celebration a poem on the story of Esther, Iggeret ha-purim, in a Romanic vernacular; later he rewrote it in Hebrew: the Romanic version was probably meant for the women and children, the Hebrew one for the men.

Text. The Hebrew version of Arnold's Regimen is still unpublished.
The Romanic Iggeret ha-purim was printed in Constantinople 1812, then again with Hebrew translation in Salonica 1853.
Criticism. Steinschneider (p. 779, 1893). Neubauer-Renan (p. 647–50, 1893). S. Kahn (JE 3, 600, 1902). Mayer Kayserling (JE 4, 353, 1903). M. Zobel (EJ 5, 709, 1930).

JUDAH BEN MOSES BEN DANIEL

Judah ben Moses ben Daniel ben Jekuthiel. Rabbi Judah ha-filosof. Judah Romano or Leone Romano, Leone de Ser Daniele. Italian philosopher, exegete, and translator from Latin into Hebrew. Cousin and friend of Immanuel ben Solomon. Born at Rome c. 1292, flourished for a time at the court of Robert of Anjou, king of Naples from 1310 to 1343, died at Rome after 1350.

It was said by Moses Rieti (1388–after 1460) that Judah ben Moses helped king Robert to read the Bible in Hebrew.

His most important activity was as a translator—be it noted—from Latin into Hebrew. His main purpose was to diffuse philosophical knowledge among the Jews, and he was one of the first to realize the value of the Latin sources. He translated:

1. Pseudo-Aristotelian De causis (V-2? Introd. 1, 404), before 1328, under the title Sefer ha-'illot or Sefer ha-sabot; also called Sefer ha-ṭob ha-gamur (De absoluto bono) and Pirḥe elahut (Flores divinitatis). He did not translate it from the Arabic, but from the Latin, probably from the version made by Gerard of Cremona: De expositione bonitatis purae (Isis 29, 426). A similar translation had been made before by Hillel ben Samuel (XIII-2), and the text had even been translated directly from Arabic into Hebrew by Zeraḥiah ben Isaac ben Shealtiel (XIII-2), Sefer ha bi'ur ha-ṭob ha-gamur. This is the more remarkable because Zeraḥiah and Hillel both flourished in Italy, even in Rome.

2. Boetius (VI-1): De uno et unitate, Ma'amar ha-eḥad ve-ha-aḥdut.

3. Ibn Rushd (XII-2): De substantia orbis, probably from the version ascribed to Michael Scot (Introd. 2, 580).

4. Thomas Aquinas (XIII-2): De ideologia, Ma'amar ha-hemshelim, before 1328.

Also other short texts by Thomas Aquinas, Albert the Great, Giles of Rome, etc.

His own writings include commentaries on the Bible, on Jewish prayers, on the Sefer ha-madda', which is the first part of Maimonides' Mishneh Torah, and possibly on the qabbalistic Sefer ma'areket ha-elahut by rabbi Perez ben Isaac Kohen "Gerondi" (if this last commentary is truly his, it would provide for the mysterious rabbi Perez a terminus ad quem). He compiled a Hebrew-Italian glossary of philosophical terms, which includes discussions of philosophical and cosmological questions.

Text. No writings of his have yet been edited, but I may mention that the Ma'areket elahut was printed at Ferrara 1558.

Criticism. M. Steinschneider: Guida Romano (Il Buonarotti 5, 3–12, 1870; reprinted in his Gesammelte Schriften 1, 507–22, 1925); (p. 183, 263, 467, 489, 1893). Ismar Elbogen (JE 10, 444, 1905). U. Cassuto (EJ 8, 1020, 1931).

HEZEKIAH BAR ḤALAFTA

Hezekiah bar Ḥalafta ha-zarmil (?). Translator from Latin into Hebrew who flourished c. 1320.

In that year he translated a Latin commentary on the Summulae logicales (or Parva logicalia) of Peter of Spain (XIII-2), adding an interesting preface. The commentary quotes Isḥāq al-Isrā'īlī, Ibn Gabirol, Ibn Rushd, Maimonides, Moses ibn Tibbon. Its Latin origin is clear; for example, Ibn Gabirol is named in Hebrew Abi Sumron (Avicebron)!

Hezekiah is the English Biblical form of the Hebrew name Ḥizqiyyahu. Ḥalafta (and variants such as Taḥlifa) is a very old Jewish name, often used by the early speakers and teachers (first to fifth cent.). See lists of tannaim and amoraim in JE (12, 40–54, 1906).

Criticism. Adolf Neubauer: Catalogue of Hebrew MSS in the Bodleian (1, 754, no. 2187, Oxford 1886). Jacob Guttmann: Die Philosophie des Salomon ibn Gabirol (p. 8, Göttingen 1889). M. Zobel (EJ 5, 495, 1930).

SAMUEL BENVENISTE

Judeo-Spanish physician and translator from Latin into Hebrew. He flourished at the end of the thirteenth century in Saragossa, later, at the beginning of the fourteenth century, in Barcelona and in Tarragona (1322). Still living in 1356, being mentioned in that year together with maestro Leon Medico, maestro Mose Medico, and maestro Yuçef Avendagot (i.e., Joseph ha-Rofe ibn abī Ayyūb).

He was attached to the court of Pedro, king of Aragon,[15] as physician in ordinary to the king's brother, Don Manuel.

A translation of Boetius' De consolatione philosophiae has been ascribed to him, but the MS of it is lost. Boetius was the only early Latin writer whose works were translated into Hebrew. (Another Hebrew translation was made in 1423 by 'Azariah ben Joseph Ibn Abba Mari under the title Neḥamat ha-filosofiya.)

He also translated Maimonides' treatise on asthma (Maqāla fī-l-rabw, see Introd. 2, 372). That translation was probably made not from the Arabic, but from the Latin.

He was one of ten great men of Catalonia whom Qalonymos ben Qalonymos had met on his journeys and desired to honor above all others.

The name Benveniste and its many Romanic variants (Benevenutus, Bienvenu, Abenbenist, etc.), all of which mean "welcome," was common among the Jews of southern France, Catalonia, and Aragon; in Aragon it goes back at least to 1079. The Hebrew forms are not translations but simply transcriptions of the Romanic ones, many new variants occurring in these transcriptions (see EJ 4, 142). See my notes on Benevenutus Grassus (XII-1) and Sheshet ben Isaac Benveniste (XII-2).

Criticism. Neubauer-Renan (p. 451, 1893). Steinschneider (p. 466, 767, 1893). Brief notes in JE (3, 41, 1902) and EJ (4, 156, 1929).

DAVID BEN YOM-ṬOB BEN BILA

David ben Yom-ṭob ben Bila (or Bilia, or Villa). Judeo-Portuguese poet, theologian, Biblical commentator, astrologer, and translator from Latin into Hebrew who flourished in Portugal in the first half of the fourteenth century. His Biblical commentaries, somewhat in the style of Abraham ben Ezra, do not concern us, nor other works of his except the following:

1. Yessodot ha-maskil. Thirteen articles of faith complementary to those of Maimonides.

2. Kelal qaṭan, concerning the relation between astrology and medicine.

3. In 1338 he translated the Salus vitae into Hebrew, Ma'amar bi-segullot 'or ha-naḥash. This singular treatise, ascribed to one Joannes Pauli (or John Paulinus, John of Spain), deals with the twelve medical or magical virtues of pulverized snakeskin. The Latin text was often copied and appeared under many titles: De pelle serpentis XII experimenta et quaedam vera, De corio serpentis, De viribus corii serpentis pulverisati, De spolio serpentis, etc. It was derived from an Arabic (Egyptian?) original composed by one Alchamus (Alchanus, Alanus, Alganus, Alcharius, Alcaus, Alcabitius?).[16] If Salus vitae is a translation of the original Arabic title, that title was probably a sort of pun (as so many are), for the Arabic words for snake and life are almost alike (ḥayyah, ḥayāh).

[15] Presumably Pedro IV the Ceremonious, king from 1336 to 1387.

[16] These names cannot be identified except the last, used to designate al-Qabīṣī, the astrologer (X-2). It does not follow that the latter was the author.

4. Treatise on logic, Kilale ha-higgayon.

In his Biblical commentaries, David gave astrological interpretations of the rainbow and of the holydays. He did not believe in metempsychosis.

He is possibly identical with David ben Yom-ṭob Bonjorn, father of the astronomer Jacob Bonet (XIV-2); if so, he flourished in Perpignan about the middle of the century. The names Bonjorn, Bongoron, and many other Romanic variants are equivalent to the Hebrew Yom-ṭob.

Text. Yessodot ha-maskil, published in the Sefer dibre ḥakamim of Eliezer ben Solomon Ashkenasi (Metz 1849). This includes a French translation by Salomon Klein.

Criticism. Introd. (2, 1093). Steinschneider (p. 499, 806, 1893); (p. 51, 1904). I. Broydé (JE 6, 520, 1904). Thorndike (2, 794–96, 1923). S. A. Horodetzky (EJ 4, 798, 1929). B. Suler (EJ 4, 950).

4b. TRANSLATIONS FROM LATIN INTO FRENCH

PROUVILLE

Jean de Prouville, French physician and translator from Latin into French, who flourished probably at the beginning of the fourteenth century.

Jean de Prouville, Joannes de Probavilla, originated probably in Prouville (near Bernaville, dépt. Somme; Picardy). He was a member ("profès") of a religious order, but authorized to be a clerk to the count of Saint-Pol, Guy de Châtillon, the king's cupbearer (bouteiller) from 1296 to his (Guy's) death in 1317. Guy de Châtillon was a patron also of the surgeon Jean Pitart (d. after 1328).

Jean de Prouville wrote a medical poem (292 lines), Liber de signis pronosticis, and he translated from Latin into French, for Guy de Châtillon, the surgical treatise of the abbé Poutrel. That translation is extant in one of the MSS formerly owned by queen Christina of Sweden (Vatican, Reg. 1211). It is an elaborate treatise (92 leaves, 24 lines per page), ending with unguents and recipes. The author of the original Latin treatise, abbé Poutrel (or Punel?), cannot be identified.

Text. Both texts are unpublished.

Criticism. Ernest Langlois: Notices des MSS français et provençaux de Rome antérieurs au XVIe siècle (Notices et extraits 33(2), 100, 1889). Antoine Thomas (HL 36, 603–7, 1927).

PIERRE DE PARIS

Translator from Latin into French.

Peculiarities of his French show that he was probably of Italian (Venetian) origin. On the other hand, his name suggests that he flourished sometime in Paris, perhaps as a student. He also lived in Cyprus (in the first decade of the century).

He translated into French the Politics of Aristotle, the Psalms, and the Consolatio philosophiae of Boetius. The first translation is lost; the second and third, extant, were made at the request of Simon Le Rat, who resided in Cyprus from 1299 to 1310, first as marshal of the Knights of St. John, then as commander of the order for Cyprus. This confirms Peter's residence in Cyprus. Peter's translation of Boetius was completed after he had left Cyprus; it includes a commentary interpolated into the text to explain its difficulties. That mediocre French commentary was soon translated into Latin by an unknown feeble-minded scholar.

Peter wrote a philosophical treatise (lost) dedicated to Amauri de Lusignan, brother of Henry II (king of Cyprus 1285–1324). Amauri usurped his brother's power, was proclaimed regent of Cyprus in 1306, and was assassinated in 1310.

Criticism. Antoine Thomas: Notice sur le ms. Latin 4788 du Vatican contenant une traduction française avec commentaire par maître Pierre de Paris de la Consolatiô philosophiae (Notices et extraits 41, 29–90, 1923). This includes long extracts and glossary. Langlois (4, 277–81, 1928). Mario Roques: Traductions françaises de la Consolatio de Boèce (HL 37, 419–88, chiefly 441–50, 1938).

Roques' study illustrates the great popularity of Boetius' Consolation among French readers. It enumerates nine translations, many being anonymous, the others by John of Meung (XIII-2), by Peter of Paris, by a mysterious Italian Bonaventura da Demena (date and place unknown), and by the Dominican Renaud de Louhans (in Saône-et-Loire; Burgundy). This last-named translation was composed at Poligny (dépt. Jura; Franche-Comté) c. 1336; it is an adaptation in verse extending to nearly 8,000 lines. The same Renaud de Louhans translated also the Liber consolationis (1246) of Albertano of Brescia (XIII-1) under the title Livre de Mélibée et de Prudence (c. 1336). For this and other translations of Albertano's moral treatises, see Mario Roques (HL 37, 488–506, 1938).

ARNOLD OF QUINQEMPOIX

French royal physician, translator from Latin into French and vice versa (d. c. 1321–26).

Arnulphus de Quiquenpoit, Arnulfus de Quinquenpoist, Adenulphus de Quinquempoix, Ernoul, Arnoul. He originated probably in the village of Quinquempoix, in the canton of St.-Just-en-Chaussée (Oise), rather than in Quincampoix near Beauvais.

One of the most popular doctors at the court of Philip the Fair (1285–1314) and his sons Louis X (1314–16) and Philip V (1316–22). He died after 1321 and before December 1, 1326. He is remembered mainly for his translations from Latin into French, French into Latin, and Hebrew (?) into French.

Arnold planned to translate all the astrological works of Abraham ben Meïr ibn Ezra (XII-1) into Latin, but the only extant translations are the Liber de questionibus and Liber de electionibus. He also translated the Liber de significationibus septem planetarum and the Liber de occultis, but his attribution of them to Ibn Ezra is doubtful. The first three translations were probably made not from the original Hebrew, but from the French translations by Hagin the Jew (Introd. 2, 721, 995). He may not have known of the translation made by Peter of Abano, but he certainly knew the translation of Ibn Ezra's Liber conjunctionum planetarum by Henry Bate (XIII-2).

Arnold is credited with translations from Latin into French of an astrological work of Abū Ma'shar (IX-1), Des elections selonc les regars et les conjonctions de la lune as planettes par les 12 signes, but without the tables, and of al-Kindī's (IX-1) De imbribus et pluviis. Also, he may have translated from Hebrew (or Latin) into French the Sefer ha-ge'ullah (Book of redemption), a treatise on the date of the Messiah's coming written (c. 1263–70) by Moses ben Naḥman Gerondi (XIII-2), which he called La redempcion des fils d'Ysrael. That is, the text entitled La redempcion des fils d'Ysrael was probably a translation of the Sefer ha-ge'ullah; but we cannot be sure, as that text is lost. The translation of al-Kindī is also lost. The Hebrew text of the Sefer ha-ge'ullah was edited by Jacob Lipschitz (London 1909).

He translated into French (Picard) the Liber Hermetis trismegisti for the queen of France, Marie of Luxemburg (d. 1324). By the way, that astrological treatise had been almost completely forgotten until its recent edition in Latin by Wilhelm Gundel: Neue astrologische Texte des Hermes Trismegistos (see complete reference under "Criticism" below). The original lost treatise was Greek, probably of the third century, and partly derived from Egyptian sources. Arnold's translation into the Picard dialect (Parisinus fr. 613) represents a tradition somewhat different from the Latin translation which Gundel has found in a composite astronomical MS of 1431 in the British Museum (Harleianus 3731). See good review of Gundel's work by Claire Préaux (Chronique d'Egypte 12, 112–15, 1937).

Criticism. Antoine Thomas: Arnoul de Quinquempoix, médecin et astrologue (HL 35, 630–32, Paris 1921). Raphael Levy: The astrological works of Abraham ibn Ezra (Johns Hopkins studies in Romance literatures and languages vol. 8, 46–50, Baltimore 1927; Isis 11, 171). Wilhelm Gundel: Neue astrologische Texte des Hermes Trismegistos. Funde und Forschungen auf dem Gebiet der antiken Astronomie und Astrologie (Abhandlungen der bayerischen Akad., phil. hist. Abt., part 12, 386 p., München 1936). E. de Strycker (S.J.): La baleine, l'aveugle et le chat dans un texte astrologique (Revue belge de philologie et d'histoire 17, 222–25, 1938).

BERSUIRE

Pierre Bersuire. French (Poitevin) Benedictine, Biblical encyclopaedist, translator of Livy's Decades from Latin into French (d. 1362).

He is best known under the name Petrus Berchorius (Pictaviensis), derived from Berchorium. Hence it is deduced, first, that his family originated in Bersuire or Bressuire (Vendée; Bas Poitou), and, second, that his French name would be something like Bersuire, Berçuire, Bercheur, Berchoire, etc.

He was born c. 1290 in St. Pierre du Chemin near Maillezais, Vendée; he assumed the Franciscan habit, but exchanged it later for the Benedictine one. In 1328 he entered the service of cardinal Pierre Després (Petrus de Pratis), vice-chancellor of John XXII; he thus resided in Avignon from 1328 on to 1342, enjoying sufficient leisure to write his main works and to cultivate Petrarca's friendship. In 1351 he was a student in Paris and camerarius of the abbey of Notre Dame des Coulombs in the diocese of Chartres. In that year he was accused of heresy and imprisoned, but was saved by the combined efforts of the University and of John the Good (king 1350–64). He then entered the king's service, being his secretary from 1352 to 1355. He was prior of the monastery of St. Eloi in Paris from 1354 to his death, and was beneficiary of various prebends. In 1361 he renewed his conversations with Petrarca, who had come to Paris as an ambassador of Galeazzo Visconti of Milano. He died in Paris at the beginning of 1362.

His main work as a Biblical scholar was done while he was in Avignon (1328–42). He compiled a kind of Biblical encyclopaedia, dealing not only with theology, but incidentally with many other subjects, even physics, biology, geography, medicine. It was divided into two main parts, the Reductorium morale, completed before 1335, and the Repertorium morale, probably completed about 1340 (second redaction 1359). During the same period he wrote three smaller works, to wit, the De mirabilibus mundi, a paraphrase of and commentary on Ovid's Metamorphoses, and the Moralizationes super totam Bibliam.

His Biblical commentaries include new interpretations and bold criticisms of the ecclesiastical conditions of his time, which may have caused his arrest in 1351. In that respect he was a forerunner of such men as Pierre d'Ailly (1350–1420), Jean Gerson (1363–1429), Nicolas de Clamanges (or Clémanges, 1360–1440?), who realized more and more keenly the disorganization and corruption of the church and the urgent need of reform.

His second great accomplishment was the translation into French of Livy's Decades, at the request of king John the Good. It was begun in 1351/52 and completed c. 1355, that is, as far as it could be completed at that time. It included only what was then known of Livy, i.e., the first and third decades, and books I to IX of the fourth. Le Rommans de Titus Livius, as the translation was called, had a very great success, and it was of great importance for the revival of ancient literature and for the blossoming out of the French Renaissance. It was also of some importance in the development of the French language. Bersuire prefixed to his translation a list of the Latin words which he had Gallicized because French equivalents were lacking. The list of new French words thus obtained includes augure, inauguration, auspice, chose publique, colonie, cirque, enseignes, expier, faction, fastes, magistrats, prodiges, station, sénat, sénateur, transfuge, triomphe, tribun du peuple, all of which are common words in the language of today. Nicole Oresme did the same in his Aristotelian translations; that is, he himself listed all the words which he had been obliged to borrow from the Greek and Latin in order to complete his task, words which were permanent acquisitions of the French language.

In the first edition of Bersuire's translation (Paris 1486–87) the missing second decade was replaced by a translation of the De bello punico of Leonardo Bruni Aretino (1369–1444) by Jean le Bègue, dedicated to Charles VII (king 1422–61).

Text. Liber Bibliae moralis, Ulm 1474, Strassburg 1474, Deventer 1477, Cologne 1477.

Repertorium morale (folio, 3 vols.), Nuremberg 1489, 1499, Paris 1521–22, Venice 1583.

Reductorium morale (folio, 1 vol.), Basel 1515, Lyon 1520, Paris 1521, Venice 1575, 1583.

Opera omnia (3 vols.), Mainz 1609, Cologne 1620, 1631. Opera omnia, sive Reductorium, Repertorium et Dictionarium utriusque Testamenti quadripartitum. Editio novissima (6 vols. in 3), Cologne 1730–31.

Les Décades (folio, 3 vols.), Paris 1486–87; Paris 1514–15; again 1530.

Criticism. Petit de Julleville (2, 260–62, 1896). Friedrich Baumann: Livius, Bersuire und Bellenden. Vergleichende Studien zu Bellenden's Liviusübersetzung (Diss. Leipzig 1905). John Bellenden (Ballenden or Ballentyne, fl. 1533–87) translated Livy for James V of Scotland (DNB 4, 186). Léopold Pannier: Pierre Bersuire, premier traducteur français de Tite Live (Bibliothèque de l'Ecole des chartes 33, 325–64, 1872). Antoine Thomas: Grande encyclopédie (6, 429); Deux documents inédits sur Pierre Bersuire (Romania 40, 97–100, 1911). Franz Fassbinder: Das Leben und die Werke des P. Berçuire (Diss., 48 p., Bonn 1917). Fausto Ghisalberti: L'Ovidius moralizatus di Pierre Bersuire (136 p. reprinted from the Studi romanzi vol. 23, Rome 1933). Richard Salomon: Opicinus de Canistris (1, 79, London 1936; Isis 26, 460–63). Wickersheimer (p. 617, 1936). Conway Zirkle: The jumar (Isis 33, 486–506, 1941), p. 488 reference to the onocentaur in the Reductorium.

NOTE ON THE GESTA ROMANORUM

The Gesta Romanorum is a collection of edifying stories for the use of preachers; the nucleus was taken from Roman history or legend, the rest from many sources, Oriental, Scandinavian, etc. The variety of origins is admitted in most of the MSS, "Incipiunt historie notabiles atque magis principales collecte ex gestis Romanorum et quibusdam aliis notabilibus gestis cum moralisationibus eorundem." The collection has been ascribed by various scholars, including Sir Frederic Madden, to Pierre Bersuire because of the latter's known authorship of the Reductorium morale super totam Bibliam and strong resemblances of style, method, and matter. This is not convincing, but it is almost certain that the Gesta Romanorum was composed toward the end of the thirteenth century or the very beginning of the fourteenth. Indeed, a terminus ante quem is given by the Decamerone of Boccaccio, composed about the middle of the century, and also by the Moralites historiarum of Robert Holcot, who died in 1349.

According to Hermann Oesterley, to whom we owe the critical edition of the Latin text (1872), the collection was originally made in England toward the end of the thirteenth century, then passed to the continent, where it was submitted to various changes and received many additions. Such a collection would naturally invite additions and other modifications. It is interesting to note that the earliest editions, containing 150 chapters (Utrecht), 151 chapters (Cologne), and 181 chapters (Ulrich Zell, Cologne), all published between 1472 and 1475, are more elaborate than any of the numerous anterior MSS. That is, the editors of these early printed collections were acting like authors free to modify the tradition or to increase its scope. Among the authors to whom some of the stories have been ascribed, it will suffice to name two Dominicans, John de Bromyarde[17] of Oxford (fl. 1390), who compiled a Summa praedicantium (Nuremberg 1485), and John Herolt of Basel, called Discipulus (fl. c. 1418). The Dominicans being especially concerned with preaching, it is not surprising that a good many collections of sermons, exempla, and moralizations were compiled by them.

There are many incunabula editions in Latin and at least one in German (Stillwell p. 219, 1940), but the earliest English edition appeared only c. 1510–15, this being also the first edition of the Gesta in England. There is no point in enumerating here all the editions.

The most important for the Latin text is Hermann Oesterley: Gesta Romanorum (764 p., Berlin 1872), with analysis of 138 MSS. The Early English versions were edited for the Roxburghe Club by Sir Frederic Madden (552 p., London 1838). Re-edited on the basis of more MSS by Sidney J. H. Herrtage for the Early English Text Society (598 p., London 1879), with glossary. The French text was first printed in Paris 1521 (thrice reprinted in less than ten years, n.d., 1525, 1529). Modern edition under the old title by Gustave Brunet: Le violier des histoires romaines (Bibliothèque elzévirienne, 480 p., Paris 1858).

A modern English translation by Charles Swan was first printed London 1824, and frequently reprinted, e.g. in the Bohn Library. I have used the reprint, with a preface by E. A. Baker, in the Broadway translations (492 p., London n.d.). Each of the editions in Latin, French, or English cited above contains discussions of the text, its origins, etc. See also Francis Douce: Illustrations of Shakespeare, with dissertations . . . on the popular tales called Gesta Romanorum, etc. (2 vols., London 1807).

NICOLAS DE LA HORBE

French translator from Latin into French (fl. 1327).

He translated the Liber astronomicus, composed by Guido Bonatti of Forlì (XIII-2), c. 1261 or c. 1277. In spite of its title, this is a general treatise of pure astrology; the names astrology and astronomy were often confused in the Middle Ages (Introd. 2, 760). The French version is divided into six parts: (1) introduc-

[17] DNB (6, 405).

toire, (2) interrogations, (3) élections, (4) révolutions, (5) nativités, (6) pluyes et mutacions de l'air. The translation of part 2 was completed on December 15, 1327.

Text. Unpublished.
Criticism. Charles Victor Langlois (HL 35, 629, 1921).

VIGNAI

Jean de Vignai. Translator from Latin into French (fl. 1326–50).

Jean de Vignai, Joannes Duvignay hospitalarius S. Jacobi de Alto passu, brother hospitaler in St. Jacques du Haut Pas, Paris, originated perhaps near Bayeux in Normandie. He was a poor writer, but the author of many important translations, as follows:

1. Epistres et Evangiles de tout l'an, in accordance with the Parisian missal. Translation made in 1326 (or 1336?) for Jeanne de Bourgogne (d. 1348), first wife of Philippe VI. It is simply a revision of the thirteenth-century translation.
2. Vegetius (IV-2): De re militari. Previously translated by Jean de Meung in 1284, and translated a third time anonymously in 1380.
3. Gervase of Tilbury (XIII-1): Otia imperialia.
4. Hugh of Saint Cher (XIII-1): Speculum ecclesie (or Expositio misse).
5. Vincent of Beauvais (XIII-2): Speculum historiale; translation made for Jeanne de Bourgogne.
6. James of Voragine (XIII-2): Legenda aurea.
7. Primat. Monk of St. Denis who wrote a chronicle of St. Louis and Philippe III le Hardi, extending from 1250 to 1286. The original is lost, but for fragments incorporated in the chronicle of William of Nangis (XIII-2); hence Vignai's translation is very precious.
8. Jacques de Cessoles: De ludo scacchorum, Jeu des eschès moralisés. Or, more fully, De moribus hominum et de officiis nobilium super ludo scacorum. Translation made for John the Good when he was still duke of Normandy, hence within the period 1332–50.

Jacobus de Cessolis was a French Dominican, who hailed probably from Cessoles in Picardy, flourished in Reims, and wrote his famous book c. 1290.[18] That book, which enjoyed more than two centuries of popularity, is not a treatise on chess, but an account of morality and courtesy explained allegorically in chess terms. There are an abundance of MSS and at least a dozen incunabula editions in five or six languages. The English version was derived by William Caxton from the French.

This book was also ascribed to Giles of Rome (XIII-2), wrongly. Jacobus' name was strangely misspelled: Carzolis, Cassalis, Cossolis, Tesselis, even de Thessalonia, Thessalonica, etc.

9. Brocard: Directorium ad passagium faciendum ad Terram Sanctam. Translation made in 1333.
10. Odoric of Pordenone: Merveilles de la Terre d'outremer. The original was dictated by Odoric in 1330.

[18] Murray (p. 538, 1913) argues that Cessoles was not a Picard, but a Lombard, and that his name was probably derived from the district Cessole, near Genoa, in southern Piedmont. That family name still exists in Nice. He would ascribe to his work a date (1275–1300) which may be earlier than the one I am giving. Charles K. Wilkinson: A thirteenth century morality (Bull. Metropolitan Museum 2, 47–55, 7 ill., New York 1943).

11. Theodoros Palaeologos: Enseignemens ou ordonnances pour ung seigneur qui a guerres et grans gouvernemens a faire. The original Latin[19] text is lost.

12. Alexandre, a form of the Alexandrian legend, translated in 1341.

These texts have been named in rough chronological order, except the last one. It should be noted that one of them, Vincent's Speculum, was exceedingly long, and that two (Primat and Palaeologos) have been preserved only in the translation.

Text. The version of Primat's chronicle was edited by Natalis de Wailly: Recueil des historiens de France (23, 5-106, Paris 1876).

Légende dorée traduite en françois par Jean de Vigny (Paris 1488). There may be other French editions of this particular version.

Jacobi de Cessolis Liber de moribus hominum et officiis nobilium super ludos scacchorum. First Latin edition, Utrecht c. 1475, reprinted Toulouse c. 1476, Milano 1479, Toulouse c. 1494. Translation into High German: Augsburg 1477, Strassburg c. 1478, Augsburg 1483, Strassburg 1483. Into Low German: Lübeck c. 1490. Into English from the French by William Caxton: Bruges 1474, Westminster c. 1478. Into Italian: Florence 1493, Venice 1534. Into Dutch: Gouda 1479, Zwolle c. 1480 (two editions, one of them much abbreviated), Delft 1483. The incunabula data are presumably complete, being derived from GW (6, 402-10, nos. 6523-38, 1934). I add a few data concerning the modern editions available to me.

Ernst Köpke: Jacobus de Cessolis (Mittheilungen aus den Handschriften der Ritter Akademie zu Brandenburg an der Havel, part 2, 44 p., Brandenburg 1879).

Caxton's edition, The game of the chesse, reprinted in phonetic spelling (2d ed., 78 p., London 1872). Verbatim reprint of the first edition, with an introduction by William E. A. Axon: Caxton's Game and playe of the chesse (274 p., London 1883). The French version, from which Caxton's English version was derived, was printed for the first time in Paris 1504, 1505, and many times reprinted.

Pietro Marocco: Volgarizzamento del libro de' costumi e degli offizii de' nobili sopra il giuoco degli scacchi (182 p., Milano 1829).

Gertrude H. Van Schaick Avelingh: Dat scaecspel (Bibliotheek van middelnederlandsche letterkunde, 288 p., Leiden 1912). Text of the Middle Dutch version, with elaborate introduction (116 p.), edited from 12 MSS.

Criticism. Samuel Berger: La Bible française au Moyen âge (p. 221-29, Paris 1884). E. Langlois: Le miroir historial. Exemplaire de Prégent de Coëtivy (Romania 14, 131, 1885). Paul Meyer: Les anciens traducteurs français de Végèce et en particulier Jean de Vignai (Romania 25, 401-23, 1896). Hermann Suchier: Das lateinische Original von Vignay's Mirouer de l'église (Zeitschrift für romanische Philologie 23, 410, 1899).

For Jacques de Cessoles, see Félix Lajard (HL 25, 9-41, 1869) and introductions to the modern editions above mentioned. Francesco Novati: Una data certa per la biografia de frate Jacopo de Cessulis (Il libro e la stampa 3, 45-50, 1909); according to this paper, Jacques was vicar to the inquisitor in Genoa 1317-18; his famous book may have been written later than is generally assumed, at the beginning of the fourteenth century. Murray (p. 537-45, 1913).

For another Jean de Vignai, grammarian, professor in Dijon, who flourished under Philippe le Bel, see Barthélemy Hauréau (HL 30, 280-93, 1888)

[19] Yes, Latin! Theodoros Palaeologos (b. c. 1287, d. 1338) was the second son of Andronicos II (ruled 1282-1328) and of empress Eirene (Iolanda of Montferrat). He succeeded his maternal uncle Giovanni I (1293-1305) as marquess of Montferrat (1305-38), thus founding the Paleologo dynasty in that marquisate (1305-1533). Theodore I of Montferrat became a Roman Catholic; in 1306, he married Argentina Spinola, scion of a powerful Genoese Ghibelline family; hence he was more of a Latin than a Greek. Montferrat is between Turin and Genoa.

4g. TRANSLATIONS FROM LATIN INTO GREEK

GUILLAUME BERNARD

Languedocian Dominican. Translator from Latin into Greek? (d. after 1317).

Guillaume Bernard (this may mean William the son of Bernard) was born in Gaillac on the Tarn (dépt. Tarn; Languedoc) and assumed the Dominican habit in Albi. In 1274 he was studying in the monastery of Carcassonne. In 1277 he taught natural philosophy there, and he taught the same subject in Montpellier from 1278 to 1281. He taught in various other places of his province and was for a year (1289) one of the general preachers. He was prior at Montauban, and later at Albi (1292). In 1298 he went from Toulouse to Rome, then to Greece, where he studied the Greek language. He then established himself with twelve brethren in Pera (Constantinople), their purpose being to preach to the Greeks and bring them back to the Roman fold. In 1301 Guillaume of Gaillac was back in his country, being lector in Arles, then in other places, finally in Bergerac 1317. That is the last we hear of him.

When his brother Dominican Bernard Gui wrote the Practica inquisitionis, in 1323, Guillaume was already dead. Gui makes the following statement about him: "Profecitque in lingua greca ita quod eam plene scivit et libros latinos fr. Thomae in graecum transtulit." This is very startling, and it is hardly credible that Guillaume could have attained within three years sufficient mastery of Greek to translate works of St. Thomas into that language. However, even if this was only an intention which was not implemented—for no MS of any such translation is known—it was noteworthy.

A few sermons of his have come down to us.

Criticism. Barthélemy Hauréau (HL 31, 100–4, 1893). Raymond Loenertz: La Société des frères pérégrinants (222 p., Romae ad S. Sabinae 1937).

4h. TRANSLATIONS FROM LATIN INTO ARMENIAN

BARTHOLOMEW OF BOLOGNA

Italian Dominican and translator from Latin and Persian into Armenian (d. 1333).

He was born in Bologna toward the end of the thirteenth century and assumed the Dominican habit in that city. Bartholomew is his religious name; his original name and surname are not known with certainty. He was called to Avignon by John XXII (pope 1316–34) and consecrated bishop of Marāgha.[19a] He started on his journey to the East c. 1320 in the company of brother John the Englishman, brother John of Florence, both priests, and brother Pietro Tarragonese, a layman.

In Marāgha he studied Persian and Armenian, and began the translation of a number of Catholic books from Latin into Armenian. He died on August 15, 1333, and was buried in the church of the Assumption in the "castello di Charnà, nella provincia Erinciach, dal volgo chiamata Alincià."[20] He received the title "blessed" from Benedict XIV in 1755.

One of Bartholomew's disciples was an Armenian monk, Johannes Kerniensis,

[19a] For Marāgha see Introd. 2, 1004 and passim.

[20] Thus Fantuzzi (p. 370), who also calls Johannes Kerniensis, Giovanni di Charnà. I think that the names Charnà, Kerniensis refer to Karīn, a center of Armenian population, near the sources of the Euphrates and the Araxes. Armenian Karīn = Greek Theodosiopolis = Arabic Arḍ al-rūm, hence Russian Erzerum. Le Strange (p. 117, 1905); EI (2, 31, 1913).

who was converted by him from Gregorian Monophysitism to Roman Catholicism. John helped his teacher to do his translations and corrected his Armenian letters. Yet it is hard to believe that they could complete all the translations into Armenian credited to them, not only the Bible, and the Dominican breviary, missal, ritual, diurnal, but also St. Thomas' Summa contra gentes, and the third part of the Summa theologica? According to a more moderate account, Bartholomew wrote commentaries on the six days of creation and the Gospel of St. John, and pastoral letters, and translated them into Armenian with the help of his disciples. He also translated into Armenian some sermons which he had first delivered in Persian, during his missionary journeys in Persia.

John of Karīn became the leader of the United Brethren, i.e., the Armenians who favored submission to Rome and the assimilation of all their creeds and rites to Roman usage, and he thus incurred the hatred of the Gregorian Armenians, who constituted the great mass of his countrymen.

Whatever be the quality and amount of his translations, Bartholomew of Bologna must be counted the first Western Armenologist, and this is the more remarkable when one considers that the next ones did not appear until the seventeenth century, the first of these being Francesco Rivola, of the Ambrosian College in Milano, whose Dictionarium armeno-latinum and Grammatica armena were printed in Milano respectively in 1621 and 1624.

Criticism. Giovanni Fantuzzi: Notizie degli scrittori bolognesi (1, 368–70, Bologna 1781). Somal (p. 130, 201, 1829). Neumann (p. 211, 219, 1836).

JACOB THE DRAGOMAN

Armenian translator from Latin into Armenian, and Catholic theologian (fl. in first third of the century).

Jacob the Dragoman (or the Interpreter) was one of the United Brethren working with Bartholomew of Bologna and John of Karīn. He also translated independently and under his own name treatises composed by the Dominican Peter of Aragon, (1) on virtues, (2) on vices, (3) on rights and judgments. The Armenian treatises on vices and virtues were much appreciated by Armenian doctors, who used them as textbooks. For example, we hear of a doctor, John Golodik (Golotik, Golodentz), who lectured on them in the second half of the fourteenth century. The same Golodik wrote commentaries on Isaiah, on Dionysios the Areopagite (V-2), etc.

Jacob wrote a treatise on the two natures and single person of Christ, defending the Catholic belief against Armenian Monophysitism.

The third treatise of Peter of Aragon, on rights and judgments, and his sermons (or the sermons alone) were translated into Armenian in 1334 by the vartabet Sergius Vasciéntz.

Text. The first and second of the treatises mentioned above, on vices and virtues, were published in Venice 1721, and again in Venice 1772. The second edition is much better.

Criticism. Somal (p. 131, 136, 1829). Neumann (p. 213, 1836). Dwight (p. 274, 1853). Patcanian (p. 84, 86, 1860).

NERSES BALÌ

Armenian translator from Latin into Armenian, flourished under Clement VI (pope 1342–52).

Nerses Balì (or Baliéntz, Bakhon, Balon), bishop of Urmīya. He was an Armenian of Cilicia, who flourished in Avignon under Clement VI. While there he improved his knowledge of Latin and translated from that language into his own the worthless but very popular chronicle of popes and emperors of Martin of Troppau (XIII-2), adding information concerning Armenian events and lists of the Armenian kings and patriarchs. On account of the mediocrity and inexactitude of Martin's chronicle, this translation exerted a very bad influence upon Armenian historiography.

Apart from the treatises translated from the Latin into Armenian for Catholic propaganda, the texts chosen for translation were mediocre. There are, however, contemporary translations by unknown authors of a treatise by Bede (VIII-1) and of the theology of Albert the Great (XIII-2).

Nerses Balì is said to have written a well documented book on the warm springs of Cilicia. Unfortunately that book is lost (Torkomian).

Criticism. Somal (p. 39, 1825); (p. 131, 1829). Neumann (p. 212, 1836). NBG (4, 309, 1855), s.v. Balon, short article containing many errors. Patcanian (p. 85, 1860). V. Torkomian: Histoire de la médicine en Arméno-Cilicie (Revue des études arméniennes 6, 25, Paris 1926).

5a. TRANSLATION FROM HEBREW INTO LATIN

JOHANNES DE PLANIS

Jean des Plans of Montréal (?) in the diocese of Albi, near Toulouse (Languedoc). Medical translator from Hebrew into Latin who flourished at the beginning of the fourteenth century.

In 1304, he translated Ibn Rushd's Canones de (sive, Articuli generales proficientes in) medicinis laxativis from Hebrew into Latin with the help of a Jew called Maynus (probably a variant of Maimon), who at the time of the expulsion of the Jews from France (1306) was baptized and called Johannes.

Criticism. Ernest Renan (HL 28, 138, 1881), only 18 lines at the end of the article Armengaud fils de Blaise. Steinschneider (p. 984, 1893), only 3 lines. Wickersheimer (p. 465, 1936).

6a. TRANSLATIONS FROM FRENCH INTO ENGLISH

MANNYNG

Robert Mannyng. English didactic poet (d. after 1338).

Also called Robert de Brunne after his native place, Brunne or Bourne, Lincolnshire. He entered the priory of the Gilbertine canons[21] at Sempringham, near Brunne, in 1288. In 1338 he was resident in the Gilbertine priory of Sixhill, Lincolnshire.

[21] As I failed to speak of the foundation of the Gilbertine order in volume 2, a few words of information are appended here. The order was founded c. 1130 at Sempringham (Lincolnshire) by St. Gilbert of Sempringham (b. c. 1086, d. 1189) in his own ancestral manor. At first it was simply an order for nuns, but later lay sisters and lay brothers were added, and later still (1148) canons. Gilbert was at first inspired by the Cistercian model, but he gave to the canons the Augustinian rule. The Gilbertine order was restricted to England (except for two houses in Westmeath county, Ireland) and was the only purely English order, owing allegiance to no superiors on the continent except the curia. Gilbert was the first prior general or "master" of the order; but, strangely enough, he made his religious profession only sometime after 1170, when old age had obliged him to resign. He was canonized by Innocent III c. 1201 and is feasted on February 11. R. Urban Butler (CE 6, 556–57, 1909).

In 1303 he wrote a long didactic poem, Handlyng synne (12,630 lines), addressed to the good men of Brunne; an English adaptation of the Manuel des pechiez (péchés) of William of Wadington.[22] It is a collection of tales and anecdotes illustrating the sins, sacraments, requisites and graces of shrift, comparable in some respects to the Confessio amantis of John Gower (composed 1390–93). It constitutes a remarkable mirror of contemporary morality and politics. Some of the stories, e.g., apropos of Robert Grosseteste's love of music, were additions to the French text, derived from local traditions.

On Friday May 25, 1338, being at Sixhill, he completed his Rimed story of England from Noah to the death of Edward I (1307). It is divided into two very distinct parts. The first, from Noah to Cadwallader, king of the Britons, and to 689, consists of 8,365 short couplets; it is largely a translation of the Roman de Brut of Wace of Jersey (XII-2), with minor additions taken from later chronicles. The second part, from Cadwallader to 1307, is a translation of the Anglo-Norman rhymed chronicle of Peter of Langtoft; it is made up of c. 9,000 alexandrines in couplets.

Mannyng's earlier work, Handlyng synne, is by far the more important. It is a document of the first order for the understanding of English society at the beginning of the fourteenth century. Mannyng's writings helped to prepare the supremacy of the East Midland dialect and hence are of special interest for the history of the English language.

Text. Frederick James Furnivall edited the English text of Handlyng synne together with the French text of Wadington's Manuel des péchés (Roxburghe Club, 534 p., London 1862). New edition of both texts for the Early English Text Society (nos. 119, 123, London 1901–3).

The story of Robert Manning of Brunne (to 689) edited by F. J. Furnivall (Rolls series, 2 vols., London 1887). Peter Langtoft's chronicle as improved by Robert of Brunne (689–1307), edited by Thomas Hearne (2 vols., Oxford 1725). Reprinted in Hearne's works (vols. 3, 4, London 1810).

St. Bonaventure's meditations on the supper of Our Lord, drawn into English verse by Robert Manning, edited by J. Meadows Cowper (Early English Text Society, no. 60, 72 p., London 1875). Apocryphal.

Criticism. C. L. Kingsford (DNB 36, 80, 1893). Alfred Kunz: Mannyng's Handlyng synne verglichen mit der anglonormannischen Vorlage (Diss. Königsberg i.P., 1913). C. Gross (no. 379, 1915). Wells (p. 199–202, 342–44, 794, 796, 816).

MICHAEL OF NORTHGATE

Author of the Ayenbite of inwyt (fl. 1340).

Michael (or Dan Michel) of Northgate, Kent, was a brother of the cloister of St. Austin, Canterbury; he completed in 1340 a translation (was he the translator or simply the copyist?) of La somme des vices et vertus, a large ethical treatise composed c. 1279 by the French Dominican Lorens.[23] The translation covers 271 pages in print, and has come down to us in a single MS, Michael's autograph copy (Arundel MS 57, British Museum).

[22] William (or Wilham) de Wadington is practically unknown. He was an Englishman and a priest and flourished in the thirteenth century (it is impossible to be more precise). His Anglo-Norman poem has survived as well as Mannyng's adaptation of it. Gaston Paris (HL 28, 179–207, 1881). Emile Jules François Arnould: Le manuel des péchés. Etude de littérature religieuse anglo-normande (460 p., Paris 1940; Speculum 20, 99–103, 1945).

[23] Lorens or Laurent (Laurentius Gallus), Dominican, was confessor to Philip III the Bold (king 1270–85). His work, being composed for the king, was also called La somme le roi, or Li

The Ayenbite of inwyt (again biting of the inner wit, or remorse of conscience) was written in the Kentish dialect. Its literary value is small, but, being a large dated monument of the southern dialect, it is of considerable value for the history of the English language. The purpose of the book is similar to that of the Handlying synne, written by Robert Mannyng in 1303, and of the Pricke of conscience, written by Richard Rolle before 1349, but Michael's treatment of the subject (or rather Lorens') is very dull. Michael's work was less popular than Richard's, but the same French text was translated into Midland dialect c. 1400, and another English version was made c. 1440; moreover, Chaucer's Parson's tale is an adaptation of the French Somme, and Caxton published a prose version of it entitled The book royal (or The book for a kyng).

To the Ayenbite is appended a Kentish version of the allegory also represented by Sawles warde (southwestern dialect; 1200–50, perhaps 1200–25), derived from Matthew 24:43, "If the goodman of the house had known in what watch the thief would come, he would have watched, and would not have suffered his house to be broken up."

Text. The Ayenbite of inwyt was first edited by Joseph Stevenson (Roxburghe Club, 227 p., London 1855), then by Richard Morris (Early English Text Society, no. 23, 360 p., 1866; reprinted 1895). Includes elaborate glossarial index but no other index.

The Tuscan version of Lorens' Somme by Zucchero Bencivenni (fl. 1310) was partly edited by Luigi Rigoli (Florence 1828); by Giuseppe Manuzzi (46 p., Florence 1848); and by Luigi Barbieri (Scelta di curiosità letterarie vol. 26, 48 p., Bologna 1863). The Dutch version was completely edited by D. C. Tinbergen: Des coninx summe (696 p., Leiden 1900–7).

Criticism. Wilhelm Eilers: Die Erzählung des Pfarrers in Chaucer's Canterbury-Geschichten und die Somme de vices et de vertus des Frère Lorens (thesis, 70 p., Erlangen 1882), Englished in Essays on Chaucer (16, 501–610, 1884). Robert W. Evers: Beiträge zur Erklärung und Textkritik von Dan Michel's Ayenbite of inwyt (120 p., Erlangen 1888). Ludwig Lusner: La somme des vices et des vertus (Programm, 12 p., Wien 1905). Wells (p. 345, 817).

6c. TRANSLATIONS FROM FRENCH INTO ITALIAN

BENCIVENNI

Zucchero Bencivenni of Florence. Flourished c. 1310–13. Translator of Arabic writings of al-Farghānī (IX-1) and al-Rāzī (IX-2) from French into Italian. I know nothing about these translations.

He also translated into Italian the explanation of the Pater noster written in French by the Dominican Laurent (Laurentius Gallus, Lorens) and dedicated by the latter in 1279 to Philippe III le Hardi (king of France 1270–85). That Italian translation is one of the testi di lingua used by the Accademici della Crusca for their dictionary.

It is said that Zucchero Benvicenni was the first to distinguish the letters u and v.

Text. Luigi Rigoli: Volgarizzamento dall' Esposizione del Pater nostro fatto da Zucchero Bencivenni per la prima volta pubblicato (quarto, 146 p., ill., Firenze 1828).

---

livres roiaux de vices et vertus, and it bore still other titles, such as Le miroir du monde, Le livre des commandements de Dieu, etc. It was very successful, judging from the number of MSS and from many translations into English, Dutch, Catalan, Spanish, and Italian. There are no less than five English translations or adaptations. Felix Lajard (HL 19, 397–405, 1838).

Trattatello delle virtù. Testo francese di frate Lorenzo de' Predicatori e toscano di Zucchero Bencivenni (Scelta di curiosità letterarie vol. 26, 48 p., Bologna 1863). This is simply an extract from the earlier edition, but it includes the French original as well as the Tuscan version.

Criticism. Libri (2, 207, 1838), only a few lines. Steinschneider (p. 7, 1904), only 3 lines.

7a. TRANSLATIONS FROM SPANISH INTO LATIN

RAIMOND DE BÉZIERS

Languedocian (Biterrois) translator from Spanish into Latin. Flourished 1305–13, probably in Paris.

Raimundus de Biterris. Raimond was born in Béziers (dépt. Hérault; Languedoc). He called himself a physicus. He undertook to translate into Latin the Castilian text of the Kalīla wa-Dimna (made from the Arabic for king Alfonso el Sabio, d. 1284) for Jeanne de Navarre-Champagne, queen of Philippe le Bel. At the time of her death (April 2, 1305) his work was interrupted,[24] and the Castilian MS was probably withdrawn from him. Sometime afterward he got to know of the Latin translation made from rabbi Joel's (?) Hebrew version by John of Capua (XIII-2), the Directorium vitae humanae. He then completed his work on the basis of the Directorium; that is, the second part of it is not a translation, but a plagiarism from John of Capua, to which he has added many interpolations of his own. He offered a magnificent copy of his completed work to king Philippe on Pentecost 1313. The Hebrew-Latin tradition of the Kalīla wa-Dimna due to John of Capua was derived from the same Arabic text as the Alfonsine Castilian translation.

I have dealt with Raimond de Béziers in spite of his insignificance, because the tradition of the Kalīla wa-Dimna is so important for the understanding of Oriental influences in the West. That cycle of animal fables can be followed along innumerable ramifications from early Egyptian and Mesopotamian sources down to Uncle Remus' stories of Brer Rabbit.

Text. The Castilian text of the Alfonsine translation was edited by Pascual de Gayangos (Biblioteca de autores españoles vol. 51, Madrid 1860).

Raimond's Liber Kalilae et Dimnae, as well as the Directorium of John of Capua, was edited by Léopold Hervieux: Les fabulistes latins depuis le siècle d'Auguste jusqu'à la fin du moyen âge, vol. 5, Jean de Capoue et ses dérivés (Paris 1899). Vol. 1 of that work began to appear in 1884.

Criticism. Gaston Paris (HL 33, 191–253, 1906). James Henry Breasted: The tales of Kalila and Dimna and the ancestry of animal fables (Oriental Institute communications 1, 82–87, Chicago 1922; also in American journal of Semitic languages and literatures vol. 38; Isis 5, 264).

For the tradition of Kalīla wa-Dimna see Introd. vols. 1, 2, passim.

8a. TRANSLATIONS FROM SANSKRIT INTO PERSIAN

NAKHSHABĪ

Shaykh Ḍiyā al-dīn al-Nakhshabī. Persian translator (or adapter) from Sanskrit into Persian (d. 1350).

The nisba refers to Nakhshab (Arabic, Nasaf), a town halfway between Bukhārā

[24] It is interesting to recall that a far more important work was interrupted by Jeanne's death, to wit, the Mémoires of Joinville.

and Samarqand, south of both cities. He probably originated in that town, but spent part of his life in Badā'ūn (or Budaun, Rohilkhand, United Provinces, India), and died in 1350.

In 1330 he composed in Persian the Ṭūṭī-nāma (Book of the parrot), derived from the Sanskrit work Śukasaptati (The seventy stories of a parrot). It is an adaptation divided into 52 chapters, and is based on an earlier Persian translation. Another Persian version was made by order of Akbar (Mogul emperor of India 1555–1605) by Abū-l-Faḍl ibn Mubārak, and still another by Muḥammad Qādirī (seventeenth cent.). This final version in 35 chapters was enormously popular, witness translations into Urdu, Bengali, Turkish, and Qazān Tatar; also into English, German, French, Russian, and Greek. Some of these translations are fragmentary, others more or less complete; some exist only in MSS, others have been printed. The earliest translation printed in the West was the partial English one by B. Gerrans (1792); the Greek translation by Demetrios Galanos was printed in Athens 1851.

Another book of Nakhshabī's, Ladhdhat al-nisā', is derived from the Sanskrit treatise on erotics composed by Kokkoka before the thirteenth century, the Koka-śāstra or Ratirahasya (Secrets of the art of love).

These two books do not interest us in themselves, but only as illustrations of the influence of Hindu upon Persian thought in the fourteenth century.

Other books of his do not concern us except the Juz'īyāt wa kullīyāt (Particularities and generalities), describing various parts of the body, their harmony proving God's greatness, and their diseases. It is divided into 40 sections called nāmūs, and therefore is sometimes called chil nāmūs. Each section deals with a special part of the body. The work also appears under the title Nāmūs-i-akbar. It was composed during the rule of Mubārak shāh Quṭb al-dīn (Khaljī sulṭān of Delhi 1316–20).

Text. For editions and translations of the Śukasaptati see Emeneau (p. 140–42, 1935), but add to this, E. Muller: Touti-nameh ou les contes du perroquet (124 p., Strasbourg 1934), French translation derived from the Persian-English edition of Francis Gladwin (London 1801). For Kokkoka and other works on kāmaśāstra, see Emeneau (p. 341).

For the Juz'īyāt wa kullīyāt, see Charles Rieu: Catalogue of Persian MSS in British Museum (2, 740, Add. 26,300, 1881). E. Denison Ross and Edward G. Browne: Catalogue of Persian and Arabic MSS in India Office (no. 147, p. 94, London 1902).

Criticism. Fonahn (p. 67, 1910). Winternitz (3, 342, 541, 1922). E. Berthels (EI 3, 841, 1934).

8b. TRANSLATIONS FROM SANSKRIT INTO TELUGU

ERRĀPRAGAḌA

Telugu-Śaiva poet (1280–1350).

Errāpragaḍa completed the translation of the Mahābhārata from Sanskrit into Telugu, the greatest monument of Telugu literature. He was a niyogin (a layman of the Brahmin caste), from Gudlūru in Kandukur Taluk (Nellore district). His father, Śrī Sūrya, was a poet in two languages (Sanskrit and Telugu) and a yogin. He himself was a disciple of the yogin Śaṅkarasvāmin and a staunch Śaiva. He wrote in the most difficult style (kadaḷi pāka), using almost as many Sanskrit as Telugu words, and was called therefore Prabandha-parameśvara (lord of literary composition). He was also nicknamed Śaṁbhudāsa (servant of Śiva).

After having completed the translation of the Mahābhārata, he translated the Harivaṁśa, which is a sort of epilogue to it, narrating the fortunes of Kṛishṇa after the war. Various other poems are ascribed to him.

The Telugu version of the Mahābhārata was begun by Nanniah (Vagānu Śāsana) at the command of the Chāḷukyā king, Rāja-rāja-narendra (1022–63); it was continued by Tikkanna Yagvi (1220–1300); finally Errāpragaḍa completed the portions of the Araṇya-parvan (book III) which were still unfinished. These three poets, who among them created the outstanding work of Telugu literature, are always praised together under the name kavitraya (the three poets).

Text. Telugu metrical version of the Āndra-bhārata or Mahā-bhārata. Books I to III by Nannaya Bhaṭṭāraka, books IV to XVIII by Tikkana Sōma-yāji; suppt. to book III by Errā Pregaḍa, Śambhu-dāsuḍu. Edited by Viñzamūru Kṛishṇamāchāryulu (3 vols., Madras 1864). Other editions: Madras 1881, 1901, etc. For the many partial versions (e.g., of the Gītā) see Lionel David Barnett: Catalogue of Telugu books in British Museum (p. 109–16, London 1912).

Criticism. P. Chenchiah and Raja M. Bhujanga Rao Bahadur: History of Telugu literature (Heritage of India p. 42, 48–50, Calcutta 1928). For the Telugu language, see my note on Raṭṭa-kavi.

8d. TRANSLATIONS FROM SANSKRIT INTO CHINESE

THE CHINESE TRIPIṬAKA

The greatest and steadiest flow of translations in the whole world was the one which was caused by Buddhist fervor, and flowed from Sanskrit into Chinese for a period of over thirteen centuries. By the fourteenth century that flow was not stopped, but had been reduced to a trickle. Out of the 173 Chinese translators dealt with by Nanjio (app. ii, 1883), only 5 belong to the Yüan dynasty; and out of some 2,990 texts translated, only 5 are credited to the Yüan scholars. Moreover, we must assume that the most important Buddhist texts were among the first to be translated, and that they were available in Chinese even before the T'ang dynasty, not to speak of the Yüan.

This matter can be investigated with remarkable precision, for the Buddhist writings were soon collected. The Pāli canon called Tripiṭaka[25] was probably established (in part) as early as the third century B.C.; around it grew a large Pāli noncanonical literature, all of which concerned only Hīnayāna Buddhism. Add to this the immense Mahāyāna literature, in pure or mixed Sanskrit, originated by Aśvaghosha (II-1), Nāgārjuna (III-1), etc.[26] The Chinese translators tried to translate everything.

Thus when we speak of the Chinese Tripiṭaka we should not think of a rigid canon like the Jewish or Christian Bible, but on the contrary of a very elastic one, the tendency being always inclusive rather than exclusive. The Chinese San-ts'ang[27] is not to be conceived as a Buddhist canon, but rather as a Buddhist library, whence each sect took the parts which it liked and thus constituted its own canon.

[25] Sanskrit, Tripiṭaka, meaning three baskets: Vinayapiṭaka, basket of discipline (of the Buddhist order); Sūtrapiṭaka, sermons, discourses; Abhidharmapiṭaka, metaphysics. See my note relative to it apropos of the Tibetan translation (Introd. 1, 467–69).

[26] For a survey, see Winternitz (vol. 2, 1912–20) or the English translation (vol. 2, 1933); see also Introd. vols. 1, 2, passim.

[27] Three treasures, translation of the Sanskrit name Tripiṭaka. In Japanese the collection is called Issaikyō. I shall use preferably the Sanskrit term, as most scholars do.

In fact, the best way of defining a sect is to indicate its favorite sūtra and to analyze the rest of its borrowings from the Tripiṭaka.

This subject being generally misunderstood by Western scholars (witness their constant reference to the Tripiṭaka as the Buddhist canon), I wish to add the following explanations to those given in previous volumes. The need of establishing a Chinese collection of Buddhist works was realized as early as 518 by Wu-ti (Liang emperor 502–49), and the first catalogue of Buddhist literature was compiled in 520 by Sêng-yu (VI-1) (Nanjio no. 1476).[28] From that time on *eleven* more collections were ordered to be made by twelve other emperors; I say twelve, because two successive emperors of the Manchu dynasty, Shih Tsung and Kao Tsung, were responsible for the last one (1735–37). Out of these twelve collections, nine are anterior to the fourteenth century. In addition to the catalogue of 520, twelve more catalogues of Buddhist books were compiled between 594 and 1600, the last one (of 1600) being the final number (no. 1662) in the Ming "canon" analyzed by Nanjio. The Chinese Tripiṭaka was printed for the first time in 972, and four more editions of that immense "library" had already been printed before the Western invention of printing! Nanjio mentions thirteen editions printed in China, Korea, and Japan. Since then at least three more have appeared: (1) the edition published by the Zōkyo Shoin in Kyōto (completed 1912), including 1,700 works in 7,140 fascicles; (2) the edition subsidized by Mr. and Mrs. S. A. Hardoon (Shanghai 1913); (3) the Taishō Issaikyō (or Taishō shinshū daizōkyō) edited by J. Takakusu and K. Watanabe (Tōkyō 1924–29), including 2,184 works, in 55 volumes of about 1,000 pages each.[29] This collection has more recently (1934) been extended to 100 volumes, to wit, 85 volumes including 3,053 Chinese texts (translations or originals), 12 volumes of illustrations, 3 volumes of index. See account by T. Matsumoto (Zeitschrift der Deutschen morgenländischen Gesellschaft 88, 194–99, 1934).

The original Pāli Tripiṭaka was divided into three "baskets" (discipline, sermons, metaphysics), of which the third (dharma, abhidharma) is by far the most important for us, as it deals with knowledge and science (physics) as well as with metaphysics; on account of their comprehensive tendencies, however, the Chinese collections needed a fourth "basket," tsa ts'ang (mixed treasure), wherein were

[28] This and similar references below are to the Catalogue of the Tripiṭaka by Bunyiu Nanjio (Oxford 1883), based on the Japanese edition of 1678–81, itself derived from a Ming exemplar. A new catalogue recently published by Bagchi (1927–38) in Calcutta is more complete, not only because it is derived from a later and fuller Japanese edition of the Tripiṭaka (Tōkyō 1882–85), but also because the author has been able to avail himself of all the additional knowledge gathered in half a century of research. The earlier work, however, is much clearer and handier, and as long as the Chinese index promised by Bagchi is unpublished, Nanjio's book, which contains all the Chinese names and titles in Chinese script, remains indispensable. It is true one may use also Alfred Forke: Katalog des Pekinger Tripiṭaka (folio, 224 p., Berlin 1916), the "Peking Tripiṭaka" being the editions of 1578, 1592, 1598, and 1735; and Daitarō Saeki: Catalogue of Ta-jih-pên-hsü-ts'ang-ching (214 p., Zōkyo Shoin, Kyōto 1915), based upon the Tripiṭaka completed by that press in 1912. There are two alphabetical indexes to Nanjio's catalogue, by Ross (1910) without Chinese type, and by Daijō Tokiwa (1930) with Chinese type but Japanese transcription. A fasciculus of Hōbōgirin (202 p., Tōkyō 1931) contains elaborate tables to the Taishō Issaikyō, with Chinese type, and Chinese, Japanese, and Sanskrit transcriptions.

[29] To these Chinese editions should be added, of course, the Pāli ones, for example, the one printed in the Siamese letters by order of the king of Thaï (39 vols., Bangkok 1893; revised ed., 45 vols., Bangkok 1928); and the Tibetan editions, for which see Introd. 1, 469.

gathered miscellaneous works by Hindu and Chinese authors.[30] Thus they contain not only translations from the Sanskrit, but also a small number of works originally written in Chinese. Some of these works are not texts in the ordinary sense, but tools for the study of texts, as for example the thirteen catalogues already mentioned, and a Sanskrit-Chinese dictionary (Nanjio no. 1640) compiled by Fa Yün (XII-2).[31] This illustrates another difference between the so-called Buddhist canon and the Jewish or Christian one; to be comparable with the Chinese library, our Bible should include not only the sacred texts, but also various books (Biblical dictionaries, bibliographies, Hebrew and Greek lexica) necessary for the correct understanding of those texts.

This excursus on the Tripiṭaka may seem too long considering that most of the translations were completed before the fourteenth century, but it should be considered as applying to the whole process of translation, of which I did not speak sufficiently in previous volumes. To be sure there are in my volume 1 notes devoted to some of the great Buddhist translators and authors, as Fa-hsien (V-1), Kumārajīva (V-1), Paramārtha (VI-2), Hsüan Tsang (VII-1), I-ching (VII-2), and I even went so far as to call three periods after them,[32] yet I did not insist enough on the importance of the translations, because I did not realize it then (1927) with sufficient strength. These translations are very important not only for the people for whom they were meant, but also for the whole Buddhist world and for scholars everywhere, because about a thousand of them, being lost in the original Sanskrit, have now themselves the value of originals. On the other hand, to deal separately with too many of these almost innumerable Chinese texts in a book concerned, not with the history of Buddhism, but with the history of science would have mystified my readers. This section of my book will have achieved its purpose if it helps to inculcate in them two fundamental ideas: (1) the importance of the Buddhist tradition in Eastern Asia, comparable, from the broad cultural point of view, with the tradition of Christianity in Europe; (2) the importance of the translations from Sanskrit into Chinese.

9. TRANSLATIONS FROM TIBETAN (?) INTO MONGOLIAN

THE MONGOLIAN TRIPIṬAKA

Kublai Khān (XIII-2), having become profoundly attached to the Tibetan (Lamaist) form of Buddhism, wished to have a complete translation of the Kanjur and Tanjur (Introd. 1, 467–69) into Mongolian. By the time of his death (1294) nothing had yet been done to realize his pious wish. His great-grandson, the emperor Wu Tsung, who ruled from 1308 to 1312 under the reign title Chih-ta (Giles no. 933), called together a conference or academy of twenty-nine Tibetan, Mongolian, Chinese, and Central Asian scholars, who were ordered to study the

[30] In the Nanjio list, 147 Hindu works are listed (nos. 1321–1467) and 195 Chinese ones (nos. 1468–1662), a total of 342 works! The first three baskets, ching ts'ang (sūtrapiṭaka), lü ts'ang (vinaya), and lun ts'ang (abhidharma), contain respectively 1,081, 85, and 154 works.

[31] This was used by the late William Edward Soothill (1861–1935) and Lewis Hodous in their precious Dictionary of Chinese Buddhist terms, with Sanskrit and English equivalents and a Sanskrit-Pali index (quarto, 530 p., London 1937). Two earlier Sanskrit-Chinese lexica (seventh and eighth cent.) were edited and translated by Prabodh Chandra Bagchi: Deux lexiques sanskrit-chinois (Sino-Indica vols. 2, 3, Paris 1929–37; Isis 33, 356).

[32] The time of Fa-hsien; the time of Hsüan Tsang; the time of I-ching.

matter and compare the Tibetan texts with the Sanskrit originals and the Chinese versions.[33]

The work of the academy appointed c. 1310 was probably facilitated by the efforts of two "Western" scholars, Pa-ssŭ-pa or Phagspa (XIII-2) and his disciple Sha-lo-pa (Nanjio p. 457, 1883; Bagchi p. 611–12, 1938). Phagspa was born in Tibet in 1239, attended a religious conference in Qaraqorum in 1253, and converted Kublai to Buddhism. In 1269 he invented a kind of Mongolian script. He wrote three treatises, presumably in Sanskrit (Nanjio nos. 1137, 1320; Bagchi p. 611, no. 2). He died in 1279/80. Sha-lo-pa was born c. 1258, and worked in Peking from 1311 to his death in 1314; he translated at least one of his master's works into Chinese (Nanjio no. 1320); five other works of his are preserved in recent editions of the Tripiṭaka.

It is possible that Sha-lo-pa took part in the translation from Tibetan into Mongolian or in the preparation thereof. The Phagspa alphabet derived from the Tibetan was not used, however, for it was insufficient and had already been superseded by another alphabet derived from the Uighūr script. The new Mongolian script, called nomoua gherel, was used for the new translation begun c. 1310. A set of that translation[34] is in the Pao-shêng monastery at Mukden, the very one which was demanded from a descendant of the Mongol emperors in the Manchu dynasty. This Mongolian script is still in use today; it was adapted to the writing of Manchu in 1599 by Nurhachu (emperor 1616–27 under the name T'ien Ming, the real founder of Ming power). See my volume 2 (p. 273, 1137), Couling (p. 323, 402, 1917), Hummel (p. 594–99, 1943).

[33] The calling of that conference was previously ascribed to Kublai himself (Introd. 2, 723). It is now established that Wu Tsung called it. See the Chung-kuo-fo-chiao shih (1928, 4/8b). For this and other data in this section I am indebted to A. W. Hummel (letter of Nov. 29, 1940).

[34] I do not know whether that translation is complete or how incomplete it is. Considering the enormous size of the Kanjur and Tanjur, it is difficult to believe they could have been completely translated between c. 1310 and the fall of the Yüan dynasty in 1368. Dr. Hummel, however, to whom I confided my doubts, answered (letter of Dec. 6, 1940): "There is a possible answer in the fact that hundreds of scholars are known to have cooperated in such tasks, and works of equal magnitude were completed in three or four years. For example, the great encyclopaedia, Yung-lo ta-tien, comprising 11,095 large transcribed volumes, was completed between the years 1403 and 1407. That enterprise had, in addition to the directors, 147 assistants to the directors, and it is stated that 2,169 men worked on it."

CHAPTER IV

EDUCATION

(First Half of the Fourteenth Century)

N.B. Only the main notes relative to education are published in this chapter. Many men who may be called educators but were primarily something else—philosophers, historians, etc.—are dealt with in other chapters. For a general survey of education, see section IV of chapter I. More information on the additional educators may then easily be obtained by means of the index.

A. CHRISTENDOM

CREATION OF NEW UNIVERSITIES

The birth and early development of the universities of Latin Christendom have been discussed for the period XII-2 (Introd. 2, 350–53), for XIII-1 (Introd. 2, 570–73), for XIII-2 (Introd. 2, 862–63).

Ten more universities were founded in the first half of the fourteenth century. The beginnings of these universities are far more definite than those of the earlier ones, for every one of them was established, after a relatively brief period of trial or negotiation, by a papal or imperial bull, or by a royal charter. I give here in chronological order the main facts concerning each. More information may be obtained from Irsay (vol. 1, 1933) or Rashdall (vol. 2, 1936); I do not cite references easily available in these volumes.

Rome (1303)

This university of the city (studium urbis) was founded by Boniface VIII in 1303; it was distinct from the curial school (studium sacri palatii) founded by Innocent IV in 1244–45. The Studium urbis died out during the Great Schism; it was renewed by Eugenius IV in 1431; the two studia seem to have merged under Leo X (1513–21) and to have been housed together in the Sapienza. There were apparently at that time more teachers than students. (Rashdall 2, 28–31, 38–39.)

Avignon (1303)

There was a school of law in Avignon in the thirteenth century, but the studium generale was established by Boniface III in 1303. The university enjoyed some popularity during the Babylonian captivity (1309–76), but it declined gradually after the removal of the papal court. (Rashdall 2, 173–81.)

Perugia (1308)

Municipal schools developed during the thirteenth century and were recognized as a studium generale by Clement V in 1308. A new bull was granted by John XXII in 1318, and an imperial bull was obtained in 1355. The university obtained some fame through its school of law, chiefly from 1316 on, when Jacobus de Belvisi was appointed professor of civil law. The canonist Joannes Andreae and the famous civilians Bartolus (XIV-2) and Baldo degli Ubaldi (XIV-2) taught there; and two centuries later one of its doctors, Alberico Gentili (1552–1608), began to teach civil law in Oxford (1587), and was one of the founders of international law. (Rashdall 2, 40–43.)

Treviso (1318)

This studium obtained its charter of foundation in 1318, not from the pope, but from the imperial claimant, Frederick of Austria (the rival of Lewis of Bavaria). It remained insignificant and died very early. Treviso was conquered by Venice in 1339, and Venetians were forbidden in 1407 to study anywhere but in Padua. (Rashdall, 2, 43.)

Cahors (1332)

This university developed from a cathedral school, having been established in 1332 by a son of Cahors, John XXII. It was never important, and was kept alive beyond the fourteenth century only by its three colleges. (Rashdall 2, 182.)

Grenoble (1339)

The University of Grenoble was established in 1339 by Benedict XII for all faculties except theology. It was never important, and after two centuries of vegetation was suppressed in 1565 by Charles IX, king of France, and incorporated with the University of Valence, founded in 1452. (Rashdall 2, 183.)

Pisa (1343)

The school of Pisa dates back to the end of the twelfth century, but it received the privileges of a studium generale only in 1343 from Clement VI. An interdict having been laid on Bologna by Benedict XII in 1338, many students emigrated from that city to Pisa. It languished after the Black Death, and the conquest of Pisa by Florence in 1406 seemed to put an end to it. It was revived in 1472, however, by Florence itself, which suppressed its own university and replaced it by the Pisan one. Pisa then had the same relation to Florence as Padua to Venice. (Rashdall 2, 45–46.)

Prague (1347)

The story of the University of Prague is at once far more complicated and more dramatic than that of the other foundations of this time, for it involved all kinds of national, linguistic, religious, and philosophical animosities. That university, which was the first in the Holy Roman Empire and which may be called the first German one, was established by Clement VI in 1347; the papal bull was soon followed in the same year by a royal bull granted by Charles IV, king of the Romans and of Bohemia. Charles IV was very much Frenchified, and the Prague university was largely modeled upon that of Paris.

This was an age of Bohemian revival in literature and religion. The university was, however, according to usage, divided into nations: (1) Bohemia, (2) Poland, (3) Bavaria, (4) Saxony. The two last ones were German, and the majority of the second was German rather than Slavic; hence only one nation out of four represented the effervescent local element. The number of Germans increased apace, because Prague was more accessible to a great many of them than Paris or Italy, and German influence increased in proportion, exciting Czech jealousy and rancor. These difficulties were considerably aggravated by the Hussite movement, and by Wycliffian tendencies. The Czech accepted Wycliffe's realism the more readily because of the German adhesion to Parisian nominalism. In Kutna Hora (Kuttenberg) 1409, king Wenceslas decreed that the Bohemian nation should have three votes, the other three nations only one among them. One can imagine the German reaction; it took partly the form of a general exodus of the Germans "zu Fuss, zu Pferd, und zu Wagen" to new German universities in Vienna (1365), Erfurt (1379, 1392), Heidelberg (1385), Cologne (1388), and Leipzig (1409). Further troubles were caused in the Prague university by struggles between Utraquists, Taborites, and orthodoxy; in 1416 the council of Constance deprived the university of all its rights. In 1555, a new school, the Clementinum, was established by the Jesuits (mostly Belgians and Germans). In 1654, the emperor Ferdinand III combined the older foundation Collegium Carolinum (1366) with the Clementinum to constitute the Carolo-Ferdinandea Universitas. It is not necessary to continue the story of these vicissitudes, which became worse than ever under Nazi tyranny.

Rashdall (2, 211–34). Dr. Souques: La querelle des universités tchèque et allemande de Prague (Bull. Société française d'histoire de la médecine 30, 17–20, 1936). Gray C. Boyce and W. H. Dawson: The University of Prague; modern problems of the German university in Czechoslovakia (127 p., London 1937; Isis 29, 587), pro-German.

Florence (1349)

A studium generale was founded in 1349 by Clement VI, but it was never very successful, and it was abolished in 1472, the remains being merged with the flourishing studium of Pisa, which became the national university of the Florentine republic.

During its brief and precarious existence, however, the University of Florence added to the city's fame because of the Dante lectures initiated by Boccaccio (1373–74), and because it was the first in Western Europe to provide for the teaching of Greek (1360–62, Leonzio Pilato; 1396–1400, Manuel Chrysoloras). Of course, Florence was the cradle of the Renaissance, but that movement was very largely independent of the university, if not antagonistic to it. On the other hand —and this is unexpected—Florence was the first university in Italy to have an effective faculty of theology. Indeed, though Perugia and Pisa were founded before Florence, respectively in 1308 and 1343, their theological faculties were constituted later, respectively in 1370 and 1367. (Rashdall 2, 47–51.)

Perpignan (1350, 1379)

The county of Roussillon was ceded to Aragon in 1344, hence the university created by royal decree in 1350 at Perpignan must be counted as Spanish, not French. When Pedro IV the Ceremonious renewed the privileges of Lerida (founded in 1300, see Introd. 2, 862) in 1347, he was contemplating the removal of that university; he did not remove it, however, but created a new one in Perpignan. Both undertakings were failures. In 1379, Perpignan received a new charter and a new lease on life from pope Clement VII, but it remained a small and precarious institution. (Rashdall 2, 96–97.)

It should be noted that most of these universities were papal institutions, and that none endured except Prague. The others, five in Italy, three in France, one in Aragon, were apparently superfluous. Students preferred to go to older institutions, which were able to attract more and better teachers as well as a larger body of students, and enjoyed more prestige. Always excepting Prague, these foundations of the first half of the fourteenth century were not important, yet each was a center of learning and contributed to the diffusion of knowledge in a new circle. The main function of each was to produce the professional men (physicians, notaries, lawyers, theologians, etc.) whom the changing times required in greater abundance.

THE COLLEGES OF OXFORD AND CAMBRIDGE

The English universities continued their development in their own way, being eclipsed by the individual colleges, which were theoretically parts of them, yet attracted most of the attention (see Introd. 2, 862–63). The best proof of the uninterrupted development of the university of Oxford (vs. the colleges) is given by its struggle against the Friars, especially the Dominicans, who had tried to make themselves entirely independent[1] in the matter of degrees and regulations. A Dominican, Hugh of Sutton (or Dutton), who refused to swear obedience to the statutes was even expelled from the university. The quarrel was submitted to arbitrators, whose decision, favorable to the university, was sanctioned by the king in 1314. That royal decree of April 7, 1314 sets forth the general principles of the university's constitution. The Friars, however, encouraged by John XXII, continued their resistance and did not submit to the university until 1320.

Their quarrel was but an aspect of the old feud between seculars and regulars (Introd. 2, 823), which smoldered at some times and in some places but was always ready to flare up at other times or in other places.

We have seen (Introd. 2, 573) that the creation of Cambridge University in 1209 was the result of an emigration of discontented students from Oxford. Similar swarmings took place c. 1238–64 to Northampton, c. 1238–78 to Salisbury, and finally in 1334 to Stamford (diocese of Lincoln). These swarmings failed to prosper, yet the Stamford one disquieted the university so much that "until 1827 an oath not to lecture at Stamford was exacted from all candidates for the mastership at Oxford" (Rashdall 3, 90).

Oxford Colleges

In addition to the monastic houses, three colleges had been founded in the second half of the thirteenth century, to wit, Balliol (c. 1260), Merton (c. 1263), and University (c. 1280). The most important of these from our point of view was Merton, fellows of which are repeatedly quoted in this volume. In addition to the stimulus which Merton gave to mathematical and physical studies in the fourteenth century, that college was responsible for two other innovations. Walter de Merton was the founder of the system of college livings which has done so much good and harm to the English universities and the Anglican church. Advowsons were acquired by other colleges, to be sure, but this was done more systematically by Merton, and without impropriation of the rectories. In the second place, Merton distinguished itself by its church, library, and other buildings, and completed a "quadrangle" which was not strictly the first, yet was the exemplar of all the later quadrangles. The first deliberate quadrangle, it is said, was that of Corpus Christi, Cambridge (founded in 1352), and since then this design has become a commonplace of college architecture in the New World as well as in the Old.

In 1269–70 the far-seeing Walter de Merton acquired a house for his college in

[1] The Dominicans had established themselves in Oxford in 1221; the Franciscans, in 1224.

Cambridge, presumably for use in case his scholars were obliged to leave Oxford. That house, Merton Hall, is the oldest secular building in Cambridge; its present name, "The school of Pythagoras," originated in the sixteenth century; without justification, for the building was neither scholastic nor Pythagorean. John Milner Gray: The school of Pythagoras (Cambridge Antiquarian Society, no. IV, quarto, 69 p., 3 pl., Cambridge 1932).

Let us speak now of the three additional colleges established in the first half of the fourteenth century, Exeter, Oriel, and Queen's.

Exeter (1314–16). The fourth Oxford college was founded c. 1314 by Walter de Stapeldon (1261–1326), bishop of Exeter (DNB 54, 92), somewhat on the model of Balliol. It was first called Stapeldon Hall. (Rashdall 3, 201–3.)

Oriel (1324). The fifth Oxford college was founded in 1324 by Adam de Brome (DNB 6, 392), rector of St. Mary's in Oxford, and was refounded in 1326 by Edward II. It was first called the House of the scholars of St. Mary. In 1327 it moved into a new house given by Edward III, known as La Oriole, hence its name Oriel. It was more important than any earlier college, except Merton. Many of its fellowships were open to much wider competition than those of other colleges, and hence permitted a better selection of scholars. In this way Oriel exerted a liberalizing and very beneficial influence. (Rashdall 3, 203–7.)

Queen's (1341). The sixth Oxford college was named after queen Philippa (1314?–69), consort of Edward III, patroness of Froissart. Indeed, it was founded in 1341 by her chaplain, Robert of Eglesfield (DNB 17, 165), and placed by him under the patronage of the queens of England. The rule of Queen's was far more elaborate than earlier college rules, aiming at regulating every detail of the domestic and spiritual life of the community. (Rashdall 3, 207–10.)

Additional information on the six earlier Oxford colleges will be found in R. T. Gunther (11, 37–134, 1937).

The earliest chained library of England was established c. 1320 by Thomas de Cobham, bishop of Worcester, in the Old Congregation House, St. Mary's, Oxford. By 1300, there were three ways of keeping books in public or semipublic libraries. They might be chained to lecterns or desks, locked up in almeries and chests,[2] or kept unchained and unlocked in a room where students would use them in carols (or alcoves) near the window under the keeper's supervision. Not all the books of a library were ever chained, but only a portion of them; other books, meant for lending, could not be chained. In the Merton library it would seem that fewer books were chained than were reserved for the personal use of the fellows. In Peterhouse, Cambridge, 1418, out of 302 books, 143 were said to be chained, 125 assigned for division among the fellows.

Though chained libraries are considered a mediaeval institution, they continued to be used during the Renaissance and later. Indeed, two of the most remarkable in existence, that of Zutphen in Holland and that of the Laurentian library in Florence, date from the sixteenth century. Fresh chains were being purchased at Chetham College, Manchester, in 1742, and at the Bodleian in 1751; books remained chained at Queen's, Oxford, from c. 1381 to 1780, at Merton until 1792, at Magdalen until 1799! Chained libraries have been re-established in our days in many English colleges and cathedrals for archaeological purposes.

[2] There is preserved in Hereford cathedral a traveling book chest of the fourteenth century (illustrated in Streeter 1931, p. 118).

Burnet Hillman Streeter: The chained library. A survey of four centuries in the evolution of the English library (390 p., 93 ill., London 1931). The preceding note was derived exclusively from canon Streeter's admirable monograph.

Cambridge Colleges

Only one college had been founded in Cambridge in the thirteenth century, namely Peterhouse, established in 1284 (Introd. 2, 863).

In 1318, Cambridge received from John XXII a bull consecrating its existence as a studium generale. On that account, it has sometimes been assimilated to the continental universities, as contrasted with Oxford. The distinction, however, is more formal than real.

Cambridge was really founded in 1209 (Introd. 2, 573); a Franciscan house was established there in the old synagogue in 1224–25, a Dominican one in 1274, Peterhouse for seculars in 1284. Before the end of the century special houses existed for Friars of the sack, Friars of Blessed Mary, Carmelites, Augustinians, and canons of Sempringham. Six more colleges were founded before 1351.

King's Hall (before 1316). This second Cambridge college was already functioning in 1316, the scholars being recruited from the choir of the Royal Chapel. The scholars were to be at least 14 years of age on admission. It is thought that King's Hall was Chaucer's model for "Solar Hall" in the Reeve's tale. It ceased to exist as a separate institution in 1546, when it was incorporated together with other houses in Trinity College, then founded by Henry VIII. (Rashdall 3, 299–300.)

Michaelhouse (1324). This college was founded by Hervey de Stanton, chancellor of the exchequer, in 1324, somewhat upon the model of Merton. It was also incorporated into Trinity in 1546. (Rashdall 3, 300–2.)

University or Clare Hall (1326). This college was founded by the university itself with royal license in 1326. It received an additional endowment from Elizabeth de Burgh, lady of Clare, granddaughter of Edward I. An elaborate history of Clare College (1326–1928) was edited by Mansfield Duval Forbes at the time of its sexcentenary (2 vols., Oxford 1928–30).

Pembroke (1347). Pembroke or Valence Marie was founded in 1347 by Marie de Valence, widow of Aymer de Valence, earl of Pembroke ("maid, wife, and widow all in a day"). She was the daughter of Guy, count of Saint-Pol, and because of her French origin, students of French birth were favored in the distribution of scholarships. (Rashdall 3, 304–6.)

Gonville (1349). This was founded by Edmund Gonville (DNB 22, 106) for the study of arts and theology. The foundation was completed after Gonville's death (1351) by his executor, William Bateman, bishop of Norwich, and rechristened College of the Annunciation. A third foundation, in 1558, was due to John Caius (1510–73), physician to Henry VIII, the earliest of Cambridge antiquaries, and master of the college from 1559 to his death. The college is now called Gonville and Caius. (Rashdall 3, 306–8.)

Trinity Hall (1350). This college was founded in 1350 by bishop William of Norwich, already mentioned apropos of Gonville, and the original full name was "College of the scholars of the Holy Trinity of Norwich." The college was meant for students of canon and civil law, and it is still today primarily a legal college.

Some information on the Cambridge colleges may be found in R. T. Gunther (1937), though this book is almost exclusively devoted to later times.

To conclude, by 1350 there were six colleges in Oxford and seven in Cambridge, but two of the latter were eventually absorbed into Trinity College (1546).

PARISIAN COLLEGES

In no place were the colleges more abundant and more diversified than in Paris. See a chronological list from 1180 to 1484 in Rashdall (1, 536–39). It begins with the Collège des dix-huit (1180) and St. Thomas de Lupara (Louvre, c. 1186); to these two no less than seventeen were added in the thirteenth century, the most famous being the Sorbonne (1257, see Introd. 2, 863), no less than twenty-seven in the first half of the fourteenth century, and eleven more in the second half. Rashdall's list does not include the Franciscan and Dominican houses.

It would take too much space to deal with each of these colleges even briefly. I shall speak of only four of them, Cardinal Lemoine, Navarre, Montaigu, and Tréguier.

The *Collège du Cardinal Lemoine* is the first of the fourteenth-century colleges, and one of the most illustrious. It was founded in 1302 by Jean Lemoine, who was born at Crécy-en-Ponthieu (near Abbeville in Picardy) c. 1250, and died in Avignon 1313. He received the red hat from Boniface VIII and was the latter's legate to France in 1302. The college was established in the rue St. Victor, and a street crossing its site, rue du Cardinal Lemoine, commemorates it to this day. An elaborate study was devoted to it by Charles Jourdain (1817–86): Le collège du Cardinal Lemoine (Mémoires de la Société de l'histoire de Paris 3, 42–81, 1877). Partly reprinted in the posthumous collection of his main essays, Excursions historiques et philosophiques à travers le Moyen âge (Paris 1888).

The *Collège de Navarre* was the first royal foundation of its kind in France. It was created in 1305 by the will of Jeanne de Navarre (1273–1305), queen of Philippe le Bel. It was located on the colline Ste Geneviève and existed until 1792. The Ecole polytechnique was established in its buildings in 1805. It was perhaps the most famous of all French colleges. Henri d'Anjou (later Henri III) and Henri de Navarre (later Henri IV) were among its alumni; Nicole Oresme (XIV-2), Pierre d'Ailly (1350–1420), Jean Gerson (1363–1429), Nicolas de Clémanges (1360–c. 1440), among its teachers. An elaborate history of this college, unfortunately not available to me, was written by Jean de Launoy: Regii Navarrae gymnasii parisiensis historia (quarto, 2 vols., Paris 1677). Brief note on it and other Parisian colleges by Victor Le Clerc (HL 24, 242–47, 1862). Général Alvin: L'Ecole polytechnique et son quartier (quarto, ill., Paris 1932; p. 22–31), with map showing the Collège de Navarre and its surroundings as they were at the end of the sixteenth century.

The *Collège de Montaigu* was founded in 1314 by Gilles Aycelin de Montaigut (born Auvergne c. 1255, died Paris 1318), archbishop, chancellor of the royal seal, who took a large part in the legal persecution of the Templars. It was placed almost on the same site as the present Bibliothèque Ste Geneviève. It was reorganized in 1483, when the Fleming Jan Standonck became its regent. Standonck[3] was a great ascetic and martinet, "a counter-reformer before the Reformation"; he created in conjunction with the college the congregation of Montaigu, and made life hard for the students. The motto of the place was Mons acutus, ingenium acutum, dentes acuti (the last because the poor students were starved). The

[3] Born in Malines 1453 (rather than 1443), died Paris 1504. See biography by Alphonse Roersch (Biographie nationale de Belgique 23, 588–99, 1922).

college existed in the rue des Sept-Voies until 1844. Erasmus, Calvin, and Ignatius of Loyola were among its alumni; it was bitterly criticized by the former of these and by Rabelais.

The last of the colleges of which I wish to say a few words was the *Collège de Tréguier*, founded in 1325 by Guillaume de Coëtmohan, precentor of the church of Tréguier in Brittany. It occupied the site of the most famous of the colleges existing in Paris today, the Collège de France, founded by Francis I in 1530.

The historian of education should deal not only with these Parisian colleges, but with many others in the country, established around cathedrals or universities or independent of them. Many were hardly more than hostelries for scholars under the tutelage of a master or proctor; in others, some form of religious exercises took place or lectures were delivered. Not to speak of the monastic houses, the constitution of which was defined by the rule of the order, there were various other kinds of religious and charity houses. Many houses were restricted to definite groups of scholars, defined geographically, or socially, or otherwise.

What I have said of France would apply to other European countries, but it is unnecessary in this volume, devoted to the history of science rather than the history of education, to expatiate on the subject.

GRAMMAR SCHOOLS

The subject of colleges subsidiary to the universities leads naturally to the consideration of other schools devoted to elementary teaching. The line is very hard to draw between "colleges" and "grammar schools." In many colleges the teaching was distinctly of an elementary nature, in others it was higher. In most cases, however, the primary teaching was given in the parishes under the direction of a priest or of a rector scholarum appointed by the priest, by the vestry, or by the town council. These parish schools were more or less formal according to the priest's peculiarities and to his interest in teaching; it is probable that in most cases no records were made or at any rate kept. The existence and functioning of these schools is proved repeatedly in many ways. For example, in the lives of mediaeval scholars, it is often stated that they studied in such or such a place, before joining a higher college; sometimes they studied in many places before going to the university. The most important elementary schools were probably those conducted by the monastic orders, primarily for their own members and the oblate children.[4]

Vanderkindere (p. 426–28, 1879). Leach (1915). Rashdall (1936 passim, chiefly 3, 345–52). Lynn Thorndike: Elementary and secondary education in the Middle Ages (Speculum 15, 400–8, 1940).

For sections B, Israel, and C, Islam, see survey in section IV B, C of chapter I.

D. FAR EAST

THE KANAZAWA-BUNKO

The Kanazawa-bunko is a famous library (bunko) originally founded by Hōjō Sanetoki (1225–75) in Kamakura. After the fire in that city in 1270, Sanetoki moved it to Kanazawa (near Yokohama); he increased it and so did his successors.

[4] That is, children "offered" to the monasteries by their parents "long before the age of discretion; sometimes even in the very cradle, though this was rare, and the limit was generally put at seven" (Coulton 2, 34, 1927; 1, ch. 14, 219–33, 1923).

After the fall of the Hōjō family in 1333 (the head of that family had virtually ruled Japan from 1200 to 1333), the library declined, but it was revived by Uesugi Norizane (c. 1450). Tokugawa Ieyasu (1542–1616), having selected Edo (now Tōkyō) as his capital, ordered the books of the Kanazawa-bunko to be moved thither.

The Kanazawa-bunko contained a great many Chinese and Japanese manuscripts and printed editions, not only the "classics," but other books on science and religion. Scholars were welcome for study, and thus that library became a center of learning in the fourteenth century.

Papinot (p. 254, 1909). Dai shakka jiten (1932).

SOSEKI

Buddhist (Zen) priest and teacher (1271–1346).

Soseki was born in 1271 in the province of Ise, being a descendant of the emperor Uda (ruled 888–97) in the ninth generation. Having lost his mother in childhood, he was brought up in the temple Hirashio-yama in the province of Kai; he became a monk at the age of 18 and then assumed the name Chikaku. Later, having dreamt of a visit to the two famous Chinese temples Sozan and Sekitō, he took the name of Soseki; he is best known, however, under his posthumous name Musō-kokushi.

He was patronized by the emperor Go-Daigo (born 1287, ruled 1319–38). In 1326, he founded the Zen-ō-ji temple in his native province, and in 1342, the Tenryū-ji in the province of Yamashiro. This second temple became the headquarters of the Rinzai-shū, a branch of Zen Buddhism (see Introd. 2, 559).

Soseki was one of the main leaders of Buddhist learning, that is, of Hindu-Chinese tradition, in his age, and exerted considerable influence upon his contemporaries.

That influence was sanctioned by the veneration of emperor and shōgun, especially that of the first Ashikaga shōgun, Takauji (ruled 1338–58); it was further increased later on, especially during the rule of the shōgun Yoshimitsu (ruled 1367–95), when Soseki's pupils Myōō and Gidō Shūshin became the spiritual leaders of the nation. They resided in Yoshimitsu's own temple, the Rokuon-ji near Kyōto. Another Zen priest who influenced Yoshimitsu, and through him the nation, was Ryōken, of the Nanzen-ji in Kyōto.

Papinot (p. 602, 1909). Brinkley and Kikuchi (p. 448, 454, 1914).

CHAPTER V

PHILOSOPHICAL AND CULTURAL BACKGROUND

(First Half of the Fourteenth Century)

N.B. Only the main notes are published in this chapter. Many men who may be called philosophers, or have influenced—sometimes deeply—the intellectual climate of their time are dealt with in other chapters, because they were primarily something else, e.g., mathematicians or physicians. For a general survey of the philosophical and cultural background, read section V of chapter I. More information on the men dealt with in that survey may then easily be obtained by means of the index.

A. WESTERN CHRISTENDOM

A1. Italy

DANTE (1265–1321)

"Dante che tutto vedea"

Preliminary remarks

This note does not aim at completeness to the same extent as most of the other notes. Because of the intrinsic importance of Dante's writings and personality, and of their immense repercussion, "Dantology" is almost a science in itself, a sufficient knowledge of which can only be the reward of a lifetime of study. I have indicated what I believed to be essential.

A complete bibliography would fill the present volume to overflowing. I have indicated the items which I consider the most important. It is quite possible that some items overlooked by me are more important than others which have been included. One cannot master Dante literature without being a lifelong Dante specialist. The notes dealing with scientific topics, however, are presumably closer to perfection.

Familiarity with the Divina commedia being taken for granted, more space has been given to Dante's minor writings than they would otherwise deserve.

Scholars writing books on Dante generally deal with the whole of his time as well as with himself; therefore, in fairness to myself, one should not compare with their books my Dante chapter only, but the whole of this work.

Contents: (1) Life. (2) Guelfs and Ghibellines. (3) Dante's works (in chronological order). (4) Divina commedia. (5) Vita nuova. (6) De vulgari eloquentia. (7) Convivio. (8) De monarchia. (9) Quaestio de aqua et terra. (10) Dante as a man of science. (11) Astronomy and cosmology (including meteorology and physics). (11 bis) Mention of lucciole. (12) Physiology and embryology. (13) Philosophy. (14) Government and law. (15) Islamic influences on the Divina commedia (with bibliography). (16) Dante's influence (with bibliography).

(17) Text: (a) Collected works, (b) Divina commedia, (c) Vita nuova, (d) De vulgari eloquentia, (e) Convito, (f) De monarchia, (g) Quaestio de aqua et terra, (h) Epistolae, (i) Canzoniere. (18) Commentaries. (19) Bibliographies. (20)

Societies and journals. (21) Dictionaries and concordances. (22) Biographies. (23) General studies. (24) Science in general. (25) Astronomy, cosmology, meteorology, and physics. (26) Geography. (27) Mathematics. (28) Chemistry. (29) Natural history. (30) Physiology and embryology. (31) Medicine. (32) Philosophy. (33) Government and law. (34) Iconography. (35) Symbolism, occultism, et alia.

1. *Life*

Dante Alighieri, son of the Florentine notary Alighiero Alighieri, was born in the quarter of San Martino al Vescovo in Florence in May 1265. At the age of nine he fell in love with Beatrice Portinari, and this unfulfilled passion had a deep influence upon his life. Not later than 1298 he married Gemma di Manetto Donati, who gave him four children, Pietro, Jacopo, Antonia, and Beatrice. He became a member of the guild of physicians (arte dei medizi e speziali) in order to be qualified for high office, and in 1300 was elected one of the priors (the highest office in the Florentine Republic). He belonged originally to the Guelf party (see explanation below), and later to the White section of that party (the Bianchi). In October 1301, the Bianchi sent an embassy to Rome, to prevent the entrance of Charles of Valois, Boniface VIII's representative, into Florence. Dante was very probably a member of that embassy, and during its absence Charles of Valois entered Florence, and proceeded to undo his adversaries. Dante was formally exiled on January 27, 1302, and that sentence was many times repeated and aggravated; he remained in exile to the end of his life. His wife stayed apparently in Florence, also his children until many years later. He wandered all over Italy and even went to Paris. He visited the Scaligeri in Verona at least twice (probably Bartolommeo della Scala c. 1303, and Can Grande della Scala c. 1316), then was for a time at Ravenna (c. 1317–18) with his children Pietro, Jacopo, and Beatrice. Upon his return from an embassy to Venice, he died in Ravenna on September 14, 1321. He was buried in that city, and his ashes have been kept there in spite of Florentine efforts to recover them.

2. *Guelfs and Ghibellines*[1]

In order to understand the political history of this time in general and Dante's exile in particular, it is well to know that the Ghibellines represented the ideals of the feudal aristocracy, of the rural districts, of the Holy Roman Empire; the Guelfs, those of the cities, of the new bourgeoisie interested in trade, manufacture, and banking, of the papacy. In reality these clear distinctions were obscured by many conflicting and obstinate traditions. These two parties were very much like our great political parties, and the allegiance of their members was determined by numberless conditions, above all by family and city pride (e.g., when Pisa was Ghibelline, her enemy, Florence, was Guelf). The Ghibellines might be compared to the Tories and Conservatives of England and the Republicans of America; the Guelfs, to the Whigs and Liberals of England, and to the Democrats of America. The wonderful organization of the Parte guelfa of Florence invites comparison with Tammany Hall. The complication was increased by secession. About 1300, the Ghibelline minority having been expelled from Florence, the Guelf party was split into two, the pure Guelfs or Neri (Blacks), and the more progressive and conciliatory

[1] The Italian words Ghibellino and Guelfo are derived from the German Waiblingen and Welf, these being the proper names of the two families which originated those parties within the Empire in the twelfth century.

or Bianchi (Whites). The Neri were partisans of Boniface VIII and his representative Charles of Valois, the Bianchi were opposed to Boniface and Charles. Dante, a Bianco, was exiled by the triumphant Neri and driven into the arms of the Ghibellines. Thus Dante, born and bred a Guelf, became a Ghibelline.

An excellent discussion of this subject will be found in Emerton (p. 255–72, 1925), by way of introduction to his English translation of Bartolus' De Guelphis et Gebellinis (not long before 1357). See also George Gordon Coulton: Guelf and Ghibelline. Dante illustrations from the autobiography of brother Salimbene of Parma (Mediaeval studies by G. G. Coulton, no. 2, 16 p., London 1905). Fra Salimbene (XIII-2) died soon after 1288.

3. *Dante's works*

The approximate chronology of his works is as follows:

1. Vita nuova. Written after Beatrice's death (1290), probably c. 1292–95. Including earlier poems.
2. De vulgari eloquentia (incomplete). Written in exile (i.e., in 1302 or later), probably but not certainly before the Convivio, possibly in or before 1305.
3. Convivio (incomplete), c. 1308? According to Pietro Fraticelli, editor of the Convivio (Opere minore di Dante Alighieri vol. 3, 8[va] ed., 1900; p. 6), books 2 and 4 were written in 1297, books 1 and 3 in 1314.
4. De monarchia, c. 1311?
5. Quaestio de aqua et terra, Verona 1320.
6. Divina commedia. Inferno, c. 1314–19; Purgatorio, not later than 1319; Paradiso, c. 1316–21.

For political events in relation to Dante's activities, see Paget Toynbee's chronological table (1300–21) in his edition of the Epistolae (p. 213–23, Oxford 1920; Isis 4, 137).

With the possible exception of the Quaestio de aqua, the genuineness of which is not certain, the Commedia was Dante's last work, the supreme fruit of his life.

To these works must be added the Epistolae, the Canzoniere, and the Eclogues. Out of some fourteen letters, ten are generally accepted as genuine; written in Latin and dealing mainly with political subjects, they range from 1304 to 1318. The poems of the Canzoniere, published independently or included in the Vita nuova and the Convivio, go back some of them to Dante's youth; two were probably written c. 1307–8, most of them are undatable. Two Latin eclogues were addressed by Dante to Giovanni del Virgilio, c. 1318–21.

We shall deal first of all with the Commedia, then with the other works (nos. 1 to 5) in chronological order.

4. *Divina commedia*

The Commedia is one of the greatest historical and philosophical poems of all time, one of the literary masterpieces of the Middle Ages. The dramatic subject is the author's journey through hell, purgatory, and paradise, which is supposed to have occurred during the Jubilee year 1300 (from Good Friday, April 8, to April 14). In hell and purgatory he was guided by Virgil at Beatrice's request, and in paradise by Beatrice herself. This visit to the three kingdoms of the next world gives the poet endless opportunities of discussing the problems of this world. The Commedia is thus a poetic encyclopaedia of mediaeval knowledge and wisdom.

The form is very symmetrical. Each of the three great divisions or cantiche (or canzoni) contains 33 canti, and there is an introductory canto at the beginning of the first cantica; there are thus in all 100 canti. These vary in length from 115 to 160 lines, but the cantiche are almost equal (respectively 4,720, 4,755, and 4,758 lines, a total of 14,233).

The original title was Commedia. The word divina is a later interpolation, due to or stabilized by Boccaccio; it occurs in some of the oldest MSS, but not in the printed editions anterior to that of 1555 (i.e., the 39th Italian edition). Dante used the name Commedia because the poem moves from evil to bliss, ending with the sublime lines:

> Ma già volgeva il mio disiro e il velle,
> Si come rota ch' igualmente è mossa,
> L'amor che move il sole e l'altre stelle.

(My will and desire were rolled with the even motion of a wheel, by the love that moves the sun and the other stars.) That idea was borrowed from Boetius; it suggests comparison with the definition of virtue given by Boetius' predecessor, St. Augustine, "brevis et vera definitio virtutis, ordo est amoris."

The success of the Commedia was almost immediate, and it has continued throughout the centuries. There are between 500 and 600 MSS, editions almost innumerable (662 listed by Mambelli in 1931), and translations in every language. The first printed edition appeared in Foligno 1472, and two other editions followed in the same year (Mantova and Iesi). There are in all sixteen incunabula editions.

The Commedia is the greatest monument of the Italian language as well as one of the earliest ones, and it stands to that language in almost the same relation as the Iliad to the Greek. Nevertheless, as Italian had not yet emerged from the vernacular (volgare) and dialectal stage in Dante's time, it was soon found necessary to translate the Commedia into Latin. Indeed, fewer educated Italians were then able to appreciate the Tuscan idiom than the Latin. A translation of the Commedia in Latin hexameters was completed by the Olivetan Ronto Matteo (and others under his direction) in 1343. The first Latin translation to appear in print, however, was that of the Jesuit Carlo d'Aquino (1654–1737), and it was not published until 1728 (G. Mambelli in Giornale dantesco 28, 202–7, 1925). There are various other Latinizations, published and unpublished.

5. *Vita nuova*

Italian prose text including thirty-one Italian poems, dedicated to the Florentine poet Guido Cavalcanti (d. 1300), to whom Dante tells the story of his love for Beatrice and how it "renewed" his life. This Beatrice, Dante's childhood love and lifelong inspiration, was probably the daughter of Folco Portinari of Florence. She was born in 1266, married Simone de' Bardi c. 1285, and died in 1290. She is the central figure not only of the Vita nuova, but also of the Divina commedia. In the Commedia she is Dante's guide and represents allegorically the divine science, theology. The Vita nuova is one of the most moving fragments of autobiography in world literature. It was not printed until 1576.

6. *De vulgari eloquentia*

Latin study on the Italian language as one of the Romance languages, examination of fourteen Italian dialects, and plea for a common literary tongue. It includes a metrical study of the canzone. Unfortunately this work was not completed: Dante wrote only two books out of four, and the second book ends abruptly.

This is one of the earliest books of its kind; one of the earliest attempts (if not the very earliest) to discuss the origins and nature of a modern language. It was first published (Vicenza 1529) in the Italian translation of Gian Giorgio Trissino (1478–1550); the Latin princeps appeared in Paris in 1577.

For the literary use of Italian before Dante, see my volume 2 (p. 577; 150, 815).

Dante had noticed that the French, Italian, and Provençal languages have many words in common, and he concluded that these languages were related (De vulgari eloquentia 1, 8). He realized that languages changed and developed; they continued to change even in heaven (Paradiso XXVI, 124–26), except Hebrew, the original tongue of mankind. See remarks on the subject by Raymond Wilson Chambers in his centenary address on "Philologists at University College," London (1927, reprinted in Man's unconquerable mind, p. 342–58).

7. *Convivio*

The "Banquet" is an Italian commentary on three of Dante's canzoni. It is divided into four books, the first being introductory, and each of the others devoted to one of these canzoni. Dante's original intention was to discuss fourteen canzoni. In the parts which he completed he renews his defense of the Italian language.

The princeps of the Convivio was published in Florence 1490; the modern title Convito did not appear until the edition of Florence 1723.

Book 2 is our main source for the study of Dante's astronomy; it may date back to as early as 1297.

8. *De monarchia*

Latin political treatise discussing the relation of church and state in three books: (1) necessity of a universal monarch; (2, 3) how far is the Roman Empire justified? Dante recognizes the pope's supremacy in spiritual matters, not in temporal ones. The temporal power of the pope is inconsistent with Christ's own teaching. God has given mankind two guides, the pope and the emperor; the former is the spiritual and theological guide, the latter the temporal ruler, whose first duty is the maintenance of universal peace. Dante praised the Eternal evangel of Joachim of Floris (XII-2), which had been edited in 1254 by Gherardo da Borgo San Donnino and promptly condemned by Alexander IV (pope 1254–61). It is not surprising that Dante's own treatise was also condemned; John XXII (pope 1316–34) ordered it to be burnt in 1329, and it was put on the Index by the council of Trent.

The De monarchia was translated into Italian by Marsilio Ficino (1433–99). The princeps appeared at Basel in 1559. For the understanding of Dante's political ideas it is necessary to study his Epistolae as well as the Monarchia.

9. *Quaestio de aqua et terra*

Latin treatise recording Dante's disputation at Verona, January 20, 1320, on the relative levels of land and water on the surface of the earth. Published by Giovanni Benedetto Moncetti (Venice 1508) on the basis of an autograph MS which is lost. The genuineness of this text is not certain, and there is no independent evidence concerning the reality of that disputation. The author (whoever he was) refutes the current opinion that the land and water surfaces are not part of the same sphere, but of two spheres, the land sphere and the water sphere, the centers of which do not coincide. This treatise being unknown until the time of Moncetti's discovery of it, that opinion continued to obtain until the end of the Middle Ages, and when Columbus in 1498 near the coast of South America noticed the steady streams of water opposing his progress (coming from the Orinoco), he thought that he was near the highest point of the sea, whence the water rushed down.[2]

10. *Dante as a man of science*

Dante had a remarkably good knowledge of astronomy, though it was not up-to-date except with regard to a few details. He had also a sufficient knowledge of physics and physiology, and, if the Quaestio de aqua et terra is authentic, of geography. With regard to other subjects he knew what one might expect him to know, considering his philosophic tendencies and the keenness of his curiosity. He was not a man of science, but a learned poet, the greatest Christian poet of the Middle Ages.

11. *Astronomy and cosmology (including meteorology and physics)*

Dante's main source of astronomical knowledge was the Elements of al-Farghānī (IX-1), which he had studied very thoroughly in the Latin translation. This very elementary work (Elementa astronomica, or Liber de aggregatione scientiae stellarum, or Liber de aggregationibus stellarum) had been Latinized in 1134 by John of Seville (XII-1) and later by Gerard of Cremona (XII-2); the Latin text was even translated into French, and the French text was translated into Italian by Zucchero Bencivenni as early as 1313. Of course Dante had no need of translations into the vernacular, as he knew Latin as well as Italian. He quoted Alfraganus or his book only twice (in the Convivio, book 2), but used him repeatedly. I do not know which Latin version he used, but John's was more popular than Gerard's, and hence the probability of his using John's is greater than that of his using Gerard's.

On account of his almost complete dependence on al-Farghānī, Dante's astronomy was far from being up-to-date. He was still upholding the Aristotelian theory of homocentric spheres at a time when Ptolemaic doctrines, having withstood reiterated criticisms, were triumphing.[3] His knowledge of Aristotle was somewhat confused because of the contradictions obtaining between the old translations from the Arabic, and the new ones (e.g., of the Meteorology) made from the Greek or revised by William of Moerbeke (XIII-2) probably at the request of St. Thomas Aquinas. Though his astronomical knowledge was on the whole a little backward, he had obtained some information at least from more modern sources; for example, his statement that the length of the tropical year is $\frac{1}{100}$ of a day less than $365\frac{1}{4}$ days was obtained probably from the Compotus major of Giovanni Campano da Novara (XIII-2) or from one of the Parisian astronomers.

Dante's cosmology may be summarized as follows (see fig. 8): The earth is a sphere concentric with the universe. Hell is a cone inside the earth reaching down

[2] Dreyer (p. 238, 1906). Salvador de Madariaga: Columbus (p. 325, New York 1940; Isis 33, 95). On December 17, 1936, being on my way from Trinidad to Demerara, I had occasion to observe the fantastic amount of muddy water thrown into the ocean by the Orinoco. Some seventy miles out at sea it was possible to distinguish the dark waters of the mighty river from the blue oceanic waters.

[3] For an account of astronomical theories at the end of the thirteenth century see Introd 2, 756–61.

FIG. 7. Portrait of Dante. From the fresco painted by Dante's friend Giotto (1266–1337), in the Bargello of Florence. Tracing made by Seymour Kirkup in 1840 before the fresco was ruined by restoration. That tracing was the basis of the Arundel Society print of 1859. Taken with kind permission from Frank Jewett Mather, Jr.: The portraits of Dante (p. 8, Princeton University Press 1921).

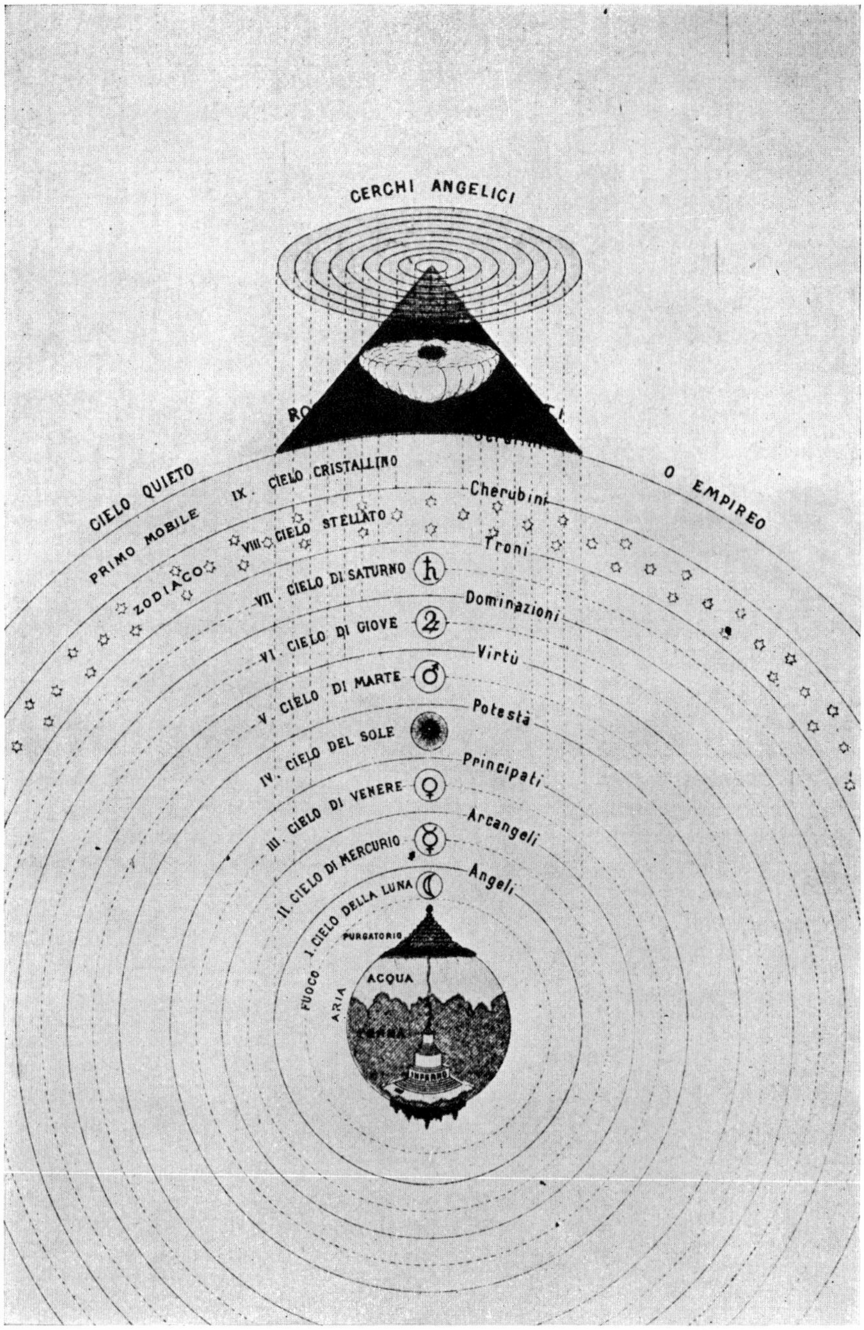

FIG. 8. The astronomical-theological universe of Dante. From the edition of the Divina commedia by Giuseppe Campi, vol. 3, Paradiso (Torino 1891).

to the very center of it, where Lucifer rules; the places of punishment become gradually more and more terrible as one goes down and approaches the center. The umbilic of the land areas (as opposed to the seas) is Jerusalem, and at the antipode of Jerusalem, rising from the middle of the ocean, there is a conical hill which is purgatory. Ten solid spheres concentric with the earth are of increasing heavenliness: the lowest is that of the moon, then follow those of Mercury, Venus, the sun, Mars, Jupiter, Saturn. The eighth sphere is that of the fixed stars or firmament, the ninth or crystalline sphere is the primum mobile, and the tenth the empyrean, the dwelling of God. That outermost, being perfect and beyond the necessity of change, is motionless; the ninth sphere moves with an exceedingly high speed (i.e., an object placed on that sphere would move very fast) which is transmitted in diminishing degrees to all the inferior spheres; the firmament has a slow eastward motion of its own amounting to one degree per century (precession of the equinoxes). The nature of the transmission of the daily rotation of the ninth to the seven inferior spheres via the eighth one is very unclear. The heavenly spheres are moved under the guidance of seraphim, cherubins, and angels.

The planets move in the ecliptic. There is no mention of eccentrics, but several allusions to epicycles. Dante explains the marks which can be seen on the surface of the moon in terms of irregular reflection (after Ibn Rushd), or in angelic terms. Similarly, his accounts of the Milky Way (Galaxy) oscillate between physics and mythology. These indecisions were natural enough, especially in one who was primarily a poet. All in all, his astronomical knowledge was amazingly good and detailed for a non-astronomer.

Duhem interpreted a passage in Paradiso (XXVII, 142–48) as a reference to the trepidation of the equinoxes (Introd. 2, 758). That interpretation is certainly wrong. There was no mention of trepidation in the Elements of al-Farghānī and none in Dante.

Dante's references to the four stars of the Southern Cross (Purgatorio I, 23; VIII, 91) are the earliest in Western literature, if one does not take into account Ptolemy's reference to them as part of the Centaur.[4] It is possible that the Southern Cross is mentioned in Arabic sources anterior to Dante (the Arabic name is 'Amūd al-ṣalīb) or that it is represented on Arabic globes (Introd. 2, 1014). At any rate, the statement (in HL 24, 488) that they are indicated on an Arabic globe of 1225, I was not able to substantiate. That globe is no. II of my list, described by G. S. Assemani. The Centaur is represented, which included the Southern Cross in the Ptolemaic manner; but the Southern Cross is not specifically designated or named.

11 bis. *Mention of lucciole* (*fireflies, glowworms*)

In the Inferno (XXVI, 29), there is a mention of fireflies, "vede lucciole giù per la vallea," which is remarkable because it is said to be the first reference to them in Italian. It is further asserted that there is no mention of them in Latin (ancient or mediaeval) letters. I publish this note on "lucciole" as a challenge, for I can hardly believe these assertions, though I am still unable completely to disprove them. Fireflies must have existed in Italy before Dante's time, and these insects were too conspicuous to remain unnoticed. One would expect them to impress any poetical and imaginative mind. Dante's lucciole are as noteworthy as Chaucer's cats.

[4] The Southern Cross is visible at least during a part of the year as far north as latitude 34° (Fez 34°8′, Beirūt 33°53′, Damascus 33°30′, Baghdād 33°20′).

Richard Thayer Holbrook: Dante and the animal kingdom (p. 346–47, New York 1902). William Warren Vernon: Readings on the Inferno (2d ed., 2, 338, London 1906). John Forster: Life of Charles Dickens, edited by J. W. T. Ley (London 1928), for Dickens' remarks on the subject.

There is an account of fireflies in Pliny (XI, 34; XVIII, 67) and there are a few other references in Latin writings, for which see the Thesaurus linguae latinae (3, 1050) s.v. cicindela. The fact remains that fireflies did not seem to make any impression upon Latin and Italian poets until Dante. Sir d'Arcy Thompson, to whom I confided my perplexity on the subject, answered (St. Andrews, Apr. 17, 1940): "There is little or no folklore about the creature, so far as I know. Rolland has hardly a word to say; Lewysohn[5] does not mention it at all. . . . Aristotle mentions the firefly, but very briefly (*πυγολαμπίς*, H. A. 523b21, 551b25). He has only a word to say about *ψυχή*, the butterfly (H. A. 532a27, 551a14, *γίνονται δ'αἱ μὲν καλούμεναι ψυχαὶ ἐκ τῶν καμπῶν*. I conjecture that it was a matter of superstition, the *ψυχή* being really a dead man's soul. I shouldn't wonder if there were something of the same kind in regard to the firefly—the less one has to do with it the better. But really we know nothing about it . . ."[6]

12. *Physiology and embryology*

Dante's physiological views are expressed in the Convivio and in canto XXV of the Purgatorio. In that canto he also explains views on the birth and development of men's bodies and souls. As I have somewhat neglected psychology (in the old meaning, the science of the soul) in my earlier volumes, I cannot account for Dante's views without a short retrospective survey.

The theological side of embryology necessitated some kind of hypothesis with regard to the beginning of each individual soul. The three main theories were (1) infusionism, (2) creationism, and (3) traducianism. According to the first of these theories, all souls were created at the beginning and are kept in a treasury; they are "infused into" new bodies at the time of conception or later; at the time of death each soul leaves the body it has been associated with, and is returned to the treasury. This theory was defended by Origen (III-1), Nemesios of Emesa (IV-2), St. Cyril of Alexandria (376–444); it was denounced by St. Jerome (IV-2) and did not survive the fifth century. It might very easily have become heretical, for it is not inconsistent with metempsychosis.

The second theory, creationism, was especially popular with the Eastern fathers of the church. According to it, God created only two human bodies, those of Adam and Eve; the bodies of all other men are begotten by their respective parents, but God creates a new special soul for each of them. This theory, after being adapted to Aristotelian psychology, was accepted by the majority of Christian doctors of the Middle Ages, including St. Thomas. In this respect Dante followed Aristotle's De anima (which he often quoted) and St. Thomas.

The third theory, traducianism, assumes that human souls are propagated by generation along with the bodies. This theory was developed early by the Latin

[5] Sir d'Arcy's references are to Eugène Rolland (1846–1909): Faune populaire de la France (13 vols., Paris 1877–1915), and to Ludwig Lewysohn (1819–1901): Die Zoologie des Talmuds (412 p., Frankfurt a.M. 1858).

[6] Gubernatis (2, 212, 1872) gives information on firefly lore, which is interesting but does not solve the present difficulty.

fathers, such as Tertullian (c. 160–c. 230), and later by St. Augustine (V-1). According to the latter, the fetus was besouled in the second month and besexed in the fourth. After having been eclipsed for centuries by creationism, which seemed more orthodox, traducianism returned to favor in proportion as Augustinianism displaced Thomism, and more completely so, of course, at the time of the Reformation. Ibn Rushd (the Averrois of Dante) was a traducianist, and it is possibly to him (or to Aristotle?) that reference is made in Purgatorio (XXV, 63) as "che più savio di te."

13. *Philosophy*

Dante was deeply interested in philosophy and theology, and was familiar with the controversies of his day. His general point of view was scholastic; he was not a pure Aristotelian and Thomist, as has often been claimed, but an eclectic philosopher, always ready to borrow from any available source, Christian or Muslim, and to make an original synthesis of his own, intermediate between the philosophy of St. Thomas and that of Ibn Sīnā and Ibn Rushd, although nearer to the latter. Thus he did not hesitate to place in Paradise (X, 136) Siger of Brabant (XIII-2), the champion of Averroism. We should bear in mind, however, that Dante was primarily a Christian poet, not a philosopher.

14. *Government and law*

Dante's views on the burning political issue of the day, the relation of empire to papacy, have been indicated above in the section on his De monarchia. See also the section on Guelfs and Ghibellines. Dante was an orthodox Christian who revered the pope but dreamt of a regeneration of the church. As a good Italian he deplored the abandonment of Rome by Clement V. Indeed, the absence of the pope destroyed whatever unity there could be at that time in Italy, and replaced it by anarchy and confusion. After Clement's death (1314) he besought the Italian cardinals to elect an Italian pope who would restore the papal see to Rome. He bitterly resented the cupidity and nepotism of the Avignon popes (Clement V and John XXII). St. Thomas Aquinas was his main guide in legal and sociological matters.

15. *Islamic influences on the Divina commedia*

It is possible that the general scheme of Dante's poem, as well as many details of it, were suggested to him (indirectly of course, for he did not know Arabic) by Muslim models. There are three cycles of Muslim traditions (ḥadīth) concerning the Prophet's miraculous journeys: (1) the isrā' (Qur'ān XVII, 1), that is, his ascension to heaven, or (according to a later and more popular interpretation) his night journey to Jerusalem; (2) the mi'rāj (Qur'ān LXXXI, 19–25; LIII, 1–12), his ascension to heaven—an event celebrated every year in the Dār al-Islām on the night before the 27th Rajab, lailat al-mi'rāj; (3) a combination of the isrā' and mi'rāj, which constitutes a complete model of Dante's visits to hell, purgatory, and paradise. These traditions were amplified and given metaphysical interpretations by Muslim philosophers, especially those of the pseudo-Empedoclean and Neoplatonic school founded by Ibn Masarra of Cordova (883–931).[7] The greatest representative of that school was Ibn 'Arabī (XIII-1), whose writings were probably one of the indirect sources of the Divina commedia.

[7] Introd. 2, 596, 598.

Another precedent is the Risālat al-ghufrān (On the remission of sins) composed c. 1031 by the Syrian poet Abū-l-'Alā al-Ma'arrī.[8] In that work, written in prose and verse, the heathen poets who have been forgiven (hence the title) are the main characters of a comedy laid in heaven; it is truly a divine "commedia," but very different in tone from Dante's. It has a Voltairian ring, and contains an account of the Manichaeans or freethinkers (zindīq, pl. zanādīq), their opinions and writings. I have used the Arabic edition by Kāmil Kīlānī (2 vols., second printing, Cairo 1925; the first printing was I think in 1923).

The Platonic love of Dante for Beatrice which is one of the fundamental motifs of the Commedia was probably also inspired by Arabic models.

The late Miguel Asín Palacios, of Madrid, in 1919 gave a brilliant exposition of all the similarities between the Commedia and various Arabic works. The weaker part of his argument concerns the transmission of the Arabic models. How did Dante know of them? If Dante had lived in Spain, this would be easier to conceive, but his travels were apparently restricted to Italy and France. Brunetto Latini (XIII-2) went to Spain, it is true, but he could hardly have been Dante's "teacher" (as he is often called), for he was already about 55 when Dante was born; he may, however, have guided him and influenced him.

Edgar Blochet: Les sources orientales de la Divine comédie (232 p., Paris 1901). Blochet tried to find Dante's models in Persia, but failed to prove his case. Miguel Asín Palacios: La escatologia musulmana en la Divina comedia (403 p., Madrid 1919). See also a pamphlet by the same author and with the same title (103 p., Madrid 1924); also published in Italian, French, and English (Isis 11, 175). This is an analysis of the world-wide discussion which followed the publication of Asín's thesis. An abbreviated edition of Asín's memorable book was published in English: Islam and the Divine comedy, translated by Harold Sunderland, with an introduction by the duke of Berwick and Alba (321 p., London 1926; Isis 10, 65-69).

Giuseppe Gabrieli: Intorno alle fonti orientali della Commedia (Arcadia vol. 3, 84 p., Roma 1919); Dante e l'Islam (43 p., in Scritti vari pubblicati in occasione del VI. cent. di Dante, Varallo Sesia 1921), summary of the question with adverse criticism and bibliography (Isis 6, 151). Augustin Renaudet: Les influences orientales dans la Divine comédie et dans la peinture toscane (Revue de synthèse historique 40, 85-103, 1925; Isis 9, 154). Miguel Asín: Sobre las fuentes islámicas de la Divina comedia (Al-Andalus 1, 451-53, 1933). John S. P. Tatlock: Mohammed and his followers in Dante (Modern language review 27, 186-95, 1932; Isis 21, 365).

For the isrā' and the mi'rāj see B. Schrieke (EI 2, 553, 1921) and J. Horovitz (EI 3, 505-8, 1931).

For Biblical influences and chiefly for the tradition of ideas concerning Eden, see Giuseppe Ricciotti: L'apocalisse di Paolo Siriaca.[8a] I, Introduzione, traduzione e commento; II, La cosmologia della Bibbia e la sua trasmissione fino a Dante (2 parts, 215 p., 9 pl., Brescia 1932).

[8] One of the greatest Arabic poets, born at Ma'arrat al-Nu'mān (between Ḥalab and Ḥimṣ) in 973; died there in 1057. See Nicholson (EI 1, 75-77, 1908), together with the latter's description and partial translation of the Risāla in Journal of the Royal Asiatic Society (1900, 1902). Brockelmann (1, 254-55; suppt. 1, 449-54).

[8a] This Paolo Siriaca should not be confused with Paul the Persian (VI-2), for he lived under Theodosios I the Great (Byzantine emperor 379-95). Ricciotti has published the Syriac text of Paul's Apocalypse with a Latin translation (Orientalia 2, 1-25, 120-49, Rome 1933).

16. *Dante's influence*

Dante's influence has been so considerable and widespread that it is impossible to outline it here. In a way it is coextensive with Italian influence. For a preliminary study of it one may consult such books as Paget Toynbee: Dante in English literature from Chaucer to Cary, c. 1380 to 1844 (2 vols., London 1909); Britain's tribute to Dante in literature and art, a chronological record of 540 years, c. 1380–1920 (British Academy, 228 p., London 1921); Arturo Farinelli: Dante in Spagna, Francia, Inghilterra, Germania (515 p., Torino 1922); and Theodor Ostermann: Dante in Deutschland. Bibliographie der deutschen Dante-Literatur, 1416–1927 (602 p., Heidelberg 1929). Also the Dante bibliographies relative to each country, for example Oga's (1930) relative to Japan, cited in another section.

Giuliano Mambelli: Le traduzioni della Divina commedia e delle opere minori (Giornale dantesco 28, 97–146, 193–224, 289–312, 1925). This bibliography is very complicated (more than 929 items), not only because it involves some 36 languages, but because it is necessary to consider not only complete translations of the works or of the Commedia, but also translations of single cantiche or canti or even smaller fragments.

Giovanni Papini: La leggenda di Dante; motti, facezie e tradizioni dei secoli XIV–XIX (128 p., Lanciano 1911). Ralph Hayward Keniston: The Dante tradition in the fourteenth and fifteenth centuries (Dante Society, Reports 31, 1–92, 1915). Albert Wesseiski: Die Legende um Dante (96 p., Weimar 1921).

In accordance with the general plan of this Introduction, we are specially interested in Arabic and Hebrew translations.

The influence of Dante upon Arabic literature seems to have been negligible. In fact, I found no trace of it until our own days. A fragment (Purgatorio XI, 1–24) was translated into Arabic in 1912; a complete Arabic translation of the Commedia was printed only in 1930–33, this being a consequence of the Italian conquest of Libya. 'Abbūd Abū-Rāshid (a Lebanese established in Libya): Al-riḥlah al-Dāntīyah fī-l-mamālik al-ilāhīyah (3 vols., Tripoli 1930–33). See review by Philip K. Hitti (Journal of the American Oriental Society 54, 435, 1934).

The Hebrew translation was almost equally late. The first complete translation was made by Saul Formiggini (1807–73), physician in Trieste, but only the Inferno was printed (214 p., Trieste 1869). The MS of the two other parts was found by S. Sabbadini, but is still unpublished. Lelio della Torre: Sull'Inferno fatto ebraico dal signor Formiggini; lettere due a Benedetto Levi. Con appendice ebraica (28 p., Padova 1871).

However, the Italian Jews who were Dante's contemporaries or their descendants had no need of Hebrew translations and no desire for them. The strength of Dante's influence upon them may be deduced from the number of Hebrew imitations of the Commedia, but before speaking of these we should mention an earlier work which may have been anterior to the Divina commedia. This was the Maḥberet ha-ṭene, a description of a journey to Paradise by Aḥiṭub ben Isaac of Palermo (XIII-2). Aḥiṭub may have been submitted to the same Islamic influences as Dante himself and reacted in a similar way, or else he felt these influences only through Dante and after him. As to the following Hebrew writings, they were undoubtedly imitations: (1) Immanuel ben Solomon ha-Romi. Author of Ha-tofet we ha-'eden. (2) Moses ben Isaac da Rieti (1388–after 1460). Author of the Miqdash me'aṭ (The little sanctuary) in Hebrew terza rima. Edited by Jacob

Goldenthal, with preface in Italian and Hebrew (Vienna 1851). (3) Moses ben Mordecai Zacuto or Zakkuth (d. Mantua 1697). Author of the Tofte 'aruk. First printed, Venice 1715. (4) Jacob (Daniel) ben Abraham Olmo (d. Ferrara 1757). Author of a supplement to Zacuto's work entitled 'Eden 'aruk, written in the same style. Printed with the Tofte 'aruk in Venice 1743-44, Metz 1777, and translated into Italian by Cesare Foà (Finale nell' Emilia 1904).

Thus the Commedia has influenced not only Hebrew thought, but also Hebrew prosody and the Hebrew language.

Michele Barbi: Della fortuna di Dante nel secolo XVI (410 p., Pisa 1890). Giuseppe Lando Passerini: Dantisti e dantofili dei secoli XVIII e XIX (7 parts including 62 contributions by various authors, Firenze 1901-5). Corrado Ricci: La Divina commedia nell'arte del cinquecento (352 p., 70 pl., Milano 1908). Arturo Farinelli: Dante e la Francia dall' età media al secolo di Voltaire (2 vols., Milano 1908). Paget Toynbee: Dante in English literature from Chaucer to Cary, c. 1380 to 1844 (2 vols., London 1909). Giovanni Papini: La leggenda di Dante; motti, facezie e tradizioni dei secoli XIV-XIX (128 p., Lanciano 1911). Ralph Hayward Keniston: The Dante tradition in the XIV and XV centuries (Dante Society, Reports 31, 1-92, 1915). Guido Biagi (editor): La Divina commedia nella figurazione artistica e nel secolare commento (2 vols., Torino 1921-31). Corrado Ricci: La Divina commedia illustrata nei luoghi e nelle persone (3 vols., Milano 1921). Elizabetta Cavallari: La fortuna di Dante nel trecento (Firenze 1921). Piero Chiminelli: La fortuna di Dante nella Cristianità reformata, con speciale riferimento all'Italia (277 p., Roma 1921). Walter Arensberg: The cryptography of Dante (505 p., New York 1921); an erratic publication to illustrate Dante's influence (Isis 4, 586). Arturo Farinelli: Dante in Spagna, Francia, Inghilterra, Germania (Dante e Goethe) (515 p., Torino 1922). U. Cassuto (EJ 5, 789-90, 1930).

17. *Text*

(a) *Collected works.* Editions of Dante's works are innumerable. I can but mention a few. The most convenient editions of the Opera omnia are the "Oxford Dante," edited by Edward Moore, first published in 1894 (3d ed., Oxford 1904, 498 p. with index by Paget Toynbee; 4th ed. revised, 1924). This text was very beautifully reprinted by St. John Hornby in the Ashendene Dante (London 1919). Two other one-volume editions of the opera are Barbèra's (Florence 1919, 466 p. plus a copious index of 157 p.), the preface signed G. B., which I take to mean Guido Biagi; and the one prepared by the Società dantesca italiana (1012 p., Florence 1921), also with index; appendix by Ernesto Giacomo Parodi (1922) containing Il fiore and Il detto d'amore with index.

English translation of the Latin works by Alan George Ferrers Howell and Philip Henry Wicksteed (435 p., London 1904).

(b) *Divina commedia.* The Commedia was printed thrice in 1472, in Foligno, Mantua, and Iesi (Ancona), and there has been much discussion as to which of these three editions should be considered the princeps. The Foligno edition, which is the only one to be dated, 5-6 (11?) April 1472, seems to be the first. The three 1472 editions can be compared in the Pierpont Morgan Library, New York.

An edition printed in Florence 1481 is famous because of copper engravings the drawings for which are traditionally ascribed to Sandro Botticelli; another edition, Brescia 1487, is illustrated with 68 full-page woodcuts. Copies of both are in the Boston Public Library and have been discussed by Zoltán Haraszti (More books, March 1943, p. 96-108). There were at least eleven more incunabula editions. Mambelli (1931) has listed 662 editions (in Italian) of the Commedia.

Facsimile del Codice Landiano della Divina commedia, con prefazione ed introduzione di A. Balsamo e G. Bertoni (Florence 1921). Facsimile of the earliest MS with an unquestioned date, 1336. This MS was made by Antonio da Fermo, otherwise unknown, for Beccario Beccaria of Pavia, podestà of Genoa; it is now preserved in Piacenza.

Edward Moore: Contributions to the textual criticism of the Divina commedia (780 p., Cambridge 1889).

English translations by Henry Boyd, in verse (3 vols., London 1802); by Henry Francis Cary, in verse, with the Italian text (3 vols., London 1814); by Henry Wadsworth Longfellow, in verse (3 vols., Boston 1867); by Charles Eliot Norton, in prose (3 vols., Boston 1892); by H. F. Tozer, in prose (Oxford 1904); by Courtney Langdon, in blank verse, with the Italian text (3 vols., Cambridge, Mass. 1918–21). Henry Boyd's was the first complete translation of the Commedia to be printed, but an English fragment of the Inferno was printed in 1773, and the whole of the Inferno, translated by Henry Boyd, was printed in London 1785. Cary's translation in blank verse is perhaps the most valuable.

Many editions of the Commedia appeared in 1921, when the sixth centenary of Dante's death was celebrated all over the world. The most remarkable were: Corrado Ricci: La Divina commedia illustrata nei luoghi e nelle persone (quarto, 3 vols., 700 fig., 100 pl., Milano 1921); first published more modestly in 1898. Guido Biagi: La Divina commedia nella figurazione artistica e nel secolare commento. Vol. 1, L'Inferno (folio, 832 p., Torino 1921–24). The publication in parts was begun in 1921; after Biagi's death (1925) the continuation of the work was entrusted to Enrico Rostagno and Giuseppe Lando Passerini. Vol. 2, Purgatorio, appeared in 1931 (folio, 741 p., 1 pl., 103 fig.).

(c) *Vita nuova.* Editio princeps, Florence 1576, including Dante's life by Boccaccio. Many later editions. Friedrich Beck: Vita nuova. Kritischer Text unter Benützung von 35 bekannten Handschriften (192 p., München 1896). Another critical edition was prepared by Michele Barbi for the Società dantesca italiana (392 p., 5 pl., Milano 1907). Many times reprinted.

First English translation by Joseph Garrow, with Italian text (160 p., Florence 1846). Other English translations by Charles Eliot Norton (incomplete, 110 p., Cambridge, Mass. 1859; complete, 149 p., Boston 1867); by Dante Gabriele Rossetti in his Early Italian poets (p. 223–309, London 1861); by Theodore Martin (London 1862). Norton's translation and Rossetti's have been many times reprinted. Rossetti's is a classic of English literature.

(d) *De vulgari eloquentia.* First published in the Italian translation by Giovanni Giorgio Trissino (folio, 26 f., Vicenza 1529). Editio princeps (62 p., Paris 1577). Critical edition by Pio Rajna (422 p., Firenze 1896), and by Ludovicus Bertalot (88 p., Friedrichsdorf near Frankfurt a.M. 1917). Bertalot's edition was based upon a newly discovered MS, the Bini MS (second half of fourteenth century), containing also the text of the Monarchia.

English translation by Alan George Ferrers Howell (152 p., London 1890).

(e) *Convito.* Princeps entitled Convivio (90 f., Florence 1490). Second edition, Lo amoroso convivio di Dante (Venice 1521). Many later editions. Il Convivio ridotto a miglior lezione e commentato a G. Busnelli e G. Vandelli, con introduzione di Michele Barbi (2 vols., Florence 1934–37).

Il Convivio riprodotto in fototipia dal Codice Barberiniano latino 4086 con introduzione di Federico Schneider (26 p., 49 pl., Vatican City 1932; Isis 24, 204).

First English translation by Elisabeth Price Sayer (286 p., London 1887). Other translations by Katherine Hillard (468 p., London 1889); by Philip Henry Wicksteed (London 1903); by William Walrond Jackson (318 p., Oxford 1909).

(f) *De monarchia.* Princeps printed by Joannes Oporinus (Basel 1559). Monarchia, cum italica interpretatione Marsilii Ficini nunc primum in lucem edita

(212 p., Florence 1839). Latin and Italian texts often reprinted. Edition based on a new MS (the Bini MS mentioned above) by Ludovicus Bertalot (110 p., Friedrichsdorf 1917).

Friedrich Schneider: Die Monarchia aus der Berliner Handschrift Cod. Lat. folio 437 als Faksimile Druck (Weimar 1930); Monarchiae liber et Epistolae ex codice vaticano palatino 1729 phototypice expressa (Rome 1930).

First English translation by Frederick John Church (136 p., London 1879). Englished again by P. H. Wicksteed (Hull 1896) and by Aurelia Henry (268 p., Boston 1904), with Latin text. French translation by B. Landry (204 p., Paris 1933; Isis 21, 364).

(g) *Quaestio de aqua et terra*. Editio princeps by Giovanni Benedetto Moncetti (quarto, 12 f., Venice 1508). The editor claimed to have edited this text from Dante's own MS. That MS is lost and there is no other. The text has been often reprinted on the exclusive basis of the princeps. Facsimile edition of the princeps with introduction by O. Zanotti-Bianco and translations into Italian, French, Spanish, English, and German (212 p., Florence 1905). Critical edition by Vincenzo Biagi (195 p., Modena 1907).

English translations by Charles H. Bromby (London 1897); by Alain Campbell White (74 p., Boston 1903); by S. P. Thompson (Florence 1905); and by Charles Lancelot Shadwell (78 p., Oxford 1909), with the Latin text.

(h) *Epistolae*. Some letters were printed as early as 1547 in Florence and 1552 in Venice. Carl Witte: Epistolae quae exstant (108 p., Padua 1827). Critical edition by Paget Toynbee: Dantis epistolae (362 p., Oxford 1920). This includes the text of ten letters dated 1304 to c. 1319 (Isis 4, 136).

Friedrich Schneider: Briefe an die Fürsten und Völker Italiens und an Kaiser Heinrich VII (Zwickau, Saxony 1930); Briefe an Can Grande della Scala (Zwickau, Saxony 1933). Facsimile editions of MSS.

First English translation by Charles Sterrett Latham (302 p., Boston 1891). Other English versions by Philip H. Wicksteed (Hull 1898) and by Paget Toynbee (Cambridge 1917-18).

(i) *Canzoniere*. There are six incunabula editions, ranging from 1477 to 1497, of the apocryphal Credo. Canzoni e madrigali (Milano 1518), unique copy in the library of Cornell University. Many editions, the handiest for English readers being the one included in the Oxford Dante.

English translation by Charles Lyell (502 p., London 1835), many times reprinted. The translator, Charles Lyell (1767-1849), was a botanist, and the father of the famous geologist Sir Charles Lyell (1797-1875).

18. *Commentaries*

Luigi Rocca: Di alcuni commenti della Commedia composti nei primi vent' anni dopo la morte di Dante (440 p., Florence 1891). The earliest important commentary was Boccaccio's, cut short by his death (in 1375) but completed by his disciple Benvenuto Rambaldi of Imola (XIV-2).

The most important modern commentaries are the ones included in Giuseppe Campi's edition of the Commedia (3 vols., Torino 1888-91), index by E. Barbero (1893); the many publications of Giovanni Andrea Scartazzini (1837-1901); and the English commentaries by William Warren Vernon derived from the commentary of Benvenuto da Imola, Readings on the Inferno (2 vols., London 1894; 2d ed. revised 1906), Readings on the Purgatorio (2 vols., 1889; 2d ed. 1897; 3d ed. 1907), Readings on the Paradiso (2 vols., 1900; 2d ed. 1909); and by the Rev. Henry Fanshawe Tozer (636 p., Oxford 1901).

19. *Bibliographies*

Paul Colomb de Batines: Bibliografia dantesca (2 vols., Prato 1845-46); index to it (174 p., Bologna 1883); supplement by G. Biagi (Florence 1888). Bibliographies by Julius Petzholdt (Deutsche Dante-Gesellschaft) from 1869. Bibliographies by W. C. Lane on the basis of the Boston and Harvard collections (1890 to 1917). Lucien Auvray: Les manuscrits de Dante des bibliothèques de France (196 p., Paris 1892).

Giuliano Mambelli: Le traduzioni della Divina commedia e delle opere minori (Giornale dantesco 28, 97–146, 193–224, 289–312, 1925); Gli annali delle edizioni dantesche (435 p., 46 pl., Bologna 1931). The latter is a catalogue raisonné of 1,091 separate editions, with elaborate notes and many facsimiles, followed by a bibliography of illustrated editions of the Commedia and sets of illustrations relative to it, and by a list of writings on Dante.

The most elaborate and the most convenient bibliography is the Catalogue of the Dante collection of Cornell University. That collection is the largest of its kind, with the possible exception of that included in the Biblioteca nazionale of Florence. Theodore Wesley Koch: Catalogue of the Dante collection presented by Willard Fiske to Cornell University (2 vols., Ithaca, N. Y. 1898–99). Mary Fowler: Catalogue of the same collection, additions 1898–1920 (152 p., Ithaca, N. Y. 1921). For the period posterior to 1920, see N. D. Evola: Bibliografia dantesca 1920–1930 (260 p., Firenze 1932). This is vol. 33 of Il giornale dantesco.

For the sake of curiosity, I may add Jukichi Oga: Bibliografia dantesca giapponese (2d ed. revised, 59 p., Firenze 1930), in Italian translation and transcription, no Japanese type. This bibliography reveals the existence of many Japanese translations (p. 9–16), not only of the Divina commedia but of all the minor works, and of a great many Japanese studies (p. 17–59). The compiler, Oga, is himself the author of some 36 papers on Dante, most of them in Japanese, a few in English.

20. *Societies and journals*

An abundance of Dante materials is collected in the publications of Dante societies or in other Dante journals. The earliest of these societies was the German one, and the first volume of its Jahrbuch, Jahrbuch der deutschen Dante-Gesellschaft, appeared in Leipzig 1867. This Jahrbuch did not appear every year. In 1920, with the fifth volume, the title was changed to Deutsches Dante-Jahrbuch. Vol. 21 was published in Weimar 1939.

L'Alighieri. Rivista di cose dantesche (Verona and Venice 1889–93). Replaced by Giornale dantesco (Florence 1893). First edited by G. L. Passerini; vol. 36, edited by Luigi Pietrobono, appeared in 1933. Index to l'Alighieri and the Giornale, 1889–1910.

The Società dantesca italiana publishes a Bullettino (vols. 1–15, Florence 1890–99; new series, vols. 1–28, 1893–1921). Index to vols. 1–10, 1893–1903. Continued in the Studi danteschi edited by Michele Barbi (Florence, vol. 1, 1920; vol. 19, 1935).

Other Dante societies were founded in Oxford 1876, in London 1881, in Cambridge, Massachusetts 1882, in New York 1890, and many other cities, and almost every one of them has issued publications. Many of these publications, however, have only a sentimental interest.

21. *Dictionaries and concordances*

Giovanni Andrea Scartazzini: Enciclopedia dantesca (3 vols., Milano 1896–1905). Paget Toynbee: Dictionary of proper names and notable matters in the works of Dante (626 p., Oxford 1898); Concise dictionary (576 p., Oxford 1914). Though the concise dictionary contains new data, it does not supersede the earlier work. Both books should be consulted; they are very convenient, yet disappointing to the historian of science, who will seldom find in them the special information he is hunting for.

Edward Allen Fay: Concordance to the Commedia (825 p., Cambridge, Mass.

1888). E. S. Sheldon and A. C. White: Concordance to the minor Italian works (748 p., Oxford 1905). Edward Kennard Rand and E. H. Wilkins: Concordance to the Latin works (585 p., Oxford 1912).

22. *Biographies*

Giuseppe Lando Passerini: Le vite di Dante, scritta da Giovanni e Filippo Villani, da Giovanni Boccaccio, Leonardo Aretino e Giannozzo Manetti (340 p., Florence 1917).

Edward Moore: Dante and his early biographers (181 p., London 1890). Corrado Ricci: L'ultimo rifugio di Dante (498 p., Milano 1891; new ed., 497 p., 22 ill., 17 pl., Milano 1921). Paget Toynbee: Dante (4th ed. revised, 340 p., 16 pl., London 1910; 6th ed. revised, 1924; 1st ed. 1900). Pierre Gauthiez: Dante (Paris 1908). Carlo Cipolla: La data della morte di Dante secondo Ferreto dei Ferreti (Atti dell' Accad. di Torino 49, 1214–1219, 1914), claiming that Dante died not on September 14, 1321, but on August 11; Ferreto's testimony is the earliest available; he died before April 13, 1337. Giovanni Livi: Dante, suoi primi cultori, sua gente in Bologna (302 p., Bologna 1918). Charles Hall Grandgent: Dante (406 p., London 1920). Gertrude Leigh: New light on the youth of Dante (286 p., London 1929). G. McCroben: Dante in the Casentino (Florence 1931). Nicola Zingarelli: La vita, i tempi e le opere di Dante (2 vols., Milano 1931). Michele Barbi: Dante (270 p., Florence 1933). Giovanni Papini: Dante vivo (445 p., Florence 1933); English translation (1934).

23. *General studies*

Karl Vossler: Die göttliche Komödie, Entwicklungsgeschichte und Erklärung (2 vols., Heidelberg 1907–10; revised ed., 2 vols., Heidelberg 1925); La Divina commedia studiata nelle sua genesi e interpretazione (2 vols., Bari 1909–27); Mediaeval culture. An introduction to Dante and his times (2 vols., New York 1929). As these ponderous volumes have appeared in German, Italian, and English and are available in one form or another in most libraries, it is worth while to analyze them. Vol. 1: After an introduction comparing the Divine comedy with Goethe's Faust, the author explains Dante's religious, philosophical, ethical, and political backgrounds. In each case this involves a history of the subject begun as far back as possible. It is a history of ideas down to Dante. Vol. 2 deals in the same manner with the literary background and Dante's poetry. There are references to scientific subjects, but no adequate treatment of them. The English edition lacks many of the references of the German one, but includes a bibliography by J. E. Spingarn (2, 389–429, dated 1928). The part of that bibliography dealing with "mediaeval science" is very inadequate. Edward Moore: Studies in Dante (Oxford, vol. 1, 1896; vol. 2, 1899; vol. 3, 1903; vol. 4, 1917). Edmund G. Gardner (ERE 4, 394–99, 1912). Giuseppe Bindoni: Indagini critiche sulla Divina commedia (664 p., Milano 1918). Francesco Torraca: Studi danteschi, Nuovi studi (Naples 1912–21). Paget Toynbee: Dante studies and researches (367 p., London 1902); Dante studies (339 p., Oxford 1921). Philip Henry Wicksteed: From Vita nuova to Paradiso (166 p., Manchester 1921).

Innumerable studies appeared in 1921 to commemorate the sixth centenary of Dante's death. For example, Omaggio dell' Olando (L'Aia 1921). Essays in commemoration, by the University of London (London 1921). Paget Toynbee: Britain's tribute to Dante in literature and art, c. 1380–1920 (British Academy, 228 p., London 1921; Isis 4, 407). Recueil d'études publiées par l'Union intellectuelle franco-italienne (277 p., 40 pl., Paris 1921; Isis 5, 218).

James Eustace Shaw: Essays on the Vita nuova (236 p., Princeton 1929). Arthur H. Norway: Dante. The Divine comedy (172 p., London 1931). Alice Curtayne: A recall to Dante (256 p., London 1932). Mary Bradford Whiting: Dante and his poetry (215 p., London 1932). Friedrich Schneider: Dante. Eine Einführung in sein Leben und sein Werk (188 p., Weimar 1935). Rudolf Palgen: Das mittelalterliche Gesicht der göttlichen Komödie; Das Quellenproblem; Neue Beiträge zum Quellenproblem (3 pamphlets, 111, 39, 47 p., Heidelberg 1933–35). Giovanni Ferretti: I due tempi della composizione della Divina commedia (458 p., Bari 1935). Gaetano Salvemini: Florence in the time of Dante (Speculum 11, 317–26, 1936). Heinz Pflaum: The structure of the Divina commedia according to Dante (Sefer Magnes p. 188–98, Jerusalem 1938), in Hebrew with English summary. Coulton (p. 207–22, 1938b).

24. *Science in general*

Antonio Garbasso: La Commedia nei commenti degli scienzati italiani (34 p., Firenze 1912). Lloyd Roberts: The scientific knowledge of Dante (Manchester 1914). Gino Loria: Dante e la scienza del suo tempo (Conferenze e prolusioni 14, 193–202, Torino 1921; Isis 4, 406). Francesco Vercelli: Le scienze fisiche e matematiche nelle opere di Dante (Rivista marittima, 1923). Jonathan Wright: The foundations of science and religion in Dante's debt to Aristotle (Annals of medical history 10, 417–28, 1928). Giuseppe Boffito: Saggio d'un commento scientifico alla Divina commedia (23 p., Firenze 1936).

Studi su Dante e sulla scienze del suo secolo insieme ad altri lavori sulla storia della scienza e della civiltà (Roma 1921–23). This is a reprint from Mieli's Archivio di storia della scienza (3, 277–344), various articles of which are cited below in other sections.

Many of the studies on Dante's scientific knowledge are really studies of the scientific activities of his time, to which time the whole of our own book is devoted.

25. *Astronomy, cosmology, meteorology, and physics*

Giovanni Antonelli: Sulle dottrine astronomiche della Commedia (Firenze 1865) and other papers. Antonio Lubin: Dante e gli astronomi italiani. Dante e la donna gentile (160 p., Trieste 1895). Giuseppe Boffito: Per la storia della meteorologia in Italia (Torino 1898). Edward Moore: The astronomy of Dante (Studies in Dante, 3d series, p. 1–108, Oxford 1903). Filippo Angelitti: Sugli accenni danteschi ai segni, alle costellazioni ed al moto del cielo stellato da occidente in oriente di un grado in cento anni (Rivista di astronomia 1912–13), and many other papers. Mary Acworth Orr (Mrs. John Evershed): Dante and the early astronomers (524 p., 54 ill., London, n.d.; preface dated October 1913, Kodaikanal Observatory, S. India). This is a very elaborate study, but a large part of it (200 p.) is devoted to the history of astronomy from primitive times until the age of Dante. Duhem (4, 222–29, 1916). Ottavio Zanotti-Bianco: La trepidazione in Dante (Atti dell' Accad. di Torino 52, 353, 1916–17), refuting Duhem's views on the subject. Calogero Vitanza: Dante e l'astrologia (2 parts, Athenaeum anno 7, 1919). J. L. E. Dreyer: The cosmology of Dante (Nature 107, 428–30, 1921). Giuseppe Boffito: Dante geodeta (Giornale dantesco 24, 96–119, 1921; Isis 8, 744); Distanze e dimensioni cosmichi secondo Dante (Archivio di storia della scienza 3, 34–44, 1922). Pio Emanuelli: L'astronomia in Dante (ibid. 301–10, 1923; Isis 5, 502). Filippo Angelitti (1856–1931), cultore di astronomia dantesca (Archeion 13, 69–73, 1931). Bruno Nardi: Dante e Alpetragio (Giornale dantesco vol. 29, 15 p., Firenze 1926). Cesare Nisi: L'ottica nella Divina commedia (Annuario Assoc. ottica italiana p. 50–68, 1931). Giuseppe Boffito: Le quattro "chiare" stelle di Dante (Pubblicazioni dell' Osservatorio del Collegio alla Querce, no. 62, p. 3–6, Firenze 1936). Hennig (3, 148–52, 1938) apropos of Dante's knowledge of southern stars.

26. *Geography*

See our notes above on the Quaestio de aqua et terra, and the discussion of that treatise by Eduard Suess in his great treatise Das Antlitz der Erde. I have used Emmanuel de Margerie's French edition, La face de la terre (2, 5–10, 1909).

Edward Moore: The geography of Dante (in his Studies in Dante, 3d series, p. 109–43, Oxford 1903), lecture delivered in the Sala Dante, Or San Michele, Florence, Easter 1900. Assunto Mori: La geografia in Dante (Archivio di storia della scienza 3, 57–69, 1921). Paolo Revelli: L'Italia nella Divina commedia. Con la riproduzione diplomatica del planisfere vaticano-palatino di Pietro Vesconte del 1320–1321 e una cartina, l'Italia di Dante (Milano 1922). Arnold Norlind: Dante som geograf (Ymer, 1924, p. 260–78, 7 fig.). R. Benini: Il lago di Circonio (Palus Lugea degli antichi) nel disegno dantesco dell'Inferno (Rendiconti dell' Accad. dei Lincei 4, 3–14, 1928; Isis 13, 163). Alberto Magnaghi: Questioni di geografia dantesca (Rivista geografica italiana 35, 195–205, 1928). E. O. von Lippmann: Dante's Schrift über Meer und Festland (Geistige Arbeit 4, 3–4, 1937; Isis 29, 213). Kimble (241–44, 1938).

27. *Mathematics*

Giuseppe Boffito: Il punto e il cerchio secondo gli antichi e secondo Dante (Rendiconti dell'Istituto lombardo 36, 1129–42, 1903). Gino Loria: Le matematiche nel secolo di Dante (Archivio di storia della scienza 3, 32–33, 1921). Giuseppe Boffito: Della "matematica" nell'uso popolare, dotto e lessicale al tempo e nell'opera di Dante (Pubblicazioni del Collegio alla Querce di Firenze, serie in 8vo, no. 36, 23 p., 1937); Dove e quando potè Dante vedere gli orologi meccanici che descrive (Giornale dantesco vol. 39, annuario dantesco 9, Firenze 1938).

28. *Chemistry*

E. O. von Lippmann: Chemisches und Technologisches bei Dante (Chemiker Zeitung p. 901, 1921); reprinted in his Beiträge (p. 192–97, 1923); also in the Archivio di storia della scienza (3, 45–56, 1921; Isis 5, 503). Julius Ruska: L'alchimie à l'époque du Dante (Annales Guébhard-Séverine, 10me année, 410–17, 1934); this paper does not deal at all with Dante.

29. *Natural history*

Levi Oscar Kuhns: The treatment of nature in the Commedia (214 p., London 1897). Richard Thayer Holbrook: Dante and the animal kingdom (390 p., New York 1902). Raffaele Sarra: Le conoscenze zoologiche di Dante (Archivio di storia della scienza 3, 237–43, 1922). Eugenio Righini: L'agricoltura nella Commedia (74 p., Ferrara 1922). Augusto Béguinot: Le piante nella Commedia (Archivio 3, 277–82, 1923). Vincenzo Cioffarri: Smeraldo (Speculum 19, 360–63, 1944).

30. *Physiology and embryology*

Antonino del Gaudio: Fisiologia della generazione umana nel canto xxv del Purgatorio (Archivio di storia della scienza 5, 101–13, 1924; 6, 121–38, 1925; 8, 176–79, 1927). Giuseppe Boffito: La circolazione del sangue secondo Cecco d'Ascoli e Dante (Pubblicazioni del Collegio alla Querce, no. 35, 20 p., Firenze 1932). Needham (p. 75–77, 1934).

31. *Medicine*

Michelangelo Asson: Intorno le conoscenze biologiche e mediche di Dante (Atti del Istituto veneto vol. 6, 27 p., Venezia 1861). Alexander G. Drury: Dante physician (90 p., Cincinnati 1908). P. H. Dernehl: Notes médicales sur la Divine comédie (Répertoire de médecine internationale, 1911–12; also in Bull. Johns Hopkins Hospital 22, 333–44, 1911). Ercole Passera: Le cognitizione oftalmologiche di Dante (Archivio di storia della scienza 3, 1–31, 1921). Arturo Castiglioni: La medicina ai tempi e nell'opere di Dante (ibid. p. 211–36, 1922). Marcel Fosseyeux: Dante et la médecine de son temps (Comptes rendus du 2e congrès international d'histoire de la médecine, Paris 1921, p. 275–81, Evreux 1922; Revue des études historiques p. 139–50, 1922). Guglielmo Bilancioni: Dante e i medici (Archivio di storia della scienza 3, 283–300, 1923). Wilhelm Haberling: War Dante ein Arzt? (Deutsches Dante-Jahrbuch 7, 59–78, 1923). Liborio Giuffre: Dante e le scienze mediche (194 p., Bologna 1924). Raffaele Ciasca: Dante e l'arte dei medici e speziali (Archivio storico italiano 15, 59–97, 1931); German translation, Dante als Arzt und Apotheker (Deutsches Dante-Jahrbuch 13, 163–96, 1931). Leopold Vaccaro: The medical side of Dante (Medical life 39, 65–71, 1932). C. Pedrazzini: Dante et la pharmacie al Canto delle Rondini à Florence (Vorträge der Hauptversammlung der Gesellschaft für Geschichte der Pharmazie p. 114–17, Basel 1934).

32. *Philosophy*

Frédéric Ozanam (1813–53): Dante et la philosophie catholique au treizième siècle (Paris 1839). A book that made a considerable stir a century ago; often reprinted and translated into English.

Carlo Pagano Paganini: Chiose e luoghi filosofici della Commedia (100 p., Città di Castello 1894). Natale Busetto: Saggi di varia psicologia dantesca; relazioni di Dante con Alberto Magno e San Tommaso (Prato, Toscana 1905). Otto Miller: Dantes Geschichtsphilosophie (Freiburg Diss., 130 p., Hildesheim 1912). Bruno Nardi: Sigieri di Brabante e le fonti della filosofia di Dante (Rivista di filosofia neo-scolastica 1912). Philip Henry Wicksteed: Dante and Aquinas (283 p., London 1913). Giovanni Busnelli: Cosmogonia e antropogenesi secondo Dante e le sue fonti (Roma 1922), defending the purity of Dante's Thomism against Nardi. Karl Weczerzik von Planheim: Die Scholastik in Dantes Weltsystem (Wien 1923). Arturo Farinelli: Der Aufstieg der Seele bei Dante (Bibliothek Warburg, Vorträge 1928–29, 191–213, 1930). Bruno Nardi: Saggi di filosofia dantesca (Milano 1930). Pierre Mandonnet: Dante le théologien (332 p., Paris 1935). H. R. Patch: The last line of the Commedia (Speculum 14, 56–65, 1939).

33. *Government and law*

Gino Arias: Le istituzioni giuridiche medievali nella Commedia (Firenze 1901). Joseph Kohler: Dante und die Homosexualität (Archiv für Strafrecht und Strafprozess 48, 63–67, 109–10, 1901). Hans Kelsen: Die Staatslehre des Dante (156 p., Wien 1905). Antonio Cappa-Legora: La politica di Dante e di Marsiglio di Padova (Roma 1906). James Williams: Dante as a jurist (72 p., Oxford 1906). Hermann Heinrich Grauert: Dante und die Idee des Weltfriedens (Bayerische Akademie, Festrede, 42 p., München 1909). Anton von Kostanecki: Dantes Philosophie des Eigentums (Archiv für Rechtsphilosophie vol. 4, 1911). Isidoro del Lungo: Dante in patria e nell'esilio errabondo (Lectura Dantis, Firenze 1914). Filippo Paleschi: Patria, politica e società delle nazioni nel pensiero e nell' opera di Dante (29 p., Parma 1920). Ezio Flori: Dell'idea imperiale di Dante (Bologna 1921?). John Joseph Rolbiecki: The political philosophy of Dante (Catholic University of America thesis, 156 p., Washington 1921). Arrigo Solmi: Il pensiero politico di Dante (Firenze 1922). Léon Prieur: Dante et l'ordre social. Le droit public dans la Divine comédie (Paris 1923). Allan H. Gilbert: Dante's conception of justice (254 p., Durham, N. C. 1925; Speculum 2, 346–49). Ettore Lombardo Pellegrino: Dante e la concezione politica (77 p., Messina 1925). Modesto Scarpini: Il sistema religioso politico di Dante (Firenze 1926). Dino Bigongiari: The text of Dante's Monarchia (Speculum 2, 457–62, 1927). Francesco Ercole: Il pensiero politico di Dante (2 vols., Milano 1927–28). Girolamo Grillo: Dante giurista (69 p., Velletri 1934). Carlyle (6 vols., 1903–36) pays very little attention to Dante (6, 111–23). W. H. V. Reade: Dante's vision of history (Proc. British Academy 25, 187–215,

1939). Helen Wieruszowski: Art and the Commune in the time of Dante (Speculum 19, 14–33, 4 pls., 1944).

34. *Iconography*

Charles Eliot Norton: On the original portraits of Dante (18 p., Cambridge, Mass. 1865). Also in Japanese translation (Tokyo 1893). Richard Thayer Holbrook: Portraits of Dante from Giotto to Raffael (quarto, 284 p., 37 pl., London 1911). P. Toynbee: Portraits of Dante (Bodleian quarterly record 2, 53–57, 1917). Frank Jewett Mather: The portraits of Dante, compared with the measurements of his skull and reclassified (100 p., 66 ill., Princeton 1921). G. L. Passerini: Il ritratto di Dante (50 pl., Firenze 1921). Cesare Foligno: Dante (Bergamo 1921). Fabio Frassetto: Dantis ossa, la forma corporea di Dante: scheletro, ritratti, maschere e busti (folio, 213 p., 93 fig., Bologna 1933). Elaborate study of Dante's remains and discussion of his iconography in function of the anthropometrical data thus obtained. The author concludes that the image of Dante is best preserved in the Giotto fresco in the Bargello, Florence, and (even better) in the miniature of the Codex Palatinus no. 320 (Biblioteca nazionale, Florence). According to Mather and others, this miniature is derived from a portrait by Taddeo Gaddi (1300–66), which was in Santa Croce and was destroyed in 1566 by Giorgio Vasari, by order of Cosimo I de' Medici.

35. *Symbolism, occultism, et alia*

Michele Angelo Caetani, duca di Sermoneta (1804–82): Della dottrina che si asconde nell'ottavo e nono canto dell'Inferno (21 p., Roma 1852). This is the origin of the symbolic or occultist interpretation of the Commedia. Giovanni Pascoli: Sotto il velame (640 p., Messina 1900; 3d ed., Bologna 1923); La mirabile visione (782 p., Messina 1902). Luigi Pietrobono: Il poema sacro (Bologna 1915). Walter Arensberg: The cryptography of Dante (506 p., New York 1921). René Guénon: L'ésotérisme de Dante (100 p., Paris 1925; Isis 8, 745). Luigi Valli: L'allegoria di Dante secondo Giovanni Pascoli (Bologna 1922); Il segreto della croce e dell' aquila (362 p., Bologna 1922); La chiave della Divina commedia (Bologna 1925); Il linguaggio secreto di Dante e dei "Fedeli d'amore" (454 p., Roma 1928). H. Flanders Dunbar: Symbolism in mediaeval thought and its consummation in the Divine comedy (500 p., New Haven 1929).

Gertrude Leigh: New light on the youth of Dante. The course of Dante's life prior to 1290 traced in the Inferno, cantos 3–13 (286 p., London 1929); The passing of Beatrice. A study in the heterodoxy of Dante (220 p., London 1932).

JACOPO ALIGHIERI

Jacopo di Dante Alighieri. Florentine didactic poet and commentator on the Divina commedia of his father (d. before 1349).

Dante had four children in the following order: Pietro (d. Treviso 1364), Jacopo, Antonia, and Beatrice. Beatrice was a nun at Ravenna in 1350 when Boccaccio brought her a present from the capitani of Or San Michele in Florence; she died before 1370. Pietro and Jacopo were mentioned together (filios) in the second decree of banishment against Dante (1315), and they were separately named in documents of 1332 and 1342. The sons were among the exiles permitted to return to Florence in 1325 on condition of paying a definite part of their fines. Jacopo was banished again soon afterward; he became a priest and was a canon in Verona in 1341–42; he died before 1349.

Sometime after 1326 he wrote a commentary (Chiose) on the Inferno. He was not the first to do so, but had two predecessors, Ser Graziolo (1324) and Guido da

Pisa (1325–26). These three early commentators did not go beyond the Inferno, but Jacopo had planned a commentary on the Purgatorio. The purpose of his Chiose alla cantica dell'Inferno was neither grammatical nor historical, but rather to underline the main allegorical aspect of the poem, a moralizing meditation on the vicissitudes of mankind.

Jacopo (or his elder brother Pietro) was the author of a canzone foretelling the conclusion of peace between John XXII and Ludwig of Bavaria. He is very probably the author of a didactic poem entitled Il Dottrinale, a kind of popular encyclopaedia in verse probably composed after his father's death (1321). It is divided into 60 chapters containing each 10 stanze of 6 lines each, that is, in all 3,600 lines, a curious sexagesimal arrangement.

The main scientific sources are al-Farghānī (probably through Dante) and Sacrobosco. Jacopo may have been acquainted with the Tesoretto of Brunetto Latini (d. 1294/95) and with the Acerba of Cecco d'Ascoli (d. 1327), and of course he knew very well his father's work. The authors quoted in the Dottrinale are Hermes, Hippocrates, Aristotle, Euclid, Ptolemy, Galen, Orosius; Māshāllāh, Abū Ma'shar, al-Farghānī, al-Kindī, Zahel (Sahl ibn Bishr), Ibn Sīnā, and a few others whom I cannot identify.

Chapters 1–5 deal with astronomy, the spherical shape of the earth, the proportion of earth and water; chs. 6–9 with the climates, chs. 10–11 with the four elements, chs. 12–15 with the motions of the planets, chs. 16–18 with the eighth sphere, ch. 19 with astrology, chs. 20–21 with the signs of the zodiac, chs. 22–26 with the planets, chs. 27–32 with meteorology (29, thunder; 30, earthquakes; 31, winds; 32, shooting stars and comets), ch. 33 with the Milky Way, ch. 34 with the cause of nights, ch. 35 with the colors of stars, ch. 36 with eclipses, ch. 37 with astrology and natural philosophy.

These 37 chapters constitute a popular account of natural philosophy; the remaining chapters are devoted to moral philosophy and theology, as follows: 38, faith; 39, hope; 40, charity; 41, providence; 42, justice; 43, fortitude; 44, temperance; 45, government of the church (reggimento di Sancta chiesa cattolica); 46, government of the empire; 47–48, kingdoms, cities, and castles; 49, government of self and family; 50, love and hatred; 51–52, conditions of human beauty (condizione delle bellezze humane); 53, Continenza del non volere e dell'odio; 54, free will; 55–59, moral commentary on the Divina commedia; 60, conclusion.

Text. Giovanni Rossi: Capitoli di M. Bosone da Gubbio e di Jacopo Alighieri (Napoli 1829). Bosone de' Raffaelli da Gubbio was a contemporary, podestà in Umbria and Toscana, vicar of Louis of Bavaria in 1327, and senator of Rome in 1337; died after 1349. Lord Vernon: Chiose alla cantica dell' Inferno (286 p., Firenze 1848). Capitolo di Jacopo Alighieri sopra la Divina commedia (8 p., published anonymously at "Utopia" 1850). Francesco Paolo Luiso: Chiose di Dante le quali fece il figliuolo co le sue mani. Vol. II Purgatorio (186 p., Firenze 1904), cited pro forma; this is not Jacopo's work. Jarro (= G. Piccini): Chiose alla cantica dell'Inferno da Jacopo Alighieri, pubblicate per la prima volta in corretta lezione con riscontri e fac-simili di codici, e precedute da una indagine critica (only 75 copies printed, folio, 164 p., 8 pl., Firenze 1915).

The Dottrinale was first edited by the marchese di Villarosa (Palermo 1817). Edition by Giovanni Crocioni (Collezione di opuscoli danteschi edited by G. L. Passerini, vols. 26–28, 336 p., Città di Castello 1895). Elaborate critical edition with long introduction, glossary, and indexes.

Criticism. Etienne Audin de Rians: Delle vere chiose di Jacopo Alighieri e del comento ad esso attribuito (24 p., Firenze 1848), dedicated to G. G. Warren, Lord Vernon. Vittorio Imbriani: Documenti su Jacopo Alighieri (Aneddoti tansilliani[9] e danteschi, edited by Francesco Fiorentino and Vittorio Imbriani, p. viii–xv, Napoli 1883). Luigi Rocca: Di alcuni commenti della Divina commedia composti nei primi vent'anni dopo la morte di Dante (Firenze 1891). Giovanni Crocioni: La materia del Dottrinale in relazione con le teorie del tempo (Rivista di fisica, matematica e scienze naturali vols. 3, 4, 1902–4). Francesco Paolo Luiso: Tra chiose e commenti alla Divina commedia (Archivio storico italiano 31, 71–96, 1903; 33, 1–52, 1904). Arnaldo Della Torre: Un documento poco noto sul ribandimento di Iacopo di Dante (ibid. p. 289–331). Sapegno (p. 115, 129, 1934). J. W. Thompson (p. 521, 1939), apropos of Pietro di Dante.

FRANCESCO PETRARCA (1304–74)

One of the greatest poets of Europe in the vernacular as well as in Latin. One of the creators of Italian language, culture, and unity. One of the pioneers of the humanistic reaction against mediaevalism, and, as such, one of the founders of modern culture and indirectly of modern science.

Contents: (1) Life. (2) Character. (3) Petrarca man of letters. (4) Petrarca's works. (5) His Christian humanism. (6) His attitude toward science. (7) His geographical views. (8) His political views. (9) His influence.

(10) General bibliography. (11) Indexes and concordances. (12) Facsimile manuscripts. (13) Printed texts. (14) Biographies and general criticism. (15) Special criticism. (16) Geographical criticism. (17) Philosophical criticism. (18) Political criticism. (19) Documents concerning Petrarca's influence.

1. *Life*

Francesco Petrarca belonged to an old Florentine family, but his father, the notary Ser Petracco (a form of Pietro) son of Parenzo, was exiled from Florence for political reasons on the same day as Dante, January 27, 1302. Ser Petracco established himself in the Ghibelline city of Arezzo. There Francesco was born on Monday, July 20, 1304 (later he changed his name to Francesco Petrarca instead of Francesco di Petracco). It would take too long to recite all his family's wanderings and his own; it will suffice to recall the main "stations." In 1313 the family moved to Avignon; from 1315 to 1318 Francesco studied in the school of Carpentras (not very far from Avignon), being taught by Convenevole da Prato; then he spent four years studying law in Montpellier and three more years at the University of Bologna.

On April 6, 1327, he beheld for the first time, in the church of Santa Clara in Avignon, "Laura," the woman who remained his main source of inspiration. Nothing very definite is known about her. She was probably a married woman, and died (of the plague?) on April 6, 1348. Petrarca took orders but was never a priest. He had two illegitimate children, born probably of the same unknown mother (not Laura): a son Giovanni (1337–61), and a daughter Francesca (1343–84), who married in Milano and gave him two grandchildren.

Petrarca's first long journey occurred in 1333, when he visited Paris, Ghent, Liége, Aix-la-Chapelle, Cologne. At the close of 1336 he sailed from Marseille for his first visit to Rome. In 1337, he retired into the solitude of Vaucluse on the Sorgue (some 15 miles from Avignon), where much of his work was done and which remained until 1353 his favorite retreat. In February 1341 he left for Naples to

[9] Luigi Tansillo, Italian poet (1510?–68).

Fig. 9. Portrait of Petrarca, discovered by Pierre de Nolhac in a MS of Petrarca's De viris illustribus (Bibliothèque nationale, Paris, fonds latin n° 6069F). That MS was completed in Padua by Lombardo della Seta, Petrarca's friend, in 1379, four and a half years after the latter's death. From Prince d'Essling and Eugène Müntz: Pétrarque (p. 66, Paris 1902).

visit king Robert of Anjou (then count of Provence and as such lord of Avignon, thus Petrarca's ruler; Avignon was sold to the popes in 1348). On Easter Sunday, April 8, 1341, he received the laurel crown of poetry on the Capitol. This is very significant, Petrarca being the first poet to be thus honored since the days of Statius (died c. 96),[10] more than twelve and a half centuries before.

In October 1350, he started on a pilgrimage to Rome for the Jubilee, and, stopping in Florence, met Boccaccio and Francesco Nelli.[11] In the following spring Florence recalled him from exile, offering him (through Boccaccio) a chair in its newly founded university; Petrarca did not accept the offer.

From 1353 to 1361 he flourished under Visconti patronage in Milano; driven out of that city by an outbreak of the plague in July 1361, he moved to Padua, then to Venice, where the republic had offered him a house (1362) and where he spent some five years. In 1369, he settled in Arquà in the Euganean hills (Colli Euganei), not far from Padua; and this was his main residence until his death there in the night of July 18, 1374.

Being an exile, Petrarca never enjoyed a permanent home, but the two places which came closest to being homes to him were Vaucluse (1337–53), the retreat of his maturity, and Arquà (1369–74), the retreat of his last years, both solitary places in hilly landscapes. Petrarca's house in Vaucluse has disappeared, but the famous fontaine de Vaucluse (the spring of the river Sorgue) still sings his fame. The little town of Arquà is now called Arquà Petrarca; it boasts the poet's house and his tomb. The tomb was violated and robbed in 1630, restored in 1843. The "casa" suffered many alterations; in 1923, it was restored and has now become a Petrarcan sanctuary and museum.

2. *Character*

In his Averroès (p. 328, ster. ed. 1869) Ernest Renan called Petrarca "le premier homme moderne." The phrase has often been repeated; it is striking, though a little misleading, and paradoxical. Petrarca himself was aware of his being at the limit of two worlds, "velut in confinio duorum populorum constitutus ac simul ante retroque prospiciens" (De rebus memorandis 1, 2). Contrast him with Dante, whose Divina commedia marked the climax and the end of an age; Petrarca's activities symbolize the adumbration of a new age. And yet he was a true "laudator temporis acti," he loathed the present and the more immediate (mediaeval) past. He was progressive, but had set his goal in classical antiquity. He was a reformer, but wanted to restore Roman culture. He was anti-mediaeval, anti-scholastic, anti-Aristotelian, anti-Arabic, and, as we shall see below, he was also anti-scientific. His hatred of ignorance and superstition, and his witty invectives, suggest comparison with Erasmus and even with Voltaire.

On the other hand, he introduced a new kind of introspection—very rare in mediaeval times—and his very nostalgia was "modern" (new) in its form of ex-

[10] The succession is rather distant but natural. The author of the Africa was the genuine heir of the author of the Thebaid and the Achilleid; and some of his shorter poems might be compared with the Silvae. Petrarca, however, was a far greater man than Statius. The same honor was given to Mussato in 1315, but in Padua, not in Rome.

[11] Francesco Nelli, called Simonide by Petrarca, prior of the Santi Apòstoli in Florence, died at Naples in 1363. He is remembered today only because of his friendship with Petrarca. Henri Cochin: Un ami de Pétrarque, lettres de F. Nelli à Pétrarque (324 p., Paris 1892); Italian edition (210 p., Firenze 1901).

pression. His interest in the sensuous world was something new; many of his descriptions remain pitifully abstract and conventional, yet they are informed with new feelings. His love of travel is remarkable. It is difficult to measure the degree of "modernism" of so many intangible qualities, yet the general statement may be accepted grosso modo: Petrarca opens a new age.

3. *Petrarca man of letters*

Petrarca, like Dante, wrote in Italian and in Latin, but, unlike Dante, he used predominantly the second language. He wrote a large amount of Latin poetry and a great many Latin letters; he expected fame and immortality from his Latin writings, but as a matter of fact he has obtained it very largely from his Italian poetry, to which he himself attached far less importance.

He seemed to believe that one's vernacular is best for domestic and sentimental purposes, the international language (such as Latin was in his days) preferable for matters of international concern.

There was nothing provincial in his use of the "vernacular," however, and so he was one of the founders of the Italian language even as he was one of the harbingers of Italian unity.

His Italian poetry is very different from Dante's in almost every respect; in spite of the love of nature which it reveals, it is often artificial and conventional. Dante was the first great Italian poet, Petrarca the first "man of letters."

It is typical of Petrarca's temperamental polarity to Dante that he did not read the Divina commedia until relatively late (in the fifties of the century and of his age), and that only upon the entreaties of his younger friend Boccaccio, who gave him a copy of it.

4. *Petrarca's works*

Italian poetry is but a small part (about one-sixteenth) of Petrarca's production, but by far the most important from the point of view of "belles lettres," and the most popular. Editions of the Canzoniere and the Trionfi are almost innumerable; the first (of both) was published by Wendelin of Speyer in Venice 1470.

To pass to the Latin writings, the most ambitious was the long epic Africa, dealing with the Punic war and the glorification of Scipio Africanus major (237-183 B.C.). Petrarca began it in his youth and was not able to complete it. It was printed half a dozen times in the sixteenth century, and a few times more later on; it was translated into Italian, French, and Swedish.

Next in importance in Petrarca's opinion was the De viris illustribus, which was not completely edited until 1874-79. The life of Caesar, however (as long by itself as all the other lives together), was printed as early as 1473 and many times afterward. A work of the same kind was the De rebus memorandis, first printed at Louvain 1484/85.

The most popular of Petrarca's Latin writings was the De remediis utriusque fortunae, wherein he speaks of a great many subjects, gives abundant illustrations of the vanity of good fortune, and offers consolation to the victims of ill fortune. The need of such a book would naturally be greater in hard times, and those times were very hard indeed. There are at least four complete incunabula editions, plus half a dozen fragmentary ones. A good index of its popularity in wide circles is the existence of many early translations: a Bohemian translation by Rehoř Hruby of Gelenije (Gregorius Gelenius), printed as early as 1501; a Spanish one by Franciscus de Madrid, printed in Valladolid 1510; a French one by Nicole Oresme, or more probably Jean Dandin, printed in Paris 1523 (this is the earliest translation of the treatise into another language); an incomplete German one printed in Oppenheim 1516, and a complete one in Augsburg 1532; an Italian one by the Florentine Dominican Remigio Nannini or Nanni (1521–81), printed in Venice 1549; an English one, Phisicke against fortune, as well prosperous as adverse, by the physician Thomas Twyne (1543–1613), printed in London 1579; a Dutch one, printed in Amsterdam 1606.

Petrarca's Secret, i.e., the treatise De contemptu mundi which he called Secretum suum, is the book I had in mind when I spoke (in §2) of his introspection. It is a discussion of some of his most intimate conflicts (e.g., on the subject of his love for Laura) in the form of a dialogue between himself and St. Augustine. It was printed as early as 1473 and many times afterward, though far less frequently than the Remedia.

Among the shorter Latin writings it will suffice to mention De vita solitaria, printed as early as 1473 (?) and soon translated into Spanish (printed 1553); De otio religiosorum; and De suiipsius et multorum ignorantia, a pamphlet against the Averroists.

Petrarca's letters are as bulky as the rest of his Latin writings put together. Some of them are almost like formal treatises, for example, the two letters De quibusdam consiliis medicinae, addressed to Giovanni of Padua (they fill 18 closely printed pages in the folio edition of 1581, p. 897–914), and the Epistola ad posteros (princeps, Louvain 1484/85), an autobiography down to his 47th year, which inspires much confidence in spite of some confusion about dates. The letters are divided into various collections, as follows: De rebus familiaribus or Epistolae familiares, some 347 letters written between 1332 and 1362 (first ed., incomplete, 1492); Epistolae variae, some 70 letters; Epistolae de rebus senilibus, 124 letters of the period 1362–74, some of which, like the two to Giovanni of Padua above mentioned, are very long; Epistolae sine titulo, some 20 letters including bitter criticisms of the Avignonese papal regime; the words "sine titulo" refer to the fact that the names of the addressees have been suppressed, probably for their safety's sake.

The corpus of Petrarca's letters is comparable to that of Erasmus' letters written two centuries later. In both cases the letters were the main instruments of contemporary influence, and they have remained monuments of their authors' fame.

5. *His Christian humanism*

Petrarca's chief achievement was his starting of what might be called the first age of humanism, the age of exploration and vague inspiration. In particular, he was a promoter of Latin studies, a passionate defender of Roman antiquity, which he admired so much that the dismal present became more dismal to him, and the future, except if redeemed with humanism, more completely hopeless.

He was well acquainted with Latin literature, but was influenced chiefly by Cicero and Virgil (the main sources of inspiration of the Italian renaissance) and secondarily by Livy, Seneca, St. Augustine; he had some very imperfect knowledge of Homer, Plato, and Aristotle through Latin versions. He knew no Greek, though some rudiments of it may have been shown to him by Bernardo Barlaam (Avignon 1339) or Leonzio Pilato (Venice 1363). He owned Greek MSS of Plato and Homer, but could not read them ("Homerus apud me mutus"). Yet he had an intuitive appreciation of the fundamental importance of Greek studies, and it was he who advised Boccaccio to learn that language.

His love of Roman literature and his interest in pagan mythology did not create any conflict in him with his religion, for his devotion was too strong and his orthodoxy unassailable (conscious paganism was unknown in his time). His humanism was a Christian humanism equally distant from the pagan humanism of the later Renaissance and from the Christian mediaevalism of Dante; he could admire equally Cicero and Augustine, and reconcile the love of classical literature and the love of nature with Christian asceticism. Though he recognized the perfection of monastic life, he was too much of a humanist to withdraw from the world; he loved solitude for the sake of his literary needs rather than for mystical reasons.

He had gradually gathered a large collection of MSS (certainly more than 200) which he agreed to bequeath to the city of Venice when he settled there in 1362. However, his library was never delivered to Venice. It fell into the hands of his last patron, Francesco I da Carrara, lord of Padua (d. 1393); it was ceded by him in 1388 to Gian Galeazzo Visconti (1347–1402) and carried by the latter to Pavia. In 1499, Pavia was sacked by the French. Thus were Petrarca's MSS scattered: some 26 volumes have been identified in the Bibliothèque nationale in Paris, 6 more in Rome, single items in Florence, Venice, Padua, and Milan.

Petrarca discovered two speeches of Cicero's (one of them pro Archia) in Liége 1333, and his letters to Atticus, Brutus, and Quintus in Verona 1345. Up to that time Cicero's letters were unknown; the letters ad familiares remained unknown until 1389.

Petrarca collected not only MSS, but also inscriptions and coins. He sent Roman coins obtained from treasure-trove to the emperor Charles IV in Mantua 1354, in order to encourage him to have similar ones made. He may have been the indirect cause of the creation of the first medals before the end of the century. The earliest medal known is the one bearing the effigy of Francesco II Novello da Carrara (1359–1406, son of Francesco I above mentioned), coined to celebrate his recapture of Padua on June 15, 1390; it is clearly inspired by Roman coins.[12]

6. *His attitude toward science*

Petrarca "the first modern man" was intensely anti-mediaeval. He was one of the first to consider the Middle Ages as "dark ages." This explains his lack of interest in Dante, who ought to have been so dear to him in many respects (e.g., Italian nationalism). The Latin renaissance of the twelfth and thirteenth centuries had been essentially, under Arabic stimulation, a scientific renaissance; indeed, the scientific, logical, and theological interests had been carried to the extreme of implying a neglect and contempt of form and style. The mediaeval renaissance had been largely anti-literary; by reaction, the new Italian renaissance initiated by Petrarca tended to be anti-scientific.

Under the influence of his Muslim, Jewish, and Christian interpreters, Aristotle had been gradually exalted to the skies. Hence Petrarca's reaction was anti-Aristotelian, and as Averroes had been the main artisan of Aristotle's triumph, it was also anti-Averroistic. Though Petrarca's knowledge of Aristotle was superficial, he was repelled by the "Master"'s lack of "eloquentia," and did not hesitate to accuse him of error in matters large and small. The more advanced and scien-

[12] Ernest Babelon: Les origines de l'art du médailleur, in André Michel: Histoire de l'art (3, 897–924, chiefly 898–917, 1908).

tific form of Peripateticism as developed by the Averroists of Padua was especially obnoxious to him. In that form, philosophy and science were not simply dry and repellent, but offensive. Averroism suggested rebellion and heresy.[13] In Petrarca it shocked not only the man, but also the Christian and the artist. He urged his friend Luigi Marsigli to write "contra canem illum rabidum Averroim."[14] His hatred of Averroism induced in him a strong dislike of everything Arabic. The strength of his dislike suggests that Arabic influences were very strong in his day; indeed, they had then reached their climax and permeated science and philosophy. Petrarca's anti-Averroism is best expressed in De suiipsius et multorum ignorantia, composed in his old age.

He was an enemy of ignorance and of superstition, but in the way of a man of good sense, who is instinctively repulsed by foolishness and blindness. He might be called a Christian rationalist; having assented to the dogmas of his faith, his mind was closed to any other form of irrationalism. His rationalism was passive, not active; his hatred of superstitions did not make of him a friend of science, for his anti-Averroistic prejudices were too strong for that. Thus he was a true humanist in the old and narrow sense: loving the classical literature, moderation, common sense, but shrinking from science.[15]

His criticism of astrology was as radical as could be expected in his time, and did not exclude a few inconsistencies (e.g., his real or pretended fear concerning the approach of his grand climacteric, i.e., his sixty-third year). In the two letters addressed in his old age to Giovanni of Padua or Giovanni de' Dondi (XIV-2), he strongly criticized contemporary medical superstitions, astrological and alchemical medicine, the irrational elements of uroscopy and coproscopy, and other quackeries, many of which were the more objectionable to him because of their Muslim origin; he also rebuked medical philosophy (or what passed for it) and medical pedantism (e.g., use of Grecisms and Arabisms). To divination and magic he was resolutely hostile.

Petrarca's aversion to Averroism and to logic was partly a healthy reaction against the abuses of scholastic argumentation. For example, see his letter to the poet Tommaso Caloria da Messina (Fam. I, 6, Dialecticorum detestatur contentiones). That letter is specially interesting because he was relatively young when he wrote it (Tommaso died c. 1341), say in his thirties. Some of his criticisms recall earlier ones made by philosophers of the school of Chartres, such as John of Salisbury; yet his reaction was largely intuitive and temperamental, hence original.

Petrarca's distrust of science is comparable to that experienced by Socrates almost eighteen centuries before, and caused in the latter's case by the excesses of sophistry. Like Socrates, Petrarca exerted a good influence upon the development of science. Indeed, the progress of experimental science required the preliminary dethronement of scholastic philosophy.

[13] For a brief discussion of Averroism, see Introd. 2, especially p. 358. Petrarca's reaction to Averroism was magnificently explained by Renan in his Averroès (p. 328–38, 1869).

[14] As quoted by Sandys (2, p. 10, 1908). Luigi Marsigli was a Florentine Augustinian, who died in 1394; a friend of Petrarca and one of the early "humanistic" group. He was used as an ambassador by the Signoria. Giulio Dolci (Enciclopedia italiana 22, 424, 1934).

[15] It is in contrast with that old humanism that I coined the phrase "new humanism" in 1918, by which I meant primarily a humanism comparable in other respects to the old one, but including science instead of excluding it. G. Sarton: Le nouvel humanisme (Scientia 23, 161–75, 1918); The history of science and the new humanism (New York 1931; new edition, Cambridge, Mass. 1937).

7. *His geographical views*

According to Flavio Biondo (1388–1463) in his Italia illustrata[16] (composed in 1451), Petrarca and Robert of Anjou had drawn together (in 1341) a map of Italy —which would then have been the first of its kind (excluding the coastal outlines found in portolani). No such map has come down to us, and we can hardly conceive Petrarca to have drawn one having any scientific value, for he was entirely unprepared for that kind of work.

On the other hand, according to Boccaccio (De montibus, fluminibus, etc.; in the last chapter) Petrarca had written a treatise on the classical geography of Italy; that is more plausible; his interest in the subject is further proved by the fact that he owned old maps (carte vetustissime)[17] and had searched Latin literature for geographical data.

In the Vita solitaria (lib. 2, cap. 3) he referred to the discovery of the Canary Islands by the Genoese Lanzarote Malocello (c. 1270–75); see Introd. 2, 1062.

He compiled for a friend an itinerary to the Holy Land (from Genoa to Jerusalem), wherein he dealt primarily with the Italian part of the journey (p. 556–64, Basel 1581). His own journey to Paris, the Netherlands, and the Rhine he described in two letters written in 1333, respectively in Aix-la-Chapelle and Lyon (Fam. I, 3 and 4; p. 574–77, Basel 1581). His descriptions are void of geographical interest.

The most picturesque event in his career was his ascent of Mt. Ventoux (i.e., ventosum), an isolated mount 1,912 m. high in the department of Vaucluse, on April 26, 1336, with his younger brother Gherardo (Fam. IV, 1; p. 624–27, Basel 1581). This ascent for its own sake (not in order to reach another country, as would be the case with Alpine passes) is almost unique in mediaeval times.[18] Pe-

[16] "Pictura Italiae quam in primis sequimur, Roberti regis Siciliae et Francisci Petrarchae eius amici opus" (Italia illustrata, p. 353, Basel 1531).

[17] P. de Nolhac: Pétrarque et l'humanisme (2d ed., 1, 149, 1907).

[18] For the sake of comparison, see extracts quoted by Coulton: Life in the Middle Ages (2d ed., 2, 3–6, 1928). The "earliest recorded Alpine climb" is found in the anonymous Chronicon novaliciense (c. 726–1050), that is, the chronicle of the Benedictine monastery of Novalese under Mt. Cenis, the event being undated. Coulton quotes two other extracts relative to early mountaineering. The second, taken from the Speculum historiale (lib. 1, c. 84) of Vincent of Beauvais, refers to Petrus Comestor (XII-2), who "saith that Mount Olympus riseth even to the clear aether, wherefore letters written in the dust on the summit of that mountain have been found unchanged after the lapse of a whole year. Neither can birds live there, by reason of the rarefaction of the air, nor could the Philosophers who have ascended it remain there even for a brief space of time, without sponges soaked in water, which they applied to their nostrils and sucked thence a denser air." The third refers to the ascent of Mt. Canigou in the Pyrénées by king Pedro III of Aragon (d. 1285), as reported in the chronicle of Fra Salimbene (XIII-2; d. c. 1288). This third account is more convincing than the two others; it refers to an ascent which was probably made by a definite person. Thus Petrarca's ascent is not unique; one should add to it at least the ascent of king Pedro. See also the note on Buridan.

Mont Ventoux has at least a second title to the gratitude of historians of science, for it was on its slope that the great entomologist Jean Henri Fabre (1823–1915) did his first great work (Isis 7, 143; 8, 335).

For more information on early alpinism see Coolidge (1904).

Nordström (p. 133, 1933) draws attention to two other facts. Gui de Bazoches (cantor at St. Etienne in Châlons-sur-Marne, crusader 1190, died 1203) gave a description of Etna. The author of the Image du monde, Gossouin or Walter of Metz (XIII-1), gave a better description of the same volcano, which suggests that he had actually made the ascent of it.

trarca's interest, however, was literary rather than sporting or scientific. To begin with, his desire to climb Mt. Ventoux had been inspired by his reading in Livy (XL, 21) about the ascent of Mt. Haimos in Thrace c. 181 B.C. by Philip V of Macedonia. Then when he reached the top, he began to read St. Augustine's Confessions. (The first Western man to take a scientific—geologic—interest in the scenery of high altitudes was probably Leonardo da Vinci.)

In short, to call Petrarca a geographer would be foolish, but he was deeply interested in the ancient geography of Italy, this being the more scientific aspect of his humanism, and he was one of the first European mountain climbers.

8. *His political views*

Petrarca was a Ghibelline, but first of all an Italian; like Dante, he thought in terms of a united Italy before the existence of any kind of unity. Indeed, the disorder in public affairs was extreme; nowhere in the peninsula was security or peace to be found. Petrarca's hatred of his own age and love of the Roman past was political as well as literary. He dreamt of a reconstruction of Roman unity, as well as of a revival of Latin letters. (I say "dreamt" advisedly, for his political views were vague and changeable.) It is impossible for him not to have known of Marsiglio of Padua, yet, as far as I am aware,[19] he never referred to him or to his great work, the Defensor pacis of 1324.

At the time of his coronation in Rome, Easter 1341, he was made a Roman citizen. In 1342 he met Cola di Rienzo, befriended him, and at the time of the latter's "coup d'état" (Rome, Pentecost 1347) set great hopes on him, trusting that Rienzo would create peace, unity, and security. He wrote at least eight letters to him to advise and restrain him; he was proceeding to Rome to join him when the fantastic scheme petered out. He wrote to the Roman people to defend him, but in vain.

After Rienzo's failure, Petrarca set his hopes on the emperor Charles IV, and from 1350 on sent many messages to him; he met him in Mantua 1354, and again in Prague 1356. These Ghibelline hopes for the restoration of peace and unity by the power of the Holy Roman Empire were frustrated.

About 1367 Petrarca wrote for the ruler of Padua, Francesco I da Carrara, a treatise on the best form of government, De republica optime administranda.

His views on church politics were dominated by his love of the church and of Italy. In his Epistolae sine titulo he denounced vigorously the degraded churchmen of Avignon. It is absurd to speak of him as a forerunner of the Reformation. He was orthodox, but dreamed of a reclaimed papacy re-established in Rome.

9. *His influence*

Petrarca, the first modern man, was sufficiently a man of his time to enjoy considerable popularity, not only among despots and popes, but even among the humbler literati. His style was unique, but his feelings were shared by many. He was the first herald of the Renaissance, and his challenge was heard not only in Italy but in Spain, France, England, and other countries. See my notes on Boccaccio and Chaucer (XIV-2). Jean de Montreuil (d. 1418), first humanist of France, regarded him as his guide and master. The Catalan poet Ausías March of Valencia

[19] I have consulted Labanca (1882) and the partial indexes available to me; there is no general Petrarcan concordance.

(1379–1459) imitated his poetry and introduced its moods and cadences into the Spanish world.

It is often repeated (e.g., Sandys 2, 99) that Petrarca's handwriting was immortalized in the "Aldine" or "italic" type. That pretty story has no factual basis. The type was founded by Francesco of Bologna and first used in 1501 by the great Venetian printer Aldus Manutius (1449–1515), in the latter's pocket editions of Virgil, Horace, Juvenal, Persius, as well as of the Cose volgare of Petrarca. Aldus himself called that style of script "cancelleresco." Nevertheless, it is significant of Petrarca's fame that a connection was imagined between that style and his own writing.

Petrarca's influence on scientific thought has already been discussed; it was indirect and negative, but considerable.

10. *General bibliography*

The best bibliography of Petrarca available today is Mary Fowler: Catalogue of the Petrarch collection bequeathed by [Daniel] Willard Fiske [1831–1904] to the Cornell University Library (quarto, 572 p., Oxford 1916). The Fiske collection in Cornell, Ithaca, N. Y. is being gradually increased, 319 books having been added to it since the publication of Fowler's catalogue (letter from curator dated Feb. 17, 1937).

11. *Indexes and concordances*

Antonio Meneghelli: Index Francisci Petrarcae epistolarum quae editae sunt et quae adhuc ineditae (p. 5–29, Padua 1818); list of incipits, jejune and incomplete. Dino Provenzali: Dizionarietto dei nomi propri della Divina commedia e del Canzoniere (122 p., 1913).

Kenneth McKenzie: Concordanza delle Rime di F. Petrarca (536 p., Oxford 1912).

12. *Facsimile manuscripts*

Il manoscritto vaticano latino 3196 autografo di Petrarca riprodotto (Roma 1895). Codice Orsini–da Costa delle Rime e dei Trionfi (38 p. + 180 fol. facsimiles, 11 pl., Roma 1904); complete facsimile, with introduction by Domenico Ciampoli. Vie de César. Reproduction facsimile du MS latin 5784 de la Bibliothèque nationale (23 p., 97 facs., Paris 1906). I codici petrarcheschi della Biblioteca vaticana (260 p., Roma 1908).

MSS owned by Petrarca: Petrarcae Vergilianus codex. Ad Publii Vergilii Maronis diem natalem bis millesimum celebrandum quam simillime expressus atque in lucem editus . . . Praefatus est Iohannes Galbiati, ascita etiam Achille Ratti (nunc Pii XI) de hoc codice commentatione (282 p., Milano 1930). Facsimile of Petrarca's Horace MS, Cod. Laurent. med. Plut. 34.1 (X–XI), with description by Enrico Rostagno: L'Orazio laurenziano già di F. Petrarca (60 p., Rome 1933). See my note on Codex Cumanicus.

13. *Printed texts*

Collected editions: The earliest edition of Petrarca's collected works was printed in Basel by John Amerbach 1496; it included letters as well as treatises, but nothing written in Italian. The Latin writings were published again in Venice 1501, 1503, etc. The first edition of the "Opera que extant omnia . . . Adiecimus eiusdem authoris quae hetrusco sermone scripsit omnia" appeared in Basel 1554, and was reprinted there in 1581. It includes the Italian verse (called Etruscan in the title!). Pending the completion of the new national edition, these Basel editions are the most complete available. I have used the edition of 1581 (folio, 4 vols., 1364 p. in all, generally bound in 1 vol.) and found it very convenient in spite of many imperfections.

In 1904, the Italian government established a commission for the preparation and publication of a new national edition of Petrarca's works. The first volume of it appeared 22 years later. It includes L'Africa, edizione critica per cura di Nicola Festa (356 p., 6 pl., Florence 1926). I have seen but two other volumes of that edition, numbered X and XI, including the Familiar letters (books I to XI) edited by Vittorio Rossi (1933, 1934).

Editions of the letters (in addition to those already cited): The first letter to appear in print was autobiographical, entitled Epistola ad posteros, or Epistola de studiorum suorum successibus ad posteritatem (Louvain 1484/85). The first collection of letters, Epistole familiares, appeared in Venice 1492. Down to 1602 there were at least twelve editions of the letters.

Epistolae de rebus familiaribus et variae tum quae adhuc tum quae nondum editae familiarium scilicet libri XXIIII, variarum liber unicus. First critical edition, by Giuseppe Fracassetti (3 vols., Florence 1859–63). This will probably be superseded by the national edition of the letters, which began to appear in 1933.

The latest edition of the Epistolae de rebus senilibus and the Epistolae sine titulo is still the one included in the Basel edition of 1581.

All the letters have been translated into Italian by Giuseppe Fracassetti: Lettere delle cose familiari libri ventiquattro, lettere varie libro unico (5 vols., Florence 1863–67); Lettere senili (2 vols., Florence 1869–70). These well indexed volumes constitute one of the best tools for Petrarcan studies.

There are a great many partial editions in Latin and in other languages. I shall mention only, because of its handiness, the Epistolae selectae edited by A. F. Johnson (286 p., Oxford 1923), a very good introduction to Petrarca.

Editions of the Canzoniere and Trionfi are innumerable. See Fiske catalogue, p. 69–190. Princeps, by Wendelin of Speyer, Venice 1470. Le rime sparse e i trionfi, edited by Ezio Chiòrboli (501 p., Bari 1930).

As to separate editions of the Latin works, I shall cite only a few items of special interest or posterior to the Fiske catalogue of 1916, to which the reader is constantly referred.

Africa sive de bello punico libri IX. Princeps in the second edition of the Latin works, Venice 1501, reprinted in the following editions of collected works. First separate edition by L. Pingaud (400 p., Paris 1872). Better edition by Francesco Corradini, in Padova a Petrarca nel quinto centenario dalla sua morte (Padova 1874, p. 77–474). Latest edition by Nicola Festa (356 p., Florence 1926), with elaborate study of the tradition (76 p.).

De viris illustribus. The text published in the early Latin collected editions is only an abridgment. First complete edition by Aloisio Razzolini (2 vols. in Collezione di opere inedite o rare, Bologna 1874–79), with Italian translation on opposite pages. The life of Caesar, however, had been printed as early as 1473 by Conrad Fyner in Esslingen, together with Caesar's De bello gallico (princeps of it). Critical edition of the life of Caesar by Karl Ernst Christoph Schneider (458 p., Leipzig 1827).

De rebus memorandis. Princeps, by Rodolph Loeffs, Louvain 1484/85.

De remediis utriusque fortunae. See account of early editions in Latin and various other languages in §4.

Secretum. Princeps by the R printer, Strassburg c. 1473. First French translation by Victor Develay: Mon secret, ou Du conflit de mes passions (Paris 1879, reprinted 1898). English translation by William H. Draper, Petrarch's Secret, or, The soul's conflict with passion, three dialogues between himself and S. Augustine (216 p., London 1911).

De vita solitaria. Printed separately in Strassburg 1473?, Milano 1498, etc. Spanish translation, anonymous (Medina del Campo 1553). English translation by Jacob Zeitlin (316 p., University of Illinois 1924), strongly criticized by Odell Shepard in Journal of English and German philology (24, 560–74, Urbana, Ill. 1925).

De suiipsius et multorum ignorantia. Separately printed by Le Preux (Geneva 1609). Critical edition by Luigi Mario Capelli (120 p., Paris 1906). Italian translation by the same in Angelo Solerti: L'autobiografia etc. (355 p., Firenze 1904). German translation by Hermann Hefele (Jena 1910).

Itinerarium syriacum. Edited by Giacomo Lombroso in the Atti dell' Accad. dei Lincei (Rendiconti 4, 390–403, 1888). Reprinted in the author's Memorie italiane del buon tempo antico (p. 16–49, 1889).

Two political treatises, A and B:

A. De officio et virtutibus imperatoris, appended to Joachim Camerarius' Latin translation of Onasandros (I-2): Στρατηγικὸς λόγος, De re militari (Nuremberg 1595). Italian translation, Libro degli uffici e delle virtù di un capitano, in Varie opere filosofiche di F. Petrarca per la prima volta ridotte in volgare favella (p. 93–137, Milano 1824; again 1833).

B. De republica optime administranda. Printed by Le Preux in Bern 1602; again 1617. Including a reprint of A. Partial French version of B by Etienne Jean Delécluze (15 p., Revue de Paris, 9 nov. 1838). Italian translation of B by Ambrogio Levati in the collection quoted apropos of A (p. 1–92, Milano 1824; 1833).

14. *Biographies and general criticism*

The only ancient biography deserving to be mentioned here is the very elaborate if uncritical one by the abbé de Sade, Jean François Paul Aldance de Sade (Avignon 1705–78): Mémoires pour la vie de Pétrarque (quarto, 3 vols., Amsterdam 1764–67), which remained authoritative for a long time and was translated into German and English (many English editions, all abridged). It was the abbé de Sade who started the "Laura controversy," by identifying Petrarca's ideal mistress with the wife of one of his ancestors, Laura de Noves. That identification has not been generally accepted. It is interesting to note that the infamous marquis de Sade (1740–1814)—after whom the term "sadism" was coined—belonged to the same family, one of the noblest families of Provence (Isis 21, 495).

Ludwig Georg Voigt: Die Wiederbelebung des classischen Alterthums (Berlin 1859); revised edition (2 vols., Berlin 1880–81); translated into French and Italian. Alfred Mézières: Pétrarque (475 p., Paris 1868), at least twice reprinted (1868, 1895). Attilio Hortis: Scritti inediti di Petrarca (388 p., Trieste 1874). The apocryphal texts edited in this book cover only p. 311–72; the rest is biographical. Gustav Körting: Petrarca's Leben und Werke (734 p., Leipzig 1878). Henry Reeve: Petrarch (148 p., Edinburgh 1878). Pierre de Nolhac: Pétrarque et l'humanisme d'après un essai de restitution de sa bibliothèque (449 p., Paris 1892); amplified and revised edition (2 vols., Paris 1907); English abridgment (120 p., Boston 1907). Pierre de Nolhac (1859–1936), who was the leading Petrarcan scholar of France, wrote many other studies on the subject, for which see the Fiske catalogue (p. 383–85). James Harvey Robinson and Henry Winchester Rolfe: Petrarch, the first modern scholar and man of letters, a selection of his correspondence (in English) with introduction (446 p., New York 1898); revised edition (490 p., New York 1914); a very good introduction to the subject. Victor Masséna (prince d'Essling, duc de Rivoli) and Eugene Müntz: Pétrarque, ses études d'art, son influence sur les artistes, ses portraits et ceux de Laure, etc. (300 p., 21 pl., 191 engr., Gazette des beaux-arts, Paris 1902); still the standard work on Petrarcan iconography. Henry Cochin: Le frère de Pétrarque et le livre Du repos des religieux (254 p., Paris 1903). Angelo Solerti: Le vite di Dante, Petrarca e Boccaccio scritte fino al secolo decimosesto (788 p., Milano 1904). Maud F. Jerrold: Petrarca, poet and humanist (362 p., 8 ill., London 1909). Murray Anthony Potter: Four essays (Harvard studies in Romanic languages vol. 3, 140 p., Cambridge 1917). Maria Sicca: L'amicizia fra il Petrarca ed il Boccaccio (165 p., Napoli 1919). Giovanni Alfredo Cesareo: F. Petrarca, la vita (Messina 1920). Edward Henry Ralph Tatham: Petrarch, the first modern man of letters, his life and correspondence (2 vols., London 1925–26). Paul Piur: Die Korrespondenz Petrarcas, in Konrad Burdach and Piur: Briefwechsel des Cola di Rienzo (vol. 2, part 2, p. 110–238, 332–59, Berlin 1928). Ernest Hatch Wilkins: A tentative chronological list of Petrarch's prose letters (24 p., Chicago 1929). Enrico Carrara: L'epistola posteritati e la leggenda petrarchea (Annali dell' Istituto superiore di magistèro del Piemonte 3, p. 297, 1929); La leggenda di Laura (34 p., Torino 1934); elaborate article in Enciclopedia italiana (27, 8–23, many ill., 1935). Theodor E. Mommsen: Petrarch's conception of the "dark ages" (Speculum 17, 226–42, 1942). John Humphreys Whitfield: Petrarch and the Renaissance (170 p., Oxford 1943).

15. *Special criticism*

Antonio Favaro: Intorno al probabile autore di una predizione di terremoto riferita da Petrarca (Atti del Istituto veneto 2, ser. 5, 16 p., Venezia 1876). The earthquake which destroyed a part of Naples November 25, 1343 was predicted by a bishop who was probably a disciple of Andalò di Negro; Petrarca referred to it in Epist. fam. V, 5. Francesco Lo Parco: Petrarca e Barlaam (128 p., Reggio Calabria 1905). Sandys (vol. 2, ch. 1, 1908). Antonio Belloni: Il Petrarca e i sogni (Padova in onore di Petrarca 1904, 2, 31–46, 1909). Giuseppina Fumagalli: Alcune idee pedagogiche di Dante e del Petrarca (128 p., Florence 1910). Neuburger (2, 416–18, 1911). E. O. von Lippmann: Petrarca über die Alchemie (Archiv für Geschichte der Naturwissenschaften 6, 236–40, 1913), reprinted in his Beiträge (p. 197–200, Berlin 1923); apropos of the dialogue de alchimia in the De remediis utriusque fortunae (Isis 5, 503). Ugo Viviani: I consigli "sulle infermitadi del corpo" di Petrarca (Rivista di storia delle scienze p. 25–28, 1921). Thorndike (3, 213–23, 1934), on Petrarch and some friars. Ernest H. Wilkins: The coronation of Petrarch (Speculum 18, 155–97, 1943).

16. *Geographical criticism*

Röhricht (p. 89, 1890). Giosuè Carducci (1836–1907): Il Petrarca alpinista (Il secolo, Milano 1882), reprinted in his Opere (10, 149–60, Bologna 1898). Giovanni Alfredo Cesareo: La carta d'Italia del Petrarca (Dai tempi antichi ai tempi moderni, Da Dante a Leopardi. Raccolta di scritti ... per le nozze di Michele Scherillo con Tereza Negri p. 221–25, Milano 1904). Medardo Morici: Le opere geografiche del Petrarca e del Boccaccio copiate da un amanuense di Rocca contrada nel 1434 (La bibliofilia 6, 321–26, 1905), apropos of the Itinerarium syriacum. Francesco Lo Parco: Il Petrarca e gli antipodi etnografici in rapporto con la concezione patristica e dantesca (Romania 37, 337–57, 1908); L'ultima Thule nell' intuizione e nella divinazione di F. Petrarca (Rivista geografica italiana 18, 459–74, 1911), apropos of Epist. fam. III, 1; Il viaggio di F. Petrarca ad extrema terrarum (Studi dedicati a Francesco Torraca p. 87–100, Napoli 1912). Hennig (3, 136–43, 1938).

17. *Philosophical criticism*

Heinrich Schmelzer: Petrarcas Verhältnis zur vorausgehenden christlichen Philosophie des Abendlandes (74 p., Bonn 1911). Pietro Paolo Gerosa: L'umanésimo agostiniano del Petrarca (Didaskaleion, Torino 1926–27). R. Klibansky: Appendix ad praefationem De dialogis de vera sapientia Petrarcae addictis (Nicolai de Cusa Opera omnia vol. 5, 45 p., Leipzig 1937; Isis 28, 546).

18. *Political criticism*

Baldassare Labanca: Marsilio da Padova (235 p., Padova 1882); for Petrarca see p. 199–204. Mario Emilio Cosenza. Petrarca and the revolution of Cola di Rienzo (334 p., Chicago 1913). Paul Piur: Petrarcas Buch ohne Namen und die päpstliche Kurie (Halle a.S. 1925). Charles Calvert Bayley: Petrarch, Charles IV and the Renovatio imperii (Speculum 17, 323–41, 1942).

19. *Documents concerning Petrarca's influence*

Petrarca e Venezia (328 p., Venezia 1874). Marius Pieri: Le pétrarquisme au XVIe siècle, Pétrarque et Ronsard, ou de l'influence de Pétrarque sur la Pléiade française (342 p., Marseille 1896). Bernardo Sanvisenti: I primi influssi di Dante, del Petrarca e del Boccaccio sulla letteratura spagnuola (480 p., Milano 1902). Arturo Farinelli: Note sulla forma del Petrarca in Ispagna nel quattrocento (Giornale storico della letteratura italiana 44, 297–350, 1904). Petrarca e la Lombardia (370 p., 8 pl., Milano 1904). Padova in onore del Petrarca (2 vols., 1906–9). Fredrik Amadeus Wulff: En svensk Petrarca-bok till jubelfästen 1304–1904 (588 p., ill., Stockholm 1905–6). Peter Borghesi: Petrarch and his influence on English literature (136 p., Bologna 1906). Joseph Vianey: Le pétrarquisme en France au XVIe siècle (Travaux et mémoires de Montpellier vol. 3, 400 p., Montpellier 1909). Union intellectuelle franco-italienne: Pétrarque. Mélanges de littérature et d'histoire (235 p., Paris 1928). Konrad Burdach: Aus Petrarcas ältestem deutschen Schülerkreise. Texte und Untersuchungen (Vom Mittelalter zur Reformation vol. 4, 290 p., 2 pl., Berlin 1929). Arturo Farinelli: Petrarca und Deutschland in der dämmernden Renaissance (70 p., Petrarca-Haus, Köln 1933). Catharina Ypes: Petrarca in de nederlandsche letterkunde (395 p., Amsterdam 1934). Parma a Petrarca (304 p., Parma 1934). A Petrarca, la deputazione di storia patria per le province parmensi (420 p., Parma 1935). Revilo P. Oliver: Petrarch's prestige as a humanist (Classical studies in honor of William Abbott Oldfather p. 134–35, Urbana, Ill. 1943).

Incomplete as this list probably is, it suffices to illustrate the diffusion of Petrarcan influences throughout the world down to our own day.

JOHN OF NAPLES

Joannes de Regina de Neapoli. Italian Dominican, Thomist (d. after 1335).

John originated probably in Naples. He assumed the Dominican habit in the convent S. Domenico Maggiore in that city, then continued his studies in Paris. He taught in Paris c. 1315–17, then returned to his country. He apparently spent the rest of his life in Naples. He took a prominent part, however, as procurator, in the process of canonization of St. Thomas, which took place in Avignon 1323 under John XXII. His name appears for the last time in a notarial document dated 1336.

He wrote a commentary on the Sentences, two Quodlibeta, forty-two Quaestiones disputatae, and a treatise De paupertate Christi directed against the Franciscan cardinal Vital du Four. That treatise was thus presumably written after 1322.

John of Naples was a defender of Thomism pure and simple.

Text. The Quaestiones variae Parisiis disputatae were edited by the Dominican father Domenico Gravina (Naples 1618).

Criticism. Carl Johann Jellouschek (O.S.B.): Johannes von Neapel und seine Lehre vom Verhältnisse zwischen Gott und Welt. Ein Beitrag zur Geschichte der ältesten Thomistenschule (144 p., Wien 1918).

GRAZIADEI D'ASCOLI

Gratiadei Aesculanus. Italian Dominican, commentator on Aristotle, who flourished until 1341. He is so little known, even to his Dominican brethren, that one is not even sure in which Ascoli he originated or after which one he was named, whether Ascoli Piceno in the Marche, or Ascoli Satriano in Apulia. He studied or taught in Padua; he is mentioned here partly because his commentaries were selected for publication by the early printers.

He wrote commentaries on the Logic of Aristotle (that is, the ars vetus, plus the Praedicabilia[19a] of Porphyry and the Sex principia of Gilbert de la Porrée) and on the Parva naturalia, also "Quaestiones" on the eight books of Physics, on the De anima, and Quaestiones theologicae et metaphysicae quas disputavit in studio Patavino. He added supplements to St. Thomas' commentaries on the second book of Perihermenias and on De physico auditu.

Text. Commentaria in totam artem veterem Aristotelis. Edited by the Dominican Theophile of Cremona (Venice 1491). Reprinted Venice 1493, 1496 (Hain 7874–6).

Quaestiones theologicae et metaphysicae (Venice 1484?).

Quaestiones super octo libros physicorum (Venice 1484). This is the only Graziadei edition mentioned by Klebs (no. 473).

Supplement to St. Thomas' commentary on Perihermenias (1477, 1481).

Acutissime quaestiones de physico auditu (Venice 1517).

Criticism. Quétif and Echard (1, 603, 1719).

ALEXANDER OF ALEXANDRIA

Italian Franciscan, commentator on the Metaphysics of Aristotle (d. Rome 1314).

Alexander ab Alexandria (junior) Lombardus, master in theology, lecturer at the curia, minister general of his order. His commentary on the Metaphysics was wrongly ascribed to the English Franciscan Alexander of Hales (XIII-1) and to Thomas Aquinas. It was translated into Hebrew. He wrote a summary of St. Bonaventure's commentary on the Sentences, and quaestiones disputatae, e.g., on usury. There are many MSS of his writings. He must be counted a Scotist but with leanings to St. Bonaventure.

I mention him here chiefly because of his confusion with Alexander of Hales and with another Alexander of Alexandria, contemporary of Hales.

Text. The commentary on the Metaphysics was printed in Venice 1572, but under the name of Alexander of Hales.

Criticism. De humanae cognitionis ratione, anecdota quaedam Sancti Bonaventurae et nonnullorum ipsius discipulorum (p. XXII, 219, Ad aquas claras 1883) includes fragment of a quaestio disputata contra errorem Averrois. Steinschneider (p. 495, 1893). Felder (p. 204, 1904). Ueberweg (p. 437, 1915). De Wulf (2, 100, 207, 1926).

[19a] The Isagoge of Porphyry (III-2) was sometimes called περὶ πέντε φωνῶν, de quinque praedicabilibus. For example, one of the undated incunabula (Pellechet 1181) is entitled Liber ysagogarum i.e. introductionum Porphyrii in Praedicamenta Aristotelis. Continet duos tractatus. Tractatus primus de quinque predicabilibus. Tractatus secundus de convenientia et doctrina predicabilium ad invicem.

GERARD OF BOLOGNA

Italian Carmelite Thomist (d. 1317).

He obtained his degree of doctor in theology in Paris, being the first of his order to be thus honored. This is said to have happened in 1295. Two years later he was elected prior general of the Carmelites. He wrote a commentary on the Sentences, a Summa theologica (built on the same plan as St. Thomas' Summa), Quaestiones ordinariae, and four Quodlibeta.

He should have been mentioned in our volume 2 as one of the early Thomists. He lacked originality and strength.

Text. The commentary on the Sentences was printed in Venice 1622.

Criticism. Hauréau (2, part 2, 266–72, 1880). Bartolomé Maria Riberta y Roqueta: De summa theologiae mag. Gerardi Bononiensis (Analecta ordinis Carmelitarum vol. 16, 1–54, 1923), not available to me. Michalski (p. 74–77, 93, 1925a). De Wulf (2, 218, 1926).

GREGORIO DA RIMINI

Italian Augustinian, theologian, Occamist (d. 1358).

Gregorio Novelli da Rimini (Gregorius de Arimino, Ariminensis). Born at an unknown date in Rimini. Became an Augustinian Hermit. Studied in Rimini, and in Paris (1323–29). Was appointed in 1345 magister regens or cathedraticus in Paris at the special request of Clement VI. In 1351 he left Paris and became "principalis lector" in the Augustinian house of his native city. When Thomas of Strassburg died, in 1357, Gregorio was elected in his place general of their order. Gregorio died in November 1358 in Vienna.

His main work is a commentary on the four books of the Sentences. He lectured on them in Paris in 1341; his commentary was completed in 1344, he may have added to it until 1351 or even later. In addition, he wrote treatises De intentione et remissione formarum, Quaestiones metaphysicales, De usuris, etc.

His main authorities were Aristotle and Averroes, St. Augustine; he made a critical use of St. Thomas. Up to his time the Augustinian Hermits had followed their most illustrious brother Giles of Rome (XIII-2), but Gregorio was deeply impressed by the Occamic traditions flourishing in Paris and became a nominalist.

His commentary on the Sentences contains discussions of mathematical continuity and infinity (categorematic and syncategorematic).

Text. Gregorius de Arimino in primo et secundo Sententiarum nupperime impressus. Edited by the Augustinian Hermit Paulus de Genazzano. Undated incunabulum. Other editions, Paris 1482, etc., Venice 1503, 1518–22. In secundo Sententiarum libro, Milan 1494.

De usuris. Rimini 1622?

Criticism. Duhem: Etudes (2, 385–99, 1909). Joseph Würsdörfer: Erkennen und Wissen nach Gregor von Rimini. Ein Beitrag zur Geschichte der Erkenntnistheorie des Nominalismus (Beiträge zur Geschichte der Philosophie des Mittelalters vol. 20, part 1, 148 p., Münster 1917). Michalski (p. 102, 1925a). De Wulf (2, 194, 1926). Hubert Elie: Le complexe significabile (260 p., Paris 1936; p. 17–40), pointing out that Gregorio was the author of the distinction between ens, res, and aliquid, and the initiator in 1344 of a logical or epistemological quarrel concerning the "complexe significabile" which exercised the schoolmen for a century and a half and has been revived in a different form recently by Alexis Meinong and Bertrand Russell.

URBANO OF BOLOGNA

Urbanus Averroista. Italian Servite, Averroist. His main work was an elaborate commentary on Ibn Rushd's commentary on Aristotelian physics, which he composed in 1334, when he was already old. Because of that work, Urbano was nicknamed the father of philosophy!

Urbano is quoted here as a representative of the Averroism which was then beginning to develop in northern Italy, not so much in Bologna, though, as in Padua, where Pietro of Abano was first to illustrate these new tendencies. Italian Averroism did not attain its maturity, however, until the fifteenth century, with such men as Paul of Venice (c. 1370–1429), Gaetano da Thiene (1387–1462?), and Nicoletto Vernia da Chieti (fl. 1481).

Text. Urbanus Averroista commentorum omnium Averroys super librum Aristotelis de physico auditu expositor clarissimus. Printed in Venice 1492 (Klebs no. 1006) by order of Antonio Alabanti (d. 1495), 21st general of the Servites, with a preface by Nicoletto Vernia.

Criticism. Renan (p. 343, 1869). G. Sarton: The date of Urbano of Bologna (query no. 86, Isis 32, 118–19).

A2. Spain

ANTONIUS ANDREAE

Antonius Andreae, Anthony son of Andrew. Catalan Franciscan, pupil of Duns Scot (XIII-2; d. 1308); died in 1320 or later. The traditional date 1320 seems too early, for he criticizes and names Peter Auriol (d. 1322). He was an ardent Scotist, nicknamed Doctor dulcifluus. He wrote a number of books on logic and philosophy which attained more popularity than they seem to have deserved. They contain rhetorical and diffuse explanations of hackneyed subjects "secundum artem doctrinae scotistae."

He wrote commentaries on the books of Sentences, on Aristotle's Metaphysics, on Aristotelian and Boetian logic, on the categories of Gilbert de la Porrée (XII-1). He also published a treatise on his own logic, and another De tribus principiis rerum naturalium, discussing matter, form, and privation. Antonius argued that though matter and form are always mixed, yet each has a separate and absolute reality.

Even if the intrinsic value of these works is small, they have some extrinsic importance because of their popularity. Note the number of incunabula editions, especially of the commentary on Aristotle's Metaphysics, and their international distribution.

Text. Quaestiones super XII libros Metaphysicae Aristotelis. Edited by Franciscus de Neritono, Naples 1473–77. Other editions: Naples 1475, Vicenza 1477, London 1480, Venice 1481, 1487, 1491, Leipzig 1495–96, Poitiers 1495, Venice 1495, after 1500?, 1514, 1523.

Scriptum aureum super Metaphysicam Aristotelis, Venice 1482.

Quaestiones de tribus principiis rerum naturalium. First edition by Thomas Penceth (d. 1487) together with the Formalitates, Padua 1475. Second edition, Ferrara 1490.

Scriptum in artem veterem Aristotelis et in divisiones Boethii, Venice 1480, Bologna 1481, Venice 1492, 1496, 1508, 1517.

Scriptum in logica sua, St. Albans 1483.

Quaestiones de libro sex principiorum Gilberti Porretani, printed with Duns

Scotus: Super universalibus Porphyrii ac libris Praedicamentorum et Perihermenias Aristotelis, Barcelona 1475?, 1485?, Venice 1492.

The incunabula are listed after GW (2, nos. 1656–74, 1926).

Criticism. Prantl (3, 276–82, 1867). Hauréau (2, part 2, 445–49, 1880). Klebs (nos. 64–66, 1938).

BERNAT OLIVER

Valencian Augustinian theologian writing in Latin (d. 1348).

Bernat Oliver (Bernardo in Spanish) was born in Valencia and assumed the monastic habit in the Augustinian house of that city. He completed his philosophical and theological studies in Paris and then returned to his country. He was a famous preacher and was often consulted by the kings of Aragon Alfons III el Benigne and Pere III el Cerimoniós; the latter praised him in his chronicle.

He was appointed bishop of Huesca in 1337, of Barcelona in 1345, and finally in 1346 of Tortosa, where he died on July 14, 1348.

He is the best representative of scholastic philosophy tempered with mysticism in his time and country. In addition to commentaries on the Books of sentences, he wrote various theological treatises, the most important of which is the Excitatorium mentis ad Deum, which was translated into Catalan, Excitatori de la pensa a Deu, in the following century. The author of that translation had a marvelous command of the beautiful Catalan language, but is unfortunately unknown.

Text. Excitatorium mentis ad Deum. Nunc primum ad fidem codicis Escurialensis edidit P. Benignus Fernández eiusdem ordinis alumnus (264 p., Madrid 1911). Including elaborate biography and bibliography.

Excitatori de la pensa a Deu. Text i anotació per Pere Bohigas (286 p., Barcelona 1929).

Criticism. EUI (39, 1093).

ALFONSUS VARGAS TOLETANUS

Spanish Augustinian commentator on Aristotle and Peter the Lombard. Alfonsus Fernandi de Toledo y Vargas, Alfonsus Hispalensis or de Hispania. He was born c. 1300, was educated at the Augustinian house of Toledo, and assumed the Augustinian habit. He continued his studies in Paris, where he commented on the Sentences c. 1345, became master in theology c. 1345–48, and was "sacrae paginae professor" by 1348. His successful teaching career was interrupted in 1353, when he was appointed bishop of Badajoz; in 1361 he became archbishop of Sevilla; he died in that city on December 26/27, 1366, "non sine nota sanctitatis."

In 1353 he took an active part in the expedition of cardinal Aegidius Alvarez de Albornoz to subdue malcontents in the papal states; he was personally responsible for the conquest of Faenza.

Only two of his works survive: his twelve questions on the De anima and his commentary on the first book of Sentences (c. 1345–48). They are among the best-known works of the "schola aegidiana" or Augustinian school, for which see my note on Thomas of Strassburg.

Text. In tres Aristotelis libros de anima subtilissimae quaestiones. First edition, Florence 1477 (Klebs no. 49). Reprinted in Venice 1566, Vicentia 1608, Rome 1609.

Lectura super primo sententiarum. Unique edition by Paganinus de Paganinis, Venice 1490.

Criticism. Josef Kürzinger: Alfonsus Vargas Toletanus und seine theologische Einleitungslehre (Beiträge zur Geschichte der Philosophie und Theologie des Mittelalters vol. 22, nos. 5–6, 244 p., Münster i.W. 1930).

A3. France

HERVÉ NÉDÉLEC

French (Breton) Dominican, Thomist leader (d. 1323).

Hervaeus Brito, Hervaeus Natalis. Natalis is the same as Noël in French, Nédélec in Breton (or Armorican, a Celtic language, closely connected with Welsh and Cornish). The time and place of his birth are not known. There is no proof that he was born at Nédellec (diocese of Tréguier); hypothesis assumed to account for his name, then written Hervé de Nédellec. He entered the Dominican order (in Morlaix?) but seems to have been a secular first.

In 1303 he attended Dominican deliberations in Paris. He was then bachelor in theology and lecturing on the Sentences; he became licentiate in 1307, and took part in the Dominican inquest on the Templars. In 1309 he was appointed prior of the province of France; in 1314 he was charged, with others, to make a list of the errors of Durand of Saint Pourçain (that list is extant); in 1318 at the chapter of Lyon he was elected master general of the order. From that time on his history can hardly be separated from that of the order. We can follow him at the various annual chapters where he presided, Cahors, Rouen, Florence, Vienne, Barcelona. At that last one (1323) he excommunicated every monk studying alchemy or refusing to burn within a week the alchemical books he might have. Upon his return from Barcelona he fell ill and was obliged to stop his journey in Narbonne, where he died on August 7, 1323. The last joy of his life was the canonization of St. Thomas Aquinas, which occurred in Avignon on July 14 of the same year.

Hervé wrote many treatises in defense of Thomism against Duns Scot and the latter's followers, against independent critics like the Flemish archdeacon Henry of Ghent (XIII-2; d. 1293) and the Walloon canon Godfrey of Fontaines (XIII-2; d. after 1303), perhaps also against that half-hearted nominalist Durand of Saint Pourçain (d. 1334). It was the first attempt to do what was accomplished later by the Rouergois Dominican Jean Capréole (d. 1444) and the Italian one Tommaso De Vio of Gaeta (alias Gaetano, Cajetan; 1469–1534).

His most systematic work of that kind is the Defensio doctrinae fratris Thomae de Aquino, written by him for the general of his order, Aimeric de' Giuliani of Piacenza—thus between 1304 and 1311—and left incomplete. He discussed selected topics of the Sentences from the Thomist point of view against the Scotists in his Quaestiones in quatuor libros Sententiarum and in his eleven Quodlibeta. These quodlibeta include the discussion of some 204 questions of philosophy, theology, and discipline (see list in HL 34, 316–24). Hervé shows a good deal of moderation, for example in solving the many difficulties obtaining between seculars and regulars. He wrote many other treatises: On beatitude. On the Word. On the eternity of the world, defending St. Thomas against the Oxford Franciscan William de la Mare (XIII-2; d. 1298). On the substance of heavens (De materia coeli), or rather on the influence of heavens on the earth; if the motions of heavens were to stop, the motions of earth would also be stopped, there would be no new generation, only decomposition. De relationibus, i.e., on the relations between the divine persons and the unity of God. De virtutibus, is one born virtuous or does one become virtuous? this implies the subject of grace. On the motions of the angels.

On the unity of forms. This is a very long treatise on a topic of very great importance, to which Hervé came back repeatedly. Any substance is made up of matter and form. One form? Yes, claimed he after Thomas. He discussed this again in a treatise Contra Henricum de pluritate formarum, in another De formis, in his Quaestiones in quatuor libros Sententiarum, in his Quodlibeta.

He wrote many other treatises against the same Henricus (Henry of Ghent): De esse et essentia, De speciebus (De materia et forma), De voluntate et intellectu, De intellectu et de speciebus. He is always coming back to the same central question of Thomist doctrine, the unity of the substantial form.

He discussed in the Thomist manner first and second intentions, i.e., simple ideas derived from the observation of particular objects, and complex or general ideas implying judgments and the use of imagination.

It will suffice to mention two other treatises of his: De potestate papae, de jurisdictione ecclesiasticae potestatis et de exemptione; he defends the pope's absolute power, and also indirectly the power delegated by him to the religious orders, but shows again his wish to conciliate the secular clergy. The De paupertate Christi et apostolarum was written c. 1322 in answer to a consultation by John XXII, against the Spirituals.

Text. Quaestiones in quatuor libros Sententiarum. First edition, Venice 1505; second, Paris 1647. Both folios.

Quodlibeta. First edition, including only four quodlibeta, Venice 1486. The second edition, annotated by Marco Antonio Zimara (d. 1532), printed in Venice 1513, contains the eleven quodlibeta, plus eight other treatises by Nédélec, De beatitudine, De verbo, De aeternitate mundi, De materia coeli, De relationibus, De unitate formarum, De virtutibus, De motu angeli.

De intentionibus secundis. Two early editions, Venice s.a., Paris 1489.

De potestate papae, de jurisdictione ecclesiasticae potestatis et de exemptione. First edition Paris 1506, second 1647?

Defensio doctrinae Thomae de Aquino. Partial edition by Engelbert Krebs (Münster 1912). See below.

Criticism. B. Hauréau (NBG 24, 532–33, 1858). Engelbert Krebs: Theologie und Wissenschaft nach der Lehre der Hochscholastik, an der Hand der bisher ungedruckten Defensa doctrinae D. Thomae (Beiträge zur Geschichte der Philosophie des Mittelalters vol. 11, nos. 3–4, 201 p., Münster i.W. 1912), including long extracts (114 p.) from the Defensa. Duhem: Etudes (3, 320, 1913). B. Hauréau (HL 34, 308–51, 1914). Michalski (p. 90–92, 1925a). Josef Santeler: Der kausale Gottesbeweis bei Herveus Natalis nach dem ungedruckten Traktat De cognitione primi principi (Philosophie und Grenzwissenschaften vol. 3, part 1, 96 p., Innsbruck 1930).

DURAND OF SAINT POURÇAIN

French Dominican, commentator on the Sentences; one of the preparers of the new nominalism (d. 1334).

Contents: (1) Life. (2) Works. (3) Philosophy. (4) Astronomy. (5) Economics.
(6) Text. (7) Criticism.

1. *Life*

Durand de Saint Pourçain, Durandus a Sancto Porciano. Born (c. 1270–75?) at St. Pourçain-sur-Sioule in the Bourbonnais (dépt. Allier). He assumed the

Dominican habit in Clermont-Ferrand, later proceeded to Paris, and in 1303 was already established in the monastery of St. James in that city; he obtained the licentia docendi there in 1312. From 1313 to 1317 he was in Avignon, being lector s. palatii (lector curiae) and probably papal chaplain. He was appointed bishop of Limoux (dépt. Aude; not far from Carcassonne) in 1317, bishop of Le Puy-en-Vélay in 1318, bishop of Meaux (dépt. Seine-et-Marne) in 1326. He died in Meaux on September 10, 1334 (not 1332 or 1333).

He was called "Doctor resolutissimus," "Doctor modernus Durandus," also "Durus Durandus."[20] The last epithet may have been due to his having been born in central France, the inhabitants of which are hard-headed. He was not really an Auvergnat, but a Sanpourcinois, that is, a Bourbonnichon. The Bourbonnais lies close to Auvergne, north of it.

2. *Works*

Durand's main work is his elaborate commentary on the Sentences of Peter the Lombard, which occupied him a good part of his life. He began the first redaction in 1308, the third in 1327. At the end of it he wrote "Scripturam super quatuor Sententiarum libros iuvenis inchoavi sed senex complevi." This work contains his philosophical and scientific views, and is the only one which we need consider.

Among his other writings it will suffice to mention a Tractatus (quaestiones) de habitibus (c. 1312–13); Disputationes de quolibet (Paris 1312, Avignon 1314); De origine potestatum et iurisdictionum quibus populus regitur (1329); De visione Dei quam habent animae sanctorum ante iudicium generale (1333), also called De visione beatifica, against the views of John XXII. In the Tractatus he argued that the faculties of sensitive life alone are capable of habitus, not the intellect or will.

3. *Philosophy*

Durand was able to combine orthodoxy with some independence of thought. He preferred reason to authority "cuiuscunque doctoris quantumcunque celebris vel solemnis" (perhaps he had St. Thomas in mind).

He abandoned the realistic point of view, which had been so convenient for the purposes of dogmatic theology, and adopted the conceptualistic one, which was a sort of halfway stopping place between realism and nominalism. Universals exist only in the form of concepts; we can apprehend only singular things and thus our knowledge begins with individuals, "primum cognitum ab intellectu non est universale sed singulare." Thus for him the problem of individuation (how to derive the individual from the universal) vanishes.

The Dominican chapter of Saragossa (1309) had declared St. Thomas' doctrines to be the official doctrines of the order. In spite of this, Durand developed anti-Thomist and nominalistic tendencies. His commentary on the Sentences was censored by a Dominican commission in 1314, then again in 1317, when, thanks to the activities of John of Naples and Petrus de Palude, a list of 235 articles was drawn up wherein Durand deviated from Thomistic orthodoxy. His treatise De

[20] Hence his legendary epitaph:

"Durus Durandus jacet hic sub marmore duro.
An sit cremandus? nec ego scio sed neque curo."

The cremation which is here referred to is of course an other-world one.

visione beatifica was examined by order of John XXII in 1333 and found to contain 11 erroneous articles.

In his fight for relative independence and mild rationalism Durand was a forerunner and companion-at-arms of his younger contemporary Occam (d. 1349). Yet there are conspicuous differences, intellectual and temperamental, between them. In 1326, Durand was a member of a commission appointed by John XXII to re-examine Occam's commentary on the Sentences; it censored 51 articles taken from it.

It is clear, however, that Durand must be counted, together with Occam, among the thinkers who accelerated the downfall of scholasticism and prepared the way for modern science. He was averse to dogmatism and rather timid in his own assertions. For example, in his discussions of infinity, he seems to hesitate, yet leans to the conclusion that God cannot create an actual infinity either in size or in number; he can only create a magnitude syncategorematically infinite; infinity can exist only in fieri, not in facto.

Durand's independence of thought is very pleasant, and the more so that it was combined with gentleness. He was reverently orthodox, but was not unduly subservient to human authorities. As he put it in his commentary on the Sentences, "Naturalis philosophia non est quod Aristoteles et alii philosophi senserint sed quod habeat veritas rerum. Unde, ubi deviat mens Aristotelis a veritate rerum non est scientia scire quod Aristoteles senserit sed potius error," "De Aristotele non est tantum curandum sicut de veritate," etc.

His writings were not popular, yet his influence was not inconsiderable, and it continued to the eighteenth century.

4. *Astronomy*

Durand was not an astronomer, but in his commentary on the Sentences he was obliged to state his astronomical views. The fixed stars are moved by the revolution of the eighth sphere. As to the planets, observations show that their distances from the earth vary, hence the need of eccentrics; and that their trajectories as compared with those of the stars are sometimes retrograde, hence the need of epicycles. His views on eccentrics and epicycles were probably derived from Ibn al-Haitham and Bernard of Verdun. He cautiously added that a correct understanding (bona imaginatio) of them does not imply any subdivision of the incorruptible heavens; moreover, division is not necessarily destructive. Neither do epicycles and eccentrics conflict with the idea that noncircular motions are inconceivable above the moon, for they can be analyzed and reduced to circular motions. Planetary motions are not unnatural, but praeter naturam. These subtle distinctions could not disguise a gradual abandonment of Aristotelian physics, but caused it to be less obnoxious.

5. *Economics*

According to various writers on economic history, Durand suggested in 1326 the organization of state banks for the lending of money, with or without interest. Being unable to find the text ad hoc, I applied to Professor Joseph Koch, of Breslau, who has devoted many years to the investigation of Durand's writings. He kindly answered (Düsseldorf, Oct. 22, 1937) that he was not aware of the existence of any writing by Durand on economic questions. This suggestion is perhaps included in the apocryphal De legibus (HL 37, p. 30, no. viii), which contains many "modern" ideas; or perhaps in some of the writings of William Durant junior, bishop of Mende?

To return to the suggestion, whoever made it, it illustrates the evolution of Christian views on the subject of "usury"; that evolution was very slow. Loans were indispensable in some critical cases, but it was felt they should be restricted to such cases; loans for immediate consumption, not for production. The first organizations for the lending of money were thus significantly the monti di pietà introduced by the Franciscans in Italy in the second half of the fifteenth century in order to provide money for people in need. Interest was charged only, if at all, to cover running expenses (not for the loan of money); in some cases these expenses were provided for by special endowments (pious bequests). That solution was recommended by the Fifth Lateran council (1512–17).

Heribert Holzapfel: Die Anfänge der Montes pietatis (p. 29, München 1903). Rambaud (p. 68, 1909). Magdeleine Beis: Monts de piété et oeuvres de prêt gratuit (Montpellier thesis, p. 17, Paris 1929).

6. *Text*

In Sententias theologicas Petri Lombardi commentariorum libri IV was first printed in Paris 1508. Then again in Paris 1515, 1550; Venice 1571; Lyon 1556, 1560, 1595. The edition of Lyon 1595 contains an elaborate index and concordance with St. Thomas' Summa.

The De origine potestatum etc. was printed in Paris 1506; the first three quaestiones in the De origine potestatum of cardinal Pierre Bertrand[20a] are by Durand (Maxima bibliotheca veterum patrum 26, 127 ff., Lyon 1677).

De paupertate Christi et apostolorum, small part published by Odorico Rinaldi (Annales ecclesiastici a. 1322, nos. 59–61, vol. 15, Cologne 1691).

De visione Dei quam habent animae sanctorum ante iudicium generale, part published by Rinaldi (Annales ecclesiastici a. 1333, nos. 49–57, vol. 15, Cologne 1691).

7. *Criticism*

Werner (vol. 4, 1887). Duhem: Etudes (2, 378, 1909); Système (4, 103–6, 1916). Joseph Koch: Die Jahre 1312–1317 im Leben des Durandus (Miscellanea F. Ehrle 1, 265–306, 1923). De Wulf (2, 172–74, 1926).

Joseph Koch: Durandus de S. Porciano. Forschungen zum Streit um Thomas von Aquin zu Beginn des 14. Jahrhunderts. Erster Teil. Literargeschichtliche Grundlegung (Beiträge zur Geschichte der Philosophie des Mittelalters vol. 26, 452 p., Münster i.W. 1927); very elaborate study including an account of the efforts of Durand's contemporary adversaries, such as Herveus Natalis, Petrus de Palude, John of Naples, Guido Terrena, Gerard of Bologna, James of Lausanne, Bernard the Lombard, Durandellus, Thomas Anglicus. This is the only part thus far published, but the author wrote to me (Sept. 5, 1937) that the second volume would probably be ready in 1940.

Flick (1, 52–53, 1930). Johann Stufler (S.J.): Bemerkungen zur Konkurslehre des Durandus von St. Pourçain (Martin Grabmann Festschrift p. 1080–90, Münster i.W. 1935). Paul Fournier (HL 37, 1–38, 1936).

[20a] Pierre Bertrand (1280–1349), of Annonay in the Vivarais (dépt. Ardèche), bishop of Nevers and Autun, later cardinal. In 1341 he founded in Paris the college named after him Collège d'Autun (ou du cardinal Bertrand). He defended the clergy against the king's advocate Pierre de Cugnières (d. 1345) and wrote the Tractatus de origine jurisdictionum, sive de duabus potestatibus. (NBG 5, 759, 1855.)

DURAND D'AURILLAC

French (Auvergnat) Dominican (fl. 1330–34).

Durand originated probably in Aurillac (in Auvergne; dépt. Cantal). He assumed the Dominican habit, perhaps in Clermont-Ferrand. He read on the Sentences in Paris 1330–31. In 1334 he took part in the deliberation of Parisian schoolmen concerning the beatific vision, and was one of the twenty-nine theologians who wrote a letter to Philippe VI denouncing John XXII's views on the subject. Then he vanishes completely.

There is but one authentic writing of his, concerning the reality of time (Queritur utrum tempus sit aliquid reale extra animum), but we speak of him here because he has been wrongly identified with one Durandellus, who wrote Evidentie contra Durandum [a Sancto Porciano]. It was claimed that he was called Durandellus to differentiate him from his greater contemporary, countryman, religious brother, and adversary, Durand of Saint Pourçain.

The Evidentie contra Durandum is from another hand, and so is the Correctorium corruptorii (or Responsiones contra corrumpentes doctrinam Thome). None of the various treatises bearing that title, Correctorium corruptorii, can be definitely ascribed to Durand d'Aurillac.

Text. The question on time is unpublished. Escorial MS RH4.

Criticism. P. Mandonnet: Premiers travaux de polémique thomiste (Revue des sciences philosophiques et théologiques 7, 46–70, 1913; p. 67). Ueberweg (p. 515, 592, 1915). Paul Fournier (HL 37, 515–17, 1938).

PALU

Pierre de la Palu. French (Bressan) Dominican and conservative theologian (d. 1342).

Petrus de Palude, Petrus Paludanus. Son of Gérard de la Palu, a Bressan lord. Pierre was born c. 1270 or 1275 somewhere in Bresse (there are many localities called La Palu in the Ain department). He studied civil law in Toulouse or Montpellier (there was then no teaching of it in Paris). He assumed the Dominican habit, perhaps in Toulouse. In 1309–10 we find him in the St. James monastery in Paris, where he had just replaced Durand de Saint Pourçain as reader of the Sentences; he was in that monastery at least until 1317, becoming a licentiate in 1314, and St. James remained his main residence for many more years. In 1317 he replaced the master general at the Dominican synod of Pamplona. In 1318 he was delegated by John XXII to help make peace between the king of France and Robert of Béthune, count of Flanders, both of whom claimed possession of French Flanders; he failed in these negotiations and found himself in trouble because of them. In 1329 he was consecrated patriarch of Jerusalem in Avignon by John XXII, and administrator of the church of Limasol in Cyprus (as Jerusalem was in Muslim hands, the patriarchal see was then in Nicosia, Cyprus). He went to Cyprus and Egypt with Guillaume Durant, jr., both charged by John XXII and Philippe le Bel to negotiate with the Ayyūbī sulṭān of Egypt, al-Kāmil Muḥammad, for the recovery of the Holy Land or at least for better treatment of the Christians. These negotiations failed. Pierre was back in Avignon in 1331. About 1336 he was elected bishop of Couserans (Fanum S. Licerii, St. Lizier, in Gascony; dépt. Ariège). He died in Paris on January 31, 1342, and was buried in St. James.

The following facts will illustrate his activity as a theologian. In 1314 he was made a member of a commission of ten Dominicans, presided over by Hervé Nédélec, charged to examine the writings of their brother Durand de Saint Pourçain. Palu and John of Naples drew up a list of 93 erroneous or dubious propositions. In 1317, they drew up a new list of 235 points of disagreement between Thomas and Durand de Saint Pourçain. The latter's appointment in the same year to the bishopric of Limoux was perhaps made by John XXII to protect him against further Dominican (Thomistic) intolerance. In 1319, Palu, Terrena, and others were ordered by John XXII to examine the Joachimite errors revived by Peter Olivi (see my note on Terrena). Finally, in 1333 Palu was a member of the theological assembly convoked by king Philippe VI in Vincennes to scrutinize the views of John XXII on the beatific vision; in 1334, he was one of those twenty-nine theologians who agreed in condemning those views and begging the pope to repudiate them.[21] In 1335, Benedict XII, assisted by Palu, decided the matter against his predecessor.

Pierre de la Palu wrote commentaries on the Bible, then scholastic commentaries in the form of Quodlibeta and Quaestiones. His main work in that line was his commentary on the Sentences, largely directed against Durand de Saint Pourçain in defense of Thomas Aquinas.

Pierre was not as good a theologian as Hervé Nédélec, but was a better canonist and civilian. His writings on canon law include many consultations and various papers against Jean de Pouilli. This concerns the old conflict between regulars and seculars; Pouilli defended the latter, Palu the former. The matter was finally settled against Pouilli by the constitution Vas electionis given by John XXII on July 24, 1321. Palu's main work against Pouilli is the De causa immediata ecclesiastice potestatis (1318 or soon after); the papal power is the fons et origo of every ecclesiastical power whether regular or secular, and thus the regulars are given as much standing against the seculars as the pope desires.

Palu composed in 1328 a treatise De paupertate Christi against the Franciscan Michele da Cesena, that is, against the Spirituals in defense of the conservative and papal party.

He was a famous preacher, and some of his sermons have come down to us, together with many apocryphal ones. He wrote a history of crusades for the Christian faith, Liber bellorum Domini; it was a pretentious compilation, of which only fragments remain. It dates probably from after his return from the East (1331 ff.), when he spent much of his time preaching a new crusade.

Palu's influence appears in the Malleus maleficarum (printed 1489 ff.; Isis 25, 147–49), wherein his arguments are taken into account. For example, the Malleus follows him in distinguishing five methods by means of which the devil causes sexual impotence.

Text. At least fifteen editions of sermons are ascribed to him, eight of which are incunabula, the others of the sixteenth century. These sermons are apocryphal; a few authentic ones exist in MS.

The commentary on the four books of Sentences was printed in Venice 1495. There are various partial editions. In IV librum, Paris 1493, Venice 1493. In III et IV libros, Paris 1514, 1530, etc.

[21] The "beatific vision" is the immediate sight of God in the glory of heaven as enjoyed by the blessed dead. John XXII claimed that it could be enjoyed only after the Last Judgment; Palu and his brethren, that it would be enjoyed immediately after death.

De causa immediata ecclesiasticae potestatis, Paris 1506, 1647.

Criticism. I have used a MS study by Jules Stanislas Doinel: Essai sur la vie et les principales oeuvres de Pierre de la Palu (folio, 75 p., undated), MS Riant 17 in Harvard Library. It is an unpublished thesis of the Ecole des chartes, 1866. Ernest Wickersheimer: Les pilules de frère Pierre de la Palud (Bull. Société française de l'histoire de médecine 16, 139–41, 1922), apropos of a recipe for pills which Peter brought back from overseas. Paul Fournier (HL 37, 39–84, 1936). Wickersheimer (p. 642, 1936). Henry E. Sigerist: Impotence as a result of witchcraft (Essays in biology in honor of Herbert M. Evans p. 541–46, Berkeley 1943).

AURIOL

Pierre Auriol. French Franciscan, theologian, conceptualist, and forerunner of Occam (d. 1322).

Petrus Aureoli, Pierre d'Auriole. Date of birth unknown. He was born in the last quarter of the thirteenth century, we do not know where, but it was neither in Verberie sur Oise in Picardy (that is, he is different from Petrus de Verberia), nor in Toulouse. His family originated in the diocese of Cahors and the county of Quercy (dépts. Tarn-et-Garonne, Lot) in Aquitania. He assumed the Franciscan habit at an unknown date and place; by 1311 he had already been for some time a brother of the Aquitanian province.

In 1304 he was a student at the University of Paris; he may have sat at the feet of Duns Scot. In 1312 he was lector in the Franciscan house of Bologna, in 1314 in Toulouse; he became doctor and magister in theology in Paris 1318. At the end of 1320 he was appointed provincial of Aquitania; on February 27, 1321, John XXII made him archbishop of Aix-en-Provence; he died in Avignon, January 1322.

Iconography. Inasmuch as we have relatively few portraits of fourteenth-century scholars, it is worth while to note that Auriol's effigy has been preserved. For a discussion of this see Dreiling (p. 47–53, 1913).

Writings. His first work, Tractatus de paupertate et usu paupere, was written in 1311. It is an attempt at conciliation between the excessive love of poverty professed by the Spirituals and the more moderate views of the Franciscan majority. The love of poverty is but one virtue among others, such as obedience, which it should not neutralize.

In 1312 he published his first philosophical treatise, De principiis naturae, an account of nature in terms of matter and form.

In 1314 and 1315, he wrote two treatises in defense of the Immaculate Conception, Tractatus de conceptione beatae Mariae virginis and Repercussorium editum contra adversarium innocentiae matris Dei. These do not concern us, but it is interesting to recall (see Introd. 2, 714, 912, 968, 1127) that that incipient dogma was defended by the Scotists and other Franciscans against the Thomists and other Dominicans.

Auriol's main work was his commentary on the books of Sentences, of which there are two redactions, the first dating back to 1314–15 (or even 1312), the second completed in Paris 1316–18.

In 1319 he completed a commentary on the Holy Bible, Compendium sensus litteralis totius Divinae Scripturae, this being by far the most popular of his works; and in 1320 he issued his Quodlibeta, wherein he discussed moot questions of metaphysics, ethics, psychology, etc. against Thomas Anglicus,[22] Hervé of Nédélec, and the Scotists.

His philosophy. Auriol's main sources, outside the Holy Writ, were Aristotle, St. Augustine, and Averroes. He was a conceptualist, trying to compromise between the Scotists and the Thomists. Like Durand of Saint Pourçain, he refused to make a distinction between essence and existence; in addition, he rejected the idea that the soul is the form of the body. His views, as well as Durand's, are historically important because they prepared the new system established by William of Occam. The latter, by the way, knew of Auriol's work, but only imperfectly after he had already completed his commentary on the first book of Sentences.

Text. The second redaction of the commentary on the Books of sentences, and the Quodlibeta were printed in Rome (folio, 2 vols., 1596–1605). The first volume, containing the commentary to book I only, extends to 1126 pages (plus elaborate indexes); it was edited with great care by the Franciscan Costanzo Boccafuoco (1531–95) of Sarnano nella Marca d'Ancona, cardinal (generally called cardinal Sarnano), and dedicated by him on December 29, 1595 to Clement VIII. It was printed in the Vatican in 1596. The second volume, containing the rest of the commentary and the Quodlibeta, was very carelessly edited after the cardinal's death, and printed without notes in Rome 1605.

De paupertate is included in Firmamenta trium ordinum beatissimi patris nostri Francisci (Paris 1512). Reprinted Venice 1513?

De conceptione beatae Mariae virginis. There are two or three incunabula editions, and at least four later ones.

Quaestiones disputatae de Immaculata Conceptione. Anonymous edition by the Franciscan fathers of Quaracchi, near Florence (178 p., 1904). This includes not only the De conceptione but also the Repercussorium, plus questions by William of Ware and John Duns Scot.

De principiis naturae is still unpublished. MSS in Padua and Avignon.

Brevarium bibliorum, sive Compendium Sacrae Scripturae. First edition, Strassburg, s.a. (c. 1476). There are a dozen more editions, the latest, provided with analytic tables, printed at Rouen 1649. The titles of these editions vary greatly.

Criticism: Noël Valois (HL 33, 479–527, 1906). Raymundus Dreiling (O.F.M.): Der Konzeptualismus in der Universalienlehre des Petrus Aureoli (Beiträge zur Geschichte der Philosophie des Mittelalters vol. 11, no. 6, 230 p., Münster i.W. 1913). De Wulf (2, 174–76, 1926). Michalski (p. 42, 93–96, 1925a); (p. 233 f., 1937).

MEYRONNES

François de Meyronnes. Provençal Franciscan theologian (d. 1325).

Also called François de Mayronnes, or Maironnes, Mairon; Franciscus de Mayronis. He hailed from Meyronnes (arr. Barcelonnette, dépt. Basses-Alpes; Provence). He probably assumed the Franciscan habit in Digne (Basses-Alpes); at any rate, he continued his studies in Paris, where he received his licentia docendi in 1323 upon the recommendation of Robert king of Sicily[23] and John XXII. In

[22] That is, Thomas of Wilton, an Englishman who, though chancellor in London, received a papal permission in 1320 to reside at the University of Paris. He was often quoted by John Baconthorpe (HL 33, 507). Not to be confused with another Thomas Anglicus, Thomas Jorz, who died in 1310 (see below).

[23] Provence was ruled by the Angevine princes of Naples and Sicily from 1246 to 1481.

1324 he preached in Avignon before the latter. He died in Perugia on July 26 of an unnamed year (probably 1325).

He did *not* introduce (whether in 1315 or 1320) the actus sorbonicus. This was an academic stunt: a teacher had to hold himself in readiness on Fridays, in summertime, to answer publicly every objection, for twelve long hours!

His main work is a commentary on the four books of Sentences, of which there are various redactions. He paid special attention to book I, dealing with God and the Trinity, and his commentary on it was used by Nicholas of Cues. As to his other writings, it will suffice to mention his Tractatus primi principii complexi; a controversy De persona et essentia with the Benedictine Pierre Roger (the future Clement VI, pope 1342–52), this being a very good specimen of the Parisian scholastic disputes of that time (one of the pieces of that controversy is dated 1320); quodlibeta, extracts (flores extracti, in veritates reducti, veritates) from St. Augustine with commentary; extracts from Dionysios the Areopagite (from the Latin versions and commentaries of John Scotus Erigena, IX-2, John Sarrazin, XII-2, and Thomas Gallus, abbot of Vercelli;[23a] commentaries on Holy Writ; Moralia; commentary on the Aristotelian Logics and Physics; De indulgenciis or De clavibus; Tractatus de principatu temporali, concluding (against Dante) that a universal monarchy is undesirable; De dominio apostolorum or Questio de paupertate Christi, a burning subject in Franciscan circles; etc. The Tractatus formalitatum secundum doctrinam Francisci Mayronis is derived from François' writings and those of Duns Scot.

François de Meyronnes, being deeply influenced by Plato, St. Augustine, and Dionysios Areopagita as well as by Duns Scot, contributed to give to "Scotism" some of its characteristics. It is an exaggeration to call him (as did Duhem) "the real creator of what has been incorrectly named Scotism," but he certainly must share the guilt of having introduced into metaphysics and theology a number of unnecessary subtleties. The undeserved popularity of many of his writings increased his unhealthy power. Happily for him, his subtleties were of such innocent nature that the defenders of orthodoxy did not prick up their ears, except perhaps in one instance, when he asked whether God was not the cause of sin (utrum Deus sit causa effectiva peccati, in commentary on book II of the Sentences, dist. 43, qu. 9, art. 4). He also argued the following question: "Dicendum quod Christi corpus in matris utero vere habuit ordinem partium in toto, et non ordinem partium in loco, sicut in hostia habet" (Sent. III, dist. 4, qu. 1, art. 6).

To return to scientific subjects, François discussed such questions as the plurality of worlds and the rotation of the earth. Apropos of the latter he quoted an anonymous opinion according to which it would be better to assume that the earth rotates than that the heavens do, but he does not press it.[24] François also questioned the traditional views on the sterility of money and the sinfulness of taking interest on loans.

Text. A part of the commentary on book I of the Sentences was printed under the title Conflatus, Trevisa 1476, and reprinted Basel 1498, Venice 1504–7, 1519,

[23a] This Thomas Gallus or of Vercelli (Piemonte) was not dealt with in vol. 2. Before becoming prior and abbot of Vercelli he taught in the abbey of St. Victor in Paris. He continued and amplified the Dionysian tendencies of Hugh of St. Victor (XII-1). He died in 1226 or 1246 (Überweg p. 331, 347, 1915).

[24] Commentary on book II of Sentences, dist. 14, qu. 5 (ed. 1520, fol. 150): "Dicit tamen quidam doctor quod si Terra moveretur et Coelum quiesceret, quod hic esset melior dispositio. Sed hoc impugnatur propter diversitatem motuum in Coelo quae non possent salvari."

1520, 1526, 1527. The Venetian editions include also the commentary on books II to IV.

Tractatus primi principii complexi. Printed Venice 1517. Also in certain editions of the Conflatus, Venice 1520, etc.

The Flores extracted from St. Augustine with François' commentary were often printed: Trevisa 1476, Toulouse 1488, Venice 1489, Lyon 1520.

There are many editions of his sermons: Venice 1491, 1493, Basel 1498, 1502, etc.

Passus super universalia, predicamenta et perihermenias, 1478; Venice 1489, 1517. The edition of 1517 is the collection edited by Gerolamo Nuciarelli (Nucerellus), containing also the Tractatus primi principii complexi quoted above, and the Tractatus de formalitatibus.

Super exposicione Decalogi, Basel 1498, Paris 1519.

Criticism. Rambaud (p. 65, 1909). Pierre Duhem: François de Meyronnes et la question de la rotation de la terre (Archivum franciscanum historicum 6, 23–25, 1913); Système (5, 231, 1917). Charles Victor Langlois (HL 36, 305–42, 1924–27). Grant McColley and H. W. Miller: Saint Bonaventure, Francis Mayron, William Vorilong and the doctrine of plurality of worlds (Speculum 12, 386–89, 1937; Isis 28, 230).

DU FOUR

Vital du Four, or Dufour; Vitalis de Furno. Gascon Franciscan theologian (d. 1327).

Vital originated, not in Four in Brittany, but in Bazas in Guyenne (dépt. Gironde). He assumed the Franciscan habit; studied the Sentences in Paris under Jacques de Carceto (otherwise unknown), and repeated his teacher's lectura in Montpellier 1295–96. He was master in theology and minister of the Aquitanian province of his order in 1307. His countryman Clement V (Bertrand de Got, born near Bazas, pope 1305–14) made Vital a cardinal in 1312 and gave him various monasteries in commendam. Vital continued to be generously treated by him and by John XXII, until 1322, when he took sides with the Franciscan Spirituals on the question of apostolic poverty. He died in Avignon on August 16, 1327, and was buried in the Franciscan church of that city.

He wrote a commentary on the four books of Sentences, a dictionary of Biblical ethics entitled Speculum morale totius Sacre Scripture (c. 1305), Postilla super Apocalipsim, Quodlibeta theologica, sermons, etc.

His most interesting work to us, the Pro conservanda sanitate tuendaque prospera valetudine, is unfortunately of uncertain authorship. It is a kind of materia medica in alphabetical order. There is no evidence that Vital had studied medicine, but he had resided in Montpellier in 1295–96 and may have followed medical courses at that time; in his commentary on the Sentences he showed interest in natural phaenomena, such as magnetic attraction and phosphorescence. The Pro sanitate is divided as follows: water and its varieties, metals, other inorganic substances, substances derived from plants, from animals. The facts collected are antiquated, being largely ancient, patristic, Salernitan, or early Muslim (not farther down than 1150 or even 1100).

Text. Speculum totale, Lyon 1513, 1563; Venice 1594, 1603.

Pro conservanda sanitate, Mainz 1531.

Criticism. E. O. von Lippmann: Das Sammelbuch des Vitalis de Furno und seine Bedeutung für die Geschichte der Chemie (Chemiker Zeitung 1922, reprint 17 p.; Isis 4, 587). Charles V. Langlois (HL 36, 295–305, 1924). F. Delorme: Le cardinal Vital du Four, huit questions disputées sur le problème de la connaissance (Revue d'histoire doctrinale et littéraire du Moyen âge 2, 151–337, 1927). Wickersheimer (p. 776, 1936). Lynn Thorndike: Little known medical works in Basel MSS (Annals of medical history 2, 285–86, 1940), giving the introduction to the Pro conservanda sanitate omitted in the very unsatisfactory edition of 1531.

BONET

Nicholas Bonet, Doctor proficuus. Franciscan, theologian, Aristotelian commentator, and member of a papal mission to China (d. 1343?).

His origins are obscure, and he has been claimed as a Sicilian and Catalan. He was more probably a Tourangeau. It is probable that he assumed the Franciscan habit in Tours, and that he studied in Paris. It is said that he was one of the disciples of Duns Scot (XIII-2; d. 1308). The only certain date of his life, however, refers to his mission to China. In 1338 he was sent thither by Benedict XII on an embassy to the great Khān under the leadership of Giovanni de' Marignolli. For a brief account of the journey, see my note on Marignolli. The embassy returned in 1346, but apparently Bonet returned earlier (certis ex causis ad Curiam est reversus, chronicle of the twenty-four generals). In 1342 he was appointed bishop of Malta; another bishop was appointed in the following year. Hence Bonet died presumably in 1343 (not in 1360).

He wrote commentaries on Genesis, on Aristotle's Metaphysics, Physics, De anima, Praedicamenta, on the Books of sentences of Peter the Lombard. His own compositions include a Theologia naturalis and a Tractatus de conceptione Beatae Mariae Virginis, dedicated to Clement V (pope 1305–14).

Text. His commentary on the Metaphysics was first printed in Barcelona 1493 (Klebs no. 199, 132 leaves). Reprinted Venice 1505.

Theologia naturalis. Printed in Venice 1505 together with the commentary on Metaphysics, Physics, and Praedicamenta.

Criticism. EIU (8, 1593, 1912). P. Martin de Barcelone: Nicolas Bonet (Etudes franciscaines 37, 638–57, 1925). Streit (p. 76–77, 80–81, 1928), referring to sources.

DEGUILLEVILLE

Guillaume Deguilleville (or Digulleville, Guileville). French (Norman) Cistercian, author of three didactic poems, "pilgrimages" (fl. 1330–58).

Deguilleville was born c. 1295, probably in Digulleville near Beaumont-Hague (dépt. Manche; Normandy), and entered the Cistercian house of Chaalis near Senlis (Oise).

He composed three "dreams" in octosyllabic French verse. (1) Pèlerinage de la vie humaine (1330–32, revised 1355). (2) Pèlerinage de l'âme séparée du corps (c. 1355). (3) Pèlerinage de Jésus-Christ (1358).

The sources are patristic literature, St. Bernard, the Roman de la rose (Introd. 2, 932); the author had some acquaintance with Aristotle and Ptolemy; he was apparently unacquainted with the Divina commedia. His own allegories are on a much lower level than Dante's.

The first pilgrimage was exceedingly popular in France for two centuries. It was "translated" into French prose in 1464 for Jeanne de Laval, queen of Jerusalem and duchess of Anjou (d. 1382), by Jean Galloppes, chaplain to the duke of Bedford. It was revised by a Cistercian monk, Pierre Virgin of Clairvaux, who flourished probably at about the same time. A dramatic interpretation was prepared in the

Walloon dialect of Liége. A fragment was translated by Chaucer, and the whole, in 1426, by John Lydgate (1370?–1451?); Lydgate's translation influenced John Bunyan (1628–88). A Castilian version was prepared by Vicente Mazuello (printed 1490). A version in German verse was composed early in the fifteenth century.

The pilgrimage of the soul was translated into French prose by Jean Galopes (Galloppes), and that text was translated into English in 1413, probably by Lydgate.

The third pilgrimage was simply a life of Christ.

Text. Le romant des trois pelerinaiges (206 leaves, Paris c. 1500). Text of the three pilgrimages.

First pilgrimage: The prose version of Jean Galloppes was printed for Henry VII by Vérard (c. 1499), facsimile reprint with note by Alfred W. Pollard (Roxburghe Club, London 1912). Le pelerinage de la vie humaine, edited by J. J. Stürzinger (Roxburghe Club, 464 p., London 1893).

Modern English prose translation by Katherine Isabella Cust (84 p., London 1859). The pilgrimage of the life of man, Englisht by John Lydgate 1426. Edited by Frederick James Furnivall, with introduction, notes, indexes by Katharine B. Locock (Early English Text Society, 3 parts, London 1899–1904). Same reprinted for the Roxburghe Club (London 1905).

The pilgrimage of the lyf of the manhode, edited by William Aldis Wright (Roxburghe Club, 262 p., 1869).

Aloys Böhmer: Die Pilgerfahrt des träumenden Mönchs (348 p., Berlin 1915), German verse translation of early fifteenth century. New edition by Adriaan Meijboom (Amsterdam thesis, Bonn 1925).

El peregrino de la vida humana (Toloza 1490). Mazuello's version.

First edition in Dutch, Haarlem 1486, with woodcuts. There is a copy of that beautiful edition in the Pierpont Morgan Library (Report for 1930–35, pl. VII), and also of an early French MS (MS 772; same Report, p. 89) written and illuminated in northern France in the third quarter of the fourteenth century. The author of the 90 miniatures may possibly be identified with Jean Bondol of Bruges (fl. c. 1370–80), le "Maitre aux boqueteaux"?

Second pilgrimage: The book of the pylgremage of the sowle (William Caxton, 1483). New edition by Katherine Isabella Cust (112 p., London 1859). Le pelerinage de l'ame, edited by J. J. Stürzinger (Roxburghe Club, 405 p., 1895).

Third pilgrimage: Le pelerinage Jhesucrist. Edited by J. J. Stürzinger (Roxburghe Club, 378 p., 1897).

Criticism. Nathaniel Hill: The ancient poem Le pèlerinage de l'homme compared with the Pilgrim's progress of John Bunyan (London 1858). Johan Erik Evald Hultman: Guillaume de Deguileville (210 p., Upsala 1902), in Swedish. James Blanton Wharey: The sources of Bunyan's allegories with special reference to Deguileville's Pilgrimage of man (Johns Hopkins thesis, 136 p., Baltimore 1904). Alfred Jeanroy: La passion Nostre Dame et le Pèlerinage de l'âme (Romania 36, 361–68, 1907). Stanley Leman Galpin: On the sources of the Pèlerinage de l'âme (Publications of the Modern Language Association 25, 275–308, 1910). Langlois (4, 199–268, 1928). Abbé Joseph Delacotte: Guillaume de Digulleville. Trois romans poèmes du XIVe siècle (288 p., Paris 1932), analysis with extracts. Fritz Goetze: Untersuchungen über die Pilgerfahrt des träumenden Mönchs (Marburg thesis, 1934).

MIRECOURT

John of Mirecourt, Joannes de Mirecuria (there is a place called Mirecourt in dépt. Vosges, Lorraine). French Cistercian, bachelor of theology who lectured on the Sentences at the Collège St. Bernard in Paris 1345. In 1347, forty propositions extracted from his lectures were condemned by the masters of theology of Paris University.

His ideas were inspired partly by those of Bradwardine (or at any rate very similar to them), considering God as the necessitating cause of every contingent activity. This led to such dangerous conclusions as these: "Quod Deus facit quod aliquis peccat et quod sit peccator . . . Quod si aliquis habens usum liberii arbitrii, incidens in tantam temptationem cui non possit resistere, moveatur ad illecebram cum aliena uxore, non committit adulterium, et sic de aliis peccatis." Other ideas of his suggest the terminism of Occam or the subjectivism of Autrecourt. The principle of causality cannot be proved.

Text. The commentary on the Sentences is unpublished, but the propositions condemned in 1347 were edited by Charles Du Plessis d'Argentrée: Collectio iudiciorum (1, 343–45, Paris 1724) and by Heinrich Denifle: Chartularium universitatis parisiensis (2, 610–14, Paris 1891).

Alexander Birkenmajer: Ein Rechtfertigungsschreiben Johanns von Mirecourt (Beiträge zur Geschichte der Philosophie des Mittelalters 20, no. 5, 91–128, Münster i.W. 1922).

Criticism. Constantin Michalski: Die vielfachen Redaktionen einiger Kommentare zu Petrus Lombardus (Miscellanea Francesco Ehrle 1, 219–64, 226 ff., Roma 1924). Michalski (p. 78, 1920); (p. 46, 109–12, 1925a); (1937 passim).

RAOUL LE BRETON

French logician and philosopher (fl. 1299–1320).

Radulphus Reginaldi Britonis. Raoul Renaud, dit Le Breton, i.e., the Breton, which may refer to family origin. Le Breton was not an uncommon family name, however, in Paris at that time. In 1299 Raoul was already teaching logic in Paris; in 1308–9, he discussed the books of Sentences. In 1316, being already a doctor in theology, he was named canon of Le Mans by John XXII. He received many other prebends. He was provisor of the Sorbonne from 1315 to 1320. The dates and places of his birth and death are unknown.

He wrote "questions" on the logica vetus or ars vetus, i.e., the Praedicamenta and De interpretatione of Aristotle, Porphyry's Isagoge, and the Liber sex principiorum of Gilbert de la Porrée (XII-1); and on the logica nova, i.e., the logical books which began to circulate in the West only in the thirteenth century, to wit, Aristotle's Topica and Analytica, and Boetius' Topica. He wrote questions also on the De anima and on the Sentences of Peter the Lombard. There are many contemporary MSS, most of them, strangely enough, out of France, chiefly in Italy. Nothing has been printed, however.

Raoul was a Thomist, that is, a moderate realist, anti-Scotist.

Criticism. Paul Fournier (HL 36, 169–180, 1924).

JEAN DE POUILLI

Joannes de Polliaco. French (Picard) theologian, born either in a village of the Beauvaisis or near Laon. He was already a fellow (socius) of the Sorbonne toward the end of the thirteenth century, and was already called magister in 1295. He was a disciple of the Belgian doctor Godefroi de Fontaines (d. after 1303). He taught at the Sorbonne, was a prebendary of the cathedrals of Cambrai and St. Quentin, and died after 1321.

He was an independent Thomist, like his master Godefroi de Fontaines (XIII-2). He wrote quodlibeta and quaestiones dealing with a number of theological and philosophical topics. He claimed against the Scotists and against the mystics that will always is subordinated to reason.

He seems to have been a narrow-minded and obstinate theologian and canonist. He took a considerable part in the theological debates caused by the persecution of the Knights Templars. The Templars were arrested in 1307 by order of Philippe le Bel, and Jean de Pouilli attended their condemnation by Clement V at the council of Vienne (1311–12). He had for them neither sympathy nor mercy. He was also one of the doctors who in 1310 caused the gentle mystic Marguerite Porrette[25] to be burnt at the stake.

We have frequently referred in volume 2 (e.g., p. 712, 823) to one of the fundamental intellectual conflicts in Western Christendom, that between the seculars (the clergy) and the regulars, especially the militant Franciscans and Dominicans. By the end of the thirteenth century the regulars were winning, for the leading philosophers were found among them. That conflict continued unabated throughout the fourteenth century. As early as 1307 if not before, Jean de Pouilli had taken sides with the seculars; he was naturally attacked by the Friars and was involved in a long series of litigations with the curia. On July 24, 1321 he was finally condemned by John XXII; three days later, he recanted publicly in his lecture room at the University of Paris.

This Jean de Pouilli should not be confused with a homonym, physician in 1370–89 to Philip the Bold, duke of Burgundy, and after 1384 to Charles VI, king of France (Wickersheimer p. 468, 1936).

Text. No writings are ascribed to the physician. Those of the theologian are unpublished, but a table of contents of them is included in Valois' memoir cited below (p. 260–70).

Criticism. Noël Valois (HL 34, 220–81, 1914). Michalski (p. 73, 1920). Joseph Koch: Der Prozess gegen den Magister Johannes de Polliaco und seine Vorgeschichte (Recherches de théologie ancienne et médiévale 5, 391–422, Louvain 1933; Isis 29, 213).

JOHN OF JANDUN

French philosopher and scientist, commentator on Aristotle and Ibn Rushd, leader of the Parisian Averroists, publicist (d. 1328).

Contents: (1) Life. (2) Writings. (3) Philosophy. (4) Mechanics and physics. (5) Astronomy. (6) Influence.
(7) Text. (8) Criticism.

1. *Life*

Jean de Jandun. Joannes de Janduno, Ganduno, Gandinio; Joannes Ghandini, Gendini, etc. Among these many spellings one was particularly misleading, de Gandavo, for on the strength of it he was wrongly connected with the city of Ghent in Flanders and called John of Ghent. That mistake was aggravated by

[25] Marguerite Porrette (or Poirette, Porete) was a Beghard (Beguine) from Hainaut, flourished in Paris. She had written before 1305 a mystical book which was burned with her. Her execution took place in Paris about Whitsunday 1310. See Barthélemy Hauréau (HL 27, 70–74, 1877). Ch. V. Langlois: Marguerite Porete (Revue historique 54, 295–99, 1894).

another, for he was also called John Dullaert, and there was a man of that name, an Aristotelian commentator, actually born in Ghent![26] To return to John of Jandun, he was born at an unknown date at the end of the thirteenth century in the diocese of Reims. He originated probably in Jandun, near Signi l'Abbaye (Ardennes) in Champagne. He studied in Paris and was already there early in the fourteenth century; about the year 1311 or before, he became acquainted in Paris with Marsiglio of Padua, who remained his lifelong friend; he was one of the first masters in the College of Navarre (Paris) 1316, and in the same year, 1316, was elected a canon of Senlis (Oise) by John XXII. It is impossible to know how much of his time was spent in Paris, and how much in Senlis; he was in Senlis in 1323. He helped Marsiglio of Padua to write the Defensor pacis, which was completed in June 1324. From that time on John and Marsiglio shared to some extent the same vicissitudes. They left Paris together clandestinely and went to Nuremberg to place themselves under the protection of the emperor Ludwig of Bavaria. John XXII denounced them in a bull of 1326 and excommunicated them in the following year. On January 17, 1328, they attended the coronation of Ludwig in Rome by Sciarra Colonna and three other syndics of the people; on May 12, 1328, they attended in Rome the popular election, confirmed by the emperor, of a new pope, the Franciscan Pietro da Corbara.[27] A few days before (May 1, 1328), John of Jandun had been appointed bishop of Ferrara by the *emperor*. He died in Todi (on the Tiber) within the same year, 1328.

2. *Writings*

As only two or three of his works are dated, they cannot be placed in chronological order, but they are almost certainly anterior to the Defensor pacis, and probably spaced out between the years 1310 (or a few years before) and 1323. I quote them in the order given in HL (33, 536–60).

1. Quaestiones super libros Physicorum. This was his main work, and one of the first if not the very first. Indeed, it begins with an encyclopaedic introduction (to all his commentaries) wherein natural philosophy is divided into six main branches, and the purpose of each is indicated as well as its standard authorities: (I) Motion. Aristotle's Physics. (II) Celestial bodies, elements. De coelo et mundo. (III) Generation and corruption, growth and change. De generatione and second book of De anima; Albert the Great, De nutrimento et nutribili; and the Colliget of Ibn Rushd. (IV) Qualities (dry and damp, hot and cold). Meteorologica. (V) Metals and stones. No Aristotelian treatise; Albert the Great, De mineralibus. (VI) Organic bodies: (a) the soul, De anima; (b) passions, Parva

[26] A theologian called John of Ghent taught in Paris in 1303, and was curé of Kieldrecht (near St. Nicholas, in East Flanders). His commentaries on the Book of sentences and his quodlibeta have been wrongly ascribed to John of Jandun (De Wulf 2, 231).

As to John Dullaert, he was born in Ghent c. 1470 and died in Paris 1513. Many of his Aristotelian commentaries have been published. While he was teaching in Beauvais, his main pupil was the famous humanist Juan Luis Vives (1492–1540). After E. H. J. Reusens, in Biographie nationale de Belgique (6, 273–74, 1878).

These names mistakenly given to John of Jandun (such as Dullaert, John of Ghent, John of Jandun of Ghent) occur repeatedly in the early printed editions, and hence are very difficult to uproot.

[27] This antipope, Nicholas V, did not last very long. He submitted to John XXII in 1330 and died in 1333.

naturalia; (c) plants; (d) animals, Aristotle's zoological treatises. To conclude, he recommends the study of a series of other (apocryphal) Aristotelian treatises, mainly the Problems, and also the De substantia orbis of Ibn Rushd. John's commentary is made out of a series of questions, each being followed with all the answers then conceivable. It is often difficult to know which answer is preferred by the author. The questions cover all the fundamental difficulties of mechanics (or physics), such as, is matter divisible per se? can nature be entirely explained in terms of matter and form? what is motion? is there a vacuum and, if so, how does motion take place in it? is circular motion perpetual? has the primum mobile infinite energy?

This treatise was quite popular; it was printed first in 1475 and five times more before the end of the century. The edition of Venice 1488 contains additions and notes dated 1485 by the Cretan Jew Elijah Delmedigo (c. 1460–97), and one edition at least (1552) interpolations by the Dominican Johann Romberch, inquisitor in Cologne (d. c. 1533).

2. Quaestio disputata super libros Physicorum. Question included in the Oxford MS but not in the printed editions, "Whether time, motion, the world have always existed?" Both answers, yes and no, are explained, but John finally concludes in favor of the negative.

3. Quaestiones super libros De coelo et mundo (printed 1501). Built in the same way as opus 1 and covering field (II) of the introduction to that opus. It includes naturally a discussion of astrology.

4, 5. Expositio et quaestiones super librum De substantia orbis (printed 1481). This is a supercommentary on Ibn Rushd's commentary on the De coelo et mundo. John gives the full text of Ibn Rushd's work, interpolating his own interpretations, then adding a series of questions and answers in his usual manner.

6. Quaestio num augmentatio sit possibilis (unpublished).

7, 8. De sensu agente. Dated 1310.

9. Quaestiones super tres libros De anima. Dated 1300, yet including a reference to nos. 7, 8, dated 1310. The date 1300, which is very early, is probably a mistake. The Quaestiones de anima were probably written after the De sensu agente. This treatise was very popular judging from the number of MSS and editions, the first in 1473 and at least ten more within less than a century.

10. Quaestiones in Parva naturalia (printed 1505). Questions relative to the seven treatises, De sensu et sensato, De memoria et reminiscentia, De somno et vigilia, De causa longitudinis et brevitatis vitae, De iuventute et senectute et de inspiratione et expiratione, De morte et vita, De motibus animalium. This includes a series of odd questions, such as, would a man born deaf be necessarily mute? what language would an abandoned child speak, to whom no one ever spoke? In this second case he concludes that the child would not speak Hebrew, nor any definite language. There are also questions on knowledge of the future, dreams, astrology.

11. Quaestiones in librum De bona fortuna (printed 1505, with no. 10). The De bona fortuna is a collection of extracts from the Eudemian Ethics.

12. Edition of Pietro d'Abano's commentary on the Problemata, with a preface. Pietro's commentary was completed at Padua in 1310, and John received a copy of it soon afterward from his friend Marsiglio of Padua. John's editing is very discreet. It is more like the work of an intelligent copyist.

13. Quaestiones in duodecim libros Metaphysicae (printed 1505).

14. Quaestiones super Rhetoricam (unpublished).

15, 16. De laudibus Silvanecti et De laudibus Parisius. Both written in 1323, the first in praise of his country retreat Senlis, the second in praise of Paris. The latter is particularly interesting, as it includes a description of Paris and of its university in 1323.

17. Defensor pacis, completed on June 24, 1324 by Marsiglio of Padua, with John's cooperation. The book and John's share in it are discussed in the note on Marsiglio.

3. *Philosophy*

John was a great admirer of Ibn Rushd and called himself "the ape of Aristotle and Ibn Rushd." On the other hand, he was antagonistic to St. Thomas. He discussed lengthily such questions as the eternity of the world and of motion, the necessary realization of the possible, the isolation, unity, and eternity of the human intellect. In many cases his attitude might be called antischolastic. He was orthodox, however, and, as if to compensate for his rationalism, he inserted many professions of faith in his writings.

For example, after having set forth the Averroistic theory of the eternity of the world, he remarks that we must believe in the Christian doctrine of creation. Whenever his philosophic views conflict with dogmatic theology, he concludes that after all the latter must be right, in spite of rational appearances. There are two fields of thought, the rational and the dogmatic, the latter being pre-eminent. This is somewhat different from the theory of twofold truth which I have discussed in volume 2 (p. 357; 354, 877). Some critics (e.g., De Wulf) have thrown suspicion upon John's sincerity, especially because of his antipapal activity together with Marsiglio of Padua in 1324 and later. However, his opposition to the pope of Avignon and the pontifical policies of his day was not at all incompatible with theological orthodoxy, and on the other hand there was nothing dishonest in showing the contradictions between reason and faith (it would have been hypocritical to hide them after having seen them). In my opinion, John the commentator was an honest man, whose rational conclusions were restrained by his orthodoxy; he was too honest, indeed, to conceal his difficulties. One might as well doubt Pasteur's sincerity as his own.

Instead of reproaching him for heterodoxy and originality, I feel that John was more eclectic than original, more critical than productive; he tried honestly to see every side of a question, but lacked creative power.

4. *Mechanics and physics*

John's commentaries on Aristotelian physics are especially interesting from the mechanical point of view. For example, he asks himself the question (De coelo et mundo, quaestio xix super librum IV): Is the cause attracting a falling body to the ground inherent in its initial position? (we would say today: has the falling body any potential energy because of its position?). As a good Peripatetician he was obliged to answer no, otherwise the argument against the plurality of worlds would have been shaken. On that question hangs another one: Is action at a distance possible? John answers again, consistently, no. But then, he asks himself, how will it be possible to account for the attraction of a magnet? He solves that difficulty by assuming that between the magnet and the piece of iron attracted by it there is medium which is gradually altered as the species magnetica is transmitted step by step. That theory and its consequences were strongly denied by William of Occam.

John maintained the Aristotelian theory of the impossibility of a vacuum, and, together with Albert of Saxony and later Marsilius of Inghen, deduced from it the impossibility, or the extreme difficulty, of separating two polished surfaces closely pressed against each other.

5. *Astronomy*

There is no evidence that John made astronomical observations, but he was well acquainted with astronomical theories. In spite of his devotion to Ibn Rushd, he defended the theory of eccentrics and epicycles[28] in agreement with "Ptolemy and modern astronomers." He tried to reformulate that theory in order to escape Averroistic criticism. According to this new formulation, each planet has three neighboring orbits, the extreme ones being contiguous to the extreme orbits of other planets; the epicycle moves within the thickness of the intermediary orbit.

John does not speculate, however, concerning the real existence of these orbits. It suffices that the theory be workable and help one to save the phaenomena (salvare apparentias).

He had read, or tried to read, the treatise of al-Biṭrūjī (XII-2) which had been put into Latin as early as 1217 by Michael Scot.

John believed moderately in astrology, and also in other superstitions of his time (see, e.g., the Quaestiones in Parva naturalia). His attitude is one of prudent skepticism, his readiness to believe decreasing as he passes from the more to the less scientific parts of astrology, and from astrology to oneiroscopy and other forms of divination.

6. *Influence*

John was considered the leader of the Parisian Averroists, and his influence must have been considerable, judging from the number of MSS and early printed editions of his commentaries. As late as Galileo's time, Cesare Cremonini (1550–1631), the last Averroist teacher, was still using them almost as much as the writings of Ibn Rushd himself.

As to his influence on ecclesiastical politics and, if you please, on the Reformation, it was also very great, but cannot be separated from that exerted by Marsiglio of Padua.

7. *Text*

The order of the writings is the same as in the text.

1. Quaestiones super libros Physicorum. First edition by anonymous printer Padua 1475, also Venice, Scotus 1481, St. Albans 1481. The edition of 1485 is a ghost. Other editions, Venice by Locatelli 1487, 1492; Venice 1488. Later ones: Venice 1501, Paris 1506, Lyon 1512, Venice 1540, 1544, 1541, 1552, 1575, 1586.

3. Quaestiones super libros De coelo et mundo. First edition by Boneto Locatelli, of the text revised by Nicoleto Vernia of Chieti (in the Abruzzi), Venice 1501. Later editions: Venice 1506, 1519, 1552, 1589, Lyon 1512.

4, 5. Expositio et quaestiones super librum De substantia orbis. Venice 1481, Vicenza 1486, Venice 1493, 1501, 1505, 1514, 1552.

The edition of 1493 by Boneto Locatelli was based on a text revised by the two Augustinian Hermits Secondo Contarini (of Venice, fl. 1482–97) and Paul of Palermo.

[28] In order to understand the implications of this, see my remarks in volume 2 (p. 16–20, 756–60): "Ptolemaism was more secure at the end of the thirteenth century than a century before" (p. 18).

9. Quaestiones super tres libros De anima. Venice 1473, 1480, 1488, 1497, 1501, 1507, 1519, 1544, 1552, 1561, 1587.

10. Quaestiones in Parva naturalia. Single edition by Boneto Locatelli, Venice 1505. The text was prepared with the cooperation of the Neapolitan Averroist Marco Antonio Zimara, and the edition includes a short article by the latter, Quaestio de movente et moto, de intentione Aristotelis et sui magni commentatoris Averroys contra modernos.

11. Quaestiones in librum De bona fortuna. Text included in the edition of no. 10, Venice 1505.

12. See note on Pietro d'Abano.

13. Quaestiones in duodecim libros Metaphysicae. Edited with notes by M. A. Zimara, dated Venice 1505, also in Venice 1525, 1553, 1560, 1586.

15, 16. De laudibus Silvanecti, De laudibus Parisius. Edited by Le Roux de Lincy and Taranne (Bull. Comité de la langue, de l'histoire et des arts de la France 3, 505–40, 1855–56); again by Le Roux de Lincy and Tisserand in Paris et ses historiens aux XIVe et XVe siècles (p. 1–79, Paris 1867), in the collection Histoire générale de Paris; this second edition includes a French translation by Alexandre Bruel.

Various texts on the relations between reason and faith and the theory of the two-fold truth (Gilson p. 70–75, 1921).

8. *Criticism*

Renan: Averroès (p. 339 ff. and by index, stereotyped ed. 1869). Karl Werner: Der Averroismus in der christlich-peripatetischen Psychologie des späteren Mittelalters (Sitzungsberichte der Kais. Akad. der Wissenschaften in Wien, phil.-hist. Classe, 98, 265–88, 1881); Die Scholastik des späteren Mittelalters (vol. 2, 1883; vol. 4, 1887). Noël Valois: Jean de Jandun et Marsile de Padoue (HL 33, 528–623, 1906). Duhem: Essai sur la notion de théorie physique (Annales de la philosophie chrétienne, Paris 1908); Etudes (2, 82–90, 1909); Système (4, 96–103, 1916). De Wulf (2, 231–35, 1926). De Waard (p. 13, 17, 1936).

BURIDAN

French (Artésien, Picard) philosopher, mechanician, astronomer, and commentator on Aristotle (d. c. 1358).

Contents: (1) Life. (2) Writings. (3) Philosophy. (4) Mathematics. (5) Mechanics. (6) Celestial mechanics. (7) Astronomy. (8) Economics. (9) Influence.
(10) Text. (11) Criticism.

1. *Life*

Jean Buridan was born at the end of the thirteenth century in Béthune (arr. Pas-de-Calais), Artois, diocese of Arras. He was rector of the University of Paris in February 1328, and a second time in 1340; benefices were given to him in the diocese of Arras in 1330 and 1342, but he was all the time lecturing in Paris. He was acquainted with the astronomer Firmin de Belleval, and with Oresme.

At some unknown time during the pontificate of John XXII (1316–34), probably toward the end of it, he traveled to Avignon, and on the way was much impressed by the mountains, i.e., the Cévennes and Mons Ventosus (Ventoux). Some remarks in his questions on the Meteorologica suggest that he may have climbed Mt. Ventoux; before Petrarca (Petrarca's ascent took place in 1336).

On July 12, 1358 a concordat between the English and Picard nations in the

University of Paris was signed by him, Albert of Saxony, Nicholas of Soissons, and others. This is the last reference to him in the university archives, and hence we may assume that he died not much later, possibly within the same year, 1358, being then in his sixties.

In the famous "Ballade des dames du temps jadis" included in the Grand testament, 1461, of François Villon (1431–c. 1489) we read the lines (341–44):

> ou est la royne
> Qui commanda que Buridan
> Fust gecté en ung sac en Saine?
> Mais où sont les neiges d'antan?

(Where is the queen who ordered that Buridan be tied in a sack and thrown into the Seine? But where are the snows of yesteryear?) The queen referred to would be Marguerite de Bourgogne, married to Louis le Hutin, king of Navarre. She was accused of adultery together with her two sisters-in-law, Blanche de La Marche and Jeanne de Poitiers. The three princesses were said to entice young men into the Tour de Nesle, and to have them thrown into the river when they were tired of them. Jeanne was declared innocent, Blanche and Marguerite condemned to lifelong confinement. Louis le Hutin became king of France in 1314, and caused queen Marguerite to be murdered in 1315. A similar story was told about Jeanne de Bourgogne, queen of Philippe V le Long, condemned in 1314 for adultery to lifelong confinement; she lived until 1325. The story of Marguerite de Bourgogne was exploited by Alexandre Dumas in his very popular drama "La Tour de Nesle" (1832), wherein a "captain" Buridan appears as her lover and the father of her two sons. We are not concerned with the royal princesses, but Buridan is certainly innocent, for if he had been implicated in such a scandal he could not have continued to teach in Paris.

It may seem futile to discuss this matter, but such stories die hard. For example, it is very fully dealt with in the Dictionnaire historique of Pierre Bayle, article Buridan (folio ed., p. 708–11, Amsterdam 1740).

2. *Writings*

He wrote a commentary on the logic of William of Occam, entitled Scriptum super summulas, which was itself commented upon somewhat later by John Dorp of Leyden.[29] He composed many commentaries, generally in the form of "questions" on the works of Aristotle, notably on the Physics, Metaphysics (also an expositio), De anima, Parva naturalia, Meteorologica, De coelo et mundo, De generatione et corruptione, Nicomachean Ethics, and Politics.

Exact criticism of his thought is especially difficult because some of these commentaries at least have not come to us in his own redaction, but in the form of students' notes (reportata) or copies of such notes. These students were German, and their notes illustrate the well known influence of the University of Paris over the new universities of Central Europe (Prague 1347, Vienna 1365, Erfurt 1389). For example, notes on the De sensu et sensato (now ascribed to Theophrastos) were taken in Paris by Albert of Ricmestorp (Albert of Saxony) and taught (pronunciate) in Prague 1365 by Johann Krichpaum of Ingolstadt. There are copies of notes on other books of the Parva naturalia written by the same Krichpaum in Prague 1367,

[29] Flourished in Paris at the end of the fourteenth century and the beginning of the fifteenth; later taught in Cologne (Ueberweg 1915, p. 621).

on the De anima, written in Prague 1365, on the Meteorologica, Prague 1366. Questions on the De generatione et corruptione are "reported" by one Conrad Verniger of Brixen, who wrote them in Vienna 1378; questions on the Physics were also reported by a student and carried to Germany, but not by Heinrich Totting of Oyta as suggested by Duhem, for Oyta's stay in Paris was too late (1377–81). Finally, there is a reportatio of the commentary on the Nicomachean Ethics dated 1372.

3. *Philosophy*

Buridan was an Occamist, but more moderate than other members of the Parisian school. He attached much importance to the study of logic. A simple means of finding the middle term of a syllogism, inventio medii, the so-called pons asinorum, is sometimes ascribed to him (it is more probably an interpolation of John Dorp). He defended the value of the principle of causality which had been attacked by Nicholas of Autrecourt; that principle was the basis of his proof of the existence of God.

He discussed the problem of freedom of the will vs. determinism. He did not separate will from intellect, but saved himself from complete determinism by assuming the possibility of a suspended decision, and of a liberum arbitrium indifferentiae. Otherwise man might die like the donkey who let himself starve between two identical bundles of hay. That famous story ("Buridan's ass") is not found in his writings, but might possibly be derived from his oral teaching. It is the kind of joke which a teacher might tell to illustrate an argument, and the students could be trusted to remember and transmit it.[30]

4. *Mathematics*

In 1335 Buridan was engaged in a controversy with a certain magister called de Montescalerio, concerning the division ad infinitum, the reality of the geometric point, and other such topics. Again, his question 18 on the third book of the Physics is "utrum in quolibet continuo infinitae sint partes."[31] He complicated the study of infinity vainly by making a distinction between syncategorematic infinity and categorematic infinity, that is, between a kind of relative and incomplete infinity, and one which is absolute. These questions had theological as well as mathematical implications.

5. *Mechanics*

Buridan's main title to immortality is his treatment of the ideas of movement and impetus. He may be considered one of the distant and indirect founders of modern dynamics. His work guided for some two centuries the nominalistic school, then the Italian mechanicians who completed the preparation of Galileo's revolution.

[30] The theme of the story is certainly anterior to Buridan, for we find it in Dante's Paradiso (beginning of canto IV). If Buridan did not invent it, he established it. The name of the ass is not known, but the phrase "Buridan's ass" has immortalized both the ass and his master. I was amused to find in the latest "Dictionary of philosophy" (edited by Dagobert D. Runes, New York 1942, p. 42) an article on Buridan's ass, none on Buridan himself! According to Giuseppe Campi's commentary on the Paradiso (p. 69, Torino 1891), the theme was discussed by St. Thomas.

[31] The idea may be Bradwardine's, as suggested by Eduard Stamm?

His chief merit lies in his opposition to Aristotelian dynamics. He was not by any means the first in this, as some of his ideas can be traced as far back as Philoponos (VI-1),[32] but his criticism was more vigorous and more effective. See, e.g., his questions 7 and 8 on book VII of the Physics. He concludes that there are no movements in nature to which the Aristotelian rules can be correctly applied. In question 12 on book VIII he asks himself what causes the motion of a projectile (Utrum projectum post exitum a manu projicientis moveatur ab aere vel a quo moveatur). He rejects the idea of antiperistasis[33] and the idea that the air pushed by the projectile pushes more rapidly the air placed in front of itself, etc. He concludes that the cause of the movement must be looked for not in the air, but in the projectile itself. The latter has received and conserves an impetus,[34] which is gradually diminished by the projectile's own gravity and by the resistance of the air. This explains why it is possible to throw a piece of iron farther away than a feather. The impetus of a body, as conceived by Buridan, is proportional to its speed, volume, and density; it is thus not essentially different from the Cartesian quantity of motion or linear momentum (mv). Buridan's concept is a weak anticipation of the concept of inertia.

As to the gravity of a falling body, is it comparable to the attraction of a piece of iron by a magnet? The latter was explained by Buridan (following Ibn Rushd, but opposing Occam) by means of an alteration gradually transmitted through the medium from the magnet to the object attracted by it. The case of the falling body is different, for its attraction to the center of the world increases with its distance from it; as the body falls, it acquires more and more impetus and speed. The final speed, however, does not depend so much on the initial position as on the length or duration of the fall.

The notion of gravity, implying that of a universal center of gravity, involved a discussion of the plurality of worlds which it is unprofitable to analyze here.

These discussions are difficult to follow because the fundamental ideas are not yet sufficiently abstract and clear, but the author often quotes observations which prove his ingenuity and refresh the reader's interest.

Buridan continued to accept implicitly the Aristotelian impossibility of a vacuum.

6. *Celestial mechanics*

It is proper to separate the subject of celestial mechanics from mechanics in general, for in Buridan's time it involved a new set of fundamental difficulties. Is it possible to apply the notion of impetus to celestial bodies as well as to sublunar ones? Indeed, the incorruptible matter of the former is essentially different from that of the latter; it is a kind of matter not subjected to form. Buridan concludes, however, that there is an impetus initially impressed by God, and not diminished since there is no resistance. It is not necessary to postulate the existence of angels or other miraculous means of motion. God gave an indestructible impetus at the beginning and then could rest. In spite of material differences between celestial and sublunar bodies, the same dynamics applies to both.

Buridan was apparently one of the first, with Francis of Marchia, to declare the possibility of extending our mechanics to the heavens. The legitimacy of that extension remained unproved, however, until the time of Kepler, or even of Newton.

[32] I take this occasion to remark that the two notes on Philoponos in my Introduction (1, 421, 480) stand in need of a complete revision (Isis 18, 447).

[33] Opposition by which the quality opposed is strengthened (ἀντιπερίστασις).

[34] Philoponos. See my Introduction by means of the index, s.v. impetus.

7. *Astronomy*

In agreement with the majority of schoolmen of his time, Buridan favored Ptolemaic astronomy against the Aristotelian. He was somewhat acquainted, however, with the work of al-Biṭrūjī, which had been available in Latin for more than a century. That may have set him thinking about the difficulties of the Ptolemaic theories, for instance, with regard to the epicycles and eccentrics. He objected to the epicycles, especially the lunar ones. The "appearances might be saved" with eccentrics alone, or with epicycles alone. It is difficult to choose between these hypotheses, which are kinematically equivalent. Thus did the Parisian nominalist recapture the point of view of Hipparchos and of the Alexandrian astronomers.

Buridan also questioned the reality of the slow motions of stars. Such motions could only be evidenced by reference to ancient catalogues, and are these trustworthy? This illustrates a fundamental difficulty of mediaeval scientists: how could they be sure of having a standard text? Science was not yet cumulative in the sense that it is today, for the transmission of the results already obtained was far too precarious.

The ninth sphere (primum mobile) may be real or simply a mathematical conception. A hypothesis is sufficient if it accounts for the facts. "Et ideo sufficit eis accipere faciliorem imaginationem secundum quam, si esset vera, corpora coelestia moverentur tot motibus et talibus velocitatibus sicut nunc moventur, et non debent curare utrum sit ita in re sicut imaginantur" (Duhem 4, 138). Similar thoughts had already occurred to Simplicios (VI-1) and to others, but Buridan expresses them very clearly.

Finally, in question 22 relative to book II of the De coelo et mundo, "Utrum terra semper quiescat in medio mundi," he explained the argument in favor of the diurnal rotation of the earth, which Oresme reproduced soon afterward in French. There can be no doubt that Oresme's text is derived from Buridan's.

8. *Economics*

In his questions on the Aristotelian Ethics and Politics, Buridan was led to review the social problems of his time. It will suffice to quote an example. In question XI on book I of the Politics, he asks "Utrum mutatio et commutatio monetarum in policia bene recta sint licite," wherein Oresme is again anticipated.[35] It is probable that as Buridan's commentaries are gradually explored, it will be possible to ascribe other ideas to his initiative.

9. *Influence*

Buridan's teaching did not affect only the Parisian scholars; it was soon transmitted by some of his own students to the new universities of Central Europe (see §2) and thus influenced the scientific thought of the fourteenth century more effectively and faster than would have been possible otherwise.

Among the scientists who followed him were such men as Oresme, then later Nicholas of Cusa (1401–64) and Domingo de Soto of Salamanca (1494–1570), and his indirect influence upon the Italian mechanicians has already been mentioned.

[35] According to Bridrey (p. 303 f., 1906), it was Oresme who influenced Buridan rather than the opposite. Buridan, it is true, died about 24 years earlier than Oresme, yet Bridrey's conclusion is not implausible; it is accepted by René Gonnard (Histoire des idées économiques 1, 137, Paris 1935).

10. *Text*

Our list of early editions is incomplete. Summulae logicae (or Summa de dialectica, or Compendium logicae) with commentary by John Dorp. Lyon 1487, 1499, Venice 1499, Paris 1504, Oxford 1637, London 1740.

Sophismata. Various Paris incunabula c. 1496–1500, one perhaps after 1500.

Consequentiae. Paris 1493, 1495, 1499?

Quaestiones super VIII libros Physicorum, edited by John Dullaert of Ghent, Paris 1509. Dullaert was born in Ghent c. 1470, but spent the best part of his life in Paris, where he taught and where he died in 1513 (Biographie nationale de Belgique 6, 273–74, 1878).

In Metaphysicen quaestiones. Early edition, Paris c. 1480? Edition by Josse Bade (Jodocus Badius), Paris 1518. Badius was born in Assche, near Brussels, in 1462; he died in Paris 1534/35 (Biographie nationale de Belgique 1, 610–20, 1866).

Quaestiones in libros de sensu et sensato, de memoria et reminiscentia, de somno et vigilia, de longitudine et brevitate vitae, de juventute et senectute. Paris 1516, 1518. This is part of a collection Quaestiones et decisiones physicales insignium virorum, including also commentaries by Albert of Saxony and Themon son of the Jew, edited by George Lokert (or Lockhart), a Scotsman who was professor at the College of Montaigu in Paris in 1516 and at the Sorbonne in 1518.

Quaestiones de anima. Paris 1516.

Quaestiones in VIII libros Politicorum. Paris c. 1480?, 1500, 1513, Oxford 1640.

Quaestiones super X libros Ethicorum ad Nicomachum. Paris 1489, 1513, 1518, Oxford 1637.

Quaestiones super libris IV de coelo et mundo. First edition by Ernest Addison Moody (Mediaeval Academy, 360 p. typescript, Cambridge, Mass. 1942; Isis 35, 226). The quaestiones of Albert of Saxony (XIV-2), hardly more than a new edition of Buridan, were often printed from 1481 to 1518.

11. *Criticism*

Duhem: Etudes (vol. 2, 1909, p. 379–84 on infinity, 420–23 gravity, 428–41 principle of individuation, quidditas; vol. 3, 1913, p. 1–260 Buridan's influence on Leonardo da Vinci and other Italians, 279–86, 350–60 dynamics, 295–301 kinematics); Système (4, 124–42, 1916), on astronomy; Dominique Soto et la scolastique parisienne (Bull. hispanique 12, 275–302, 1910, etc.); Le temps et le mouvement selon les scolastiques (Revue de philosophie 25, 109–52, 1914), and previous articles, this being the seventh, bearing the same title.

Emile Bridrey: La théorie de la monnaie au XIVe siècle. Nicole Oresme (p. 727–36, Paris 1906), contains the text of Buridan's question concerning money. J. Bulliot: Jean Buridan et le mouvement de la terre. Question 22 du second livre du De coelo (Revue de philosophie 25, 5–24, 1914), including the text of Buridan's question concerning the diurnal motion of the earth. Léon Gauthier: L'argument de l'âne de Buridan et les philosophes arabes (Mélanges René Basset 1, 209–33, Paris 1923; Isis 15, 284). E. J. Dijksterhuis: Val en worp (p. 68–78, Groningen 1924; Isis 8, 378–79), re-examination of the MSS used by Duhem and correction of his readings. De Wulf (2, 191–93, 1926). Michalsky (p. 81–86, 1920); (p. 55 f., 1925a); (p. 202–9, 1925b); (p. 113–18, 144–49, 1927). Ernst Borchert: Die Lehre von der Bewegung bei Nicolaus Oresme (Münster i.W. 1934; Isis 25, 534). De Waard (p. 16–17, 1936). Albert Hyma: Christianity, capitalism and communism (p. 23, Ann Arbor, Mich. 1937). S. Pines: Les précurseurs musulmans de la théorie de l'impetus (Archeion 21, 298–306, 1938, really 1939), pointing out the similarity between Buridan's explanation of the acceleration of falling bodies and that given by Hibatallāh ibn Malkā (XII-2). Ernest A. Moody: Buridan and the habitability of the earth (Speculum 16, 415–25, 1941), including text of his commentary on De coelo II, quaestio 7. Lynn Thorndike: Buridan's questions on the Physiognomy ascribed to Aristotle (Speculum 18, 99–103, 1943; Isis 36).

LE MIESIER

Thomas Le Miesier. French physician and Lullist (d. in or after 1336).

Thomas of Arras (Thomas Atrebatensis) called Le Miesier (or Li Miesiers), a not uncommon name at that time, meaning hydromel brewer. He studied probably in Paris, being a member of the Sorbonne in 1299. Later he returned to his "pays" (Artois, dépt. Pas-de-Calais), was canon of Arras and physician to Mathilde (or Mahault), countess of Artois and Burgundy, from 1310 or 1315 on, in Arras and Hesdin; he was with her at the time of her death, in Paris 1329. He made his will in 1336.

Ramon Lull's Disputatio eremitae et Raymundi super aliquibus dubiis quaestionibus sententiarum Petri Lombardi (Paris 1298; Introd. 2, 903) having attracted Thomas' attention, the latter formulated fifty more questions, Quaestiones atrebatenses, which are preserved in a text dated June 1299, together with Ramon's answers.

Thomas was then (or became later) a regular disciple of Ramon Lull, and in a contemporary Parisian MS (now in Karlsruhe) there are two miniatures each of which represents the master and the pupil. Thomas prepared commentaries on the Lullian doctrines in three stages (as was done by Ibn Rushd for Aristotle; Introd. 2, 356): a brief one, Breviculum; a medium one, Electorium medium; and the large Electorium. The Karlsruhe MS includes the Breviculum; the middle commentary is lost; the Electorium is preserved in another contemporary MS (Bibliothèque nationale, lat. 15450), wherein it is preceded by a biography of Lull and two lists of his writings (the first dated 1311; the second a little later).

Thomas wrote a preface to the Liber de gentili et tribus sapientibus, a discussion between a Jew, a Christian, and a Muslim, written by Lull in Majorca c. 1272 (Introd. 2, 904).

Criticism. Langlois (4, 338–43, 1928), with reproductions of the two double portraits. Wickersheimer (p. 763, 1936). Ch. V. Langlois (HL 37, 509–10, 1938).

AUTRECOURT

Nicholas of Autrecourt. French theologian, "the mediaeval Hume" (d. after 1350).

Nicolaus de Autricuria (Altricuria, Utricuria). Born toward the end of the thirteenth century in Autrecourt, near Bar-le-Duc (dépt. Meuse). Studied in Paris, being a member of the Sorbonne c. 1320–27. In 1338 he became a prebendary of the cathedral of Metz, having obtained before that his degree of M.A. and licentiate in theology. He addressed nine very bold philosophical letters to the Franciscan Bernard of Arezzo, and was ordered by Benedict XII on November 21, 1340 to appear before the curia; he was censured by Clement VI in 1342 and took refuge at the court of Ludwig of Bavaria. His final condemnation and the burning of his writings was ordered by Clement VI on November 25, 1347. In 1350 he was dean of the cathedral of Metz.

His main ideas are known only indirectly, e.g., through the answer written to him by one master Giles. These ideas were extremely daring. He claimed that the existence of the external world cannot be proved, and that the principle of causality has no objective validity. The only certainties are the principle of contradiction and the existence of God. Everything else is uncertain unless it can be reduced to them. There are no degrees of certainty; a thing is certain or not. The only substance which a man can know is his own soul. Knowledge is restricted to individual intuitions; there is no general knowledge of any kind. He apparently accepted the atomic hypothesis, however, and used it to account for generation and corruption, which are simply integrations and disintegrations of atoms. This implied the assumption of a vacuum, an assumption which he was practically alone in his time in making.

Text. For master Giles' answer, which summarizes Nicholas' theory and other documents, see Barthélemy Hauréau (Notices et extraits 34, part 2, 332–41, 1895). See also Lappe (1908).

J. Reginald O'Donnell: Nicholas d'Autrecourt (Mediaeval studies 1, 179–280, New York 1939). Edition of the Tractatus universalis ad videndum an sermones peripateticorum fuerint demonstrativi, with an appendix Quaestio de qua respondet Nicholaus de Ultricuria, based upon a unique MS in the Bodleian. It deals with such topics as the eternity of the world, whether the continuum is made up of indivisibilia, vacuum, whether substance and quantity are different, whether everything is what it seems to be, whether a single effect can be the result of various causes, etc.

Criticism. Hastings Rashdall: Nicolaus de Ultricuria, a mediaeval Hume (Proceedings of the Aristotelian Society, 1907). Joseph Lappe: Nicolaus von Autrecourt (Beiträge zur Geschichte der Philosophie des Mittelalters vol. 6, no. 2, 80 p., Münster i.W. 1908), includes 40 p. of texts. G. M. Manser: Drei Zweifler am Kausalprinzip im 14. Jahrhundert (Jahrbuch für Philosophie und speculative Theologie 27, 405–37, 1912), dealing with Occam and Pierre d'Ailly (1350–1420) as well as with Autrecourt. Michalski (p. 59 f., 77, 1920); (p. 41 f., 106–9, 1925a). De Wulf (2, 238–41, 1926). P. Vignaux (DTC 11, 561–87, 1931), elaborate study. Julius R. Weinberg: The fifth letter of Nicholas of Autrecourt to Bernard of Arezzo (Journal of the history of ideas 3, 220–27, 1942). J. Reginald O'Donnell: The philosophy of Nicholas of Autrecourt (Mediaeval studies 4, 97–125, 1942; Isis 35, 59).

JEAN BONNET

Parisian priest who flourished under Philippe le Bel (king 1285–1314) and was perhaps the author of the philosophical and scientific dialogue called Placides et Timéo ou Livre des secrets aux philosophes.

According to the preface of the best MS, a magnificent one written at the end of the fifteenth century for Louis of Bruges, lord of the Gruthuyse, and owned by the kings of France from Louis XII on, Jehan Bonnet, priest, doctor in theology, born in Paris is the author. That is not certain but probable. The work is certainly anterior to 1304; but it may date from the end of the thirteenth century as well as from the beginning of the fourteenth.

It is given as a translation from Latin into French, yet the text is very different from that of the Secretum philosophorum, a collection of "experiments," riddles, tricks, illusions, etc. which was composed in the thirteenth century perhaps in England.

Les secrets aux philosophes is a dialogue between the young prince Placides and his tutor Timéo, dealing with metaphysical and scientific discussions. In the preface bearing Bonnet's name, the latter claims to have studied and translated extracts from Aristotle, Plato, and others. In particular, he refers to Plato's book on the shape of the world (La figure du monde), which is a kind of encyclopaedia of natural science (I do not know which book is meant, Timaeos?). Les secrets aux philosophes is one of the earliest works of its kind in the French language. It is comparable in some respects to the Secreta secretorum (IX-1?) and to the Quaestiones naturales of Adelard of Bath (XII-1). It has in common with Adelard's questions much naïveté as well as a genuine interest in concrete realities vs. scholastic abstractions; moreover, it betrays sometimes a timid Averroistic or materialistic point of view.

In the first edition (Paris c. 1504) and many other sixteenth-century editions, all entitled Le coeur de philosophie, the dialogue Placides et Timéo is followed by two other texts: (1) L'espere du ciel et du monde, which is an adaptation of the Sphere of John of Sacrobosco (XIII-1); (2) a treatise on the computus, traictié du compost et kalendrier. In the preface to these printed editions Bonnet's name is omitted, but as there is no MS tradition for the "heart of philosophy" as a whole, it is possible that these three French treatises were put together for the first time not for Philippe le Bel, but by or for the printer Antoine Vérard. The relative popularity of that work and especially of the Secrets aux philosophes in the first half of the sixteenth century is noteworthy.

In the Gruthuyse MS the Secrets aux philosophes is followed by a similar text, ascribed to the unknown Albert of Trebizond, dealing with the four complexions, and questions of gynaecology and obstetrics, a kind of Secreta mulierum wherein many questions already treated are discussed again, sometimes in the same words. It is possible that Albert of Trebizond is but another name of the pseudo Albert the Great (Introd. 2, 941).

The name of the tutor Timéo is certainly an echo of the Platonic Timaeos, as translated (partly) by Chalcidius (IV-1) and commented upon by Guillaume de Conches (XII-1). The author of the Secrets aux philosophes knew that commentary as well as Guillaume's Philosophia mundi, the Imago mundi of Honorius Inclusus (XI-2), and perhaps the Fontaine de toutes les sciences or Romance of Sidrach (XIII-1).

Text. Manuscript tradition. Three different forms of it exist: (1) A MS of the end of the fifteenth century (Bibliothèque nationale, MS fr. 212) made for Louis of Bruges, lord of the Gruthuyse;[36] this is Langlois' B text. It is by far the best. (2) A MS of the beginning of the fourteenth century (Bibliothèque nationale, MS fr. 19958); Langlois' A text. A is much inferior to B but much earlier. (3) There are no MSS of the third form, which is represented only by the edition printed c. 1504 by Antoine Vérard, Paris, under the title Le cueur de philosophie. Often reprinted during the sixteenth century. I have used the edition printed at Paris by François Regnault in 1529 (copy in Harvard Library). The text of (3) follows largely that of (2)—that is, the inferior version—but is offered as being a translation from the Latin made at the request of Philippe le Bel, king of France from 1285 to 1314.

Le coeur (des secrets) de philosophie. First printed by Antoine Vérard (Paris c. 1504). Many other sixteenth-century editions. I have seen two Parisian undated ones (1529, c. 1538–41).

Criticism. Ernest Renan: Le livre des secrets aux philosophes (HL 30, 567–95, 1888). Thorndike (2, 791–92, 1923). Langlois (3, 276–334, 1927).

[36] I.e., the Great House, a manor in Bruges.

A4. England

BASSOLES

John of Bassoles, or Bassols. Franciscan, favorite disciple of Duns Scot (XIII-2; d. 1308); died on July 4, 1333. The date of his death is known from an obiit in the calendar of the famous abbey of Tewkesbury (Gloucestershire). Was he an Englishman, or a Frenchman, or a Catalan? There is a place named Bassoles near Couci, in Aisne (Picardy).

At any rate, he attended Duns Scot's lectures in Paris, and the latter appreciated his presence so much that when he saw him (even if there was nobody but him) he would say, "Bassolius adest; en auditorium est." The story may be apocryphal, the more so because a similar one is ascribed to Plato speaking in the same way of Aristotle.

John of Bassoles wrote a commentary on the four books of Sentences, of which there are many printed editions (some of them incunabula) but no MSS!

There was a "master regent" in the faculty of medicine of Paris, in 1325–26, named Jean de Bassoles (de Bazoliis). Were these two men, the commentator on Peter the Lombard and the physician, one and the same? It does not seem possible for a Franciscan to have been thus employed in the faculty of medicine.

Text. In quatuor libros Sententiarum. Various incunabula editions, one of which is dated Cologne 1488. Improved edition published in two parts, Paris 1516–17, edited by Oronce Finé (1494–1555), who contributed various prefaces.

Criticism. Duhem: Etudes (2, 373–78, 1909), apropos of Bassoles' discussion of infinity. Short note in EUI (7, 1094, c. 1912), wherein Bassoles is said to have been a Franciscan, born in Barcelona, and to have assumed the habit of his order in that city. Michalski (p. 221–24, 228, 1925b). Ch. V. Langlois (HL 36, 349–55, 1927). Wickersheimer (p. 358, 1936).

OCCAM

William of Occam. English Franciscan, logician (d. c. 1349).

Contents: (1) Life. (2) Works. (3) Logic. (4) Metaphysics and philosophy of science. (5) Mechanics. (6) Politics. (7) Influence.
(8) Text. (9) General criticism. (10) Special studies.

1. *Life*

William of Occam, or better Ockham, was born about the end of the thirteenth century, probably in Ockham, Surrey. He became a Franciscan friar and studied in Oxford, probably in the Franciscan College, not in Merton College. He studied there from c. 1312 to 1318. Thus he cannot have been Duns Scot's disciple, for the latter died in 1308, and had left Oxford some time before. William did not become a master of theology, and did not teach in Paris. He taught in Oxford as a bachelor until 1324. In that year he was ordered to appear before the curia in Avignon in order to justify his views on many subjects put forward in his commentary on the Sentences of Peter Lombard; he was not condemned. In the meanwhile the Franciscan order had been very much shaken because of differences of opinion on evangelical poverty. The fundamental importance of evangelical poverty had been emphasized at the Franciscan chapter of Perugia 1322, and that doctrine[37] had

[37] I.e., the main doctrine of the Spiritual Franciscans (Introd. 2, 333, 545, 1033; see also this volume by index.

afterward been condemned by John XXII (pope 1316–34). William took up the defense of his order against the curia. In 1328 he was detained in Avignon while his case was being investigated. He managed to escape on May 25, 1328, together with other friars including Michele da Cesena, general of the order. They took refuge in Pisa, where Ludwig of Bavaria (emperor 1328–47) was then residing.[38] The fugitives were excommunicated on June 6, 1328. They remained under the emperor's protection and returned with him to Bavaria in February 1330. They lived in the Franciscan convent of Munich. According to an old tradition, William said to the emperor: "Tu me defendas gladio, ego te defendam calamo." Whether these words were uttered or not, they represent the situation fairly well. For William spent the rest of his life under imperial protection and devoted considerable time to the writing of treatises defending imperial vs. papal sovereignty. After the death of Michele da Cesena, in 1342, William became the sole leader of the anti-papal Franciscans, and continued the resistance. His activities from then on become more obscure than ever. The emperor died in 1347. It would seem that William tried to be reconciled with the church, but there is no record of his absolution, if he was absolved. He died in Munich (?) on April 10, 1349 (or 1350).

2. *Works*

We shall divide the works into the following groups: (a) philosophy, (b) logic, (c) politics, (d) varia. The dates in parentheses refer to the first early printed edition, if any.

(a) *Philosophy.* 1. Super quattuor libros Sententiarum (I in 1483, I–IV in 1495). Written in Oxford before 1324. His longest work and probably his earliest.

2. Quaestiones in octo libros Physicorum (1491).

2 bis. Expositio physicae.

3. Summulae in octo libros Physicorum (1494), or Philosophia naturalis.

4. Quodlibeta septem (1487).

(b) *Logic.* 5. Expositio aurea super artem veterem (1496). Commentaries on Aristotle's Categoriae and De interpretatione, and on Porphyry's Isagoge.

6. Summa totius logicae (1488). This work, which may be considered William's masterpiece, was written at the request of his disciple Adam de Anglia, and hence presumably begun if not completed during his Oxford days. Adam de Anglia is perhaps identical with Adam Wodeham (q.v.).

The Summa was translated into Hebrew by Elijah ben Joseph Ḥabillo (fl. Aragon c. 1471). The same translated also William's Quaestiones philosophicae (?), perhaps the same as our no. 4. Steinschneider (p. 470, 1893).

(c) *Politics.* We use the term "politics" here rather loosely to include all the pamphlets written by William in defense of his opinions not only in political matters, but also in matters of ecclesiastical policy.

7. Opus nonaginta dierum, answering the sentence of excommunication and the tract written by the pope against the general of the Franciscans, Michele da Cesena; written in 1330 (1481).

8. De dogmatibus papae Johannis XXII, written c. 1333–34.

9. Epistola ad fratres minores, written 1334.

10. Compendium errorum Johannis papae XXII. Imputing to John XXII seventy errors and seven heresies. Written c. 1334–38, after John's death (1476).

11. Defensorium contra Johannem papam, written c. 1338–39 (1513).

[38] The emperor was already sheltering Marsiglio of Padua and John of Jandun.

12. Tractatus ostendens quod Benedictus papa XII nonnullas Johannis XXII haereses amplexus est et defendit, written c. 1338.

12 bis. Tractatus adversus Clementem papam VI.

13. De potestate pontificum et imperatorum, written c. 1339–42.

13 bis. De imperatorum et pontificum potestate, written c. 1346–47. It is apparently different from no. 13.

14. Tractatus de iurisdictione imperatoris in causis matrimonialibus, written 1342.

15. Dialogus inter magistrum et discipulum (1476). Elaborate treatise reviewing all the questions implied in the conflicts between pope and emperor, church and state. This includes, or was meant to include, some of the treatises already mentioned, wholly or partly. It was not completed. The text which has come down to us was already available in 1343.

16. Disputatio inter militem et clericum (1470). Probably apocryphal. It has been ascribed also to Pierre du Bois. This treatise was translated into English, and the English version twice printed in the first half of the sixteenth century.

(d) *Varia.* 17. De sacramento altaris (c. 1490).

18. De corpore Christi (1491). These two treatises were written by Occam probably to show that he was not heretical.

19. Centilogium theologicum (1495). Brief explanation of a hundred theological conclusions.

20. Tractatus de principiis theologiae (doubtful).

This list is probably incomplete (at least with regard to the political writings), or it may contain other spurious titles than no. 16. It is exemplative rather than final. The criticism of the texts is still far too imperfect to enable one to judge Occam's writings in their totality, or to attempt a strict chronology of them. All we can say is that the commentary on the Sentences is anterior to 1324, and that his other philosophical works, including the Logic, are probably of the early period of his life (before 1324, or before 1328), whereas the polemical treatises (grouped under c) are certainly posterior (1330 and later). A critical edition of the Logic is especially needed; it may reveal that William continued to work at it during his Munich days (1330–49). There are two reasons for considering that possibility: first, the mass of his philosophical and logical writings is so great that it would hardly have been possible for him to complete them before 1324 or 1328; second, his political activity seems to have stopped c. 1342 or 1346.

3. *Logic*

William's views on logic are found mainly in the two works quoted above under (b), but also in other writings, as his commentary on the Sentences or his Quodlibeta. His sources are mainly Aristotle and Porphyry, then subsidiarily Boetius, St. John Damascene, Ibn Sīnā, St. Anselm, Ibn Rushd, Robert Grosseteste, and Peter of Spain. On the other hand, he hardly ever referred to St. Augustine. This illustrates one singular aspect of William's thought: as contrasted with the majority of scholastics or with such a master as St. Thomas, he was not very much interested in the historical development of problems, but rather in the problems themselves.

His logic has sometimes been called "Byzantine logic" because of a misunderstanding fostered by Prantl (1867). According to the latter, the Summulae logicales of Peter of Spain was simply an adaptation of the Greek summary of Aristotelian logic by Michael Psellos (XI-2).[39] This is now proved to be untrue. Peter of Spain had Western sources, such as Lambert of Auxerre. Thus William's new logic is partly derived from the Summa of Lambert of Auxerre,[40] and also from the Parva logicalia of William of Shyreswood,[41] both of whom discussed the proprietates terminorum. William was influenced also by the revival of grammatical studies, a philosophical reaction against the stereotyped grammars of Donatus and Priscian. The "speculative" grammarians or "modistae" were led by John of Garland (still living in 1272); they attracted the attention of scholars as different from one another as Boetius of Dacia and Duns Scot. The "logica nova" or "logica modernorum" was a product of the thirteenth century, fully prepared at the time of Occam's studies. "Occamism" must thus be considered a climax as well as a new departure.

It is often said that William revived nominalism, or was the founder of a new form of it, of a new nominalism, called "terminism." In fact, the words "terminism" and "Occamism" are considered interchangeable. This is somewhat misleading. The distinctions made concerning the "proprietates terminorum" are more frequent in Duns Scot than in Occam, and the latter was far from being the first to insist on correct definitions, or to stress the formal aspect of logic, but he restated Aristotelian logic in the light of the new logic. His merit was less in introducing new terms than in explaining the meaning and function of terms. He insisted that universals have no real existence, but only a formal one; this was a way—the only way—of solving the old problem of universals.[42] That is, universals are simply terms, and logic cannot deal with things or with thoughts, but only with terms.

William's fundamental source being the Organon, discussions of the logical aspect of Occamism hinge necessarily on his interpretations of Aristotle. Considering the vastness and complexity of that subject, and the fact that many necessary texts are not yet available in critical editions, considering also that nonscientific issues are intertwisted with the purely scientific ones, it is not surprising that William's logic or his interpretations of Aristotelian logic have been judged in many different ways. One extreme is to say that he has corrupted Aristotelian thought; another, that he has purified it by getting rid of Neoplatonic and Augustinian excrescences. The truth is probably nearer to the second extreme than to the first. Remember that the discussion of Maimonidism and Averroism involved similar difficulties, but the scandal caused by Occamism was perhaps the greatest of all, for it is no exaggeration to say that it hastened the disintegration and the downfall of scholasticism.

Occam's name has been immortalized by the phrase "Occam's razor," representing the law of parsimony, "Entia non sunt multiplicanda praeter necessitatem." That sentence has not yet been found in Occam's writings; but the same idea occurs

[39] I repeated that mistake in my note on Psellos (Introd. 1, 750), but corrected it in my note on Peter of Spain (Introd. 2, 890).

[40] Lambert of Auxerre, Dominican who flourished in Auxerre (dépt. Yonne) c. 1250. His Summa is a commentary on the Aristotelian Organon. He insisted on the fundamental importance of proper definitions. See Hauréau (2, part 1, 188–91, 1880).

[41] William of Shyreswood or Shirwood flourished in Oxford, was warmly praised by Roger Bacon. See short and incorrect note by C. L. Kingsford (DNB 52, 146, 1897). Moody says he died in 1249 (p. 25, 1935); according to DNB he flourished in 1260 (?).

[42] That problem goes back to St. Anselm and Roscelin (XI-2), if not earlier. See Introd. 1, 749.

in them many times under other forms, such as "Pluralitas non est ponenda sine necessitate" and "Frustra fit per plura quod potest fieri per pauciora" (Abbagnano p. 159, 1931). In other words, the best explanation or theory is the one implying the smallest number of assumptions; logical analysis must be carried as far as possible. Occam did not invent this principle, which may be found in the works of earlier schoolmen (e.g., Duns Scot), but he understood it more deeply and expressed it more forcibly. "Occam's razor" is very typical of his point of view, and a splendid illustration of it.

4. *Metaphysics and philosophy of science*

The fundamental characteristic of his philosophy is its extreme individualism. Every existent thing is individual, unique, different from all others. Our intuitive knowledge of these individuals, however, may lead to general ideas, and these may be represented by terms or signs. Our final knowledge concerns only the relations between such signs; it is thus twice removed from reality, because the relations between our intuitions of individuals and general ideas on the one hand, and between those ideas and the signs, are imperfect. Such knowledge as we have is thus purely formal.

Applying this point of view to theology, Occam concluded, e.g., that the existence, unity, and attributes of God cannot be demonstrated, "Non potest scire evidenter quod Deus est." Theological dogmas are irrational; religion is essentially a matter of faith, not of reason.

The radical application of such a method was bound to lead to religious agnosticism and to a real impoverishment of metaphysics, as well as to modern science. The scope which he gave to formal logic is comparable to that given in our own days to mathematical physics. The modernity of his thought is very striking, in spite of the fact that its application was necessarily restricted either to very general problems (such as theological questions) or to undifferentiated ones (such as the immature scientific questions of his time).

5. *Mechanics*

It is difficult to characterize briefly Occam's criticism of Aristotelian mechanics, for example his views on movement, without the use of a scholastic jargon corresponding to irrelevant distinctions. The question whether motion is due to a forma fluens (as Duns Scot claimed) or to a flexus formae (as Occam claimed) is indeed irrelevant and its discussion not very helpful. It would seem that Occam conceived the possibility of action without contact.

6. *Politics*

Occam's opposition to the pope was determined by the defense first of his order, and later of his imperial patron. He used his dialectic to prove that the pope's power was purely spiritual, not temporal; the church of Christ should remain dissociated from temporal matters as it was at the beginning. Thus his defense of the emperor's sovereignty against the pope's was in line with his defense of the Spiritual Franciscans against the pope's authority. If the pope had temporal as well as spiritual power, men would be reduced to slavery. He went so far as to suggest that Christ and not the pope was the true head of the church, and that it might conceivably be better to have several popes! He attacked with special vigor the abuses of the Avignon curia, abuses which were many and tangible enough.

He invoked against the pope the authority of a council including laymen as well as clergy, and women[43] as well as men. In his writings he prepared weapons for the reformers within and without the church, for the defenders of the conciliar idea, and for the advocates within each council of the council's rights against the pope's.

7. *Influence*

Occam's political influence has already been indicated. The main reformers from Wycliffe to Luther acknowledged it; the latter called him "mein lieber Meister Occam."

His philosophical influence was even greater. He started a new school of thought or a new way (the via moderna). His disciples, called terministae, conceptistae, and more generally nominales (as opposed to reales), were found not simply in Oxford and Paris, but in many universities of Central Europe. We shall meet a few of them. In spite of a very natural opposition from those who followed the via antiqua, Occamism became increasingly popular among thinking people, and was widely diffused by the end of the century.

The titles Doctor invincibilis and Venerabilis inceptor given to Occam reflect his fame. It is true, a more literal explanation of the second title has been offered. When Occam lectured in Oxford he was an "inceptor," that is, a bachelor who had not yet received license to teach. It is probable, however, that the European writers who called him "venerabilis inceptor" did not think of his technical status in his early Oxford days, but rather of the new way he had opened.

As Occamism was not a dogmatic system, but simply a method, a way, his disciples did not constitute a united group, as did, say, the Thomists or Scotists. Each disciple was or might be different from the others according to his own genius. A ferment of disintegration was thus introduced into scholasticism. Modern science could not have grown within the rigid frame of dogmatic systems. Occamism helped its development, negatively, by preparing the dissolution of those dogmatic systems, and positively, by creating proper spiritual conditions and improving the logical tools.

8. *Text*

The various works bear the same numbers as in §2.

1. Super quattuor libros Sententiarum subtilissimae quaestiones earumque decisiones. First edition of the commentary on book I, Strassburg 1483. First edition of the whole work, Lyon 1495. This edition includes also no. 19.

Tabulae ad diversas huius operis super quattuor libros Sententiarum, Lyon 1495.

Detailed tables of these commentaries in Etudes franciscaines 31, 644–56, June 1914.

2. Quaestiones in octo libros Physicorum. Strassburg 1491, 1506, Venice 1506, Rome 1637.

3. Summulae in octo libros Physicorum. Bologna 1494, Venice 1506.

Philosophia naturalis. Rome 1637.

4. Quodlibeta septem. Paris 1487, 1488, Strassburg 1491. The edition of 1491 includes also nos. 17 and 18.

5. Expositio aurea et admodum utilis super totam artem veterem edita per

[43] Occam argued that, the essential function of councils being to assist the salvation of souls, and women having souls as well as men, they should be entitled to take part in the proceedings. It is interesting to note that Occam's feminism was continued and intensified by another Englishman, Sir Thomas More (1478–1535), notably in the latter's Utopia (1516).

venerabilem inceptorem fratrem Guilielmum de Occham, cum quaestionibus Alberti parvi de Saxonia. Bologna 1496. This was edited by Marco di Benevento, a Celestine monk, who introduced nominalism into Bologna about the end of the fifteenth century. The edition includes a prologue, commentary on Porphyry's Libri praedicabilium and Libri praedicamentorum, commentary on the De interpretatione, a treatise De futuris contingentibus. Together with the notes of Albert of Saxony and Marco di Benevento and a brief appendix by Riccardo di Capsalo (Abbagnano p. 28, 1931).

6. Summa totius logicae. Paris 1488, Bologna 1498, Venice 1508, 1522, 1591, Oxford 1675. The title is sometimes Tractatus logicae divisus in tres partes (Paris 1488). The edition of 1508 was prepared and partly written by Marco di Benevento.

7–16. Five of the political treatises (nos. 7, 8, 10, 13, 15) were edited by Melchior Goldast (1578–1635), in his collection Politica imperialia sive Discursus politici, acta publica et tractatus generales de imperatoris et regis Romanorum etc. (Frankfurt 1614). Same collection in German, Politische Reichshandel usw. (Frankfurt 1614). The Latin collection was reprinted under a new title, Monarchiae s. romani imperii, sive Tractatus de jurisdictione imperiali seu regia et pontificia seu sacerdotali (folio, 3 vols., Frankfurt 1668). Occam's writings are in vol. 2 of the edition of 1614, and in vol. 3 of the reprint of 1621.

Richard Scholz: Unbekannte kirchenpolitische Streitschriften aus der Zeit Ludwig des Bayern (2, 392–480, Rome 1914). This includes no. 13 bis, and the four following works: Contra Johannem XXII (2, 396–403). Tractatus contra Benedictum XII [1334–42] (2, 403–17). Allegationes de potestate imperiali (2, 417–31). An rex Angliae [Edward III, 1327–77] pro succursu guerrae possit recipere bona ecclesiarum (2, 432–53).

7. Opus xc dierum. Louvain 1481, Lyon 1495, 1496; edited by Goldast (2, 993–1236, Frankfurt 1614).

8. Tractatus de dogmatibus Johannis XXII papae. Edited by Goldast (2, 740–70).

9. Epistola ad fratres minores. Edited by C. Kenneth Brampton (90 p., Oxford 1929).

10. Compendium errorum Johannis papae XXII. Paris 1476, Louvain 1481, Lyon 1494, 1495; edited by Goldast (2, 957–76).

11. Defensorium (a paupertate Christi) contra Joannem XXII. Venice 1513.

12 bis. Tractatus adversus Clementem papam VI. Edited by Karl Müller (26 p., Giessen 1888).

13. Super potestate summi pontificis octo quaestionum decisiones, or De potestate pontificum et imperatorum. The edition printed by Goldast: Monarchiae (1, 588–647) is the one revised by Jacob Almain (theologian of Sens, died 1515): Expositio de suprema potestate ecclesiastica et laica; circa quaestionum decisiones magistri G. de Ockam super potestate summi pontificis (1512). A shortened form of this work is known as Octo quaestiones; Lyon 1496, Goldast (2, 313–91).

13 bis. De imperatorum et pontificum potestate. Edited by Richard Scholz: Unbekannte kirchenpolitische Streitschriften aus der Zeit Ludwig des Bayern (2, 453–80). This edition breaks off in the first part of ch. 27. Brief résumés of the first 26 chapters and a complete edition of ch. 27 have been edited by W. Mulder (Archivum franciscanum historicum 16, 469–92, 1923; 17, 72–97, 1924). New but incomplete edition by C. Kenneth Brampton (146 p., Oxford 1927), see Speculum 2, 455, 1927.

15. Dialogus inter magistrum et discipulum. Paris 1476, Louvain 1481, Lyon 1491, 1494, 1495, c. 1500; edited by Goldast (2, 392–957).

16. Probably not by Occam; Dialogus inter clericum et militem super dignitate papali et regia, Cologne c. 1470, 1475, Vienna c. 1480, Ulm c. 1485, Augsburg c.

1490, etc.; edited by Goldast (1, 13–18). English translation by Trevisa (XIV-2): A dialogue between a knyght and a clerke concernynge the power spiritual and temporall, printed by Thomas Berthelet, London 1533, c. 1540, 1559. Also edited by Aaron Jenkins Perry in Early English Text Society (vol. 167, 1–38, 1925).

17. De sacramento altaris. Paris c. 1490, Strassburg 1491, Venice 1504, 1516. Critical edition by T. Bruce Birch (624 p., Burlington, Iowa 1930), with English translation.

18. De corpore Christi. Strassburg 1491. The edition of 1491 includes as well nos. 4 and 17.

19. Centiloquium theologium. Lyon 1495. Together with no. 1.

20. Tractatus de principiis theologiae, ascribed to Occam. Edited by L. Baudry (Etudes de philosophie médiévale 23, 161 p., Paris 1936); that treatise was written in the second quarter of the fourteenth century, not by Occam, but by a good Occamist.

A new edition of Occam's Opera politica, most of them as yet unpublished or badly published, is being prepared by the University of Manchester; the work was begun under the direction of the late Jeffrey Garrett Sikes. Vol. 1 (382 p.), edited by him, appeared in Manchester 1940 (see American historical review 48, 82–83, 1942). It contains Octo quaestiones de potestate papae; An princeps pro suo succursu, scilicet guerrae, possit recipere bona ecclesiarum, etiam invito papa; Consultatio de causa matrimoniali; Opus nonaginta dierum (ch. I-VI).

Breviloquium de potestate papae, edited by L. Baudry (200 p., Paris 1937).

9. *General criticism*

Adolphe Franck: Réformateurs et publicistes de l'Europe (Paris 1864). Prantl (3, 327–420, 1867). Hauréau (2, part 2, 356–430, 1880). Poole (1884). Little (1892). R. L. Poole (DNB 41, 357–62, 1895). De Wulf (2, 176–86, 1926). Nicola Abbagnano: Guglielmo di Ockham (400 p., Lanciano 1931), elaborate general study of Occam's work and personality. Stephen Chak Tornay: Ockham. Studies and selections (216 p., La Salle 1938; Isis 29, 487).

10. *Special studies*

James Sullivan: Marsiglio and Occam (American historical review 2, 409–26, 593–610, 1897). Duhem: Etudes (2, 72–90, 1909), dealing with plurality of worlds, action at a distance. Alfred Kühtmann: Zur Geschichte des Terminismus (Leipzig 1911). Lothar Kugler: Der Begriff der Erkenntnis bei Occam (63 p., Breslau 1913). C. Delisle Burns: William of Ockham on continuity (Mind 25, 506–12, 1916), note on continuity and motion. W. M. Thorburn: The myth of Occam's razor (Mind 27, 345–53, 1918). Philip E. B. Jourdain: The logical significance of Ockham's razor (Monist 29, 450–51, 1919; Isis 4, 586). C. Delisle Burns and Philip E. B. Jourdain (ERE 10, 583–87, 1919). James Lindsay: The logic and metaphysics of Occam (Monist 30, 521–47, 1920). Erich Hochstetter: Studien zur Metaphysik und Erkenntnislehre Wilhelms von Ockham (187 p., Berlin 1927). L. Baudry: Fragments inconnus d'Occam, le Tractatus de principiis theologiae (Académie des inscriptions, Comptes rendus p. 46–55, 1927; Isis 11, 176; 25, 200). Simon Moser: Grundbegriffe der Naturphilosophie bei Wilhelm von Ockham. Kritischer Vergleich der Summulae in libros physicorum mit der Philosophie des Aristoteles (Philosophie und Grenzwissenschaften vol. 4, parts 2–3, 184 p., Innsbruck 1932). Ernst Borchert: Die Lehre von der Bewegung bei Nicolaus Oresme (p. 34–36, Münster i.W. 1934; Isis 25, 534). Ernest A. Moody: The logic of William of Ockham (336 p., New York 1935; Speculum 12, 274–77), elaborate study. Stephen Chak Tornay: The nominalism of Ockham (Philosophical review 45, 245–67, 1936). T. Bruce Birch: The theory of continuity of Ockham (Philosophy of science 3, 494–505, 1936). Michalski (p. 63–68, 1920); (p. 43–45, 96–97, 1925a); (p. 197–200,

216-21, 1925b); (p. 255-61, 297 f., 1937). J. Koch: Neue Aktenstücke zu dem gegen Wilhelm Ockham in Avignon geführten Prozess (Recherches de théologie ancienne et médiévale 7, 353-80, 1935; 8, 79-93, 168-97, Louvain 1936). Sytse Ulbe Zuidema: De philosophie van Occam in zijn commentaar op de Sententiën (Amsterdam thesis, 2 vols.; vol. 1, 534 p., vol. 2, 400 p., Hilversum 1936). Vol. 2 contains only quotations from Occam's commentary on the Sentences, and some of the 51 Occamist propositions censored in Avignon in 1326.

JOHN RODINGTON

English Franciscan theologian (d. 1348).

He probably derives his name from the village of Ruddington, Nottinghamshire. He studied in Oxford, where he obtained his D.D., and in Paris. He assumed the Franciscan habit, lived in the monastery of Stamford, and became eventually the nineteenth provincial of his order in England. He died in 1348, probably of the plague, at Bedford, and was buried there.

He wrote commentaries on the Books of sentences, at least on books I and IV. He was much influenced by Occam. He discussed such topics as God's omnipotence and His knowledge of the things which do not partake of His essence, refuting Ibn Rushd.

Text. The commentary on Sentences I was edited by the Franciscan Jean Picard (fl. end of fifteenth cent.), and included in his Thesaurus theologorum (Milano 1506).

Criticism. A. F. Pollard (DNB 49, 81, 1897). Michalski (p. 46, 77-79, 101, 1925a).

ADAM WODEHAM

Adam Woodham or Goddam, Godham. (There are five places called Wodeham in England.) English Franciscan and Occamist (d. 1358).

Born at the end of the thirteenth century, attended Occam's lectures on the Liber sententiarum of Peter the Lombard in Oxford (i.e., before 1324), then other lectures (critical of Occam's tendencies) by Walter Catton[44] in Norwich. He was one of Occam's first disciples, and may be the Adam de Anglia for whom Occam wrote his Summa totius logicae. He taught in London, then in Oxford (1332 or c. 1340), where he lectured on the Sentences. Later he became a doctor in theology. He is said to have died in Bury St. Edmunds in 1358.

His commentary on the Sentences was abridged by Henry of Oyta c. 1373-77. He also wrote Quaestiones variae philosophicae et theologicae, etc. He was not by any means a slavish follower of Occam, but disagreed with him more than once.

Text. See note on Henry of Oyta.

Criticism. R. L. Poole: Goddam (DNB 9, 23, 1890). Little (p. 172, 1892). Michalski (p. 71-72, 1920); (p. 45, 1925a); (p. 200, 221, 229, 1925b); (1937 passim). De Wulf (2, 177, 188, 1926).

JORZ

Thomas Jorz. English Dominican, Thomist (d. 1310).

Thomas Jorz, or Jorse, Joyce. Also called Thomas Anglicus, which caused

[44] Walter Catton or Chattodunus, Franciscan of Norwich. Author of a commentary on the Sentences, and of other books, one of them "adversus astrologos." His works are apparently lost. He was called to Avignon by the pope and died a penitentiary in that city 1343 (DNB 9, 325, 1887).

confusion with other contemporary English Thomases, e.g. Thomas of Sutton, and Thomas Wallensis, himself confused with Thomas Waleys. He is said to have been of Welsh ancestry but born in London. He and his five brothers all assumed the Dominican habit, and two of his brothers, Walter and Roland, were archbishops of Armagh (Walter in 1306–7, Roland in 1311–21).

Thomas studied in Oxford and Paris. He taught in Paris, London, Oxford. He was prior of the Dominicans of Oxford, then of England (1296–1303). He attended councils of his order in Marseille 1300 and Cologne 1301. At the end of 1305 he was sent by Edward I, whose confessor he was, on a mission to Clement V in Lyon; he was then created cardinal-priest. He continued to represent Edward I and II at the curia, and was charged with various diplomatic negotiations as well as with the examination of moot questions, such as evangelical poverty. While he was on his way to negotiate with Henry VII of Luxemburg, he died in Grenoble, on December 13, 1310. He was buried in the Dominican church of Oxford.

His scientific activity probably took place before 1305, and much of it may belong to the thirteenth century, but I forgot to deal with him in my volume 2, and must include him now, if only because of confusions with Thomas Sutton and Thomas Waleys. For example, the commentary on the first book of Sentences printed in Venice 1523 under his name is now ascribed to Sutton; the commentary on Psalms printed in Venice 1611 under his name is now ascribed to Waleys. Other commentaries on the Bible, on Augustine's Civitas Dei, etc. have also been restored to Waleys.[45]

His writings include Quodlibeta, commentaries on Aristotelian logic and physics, etc. A commentary on Boetius' Consolatio philosophiae printed under the name of Thomas Aquinas is probably the work of Thomas Jorz or Thomas Waleys.

Text. Super Boethium de consolatione philosophiae. Louvain 1484, 1487, 1495, 1499, Lyon 1514.

Criticism. C. L. Kingsford (DNB 30, 203–4, 1892). De Wulf (2, 212, 1926).

SUTTON

Thomas of Sutton. Thomas Anglicus. English Dominican, born probably c. 1260. His name occurs for the first time c. 1285, when he was a student in Oxford; in 1292/93 he was already preaching in the Dominican church of that city. He was occupying the Dominican chair of Oxford c. 1298. He died after 1311.

He was one of the earliest defenders of Thomism in England. Before the end of the thirteenth century, he wrote commentaries on the Organon, and treatises De unitate formae, De productione formarum, De pluritate formarum, and two Quodlibeta. After 1300 he composed two more Quodlibeta, Quaestiones disputatae, and treatises against John Duns Scot and Robert Cowton.[46] According to father Pelster, he was also very probably the author of a concordance of some of St. Thomas' sayings, beginning "Veritatis et sobrietatis verba loquor."

Text. Liber propugnatorius super primum librum Sententiarum contra Joannem ordinis Minoritani (Venice 1523). This is one of his treatises against Duns Scot; it has been wrongly ascribed to Thomas Jorz.

[45] Thomas Waleys (Waleis, Walleys, Galeys), Thomas Anglicus s. Wallensis. English (or Welsh) Dominican. Educated in Oxford and Paris. Imprisoned by the Inquisition for seventeen months because of his defense (Avignon 1333) of the doctrine of the saints' immediate vision of God (Mary Bateson, DNB 59, 121, 1899).

[46] Robert Cowton. English Franciscan who flourished about the turn of the century. Studied in Oxford and Paris (DNB 12, 402).

A treatise of his Contra pluritatem formarum is included in Michael De Maria: Opuscula philosophica et theologica selecta S. Thomae Aquinatis (1, 393–436, Città di Castello 1886).

Franciscus Pelster (S.J.): Thomae de Sutton O.P. Quaestiones de reali distinctione inter essentiam et esse (Opuscula et textus historiam ecclesiae eiusque vitam atque doctrinam illustrantia, no. 5, 64 p., Monasterii 1928). That is, the text of the Quaestio disputata XXVI and of the Tertium quodlibet, quaestiones VIII–IX, with notes and bibliography.

Criticism. F. Ehrle: Thomas de Sutton, sein Leben, seine Quolibet und seine Quaestiones disputatae (Festschrift Georg von Hertling p. 426–50, Kempten-München 1913). F. Pelster: Thomas von Sutton, ein Oxforder Verteidiger der thomistischen Lehre (Zeitschrift für katholische Theologie 46, 212–53, 361–401, 1922). De Wulf (2, 49–51, 1926).

HOLCOT

Robert of Holcot. English Dominican, philosopher (d. 1349).

Robert of Holcot or Holkot. The place and date of his birth are unknown. There is a village called Holcot in Northamptonshire. Robert was probably brought up in the Dominican house of Oxford, and obtained his doctorate of theology in that university. He was stricken by the plague in 1349 while lecturing on Ecclesiasticus, and died in that same year. He was buried in Northampton (?).

He wrote many Biblical commentaries and a commentary on the Books of sentences, wherein his philosophical views are stated. He had been influenced by Occam, and there are also points in common between Holcot and Bradwardine on the one hand and between him and Gregorio da Rimini on the other. Thus, though he was a Dominican he was not by any means a pure Thomist. His fastidious definition of actual and potential infinity is similar to Gregorio's, though less clear. He also discusses at great length the plurality of worlds. God, being absolutely omnipotent, could create many worlds, just as he could cause man to hate him. But if there be more than one world, the existence of a vacuum cannot be denied. It is not quite clear whether this should be taken as an argument against the plurality of worlds or for the possibility of a vacuum. Science is concerned, not with real things, but rather with the formulation of judgments.

The Philobiblon sive De amore librorum has been ascribed to him as well as to Richard de Bury; the balance of probability seems to be in the latter's favor.

In addition to the commentaries already mentioned, he wrote various theological tracts, logical tracts, Moralitates historiarum (or Moralizationes), sermons, De ludo scaccorum libri IV, and treatises on astrology, De umbra stellarum, De amore stellarum, De natura, de motibus et de effectibus stellarum.

The alchemical treatise De serpente alchemico breviloquium bearing his name (in a fifteenth-cent. British Museum MS, Harley 3528) is ascribed in that MS, but by a later hand, to one Thomas Holcote, disciple of Geoffrey Chaucer, who wrote "in ryme royall the moralization of the chesse in Englische." It is true a Latin treatise on chess was ascribed to Robert Holcot (see above), but until further notice we must distinguish a Thomas Holcot who lived toward the end of the fourteenth century from Robert, who died in 1349.

Text. Quaestiones on the Sentences. Lyon 1497, 1510, 1518.
For Biblical commentaries see DNB; there are a few incunabula editions.
Moralitates historiarum. Venice 1505, Paris 1510, Basel 1586.
For Philobiblon, see note on Richard de Bury.

The alchemical treatise of "Thomas Holcot" was printed by Zetzner (5, 787-98, 1660) in the form of a treatise De lapido philosophico addressed by Aristotle to Alexander the Great.

Criticism. R. L. Poole (DNB 27, 113-15, 1891). Duhem: Etudes (2, 399-403, 417-20, 1909). D. W. Singer (1, no. 300, 1928). Thorndike (3, 218, 1934). Michalski (p. 70, 1920; p. 47, 1925a; p. 102-11, 125-33, 1927; 1937 passim).

BURY

Richard de Bury. English Benedictine, humanist, bibliophile (1287-1345).

Richard of Aungerville, son of Sir Richard d'Aungerville, was called de Bury, because he was born in or near Bury St. Edmund's in Suffolk. He was born in 1287 (not 1281), was educated by his uncle John of Willoughby; later in Oxford. He assumed the Benedictine habit in Durham. Edward II appointed him tutor to his eldest son (born 1312). When the latter became king (Edward III) in 1327, he patronized his former teacher in many ways, entrusted to him many important offices and missions, and made him a member of his household. Richard was treasurer of Guienne, then dean of Wells. The bishopric of Durham falling vacant in 1333, Robert of Graystanes[47] was canonically elected and consecrated to it, yet was refused the temporalities of it and obliged to make place for the king's protégé. Thus was Richard elected bishop of Durham in 1333. He was appointed lord chancellor (1334-35), then lord high treasurer, and was sent on royal missions to the Low Countries, France, Germany, Scotland. In spite of all these honors and preferments he was often involved in financial difficulties, and was heavily in debt at the time of his death at Auckland castle (near Durham) on April 14, 1345. He was buried in the cathedral of Durham; his collection of MSS was probably sold to satisfy his creditors. A monument was built over his tomb, a short time before 1910, at the expense of the Grolier Society of New York.

He was a great bibliophile and assembled a large collection of MSS, buying many and obtaining others in other ways. As was stated in the Philobiblon, "Those who needed his help or influence" (and we must remember that his influence was considerable) "saw that he could be won better by MSS than by bribes of money." (Examples quoted in the Surtees Society vol. of 1910, p. xv.) It was his intention to give his library to Durham College, Oxford, but that intention was not realized and the books were dispersed. Only a few of these books have been traced and identified today (in the British Museum, the Bodleian, and the cathedral library of Durham). He patronized many of his contemporaries dealt with in this volume, such as Thomas Bradwardine, Walter Burley, John Mauduith, Robert Holcot.

He wrote the Philobiblon, completing it in his manor of Auckland on January 24, 1344 (i.e., 1345), a few months before his death. This is a sort of handbook to his library, but, in addition to that, a treatise on the love, use, and care of books; one of the earliest, possibly the earliest, of its kind. It is a typically bibliophilistic publication, with all the earmarks of such publications to these days—facile enthusiasm, mannerisms, jingle jokes, dilettantism. No wonder that he has been warmly praised by modern bibliophiles but less so by scholars. For example, the late provost of Eton, Montague Rhodes James (1862-1936), spoke rather contemptu-

[47] Subprior of Durham, continued the chronicle of Durham begun by Simeon of Durham (fl. 1130) and Geoffrey de Coldingham (fl. 1213), from 1213 to 1333. It was edited by Henry Wharton in his Anglia sacra (1, 732-64, London 1691). Robert died c. 1336 (T. A. Archer, DNB 23, 30, 1890). Under the date March 1320, Graystanes referred to a prodigy which may have been northern lights.

ously of him in his "Wanderings and homes of manuscripts" (p. 78, London 1919; Isis 3, 470): "I am inclined to think that he was a humbug; his book is of the kind that it is proper to translate, print on hand-made paper, and bind in a vellum wrapper, but it tells us just nothing of what books De Bury had or read, and I could not point to a single work of any importance which he was instrumental in bringing to light or preserving. Persons who take pains to advertise themselves as book-lovers or bibliomaniacs are rarely those who render great services to literature."

The accusation of dilettantism had been made a long time ago by no less a person than Petrarch, whom he had met in Avignon (in 1330 or 1333). Petrarch speaks of him with dubious praise in a letter to Tommaso di Messina, 1337 (Epistolae de rebus familiaribus III, 1; Fracassetti's ed., 1, 137, 1859). Richard had promised to give him information about the "ultima Thule" after his return to England, but failed to do so in spite of numerous inquiries.

It must however be said to Richard's credit that he made a plea (Philobiblon, c. X) for a better study of Greek, Hebrew, and Arabic; these languages should be studied in a living manner; "nothing but the hearing of the ears can represent to the learner's intelligence the true nature and qualities of any language." The prophetic value of that remark will be better appreciated if we bear in mind that it is not yet generally understood today, and that many pedagogues continue to teach as if those languages were dead, not alive. During one of his visits to Paris, Richard observed that astronomy was well studied in that city.[48]

It has been claimed that the Philobiblon was composed not by Richard, but by one of his clerks, the Dominican Robert of Holcot. Various MSS bear Holcot's name. The discussion of this is complicated; it may be summed up as follows: though external evidence is strong against Richard's authorship, the internal proofs are heavily in his favor (Surtees vol. of 1910, p. xl).

Text. Editio princeps of the Philobiblon, Cologne 1473. Later editions, Speier 1483 or after, Paris 1500, Leipzig 1574, Oxford 1599.

Latin-English edition by John Bellingham Inglis (London 1832), reprinted in America (Albany, N. Y. 1861; New York 1899). New Latin-English edition by Ernest C. Thomas (346 p., London 1888), often reprinted. Latin-English edition by Andrew Fleming West (Grolier Club, 3 vols., New York 1889). There are various editions "de luxe" for bibliophiles. Latin-French edition by Hippolyte Cocheris (Paris 1856).

Latin-Italian translation by Marco Besso (Roma 1914). Catalan translation by J. Pin y Soler (Barcelona 1916). German edition by Max Joseph Husung based on the translation of Franz Pattloch (Weimar 1931).

Richard d'Aungerville of Bury. Fragments of his register and other documents (Publications of the Surtees Society vol. 119, 338 p., Durham 1910), valuable collection of documents, edited and introduced by the dean of Durham. Parts of Richard of Bury's Register not included in the Surtees Society volume are found in Registrum Palatinum Dunelmense edited by Thomas D. Hardy (Rolls series vol. 62, London 1875; 3, 208–523); these are not under the name of Richard of Bury; but see Surtees Society vol. 119, p. viii–ix.

Criticism. Mandell Creighton (DNB 8, 25–27, 1886). Samuel Lane Boardman: Richard de Bury (67 p., Bangor, Maine 1902). J. W. Thompson (p. 383–86, 1939).

BACONTHORPE

John Baconthorpe (alias Bacon, Bacho). English Carmelite and philosopher (d. England 1346).

[48] G. Bigourdan (Comptes rendus de l'Acad. des sciences 161, 757, 1915).

His name is probably derived from that of Baconsthorpe, in Norfolk. It is said that he was the third son of Sir Thomas Bacon of Baconsthorpe, and, if so, a grand-nephew of Roger Bacon. He was educated in the Carmelite monastery of Blakeney, Norfolk, then in the Carmelite house of Oxford, finally in Paris. After his return to England he probably taught in Oxford; and it was perhaps then that he became acquainted with Richard Fitzralph (archbishop of Armagh, Ireland, 1347, d. 1360). John and Richard anticipated Wycliffe in their defense of the subordination of clerical to royal power. John Baconthorpe attended Carmelite chapters in Albi 1327 and Valence 1330. From 1329 to 1333 he was the head of the English Carmelites. In 1333, he was summoned by the general of his order to Rome; then he attended the chapter of Nîmes (or Narbonne) 1333. He led the Parisian Carmelites in their opposition to some theological errors of John XXII (pope 1316–34).

Baconthorpe was a voluminous writer (jokes were made about the great mass of his writings as compared with the very small mass of his own body, for he was extremely small). He wrote commentaries on the Bible, the Apocrypha, Aristotle's Metaphysics, Ethics, Politics, St. Augustine's Civitas Dei, the Libri sententiarum of Peter the Lombard, etc. His commentary on the Sentences was the only one of these works to be printed, being published as early as 1484–85. His other writings are now practically unknown, in spite of his earlier fame.

He was called Doctor resolutus, and more significantly—though deceivingly—princeps Averroistarum. He was *the* Carmelite doctor, even as St. Thomas was the Dominican one, Duns Scot the Franciscan, and Giles of Rome the Augustinian. He was not a pure Averroist, but a compromiser; he helped to prolong the Averroistic influence by his mitigation of its acerbities. His own influence continued until the end of the seventeenth century, at least at Padua, the main stronghold of Averroism, witness such commentaries as those of H. Aymus (3 vols., Turin 1667–69) and Giuseppe Zagalia of Ferrara (folio, 7 vols., Ferrara 1696–1706). A curious incident illustrating the continuation of his influence is the claim made by the unfortunate Giulio Cesare Vanini (1585–1619) that he had been Baconthorpe's own pupil!

Text. For account of the incunabula see GW (3, 261–63, items 3150–52). Super I Sententiarum, Paris 1484–85; Super III Sententiarum, Paris 1484–85; Super IV Sententiarum, Paris 1485. First edition of the complete commentary, Milan 1510/11.

In the incunabula editions the author is called Joannes Baco.

Criticism. Prantl (3, 318, 1867). Renan: Averroès (p. 318–20, 420, 1869). T. A. Archer (DNB 2, 379–81, 1885). Michalski (p. 53–55, 1925a; p. 226–28, 1925b). De Wulf (2, 234, 1926).

FAVERSHAM

Simon of Faversham, Simon Anglicus. English commentator on Aristotle (d. 1306).

Simon was parson in Harrow, Middlesex, from 1270–72 to c. 1306. In 1304, he was master of theology and chancellor of the University of Oxford. He died in 1306 on his way to the curia or at the curia itself.

He wrote a number of commentaries (or questions) on the Organon, Metaphysics, De anima, Physics, De coelo et mundo, De generatione et corruptione, Meteorologica, etc. In all probability a substantial part of these abundant writings goes back to the thirteenth century, and it might have been better to deal with him in my volume 2. It is not too late, however, to do it now, as his work was certainly continued into the fourteenth century. In a Merton MS his questions on the third book of De anima are coupled with questions of Siger of Brabant on the same book. His interest was apparently restricted to philosophy (vs. theology), which is in itself remarkable.

With regard to the problem of universals, his position is the same as that of St. Thomas (vs. Scotism).

Text. Carmelo Ottaviano: Le Quaestiones super libro Praedicamentorum (Memorie Accad. dei Lincei, sci. morale, vol. 3, fasc. 4, Roma 1930).

Criticism. Short note by Miss A. M. Clerke (DNB 52, 263, 1897). F. M. Powicke: Master Simon of Faversham (Mélanges d'histoire du Moyen âge, offerts à Ferdinand Lot, p. 649–58, Paris 1925). Carmelo Ottaviano: Le opere di Simone di Faversham e la sua posizione nel problema degli universali (Archivio di filosofia 1, 15–29, Roma 1931). Martin Grabmann: Die Aristoteleskommentare des Simon von Faversham. Handschriftliche Mitteilungen (Sitzungsberichte der Bayerischen Akad. der Wissenschaften, phil. Abt., 1933, no. 3, 40 p., München).

BURLEY

Walter Burley. English commentator on Aristotle (d. after 1337).

Walter Burley or Burleigh, Gualterus Burlaeus. Born in England (Herefordshire?) c. 1275. He studied at Merton College, Oxford, and was apparently a fellow in 1305 (the implication being that he was then a secular, not a regular). He also studied in Paris and may have had Duns Scot for a teacher, and Occam for a classmate. In 1327 he was appointed almoner to Philippa of Hainaut in preparation for her marriage to Edward III (1328). Earlier in the same year 1327 he had been sent on a special mission to Avignon to plead for the canonization of Edward III's cousin, Thomas of Lancaster (1277?–1322). He was appointed tutor to Edward prince of Wales (1330–76), the Black Prince, as soon as the latter was old enough "to learne his booke." This suggests that Burley may have lived many years after 1337 (to 1345?).

Burley wrote many commentaries on Aristotle's works, to wit, on the Organon (including Porphyry's introduction), on the Nicomachean Ethics, dedicated to Richard de Bury, on the Politica, Problemata, Meteorologica, Physica, De coelo et mundo. He also wrote an Expositio super Averroem de substantia orbis, and various treatises, De fluxu et refluxu maris Anglicani, De intentione et remissione formarum, De materia et forma, De potentiis animae.

His commentaries were comprehensive and precise if not very original; a combination of qualities which accounts for their success. His Expositio super decem libros Ethicorum Aristotelis was almost slavishly copied by Albert of Saxony, who however did not mention him. Burley enjoyed some fame, being called Doctor planus et perspicuus.

Judging from the number of MSS and early editions, his commentaries were very popular, but far less so than another work of his, De vita et moribus philosophorum, a collection of short anecdotal biographies of some 132 poets and philosophers, from Thales to Priscian the grammarian (VI-1). It is a compilation from ancient authors, many being quoted second hand; the main source is Diogenes Laërtios (III-1). It contains many gross errors (e.g., confusion of Ptolemy the astronomer with Ptolemy the king). Indeed, it is a very mediocre compilation, a fact which may explain its remarkable popularity. There were no less than thirteen incunabula editions, twelve of them in Latin, one in German. An early Italian version was printed in 1521; there was also an early translation into Spanish, but it remained unprinted until the last century. As late as 1603 the Latin text was reprinted for one Antonius a Sala, claiming to be the author! (DNB 7, 375).

To return to Burley's main work, his commentaries and his own studies, it reveals him as an independent Scotist. He was more of a realist than a nominalist, and would refer to Occam but criticize him. He created a series of new entities, attributing reality even to such concepts as "privatio" or "forma totius." Qualities such as love or justice grow in a different manner from quantities, and as they pass from one level to another, they become new entities. This might be considered a very pale adumbration of the theory of emergent (or creative) evolution?

In his commentary on the Physica he argues that if one believes in the creative power of God one cannot reject the reality of a vacuum and the plurality of worlds.

Text. For the incunabula editions I was able to avail myself of GW (5, 668–89, items 5765–93, 1932).

Expositio in artem veterem Porphyrii et Aristotelis. Without text, Venice c. 1476–78, c. 1480; with text, Venice 1481, 1485, 1488, 1492–93, 1493, 1497.

Expositio in Aristotelis Analytica posteriora. Padua c. 1477, Oxford 1517, Venice 1514, 1521, 1537.

Expositio in Aristotelis Physica. Without text, Padua 1476; with text, Venice 1482, Pavia 1488, Venice 1491, 1501, 1580, 1609.

Expositio in Aristotelis Ethica Nicomachea. With text, Venice 1481, 1500, 1521.

De intentione et remissione formarum. Printed together with Jacopo della Torre of Forlì (d. 1414): De intentione et remissione formarum, and Albert of Saxony: De proportionibus. Venice 1496.

De materia et forma. Oxford 1518.

De vita et moribus philosophorum. Complete editions, Cologne c. 1470, after 1479; with various additions, Cologne 1472, not after 1473. Incomplete editions, Nürnberg c. 1472, 1477, 1479, Louvain c. 1479–82, Toulouse c. 1480, Speyer c. 1483. Elaborations, in Latin, Cologne c. 1486, in southern Netherlands? c. 1486–90. A total of twelve incunabula Latin editions.

The German translation, Das Buch von dem Leben und Sitten der heydnischen Maister, was first printed in Augsburg 1490.

The Italian translation, Vite de' philosophi moralissime, was first printed in Venice 1521.

There is no French translation, but a large part of the work (69 chapters, among them some of the longest) is included in the Mer des histoires (Paris 1488, etc.).

The early Spanish translation (Escorial MS) was edited by Hermann Knust together with the Latin text of the Cologne edition of after 1479 (the second in our list above) (442 p., Tübingen 1886). This is a valuable edition, Knust having taken pains to trace the author's sources.

Criticism. T. A. Archer (DNB 7, 374–76, 1886). Duhem: Etudes (2, 414, 1909). Georg Heidingsfelder: Albert von Sachsen (p. 87–94, Münster 1921). De Wulf (2, 208, 1926). Michalski (p. 95–102, 120–25, 142–44, 1927).

DUMBLETON

John of Dumbleton (fl. 1331–49). English logician and philosopher. He originated probably in the village Dumbleton in Gloucestershire. He became a fellow of Merton College in Oxford in 1331 or before. In 1332–34, he was a curate in the country near Henley; then apparently returned to Merton, where he was in

1338-39. He was one of the original fellows of Queen's in 1340-41, but later (1344, 1349) returned to Merton. The end of his life is as obscure as its beginning.

His main work was a Summa logicae et naturalis philosophiae (Summa de logicis et naturalibus) divided into 10 books, though some MSS contain only 8 or 9. He also wrote two smaller treatises, De logica intellectuali (Liber de insolubilibus, de significatione et suppositione terminorum, etc.) and a Summa theologiae minor (vs. the main work, strangely called Summa theologiae maior). None of these works has yet been edited; their various titles are confusing and their contents practically unknown.

A summary of the fourth part of Dumbleton's Summa logicae was prepared by a later Mertonian, John Chilmark, under the title De actione elementorum. This Chilmark[49] (or Chylmark) was connected also with Exeter College, in 1386 (this being the only dated event of his life). He wrote various other treatises, De motu, De qualitate, De alteratione, De augmentatione, De prioritate, De aggregatione, De accidentiis planetarum (?), but his fame, whatever there was of it, was derived from the De actione elementorum, that is, it was but a reflection of Dumbleton's. His writings are not better known than those of his master.

Criticism. Reginald L. Poole (DNB 10, 257, 1887; 16, 146, 1888). Duhem: Etudes (3, 410-12, 1913). R. T. Gunther (1, 98, 1920; 2, 43, 63, 1923).

HEYTESBURY

William Heytesbury. English logician, mechanician, and physicist (fl. 1330-71).

There are many variants of his name, Hethelbury, Hegterbury, Hetisbury, Hentisberus, Entisberus, Tisberius, Tysberus, etc. Places and dates of birth and death are unknown. He was a fellow of Merton College, Oxford, in 1330, bursar of it in 1338, D.D. and chancellor of the university in 1371. Assuming him to be identical with William Heightilbury, he was one of the original fellows of Queen's College in 1340.

Heytesbury wrote five treatises dealing with logical and physical questions:

1. Sophismata. This is the largest one; it is devoted to the discussion of 32 sophisms. It is possible that the original edition contained only 30, to which were added later the two significant ones: Necesse est aliquid condensari si aliquid rarefiat. Impossibile est aliquid calefieri nisi aliquid frigefiat (adumbration of the principles of conservation of mass and energy).
2. De sensu composito et diviso. A very short treatise including the important observation that the path of a falling body is three times longer during the second second of fall than during the first (fol. 40 in edition of 1444).
3. Regulae solvendi sophismata. This is a collection of six little treatises, De insolubilis, De scire et dubitare, De relativis, De incipit et desinit, De maximo et minimo, De tribus praedicamentis (i.e., De motu locali, De motu augmentationis, De motu alterationis).
4. Probationes profundissimae conclusionum in regulis positarum. Proofs of the Regulae.
5. De veritate et falsitate propositionis.

Heytesbury was one of the pioneer logicians in the discussion of such topics as obligatoria and insolubilia, and he may have influenced Oresme with regard to the intensity of forms, their longitude, latitude, uniformity, and difformity (it is difficult

[49] There is a place of that name in Wiltshire, 11 miles from Salisbury.

to say, his writings being undated). His Regulae were commented upon by the Italian schoolman Gaetano da Thiene (1387–1465).

In his will of 1368 Simon Bredon bequeathed two volumes to his friend Heytesbury.

Text. The incunabula editions are cited after Klebs (nos. 512–15, 1938). The numbers following them refer to the list above.

Regulae solvendi sophismata. Pavia 1481 (contains 3).

Probationes conclusionum in regulis positarum. Pavia 1483 (contains 4).

De sensu composito et diviso. Venice 1491 (contains 1, 2, 3), 1494 (contains 1, 2, 3, 4, 5), 1501. Later edition with commentary by B. Victorius, Bologna 1504.

Quaedam consequentiae (Italian impression 1500). Consequentiae subtiles Tisberii, Venice 1517.

Gaetano da Thiene: Expositio regularum Hentisberi. Pavia 1483, Venice 1483 (Klebs no. 429).

Criticism. Prantl (4, 89–93, 1870). Reginald L. Poole (DNB 26, 327, 1891). Duhem: Etudes (3, 406–8, passim, 1913). R. T. Gunther (2, 53, 1923). Edmund Hoppe: Geschichte der Physik (p. 20, 1926).

ROLLE

Richard Rolle. English mystic (d. 1349).

Often called Richard Rolle of Hampole, from the place where he spent the end of his life and attained fame and sanctity. He was born c. 1300 in Thornton in Yorkshire. He was educated in Oxford, but he soon developed ascetic tendencies, and became a wandering hermit. He visited Dalton, near Rotherham, and resided there under the patronage of the squire John de Dalton. Then he moved to Anderby, Richmondshire, where he encouraged a kindred spirit, dame Margaret Kyrkby (or Kirkby), whom he called "dilecta sua discipula." Finally he established himself in Hampole, near Doncaster (southern Yorkshire), in the vicinity of the Cistercian nunnery of St. Mary. He died in Hampole on September 29, 1349.

He had the gift of healing and performed many miracles, which were recorded with a view to his canonization, but the latter was not effected. That failure may have been due to his singular independence; for he never joined a monastic order, and was not ordained. He was a lay hermit, orthodox but nonconformist and anti-scholastic. Moreover, his writings were eagerly read by Lollards.

He translated parts of the Bible from Latin into English, to wit, the Psalms and extracts from Job and Jeremiah. He wrote abundantly in Latin and in English; some treatises exist in both languages, and it is not always possible to say in which language Rolle wrote them, or if he wrote them at all.

Two devotional works, De emendatione vitae and De incendio amoris, were certainly written by him in Latin, but they are best known in the English versions made by Richard Misyn, the Mending of life (1434) and the Fire of love (1435). His main English work is a long ethical poem, the Pricke of conscience (9,624 lines),[50] which was soon translated into Latin, Stimulus conscientiae. It is not necessary to enumerate his other writings, all of which answer essentially the same purpose, to teach practical mysticism, the good life, union of the soul with God. This implied

[50] The ascription of the Pricke of conscience to Rolle is now generally disputed (Wells p. 1275, passim). The popularity of that particular work may be inferred from the number of extant MSS, 114 as against 64 MSS of the Canterbury tales and 50 of Piers Plowman. Carleton Brown and Rossell Hope Robbins: Index of Middle English verse (p. 737, New York 1943; Isis 34, 443).

some explicit or implicit criticism of the social order and of the ecclesiastical order, but he was always gentle and moderate. The abundance of MS copies of his writings in the English libraries proves his popularity.

His English language (Northumbrian dialect) is vigorous, but with occasional tendencies to affectation, a kind of anticipation of John Lyly's euphuism ("Euphues" 1579).

Text. Early editions. Rycharde Rolle hermyte of Hampull in his contemplacyons of the drede and love of God (Wynkyn de Worde 1506; again 1520?). The remedy against the troubles of temptacyons (Wynkyn de Worde 1508; again 1519). Explanationes notabiles super lectiones beati Job (Oxford 1483, Paris 1510). De emendatione vitae (Paris 1510); reprinted with extract from the Incendium amoris (Antwerp 1533). Editions including many Latin treatises, Cologne 1535, 1536, Paris 1618, Cologne 1622, Lyon 1677.

George Gresley Perry: English prose treatises edited from Robert Thornton's MS, c. 1440, in the library of Lincoln cathedral (Early English Text Society no. 20, 172 p., London 1866). New and revised text of same with glossary (London 1867, 1921). This second edition, prepared by Frederick James Furnivall, should be used, not the first. It includes a corrected text of the Officium de sancto Ricardo de Hampole (27 p.) prepared with a view to Richard's uneffected canonization.

Carl Horstman: Yorkshire writers. Richard Rolle of Hampole, an English father of the church and his followers (2 vols., London 1895–96), large collection of English writings.

Hope Emily Allen: Writings ascribed to Richard Rolle and materials for his biography (Modern Language Association of America, 584 p., New York 1927).

Margaret Deanesly: The Incendium amoris (305 p., Manchester 1915); first complete edition of the Latin text, based on MS written in 1414 by John Newton of York and collated by him with Rolle's own MS. Ralph Harvey: The Fire of love and the Mending of life or the Rule of living. Translations made by Richard Misyn in 1434–45 (Early English Text Society no. 106, 152 p., London 1895). Edition of both treatises in modern English by Frances M. M. Comper (340 p., London 1914), with an introduction by Evelyn Underhill. W. H. Hulme: Mending of life (Cleveland 1918). George Coulehan Heseltine: The Fire of love (212 p., London 1935).

Richard Morris: The Pricke of conscience. A Northumbrian poem by R. Rolle (369 p., Berlin 1863).

Henry Ramsden Bramley: The Psalter and certain canticles with a translation and exposition in English (580 p., Oxford 1884).

Frances M. M. Comper: The life of R. Rolle together with an edition of his English lyrics (360 p., London 1928).

Harald Lindkvist: Meditatio de passione Domini (78 p., Uppsala 1917).

G. C. Heseltine: Selected works (280 p., London 1930). Hope Emily Allen: (selected) English writings (244 p., Oxford 1931).

Criticism. The most valuable criticism is included in the editions above mentioned by Carl Horstman, Hope Emily Allen, Frances M. M. Comper. Unsigned article in DNB (49, 164–66, 1897). John Philip Schneider: The prose style of R. Rolle with special reference to its euphuistic tendencies (Johns Hopkins thesis, 84 p., Baltimore 1906). Reginald Maxwell Woolley: The officium and miracula of R. Rolle (98 p., Society for Promoting Christian Knowledge, London 1919). Wells (p. 444–60, 1678–79, etc.). Eugen Schnell: Die Traktate des Richard Rolle Incendium amoris et Emendatio vitae und deren Übersetzung durch Richard Misyn (Erlangen thesis, 192 p., 1932). Max Lehmann: Untersuchungen zur mystischen Terminologie R. Rolles (Berlin thesis, 78 p., Jena 1936). A. J. Collins: Middle-English devotional pieces (British Museum quarterly 14, 87–88, 1940).

A5. Germany

BERTHOLD OF MOSBURG

German Dominican and physicist, meteorologist (fl. 1318).

Nothing is known about his life. There is no place called Mosburg, but he may have come from Mosberg, or Mosbruch (near Koblenz), or from Maisberg in Lower Austria? He was lector in Cologne. In 1318 he wrote a commentary on the three books of Meteorologica of Aristotle. His main work is a very elaborate commentary on Proclos' metaphysics, Expositio in Elementationem theologicam Procli (Isis 29, 427). This was much praised by Nicholas of Cusa.

Text. The Expositio is unpublished. There are two MSS of it, the one in Balliol, Oxford, the other in the Vatican. There is a complete photostat (362 fol.) of the second MS in the Harvard Library.

Criticism. Ueberweg (1915, by index), bibliography on p. 190*.

ECKHART

German Dominican; Neoplatonist, the first of the great mystics in the Christian West (d. 1327).

Contents: (1) Life. (2) Writings. (3) Philosophy.

(4) Text. (5) General criticism. (6) Special criticism. (7) Western vs. Hindu mysticism.

1. *Life*

Meister (magister) Eckhart, as he is generally called (with many variants: Eckhard, Eckart, Eckehart), was born about 1260 in Hochheim, near Gotha (in Thuringia). He assumed the Dominican habit and was soon sent to the studium generale of his order in Cologne.[51] He graduated as master of theology at Paris in 1302, and was appointed the first provincial of Saxony in 1303 (in charge from 1303 to 1311). In 1314 he was prior in Strassburg, where he preached many sermons, and later we find him as prior in Cologne. Toward the end of his life his orthodoxy fell under suspicion, and proceedings were taken against him by the archbishop of Cologne (1326). In the following year he appealed to the curia, protested his innocence, and declared his readiness to recant any error he might have unwittingly committed. He died, presumably in Cologne, in 1327. In 1329 twenty-eight propositions of his were condemned by John XXII, seventeen of them as being heretical and the others as objectionable.

2. *Writings*

Eckhart has left abundant writings in Latin and in German. A large proportion are in the form of sermons, but there are also treatises, many of which were collected under the title Opus tripartitum (opus propositionum, opus quaestionum, opus expositionum). The first two parts are apparently lost, the third includes commentaries on Genesis, Exodus, Wisdom, John's Gospel, and sermons.

The genuineness of many of Eckhart's works is difficult to prove or disprove, and there are many textual difficulties; there is no doubt, however, as to the general tendencies of his mind. The dating is also difficult, but it would seem that many of his writings go back to the end of the thirteenth century.

[51] The very college where Albert the Great (d. 1280) had been teaching, and where St. Thomas (d. 1274) had sat at his feet.

3. *Philosophy*

Eckhart being a mystic and a poet, one cannot expect his thoughts to be as sharply defined as those of an ordinary schoolman. He claimed that in God, and in God alone, essence and existence are identical. Moreover, the essential existence of God is the only existence; nothing can really exist outside of God. From God's point of view, there is neither past nor future, but only an eternal present; thus creation is eternal. He compares God to an infinite sphere the center of which is everywhere, the surface nowhere. His psychology and ethics are equally mystical.

It is clear that such views savor of pantheism. Eckhart protested his orthodoxy, but, whatever his intentions, his winged words might easily lead far away from Christian doctrine. This has been strikingly illustrated by comparisons of his thoughts with those of Plotinos, with Mahāyāna Buddhism, and above all with Vedantic philosophy, as explained by Śaṅkara (IX-1). Eckhart could obtain some knowledge of Neoplatonism in various ways, but the possibility of his having access to Buddhist writings or to the Upanishad can hardly be contemplated. The many striking resemblances between his thought and Hindu thought can only be accounted for by the essential alikeness of mystical tendencies all over the world.[52]

Eckhart's influence on Western philosophy, especially on German philosophy, was quite considerable. It even influenced indirectly the philosophy of science ("Naturphilosophie," etc.).

4. *Text*

For incunabula editions of some of Eckhart's sermons, whether under his own name or under Tauler's, see Klibansky's preface to his edition of the Super oratione dominica (Leipzig 1934; Isis 24, 134–36).

The earliest and largest collection of Eckhart's writings was the one edited by Franz Pfeiffer: Deutsche Mystiker des vierzehnten Jahrhunderts (2 vols., Leipzig 1845–57). Editio quarta stereotypa (Göttingen 1924). English translation, with some omissions and additions, by C. de B. Evans: Meister Eckhart (504 p., London 1924). This edition includes 104 sermons, 19 tractates, various sayings, and the Liber positionum. It is a very convenient compendium of Eckhartian thought.

Two editions of Eckhart's collected works are now in course of publication. The one is directed by the French Dominican Gabriel Théry, rector of the Dominican historical institute of Santa Sabina in Rome, and Raymond Klibansky, editor of Cusanus, Magistri Eckardi opera latina, auspiciis Instituti Sanctae Sabinae ad codicum fidem edita. It will include (I) Super oratione dominica, edited by Klibansky (34 p., Leipzig 1934; Isis 24, 134–36). Opus tripartitum: (II) Prologi, edited by Hildebrand Bascour (52 p., 1935). Opus expositionum: (III, IV) Commentarium in Genesim, edited by the same. (V) C. in Exodum, edited by P. Castagnoli. (VI) C. in Sapientiam, edited by Klibansky and Théry. (VII, VIII) C. in Evangelium Ioannis, edited by Antonius Dondaine and Klibansky. (IX–XI) Opus sermonum, edited by Maiolus Cappuyns, Klibansky, and Théry. (XII) Sermones de ecclesiastico in capitulis provincialibus habiti. Sermo reportatus, edited by J. G. Sikes. (XIII) Quaestiones parisienses, edited by A. Dondaine. Commentariolum de Eckardi adiunxit Klibansky (96 p., 1936). (XIV) Fragmenta, edited by Dondaine. (XV–XVII) Apologia, processus coloniensis et avenionensis, edited by Théry and M. H. Laurent.

The rival edition is entitled Meister Eckhart. Die deutschen und lateinischen Werke herausgegeben im Auftrage der deutschen Forschungsgemeinschaft. Die lateinischen Werke (Stuttgart 1936–), to be completed in 5 volumes, plus a

[52] For the extension of this to Muslim mysticism, see Asín (1931).

volume of indexes. The editors of the Latin works are Konrad Weiss, Joseph Koch, Karl Christ, Ernst Benz, Bernhard Geyer, and Erich Seeberg. Die deutschen Werke (Stuttgart 1936–), edited by Josef Quint.

Apropos of these two editions read F. M. Powicke's letter to the Times literary supplement (p. 463, July 18, 1935) published under the title Nationalism and scholarship, or Isis 24, 136.

Franz Jostes: Meister Eckhart und seine Jünger, ungedruckte Texte zur Geschichte der deutschen Mystik (188 p., Freiburg, Schweiz 1895). Gustav Landauer: Eckharts mystische Schriften in unsere Sprache übertragen (246 p., Berlin 1903). Philipp Strauch: Paradisus anime intelligentis, Paradis der fornuftigen sele (210 p., Berlin 1919). Augustinus Daniels: Eine lateinische Rechtfertigungsschrift des Meister Eckhart (Beiträge zur Geschichte der Philosophie des Mittelalters vol. 23, no. 5, 86 p., Münster i.W. 1923). Otto Karrer: Meister Eckhart, das System seiner religiösen Lehre und Lebensweisheit. Textbuch aus den gedruckten und ungedruckten Quellen mit Einführung (380 p., pl., München 1926). Bernhard Geyer: Quaestiones et sermo parisienses (36 p., Bonn 1931).

5. *General criticism*

Hornstein (1922). Erich Seeberg: Meister Eckhart (Vortrag, 64 p., Tübingen 1934). Käte Oltmanns: Meister Eckhart (213 p., Frankfurt a.M. 1935).

6. *Special criticism*

Karl Pearson: Meister Eckehart the mystic (Mind 11, 20–34, 1886), interesting discussion from the rationalistic point of view. Heinrich Denifle: Meister Eckeharts lateinische Schriften und die Grundanschauung seiner Lehre (Archiv für Literatur und Kirchengeschichte des Mittelalters vol. 2, 1886); Denifle wrote (from 1875 on) many other papers dealing directly or indirectly with Eckhart. Max Pahncke: Untersuchungen zu den deutschen Predigten M. Eckharts (Diss., 68 p., Halle a.d.S. 1905). Hans Zuchhold: Des Nikolaus von Landau Sermone als Quelle für die Predigt M. Eckharts und seines Kreises (Hermaea 2, Halle 1905). Alfred Lotze: Kritische Beiträge zu Eckhart (Diss., 68 p., Halle 1907). Philipp Strauch: M. Eckhart-Probleme (Rektorat-Rede, 18 p., Halle 1912). Max Pahncke: Eckehartstudien, Texte und Untersuchungen (Progr., 41 p., Neuhaldensleben 1913). Henri Lichtenberger: Le mysticisme de Maître Eckhart (Vers l'unité 1, 6–13, Genève 1921). De Wulf (2, 125–34, 1926). Gabriel Théry: Edition critique des pièces relatives au procès d'Eckhart contenues dans le MS 33 de la bibliothèque de Soest (Archives d'histoire doctrinale et littéraire du moyen âge 1, 129–268, 1926–27); Contribution à l'histoire du procès d'Eckhart. Première phase, 1325–1326 (La vie spirituelle, 151 p., Ligugé, Vienne 1926). Ephrem Longré: Questions inédites de M. Eckhart et de Gonzalve de Balboa, O.F.M. (Revue néoscolastique 27, 69–85, 1927; Isis 11, 176). Martin Grabmann: Neuaufgefundene Pariser Quaestionen M. Eckharts und ihre Stellung in seinem geistigen Entwicklungsgange, Untersuchungen und Texte (Abhandlungen der Bayerischen Akad. der Wissenschaften, phil. Kl., vol. 32, no. 7, 124 p., 1927). G. Théry: Le commentaire de M. Eckhart sur le livre de la Sagesse (Archives d'histoire doctrinale et littéraire du moyen âge vols. 3, 4, 1928, 1929). Galvano della Volpe: Il misticismo speculativo di Maestro Eckhart nei suoi rapporti storici (300 p., Bologna 1930); the author's survey extends from Plotinos to Cusanus and Luther. Josef Quint: Die Überlieferung der deutschen Predigten M. Eckeharts textkritisch untersucht (1002 p., Bonn 1932). Marianus Müller: Meister Eckharts Seelenlehre und ihr Verhältnis zur Scholastik insbesondere zur Lehre des hl. Thomas (Diss., Bonn 1935). Herma Piesch: M. Eckharts Ethik (200 p., Luzern 1935). Theophora Schneider: Der intellektuelle Wortschatz Meister Eckeharts. Ein Beitrag zur Geschichte des deutschen Sprachinhalts (130 p., Berlin 1935). Franz Pelster: Ein Gutachten aus dem Eckehart-

Prozess in Avignon (Martin Grabmann Festschrift p. 1099–1124, Münster i.W. 1935), including text. Josy Seitz: Der Traktat des "unbekannten deutschen Mystikers," bei Carl Greith [1807–82], ein Beitrag zur Eckhart Forschung (Leipzig 1936). Bernard Joseph Muller-Thym: The university of being in Eckhart (St. Michael's mediaeval studies, 162 p., New York 1939). Isidoro Flaumbaum: Meister Eckhart y Martin Heidegger (Minerva 1, 50–54, Buenos Aires 1944).

7. *Western vs. Hindu mysticism*

Karl Eugen Neumann: Die innere Verwandschaft buddhistischer und christlicher Lehren (109 p., Leipzig 1891); this includes (p. 75–91) the text of Eckhart: Über die Abgeschiedenheit. Rudolf Otto: West-östliche Mystik, Vergleich und Unterscheidung zur Wesensdeutung (412 p., Gotha 1936); Englished by Bertha L. Bracey and Richenda C. Payne, Mysticism East and West, a comparative analysis of the nature of mysticism (278 p., New York 1932), based on lectures given at Oberlin College, Oberlin, Ohio in 1923–24, and largely devoted to Eckhart and Śaṅkara. Ananda K. Coomaraswamy: The transformation of nature in art (Cambridge, Mass. 1934; Isis 23, 475–77); ch. II (p. 61–95) is devoted to Eckhart's view of art, and the author remarks that Eckhart's sermons might well be termed an Upanishad of Europe. Hilko Wiardo Schomerus: Meister Eckehart und Māṇikka-Vāśagar. Mystik auf deutschem und indischem Boden (201 p., Gütersloh 1936). The bibliography of this subject could easily be extended, but these titles will be sufficient to begin with.

TAULER

Johann Tauler. German mystic, disciple of Eckhart. Born at Strassburg c. 1300, assumed the Dominican habit, and studied in the Dominican school of Strassburg, and probably also in the studium generale of Cologne. In or before 1339 he was established in Basel, which was then headquarters of a mystical group known as "the Friends of God." From Basel he traveled in various directions, preaching in many Dominican monasteries and nunneries. At an unknown time he moved back to Strassburg, where he died on June 15, 1361. His tomb can still be seen in the Dominican monastery, bearing the date June 16 (instead of 15), 1361.

Tauler was one of the greatest German preachers of the fourteenth century. He was inferior to Eckhart in knowledge, not in poetic originality. He continued the tradition of Eckhartian mysticism and popularized it.

Text. Editio princeps of his sermons, Sermon des groszgelarten . . . doctoris Iohannis Tauler . . . weisende auff den nehesten waren wegk . . . (Leipzig 1498), including 84 sermons in Saxon dialect. Second edition, Augsburg 1508, equivalent to the first but in Augsburgian dialect.

Third edition, Basel 1521, containing 42 more items. Reprinted Strassburg 1522. Edition in Low Saxon, Halberstadt 1523. Edition partly based on new MSS by Peter of Nijmegen, Petrus Noviomagus, Cologne 1543. Dutch translation of it, Frankfurt 1565, Amsterdam 1588.

Latin version by the Carthusian Laurentius Surius (Cologne 1548), chiefly based on the German edition of 1543 and itself the basis of many other versions, for example the French one by E. Pierre Noël: Oeuvres complètes de Jean Tauler, traduction littérale de la version latine du chartreux Surius (8 vols., Paris 1911–13), elaborate index appended to vol. 8, 138 p.

First critical edition by Ferdinand Vetter: Die Predigten Taulers, aus der Engelberger und der Freiburger Handschrift sowie aus Carl Schmidts Abschriften der ehemaligen Strassburger Handschriften herausgegeben (Deutsche Texte des Mittelalters vol. 11, 534 p., 3 facs., Berlin 1910).

For separate editions of treatises by Tauler or ascribed to him, refer to studies quoted below. The early editions of Tauler's works contain many items which are now considered apocryphal.

Julius Hamberger: Predigten. Nach den besten Ausgaben in die jetzige Schriftsprache übertragen (1826; 2d ed., 2 vols., Frankfurt 1864). Leopold Naumann: Ausgewählte Predigten (Kleine Texte für Vorlesungen, 62 p., reprinted Berlin 1933).

Susanna Winkworth: History and life of Tauler with twenty five of his sermons. Translated with additional notices of Tauler's life and times. Preface by Charles Kingsley (London 1857).

G. I. Lieftinck: De middelnederlandsche Tauler-Handschriften (Groningen 1936).

A. L. Corin: Sermons de Jean Tauler et autres écrits mystiques (2 vols., Liége 1924–29).

Criticism. Carl Schmidt: Bericht von der Bekehrung Taulers (64 p., Strassburg 1875). Auguste Jundt: Les amis de Dieu au XIVe siècle (thèse, Paris 1879). Heinrich Denifle: Taulers Bekehrung, kritisch untersucht (154 p., Strassburg 1879). Frances Bevan: Three friends of God; records from the lives of John Tauler, Nicholas of Basle, Henry Suso (London 1887). A. Jundt: Rulman Merswin et l'Ami de Dieu de l'Oberland (153 p., 2 pl., Paris 1890). Karl Rieder: Der Gottesfreund von Oberland, eine Erfindung des Strassburger Johanniterbruders Nikolaus von Löwen (560 p., 12 pl., Innsbruck 1905). Fred. J. Powicke: Friends of God (ERE 6, 138–41, 1914). Rufus M. Jones: Studies in mystical religion (ch. 13, p. 242–97, London 1919). A. Chiquot: Jean Tauler et le Meistersbuch (Strasbourg 1922). Hornstein (1922). Edmund Ludwig Stein: Deutsche Mystiker des Mittelalters, Eckhart, Tauler und Seuse (42 p., Paderborn 1926). Käte Grünewald: Studien zu Johannes Taulers Frömmigkeit (68 p., Berlin 1930).

THEOLOGIA DEUTSCH

Eckhart's and Tauler's theological views are faithfully reflected in a German text which has enjoyed considerable popularity, especially in German lands, and has thus been one of the main vehicles, if not the main one, of those views. It was discovered and first published by Martin Luther (1483–1546), "Eyn geystlich edles Büchleynn von rechter Underscheyd und Vorstand . . ." (Wittenberg 1516), with a preface. This was reprinted in Leipzig 1518. In that same year 1518 Luther published a new edition, much larger than the first, with a second preface, and a new title, "Eyn deutsch Theologia."

The second Lutheran edition of 1518 included 56 chapters, plus Luther's two prefaces; the princeps of 1516 omitted chapters 1 to 7 and 26 to 56; that is, it included only 18 chapters. Moreover, the text of the chapters common to the two editions is not exactly the same in both; e.g., the orthography is very different. We conclude that the two Lutheran editions were based upon two different MSS; unfortunately, no early MS is extant.

The complete original text (Luther 1518) seems to have been put together about the middle of the fourteenth century; the unknown author was probably a knight of the Teutonic Order (XII-2) who lived in Francfort. Luther said that he owed more to this book than to any other, except the Bible and St. Augustine's.

The text of 1518 attained much success, being frequently reprinted not only in German, but also in Flemish, Latin, French, and somewhat later in English. The first Flemish translation (55 chapters) appeared within three years of the publication of the complete text (Antwerp 1521). First Latin version, Theologia germanica. Libellus aureus hoc est brevis et pregnans, quomodo sit exuendus vetus homo, induendusque novus (Basel 1557), reprinted by Christopher Plantin together with Boetius' De consolatione (Antwerp 1558).[53] The same printer published the first French translation in the same year (Antwerp 1558). First English edition, based on the Plantin Latin text of 1558 (London 1648); an earlier English translation, however, had long circulated in MS. Critical editions by Hermann Mandel: Theologia Deutsch (Quellenschriften zur Geschichte des Protestantismus no. 7, Leipzig 1903); by Hermann Büttner: Das Büchlein vom vollkommenen Leben (Jena 1907), arbitrarily redivided into 17 chapters; by Gottlob Siedel: Theologia Deutsch, mit einer Einleitung über die Lehre von der Vergottung in der dominikanischen Mystik (210 p., Gotha 1929). Maria Windstosser: Etude sur la Théologie germanique, suivie d'une traduction française faite sur les editions originales de 1516 et 1518 (thesis, 230 p., Paris 1911).

The first MS was discovered only in 1843, by Professor Reuss of Würzburg; it is dated 1497 (incipit: "Dyses Buchlein hat der almechtig, ewig Got aussgesprochen . . . "; explicit: "Hie endet sich der Franckforter 1497") and was first edited by Franz Pfeiffer: Theologia Deutsch. Nach der einzigen bis jetzt bekannten Handschrift hrg. und mit einer neudeutschen Übersetzung versehen (Gütersloh 1851). That text has been frequently reprinted (4th ed. 1900). It was soon translated into English by Susanna Winkworth: Theologia germanica, with preface by Charles Kingsley (London 1854; Andover, Mass. 1856). New edition by Willo Uhl: Der Frankforter (Bonn 1912).

For criticism, see the elaborate introductions to the modern editions, e.g., Windstosser (1911). See also my notes on Eckhart and Tauler, and Greith (1861).

SUSO

Swabian mystic (c. 1295–1366) writing mainly in German.

Heinrich von Berg. Amandus; Suso, Joannes a Suevia, born near the Lake of Constance (Bodensee) on March 21, c. 1295. His father, von Berg, was patrician of Constance; Suso (Sus, Seuse, etc.; the form Suso is a Latinization) was the name of his mother, who came from Überlingen (near Constance). Heinrich was born in Constance or in Überlingen. He assumed the Dominican habit at Constance at the age of 13, but five years later experienced a kind of "conversion." He studied in his order's schools at Constance and Strassburg (?), and was Eckhart's disciple at the studium generale of Cologne in 1324. He returned to Constance c. 1327, was lector in the monastery c. 1329–34, and prior c. 1343–44. He was then disgraced for some reason. He died on January 25, 1366 in Ulm. His beatification was authorized without process, per viam cultus, by Gregory XVI in 1831.

He continued the mystical tendencies of Eckhart and Tauler, being perhaps more practical than either of them, and more poetical, "der Minnedichter der Gottesliebe." His works, the main part of which were collected toward the end of his life, form a more complete body than those of Eckhart and Tauler. Some of his letters, and perhaps other writings, were also preserved thanks to the devotion of a Dominican nun, Elsbeth Stagel. Suso was a popular preacher all over Swabia, and his sermons and other writings were eagerly read, especially in the Dominican nunneries. Hence an abundance of MSS, for some of them have been found in almost every Dominican convent of the Germanic and Dutch countries.

His main writings were collected within his lifetime, and probably by himself, under the general title Das Exemplar, being divided into four parts with a Prologus

[53] This edition was examined by the duke of Alba's inquisitors and authorized. In 1580 the text was re-examined and forbidden. It was put on the Index in 1612, and has remained there ever since.

(all in German): (I) Vita, (II) Büchlein der ewigen Weisheit, (III) Büchlein der Wahrheit, (IV) Briefbüchlein (collected by Elsbeth Stagel or with her help).

In addition we have Das grosse Briefbuch, the Horologium aeternae sapientiae, which is a free Latin translation of II, various sermons (Predigten), Das Minnebüchlein, represented by a single MS, and Das Büchlein von den neuen Felsen (The little book of the nine cliffs, probably apocryphal). The dates of these writings are difficult to determine, but the main ones, II and III, as well as the Latin adaptation of II, are probably anterior to 1341 (say, 1327–41).

The "Book of truth" is extremely difficult; it is essentially a defense of Eckhart's mysticism against dangerous exaggerations, such as the heretic extravagances of the Brethren of the Free Spirit (Adamites) and the Beghards. Suso's main sources were Aristotle, St. Augustine, Gregory the Great, St. Bernard, St. Thomas Aquinas, Neoplatonic fancies derived from many channels, and above all Eckhart.

Suso's influence was great in the fourteenth century, e.g., on Rulman Merswin (d. 1382),[54] Jan Ruisbroeck (d. 1381), and Gerrit de Groote (d. 1384). It continued for some time in the fifteenth century and even more in the sixteenth, for we have many fifteenth- and sixteenth-century editions of his writings. In 1576, however, Eberhard Mercurian, general of the Society of Jesus, forbade the reading of various mystical books, including Suso's. The pietistic tendencies of the seventeenth and eighteenth centuries brought Suso back to the surface. Mystical writings, as opposed to scientific ones, can never be proved or disproved, and hence they can never be entirely superseded.

Text. The first collection of Suso's works was edited by the Dominican Felix Fabri (Augsburg 1482). That edition was reprinted in the same city, 1512. These two editions are illustrated with interesting woodcuts, which continued a MS tradition and exerted some influence on German art.

There also are early editions of separate writings, as of the Horologium, the first s. l. et a., Paris 1470?, reprinted Paris 1479, Nuremberg 1479, Venice 1492, Cologne 1496, 1501, 1503, 1509, Paris 1511, Venice 1536, Paris 1578, etc. Der ewigen Wizheit Betbüchlein (Basel 1518). Manual oder Handbüchlein der ewigen Weyszheit (Constance 1622), etc.

To return to the collected editions, the third was prepared by Melchior von Diepenbrock, with a preface by Joseph Görres: Heinrich Suso's, genannt Amandus, Leben und Schriften (Regensburg 1829; reprinted, 611 p., Regensburg 1837). This was hardly better than the early editions.

The fourth edition, by F. H. S. Denifle: Deutsche Schriften (vol. 1, München 1880), was far superior, but not yet a critical edition, the whole being rewritten in modern German.

The fifth edition, by Karl Bihlmeyer, prepared for the state of Württemberg, was the first critical edition (808 p., Stuttgart 1907).

Nikolaus Heller: Deutsche Schriften. Vollständige Ausgabe auf Grund der Handschriften eingeleitet, übertragen und erläutert (Regensburg 1926).

Wilhelm Preger: Die Briefe Heinrich Susos (100 p., Leipzig 1867).

In addition to the early edition of the Latin treatise Horologium, there were also early editions of the German works in Latin translation. A Latin translation (lost) was prepared in the fifteenth century, and a new one was made by the Carthusian Laurentius Surius (d. 1578), on the basis of the German edition of 1512. It was printed in Cologne 1555, 1588, 1615, Naples 1658.

[54] For Rulman Merswin, see Philipp Strauch (ADB 21, 459–68, 797, 1885), also J. Baechtold: Gottesfreund im Oberland (ibid. 9, 456–60, 1879; 14, 453).

The oldest French translation of the Horologium was made by a Franciscan of Lorraine in 1389, under the title Orloge de sapience (Paris 1493, 1499, 1530).

Surius' Latin translation was translated into French by the Dominican Le Cerf (Paris 1586, 1614). Other French versions were made via an Italian one, by father del Nente (Firenze 1642, etc.). The best is the one by G. Thiriot: Oeuvres mystiques du bienheureux Henri Suso (Paris 1899), derived from Denifle.

Francis Knox: The life of blessed Henry Suso by himself, translated from the German (London 1865; reprinted 1913).

Portuguese translation of same (Lisboa 1642, 1764).

C. J. Brandt: Suso's Gudelig visdoms bog (224 p., Copenhagen 1858), Danish version of the fifteenth century.

Rich. Bergström: Susos gudeliga snilles väckare, Horologium aeternae sapientiae (492 p., Stockholm 1878–80), old Swedish version.

Hildegarde Van de Wijnpresse (Franciscan nun): De dietse vertaling van Suso's Horologium aeternae sapientiae (208 p., Groningen 1926), old Dutch version.

Criticism. See the note devoted to Tauler. Ferdinand Vetter: Ein Mystikerpaar des vierzehnten Jahrhunderts, Schwester Elsbeth Stagel und Vater Amandus (Suso) in Konstanz (64 p., Basel 1882). Wilhelm Preger: Eine noch unbekannte Schrift Susos (Abhandlungen der Bayerischen Akad. der Wissenschaften, hist. Cl., 21, 426–72, München 1895), apropos of the Minnebüchlein. Anna Nicklas: Die Terminologie des Mystikers H. Seuse (Diss., 161 p., Königsberg i.P. 1914). Renée Zeller: Le serviteur de l'éternelle sagesse, le bienheureux Henri Suso (284 p., Paris 1922). Reinhard Senn: Die Echtheit der Vita Heinrich Seuses (146 p., Bern 1930). Richard Schwarz: Das Christusbild des deutschen Mystikers Heinrich Seuse, eine Begegnung von Germanentum und Christentum (95 p., Greifswald 1934).

ENGELBERT OF ADMONT

Engelbertus Admontensis. Austrian Benedictine; moralist, publicist, encyclopaedist (d. 1331).

The time and place of Engelbert's birth are unknown. He came probably from Styria. He was sent to Prague in 1271 and remained there studying grammar, logic, and natural history until 1274, when political friction between Germans and Czechs (Rodolph of Hapsburg vs. Ottokar of Bohemia) obliged Austrian and Styrian students to leave. He proceeded to Admont on the Enns, in Styria (was it then that he assumed the Benedictine habit?). In 1279 he went to Padua to continue his education; he spent five years at the university studying philosophy and logic (under William of Brescia) and four in the Dominican house for the study of theology. In 1288 he returned to Admont, and became abbot of that Benedictine monastery in 1297. The rest of his life was spent in Admont. He resigned the abbacy in 1327 and died in 1331.

His literary activity was encyclopaedic in scope, and he was called the "Austrian Albertus Magnus." He hardly deserved that nickname, for his writings are more abundant than original. He was not in any sense a precursor, but a good mirror of his times. He illustrates the best thoughts of his contemporaries, but is not free of their superstitions. About the year 1320 he addressed to a friend, magister Ulrich of Vienna, a sort of autobiography and autobibliography, De studiis et scriptis suis, wherein he enumerates 33 works; he probably wrote a few more before the end of his life.[55]

[55] Autobibliographies were not so common in ancient and mediaeval times as they are now, yet there are many examples. It will suffice to recall Galen (II-2), see facsimile of his autobibliography in Osiris 5, 137; and the Retractations of St. Augustine (V-1).

He divides his writings into three groups, theology (16), natural philosophy (8), and moral philosophy (9).

The first group includes his very elaborate treatise De gratiis et virtutibus Beatae Mariae Virginis; a treatise De libero arbitrio, wherein he discusses free will according to Thomist psychology; De providentia Dei, wherein he remarks that rulers are instruments of divine providence and "si principes regulam iustitiae distorquent . . . corruet totum aedificium civitatis."

It is worth while to mention all the writings of the second group:

1. Commentary on the De mundo.
2. Commentary on the pseudo-Aristotelian treatise on the rising of the Nile (Introd. 1, 135).
3. De fascinatione. A treatise on fascination wrongly ascribed to Oresme, who, it is true, discussed the subject in his De configuratione qualitatum. Remember that Engelbert's treatment of it is at least half a century earlier. Fascination is the "impression of suffering or infection made on a human being or other animal by the glance of another man or animal" (Engelbert as freely quoted by Thorndike 3, 434).[56] As fascination is caused by the soul, through the eye, Engelbert is led to discuss the soul, its power over the body, the rays issuing from the eye, the detection of evil thoughts by means of a mirror (psychological means of detecting lies and crimes!), magnetic influences (description of a mariner's compass which he had seen in Venice), and similar questions.
4. De naturis animalium.
5. De quibusdam naturalibus.
6. De causis et signis mutationis aëris et temporum.
7. De causa longaevitatis hominum ante diluvium. If earth is reduced to water, its volume increases ten times; if to air, one hundred; if to fire, a thousand times (Thorndike 3, 433). The flood weakened human bodies as well as everything else. This was irreversible.
8. De musica.

The treatises of his third group, though of less immediate concern to us, include his most important contributions. I quote them in his own order:

1. De regimine principum.
2. Speculum virtutum.
3. De officiis et abusionibus eorum.
4. De ortu et fine romani imperii (c. 1307–10). A philosophical study of the origin, progress, and fall of the Roman Empire, including a discussion of the political art.
5. Utrum sapienti competat ducere uxorem. Concluding naturally for the negative.
6. Dialogus concupiscentiae et rationis.
7. Tractatum metricum de consilio vivendi.
8. De electione regis Rudolphi (i.e., Rodolph I of Hapsburg, 1218–91, elected king in 1273; founder of the Austrian monarchy).
9. De passione beatae Katherinae. (This refers, I assume, to Catherine of

[56] Three centuries later fascination was defined by Francis Bacon as follows: Fascinatio est vis et actus imaginationis intensivus in corpus alterius (De dignitate et augmentis scientiarum, lib. 4, cap. 3, 1623). That is exactly what was called two centuries later still "animal magnetism," and is believed in by Christian Scientists and other people.

Alexandria, virgin and martyr, who died in 310, to whom the famous Mt. Sinai monastery is dedicated.)

The most important of all his writings are probably the first two of the third group, Regimen principum and Speculum virtutum, which cover virtually the same ground. They are treatises for the education of princes, which had become commonplace at this time. The mediaeval interest in them began with the Polycratus of John of Salisbury, completed in 1159. It received a tremendous fillip a century later when William of Moerbeke translated Aristotle's Politics (1260), and special treatises were written by Vincent of Beauvais for Marguerite of Provence, by Thomas Aquinas and Ptolemy of Lucques for the king of Cyprus, and by Giles of Rome for the king of France. The last-named treatise was translated into eight languages, and so it would have been impossible to overlook it. Engelbert was probably acquainted with some of the other writings, if not with all, and he was certainly familiar with Aristotle, Cicero, Seneca, Boetius. In short, under the internal pressure of Aristotelianism and the external one of their own political and social vicissitudes, at the beginning of the fourteenth century the leading thinkers of Western Europe had become conscious of the need of political science, ethics, and canons. To return to Engelbert's treatises, the Regimen principum was written first, after 1290; then the Speculum virtutum, after 1298, for it was dedicated to the sons of Albert I of Austria, rex Romanorum (1298–1308). The Speculum is divided into three parts dealing respectively with the aims of men and especially of rulers, the qualities needed to reach these aims, the subordination of these qualities to the aims.

Text. The Epistola ad Ulricum scholasticum Wiennensem de studiis et scriptis suis was edited by Bernard Pez: Thesaurus anecdotorum (vol. 1, part 1, 427–36, Augsburg 1721). The same volume contains the Liber de causis longaevitatis hominum ante diluvium (p. 437–502), and the De gratiis et virtutibus Beatae Mariae (p. 503–762).

De regimine principum, edited by J. G. Th. Huffnagl: Engelberti opuscula philosophica (Ratisbon 1725).

De ortu, progressu et fine romani imperii, edited by Gaspard Brusch, together with the latter's Hodoeporicon bavaricum or Bavarian itinerary (165 p., Basel 1553). Reprinted many times (Potthast p. 406).

De libero arbitrio, edited by Bernard Pez: Thesaurus anecdotorum (vol. 4, part 2, 120–48, Augsburg 1721).

Various works have been edited by John Konrad Peez: Opuscula philosophica (Ratisbon 1725), including De summo bono hominis, Dialogus concupiscentiae et rationis, etc.

Other works by Bernard Pez: Bibliotheca ascetica (Ratisbon 1720), including Speculum virtutum, De providentia Dei, De statu defunctorum.

De musica, edited by Gerbert (2, 287–369, 1784).

Criticism. Schulte (ADB 6, 128, 1877). Andreas Posch: Die staats- und kirchenpolitische Stellung Engelberts von Admont (Görres-Gesellschaft zur Pflege der Wissenschaft im katholischen Deutschland no. 37, 144 p., Paderborn 1920). Zinner (notes 10866, 10933, 1925). Thorndike (3, 433–37, 1934).

THOMAS OF STRASSBURG

Thomas de (ab) Argentina. Alsatian Augustinian schoolman, commentator on the Sentences (d. 1357).

Born in Hagenau, Alsace, at an unknown time, assumed the Augustinian habit in that place, then studied philosophy and theology in the school which his order had established in Strassburg in 1306. In 1315 he was sent to Padua to complete his studies; while there he witnessed (in 1316) the burning of the bones of Pietro d'Abano.

After his return to Strassburg he became lector in the school of his order, and inquisitor for the diocese. In 1335 he went to Paris, completed his lectures on the Sentences in 1337, and received his doctorate in theology in the same year. It is not known how long he remained in Paris. In 1343 he was elected provincial of the Rhenan-Swabian province, and in 1354 prior general; he held that office until his death, in Vienna 1357.

He made some additions to the constitution of his order (dating from 1290), and wrote or planned to write many treatises, including one on the stars and planets; if he did actually write that particular treatise, it is lost. His main work is his commentary on the Sentences, completed in 1337.

He is quoted here as a distinguished representative of a small but distinguished school, the Schola aegidiana, thus called after its founder, Giles of Rome (XIII-2). Giles was an eclectic and moderate Thomist. Thomas continued in that direction, explaining the views of Aristotle as far as they could be reconciled with the Christian dogmas, defending a moderate realism against the aggressive Averroism and nominalism of his time. The affective side of theology was stressed, as opposed to the speculative side of Thomism and the practical one of Scotism (Dilectio Dei sive affectio . . . proprius finis nostrae theologiae est).

Thomas' commentary is very methodical and clear; his sources are abundant, the leading ones being St. Augustine, Thomas Aquinas, and Giles of Rome (doctor noster).

Text. Scripta super quattuor libros Sententiarum (Strassburg 1490). This was reprinted in Vienna 1564. The Viennese edition, at least, contains the author's biography.

Criticism. Benedict (Max) Lindner (O.E.S.A.): Die Erkenntnislehre des Thomas von Strassburg (Beiträge zur Geschichte der Philosophie und Theologie des Mittelalters vol. 27, no. 4/5, 151 p., Münster i.W. 1930). The first part of this was printed, under the title Prolegomena zu Thomas von Strassburg, in the form of a doctor's thesis (50 p., 1930).

Thomas is often quoted (e.g., by Duhem and Thorndike) apropos of his witnessing the burning of Pietro d'Abano's bones; no other information being given about himself.

EBERHARD VON WAMPEN

Low German author of a didactic poem. He originated in Wampen near Greifswald or in another Wampen on the island of Rügen, the two localities being in the same Baltic region. Nothing is known of his life except that he was in Sweden in 1325 and wrote for the young king Magnus Ericson (1316–74, king of Sweden 1319–65 and of Norway 1319–43, regent for his son 1343–55) a Low German poem entitled De spegel der naturen (Speculum nature), of which 1,775 lines are extant. He may be identical with one magister Evert von Wampen who was in Stralsund (in the same region) in 1330.

His presence at the court of Magnus Ericson is easily explained by the fact that the king's mother, Ingeborg, was partly of German origin, her mother being Euphemia, queen of Norway, daughter of Wizlaw II, prince of Rügen. Eberhard may have been in the service of queen Euphemia as physician, until her death in 1312, and then have passed into Ingeborg's service, for the latter became a Swedish duchess in that same year. Ingeborg took special pains to attract foreigners to her court, to such an extent that her council revolted against her in 1322, curtailed her powers, and forbade the introduction of more foreigners without their approval.

The poem is divided into four books arranged as follows: Book I begins with a kind of introduction explaining the doctrine of four elements, four fundamental qualities, and four complexions or temperaments. The temperaments are described in book I, the description of each being preceded by two lines taken from the Flos medicinae (Introd. 2, 434). Book II deals with the ailments relative to each temperament, and with their causes and remedies. This implies the consideration of relations between the temperaments on the one hand, and seasons, ages, celestial, meteorologic, and climatic conditions, months, hours, planets, signs of the zodiac, foods and drugs, on the other. Book III (incomplete) treats the properties of animals, herbs, and stones, the various kinds of souls, planets, signs, etc. It includes various dietetic and medical rules, e.g., with reference to bloodletting. Book IV (very incomplete, only 74 lines) contains various rules for the preservation of health. The titles and subtitles are in Latin, and there are a few Latin quotations from the Flos medicinae; the poem itself is in Low German.

The scientific value of this poem is small, but it is interesting because it is unlike any other poem of that time. The exact sources, outside the Flos medicinae, are unknown. It is unnecessary to assume that the author had obtained a doctor's degree in Italy, or even visited that country, for in his day Salernitan knowledge had spread all over Europe, even into Scandinavia,[57] and the doctrine of complexions or temperaments was the fundamental physiological theory of the time.

Text. First complete edition based upon the unique Gotha MS by Erik Björkman: Everhards von Wampen Spiegel der Natur, ein in Schweden verfasstes mittelniederdeutsches Lehrgedicht (84 p., Upsala Universitets Årsskrift 1902).

Criticism. Roethe (ADB 41, 132–33, 1896). Schelenz (p. 331, 1904).

BONER

Ulrich Boner. Swiss didactic poet writing in German (d. c. 1350).

Boner belonged to an old Bernese family and became a monk. There are records of his existence in Bern from 1324 to 1349. Toward the end of that period he composed in German verse a collection of a hundred fables, entitled Der Edelstein, and dedicated it to the Bernese patrician Johann von Ringgenbern. These fables are derived from German folklore and from the Aesopic cycle as represented by Flavius Avianus (fourth cent.) and the anonymous collection first edited by Nevelet.[58] They are also derived directly or indirectly from such sources as Valerius Maximus (fl. under Tiberius, emperor 14–37), St. Jerome (IV-2), the Latin Barlaam and Ioasaph, Petrus Alphonsi (XII-1), Jacques de Vitry (XIII-1), perhaps Bartholomew the Englishman (XIII-1), Etienne de Bourbon (a Dominican of the Lyon diocese who preached against the Albigenses, d. c. 1260), Martin von Troppau (XIII-2), Jacques de Cessoles,[59] Etienne de Besançon (Dominican who became general in

[57] See note on Henrik Harpestraeng (XIII-1), Introd. 2, 659–61.

[58] Isaac Nicolas Nevelet: Mythologia aesopica (Francfort 1610). Critical edition by Wandelin Förster appended to his edition of the Lyon Yzopet (Heilbronn 1882). The authors of that collection lived before the thirteenth century.

[59] See my note on Vignai.

1292 and died in 1294). Boner's collection of exempla is of special importance because it was written not in Latin, like its sources, but in German; and its first edition (Bamberg 1461) was the first book printed in that language.

After being neglected for centuries, the Edelstein (Precious stone, Jewel) was brought back again to the surface by the first critical edition (1757), and even more by the commentaries of no less a person than Lessing (1773). Yet no one has yet thought of investigating that text from the point of view of our studies.

Text. First edition printed by Albrecht Pfister (88 leaves folio with many woodcuts, Bamberg 1461). There is but one known copy of it, the one discovered by Lessing in the Wolfenbüttel Library and described by him. Another early edition (without place or date) is also known through a single copy, now in the state library in Berlin. That other edition may be described as contemporary with the "first"; it may be actually a little anterior to the "first." The experts disagree.

The Berlin edition is available in a complete facsimile, edited by the Graphische Gesellschaft (Berlin 1908) with a short preface by Paul Kristeller (156 plates folio, plus 6 plates taken from the Bamberg edition for comparison). These two early editions are very beautiful, and the abundant woodcuts representing various scenes, many animals, etc., most interesting. J. J. Bodmer and J. J. Breitinger reedited the text under the title: Fabeln aus den Zeiten der Minnesinger (Zürich 1757). George Friederich Benecke: Der edel Stein getichtet von Bonerius. Aus Handschriften berichtiget und mit einem Wörterbuche versehen (528 p., Berlin 1816). Franz Pfeiffer: Der Edelstein (in Dichtungen des deutschen Mittelalters vol. 4, 254 p., Leipzig 1844).

A translation in modern German by Carl Pannier was published in the Reclam Bibliothek (Leipzig c. 1895).

Criticism. Gotthold Ephraim Lessing: Zur Geschichte und Litteratur aus den Schätzen der herzoglichen Bibliothek zu Wolfenbüttel (Braunschweig 1773 et seq.). See collected editions, e.g., vol. 11 of the Lachmann-Muncker edition, and other vols. according to general index.

K. Bartsch (ADB 3, 121, 1876). Spölgen: Ulrich Boner als Didaktiker (Progr., 24 p., Realgymn. Aachen 1888). Christian Waas: Die Quellen der Beispiele Boners (Giessen Diss., 82 p., Dortmund 1897).

A6. Flanders

RUYSBROECK

The greatest mystic of the Netherlands (1293–1381). Jan van Ruysbroeck or Ruusbroec[60] was born in 1293 in the village of Ruysbroeck near Brussels. He was educated by his mother, then at the age of 11 by his uncle Jan Hinckaert, canon of St. Gudule in Brussels. He was ordained a priest at the age of 24 and became chaplain of St. Gudule. In 1343 he and two friends established themselves in a hermitage in Groenendaal (Viridis vallis, Vauvert) in the Forest of Soignes, near Waterloo. Other seculars joined them. In 1349 the whole group was affiliated to the Augustinian Canons. Ruysbroeck spent the rest of his life in Groenendaal, where he was visited by Tauler c. 1350 and by Gerrit de Groote c. 1375 and on various later occasions. He died in Groenendaal on December 2, 1381.

Being influenced by the widely diffused teachings of Christian Neoplatonism, and chiefly by Meister Eckhart, he wrote in Flemish (Dutch) a number of mystical

[60] There are many other variants. We are already acquainted with that name through William of Ruysbroeck (Rubruquis) (XIII-2), Flemish Franciscan who traveled to the Far East c. 1254 (Introd. 2, 1053). It does not follow that Jan and William were related or even that they originated in the same place.

treatises which will be named presently. He was one of the greatest Dutch writers of the Middle Ages, and one of the founders of the Dutch philosophical language. His works are:

1. Van den rike der ghelieven (The kingdom of lovers).

2. Van der cierheit der gheesteliker brulocht (The adornment of spiritual marriage). This is often considered his masterpiece.

3. Van den blinckenden steen (The sparkling stone).

4. Van den vier bekoringen (The four temptations). Criticism of the four main sins of monks and clerks: indolence, hypocrisy, the desire of understanding everything without divine grace, the unruled freedom of the spirit. It is probable that his criticism of the third sin was aimed at Eckhart, and that of the fourth at the Brothers and Sisters of the Free Spirit.

5. Van den kersten ghelove (On Christian faith).

6. Van den gheesteliken tabernacule des orconscaps (Spiritual tabernacle of the Old Testament). This is the longest of his works.

7. Van den seven sloten (The seven enclosures). Written for a Poor Clare of Brussels; it is a rule of conduct for nuns.

8. Spieghel der ewigher salicheit, or, Van den sacramente (Mirror of eternal salvation, or, On the sacrament of the Eucharist).

9. Van seven trappen in den graet der gheesteliker minnen (Seven degrees of spiritual love).

10. Van der hoechster waerheit, or, Samuel (On the highest truth).

11. Van den twaelf beghinen (On twelve Beguines). The longest treatise after 6.

12. Van den twaelf dogheden (On twelve virtues).

13. There are also a few letters.

I have not tried to analyze these writings, as this would take too much space and would hardly serve our purpose. It suffices to note the existence in the Flemish world of a great mystical voice, explaining the same secrets which were explained at the same time by others in Italy and Germany. One of the theories upon which Ruysbroeck liked to insist was that of the spiritual ladder, enabling different men to reach different levels: (1) active life, (2) inward life, (3) contemplative life. He remarked that even on the highest level the self remains separate from God. In spite of this remark and of other apologies, Ruysbroeck, like other mystics, was accused of pantheism and heresy, e.g., by Jean Gerson (1363–1429). Gerson's accusations were answered in 1406 by one of Ruysbroeck's disciples, Jan van Schoonhoven. Another disciple, Henri van den Bogarde (Henricus a Pomeris, or Pomerius), wrote his biography before 1420.

Some of Ruysbroeck's writings contain bitter criticisms of the clerical morality and customs of his time.

Judging by the large number of MSS (c. 250) in Dutch, in various German dialects, and in Latin, Ruysbroeck enjoyed much popularity. The first printed edition, however, appeared only in 1512.

Ruysbroeck did not influence the Friends of God, as they were contemporary results of the same causes, but he did influence Gerrit de Groote and through him the Brothers of the Common Life, who became the main educators of their time in Christendom. This is one of the reasons why it is necessary to speak of him, though he belongs chiefly to the history of religion and the history of literature.

Text. The first printed text was the Latin translation, De ornatu spiritualium mysticarum libri tres (Paris 1512).

The first complete edition was the Opera omnia, translated by the Carthusian Laurence Surius (d. 1578). This appeared in Cologne 1552. It contains a biography by Surius, which is hardly different from the earlier one by Pomerius. Surius' edition was reprinted in 1608, 1609, 1692, always in Cologne. It was the main channel of Ruysbroeckian thought for a long time, either directly, or through translations and anthologies derived from it. For example, the Benedictine François-Louis de Blois (Blosius, 1506–66),[60a] abbot of Liessies (near Avesnes, diocese of Cambrai), included many Ruysbroeckian extracts in his Pusillanimium consolatio (Venice 1571) and other compilations.

The first Italian text was printed in Venice 1565, the first French one in Toulouse 1606, etc. It is interesting to note that the first printing in Dutch was in the Spiegel der volcomenheyt (Antwerp c. 1525; Nijhoff, no. 1941). The Gheestelike brulocht was first printed in Brussels 1624.

The first scholarly edition of the Flemish original was published by the Maatschappij der vlaemsche bibliophilen (6 vols., 1858–68). Vols. 1 to 5 were edited by Jean Baptiste David (1801–66), vol. 6 by Ferdinand Augustin Snellaert (1809–72). A new edition was begun in 1912 by H. W. E. Moller: Alle de werken van Jan van Ruusbroec de wonderbare in nieuwere taal overgezet (vol. 1, 556 p., Bussum 1912); this is in modern Dutch. Only vol. 1 was published.

Oeuvres de Ruysbroeck l'admirable. Traduction du flamand par les Bénédictins de Saint Paul de Wisques (in Oosterhout, near Beda). Thus far 3 vols. have appeared (Bruxelles 1920, 1921, 1922).

Other French translations were published by Ernest Hello: Oeuvres choisies (Paris 1869), and by Maurice Maeterlinck: L'ornement des noces spirituelles (Bruxelles 1891, again Bruxelles 1900). Maeterlinck's introduction was Englished by Jane T. Stoddart (160 p., London 1894).

The adornment of the spiritual marriage, The sparkling stone, The book of supreme truth, translated from the Flemish by C. A. Wijnschenk, with introduction by Evelyn Underhill (292 p., London 1916). The kingdom of the lovers of God, translated from the Latin edition of Surius, with introduction by T. Arnold Hyde (232 p., London 1919).

Of German editions, I shall cite only a modern translation of old Blosius' anthology: Lichtstrahlen aus den Schriften gesammelt . . . (100 p., München 1876). Die Zierde der geistlichen Hochzeit, Vom glänzenden Stein, Das Buch von der höchsten Wahrheit, translated from the Flemish by Franz A. Lambert (Leipzig 1901). Die Zierde der geistlichen Hochzeit und die kleineren Schriften, by Friedrich Markus Huebner (406 p., Leipzig 1924).

Criticism. Johann Georg Veit Engelhardt: Richard von St. Victor und Johannes Ruysbroek (416 p., Erlangen 1838). Vanderkindere (p. 332, 435, 1879). A. A. van Otterloo: Ruysbroeck. Opnieuw uitgegeven door J. C. van Slee, inleiding van Paul Fredericq ('s Gravenhage 1896). Willem de Vreese (Biographie nationale de Belgique 20, 507–91, 1908–10), very elaborate study with long bibliography. Evelyn Underhill: Ruysbroeck (The quest series, 194 p., London 1915). Alfred Wautier d'Aygalliers: Ruysbroeck l'admirable (Paris 1923), Englished by Fred Rothwell (370 p., London 1925). Melline d'Asbeck: La mystique de Ruysbroeck (thèse, Paris 1928); Documents relatifs à Ruysbroeck (thèse complémentaire, Paris 1928).

A8. Alia

POPULAR ENCYCLOPAEDIAS

The Lumen animae (Light of the soul) is a dictionary containing 267 articles arranged in alphabetical order, most of them dealing with moral subjects, such as

[60a] For (François) Louis de Blois see Biographie nationale de Belgique (2, 499–507, 1868).

amicitia, voluntas, voluptas, uxor, etc., yet with various references to natural history. It is claimed to have been written for John XXII (pope 1316–34). Some statements in the text which do not tally with that date, e.g., references to Guy de Chauliac, may be later interpolations.

The scientific level is low, but the book was not written by a scientist for scientists. It was written by a clerk for the needs of preachers.

It was edited in 1477 by Matthew Farinator, Viennese Carmelite, and first printed in Augsburg 1477. It was reprinted in Reutlingen 1477, 1479, Strassburg 1482; a partial edition appeared in Augsburg 1518, wherein the text is ascribed to Berengarius, archbishop of Compostela (1317–25). The first editor, Matthew Farinator, was wrongly thought to be the author, as well as the author of Exempla naturarum (ADB 6, 576, 1877).

Thorndike's History of magic gives an analysis of the Lumen animae (3, 546–60, 1934), and the same chapter, "Encyclopedias of the fourteenth century" (p. 546–67), contains brief references to two other contemporary encyclopaedias, the De originibus rerum libellus of Guglielmo di Pastrengo, Petrarca's friend, and the anonymous Multifarium compiled at Bologna in 1326.

The Multifarium is divided into ten books: signs and planets, parts of the body, diseases, flying animals, terrestrial ones, herbs and plants, stones, stories of the poets, sayings of the philosophers, other histories. It is unpublished (MS Wolfenbüttel 4504). It seems largely derived from the Speculum of Vincent of Beauvais (XIII-2).

Thorndike ends this chapter with an analysis of the Fons memorabilium universi of Domenico Bandini (XIV-2).

B. EASTERN CHRISTENDOM

B1. Latinizing Byzantine Theologians

BARLAAM

Italian (Calabrian) theologian, humanist, logician, and mathematician (d. c. 1348, probably 1350).

Life. Bernardo of Seminara[61] (Reggio di Calabria), generally called Barlaam, Βαρλαὰμ ὁ Καλαβρός, which may have been either his family name or his monkish name. He was born toward the end of the thirteenth century, presumably in Seminara, and became a monk in the Basilian monastery of S. Elia de Copressino in Galatro. This Basilian community had come from Sicily, and constituted one of the centers of Byzantine culture in Calabria. Thus Barlaam was certainly well acquainted with Greek before leaving Italy; he could hear it spoken in the town and cloister, and the Basilian ritual was in Greek.[62]

He traveled to Constantinople during the rule of Andronicos III (1328–41) and

[61] Seminara is the Italian form, Seminaria the Latin one.

[62] A simple way of measuring the persistence of Greek influence in Italy is to read Isabella Stone's short article on the libraries of the Greek monasteries in southern Italy, in J. W. Thompson (p. 330–37, 1939). A number of pagan texts were preserved in those libraries, as well as Christian ones. Greek was still used as a living language in Calabria as late as the eighteenth century. Thus the great jurist Gian Vincenzo Gravina (1664–1718), founder of the Accademia degli Arcadi (Rome 1695), having adopted the young poet Pietro Trapassi (1698–1782), sent him to Calabria to learn the Greek language from the lips of the people. Under his Hellenized name Pietro Metastasio became one of the most illustrious poets and playwrights of his time. Gerhard Rohlfs: Scavi linguistici nella Magna Grecia (320 p., 1 map, Roma 1933). Very elaborate account of Greek linguistic remains in southern Italy.

became popular because of his eloquence. It was then, I assume, that he lectured on Aristotelian logic, Platonic philosophy, and Dionysios the Areopagite (V-2). He became abbot (ἡγούμενος) of the monastery of the Saviour (τοῦ Σωτῆρος) in Constantinople.

He was in good favor at the imperial court, especially with the empress Anna,[63] who was anxious to reconcile the Orthodox and Roman churches. In 1333, he was engaged in preparatory discussions with the papal legates Francesco da Camerino and frate Riccordo, and in 1339 was sent to Avignon to negotiate in the emperor's name, with Benedict XII. The aim of these negotiations was twofold: to explore the possibilities of religious union; to obtain Latin help against the Turks. Barlaam failed (how different the world might have been if he had not? but perhaps it was too late in any case?) and went back to Constantinople. He continued his fight against the Hesychasts (see below), which ended in his defeat 1341. He then returned to Italy, that is, to Naples, where he met Boccaccio, then to Avignon, where he met Petrarca, and was for a time a Greek reader at the curia. In 1342 he was appointed bishop of Gerace (Reggio di Calabria). In 1346 he was sent on a new mission to Constantinople, but was defeated again, this time by John VI Cantacuzenos; he soon returned to Avignon. In 1348 he was succeeded in the bishopric of Gerace by Symeon Atumanos.

The Hesychastic controversy. As Barlaam took a great part in this controversy and seems to have started the main trouble, it is necessary to explain it here. Hesychasm was a mystical movement in the Orthodox church, the success of which at this time was partly due to a reaction against the growing introduction of Western scholasticism. The main champion of Hesychasm was Gregorios Palamas (q.v.), and the main opponent Barlaam. It has been recalled above that Barlaam lectured on the Organon and on Platonism, and his success may have irritated the Palamas party. He seems to have been obliged c. 1336 to move to Salonica, and thence visited Mt. Athos. He found there Hesychasm in its crudest form, ridiculed the monks, and caused considerable scandal.[64]

The ἡσυχασταί (from ἡσυχία, quietness) were "quietists," some of whom carried their practice so far as to suggest comparison with yoga in India. These extremists were called ὀμφαλόψυχοι or umbilicanimi, because they tried to reach mystical ecstasy by strange ascetic exercises. According to their foremost leader, Palamas, they were able under favorable circumstances to see a light comparable to the Uncreated Light which the disciples had seen above Christ at the time of his transfiguration on Mt. Tabor (Matthew 17; Mark 9).

The Hesychastic movement developed with great intensity in the fourteenth century, for various reasons. It was a continuation of the old struggle between the secular clergy and the monks; the monks triumphed, and with them Hesychasm, because of the endless anxieties due to foreign menace (Turkish, later Servian) and to internal anarchy (struggle between the two Andronicoi and later between John Palaeologos and John Cantacuzenos), and on top of that because of the irritation

[63] Anna (c. 1306–60) was the daughter of Amedeo V, conte di Savoia. She married Andronicos III in 1326 and embraced the Orthodox religion at that time; after her husband's death in 1341 she was regent. She took much part in politics, especially in the projected reconciliation of the two churches.

[64] An amusing account of this was given by the hegumenos of the monastery of Caracállu on the Holy Mountain to Robert Curzon, jr., who related it with gusto at the end of his famous book "Visit to the monasteries in the Levant" (London 1849).

due to the teaching of Occidental "science," equally obnoxious to Greek minds and to Greek souls.

The matter was discussed at a synod in Hagia Sophia in 1341, and Barlaam was defeated and anathematized. The theory and practice of Hesychasm was especially popular on the Holy Mountain and in monasteries of the Balcanic peninsula; conversely, it helped to increase the mystical prestige of those monasteries, especially the Mt. Athos ones. The Athonite and the Hesychastic points of view converge to the extent that these names are frequently interchanged.

Hesychasm (or Athonism) was irreducibly opposed to union with Rome; and every attempt of the Orthodox leaders to compromise with Rome strengthened the Hesychastic reaction.

Barlaam's influence on humanism. Though Barlaam was hardly a humanist,[65] but rather a theologian and scientist, he had the advantage of having a living knowledge of the Greek language, and made a deep impression on Petrarca and Boccaccio because of that quality, which was then excessively rare in Italy. When he arrived in Naples in 1341 he helped king Robert's learned librarian Paolo da Perugia to select Greek MSS, and through him very probably met Boccaccio (Paolo's admirer and disciple); then he proceeded to Avignon, where he met Petrarca and taught him some Greek, not much. These lessons were soon cut short by Barlaam's new mission to Constantinople, but were resumed soon after his return in 1346. Petrarca often spoke of him in his letters, and Boccaccio praised him exceedingly (Genealogia deorum, XV, 6). Hence Barlaam's somewhat undeserved fame among the early humanists.

His writings. Most of his writings are theological or deal with ecclesiastical politics. He wrote for the union of the Catholic and Orthodox, and marshaled arguments against the Latin as well as for them. This involved discussion of the procession of the Holy Ghost.[66] He addressed a treatise on this subject to Demetrios Cydones, and another on the need of union to Alexios Calochetos. He delivered a lecture on that need before Benedict XII.

Barlaam's theological and political tracts are some of them in Greek, others in Latin. What is more startling, some are anti-Roman (or anti-Latin), others pro-Roman, the latter having probably been written when he became bishop of Gerace. Many of his Greek tracts against the Latins are still unpublished. According to Jan (1897), he was for a time violently antipapal and was largely responsible for the diffusion of the fantastic story of the female pope ("pope Joan").

He wrote a manual on Stoic ethics, Ethica secundum Stoicos ex pluribus voluminibus eorumdem Stoicorum sub compendio composita.

His scientific writings are dealt with separately in the following section.

[65] Petrarca remarked that Barlaam knew Greek very well but little Latin, Petrarca's own knowledge of Greek being rudimentary. On the other hand, Nicephoros Gregoras conceded that Barlaam may have known Latin but that his Greek was poor! (Hortis p. 500, 1879). Gregoras' opinion should be discounted because of enmity and jealousy, but the fact remains that Barlaam was not a man of letters.

[66] After the words "qui ex patre" in the Nicene Creed (325), the third Spanish council of Toledo (589) inserted "filioque," and the Catholic dogma of the Trinity developed on that basis, which the Orthodox considered most heretical. The Orthodox held that the Holy Ghost proceeds from the Father; the Catholics, that it proceeds from the Father and the Son. This was the main doctrinal difference between Eastern and Western Christendom, and a source of infinite hatred.

Scientific writings, chiefly mathematical. Barlaam wrote arithmetical demonstrations of the propositions in book II of Euclid.

He composed a Logistica (λογιστική), that is, a treatise in six books on computations with integers, ordinary fractions, and sexagesimal fractions, possibly with astronomical applications. I say possibly because that book, apparently very rare, was not available to me. Barlaam was acquainted with the Heronian method of approximating to the square root of a non-square number, and knew that it could be applied indefinitely. If A is that number and a^2 the nearest square to it, the first approximation to $\sqrt{A}$ is $\alpha_1 = \frac{1}{2}\left(a + \frac{A}{a}\right)$, the second $\alpha_2 = \frac{1}{2}\left(\alpha_1 + \frac{A}{\alpha_1}\right)$, etc.

He wrote a commentary on the theory of solar (not lunar) eclipses in the Almagest.

He solved a number of problems submitted to him by Georgios Lapethis (or Lapithes, Γεώργιος ὁ Λαπήθις or Λαπίθης), a scholar who flourished in Cyprus in the first half of the fourteenth century, was a friend of the Lusignan royal family, and corresponded not only with Barlaam, but also with Nicephoros Gregoras, Gregorios Acindynos, etc. The MS (Cod. Marc. 155 f. 67v) is entitled Βαρλαὰμ μοναχοῦ λύσεις εἰς τὰς ἐπενεχθείσας αὐτῷ ἀπορίας παρὰ τοῦ σοφωτάτου Γεώργιου τοῦ Λαπίθου (Krumbacher p. 781).

He criticized the completion and rearrangement of Ptolemy's treatise on music (ἁρμονικά) by Nicephoros Gregoras.

Text. Many of the theological writings are included in PG (151, 1243–1342, 1865), forming a sort of appendix to the works of Gregorios Palamas. Others are in other ecclesiastical collections or unpublished.

The Ethica secundum Stoicos was first printed at Ingolstadt 1604; it is included in PG (151, 1342–64, 1865).

Arithmetica demonstratio eorum quae in secundo libro Elementorum sunt in lineis et figuris planis demonstrata. Inserted in the Euclid edited by Conradus Dasypodius (1529–1600) in Greek and Latin (p. 70–117, Strassburg 1564). New edition in Heiberg's Euclid (5, 725–38, Leipzig 1888), Ἀριθμητικὴ ἀπόδειξις τῶν γραμμικῶς ἐν τῷ δευτέρῳ τῶν στοιχείων ἀποδειχθέντων.

Λογιστική sive arithmeticae, algebricae libri VI. Edited by the same Dasypodius in his Sphericae doctrinae propositiones graecae et latinae (Strassburg 1572). New editions with commentary by John Chamber (1546–1604), fellow of Merton, Oxford (DNB 10, 1) (Paris 1594?, again 1599?). Logistica nunc primum latine reddita et scholiis illustrata a Joanne Chambero, Greek and Latin edition (Paris 1600).

Barlaam's refutation of Gregoras' completion of the Ἁρμονικά of Ptolemy was edited by Joannes Franz: De musicis graecis commentatio (Berlin 1840). Gregoras' own text was edited by John Wallis (Oxford 1682), also in Wallis' Opera (vol. 3, Oxford 1699).

Criticism. Edward Gibbon: Decline and fall of the Roman Empire (chs. 63, 66, 1788). Attilio Hortis: Studj sulle opere latine del Boccaccio (p. 498, Trieste 1879). Th. Uspenskij: Skizzen zur Geschichte der byzantinischen Kultur (p. 283–364, Petersburg 1892). Pierre de Nolhac: Pétrarque et Barlaam (Revue des études grecques 5, 94–99, 1892). Krumbacher (passim, 1897). Carl v. Jan: Barlaam (PW 5, 23, 1897). Francisco Lo Parco: Petrarca e Barlaam (125 p., Reggio Calabria 1905); Gli ultimi oscuri anni di Barlaam e la verità sullo studio del greco del Petrarca (Napoli 1910). P. de Nolhac: Pétrarque et l'humanisme (2d ed., 2, 135–39, Paris 1907). Henri Hauvette: Boccace (p. 33, 362, Paris 1914). F. Vernet (DTC 2, part 2, 407–10, 1923). Ἐγκυκλοπαιδικὸν λεξικὸν Ἐλευθερουδάκη (2, 947, 1927). Vasiliev (2, 362–67, 423–27, 1932).

Scientific criticism. Bernardino Baldi: Vite di matematici italiani (Boncompagni's Bullettino 19, 598–600, 1886). Carl v. Jan: Die Harmonie der Sphären (Philologus 52, 13–37, Göttingen 1893). Heath (2, 324, 554, 1921). G. Sarton: Barlaam's Logistica, query no. 88 (Isis 32, 119, 1946).

ACINDYNOS

Γρηγόριος ὁ Ἀκίνδυνος. Byzantine theologian (d. before 1351).

Acindynos was of Bulgarian origin; he was brought up in Pelagonia (Macedonia) and educated in Salonica. He wrote in prose and verse against Barlaam as well as against Palamas, and addressed letters and poems to Nicephoros Gregoras. Hence he is a little difficult to classify. On the whole, however, he must be counted as an ally of Barlaam against the Hesychasts, and during the rule of Joannes Cantacuzenos, at the synod held in 1351 at the Blachernae (*αἱ Βλαχέρναι*, a castle near the Golden Horn end of the land wall), Barlaam and Acindynos were both posthumously anathematized.

His importance was unduly magnified for centuries by the accidental ascription to him of the Thomist treatise *περὶ οὐσίας καὶ ἐνεργείας* by the earliest editor (Jacob Gretser in 1616). Acindynos could not have written it, for there is no evidence that he knew Latin, and Demetrios Cydones' translation of the Summa contra Gentiles (main source of the *περὶ οὐσίας*) was completed only in 1354. The MSS of *περὶ οὐσίας* are anonymous, but Bessarion (d. 1472) ascribed it to Prochoros Cydones, ascription fully confirmed by Mercati in 1931. For further details see my note on Prochoros (XIV-2).

Text. PG (vol. 151, 1865).

Criticism. Krumbacher (p. 100–2, 1897), obsolete. Giovanni Mercati: Notizie di Procoro e Demetrio Cidone (p. 1–13, Vaticano 1931).

B2. Anti-Latin Hesychasts

NICEPHOROS CHUMNOS

Νικηφόρος ὁ Χοῦμνος. Byzantine philosopher, theologian, and rhetorician; flourished under the Palaeologoi, Michael VIII (1261–82) and Andronicos II (1282–1328).

The date of his birth is unknown, but it was probably in the third quarter of the thirteenth century, for he is counted among the disciples of Gregory of Cypros.[67] Under Andronicos II he reached the high offices of *ὁ ἐπὶ τοῦ κανικλείου* (the emperor's inkstand-holder, chancellor, or private secretary) and army commander (*στρατοπεδάρχης*), and he married his daughter Irene to Andronicos' son, the despot Joannes Palaeologos. In 1320 he withdrew to a monastery, assuming the name Nathanael.

In addition to many rhetorical writings (showing the influence of Gregory of Cypros) and many letters, he wrote a theological treatise against the Latins, *Ἀνασκευὴ τοῦ δόγματος τῶν Λατίνων περὶ τῆς ἐκπορεύσεως τοῦ ἁγίου πνεύματος* (Refutation of the Latin dogma of the procession of the Holy Spirit).

[67] That is, Georgios born in Cypros 1241, who was patriarch from 1283 to 1289 under the name Gregorios II Cyprios. After having received a Frankish education in Cypros, he went to Nicaea to acquire a Greek one, and then to Constantinople as soon as the city was delivered in 1261. He was one of the leading men of letters of his time, and wrote a delightful autobiography; as a theologian he took a notable part in the controversy between the Orthodox and Catholic churches. See PG (vol. 142, 1865).

We are chiefly interested in his philosophical and scientific (?) writings, though the real value of the latter cannot yet be appraised. He wrote against Platonists, Neoplatonists, Aristotelians; a dialogue of his on the soul, 'Ο περὶ ψυχῆς διάλογος, was directed against Plotinos (III-2). Other treatises of his are entitled Περὶ κόσμου φύσεως (Nature of the world), Περὶ τῶν πρώτων καὶ ἁπλῶν σωμάτων (First and simple bodies). He wrote a treatise on matter (Περὶ τῆς ὕλης) and another on meteorology, discussing such subjects as the cooling of air by winds, hail, origin of winds.

Text. Theological writings in PG (vol. 140, 1865). This includes the treatise against Plotinos (p. 1403–37), which is also printed in Plotinos' editions.

Many essays edited by Jean François Boissonade: Anecdota graeca (1, 293–312; 2, 1–187; 3, 356–408; 5, 183–350, 1829–33); the letters and the treatise on matter were edited by the same in Anecdota nova (p. 1–201, Paris 1844).

Criticism. Krumbacher (p. 478–83, 1897). A. Palmieri (DTC 2, 2395, 1905).

PALAMAS

Gregorios Palamas, Γρηγόριος ὁ Παλαμᾶς. Byzantine theologian (d. c. 1357/58).

Palamas flourished at the court of Constantinople, where his father held an important position. He belonged to a distinguished Anatolian family, yet we do not know when and where he was born. He studied Neoplatonism, and very early in life developed mystical tendencies which obliged him to withdraw to the Holy Mountain. He became the main leader of the Hesychasts against Barlaam, so much so that the Hesychasts were sometimes called after him Palamites. He took a decisive part in two synods, during which he caused the Athonite cause to triumph (Constantinople 1341, 1351). In the civil war between John Palaeologos and John Cantacuzenos, he naturally sided with the latter, who was strongly Hesychastic, and when the latter triumphed, Gregorios was consecrated archbishop of Salonica (1349) by Isidoros I (patriarch 1347–49). The people of Salonica refused to accept him, and he withdrew to the island of Lemnos, not very far from Mt. Athos. It would seem that he occupied his see later, and he died after a long illness in or after 1357/58.

He wrote a great many treatises and homilies, developed new views on ascetic contemplation (θεωρία), and explained Hesychastic mysticism in his Κεφάλαια (Capita physica, theologica, moralia, et practica). Many of his writings were directed against Barlaam and Acindynos, whom he accused of harboring Arian and Sabellian[68] heresies and Epicureanism. He also wrote against Nicephoros Gregoras (Περὶ τῆς τοῦ Γρηγορᾶ ψευδογραφίας ὁμοῦ καὶ δυσσεβείας), against Joannes XI Beccos, patriarch of Constantinople from 1275 to 1282 (d. 1293), defender of the Latins and of the union with them, and against Joannes XIV Calecas, patriarch of Constantinople from 1334 to 1347. In short, he was the main exponent of Hesychasm (about which see my note on Barlaam), as well as the main defender of Byzantine Orthodoxy against Rome.

A curious rhetorical work of his must still be quoted, the Προσωποποιία (personification of the soul accusing the body, and of the body justifying itself), a Platonic discussion on the soul.

[68] Called after Sabellios of Libya (or Italy), who was an anti-Trinitarian, or more exactly a modalistic monarchianist (Christ is divine but indistinguishable from God the Father, for there is but one divine essence). His dates of birth and death are unknown, but he was excommunicated by Callistus I (pope 218–23). For Arianism see Introd. 1, 348.

Text. Many of Palamas' writings are included in PG (vols. 150, 151, 1865). The Prosopopoeia was first edited by G. Morelius (Paris 1553); the Greek text and Latin version are in PG (150, 959–88, 1347–72). For other editions, see Krumbacher.

Criticism. Krumbacher (p. 103–5, 485, 1897). Tafrali (1912), giving the date c. 1357–58 for Palamas' death. Vasiliev (2, 363–64, 366–68, 403, 1932). P. S. Guichardan: Le problème de la simplicité divine au XIVe et XVe siècles, Grégoire Palamas, Duns Scot, Georges Scholarios (Lyon thesis, 224 p., 1933).

B3. Other Byzantine Philosophers

MAGENTINOS

Leon Magentinos, Λέων Μαγεντῖνος. Byzantine logician, fl. first half of fourteenth century. He was a monk and later archbishop of Mytilene.

He wrote commentaries on Aristotle's Interpretation, Prior analytics, etc., and on Porphyry's Isagoge.

Text. The scholia to περὶ ἑρμηνείας were printed in an Aldine edition, together with the commentary of Ammonios son of Hermias (VI-1) and Michael Psellos' (XI-2) paraphrase (Venice 1503).

The commentary on the Prior analytics, together with Philoponos' (VI-1) commentary, was edited by Vittorio Trincavelli (1496–1568) of Venice (Venice 1536).

Both works were translated into Latin by Giovanni Battista Rasario (1517–78) of Valduggia (Lyon 1547), many times reprinted.

Criticism. Nicolaos Comnenos Papadopulos: Praenotiones mystagogiae ex jure canonico (p. 227, 230, 233, Padua 1696); according to Papadopulos Leon fl. c. 1300. Le Quien (1, 959, 1740); according to Le Quien, Leon flourished sometime before 1381 [1383], when Armenopulos died. These two reference books, the first of which remained out of my reach, were drawn to my attention by professor Michael Stephanides, of Athens. Neither gives the date of Leon's archbishopric. NBG (30, 731, 1859). Krumbacher (p. 431–32, 1897).

C. ISRAEL

C1. Jews in Southern France

JOSEPH KASPI

Joseph ben Abba Mari ben Joseph Kaspi (or Caspi). Languedocian philosopher, grammarian, and exegete. Born c. 1280 at Largentière (Ardèche); moved to Tarascon, probably after the expulsion in 1306, and seems to have resided mainly in that city, but he traveled considerably in Spain, Majorca, North Africa. In 1314, he went to Egypt hoping to obtain information on Maimonides from the latter's descendants, but failed. In 1317, he was at Arles with Qalonymos ben Qalonymos; in 1329/30 in Tarascon. He is said to have died in 1340, place unknown.

His name Kaspi (or ibn Kaspi, ha-Kaspi, mi-Kaspi) is derived from the name of his native city, Largentière (argent = kesef). In Provençal he was called Don (or En) Bonafous (or Bonfos) de Largentera. He wrote about thirty books, most of which bear the word kesef in the title (The offering of silver; The silver sticks; The silver cups; The silver bundle, etc.), this being a deliberate reference to his name.[69] Two-thirds of these books deal with Biblical exegesis and need not detain us; the others, devoted to philosophy or grammar, come a little closer to our field.

[69] See preface to his Sefer ha-shoreshim.

Grammatical works. 1. Notes on Ibn Janāḥ (XI-1), on the basis of the Hebrew translation, probably the one by Judah ben Tibbon (XII-2); lost.

2. Retuqot kesef (Silver chains). Principles of Hebrew grammar, a work conceived as a kind of sequel to his logical treatise, and as introduction to his dictionary; 73 chapters. In ch. 1, symbolic interpretation of the letters of the Hebrew alphabet. Saadia Gaon (X-1), Ibn Janāḥ, and Abraham ben Ezra are quoted.

3. Sharshot kesef or Sharsherot kesef (Silver chains) or Sefer ha-shoreshim (Book of roots). In this book he develops a logical theory of Hebrew roots and tries to determine for each one a fundamental meaning, from which the other meanings are to be derived; this leads naturally to farfetched explanations. Written after his return from Egypt, hence after 1314. In this and other books of his, Provençal words are occasionally quoted.

These grammatical works were conceived by the author (according to the mediaeval usage of Hebrew grammarians) as a foundation for scientific exegesis.

Philosophical works. 4. Ẓeror ha-kesef (The bundle of silver), also called by the author Qiẓẓur qaṭan bi-meleket ha-higayon. This is the logical treatise mentioned under no. 2. It is supposed to contain the essentials of the treatises of al-Fārābī and Ibn Rushd, which he probably studied in Hebrew. He composed this treatise for his younger son Solomon, to serve as a foundation for the latter's Biblical studies; it begins with the Isagoge and ends with the Sophistics; the Topics, Rhetoric, and Poetics being omitted, as they are superfluous for the understanding of the Bible.

5. Terumat ha-kesef (Silver offering). Summary of Ibn Rushd's commentaries on the Ethics of Aristotle and the Republic of Plato as translated by Samuel ben Judah of Marseille. He completed the summary in Tarascon, December 1329, for his elder son Abba Mari, who was then married and living in Barcelona.

6. Ẓawa'at Kaspi[70] (Kaspi's testament), or Sefer ha-musar (Book of ethics), or Yoreh de'ah (Guide to knowledge), divided into 21 chapters. Written at Valencia, in 1332; he thought of it as he was contemplating a risky journey to Fez, but seems to have written it only after his return, for his younger son Solomon, living in Tarascon and then twelve years old. It contains moral advice and the outline of a course of study for that son from his fourteenth year to the eighteenth, then for two more years, in preparation for his marriage at twenty. During the first two years Solomon should study the Sefer ha-mispar of Abraham ben Ezra, Euclid, al-Farghānī, the Ḥeshbon ha-mahlakot of Abraham bar Ḥiyya, the Wisdom literature of the Bible and the Rabbis (Pirqe abot with Maimonides' commentary), the Madda' section of Maimonides' Mishneh Torah, Aristotle's Ethics in Kaspi's own summary, the Musre ha-pilosofim of Ḥunain ben Isḥāq as translated by al-Ḥarizi. During the following two years he should study the Bible, the Mishneh Torah, the Halakot of Isaac ben Jacob Alfasi, the Sefer ha-miẓwot of Moses ben Jacob of Coucy, and logic. When he reaches the age of eighteen he should continue the study of the sciences already mentioned, plus natural science. At twenty he should select a good wife, and establish a home of his own, but continue the study of philosophy: mainly, Aristotle and his disciples, the Moreh nebukim, and his father's own books.

7. Commentary on the Moreh nebukim divided into two parts entitled 'Ammude kesef (Silver columns) and Maskiyot kesef (Silver images). This might be classified with the Biblical commentaries, for it deals mainly with Maimonides' exegesis. It is divided into 177 chapters, a number equivalent to the numerical value of the

[70] Apropos of that typical form of Jewish literature, the Ẓawa'ot, see Introd. 2, 346, 889.

words "gan 'Eden," and was written (c. 1331?) for his elder son Abba Mari in Barcelona. Kaspi used the Moreh ha-moreh, an earlier commentary on the Moreh nebukim, composed in 1280 by Shem-ṭob ben Joseph Falaquera, and also al-Fārābī's treatise on principles, Kitāb al-mabādī', translated in 1248 by Moses ben Samuel ibn Tibbon, and al-Baṭalyūsī's Kitāb al-ḥadā'iq, translated by the same (Introd. 2, 848). According to Kaspi, Maimonides did not know of al-Baṭalyūsī's work, nor of those of Ibn Rushd. Kaspi's commentaries were much used, quoted from, and discussed by later Jewish commentators.

In ch. 14 of his Ẓawa'ah, Kaspi remarked that the Christians had translations of the Moreh nebukim, the Muslims of Fez read it in the original, in Egypt it was held in high honor, yet Western Jews despised it or at best cared little for it.

Biblical commentaries. Most of Kaspi's books were devoted to exegesis. I shall deal more briefly with them, though a student of his thought should naturally examine them just as carefully as the other works, every kind of knowledge being marshaled in them in order to obtain the supreme knowledge represented by the Torah and other parts of the Bible.

Kaspi made considerable use of the commentaries of Abraham ben Ezra and Maimonides, frequently discussing their opinions, and explaining when necessary the reasons for his disagreement. Out of some twenty exegetical works, I shall mention only four.

8. The Ṭirat kesef (Silver palaces) or Sefer ha-sod (Book of mystery), composed at Arles 1317, attracted at once much attention, and was criticized by various rabbis, notably Moses of Beaucaire, Abba Mari ben Eligdor, and Qalonymos ben Qalonymos. It is a sort of exegetical introduction to the study of the Torah.

9. Shulḥan kesef (Silver table). Discussing prophecy and miracles and including a good defense of the Hebrew language. The Old Testament should be read in Hebrew, rather than in a Latin or an Arabic translation, for fear of misunderstandings. (Should we conclude from this that some Jews did read it in Arabic or Latin?)

10. Menorat kesef (The silver lamp). A theological introduction written for his son Solomon. In the preface, entitled Ner elohim (God's lamp), he explains the theories of existence of Aristotle, Alexander of Aphrodisias, Ibn Sīnā, Ibn Rushd, and others.

11. Gabi'a kesef (Silver cup, or bowl), also called, like the Sefer ha-musar (no. 6), Yoreh de'ah (Guide to knowledge). This is also a kind of theological treatise, dealing with such mysteries as God's anteriority, his names, the tetragram. It includes discussions of a number of moot questions: contradictions concerning the flood, Abraham's vision, the idea of Trinity. His conciliatory views on Trinity may be one of the origins of the Judeo-Christian movement continued in Spain by Pablo de Heredia (1405–86), by other Jews, and even by Christians such as Pico della Mirandola and Reuchlin (Introd. 2, 880).

12. The last work to be considered here is Kaspi's autobibliography, Qebuẓat kesef (Silver collection), beginning with a brief autobiography. The autobibliography is not complete, as he mentions only twenty works, saying that he wrote twenty in remembrance of his namesake Joseph, who was sold for twenty pieces of silver.

Kaspi was not as great as Maimonides, but he was a man of the same intellectual type, and my remarks on Maimonides' rationalism (Introd. 2, 374) might be applied almost equally well to him. In both cases, strong leanings toward objective science and rationalism are tempered by an orthodoxy which is still stronger. In his Ẓawa'ah Kaspi warns his son against the philosophers who are too bold and would explain the Bible away with allegories, but as well against the men who ignore philosophy; we would say, he warns him against the radicals on the left and the fundamentalists and mystics on the right. He quotes Aristotle and Plato to prove his point. He shows no interest in casuistry, or in magic and astrology, and though very fond of symbols, allegories, and symmetries, he is remarkably free from superstitions.

Of course his efforts to reconcile Jewish theology with Greek philosophy led him into great difficulties. Being able to avail himself of the commentaries of Ibn Rushd, he went farther in this respect than Maimonides, though he remained in general less radical than Isaac Albalag, Levi ben Gerson, or Moses ben Joshua of Narbonne. He tried to save the theory of the eternity of the world by explaining it in a Platonic sense: formless matter is eternal, God is logically if not chronologically anterior.

In spite of his fundamental moderation, these philosophical compromises earned him the ill will of such men as Simeon ben Ẓemaḥ Duran (Majorca 1361—Algiers 1444) and Isaac ben Judah Abravanel (Lisbon 1437—Venice 1508), who were less scientifically minded. On the other hand, his fondness for allegories and for the more mysterious texts of the Bible endeared him to qabbalists like Moses ben Isaac Rieti (Rieti, Perugia, 1388—Rome c. 1460) and Johanan Allemanno (born in Constantinople; teacher of Pico della Mirandola; Pico's dates 1463–94).

His commentaries were essentially based on Hebrew texts or translations, but he knew Provençal and Latin, both of which he calls rumi (in the Kappot kesef, Silver cups; commentary on Ruth and Lamentations; no. 13 below), and he had some knowledge of Arabic, enough, e.g., to check Samuel ibn Tibbon's translation of the Moreh nebukim with the original; he also refers (in Kappot kesef) to the Arabic translation of the Torah by Saadia Gaon.

Text. The numbers correspond to those given above.

1. Lost.
2. Unpublished.
3. Sharshot kesef. Extracts given by Dukes in Literaturblatt des Orients, 1848.

4, 5. Unpublished.

6. Ẓawa'at Kaspi. Edited by Eliezer Ashkenazi in Ṭa'am zeqenim (fol. 49v, Frankfurt a.M. 1854); by Wolf Pascheles in E. Bondi: Hebräische Chrestomathie (Prag 1857); by Neubauer-Renan (p. 535–45, 1893); by Isaac Last: 'Asara kele kesef (2, 59, Pressburg 1903); by Israel Abrahams: Hebrew ethical wills (1, 127–62, Philadelphia 1926), in Hebrew and English; this is a very elegant and convenient edition.
7. 'Ammude kesef u-Maskiyot kesef. Edited by Solomon Zalman Werbluner: Die Kommentare von Joseph Kaspi zu Dalalat al-hairin von Moses Maimuni, nebst verschiedenen Verbesserungen und Zusätzen von Raphael Kirchheim (Frankfurt a.M. 1848).
8. Ṭirat kesef. Edited by Isaac Last: Mishne kesef (vol. 1, 1905).
9. Shulḥan kesef. Extracts in B. de Rossi: De praecipuis causis et momentis neglectae a nonnullis hebraicarum litterarum disciplinae disquisitio elenchtica (Torino 1769). Edited by Last (vol. 1, 1903).
10. Menorat kesef. Edited by Last (vol. 2, 1903).
11. Gabi'a kesef. Unpublished.
12. Qebuẓat kesef. Short text edited in Isaac Benjacob: Debarim 'aṭṭiqim (vol. 2, Leipzig 1846). Longer text in Neubauer-Renan (p. 535–44, 1893). Also edited by Last (1903).
13. Kappot kesef. Partly edited. Isaac Samuel Reggio: Iggerot (vol. 2, Vienna 1836). Edited by Last (1903).

Criticism. Munk (p. 496, 1859). Joseph Perles: Kalonymos b. Kalonymos' Sendschreiben an Joseph Kaspi (Munich 1879). M. Steinschneider: Ersch und Grubers Allgemeine Encyklopädie (sec. 2, vol. 31, 58–73, 1855), and in Nehemias Brüll: Jahrbücher für jüdische Geschichte und Literatur (9, 75–79, Frankfurt a.M. 1889), both reprinted in his Gesammelte Schriften (1, 89–135, Berlin 1925). Neubauer-Renan (p. 477–547, 1893), including many Hebrew texts. Abrahams (p. 370, 1896). Isaac Broydé (JE 3, 600, 1902). Wilhelm Bacher: Joseph ibn Kaspi als Bibelerklärer (Festschrift Cohen p. 119–33, Berlin 1912); Aus der Bibelexegese Joseph ibn Kaspis (Monatschrift für die Geschichte und Wissenschaft des Judentums 56, 199–217, 324–33, 449–57, 1912; 57, 559–66, 1913). Bruno Finkelscherer: Die Sprachwissenschaft des Josef ibn Kaspi (140 p., Göttingen 1930; OLZ 35, 578–580, 1932). Jakob Gordin (EJ 9, 1025–30, 1932).

JEDAIAH BEN ABRAHAM HA-BEDERSI

Judeo-Languedocian poet and philosopher, also translator from Arabic into Hebrew. Jedaiah[71] ben Abraham ha-Bedersi (he of Béziers, the Biterrois) was born in Béziers or Perpignan in or before 1270, and died c. 1340. He was also called Jedaiah ha-Penini (short for Perpinini? he of Perpignan), and in Provençal En Bonet Abram or Don Bonet Profiat (Bonet is the same as the Hebrew Ṭobiyah). He was nicknamed ha-meliẓ (rhetorician). His father, Abraham ben Isaac Bedersi, was one of the most famous Hebrew poets of Languedoc.[72]

Aside from various poems and prayers, he wrote c. 1287 the Sefer ha-pardes (Book of paradise), divided into 4 chapters: (1) service of God, (2) friends and enemies, (3) worthlessness of earthly matters, (4) various things which man ought to study and to know in order to improve himself. This last chapter is particularly important, for it underlines the value (even from the purely religious point of view) of scientific knowledge. It deals with the order of the sciences, medicine, law, logic, etc. In spite of his deep religious fervor, Jedaiah had a genuine craving for encyclopaedic knowledge. He believed that perfection required knowledge as well as piety.

His second work of importance to us is the apologetical letter, Iggeret hitnaẓẓelut, which he addressed from Montpellier c. 1305 to Solomon ben Adret of Barcelona in defense of Maimonides, that is, in defense of positive science and moderate liberalism against Talmudic orthodoxy.

It would seem that Jedaiah spent a good part of his life in Perpignan, then after his father's death moved to Montpellier. When the Jews were expelled from France in 1306,[72a] he returned probably to Perpignan (Roussillon was then a part of the kingdom of Majorca). It was probably after 1306, and in Perpignan, that he wrote the philosophical poem upon which his fame is largely based, the Beḥinat ha-'olam (Examination of the world). This is one of the most popular books of mediaeval Jewish literature, witness the number of editions in Hebrew and translations in many other languages. The burden of this poem is to prove the instability and negligibleness of earthly matters and the supreme value of religion

[71] I write Jedaiah in conformity with the English Bible, but the Hebrew name is Yedayah.

[72] Abraham ben Isaac Bedersi or Abraham Profiat (c. 1235–c. 1298). Quoted in Introd. 2, 857. Neubauer-Renan (p. 707–19, 1877). M. Zobel (EJ 3, 1210–12, 1929).

[72a] Montpellier was then Majorcan, not French, territory, but Bérenger of Frédol, bishop of Maguelonne (and Montpellier) from 1263 to 1296, had ceded his Jews to Philip the Fair, and therefore those Jews were expelled in 1306 together with the French Jews. In 1319 Sancho (king of Majorca and Montpellier 1312–24) recalled the Jews to Montpellier, where they were allowed to live for some time in peace. Montpellier became French in 1382; the Jewish community was suppressed by royal edict in 1394.

and morality, which afford our only consolation. Its charm was increased by the frequent use of familiar Biblical and Talmudic phrases. It ends with warm praise of Maimonides, whom he calls the last gaon in point of time, the first in merit.

In addition to writing commentaries on the haggadah of various Midrashim, and on Abraham ben Ezra's commentary on Genesis, Jedaiah revised the Hebrew translation of al-Fārābī's Kitāb al-'aql wal-ma'qūl (De intellectu et intellecto, or intelligibili), his Hebrew version being called Sefer ha-sekel (Book of understanding) or Ketab ha-da'at (same meaning), and he wrote commentaries on the following Arabic writings: (1) Ibn Sīnā: Qānūn, commentary in the form of a catechism; (2) Maimonides: twenty-five fundamental propositions of the Moreh nebukim (introduction to second part); (3) Ibn Rushd: Logic, Biurim le-higgayon; Physics; De coelo I, 6, Ma'amar be-hefke ha-mahalak (On the opposite of movement). He also wrote a few independent treatises wherein he discussed some points of Aristotelian metaphysics.

Jedaiah's more technical writings being still unpublished, it is not possible to estimate exactly his philosophic importance.

Text. Sefer ha-pardes. Printed in Constantinople 1515 or 1516?

Iggeret hitnaẓẓelut. Included in the responsa of Solomon ben Adret (Venice 1546). Separate edition with notes by Samson Bloch (Lemberg 1809).

Beḥinat ha'olam. First edition by Estellina Conat (Mantua c. 1476–80). Reprinted at least once in the fifteenth century (Soncino 1484) and many times in the sixteenth century and later. Many Hebrew commentaries, printed and unprinted; I quote only those of the fifteenth century, by Moses ben Shemṭob ben Ḥabib (Ferrara 1551), Joseph ben Shemṭob ben Shemṭob, Judah ben Jehiel Rophe (called Messer Leo).

French translations with text by Philippe d'Aquin, formerly Mordecai (Paris 1629), and Michel Berr (Metz 1808). Latin translation from the French, with text, by Allard Uchtmann (Leiden 1650, again 1668). English translation, with text, by Tobias Goodman (London 1806). Many German translations, generally with text, by Joel ben Joseph Wust (Dessau 1807), by S. Hamburger and C. H. Schwabacher (Fürth 1807), by J. J. Levy (i.e., Wust) (Sondershausen 1827), by Joseph Hirschfeld (Berlin 1838), by Isaac Reis Auerbach (Sulzbach 1843), by Max Emanuel Stern (Wien 1852) with Hebrew introduction by Joseph Weisse, etc. Italian translation by E. Sarker (Trieste 1796) and in the Antologia israelita (1880). There are also translations in Yiddish, Dutch, and Polish. Extract in Benzion Halper: Post-Biblical Hebrew literature (2 vols., Philadelphia 1921). Chapters 8 and 9 after the Soncino edition of 1484, entitled The nothingness of man and his pursuits (Isis 11, 512).

Criticism. Munk (p. 495, 1859). Isaac Broydé (JE 2, 625–27, 1902). M. Zobel (EJ 3, 1210–18, 1929).

LEVI BEN GERSON (1288–1344)

Contents: (1) Life. (2) Milḥamot Adonai. (3) Arithmetic and algebra. (4) Geometry. (5) Trigonometry. (6) Astronomy. (7) Cross-staff. (8) Physics. (9) Medicine. (10) Astrology and superstition. (11) Commentaries on Ibn Rushd. (12) Biblical and Talmudic commentaries. (13) Philosophical views. (14) Chronological summary. (15) Influence.

(16) Text. (17) General criticism. (18) Philosophic criticism. (19) Scientific criticism.

1. *Life*

Levi ben Gerson (Hebrew spelling with sin or shin, and final nun or mem), also called Ralbag (i.e., R. L. b. G.), Gersoni (Gersonides), Leon de Bagnols, Leo de Balneolis, Leo Hebraeus.

Judeo-Provençal philosopher, theologian, mathematician, astronomer, physicist. The greatest representative of mediaeval Judaism after Maimonides, and their boldest philosopher.

Born in 1288 at Bagnols (sur Cèze, dépt. Gard), which was then a part of the county of Orange enfeoffed to the county of Provence. He belonged to a learned family; his father, Gerson ben Solomon (XIII-2), and paternal grandfather were learned men; it has been said that Naḥmanides (XIII-2) was his maternal grandfather; Simeon ben Ẓemaḥ Duran (1361–1444) was a son of his daughter. He flourished in Orange, Perpignan, and Avignon; in or before 1338, being in the last-named city, he was not able to find copies of the Talmud and the Hebrew Bible to revise his commentary on the Torah; in 1338, 1342 he was living in Orange. He died on April 20, 1344; the place of his death is unknown (it has been said by Abraham Zacuto, and repeated by many others, that he died in Perpignan 1370; the date 1370 is certainly wrong).

His knowledge of Arabic was rudimentary and his knowledge of Latin, which he called "the language of the Christians," not deep; he often explained Hebrew words in Provençal (not in Latin). He was probably unable to read Arabic texts, and it is certain that his knowledge of Greek and Arabic philosophy and science was derived almost exclusively from Hebrew versions.

The Latin dedication of his Tractatus instrumenti astronomie to pope Clement VI "anno incarnationis Chr. 1342" has been interpreted as implying a conversion to Christianity. As this would be completely at variance with all we know of his life and thought, and as there was no need of apostasy, the Jews being very kindly treated in Avignon, it is simpler to consider that dedication either as an interpolation for which he was not responsible, or as a pure matter of form.[73]

2. *Milḥamot Adonai* (*The wars of the Lord*)

As this not only is Levi's main philosophical work, but includes his main astronomical one, it is expedient to consider it first. He devoted to it the golden years of his life, for it was begun at the end of 1316 or beginning of 1317, and completed on January 8, 1329. The purpose was to explain Aristotelian philosophy, harmonizing it as well as possible with the Jewish faith, with special reference to the most difficult problems, the very problems which Maimonides had been unable to solve completely. The treatise is divided into six books: (1) immortality of the soul, 14 chapters; (2) dreams, divination, prophecy, 8 chapters; (3) God's omniscience, 6 chapters; (4) providence, 7 chapters; (5) astronomy: (a) explanation of the Almagest (often omitted), (b) movements of the celestial bodies, 9 chapters, (c) their motor, i.e., the active intellect (νοῦς ποιητικός), 13 chapters (completed November 1328); (6) creation of the world, including a discussion of miracles, and of true and false prophets.

[73] When I write in Arabic to Muslim scholars, I date my letters according to the Hijra. I do this in order that my correspondents may understand the date at once. It is a matter of pure courtesy which does not imply any conversion to Islām!

The Milḥamot ha-shem is of great philological interest, for it shows how well the Hebrew language had adapted itself to its new duties. It had become in Levi's personality a philosophical instrument of great subtlety and precision. This is the more remarkable when one bears in mind that the adaptation of the Hebrew language to the needs of Greco-Arabic thought was not earnestly begun until the time of Judah ben Saul ibn Tibbon (XII-2).

3. *Arithmetic and algebra*

Levi's first mathematical work was the Sefer ma'aseh ḥosheb (Work of the computer), completed in April 1321. Divided into two treatises (ma'amarim): (1) principles, based on books VII to IX of Euclid; (2) applications, 6 chapters. A manuscript of the same work is entitled Sefer ha-mispar (Book of number), like the similar book of Abraham ben Ezra (XII-1). Abraham's book, however, was very popular throughout the Middle Ages, whereas Levi's was neglected. This is not surprising, especially with regard to Levi's first treatise, which was severely Euclidean. The geometric origin appears clearly in the terminology, e.g., sheṭaḥ and ẓela', meaning surface and side, used for product and factor; geometrical demonstrations, however, are generally abandoned. In this arithmetization Levi may have been influenced by the Rasā'il ikhwān al-ṣafā' (Introd. 1, 660–61),[74] but that is unproved. Summation of series as in al-Karkhī (XI-1),[75] e.g.,

$$\Sigma i^3 = (\Sigma i)^2 \qquad i = 1 \text{ to } n.$$

Development of combinatorial analysis. To determine the number of simple permutations of n objects, he obtains the correct result (which we call factorial n) by the use of mathematical induction. It is remarkable that the solution of equations is almost completely neglected (a few determinate and undeterminate equations of the first degree are solved incidentally).

The second part, on numerical applications, begins with a dissertation on unity. Levi could not abandon the old idea of opposing the number one to the others, yet realized that such distinction was inconvenient, e.g., when one considers the series of odd or square numbers. The position system is awkwardly explained, as no numerals are used except Hebrew letters. The importance of astronomical or sexagesimal (vs. ordinary) fractions is emphasized, which still increases the confusion of the decimal idea. The treatment of operations is divided into six "doors": (1) addition and subtraction, (2) multiplication, (3) series, (4) permutations and combinations, (5) division and root extraction, (6) proportions. In the fourth door, the theory of permutations is completed: (a) simple permutations of n elements taken all together,

$$P_{n,n} = n!$$

(b) permutations of n elements taken m at a time,

$$P_{n,m} = n(n-1)\cdots(n-m+1)$$

[74] The suggestion is made by Carlebach (p. 55, 1910), who refers to the Hebrew translation of the Rasā'il made in 1316. However, that translation by Qalonymos ben Qalonymos (Arles 1316) was restricted to the books on animals. Steinschneider (p. 860–62, 1893).

[75] I am not aware of the existence of any Hebrew or Latin translation of al-Karkhī, but Samū'īl ibn 'Abbās (XII-2) wrote an Arabic summary of the Kāfī fīl-ḥisāb (Introd. 2, 401).

(c) combinations of n elements taken m at a time,

$$C_{n,m} = n(n-1) \cdots (n-m+1)/m! = P_{n,m}/P_{m,m} .$$

Levi also realized that $C_{n,m} = C_{n,n-m}$.

His second arithmetical book is known only in Latin, De harmonicis numeris (De numeris armonicis); this being presumably the translation of the lost Hebrew text. Dated "In Christi incarnationis anno 1343," written for Philippe de Vitry, the musician. The purpose is to prove that the numbers 2^n, 3^m, 2^p3^r (the so-called harmonic numbers) differ by more than a unit, except the pairs 1-2, 2-3, 3-4, 8-9 Euclid is the source (he is quoted six times), and the method is Euclidean.

These two arithmetical treatises being, the first, one of his first works, and the second, one of his last, encompass the whole of his scientific life.

Note on the history of mathematical induction (or complete induction, reasoning by recurrence). We have seen above that Levi ben Gerson used that method to establish the result $P_{n,n} = n!$. The discovery of that method is generally but incorrectly ascribed to Pascal, who died in 1662. It is formulated in his Traité du triangle arithmétique, one of the treatises found already printed among his papers, and published only after his death in 1665. The printing occurred sometime after 1654. Pascal had clarified an idea borrowed by him from Francesco Maurolico (1575). G. Vacca: Maurolycus, the first discoverer of the principle of mathematical induction (Bull. American Mathematical Society 16, 70–73, 1910); W. H. Bussey: The origin of mathematical induction (American mathematical monthly 24, 199–207, 1917). We must still say that Maurolico was the discoverer, for there is a great difference between applying a method, as Levi did, and formulating it, as did Maurolico and later, more effectively, Pascal.

4. *Geometry*

Levi's main geometrical work is a commentary on books I to V of Euclid, the first of its kind in Hebrew. We may recall that Euclid had become available in Hebrew not long before Levi's birth, having been translated by Jacob ben Maḥir, then again by Moses ibn Tibbon, Montpellier 1270 (Introd. 2, 851, 849). Levi used the second translation. The Euclidean text and the commentary are regularly introduced by the words "Said Euclid" (amar E.); "said Levi." The formis thus similar to that of Levi's commentary on Ibn Rushd.

This commentary, meant to facilitate the study of Euclid for beginners, contains various interesting elucidations. In the part dealing with book V he discusses the concept of proportion of two magnitudes, and bases upon it a new theory of fractions.

He was especially interested in the axioms and postulates, and tried to prove them and to build an axiomless geometry! Of course he unwittingly introduced other axioms, or based geometry on philosophical or mechanical principles. These preoccupations caused him to write another book entitled Ḥibbur ḥokmat ha-tishboret (Science of geometry), which is lost except for a fragment, dealing with the fifth (parallel) postulate, extant in a single manuscript (namely, the great Hebrew codex 36 of Munich, a collection of mathematical texts including Moses ibn Tibbon's translation of Euclid, the Mishnat ha-middot, and other writings by al-Fārābī, Abraham ben Ezra, Levi, etc.).

His terminology is generally Tibbonidian, but he occasionally introduced new terms, such as sheṭaḥ for plane, instead of fishshuṭ.

5. *Trigonometry*

Levi wrote a trigonometrical treatise which was translated into Latin under the title De sinibus, chordis, et arcubus, the translation being made for Clement VI by the Augustinian Hermit Peter of Alexandria in 1342. That treatise is very important, as it is one of the first original non-Arabic treatises on the subject. It was not the first trigonometrical treatise in Hebrew, for the Almagest had been translated from the Arabic by Jacob Anaṭoli c. 1231–35, the Iṣlāḥ al-majisṭī of Jābir ibn Aflaḥ (XII-1) had been translated by Moses ibn Tibbon in 1274 (however, see Introd. 2, 849), and Isaac Israeli had given an elaborate explanation of trigonometry in 1310. But Isaac Israeli's account, being subordinated to astronomical needs, was restricted to spherical trigonometry, and Jābir's plane trigonometry was strangely retrograde, for it was still based on the use of chords. As the Latin title of Levi's treatise indicates, it was based on chords and on sines, and thus represented at once the Hipparchian and the Hindu-Arabic traditions. Levi rediscovered independently the sine theorem in the case of plane triangles (proportionality of sines to opposite sides); that theorem had been formulated before by Nāṣir al-dīn al-Ṭūsī (XIII-2), but Levi could not know of Nāṣir al-dīn's work, which was not translated either into Latin or into Hebrew. Regiomontanus (c. 1464) knew Levi's work and he probably obtained the sine theorem from it, though his proof of the theorem was different from Levi's, and more like that of Nāṣir al-dīn.

The originality of Levi's plane trigonometry is better appreciated if one compares it with a contemporary anonymous treatise available in the same MS,[76] which is still purely Geberian, i.e., based on the use of chords instead of sines. The slowness of the introduction of sines in plane (vs. spherical) trigonometry affords another excellent illustration of the essential timidity of the human spirit.

The trigonometrical elements considered by Levi are four in number: chord, versed sine (sagitta, defined as the projection of the chord on the radius), sine (half of the chord of the double angle), and cosine (sinus residui arcus 90 graduum; distantia sinus a centro circuli). Strangely enough, he was not acquainted with the tangent.

His table of sines is derived from the known sines of 90°, 30°, 18°; by means of the addition formulas and of continued dimidiation he finally obtains the value of sin 15′ with reference to a sexagesimal radius (length 60^p) divided into degrees, minutes, and seconds. Levi was thus obliged to consider simultaneously two kinds of degrees (gradus): those of the radius, and those of the angle. For example, $\sin 15' = 0°15'42''28'''12^{iv}27^{v}$. His tables are correct to the fifth decimal. His method of computing the sines suggests comparison with Abū-l-Wafā' (X-2), but I do not know how that tradition could have reached him, and if he was acquainted with it, how can his ignorance of the tangent be justified?

He explains the trigonometrical solution of plane triangles when (a) the three sides are known, (b) two sides and one of the opposite angles, (c) two sides and the angle included between them. Problem (b) led him to the formulation of the general sine theorem. Problems (a) and (b) were solved by means of perpendiculars

[76] Cod. Vindobon. Palat. 5277. See Braunmühl (1, 106, 1900). "Geberian" refers to Jābir ibn Aflaḥ (XII-1).

drawn from the apices to the opposite sides. Different cases arise then according to whether these perpendiculars fall within or without the triangle. It is very remarkable that Levi solved these different cases simultaneously.

6. *Astronomy*

Levi's main astronomical work is included in book 5, part 1 of the Milḥamot Adonai, a part completed in November 1328, and revised in 1340. That part is generally omitted from the MSS, and on the other hand it is often considered an independent work, bearing the title Sefer tekunah, or another similar one. The treatise was translated into Latin. It is divided into 136 chapters, and is a very elaborate account of the motions of celestial bodies. Nine chapters of it at the beginning are devoted to an instrument invented by him, Levi's staff (see §7). Before discussing his astronomical theories, it is well to mention two other works.

Levi compiled astronomical tables, Luḥot, at the request of prominent Jews and Christians. These tables are computed for the meridian of Izop (Orange) and the year 1320. They are also included in the Milḥamot Adonai, but are generally separated from it. They are divided into five parts: (1) explanation of the tables, (2) how to find an average opposition or conjunction, (3) how to deduce the true opposition (or conjunction) from the average one, (4) determination of true solar time, (5) eclipses. Positions of the moon for every day. A Paris MS contains the additional explanations written by the copyist Samuel ben Meir in 1342.

Levi wrote a Prognosticon de conjunctione Saturni et Jovis [et Martis] A.D. 1345. This was translated into Latin by Peter of Alexandria, helped by Levi's brother, Solomon ben Gerson.

To return to the Sefer tekunah, it contains an elaborate criticism of the Almagest and of the Kitāb al-hai'a of al-Biṭrūjī. Both works had been translated into Hebrew, the first by Jacob Anaṭoli c. 1231–35, the second by Moses ibn Tibbon in 1259. Levi derived his criticism of Ptolemy partly from Jābir ibn Aflaḥ, translated by Moses ibn Tibbon in 1274, and from al-Biṭrūjī, partly from other sources. He tried to find a new theory accounting for the positions of the stars and planets, and for the changes in apparent size of the latter, and yet in agreement with the principles of physics (this was a relative novelty, the tendency of contemporary astronomers being on the contrary to be satisfied with a purely geometrical description of celestial motions). He rejected the Ptolemaic epicycles, and postulated the existence of a number of nonhomocentric spheres, as many as may be needed to account for the positions of the celestial bodies, 48 in all. Motion is transmitted from one sphere to another by means of an intermediary resistless fluid. Each sphere or at least each planetary group of spheres is moved by a spirit; there are thus 48 such spirits, or at least 8. According to ancient astronomy and to al-Biṭrūjī, the motion was transmitted from sphere to sphere inward, the primum mobile being the most external sphere; according to Levi, on the contrary, the motion is transmitted outward, and the active intelligence, second only to God, which initiates every movement is in the heart of the whole system, that is, in the earth or near it. Counting God and the active intelligence, there are thus in all 50 separate substances or at least 10 (hence the sacredness of the numbers 10 and 50 in the Bible). This strange sliding back from astronomy into metaphysics and mysticism is characteristic of Levi's thought.

And yet he had carefully studied astronomical details, making observations and following one authority for one question, and another authority for another question, remaining always critical and independent. For example, with reference to the movement of the apogees he followed al-Farghānī (IX-1), whose work had been translated into Hebrew by Jacob Anaṭoli c. 1231–35. According to Ptolemy, the apogees of all bodies except the sun moved with the stars. Al-Farghānī taught that the precession of the equinoxes affected the solar apogee in exactly the same way as the other apogees. The other Muslim astronomers and the compilers of Western tables followed al-Farghānī, and so did Levi.

He was acquainted with the arguments according to which Mercury and Venus (the inferior planets) should be placed between the moon and the sun, and he duly examined the theory of Jābir according to which both planets were above the sun, and that of al-Biṭrūjī according to which Mercury was below and Venus above; he concluded in favor of Jābir's hypothesis. This wrong conclusion based upon a good analysis illustrates the difficulties entailed by the geocentric cosmology.

On the other hand, he rejected the erroneous notion of the trepidation of the equinoxes (Introd. 2, 758), to which Alpetragianism had given a new lease on life. This rejection is the more remarkable if one bears in mind that that old error continued to be accepted by astronomers until it was finally driven out by Tycho Brahe after 1588.

While admiring Levi's originality, one cannot give him a high rank as an astronomer, because his scientific views were vitiated by mystical conceptions. He realized the imperfections of Ptolemy and al-Biṭrūjī, but it is misleading to call him a forerunner of Copernicus. In fact, as far as the main issue was concerned (geocentrism vs. heliocentrism), he stood on the wrong side; in one of his Biblical commentaries (Genesis), he criticized the people who thought that the earth moves around the sun (thus there must have been such people in his time), and stated that Hipparchos had already seen the truth on that subject!

Levi's astronomical views were well received, not only among Jews, but also among Gentiles. The Latin translations mentioned above spread them in the Latin world. Pico della Mirandola praised him[77] and so did Zacuto, whose tables were used by the Portuguese junta of which Martin Behaim was a member.[77a] Joannes Remus Quietanus, writing to Kepler, expressed the hope that the latter might find a copy of Levi's treatise "Utinam apud rabbinos invenire posses tractatum Rabbi Levi V. defensionum Dei."[78]

7. *Cross-staff*

Levi invented a new astronomical instrument bearing the name of cross-staff and many other names. It is a long, graduated staff with a short perpendicular crosspiece, later called transversary. To measure an angle, e.g., the altitude of the sun, the observer holds the staff in his hand and, sighting from one end of it, moves the crosspiece until one end touches the horizon and the other the center of the sun. A lead ball at D helps to keep the transversary vertical. The angle $2a$ to be measured can be easily deduced from the graduation of the staff.

One sees that tang a would be immediately given by the ratio of the constant AC to AB, but Levi was not acquainted with the tangent, and he used the sine,

[77] Disputationes in astrologiam (book IX, ch. 8).

[77a] Abraham ben Samuel Zacuto (Salamanca c. 1450, Turkey c. 1515). Martin Behaim (Nuremberg 1459?, Lisbon 1507).

[78] Ch. Frisch: Kepleri omnia (6, 66, 1866).

$\sin \alpha = \frac{AC}{\sqrt{AC^2 + AB^2}}$. To every value of BA, that is, to every point on the long staff, there corresponds a value of sin α. Levi compiled a table of sines for every 15′, to be used with his staff.

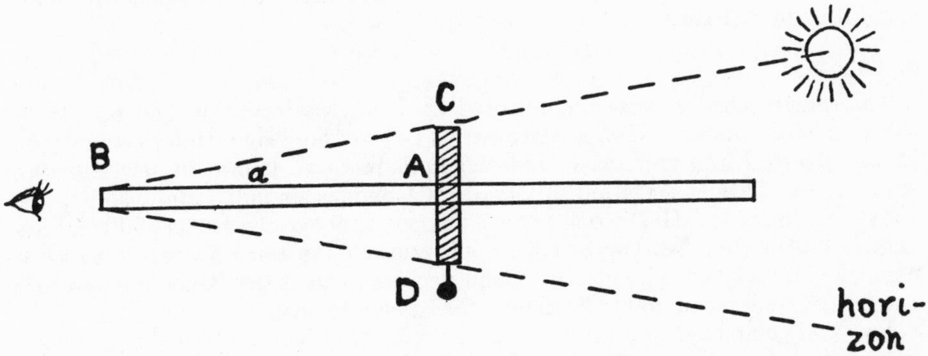

To be sure, the principle of the instrument may have occurred to others before Levi, though earlier ascriptions seem to be due to misunderstandings. For example, see my notes on al-Muẓaffar al-Ṭūsī (XIII-1) and on Jacob ben Maḥir ibn Tibbon (XIII-2) in Introd. 2, 623, 851. In any case, Levi completed and "clinched" the invention, explained its manifold applications, and embodied it in astronomical practice. The ascription to any predecessor is unproved; on the other hand, the ascription to Regiomontanus (1436–76) is certainly wrong, for we know that the latter was acquainted with Levi's work. Levi's invention was truly important, for the cross-staff continued to be used, especially by sailors, in various improved forms (notably the English quadrant or backstaff invented by captain John Davis c. 1540), until it was finally displaced by the reflecting type of instruments about the middle of the eighteenth century.[79]

Levi described his instrument and the means of using it in chs. 4–11 of his Sefer tekunah, and gave a more popular account of it in two Hebrew poems (ch. 9). The technical description was translated into Latin by Peter of Alexandria for Clement VI in 1342, Tractatus instrumenti astronomie magistri Leonis Judei de Balneolis. The fair copy, including very accurate geometrical drawings, which was preserved in the pontifical palace in Avignon, is now in the Bibliothèque nationale in Paris (Latin MS 7293). The Latin text is divided into 9 chapters. The multiplicity of Latin MSS proves that this text was widely used. In some of these MSS Levi's staff or baculus is called baculus Jacobi (Jacob's staff); this has suggested the ascription of the invention to some Jacob, as Jacob ben Maḥir, but it was in all probability simply an allusion to Genesis 32:10 (maqqel), for we find that allusion in Levi's Hebrew poem. In his treatise, on the contrary, Levi calls his instrument s mply keli (instrument); he never calls it staff (maqqel, moṭah). Peter of Alexandria called it secretorum revelator (megalleh 'amuqqot, Job 12:22). The word

[79] The principle of the modern sextant was indicated by Robert Hooke in 1666, and by Newton in 1700, but was not worked out until the following thirties: John Hadley 1731; Thomas Godfrey of Philadelphia c. 1730.

staff, however, was the most commonly accepted: baculus Jacobi, b. geometricus, b. astronomicus, balestilha, . . . cross-staff, etc.

Levi realized the importance of observing eclipses with the utmost precision, and he had the idea of using a camera obscura for such observations together with his cross-staff (e.g., lunar eclipse of 1321). The name "revelator secretorum" applies really to the combination of the two instruments (see prologue to Peter's translation in BM 1898, p. 99).

8. *Physics*

The camera obscura was not invented by Levi; the invention had been made three centuries earlier by Ibn al-Haitham (XI-1). There is no Hebrew translation of the latter's Kitāb al-manāẓir, but the work was well known in Jewish circles, either in the Latin translation of Gerard of Cremona or indirectly. Joseph ben Judah ibn 'Aqnīn (XII-2) went so far as to put it above the books of Euclid and "king" Ptolemy![80] Neither was the application of the camera obscura to astronomical purposes Levi's invention. John Peckham and Roger Bacon referred to it, and in 1285 William of Saint Cloud used the camera to observe the sun.

But Levi completed that invention in the sense that he rationalized it and popularized it. He corrected the confusing explanations of Witelo and Roger Bacon, made a distinction between the clear images obtained with a pinprick aperture and the blurred images obtained with a larger one. He tried to account for the dimensions of the images.

He used the camera and staff to determine more exactly the variations in the apparent diameters of sun and moon, these determinations being important elements in the comparison of conflicting planetary theories. He realized the prodigious distances of the stars from the earth: the stars may be considered as points, their rays as parallel, and the size of their images in the camera depends only on the size of the aperture. He explained carefully how to observe the progress of lunar and solar eclipses.

Levi tried to understand the heating effect of sunrays. He naturally failed, even as did Bacon when he tried to account for similar "actions at a distance" (Introd. 2, 957), but it was very creditable to raise the problem. Like Bacon, he was led to consider the transmission of physical influences (such as light and heat) and of astrological influences as different phases of the same problem. If heat can be transmitted from the sun, why not other influences?

9. *Medicine*

It is possible that Levi practiced medicine, as did most of the Jewish learned men of his time, but no medical writings of his are extant, except a prescription relative to gout (Neubauer-Renan p. 608, 1893).

10. *Astrology and superstition*

We have already indicated (§8) one of Levi's reasons for accepting the reality of astrological influences. He remarked, however, that those influences were difficult to understand because they were very numerous (think of the number of planets and stars) and could not be isolated. His point of view was somewhat comparable to that of the modern meteorologist, who claims a theoretical knowledge of the

[80] A statement repeated by Levi ben Abraham ben Ḥayyim (XIII-2). Steinschneider (p. 558, 1893).

weather, but disclaims a practical one because of the infinite complexity of the factors which have to be considered all at once. He conceived the possibility, however, of man's sometimes circumventing astral forces, this possibility increasing with his own spiritual power. He thus countenanced under certain circumstances divination and even witchcraft. This mixture of rationalism and mysticism was universal in his time; the proportions varied from man to man, but no one was entirely rational (is anybody entirely rational today?). What we would call Levi's superstitious tendencies were partly due to the tradition of Abraham ben Ezra (XII-1), with which he was sufficiently familiar.

Levi wrote an astrological notice on the seven constellations.

11. *Commentaries on Ibn Rushd*

Levi's most important activity was perhaps his composition of a series of commentaries on Ibn Rushd's commentaries. Thus was a purer Aristotelian tradition handed down to the Hebrew reading world. These commentaries were based exclusively on Hebrew versions of Ibn Rushd's short and middle commentaries (jāmi', talkhīṣ). Levi devoted at least five years to them, 1319–24. I shall cite them as far as possible in chronological order:

1. Sefer ha-heqqesh ha-yashar (On the right syllogism). Discussing some inaccurate reasonings in the Posterior analytics. Composed in 1319. Divided into two parts (ma'amarim), of 10 and 14 chapters. It was translated into Latin: Liber syllogismi recti . . . in quo adversatur pluribus eorum que in Prioribus Aristotelis traduntur.
2. Summary of Physics, June 1321.
3. Middle commentary on Physics, July 1321. Based on the translation by Qalonymos ben Qalonymos.
4. Summary of De generatione et corruptione, September 1321.
5. Summary of De coelo, September 1321.
6. Explanation of Meteorologica, December 1321. The Aristotelian text had been translated into Hebrew, by Samuel ibn Tibbon (XIII-1) in 1213.
7. Middle commentaries on the Organon. Levi's commentaries on the Categories and De interpretatione, and on Porphyry's Isagoge, were translated into Latin by Jacob Mantino. His commentaries on the Prior analytics, Posterior analytics, Topica, and Sophistici were completed between February and August 1323.
8. Summary of Zoology, books XI–XIX, De partibus animalium, De generatione animalium, January 1323. Latin translation by Jacob Mantino.
9. Summary of De anima, November 1323. The Aristotelian text had been translated into Hebrew in Rome c. 1284 by Zeraḥiah ben Isaac for Shabbethai ben Solomon.
10. Summary of De sensu et sensibili, February 1324. Based on Moses ibn Tibbon's translation.
11. Three epistles on the conjunction of the separate intellect with man. These epistles had been translated into Hebrew by Samuel ibn Tibbon. According to Levi, two were written by Ibn Rushd, the third by the latter's son ('Abdallāh ibn Muḥammad?). Levi's commentary is undated but posterior to his commentary on De anima.
12. Middle commentary on Metaphysics (lost).
13. Commentary on De plantis (lost).

Levi often complained of the defects and obscurities of the Hebrew MSS of Ibn Rushd's commentaries available to him. His glosses became almost inseparable from Ibn Rushd's text.

12. *Biblical and Talmudic commentaries*

Levi wrote a commentary, Sha'are ẓedeq (Doors of justice), on the thirteen logical rules for the interpretation of the Torah. These hermeneutical rules are ascribed to rabbi Ishmael, a tanna of the third generation (first half of second cent.).[81] In this commentary Levi quotes one R. Nissim, probably Nissim ben Jacob ibn Shahin, gaon of Qairawān,[82] author of the Kitāb miftāḥ maghālīq al-Talmud (Sefer mafteaḥ man'ule ha-Talmud, Key to the locks of the Talmud).

Levi wrote a commentary on Job, completed at the very end of 1325. The first four chapters were translated into Latin by the apostate Louis Henri d'Aquin (d. 1696). He wrote a series of other Biblical commentaries: on Song of songs (1325 or 1326), Ecclesiastes (1328), Ruth (1329), Esther (1329?), Genesis (1329), Exodus (1330), Leviticus (n.d.), Numbers (1337), Deuteronomy (Orange 1338), Prophetae priores (1338), Proverbs (1338), Daniel (1338), Ezra, Nehemiah, and Chronicles (1338).

His commentaries on the Torah were based on Abraham ben Ezra, Maimonides, and his own Milḥamot Adonai; he used the two Talmuds, the Tosefta, the Sifra, the Sifre, and the Mekilta. He condemned allegorical interpretations.

13. *Philosophical views*

Though he knew Aristotle's thought only through Hebrew translations of Ibn Rushd's commentaries, Levi had a deeper knowledge of it and was a more thoroughgoing Aristotelian than Maimonides. He was also more rationalistic and more daring than his great predecessor, yet his fundamental purpose was the same: to reconcile Peripateticism with Jewish orthodoxy. This statement must be qualified in two ways. First, the basis of his metaphysics was still largely Platonic; he did not hesitate to defend realism (as against nominalism) for the sake of maintaining the principle of immortality. Thus he was at once the greatest Jewish Averroist and the only realist among Jewish (and Muslim) philosophers. In the second place, under the pressure of philosophic and scientific ideas his orthodoxy was sometimes open to doubt: it was not very difficult for his enemies to denounce him as a heretic. In the introduction to his Milḥamot he goes so far as to say, "The Law cannot prevent us from considering to be true that which our reason urges us to believe" (JE 8, 29). In his commentaries he carefully reviews the opinions of his Greek and Arabic predecessors, then states his conclusions with remarkable freedom.

The universe is finite; outside of it there is neither a vacuum nor a plenum—absolutely nothing; it had a beginning but may have no end. Yet Levi rejected the idea of creatio ex nihilo: the cosmos began at a definite time; it did not proceed from another cosmos, but from an undetermined and formless chaos. Thus did he compromise between the Jewish idea of creation and the Greek idea of the eternity of matter.

He conceived individual immortality as somehow proportional to each soul's

[81] Not dealt with in Introd. vol. 1, but see D. J. Bornstein (EJ 8, 592–96, 1931).

[82] Unfortunately omitted from Introd. vol. 1. He flourished in Qairawān in the first half of the eleventh cent. His Miftāḥ maghālīq was composed c. 1039 in a strange mixture of Arabic and Hebrew. Steinschneider (p. 103–4, 1902). Max Schloessinger (JE 9, 315–17, 1905).

degree of perfection. It is clear that his anxiety to find acceptable compromises between theology and philosophy could not but irritate the fundamentalists of Israel.

His philosophical views are found in his Averroistic commentaries and in his Milḥamot, but also in his Biblical books: philosophy and exegesis were necessarily mixed in his writings, because they were not separated in his mind.

14. *Chronological summary*

1288. Levi's birth at Bagnols.
1316. Beginning of Milḥamot Adonai.
1319. Sefer ha-heqqesh ha-yashar.
1320. Luḥot (astronomical tables).
1321. Sefer ma'aseh ḥosheb.
1321. Commentaries on Ibn Rushd: Physics, De generatione, De coelo, Meteorologica.
1323. Comm. on Organon, Zoology (books XI–XIX), De anima.
1324. Comm. on De sensu et sensibili.
1325–26. Comm. on Job, Song of songs.
1328. Comm. on Ecclesiastes.
1328. Sefer tekunah (astronomical part of the Milḥamot).
1329. Milḥamot completed. Commentary on Ruth, Genesis.
1330. Comm. on Exodus.
1337. Comm. on Numbers.
1338. Comm. on Deuteronomy, Prophetae priores, Proverbs, Daniel, Ezra, Nehemiah, Chronicles.
1340. Revision of astronomy.
1342. De sinibus, chordis, et arcubus. Tractatus instrumenti astronomie. (1342 is the date of the Latin translation.)
1343. De numeris harmonicis.
1344, April 20. Death.
What happened to Levi during the years 1331–36?

15. *Influence*

On account of his boldness and of the suspicion of heresy fastened to him, Levi's influence was much smaller than it would have been otherwise; it was certainly less open. The Milḥamot Adonai was a forbidden book. Shem-ṭob ben Shem-ṭob (fl. 1390–1440) suggested that it should be called Milḥamot 'im Adonai (The battles with God)! Isaac ben Sheshet Perfet (1326–1408) spoke of Levi as a great Talmudist whom philosophy had led astray from the right path. Don Isaac Abravanel (1437–1508) and Judah Messer Leo of Mantua (rabbi in Mantua until his expulsion in 1475; JE 8, 505) treated him even more severely. The first editor of the Milḥamot, the physician Jacob ben David Marqaria, added a cautious preface lest he be himself accused of heresy (1560). However, Isaac ben Judah Lattes and Simeon ben Ẓemaḥ Duran (1361–1444) praised Levi; there is evidence that Ḥasdai Crescas (XIV-2) used extensively his commentary on Physics, and even Spinoza was influenced by him. The more favorable reception of his astronomy has already been indicated in §6.

16. *Text*

First edition of the Milḥamot ha-shem with preface by Jacob ben David Marqaria (Riva di Trento 1560). Second edition, Leipzig 1868. Neither of these editions contains the astronomical treatise. Benzion Kellermann: Die Kämpfe Gottes. Übersetzung und Erklärung des handschriftlich revidierten Textes (Schriften der Lehranstalt für die Wissenschaft des Judentums, 2 parts, Berlin 1914–16); incomplete translation with notes. Third Hebrew edition, Berlin 1923.

Gerson Lange: Die Praxis des Rechners (239 p., Francfort a.M. 1909). First edition of the arithmetical treatise of 1321, with German translation.

Joseph Carlebach: De numeris harmonicis. First edition of that treatise in his book on Levi (p. 125–44, Berlin 1910).

The parts of the Sefer tekunah translated into Latin by Peter of Alexandria have been partly published. Prince B. Boncompagni edited the beginning of the Latin text in the Atti dell' Accad. dei Nuovi Lincei (1863, 741 ff.). Other parts edited by Maximilian Curtze: Die Abhandlungen des Levi ben Gerson über Trigonometrie und den Jacobstab (BM 1898, 97–112); Urkunden zur Geschichte der Trigonometrie im christlichen Mittelalter (BM 1, 372–80, 1900). The titles of the 136 chapters of Levi's astronomy are given by Neubauer and Renan in Hebrew and Latin (p. 624–41, 1893).

Commentaries on Ibn Rushd. The commentaries on Isagoge, Categories, De interpretatione, translated into Latin by Jacob Mantino are included in the early Venetian editions of the works of Aristotle (vol. 1, 1552, etc.). See also in the same volume, part 2, quaesitum IV of the Quaesita in libros logicae (fol. 81 ff.), and the commentary on De plantis.

The Sha'are ẓedeq, Levi's commentary on the thirteen middot of R. Ishmael, is included in Jacob ben Abraham Faitusi: Sefer brit Jacob (Livorno 1800). Second edition, Jerusalem 1884.

Ferush Job. First edition by Abraham Pesaro (Ferrara? 1477). Again 1486, 1525, etc. Chapters 1–4 with Latin translation by Ludovicus Henricus Aquinas (Paris 1623).

Ferush ḥamesh megillot, with preface by Jacob Marqaria (Riva di Trento 1560). Königsberg 1860; in the rabbinical Bible of 1724–27. The "five rolls" are the Song of songs, Ruth, Lamentations, Ecclesiastes, and Esther, but there is no commentary by Levi on Lamentations.

Ferush 'al ha-torah. First edition (410 fol. in 2 vols.), Mantua before 1480, c. 1476 (see title page in JE 8, 27). Other editions in Venice 1547 and the rabbinical Bible mentioned above.

Ferush 'al nebi'im roshonim. In the Bible of Leiria 1494, etc.

Practical rules extracted from the two last-named commentaries, on the Pentateuch and Prophetae priores, edited by Joseph Oṭṭolenghi and Jacob Marqaria (Riva di Trento 1560).

Ferush mishle. In the Bible of Leiria 1494, etc. Latin translation by Antonius Giggeius (Milan 1620).

Ferush Daniel. First edition in Italy before 1480. Practical rules published separately by Jehiel ben Solomon (Warsaw 1865).

Commentary on Ezra, Nehemiah, and Chronicles, edited by Mordecai (or Marco) Mortara in the Bet oẓar ha-sifrut (vol. 2, Cracow 1888) of Shealtiel Eisig Gräber.

Liqquṭim mi kitbe RLbG, extracts from Levi's writings collected and edited by Joseph Carlebach in the Jubiläumschrift dedicated to his father, rabbi Salomo Carlebach (32 p. in Hebrew only, Berlin 1911).

17. *General criticism*

Moritz Steinschneider: four general studies, dated 1889, 1869, 1893, 1903, are reprinted in his Gesammelte Schriften (1, 233–70, Berlin 1925). Neubauer-Renan (p. 586–644, 1893). Max Seligsohn and Isaac Broydé (JE 8, 26–32, 1904). Richard Gottheil (ERE 7, 898–900, 1915). Nima H. Adlerblum (daughter of R. Chajim Hirschensohn): A study of Gersonides in his proper perspective (150 p., Columbia University 1926). Isaac Husik (EJ 7, 324–38, 1931).

18. *Philosophical criticism*

Munk (p. 497–501, 521, 1859). Manuel Joel: Lewi ben Gerson als Religionsphilosoph (Breslau 1862). Isidore Weil: Philosophie religieuse de Levi ben Gerson (274 p., Paris 1868). Husik (p. 328–61, 1916). Julius Guttmann: Levi's Theorie des Begriffs (Festschrift zum 75-jährigen Bestehen des Jüd. theol. Seminars **2**, 131 f., Breslau 1929). Harry Austryn Wolfson: Crescas' critique of Aristotle (Cambridge, Mass. 1929; Isis 14, 240–44).

19. *Scientific criticism*

M. Steinschneider: Baculus Jacobi (BM 1889, p. 36; 1890, p. 107); Die Mathematik bei den Juden (BM 1897, p. 103–7). Siegmund Günther: Die erste Anwendung des Jakobsstabes zur geographischen Ortsbestimmung (BM 1890, p. 73–80); Der Jakobsstab als Hilfsmittel geographischer Ortsbestimmung (Geographische Zeitschrift, Leipzig 1898). Braunmühl (vol. 1, 1900). Maximilian Curtze: Anonyme Abhandlung De tribus notis (BM 1, 380–90, 1900, dealing with the treatise referred to in §5); Die Dunkelkammer. Eine Untersuchung über die Vorgeschichte derselben (Himmel und Erde, Berlin 1901). See also Curtze's memoirs mentioned in §16. Joseph Carlebach: Lewi als Mathematiker (238 p., 2 pl., Berlin 1910). G. Eneström (BM 14, 261, 1914); short note on combinatorial analysis. Duhem: Système (4, 39–41, 1916, astronomy; **5**, 201–29, 1917, astronomy, immortality of the soul, creation, the Great Year and the Peripatetic theory of time, end of the world). R. T. Gunther (1, 351 f., 1923); Levi's cross-staff and similar instruments preceding the sextant. Alexander Marx: The scientific work of some outstanding mediaeval Jewish philosophers (Essays in memory of Linda R. Miller p. 154–60, New York 1938).

MOSES BEN JOSHUA OF NARBONNE

Moses ben Jacob ben Mar David ha-Darshan, Moses Narboni, Maestro Vidal Bellsom Narboni (Belhomme, Blasom). Judeo-Languedocian or Catalan philosopher and physician. He belonged to a family of Narbonne (i.e., Languedocians), but the family moved to Perpignan, in Roussillon, which was probably his birthplace. He was born at the end of the thirteenth century or the beginning of the fourteenth. He spent much of his life in Castile (e.g., in Soria and Toledo), also in Valencia and Cervera (Catalonia). He died in 1362 or very soon after, being then fairly old.

He learned Arabic in Spain and was also well acquainted with Latin and Catalan. He began early the study of philosophy especially in the writings of Maimonides, Ibn Rushd, and Levi ben Gerson. His main teacher was Abraham ben David Caslari, who taught him medicine.

His writings are abundant, most of them being in the form of commentaries. We shall deal first with two original works, then with the commentaries in chronological order of the authors commented upon. We shall thus end with his commentaries on Ibn Rushd, which are his most important compositions, and constitute his main title to fame. Indeed, Moses ben Joshua must be thought of primarily as one of the greatest Averroists of his time, second only to Levi ben Gerson.

Original works. 1. Oraḥ ḥayyim (Road of life). Medical treatise; the only one composed by him, all other writings being philosophical. It was written about 1350, and is represented by many MSS; there are apparently two somewhat different versions. Technical terms are given in Arabic and Latin as well as in Hebrew. It is a collection of remedies for various diseases, and is arranged somewhat after the method of the Kitāb al-taṣrīf of Abū-l-Qāsim al-Zahrāwī (X-2). That author, however, is not quoted, though Moses mentions many others, such as Dioscorides, Galen, 'Alī ibn Rabbān al-Ṭabarī (IX-1), Ibn Zuhr al-Samarqandī (?), Abraham ben David Caslari, Bernard of Gordon, etc. Like many of the contemporary physicians, Moses explained the Black Death by astrological arguments, referring it to the conjunction of Saturn and Jupiter in 1345. The plague increases for 55 days, then decreases during the same interval. The purer the air of a place, the more terrible is the pestilential destruction.

2. Ma'amar bi-beḥirah. Treatise on free will, written at Soria 1361. This was a refutation of the Iggeret ha-gezerah written after c. 1320 by Abner of Burgos to justify his apostasy. For a third original treatise see no. 15.

Commentaries. 3. On the Lamentations of Jeremiah (Liber threnorum, eikah). Written in 1343 or 1344. References to Maimonides, Moses ben Naḥman, etc.

4. Iggeret 'al shi'ur qomah. On the treatise Shi'ur qomah (Measurement of the size [of God]), ascribed to the high priest Ishmael ben Elisha, who flourished in Jerusalem during the last years of the second temple, i.e., in the third quarter of the first century. It includes remarks on the tetragram and the Song of songs. Written in 1343.

5. Ibn Sīnā (XI-1). Commentary on the fourth part of his Qānūn, including remarks by Jedaiah ben Abraham Bedersi. Undated.

6. Al-Ghazzālī (XI-2). Commentary on his Maqāṣid al-falāsifa. That book had been Hebraicized by Isaac Albalag (XIII-2) in 1292 or later, by Judah ben Solomon Nathan (XIV-2) before 1340, and a third time by an unknown translator. It would seem that Moses used the third of these translations; at any rate, his commentary is generally found in MSS together with it (the MSS are very numerous). Composed c. 1342, this commentary was one of his first writings.

7. Ibn Ṭufail (XII-2). Ḥaiy ibn Yaqẓān translated into Hebrew by an unknown scholar under the title Jehiel ben 'Uriel. Moses completed his commentary in Cervera 1349. He included it in an analysis of the Kitāb tadbīr al-mutawaḥḥid (De regimine solitarii) of Ibn Bājja (XII-1), which was one of Ibn Ṭufail's main sources. This analysis is particularly important because we know Ibn Bājja's work only through it.

8, 9. Maimonides (XII-2):

8. Perush mi-millot ha-higgayon. Explanation of the logical terms used by Maimonides. References to many Arabic philosophers: Ibn Sīnā, al-Ghazzālī, Ibn Bājja, Ibn Rushd.

9. Maimonides. Commentary on the Moreh nebukim. Begun in Toledo, completed seven years later in Soria 1362.

10–16. Ibn Rushd (XII-2):

10. Commentary on Ibn Rushd's commentary on the treatise of Alexander of Aphrodisias (III-1) on The intellect, Ma'amar Aleksandr be-sekel.

11. Ibn Rushd. On the talkhīṣ on the Physics.

12. Ibn Rushd. On the jāmi' on the Organon, to the Topics inclusive. Moses did not use Levi ben Gerson's commentary.

13. Ibn Rushd. On the jāmi' on Aristotle's De sensu et sensibili. Moses' authorship doubtful.

14. Ibn Rushd. Commentary on the treatise on the possibility of the conjunction and the hylic intellect, Ma'amar be-afsharut ha-daboqot, or Ma'amar be-sekel ha-hiyulani. Moses completed this commentary in Perpignan 1344.

15. Ibn Rushd. Commentary on the talkhīṣ on De anima, followed by a treatise,

Shelemut ha-nefesh (Perfection of the soul), which Moses composed for his son between 1344 and 1349, with the purpose of replacing the treatises of Aristotle and Ibn Rushd on the subject. This might be classified as an original treatise, rather than a commentary; the line is sometimes difficult to draw.

16. Ibn Rushd. Commentary on his physical treatises and on the De substantia orbis, entitled in Hebrew Ha-derushim ha-ṭib'iyim and Ma'amar be'aẓem ha-galgal. Completed in 1349.

A few other writings of little importance are ascribed to him.

Text. Ma'amar be-beḥirah. Included in the collection Dibre ḥakamim, edited by Eliezer Ashkenazi II (Metz 1849).

Bi'ur le moreh nebukim. Edited by Jacob Goldenthal (Vienna 1852).

Criticism. Munk (p. 502–6, 1859). Neubauer-Renan (p. 666–81, 1893). Steinschneider (1893). H. Gross (1897). Isaac Broydé (JE 9, 71, 1905). Alexander Marx: Scientific work of some outstanding mediaeval Jewish scholars (Essays in memory of Linda R. Miller p. 161–65, New York 1938).

JUDAH BEN ISAAC COHEN

Judah ben Isaac ben Moses ben Judah ben R. Samuel Cohen. Judeo-Provençal philosopher who was a pupil of Samuel ben Judah Barbaveri of Marseille and was writing his own work after the latter's death. Hence we must place him about the middle of the fourteenth century; his dates of birth and death are unknown; he visited Bologna in his youth and saw there the great master Niccolò da Pavia (?).

He wrote a commentary on Ibn Rushd's talkhīṣ on the Organon; the parts dealing with the Isagoge (mabo') and the Categories (ma'amarot) are extant. He wrote that commentary for his friend and relative Shelemyah of Lunel (?). It is elaborate and bold. Judah used not only the Hebrew version of Ibn Rushd's talkhīṣ by Jacob Anaṭoli (XIII-1), but also the Arabic text. He did not hesitate to criticize Ibn Rushd, and to defend Levi ben Gerson against his own master Samuel Barbaveri.

Criticism. Steinschneider (p. 73, 1893). Neubauer-Renan (p. 653–55, 1893). I. Broydé (JE 4, 150, 1903), 14 lines. B. Suler (EJ 10, 172, 1934).

ABBA MARI BEN MOSES

Judeo-Languedocian theologian (fl. c. 1303–10).

Abba Mari ben Moses ben Joseph ha-Yarḥi (i.e., of Lunel, yeraḥ meaning moon). Also called Don Astruc of Lunel (En Astruc, Nastrug). The name En Duran seems to be due to a confusion with Abba Mari's main associate, Simon ben Joseph of Lunel.

Dates of birth and death unknown. He was a descendant of Moses ben Joseph of Narbonne and Meshullam ben Jacob of Lunel, both of whom were teachers of Abraham ben David of Posquières; he was also connected with Qalonymos ben Ṭodros ha-Nasi of Narbonne. He was born presumably at Lunel (near Montpellier), where his grandfather and father had been rabbis before him. In 1303 he was in Montpellier; when the Jews were expelled from France by Philip the Fair on July 22, 1306, he moved to Arles, then to Perpignan. He was still living in 1310.

Abba Mari was one of the leaders of conservative Judaism in southern France and Catalonia against the followers of Maimonides. That struggle against Aristotelianism and relative liberalism had begun in Montpellier c. 1231–35; by 1290 it had spread to the East, but it was renewed in southern France and Catalonia at the beginning of the fourteenth century with unprecedented passion and asperity. The main leader of the Maimonideans was Jacob ben Maḥir ibn Tibbon (XIII-2; d. c. 1304). Abba Mari wrote many letters to Solomon ben Adret of Barcelona and stirred up other rabbis until he obtained the sentence of excommunication formulated by Solomon ben Adret at a synod held at the synagogue of Barcelona in 1305 (Introd. 2, 884).

The quarrel was temporarily stopped by the expulsion of the Jews from France in 1306. While in exile Abba Mari edited a collection of 104 letters relative to the controversy, together with a preface and introduction in 18 chapters. This work is entitled Sefer minḥat qenaot (Offering of zeal). The author's purpose (according to his preface) was to induce the young people to abstain from reading dangerous books. In the introductory treatise Abba Mari explains his own faith. One must believe implicitly in the Torah without trying to find reasons for one's belief in this or that commandment. The three fundamental principles of faith are the knowledge of God, the creation of the world, and providence. God is eternal, unique, incorporeal, omniscient; he has created the world out of nothing. When one's faith is solidly anchored on these principles, it will not occur to him to doubt the Torah or to search for new interpretations of miracles and precepts, as some of the contemporary scholars are trying to do.

Such a controversy would easily have led to a schism, but for the fact that there is no ecclesiastical hierarchy in Israel. The controversy began and ended with the documents edited by Abba Mari (and others of the same kind) and local excommunications like the one of Barcelona 1305. In reality the development of Jewish Maimonidism or liberalism was remarkably strong in the fourteenth century.

Text. The Minḥat qenaot was edited, with a letter of Shem-ṭob Palquera (d. after 1290), by Mordecai Loeb Bisliches in Pressburg 1838. There are many MSS, which differ in various particulars from the printed text. A critical edition with English translation, notes, and index would be a useful contribution to the study of the intellectual life of that time.

Criticism. Neubauer-Renan (p. 647–95, 1877). Includes an elaborate analysis of the Minḥat, letter by letter. Michael Friedländer and Kaufmann Kohler (JE 1, 33–34, 1901). J. Freimann (EJ 3, 608–10, 1929).

C2. Jews of Spain

VIDAL DE TOLOSA

Judeo-Spanish scholar who flourished probably in Catalonia in the first half of the fourteenth century, and wrote in Arabic and in Hebrew. I do not know whether his name refers to Toulouse in Languedoc (Tolosa in Latin) or to Tolosa in Guipúzcoa; the Spanish origin is more plausible than the French.

He wrote in Hebrew the Maggid mishneh, a commentary on the Mishneh Torah (or Yad) of Maimonides (XII-2). The commentary covered the whole work, but much of it is lost.

He wrote in Arabic a commentary (or marginal notes) on the Maqāṣid al-falāsifa of al-Ghazzālī (XI-2), which was translated into Hebrew under the title To'elet ha-higgayon (Usefulness of logic) by Moses ben Joshua of Narbonne. Now Moses wrote his own commentary on the Maqāṣid before the middle of the century, and he died c. 1362. Moreover, Vidal was a friend of Nissim ben Reuben Gerondi

(d. c. 1376); and his son Isaac ben Vidal, who lived in Alcala, was a correspondent of Isaac ben Sheshet (1326–1408). Putting all these facts together, it is necessary to place Vidal in the first half of the fourteenth century.

Text. The Maggid mishneh is printed in editions of the Yad beginning with the third (Constantinople 1509).
Criticism. Schulim Ochser (JE 12, 426, 1906).

MŪSĀ IBN ṬŪBĪ

Abū 'Imrān Mūsā ibn Ṭūbī (or Tobiah?) al-Ishbīlī al-Isrā'īlī. Jewish Arabic writer living in (or connected with) Seville probably in the first half of the fourteenth century. He wrote an Arabic poem entitled Al-sab'īniyya (because it consists of 70 verses) in praise of philosophical study. It includes a new classification of the "seven" sciences, to wit: religion, medicine, physics, metaphysics, logic, astronomy, geometry. This was translated into Hebrew and commented upon by Solomon ben Immanuel Dapiera (or da Piera)—who died probably not long before 1363—under the title Bate ha-nefesh (allusion to Isaiah 3:20; these words in the Authorized Version are strangely translated "tablets"; here bate ha-nefesh means houses or faculties of the soul; bate also means verses, as in Arabic). In the Hebrew text the classification of the seven sciences is somewhat different from that of the Arabic original: theoretical medicine, practical medicine, physics, metaphysics, logic, mathematics, astronomy.

Text. Hartwig Hirschfeld: Assab'īniyya, a philosophical poem in Arabic by Mūsā b. Ṭūbī. Together with the Hebrew version and commentary styled Batte hannefeš by Solomon Immanuel Dapiera. Edited and translated (Report of the Montefiore College, 62 p., London 1894).
Criticism. Steinschneider (p. 932, 1893); (p. 169, 1902), only 8 lines. H. A. Wolfson: Additional notes to the article on the classification of the sciences in mediaeval Jewish philosophy (Hebrew Union College annual 3, 371–75, 1926, see p. 373; Isis 10, 243).

ISAAC BEN JACOB HA-KOHEN

Spanish qabbalist. Born in the second half of the thirteenth century in Soria, Old Castile; flourished in Narbonne, Arles, Béziers, and c. 1307 at Capestang (near Béziers).[83] Under Neoplatonic and Gnostic influences he developed a theory of higher spheres, and a theory of sinister emanation.

One of his works deals with that theory of evil emanation, Ma'amar 'al ha'aẓalah ha-sema'ali, and is considered one of the most important among the early qabbalistic treatises. Another work of his, the Ma'amar al-middat ha-din weha-raḥamim, deserves to be mentioned because it was one of the qabbalistic treatises translated into Latin by Flavius Mithridates,[83a] by order of Sixtus IV (pope 1471–84).

Text. The two treatises mentioned and Flavius' Latin translation of the second have been edited by Gerhard Scholem: Madda'e ha-Yahadut (2, 165–293, Jerusalem 1927).
Criticism. Joseph Heller (EJ 8, 515–16, 1931).

[83] Hence the denomination Isaac ha-Kohen of Capestang.

[83a] "Flavius Mithridates" is the nom de plume of a Jewish scholar who c. 1486 taught Aramaic to Pico della Mirandola (JE 5, 407, 1903). He translated many Hebrew books into Latin. His Jewish name is unknown, but it has been suggested that he was perhaps identical with Pico's Hebrew and qabbala teacher, Johanan Allemanno (or Aleman, Alaman) ben Isaac (JE 1, 412, 1901).

SHEM-ṬOB BEN ABRAHAM IBN GAON

Spanish qabbalist and Talmudist. Born c. 1287 in Segovia, studied in Barcelona under Solomon ben Adret and the qabbalist Isaac ben Ṭodros, lived in Tudela and Soria, then for a time at Ṣafad in the Holy Land, returned to Spain, where he died after 1330.

He wrote:

1. Keter Shem-ṭob (Crown of the good name), commentary on Naḥmanides' commentary on the Torah. Composed c. 1315 and partly based on the oral tradition of Solomon ben Adret (XIII-2). Insistence on the deeper mystical meaning of some difficult passages.

2. Bade Aaron, or Migdal ḥananel. Qabbalistic interpretation of the story of creation.

3. Migdal 'oz, commentary on Maimonides' Mishneh Torah (Introd. 2, 374), completed only for the first 6 (out of 14) books. Shem-ṭob defended Maimonides against his adversaries, chiefly Abraham ben David of Posquières (XIII-2), but under the influence of his own qabbalistic ideas he tended to exaggerate Maimonides' qabbalistic leanings. He claimed to have found in Spain a qabbalistic treatise of Maimonides (?). While in Ṣafad he had occasion to use an autograph MS of the Mishneh Torah, and he had access to Maimonides' correspondence with the rabbis of Lunel. Shem-ṭob's writings are important for the study of the Maimonidean and Naḥmanidean traditions.

Text. Keter Shem-ṭob. First complete edition in Judah Qoriyyaṭ ii ben Abraham: Ma'or wa-shemesh (Livorno 1839).

Bade Aaron. Only the part dealing with the taggin (the decorative crowns of the Hebrew letters) and the Sefer ha-taggin (their mystical interpretation) has been edited, by J. J. L. Bargès: Sepher taghin, liber coronularum (Paris 1866).

Migdal 'oz. Often printed together with the Mishneh Torah, first time in Constantinople 1509.

Criticism. S. A. Horodezky (EJ 7, 100–1, 1931).

On the taggin, see J. D. Eisenstein (JE 11, 666–67, 1905).

ELḤANAN BEN ABRAHAM

Qabbalist who flourished probably in the first half of the fourteenth century in Spain. He wrote a treatise entitled Yesod 'olam (Foundation of the world), which includes extracts from a Hebrew translation of the pseudo-Empedoclean Kitāb al-dhawāt al-khamsa (The five substances). I have not been able to discover that Arabic text, but it is obviously the very one mentioned by Shem-ṭob ben Joseph ibn Falaquera (XIII-2) in the preface to his translation of Ibn Gabirol's Yanbū' al-ḥayāt (Meqor ḥayyim). A new stream of pseudo-Empedoclean, Neoplatonic, mystical ideas had originated in Andalusia with Muḥammad ibn 'Abdallāh ibn Masarra (883–931), and had become an essential part of the philosophy of Ibn Gabirol (XI-1), through which it deeply influenced Jewish and Christian thought. Elḥanan's unpublished Yesod 'olam is an interesting link in that pseudo-Empedoclean tradition.

Criticism. Munk (p. 3, 1859). Miguel Asín Palacios: Abenmasarra y su escuel (168 p., Madrid 1914; Isis 11, 168; Introd. 2, 596). M. Zobel (EJ 6, 389, 1930).

JOSEPH BEN ABRAHAM IBN WAQAR

Castilian Talmudist and qabbalist. Flourished in Toledo in the first half of the fourteenth century; he was already old in 1355 and died before c. 1370.

He wrote in Arabic or/and Hebrew:

1. A treatise on the sefirot[84] and the principles of the qabbala, wherein he discusses the emanation of the sefirot from God, and whether they are extrinsic to Him (as he believes) or intrinsic.
2. Ha-ma'amar ha-kolel (General treatise), the purpose of which is to reconcile qabbala and philosophy.
3. Shir ha-yiḥud, poem on the unity of the sefirot.
4. Sefer ha-yiḥud, treatise on the unity of God.

He was well acquainted with the main Talmudic and qabbalistic writings, but warned students against the many errors of the Zohar.

He may be the author also of a treatise on medicine, (5) Sefer ha-refuot.

He may have written some of these books originally in Arabic. This seems to be specially the case for nos. 2, 4, and 5.

One Joseph ibn Waqar made in 1293 or 1295 a new Hebrew translation of the first part of the Kitāb al-taṣrīf, the great medical treatise of Abū-l-Qāsim al-Zahrāwī (X-2). That treatise had been translated into Latin by Gerard of Cremona (XII-2) and into Hebrew by Shem-ṭob ben Isaac of Tortosa (XIII-2), Meshullam ben Jonah, and perhaps Nathan ha-Me'ati (XIII-2), hence Joseph's translation was somewhat superfluous and unimportant. This Joseph ibn Waqar may be identical with the qabbalist. There is nothing to prove the identity, but it is not chronologically impossible.

Text. The Shir ha-yiḥud is included in Jewish prayer books (1591, etc.).

The Sefer ha-yiḥud was translated from the Arabic and edited with notes by Menasseh Grossberg (Vienna n.d.). Not seen.

Criticism. Assemani: Bibliothecae vaticanae catalogus (1, 349, Rome 1756). Steinschneider (p. 746, 1893); (p. 168, 1902). Max Seligsohn (JE 6, 552, 1904).

THE SONS OF RABBI ASHER BEN JEHIEL

The note devoted to Asher ben Jehiel (the Hebrew form is Yeḥiel) or Rosh in volume 2 (p. 888) might have been placed in this volume, for he died at the end of 1327, in Toledo. The whole Spanish phase of his life, which is perhaps the most important, falls in the fourteenth century. Two of his children must be mentioned here, in order of seniority, Judah and Jacob.

Judah ben Asher

German rabbi and Talmudist. Born in Cologne, on July 28, 1270. He went to Toledo for commercial reasons (the date is uncertain, 1285, more probably 1305), and when his father was driven out of Germany, he prepared his reception in Toledo. He began to assist his father as rabbi and judge of the Toledo community in 1321 and succeeded him in 1327. He died in Toledo on July 4, 1349.

Some of his decisions were included in his brother's Ṭurim, and his responsa separately published. My reasons for including him are his relationship to his famous father and brother, and the ascription to him of an astronomical (?) work

[84] Introd. 2, 606, and passim.

entitled Ḥuqqat ha-shamayim (Laws of heaven). The same work is also ascribed to his grandson Judah ben Asher II, also a rabbi and Talmudist, who flourished in Burgos and Toledo and died a martyr in 1391.

Text. Zikron Judah, edited by Judah Rosenberg and David Cassel (Berlin 1846). Collection of responsa.

Israel Abrahams: Hebrew ethical wills (2, 163–200, Philadelphia 1926). Hebrew and English text of Judah's ẓawa'ah.

Criticism. Max Seligsohn (JE 7, 340, 1904). S. A. Horodezky (EJ 8, 936–37, 1931).

Jacob ben Asher

Also called Ba'al ha-ṭurim. German Talmudist. Younger brother of Judah ben Asher. Born in western Germany; went into exile with his father and the rest of his family and settled with them for a short time in Barcelona, then in Toledo, where his father was appointed chief rabbi (d. 1327). He died in or before 1340.

The main work of his life was a new codification of Jewish law and usage which superseded the Mishneh Torah of Maimonides. It is entitled Arba' ṭurim (Four rows, allusion to the four rows of precious stones in the high priest's breastplate, Exodus 28:17–20). The four rows are: (1) Oraḥ ḥayyim (Path of life), dealing with liturgical law, daily duties, sabbath, new moons, festivals, visits to the synagogue; (2) Yoreh de'a (Guide to knowledge), ritual law, things permitted and forbidden; (3) Eben 'ezer (Stone of help), marriage law; (4) Ḥoshen mishpaṭ (Breastplate of judgment), civil law, procedure.

It is based upon the Babylonian and Jerusalem Talmud, the responsa of the Gaonim, Rashi, Maimonides, Tosafists,[85] and other rabbis, including his father.

The Arba' ṭurim is of no scientific interest, but it was a book of such fundamental importance in Jewish life and of such influence upon Jewish thought for at least two and a half centuries that the historian of science must know of it, even if he need not know much of it. It owed its authority to its comprehensiveness and to its clearness of arrangement and expression, and remained the standard work of its kind for both Sephardim and Ashkenazim down to the publication of the Shulḥan 'aruk (Venice 1565).

Even as the Mishneh Torah, it was the subject of many commentaries. The two foremost commentators were the Sephardi Joseph ben Ephraim Qaro[86] (1488–1577), who based upon it his Bet Joseph and his Shulḥan 'aruk (The prepared table), built on the same plan as the Arba' ṭurim; and the Ashkenazi Moses ben Israel Isserles (c. 1520–72), who based upon it his Darke moshe and Ha-mappa (The table cloth), a collection of corrective notes to the Shulḥan 'aruk (first published in Rashi type in the Cracow edition of that work 1571).

Jacob wrote various other books which concern us even less than the Arba' ṭurim. He was not a rabbi, simply a Talmudic scholar and a saint. He was interested in rites and ceremonial minutiae, but not in omens, dreams, and other superstitions. In that respect he was more rationalistic than other members of his family and than the majority of his contemporaries, but his rationalism was that of a legalistic and ritualistic mind, not of a scientific one. He had no interest in science.

Text. The editio princeps of the Arba' ṭurim, in 4 volumes, was completed at Piove di Sacco, near Padova, on July 3, 1475. Only one other Hebrew book bears

[85] Introd. 2, 190.

[86] More usually transcribed Karo.

an earlier date, namely, the Rashi printed at Reggio five months earlier. But the first volumes of the Arba' ṭurim were in all probability printed before the Rashi and are thus the earliest Hebrew printed books. There is only one complete copy of the four parts, in the Turin library (a perfect vellum copy which remained for generations in the possession of the printer's family). The Jewish Theological Seminary of New York has parts I, II, IV; parts I and II exist only in the two libraries already named, but there are various copies of parts III, IV.

Not less than two complete editions and seven partial editions of the Arba' ṭurim appeared within twenty years. It was thus, next to the Old Testament itself, the most popular Hebrew incunabulum. The later folio editions generally include commentaries.

Another early edition of the Arba' ṭurim deserves mention, the one printed at Constantinople in 1493, this being the first book printed in the Balkans and the only incunabulum printed there.

Jacob's ẓawa'ah was partly edited by Israel Abrahams: Hebrew ethical wills (2, 202–5, Philadelphia 1926). The same work contains the ẓawa'ot of Jacob's father and brother.

Criticism. Heinrich Graetz: History of the Jews (vol. 4, 1894). Max Seligsohn (JE 7, 27–29, 1904). Alexander Marx (Register for 5690 of the Jewish Theological Seminary p. 149–50, New York 1929–30). S. A. Horodezky (EJ 8, 804–10, 1931). Report of the Librarian of Congress (p. 221, 1935).

C3. Italian Jews

IMMANUEL BEN SOLOMON

Immanuel ben Solomon ben Jekuthiel ha-Romi. In Italian, Manoello Giudeo. Judeo-Italian poet (d. after 1328).

Born at Rome c. 1270, of the Judeo-Roman family Zifroni; he was a member of the intellectual leading circles of Rome, until, after mysterious incidents, having lost his wealth, he left the city and wandered in Italy, being tutor in various families —in Perugia, Fabriano, Camerino, Ancona, Verona. In 1328, he found refuge in Fermo (Ascoli Piceno) in the March of Ancona; he died a few years later, probably in Fermo.

He had some knowledge of science and philosophy; wrote in Hebrew and Italian, and was acquainted with Arabic, Latin, and perhaps Greek.

He wrote a philosophical letter to Hillel ben Samuel of Verona and many Biblical commentaries, but is mentioned here chiefly because of his poetry in Hebrew and Italian. While in Fermo he made a dīwān of his Hebrew poems, fastening them together by means of rhyming prose, in imitation of the Maqāmāt of al-Ḥarīrī (XII-1) and the Taḥkemoni of al-Ḥarizi (XIII-1). This dīwān, entitled Maḥbarot, contains 28 poems, which are mainly good-natured satires on Jewish life. The author has been called "the Heine of the Middle Ages" or "the Jewish Voltaire," designations which are suggestive but misleading. The last poem (28) is a vision entitled Hell and paradise (Ha-tofet we ha-'eden), which was very obviously inspired by the Divina commedia, with reference not only to plan, but also to style and expression. Immanuel's poetic sources were Arabic-Spanish but also Italian; he was strongly influenced by the "dolce stil nuovo" and even adapted Hebrew poetry to Italian meters.

Immanuel and Dante may have met, either at the court of Can Grande della Scala in Verona, or in Gubbio; this cannot be proved, but he was certainly in touch with the Italian poets Cino da Pistoia (Guittone Sinibaldi) and Bosone Raffaelli da Gubbio.

With regard to the Ha-tofet we ha-'eden, it is interesting to recall the Maḥberet ha-ṭene of Aḥiṭub ben Isaac (XIII-2), describing a journey to Paradise; that was anterior to Dante. Immanuel's interpretation of the Divina commedia was the re-Orientalization of a theme the Oriental origins of which have been obnubilated by Dante's genius.

Text. The letter to Hillel ben Samuel was edited by M. Steinschneider in the Israelietische Letterbode (vol. 7, Amsterdam c. 1881).

First edition of the Maḥbarot by Gershon Soncino (Brescia 1491). Many later editions: Constantinople 1535, Lemberg 1870, and translations. Also separate editions of the Tofet we ha-'eden (Prague 1613, Francfort a.M. 1713, etc.) and translations of same in Yiddish (Prague c. 1660), in German by Max Emanuel Stern (Vienna 1865), in English by Hermann Gollancz (London 1921), etc.

The commentary on Proverbs was printed at Naples in 1487. Other Biblical commentaries were published much later (1806, etc.); others are still unpublished.

Criticism. Various articles by M. Steinschneider, dating from 1843 to 1873, are reprinted in his Gesammelte Schriften (1, 271–326, 1925). Hermann Vogelstein: Dante (JE 4, 435, 1903). Ismar Elbogen (JE 6, 563–64, 1904). Joseph Chotzner: Hebrew humour (p. 82–102, London 1905). Umberto Cassuto: Dante e Manoello (Firenze 1921); (EJ 8, 402–6, 1931). Harry S. Lewis: Immanuel of Rome (Proceedings of the American Academy of Jewish Research 5, 277–308, 1935).

C4. Eastern Jews

ISAAC BEN SAMUEL OF 'AKKĀ

Palestinian qabbalist who was driven out of 'Akkā in 1291 when it was destroyed by the sulṭān al-Malik al-Ashraf, who thus put an end to Christian power in the Holy Land. He went to Italy and to Spain, being in 1305 in Toledo. He died c. 1340.

When he arrived in Spain he began to investigate the authenticity of the Zohar, of which he had never heard in Palestine. He met in Valladolid Moses ben Shem-ṭob of Leon (XIII-2), who swore to him that a Zohar MS in his possession ascribed to Simeon ben Yoḥai was genuine (Introd. 2, 878–81). After Moses' death, in 1305, Isaac continued his investigations in Avila, Talavere, etc. and finally satisfied himself that the Zohar was what it claimed to be. He describes these investigations in his diary, Sefer ha-yamim. He flourished in Toledo, wrote qabbalistic commentaries on the Perush ha-Torah of Moses ben Naḥman (XIII-2) and on the Sefer yeẓirah (Introd. 2, 367), and composed other qabbalistic works, which are practically unknown. He seems to have been especially interested in "practical qabbalah" (gematria and the like, Introd. 2, 881), and to have been the first to develop the theory of the four worlds, outlined in the Zohar (Introd. 2, 879).

He exerted some influence upon later qabbalists, e.g., upon the two sixteenth-century Ṣafadians Ḥayyim ben Joseph Vital and Elijah ben Moses de Vidas.

A study of his life and works, together with the edition and translation of at least his diary, is very desirable.

Criticism. Josef Heller (EJ 8, 546–48, 1931).

'ABD AL-DĀ'YIM

'Abd al-Dā'yim ibn 'Abd al-'Azīz ibn Muḥassan al-Isrā'īlī. Jewish physician who flourished in the Near East (Egypt or Syria?) c. 1316. In August of that year he completed a dialogue in Arabic, entitled Kitāb al-'ilmain (The two sciences), dealing with physics and metaphysics. The MS of it (in the Bodleian) is written in Hebrew script (Syr. Rabb.). It covers some 150 quarto pages. An elaborate analysis of it, if not an edition, is very desirable.

Criticism. Adolf Neubauer: Catalogue of Hebrew MSS in the Bodleian (no. 814, 5, Oxford 1886). Kaufmann Kohler (JE 1, 43, 1901). M. Goldmann (EJ 1, 193, 1928).

AARON BEN ELIJAH THE QARAITE

Often called Aaron the Younger, to distinguish him from another Qaraite, Aaron ben Joseph (XIII-2), who is then called Aaron the Elder. Aaron the Younger is also named Aaron ha-Nicomedi, or ha-Constantini, after the two cities where he spent his life. He was born at Nicomedia (i.e., Ismid or Iznikmid, at the eastern end of the Sea of Marmora) c. 1300, and flourished probably in that city until c. 1350; he then moved to Constantinople, where he died in 1369.

He was the greatest and the last of the Qaraite philosophers, being sometimes nicknamed the Maimonides of Qaraism. About the middle of the fourteenth century Constantinople had become, partly through him, the center of Qaraite learning. For the beginnings of Qaraism see my note on Anan ben David (VIII-2); to the directions there given (Introd. 1, 525) concerning the study of Qaraism in general, add the article Karäer by various authors in EJ (9, 923–54, 1932).

Whereas Maimonides and his disciples had accomplished the harmonization of Jewish theology with Aristotelian philosophy, the Qaraites (and mainly Aaron ben Elijah) tried to harmonize the same theology with the earlier Arabic philosophy of the Mutakallimūn and especially with the teaching of the more liberal of those Muslim schoolmen, the Mu'tazila. The Qaraites of the fourteenth century are thus belated representatives of an earlier Arabic tradition, which Maimonides had already driven out of Jewish (and international) theology.

Aaron ben Elijah knew enough Arabic to read the Muslim sources, but his knowledge of Aristotelianism was mainly derived from Maimonides. He had a good knowledge of the rabbinical grammarians and theologians, e.g., of Judah ben Quraish (IX-1), Saadia Gaon (X-1), Ḥayyuj (X-2), Ibn Janāḥ (XI-1), Moses ben Samuel Giqaṭilia and Rashi (XI-2), Abraham ben Ezra (XII-1), David Qimḥi and Maimonides (XII-2), Samuel ben Tibbon (XIII-1), Judah ben Moses ha-Kohen and Naḥmanides (XIII-2), Shemariah ha-Iqriṭi. The two men who influenced him most, outside of his Qaraite masters, were Abraham ben Ezra and Maimonides. His works constitute a kind of Qaraite summa. His synthesis is historically interesting, but far less masterly and original than that of Maimonides, and its influence was negligible outside the Qaraite cul-de-sac.

Outside of piyyuṭim (hymns) and prayers, some of which are preserved in the Qaraite prayer books, he wrote three works:

1. 'Eẓ ḥayyim (The tree of life), completed in 1346. This is a treatise on theology and religious philosophy divided into 114 chapters, modeled upon the Moreh nebukim. It is in this book that the views of the Mu'tazila (e.g., views favoring the freedom of the will) are applied to Jewish beliefs, and opposed to the "philosophic" or Aristotelian theories represented by long verbatim extracts from the Moreh nebukim. The 'Eẓ ḥayyim includes an elaborate theory of prophecy; the prophets are sent by God to help men find the truth and act rightly.

The 'Eẓ ḥayyim was as important to the Qaraites as the Moreh nebukim to the

Rabbinists, and to that extent at least it is permissible to compare Aaron to Maimonides. Its influence within the Qaraite fold is proved by the writings of Caleb Afendopoulo or Efendipulo (Adrianople bef. 1430—Constantinople c. 1499),[86a] who compiled in 1497 an index to it entitled Derek 'eẓ ḥayyim, and by three commentaries, the Or ha-ḥayyim by Simḥa (Isaac) ben Moses Luẓqi (d. 1766), the 'Eẓ ha-da'at by Moses ben Samuel Qala'i, and the Derek selula by Simḥa ben Solomon (I have not been able to identify the two last-named commentators).

2. Gan 'eden (The garden of delight), a treatise on the commandments, hence called by the author Sefer ha-miẓwot. It was completed at Constantinople in 1351-52 and is divided into themes ('inyanim), orders (sedarim), and 194 chapters. It is the most comprehensive account of Qaraite law, and is thus somewhat the Qaraite equivalent of the Arba' ṭurim of Jacob ben Asher, composed but a little earlier; or, to continue the parallel with Maimonides, it is compared by Qaraites to the Yad ha-ḥazaqah. According to Aaron, the laws are derived from four sources: Bible, intelligence, tradition ('tqh), and consensus omnium (qibbuẓ), a view which reminds one of Muslim theology. For example, according to al-Shāfi'ī (IX-1) the four sources of law are: Qur'ān, qiyās (analogy, legal fiction), ḥadīth, and ijmā' (Introd. 1, 550). Like Aaron the Elder, Aaron the Younger defended the idea of temurah, i.e., the law of compensation for grief and pain, applying it even to animals.

Caleb Afendopoulo wrote a defense of Gan 'eden against Moses ben Jacob ha-Ashkenazi (Lithuania 1449, Crimea beginning of sixteenth cent.; JE 9, 70), and also an astronomical commentary, Miklal yofi (Perfection of beauty), on a part of it.

3. Keter Torah (The crown of the law), a commentary on the Pentateuch written in 1362. Aaron defends the literal interpretation against the "psychologists" (ba'ale ha-nefesh); yet he indulged occasionally in allegories. In this commentary he was influenced chiefly by Abraham ben Ezra.

Text. 1. 'Eẓ ḥayyim. First edition together with the Or ha-ḥayyim (Eupatoria, i.e. Kozlov in Crimea, 1835). M. Steinschneider: System der Religionsphilosophie nebst einem einleitenden Tractat des Karäers Kaleb Afendopolo zum ersten Male hrg. und durch Anmerkungen zum Theil von M. Steinschneider, so wie durch reichhaltige Excerpte aus arabischen Handschriften usw. erläutert von Franz Delitzsch (Leipzig 1841). Includes Afendopoulo's work, a glossary, and a comparison with the Moreh nebukim.

2. Gan 'eden. Extracts edited by Johann Gottfried Schupart (1677-1730): Secta Karaeorum dissertationibus aliquot historico-philologicis adumbrata (Jena 1701). Complete edition by Judah Savskan: Sefer miẓwot ha-gadol (Kozlov 1864-66).

3. Keter Torah. Extracts edited in Hebrew and Latin by J. G. L. Kosegarten: Liber coronae legis (Jena 1824). Complete edition by Judah Savskan (Kozlov 1866-67).

Criticism. Munk (p. 506, 1859). M. Steinschneider: Die Mathematik bei den Juden (BM 12, 34-36, 1898). Kaufmann Kohler (JE 1, 9-10, 1901). Husik (p. 362-87, 1916). S. Dörfler: Ahron ben Elia über die Manichäer (Muséon 38, 57-65, 1925); extract from the 'Eẓ ḥayyim. J. N. Simchoni (EJ 1, 37-42, 1928). Mann (vol. 2, 1935).

[86a] According to I. Markon (EJ 1, 922-27, 1928), Caleb ben Elijah Afendopoulo was born in Adrianople in 1454 and died after 1523. The dates given by me had been taken from JE (1, 222-23, 1901).

D. ISLAM

D1. Yaman

AL-MU'AIYAD BILLĀH

Al-Mu'aiyad billāh Yaḥyā ibn Ḥamza. Zaidī theologian who flourished in Yaman (1270–1348).

He is quoted here as a representative of many Zaidī theologians. He wrote many books, the main one being the Kitāb al-intiṣār, said to be the outstanding book of Zaidī law.

The Zaidīya is a group of the Shī'a, distinguished from the Ithnā 'asharīya (or twelvers) and from the Sab'īya (seveners), who recognized respectively twelve and seven a'imma (pl. of imām), in that they recognize Zaid ibn 'Alī[87] and revere him as a martyr. It is difficult to know exactly how many other a'imma they recognize.

Criticism. Brockelmann (2, 186, 1902; suppt. 2, 242, 1938). R. Strothmann: Al-Zaidīya (EI 4, 1196–98, 1933).

AL-YĀFI'Ī

Arabian ṣūfī (d. 1367).

'Abdallāh ibn As'ad al-Yāfi'ī al-Shāfi'ī was born at the end of the thirteenth century in Yāfi', Yaman. He studied theology and the Qur'ān in 'Aden, and made his first pilgrimage to Mecca in 1313. From 1318 on, his life was spent in Mecca and Madīna, but for journeys to Egypt and Syria, and to Yaman. He died in Mecca on February 21, 1367.

His mind was soon turned in the ṣūfī direction, and he sat at the feet of many mystic teachers, first and last another Yamanī, 'Alī al-Ṭawāshī (the eunuch?). Several gave him the khirqa (pl. khiraq; woolen coat which a master gave his favorite disciple, a kind of licentia docendi). He was strongly influenced by al-Ash'arī (X-1), "the founder of Muslim scholasticism," and by the Spanish mystic Ibn 'Arabī (XIII-1); on the other hand, he criticized the puritanism of his contemporary Ibn Taimīya.

Enumeration of his writings (some 20) and their editions will be found in Brockelmann and Krenkow. They deal with the history of Islām, biographies of ṣūfī saints, pious anecdotes, the consistency of Shāfi'ī doctrine with taṣawwuf, the refutation of Mu'tazila errors,[88] the licitness or illicitness of music, etc.

Criticism. Brockelmann (2, 176–77, 1902; suppt. 2, 227–28, 1938). Otto Spies: Beiträge zur arabischen Literaturgeschichte (p. 76–78, Leipzig 1932), apropos of the Mir'āt al-janān wa 'ibrat al-yaqẓān, a history of Islām to 1349, largely biographical, which al-Yāfi'ī derived from 'Umar ibn 'Alī ibn Samura al-Ja'dī (d. 1190), Ibn Khallikān (XIII-2), and al-Dhahabī. F. Krenkow (EI 4, 1144, 1933). H. G. Farmer (no. 225, p. 53, 1940).

[87] This Zaid was the son of 'Alī Zain al-'Ābidīn, who was the son of al-Ḥusain, who was the son of 'Alī and the prophet's daughter Fāṭima. In the course of a revolt against the Umayya caliph, Zaid was killed, c. 740. Some of his followers gained control of Yaman in the second half of the ninth century, where they established a Zaidī dynasty. The present ruler, the imām Yaḥyā, and the aristocracy belong to the Zaidī sect.

[88] Introd. 1, 557. H. S. Nyberg (EI 3, 787–93, 1934).

D2. Mamlūk Kingdom

AL-NUWAIRĪ

Shihāb al-dīn Abū-l-'Abbās Aḥmad ibn 'Abd al-Wahhāb al-Nuwairī al-Bakrī al-Kindī al-Shāfi'ī. Egyptian historiographer and encyclopaedist (1279–1332).

Al-Nuwairī was born on April 5, 1279, in Upper Egypt. His father (d. 1299/1300) was a government secretary. Al-Nuwairī continued the same profession, becoming a favorite of the Mamlūk sulṭān al-Nāṣir Muḥammad ibn Qalā'ūn (ruled 1293–94, 1298–1308, 1309–40). He was for a time intendant of the army in Tripolis, Syria; then intendant of the administration in the Egyptian provinces of al-Dakhālīya and al-Murtāḥīya. He died in Cairo on June 16, 1332.

He wrote a single work, but that one very large, to which he devoted at least twenty years of his life, continuing almost to his death. It is an encyclopaedia entitled Nihāyat al-arab fī funūn al-adab (Aim of the intelligent in the arts of letters), and is dedicated to al-Nāṣir. His aim was to collect together all the information needed by an educated administrator; he did not try to be original, but rather to compile data taken from many sources duly quoted by him. The Nihāyat is divided into 5 parts (funūn), dealing respectively with (1) heavens and earth (cosmology, geography), (2) man (including ethics and politics), (3) animals, (4) plants, (5) history. In order to give a better idea of the contents of this enormous work, I shall now give a more detailed analysis of it. For each fann or part, I provide a special title; each fann is divided into 5 sections (aqsām), and I use a Roman numeral for each section (qism); each qism is subdivided into chapters (abwāb), for each of which (bāb) I use an Arabic numeral if I find it necessary to enumerate them (their number varies from 2 to 14).

First part. Heavens and earth

I. Heavens. (1) Their creation, (2) their form, (3) angels, (4) planets, (5) stars.

II. Meteors. (1) Clouds, snow, coldness, (2) thunder and lightning, (3) the element air, (4) the element fire.

III. Divisions of time. (1) Days and nights, (2) months and years, (3) seasons, (4) feasts and holy days (mawāsim, a'yād).

IV. Earth. (1) Its creation, (2) names, (3) size, (4) seven climates, (5) mountains, (6) seas and islands, (7) rivers, lakes, and springs.

V. Regions of the earth. (1) Nature of each region and character of its inhabitants, (2) characteristics, (3) ancient buildings, (4) castles, (5) palaces and houses.

Second part. Man

I. Etymology of man's name; names of his members, etc.

II. Proverbs. Various superstitions and mancies of the Arabs.

III. Virtues and vices. This includes a digression on the use and abuse of wine and why Islām has forbidden it; also on song and music.

IV. Felicitations, dirges, condolences, austerity, vows, and prayers.

V. Politics. Duties of the spiritual guides, of the kings, governors, military commanders, judges, secretaries and chancellors, etc.

Third part. Animals

I. Wild beasts, like the lion, tiger, etc.

II. Other beasts, like the elephant, rhinoceros, etc.

III. Horses, cattle, mules, asses, camels.

IV. Venomous animals. (1) Those whose poison is lethal, (2) idem nonlethal.

V. Birds and fishes. This is divided into 8 chapters, the last of which deals with the methods of hunting and fishing.

Fourth part. Plants

I. (1) Origin of plants and soil they need, (2) plants proper to each region, (3) food plants, vegetables.

II. Trees. Distinguished with regard to their fruits, (1) skin or burr not eatable, (2) stone or seed not eatable, (3) fruits without skin or burr or stone.

III. Perfumed flowers. (1) Those whose perfume can be distilled, like the rose and water lily, (2) those whose perfume is generally not extracted, like the violet, narcissus, jasmin.

IV. (1) Gardens, (2) flowers, (3) gums, of which there are 18 kinds, (4) mannas (mann, amnān).

V. Aromatics and drugs. (1) Musk and its varieties, (2) ambergris, (3) aloe ('ūd), (4) sandal, (5) Indian ear (sinbal hindī) and clove (qaranful), (6) costus (qisṭ), aromatic used by Muslims for their ablutions, (7) composition of galia (ghāliya, pl. ghawālī) and nadd (pl. nadūd), cosmetics used for hairdressing, (8) composition of the preparation called rāmik (or rāmak) and sukk, (9) composition of naḍūḥāt and of distilled and nondistilled waters, (10) aphrodisiacs, (11) properties of drugs.

Fifth part. History

I–III. Old Testament history; the end of section III deals with New Testament history.

IV. Oriental and Muslim history. The fifth part is by far the largest, and this fourth section of it is as large as all the rest of the work.

Al-Nuwairī was known to European Orientalists as early as the seventeenth century; they were mainly interested in the historical part, but did not realize that the most valuable historical information concerned, as usual in such compilations, not the ancient past, but rather the author's contemporary period, down to 1331.

Part of the Nihāyat al-arab is preserved in holograph MSS. It is said that al-Nuwairī made at least four copies of the whole work; indeed, he was a professional calligrapher able to copy as many as eighty pages a day; he made eight copies of the enormous collection of traditions the Ṣaḥīḥ of al-Bukhārī (IX-1), and sold them at a thousand dirham apiece; he was also an expert bookbinder. One wonders how he could carry on all these activities abreast.

This was an age of great encyclopaedic activity in the Mamlūk kingdom (Egypt and Syria). In addition to the Nihāyat al-arab, we have the Mukhtaṣar ta'rīkh al-bashar and the Taqwīm al-buldān, both by Abū-l-Fidā' (d. 1331), the Masālik al-abṣār of Ibn Faḍlallāh al-'Umarī (d. 1349), and a little later the Ṣubḥ al-a'shā of al-Qalqashandī (XIV-2; d. 1418).

Text. Early partial editions restricted to the historical part are listed by Wüstenfeld and Kratschkowsky (see below). A more recent work relative to that part is the Arabic-Spanish edition by Gaspar Remiro: Historia de los Musulmanes de España y Africa (2 vols., Granada 1917–19; Isis 13, 434), restricted to Spanish and Maghribī history.

The following German translations and commentaries, all by Eilhard Wiedemann, are of special interest to historians of science: Zur Geschichte des Zuckers (Sitzungsberichte der Physikalisch-medizinischen Sozietät in Erlangen, Beitrag 41, vol. 47, 83–92, 1915); Über Parfüms (Archiv für Geschichte der Naturwissenschaften 6, 418–26, 1913); Über arabische Parfüms (Archiv für Geschichte der Medizin 8, 83–88, 1914); Über von den Arabern benutzte Drogen (Erlangen Sitzungsber., Beitrag 49, vol. 48, 16–60, 1918; Isis 4, 431); Über den Abschnitt über die Pflanzen (ibid., Beitrag 51, vol. 48, 151–76, 1918; Isis 4, 407).

A complete edition of the Nihāyat al-arab was prepared by Aḥmad Zakī pāshā (d. 1934), who collected photographs of all the scattered MSS, some of them holograph, and deposited them in the Royal Library in Cairo (Dār al-kutub al-miṣrīya). On the basis of these documents, the Dār al-kutub began the publication of a beautiful edition in 1923/24, when vols. 1 to 3 appeared. There will be in all some 24 vols., of which 14 have thus far been issued. See review of the first 3 vols. by F. Krenkow, enumerating their sources (Journal of the Royal Asiatic Society p. 769–72, 1925). Vol. 14 appeared in 1943.

Criticism. Johann Jacob Reiske: Animadversiones ad Abulfedam et prodidagmata ad historiam et geographiam orientalem, appended to Johann Bernhard Koehler: Abulfedae Tabula Syriae (p. 232–34, Leipzig 1766). J. T. Reinaud: Géographie d'Aboulféda (vol. 1, p. CLI, 1848). Ḥājjī Khalīfa (6, 397, no. 14069, 1852). Wüstenfeld (p. 166, no. 399, 1881). M. J. De Goeje and M. Th. Houtsma: Catalogus codicum arabicorum (2d ed., 1, 5–17, Leiden 1888), in Arabic. Brockelmann (2, 139, 1902; suppt. 2, 173, 1938). Ferrand (p. 50, 394–97, 614–25, 1914). Sarkis (col. 1884–85, 1930). Ignace Kratschkowsky (EI 3, 968–69, 1935).

'ALĪ AL-SUBKĪ

Egyptian Shāfi'ī theologian and man of letters (1284–1355).

Shaikh al-Islām Taqī al-dīn Abū-l-Ḥasan 'Alī ibn 'Abd al-Kāfī al-Subkī was born in April 1284 in Subk, in the Manūfīya district of Egypt. He studied in Cairo, Alexandria, Damascus, and made the Pilgrimage in 1310. In 1339 he was appointed chief qāḍī of Syria, in 1341 khaṭīb (preacher) in the great mosque of Damascus. He was also teaching in various schools. He held similar positions in Egypt. In 1355, he resigned his magistracy in favor of his son Tāj al-dīn Abd al-Wahhāb (XIV-2), and died in Cairo in June of the same year.

Some fifty writings are ascribed to him, dealing mainly with theological and religious questions, e.g., Al-saif al-maslūl 'alā man sabba al-rasūl (The drawn sword against him who spurns the Prophet), and the Bai' al-marhūn fī ghaibat al-madyūn (Sale of the mortgage in the absence of the debtor), which, according to Ḥājjī Khalīfa (2, 84), deals with the 'ilm al-baiṭāra (veterinary art).

The Subkī family was a distinguished family which gave many scholars, judges, professors to the Mamlūk kingdom of Egypt and Syria. The history of scholarship makes one realize the unity of that kingdom, for scholars are often moving from Egypt to Syria and vice versa, and if they teach in Damascus they are likely to teach also in Cairo. Three sons of Taqī al-dīn 'Alī distinguished themselves as judges, teachers, and writers, to wit, Bahā al-dīn Aḥmad (d. Mecca 1371–72), Jamāl al-dīn al-Ḥusain (d. 1354–55), Tāj al-dīn 'Abd al-Wahhāb (d. 1370). We shall come back to the last named in another chapter.

Criticism. Brockelmann (2, 86–88, 1902; suppt. 2, 102–4, 1938). Adolf Grohmann (EI 4, 493, 1927).

IBN RAJAB

Syrian Ḥanbalī theologian (1309–93).

Zain al-dīn Abū-l-Faraj 'Abd al-Raḥmān ibn Aḥmad ibn Rajab al-Sālimī[89] al-Baghdādī al-Ḥanbalī. Born in Baghdād in the summer 1309, moved with his father to Damascus; became a preacher in Damascus and died there in the spring 1393.

A number of philosophical and theological writings are ascribed to him: (1) Risāla fī ma'nā-l-'ilm, on the meaning of science; (2) Kitāb al-tawḥīd, on the unity of God; (3) Aḥwal al-qubūr, on the situation of the souls between death and resurrection; (4) Ṭabaqāt aṣḥāb al-imām Aḥmad ibn Ḥanbal, biographies of Ḥanbalī doctors, also called Dhail ṭabaqāt al-ḥanābila because it is a continuation of the Ṭabaqāt of Abū Ya'lā Muḥammad ibn al-Ḥusain Ibn al-Farrā al-Baghdādī (990–1065).

Criticism. Brockelmann (2, 107, 1902; suppt. 2, 129, 1938). Otto Spies: Beiträge zur arabischen Literaturgeschichte (Abhandlungen für die Kunde des Morgenlandes 19, no. 3, 12–14, Leipzig 1932).

AL-KHALLĀL

Shams al-dīn Muḥammad ibn Sālim al-Khallāl. Author of a book on jafr, who flourished c. 1335 probably in the Mamlūk kingdom.

This is quoted here for the sake of curiosity, in order to justify a reference to a form of Muslim superstition called jafr, or 'ilm al-jafr, divination especially by means of camel membranes (Freytag: Lexicon 1, 287). It is naturally connected with other superstitions, such as malāḥim (predictions, chiefly political), siḥr (magic), sīmiyā' (σημεῖα), etc. Jafr is part of the group of superstitions commonly traced back to the miraculous powers (karāmāt) of 'Ali ibn abī Ṭālib, the fourth orthodox caliph (d. 661). Thus jafr is a part of the Shī'a tradition, yet it was soon diffused throughout the Muslim world, even as far as the Maghrib.

The book bearing al-Khallāl's name is entitled Kitāb al-jafr al-kabīr.

Criticism. Brockelmann (suppt. 2, 171, 1938). Ibn Khaldūn: Prolégomènes (2, 205–25). See various articles by Duncan Black Macdonald in EI: djafr (1, 994–95, 1912), malāḥim (3, 188, 1929), siḥr (4, 409–17, 1927), sīmiyā' (4, 425–26, 1927), etc.

D3. Anatolia

'ĀSHIQ PĀSHĀ

'Alī ibn al-Mukhliṣ ibn Shaikh (or Bābā) Ilyās, called 'Āshiq pāshā (the loving pasha). Turkish poet born in 1271–72 in the Anatolian state of Qarāmān, and died on November 3, 1332.

It is said that he came to live in Qīrshahr (in another part of Anatolia, east of the middle Halys) in order to be with Ḥājjī Baktāsh (the legendary saint and creator of the darwīsh order Baktāshīya; d. 1337/38?). At any rate, he flourished in that city and completed there in 1329/30 his great poem called Gharīb-nāma (Book of the stranger) or Ma'ārif-nāma (Book of the sciences).

The purpose is to teach ṣūfī doctrine, and 'Āshiq was, if not the first Turkish

[89] I am puzzled by this name, which would seem to refer to the Sālimīya, a school of theology founded in Baṣra at the end of the ninth century; but that school was opposed by the Ḥanbalī theologians (EI 4, 115). Hence the titles Sālimī and Ḥanbalī cannot stand together?

poet, the first teacher of taṣawwuf in the Turkish language and prosody. His poem is often called Dīwān 'Āshiq pāshā; it is not a dīwān (collection of separate poems), but a single poem curiously divided into 10 parts (bāb), each bāb into 10 tales (dāstān). It is a very remarkable example of that number mysticism then so widespread, East and West, in that the tales of bāb I deal only with unity or tawḥīd, the tales of bāb II are associated with the number 2, etc. Thus in bāb IV there is a tale connected with the four elements, in bāb V, one illustrating the five senses, in bāb VII, tales relative to the seven planets and the seven ages of men. That symmetrical arrangement associated to the ṣūfī purpose led to much obscurity and artificiality and to precious little genuine science or poetry.

Not to mention folk poetry, of which more is discovered every day, 'Āshiq is not the earliest Turkish poet. A few Turkish poems were composed by Jalāl al-dīn-i-Rūmī (XIII-2), author of the immense philosophical poem Mathnawī (in Persian), and there are 156 couplets in Saljūq Turkish in the Rabāb-nāma (Book of the rabāb) of Jalāl al-dīn's son, Bahā' al-dīn Sulṭān Walad. There are also a few Turkish poems in the latter's dīwān. Now Jalāl al-dīn died in 1273 and the Rabāb-nāma was written in 1301. The Ma'ārif-nāma of 1330 is a work of far greater importance than the Turkish compositions of Jalāl al-dīn and Sulṭān Walad. The three poets used the same meter (ramal-i museddes, hexametric ramal).

Leaving Jalāl al-dīn's few Turkish poems out of account, we may say that Turkish poetry and Turkish literature began immediately after the end of the thirteenth century. This is significant, for the Saljūq empire ended in 1300 and the first 'Uthmānlī sulṭān, 'Uthmān I, ruled from 1299 on. The Mongol invasions plus the Saljūq downfall, however, had created a state of chaos in Anatolia, and in the fourteenth century there were ten rival western Turkish states. As these will be many times mentioned in my Turkish notes, a list of them with their Hellenistic approximate equivalents and their approximate position in the Anatolian peninsula is given:

1. Qarāmān. Lycaonia. Inland center south.
2. Tekkeh. Lycia, Pamphilia. South coast.
3. Ḥamīd. Pisidia, Isauria. Inland south.
4. Germyān. Phrygia. Inland west.
5. Qizil Aḥmadlī territory (or Isfandiyār). Paphlagonia. Middle north coast.
6. Menteshā. Caria. Southwest corner.
7. Aydīn } Lydia. Middle west coast.
8. Ṣārūkhān }
9. Qarāsī. Mysia. Northwest corner.
10. 'Ūthmānlī territory. Northern Phrygia (Phrygia Epictetos) plus part of Bithynia taken from the Greeks. North coast, south of Marmara.

Le Strange (p. 144, map IV, 1905). I. Hakkı Uzunçarşılıoğlu: Anatolian states and the Ak koyunlu and Kara koyunlu governments (134 p., Ankara 1937), in Turkish, with map (Isis 32).

The last named of these states gradually absorbed all the others and constituted the 'Uthmānlī empire, but that process was brutally stopped at the end of the century by a new Mongol invasion led by Tīmūr Lang. Yildirim Bāyazīd (= Abū Yazīd, the thunderbolt, sulṭān 1389–1402) was defeated and made prisoner by Tīmūr at the battle of Ankara (1402). Tīmūr's invasion, however, was not a true conquest, but rather a gigantic raid (ghazū) which delayed but did not suppress the 'Uthmānlī unification.

To return to Turkish literature, the fourteenth century constitutes its first period. Tīmūr brought Persian men of letters in his train, and thus Persian influences increased in the fifteenth century. The fourteenth century saw the gradual creation at one and the same time of the Turkish nation and Turkish literature.

The poet 'Āshiq pāshā should not be confused with his great-grandson, generally called 'Āshiq pāshā zāde, the earliest 'Uthmānlī historian. The latter's Ta'rīkh was composed at the end of the fifteenth century, but only published in this century, namely by order of the Turkish ministry of public education (Istanbul 1913/14), new edition by Friedrich Giese: Die altosmanische Chronik des 'Ašikpašazade auf Grund mehrerer neuentdeckter Handschriften (Leipzig 1929). There are many references to 'Āshiq pāshā zāde in Birge (1937).

Text. The Gharīb-nāma is still unpublished. MSS are numerous.

Criticism. Gibb (1, 176–200, 1900), including long extracts in English. F. Giese (EI 1, 482, 1911). Nicholas N. Martinovich: A Muslim mystic's plea for international unity (Moslem world 32, 26–30, 1942), including partial translation into English.

YŪNUS EMRE

Western Turkish folk poet and ṣūfī (fl. 1307).

Yūnus Emre was born in or near Boli, in what was then Qizil Aḥmadlī (later, province of Qasṭamūnī, northern Asia Minor; Boli is the ancient Claudiopolis, Bithynion). He is one of the greatest Turkish poets, but remained for a long time unappreciated because he was truly a folk poet, writing in West Turkish, using Turkish meters and an unconventional style which seemed rugged to the conventional literati dominated by Arabic and Persian conventions. He was supposed to be illiterate for that very reason, and, being a true poet and a true mystic, it may be that he borrowed relatively little from others. It is probable, however, that he had some acquaintance with the Mathnawī of Jalāl al-dīn-i-Rūmī (XIII-2).

He is quoted here because he popularized ṣūfī doctrines among the Turkish people.

In the lithographed edition of Istanbul 1884/85, his verses include 600 couplets in mathnawī style, and from 300 to 400 ghazal. All his poems are devoted to mystical ideas. He was a very poor and simple man, and traditions connect him with Ḥājjī Baktāsh Walī (d. 1337?), the legendary founder of the darwīsh order Baktāshīya (EI 1, 691–92, 1911). Birge (1937).

Text. Dīwān of Yūnus Emre. Lithographic editions (Istanbul 1884/85, 1921/22).

Criticism. Gibb (1, 164–75, 1900), examples quoted. J. Kingsley Birge: Yunus Emre, Turkey's great poet of the people (Macdonald presentation volume p. 45–60, Princeton 1933; Isis 21, 226), including Turkish bibliography and list of MSS containing various numbers of poems; (p. 53–55, 107–9, 1937).

GÜLSHEHRĪ

Aḥmad al-Gülshehrī.[90] Turkish poet who flourished c. 1317 and wrote in Persian and Turkish.

Gülshehrī composed in 1317–18 a Turkish version of the Persian poem Manṭiq al-ṭayr (Reasoning of the birds), a mystical allegory written by Farīd al-dīn 'Aṭṭār

[90] The initial of this word is the Persian-Turkish letter gāf.

(XIII-1). The birds in quest of the truth are led by the hudhud (hoopoe), who answers their learned questions.

Inasmuch as I spoke of the original Persian poem (Introd. 2, 601), it is well to speak of its Turkish translation, and the more so because the latter is the oldest literary work of some importance in the Turkish ('Uthmānlī) language.

In his Turkish work Gülshehrī considers six Persian poets as classical, to wit Sanā'ī (1048–1141), Niẓāmī of Ganja (1141–1203), Fāriḍ al-dīn 'Aṭṭār (XIII-1), Sa'dī (XIII-2), Jalāl al-dīn-i-Rūmī (XIII-2), and the latter's son Sulṭān Walad. In addition to his version of the Manṭiq al-ṭayr, he wrote in Turkish other poems and a treatise on theological terms, Gülshen-nāma; and in Persian, the poem Falak-nāma.

The fact that Gülshehrī mentions both "Mawlānā" Jalāl al-dīn and Sulṭān Walad, who were the first two masters of the Mawlawīya fraternity,[91] suggests that he belonged to it himself.

Criticism. Franz Taeschner: Das Futuvvetkapitel in Gülšehris altosmanischer Bearbeitung von 'Aṭṭārs Manṭiq uṭ-ṭayr (Sitzungsberichte der Preussischen Akad. der Wissenschaften zu Berlin, phil. Kl., 1932, 744–60), with facsimile of the text of that chapter.

AL-QAIṢARĪ

Dā'ūd ibn Maḥmūd al-Rūmī al-Qaiṣarī. Turkish ṣūfī writing in Arabic (d. 1350).

He was born in the Qarāmān country; his nisba connects him with the town of Qaiṣarīya (Caesarea Mazaca); he was educated there and in Cairo. After his return, the second 'Uthmānlī sulṭān, Urkhān (ruled 1326–60), built for him the first madrasa in his empire, at Iznīq (ancient Nicaea). He wrote various mystical treatises, such as his Risāla fī-l-taṣawwuf, and commentaries on others, such as the Manāzil al-sā'irīn of 'Abdallāh ibn Muḥammad al-Harawī (1005–88), the Fuṣūṣ al-ḥikam of Ibn 'Arabī (XIII-1), the mystic elegy Al-tā'īya al-kubrā of Ibn al-Fāriḍ (XIII-1), the Ta'wīlāt al-Qur'ān of 'Abd al-Razzāq al-Kāshānī.

It is interesting to note that the first Turkish madrasa was entrusted to a ṣūfī doctor, that is, to a man who was probably less literal and more liberal than the more conventional Muslim theologians.

Criticism. Brockelmann (2, 231, 1902; suppt. 2, 323, 1938). Adnan (p. 9, 1939).

D4. 'IRĀQ

IBN AL-MUṬAHHAR AL-ḤILLĪ

Shī'a theologian of 'Irāq (1250–1325).

Jamāl al-dīn al-Ḥasan ibn Yūsuf Ibn al-Muṭahhar al-Ḥillī al-Shī'ī, often called al-'allāma al-Ḥillī (the wise or learned man of Ḥilla, on a branch of the lower Euphrates). He was born in December 1250, was a pupil of Nāṣir al-dīn al-Ṭūsī (XIII-2); was chief of the Imamites under Uljāi'tū Khudābanda Muḥammad (Īl-khān 1303–16), died in December 1325.

He wrote a great many treatises (39 to 75) on Shī'a and Imāmīya theology, apologetic, and biography, and many of these treatises have been the occasion of series of commentaries. I quote only the Nahj al-ḥaqq wa-kashf al-ṣidq, a treatise

[91] The so-called "whirling dervishes." See Introd. 2, 874, and D. S. Margoliouth (EI 3, 418–19, 1931).

against the Sunnī school and especially against the followers of al-Ash'arī (X-1), written for the sulṭān Khudābanda; the Taḥrīr al-aḥkām al-shar'īya 'alā madhhab al-Imāmīya, a compendium of Imāmīya law; and Īḍāḥ al-ishtibāh fī asmā' al-ruwāh, including biographies of doctors of his persuasion. He apparently compiled a bibliography of his own writings and of the writings of others which he had studied.

Ibn al-Muṭahhar belonged to a famous family of theologians, which produced ten mujtahidīn (mujtahid is the highest dignity among Muslim theologians), including his father and his son Muḥammad, nicknamed Fakhr al-muḥaqqiqīn (1283–1369).

Text. The Taḥrīr al-aḥkām has been utilized in the Digest of Mohummudan law . . . edited by William Jones (vol. 1, the only one published, Calcutta 1805).

The Īḍāḥ is the basis of the 'Alam al-hudā', Notes on Shy'ah biography (Bibliotheca indica vol. 19, Calcutta 1848).

There are Persian and Indian editions of other treatises of his, or/and of commentaries upon them.

Criticism. Brockelmann (2, 164, 1902; suppt. 2, 206–9, 1938). Browne (4, 406, 1924).

'ABD AL-RAZZĀQ

'Abd al-Razzāq Kamāl al-dīn al-Kāshānī. Iraqian ṣūfī (d. 1329–30).

There are many divergences in the names given to him, Jamāl al-dīn instead of Kamāl al-dīn, then ibn abī-l-Faḍā'il (or Ghanā'im) or ibn Muḥammad, al Kāshānī, or Qāshānī, or Kāshī. The circumstances of his life are unknown except that it ended in Kāshān 1329–30. Kāshān (or Qāshān) is a place in al-Jibāl ('Irāq 'Ajam) between Qumm and Iṣfahān.

'Abd al-Razzāq was a disciple of Ibn 'Arabī al-Andalusī (XIII-1), that is, he continued the tradition of Neoplatonism as revived by Ibn Masarra of Cordova (883–931), being careful not to carry his mysticism too far, beyond the border of orthodoxy. His main work is a dictionary of the technical terms used by mystical philosophers (Kitāb iṣṭilāḥāt al-ṣūfīya), but he wrote many other books, the best known of which is one on predestination and free will (Risāla fī-l-qaḍā' wal-qadar).

He wrote commentaries on the Manāzil al-sā'irīn, a ṣūfī treatise by 'Abdallāh ibn Muḥammad al-Harawī (d. Herat 1088–89), on two treatises of Ibn 'Arabī, the Mawāqi' al-nujūm and the Fuṣūṣ al-ḥikam, and on the Qur'ān. It was the preparation of these commentaries which caused him to compile his dictionary of ṣūfī technical terms.

'Abd al-Razzāq Kamāl al-dīn al-Kāshānī has been confused (even by Ḥājjī Khalīfa and Brockelmann) with 'Abd al-Razzāq Kamāl al-dīn ibn Isḥāq al-Samarqandī, Persian historian, author of the Maṭla' al-sa'dain wa-majma' al-baḥrain (1413–82), about whom see W. Barthold (EI 1, 63, 1908). The variety of names given to our author is partly the result of that confusion.

Text. The first part of the Iṣṭilāḥāt was edited by Aloys Sprenger: Dictionary of the technical terms of the Sufies (178 p., Calcutta 1845).

The Risāla fī-l-qaḍā' wal-qadar was edited by Stanislas Guyard (32 p., Paris 1879), who had previously published a French translation of it in the Journal asiatique (Feb. 1873); revised and reprinted (45 p., Nogent le Rotrou 1875).

Criticism. Analysis of the Iṣṭilāḥāt by Hammer-Purgstall (Jahrbücher der Literatur vol. 82, Anzeige-Blatt p. 62–69, Wien 1838). Brockelmann (2, 204, 1902; suppt. 2, 280, 1938). D. B. Macdonald (EI 1, 61–63, 1908). Reynold A. Nicholson (ERE 1, 12–14, 1908).

D5. Īrān

ṢADR AL-SHARĪ'A AL-THĀNĪ

Persian encyclopaedist and theologian writing in Arabic (d. 1346).

'Ubaidallāh ibn Mas'ūd al-Maḥbūbī al-Bukhārī al-Ḥanafī. He is called Ṣadr al-Sharī'a al-thānī (the second) to distinguish him from an ancestor, Ṣadr al-Sharī'a al-awwal (the first), who was also a Ḥanafī theologian (fl. c. 1232). Ibn Baṭṭūṭa met him in Bukhārā in 1333, where he (Ṣadr) had arrived from Herāt (Defrémery's ed., 3, 28). Ṣadr al-Sharī'a died in 1346.

Among his writings two are especially important:

1. Ta'dīl al-'ulūm (Equalization of the sciences), an encyclopaedia of philosophy and of the natural sciences. The third part, Ta'dīl al-hai'at al-aflāk, dealing with astronomy, appears also separately.

2. Tanqīḥ al-uṣūl. A discussion on the principles of jurisprudence (fiqh) which was the basis of endless commentaries. It was itself derived from the Kanz al-wuṣūl ilā ma'rifat al-uṣūl of an earlier Ḥanafī doctor, 'Alī ibn Muḥammad al-Pazdawī (d. Samarqand 1089).

Text. The Ta'dīl al-'ulūm is unpublished. The Tanqīḥ al-uṣūl was printed in Delhi 1850–51 with two commentaries.

Criticism. Suter (p. 165, 1900). Brockelmann (2, 214, 1902; suppt. 2, 300–1, 1938).

AL-ĪJĪ

Persian Shāfi'ī theologian writing in Arabic (d. 1355).

'Aḍud al-dīn 'Abd al-Raḥmān ibn Aḥmad al-Ījī al-Shīrāzī. Born after 1281 in Īj near Shīrāz, flourished in Sulṭānīyah (Jibāl), then was qāḍī in Shabānkāra (Fārs), then chief judge (qāḍī al-quḍāt) under Abū Sa'īd (īl-khān of Persia 1316–35). He returned to Īj and died in 1355 in Diraimiyān, where he had been thrown into prison because of a difference of opinion with the lord of Kirmān.

He wrote in Arabic a dozen treatises dealing with scholastic philosophy (kalām), dialectics, psychology, ethics, and the Muslim creed. He discussed theology with the Shī'a doctor Muḥammad ibn Maḥmūd al-Āmilī. Many of his works were the basis of commentaries by al-Jurjānī (XIV-2) and others, and of supercommentaries, in Arabic and also in Turkish. Before dealing at greater length with the most important, the Mawāqif (the Stations), I shall say a few words of some of the others:

Ādāb al-baḥth, on dialectics, commented upon by many scholars.

Al-risālat al-waḍ'īya al-'Aḍudīya, on the expression of concepts, also frequently commented upon.

Al-shāhīya fī 'ilm al-akhlāq. Compendium on practical philosophy, that is, psychology, politics, domestic economy, ethics.

Al-'aqā'id al-'Aḍudīya, on the articles of faith.

Al-fawā'id al-Ghiyāthīya. Commentary on the third part, dealing with rhetoric, of the Miftāḥ al-'ulūm of al-Sakkākī al-Khwārizmī (XIII-1), dedicated to the wazīr Ghiyāth al-dīn.

Sharḥ mukhtaṣar al-uṣūl. Commentary on the compendium of Mālikī law by the Egyptian Ibn al-Ḥājib (XIII-1).

Ishrāq al-tawārīkh, history of the patriarchs, of the Prophet, and of his companions. This was translated into Turkish by Muṣṭafā ibn Aḥmad Chelebī (d. 1599).

Al-Ījī's main work is the Kitāb al-mawāqif fī 'ilm al-kalām (Stations in scholastic philosophy). It is a well documented and very well thought-out summary of scientific knowledge and systematic philosophy. It is relatively short and written with remarkable austerity, but it was developed again and again by various commentators, the most important of whom is the saiyid al-Jurjānī (XIV-2); the MS or printed editions of the text almost always include one commentary or more. According to the author, he wrote the Mawāqif for the sake of reviving kalām (theology, scholastic philosophy), which had become very much neglected in his day. Therefore, he read all the books available to him, and took great pains in digesting them and explaining their contents as clearly as possible and more or less in a new way. His sources are exclusively Arabic; of course, they were Greek by implication, but he hardly mentions Greek philosophers, though he mentions Euclid with regard to infinite divisibility. His main source was apparently Ibn Sīnā, but he was well acquainted with most scholastic philosophers, orthodox or not (mu'tazila).

The treatise is divided into 6 books called stations (mawāqif).[92] Each mawqif is divided into "observatories" (maraṣid), and each marṣad is divided into aims or points of view (maqṣad, maqāṣid). Contents of each mawqif: (I) logic, science in general, first principles, truth and error; (II) metaphysics, being and nonbeing, matter, necessity and possibility, monism and pluralism, causes and consequences; (III) theory of accidents; (IV) physics, divisibility of matter, vacuum, motion; cosmology; geography, psychology; (V) theodicy; (VI) prophecy, resurrection, last judgment. A sort of appendix deals with the various Muslim sects.

Though the Mawāqif is already very condensed, al-Ījī wrote an abridgment of it, Jawāhir al-kalām, mukhtaṣar al-mawāqif. That abridgment was reamplified by 'Alī ibn Muḥammad al-Bukhārī and dedicated by him to the wazīr Ghiyāth al-dīn in 1368.[93]

Text. The Mawāqif have been printed together with three commentaries, one of which is al-Jurjānī's (2 vols., Constantinople 1823–24). Th. Soerensen: Statio quinta et sexta et appendix libri Mevākif, operis dogmatici de disciplina kelām (384 p., Leipzig 1848).

For the other works, see Brockelmann.

Criticism. Wüstenfeld (p. 9, 1882). Brockelmann (2, 208–9, 1902; suppt. 2, 287–93, 1938); (EI 2, 447, 1918). Carra de Vaux (4, 137, 186–94, 1923). Plessner (p. 126–31, 1928), apropos of Al-shāhīya fī 'ilm al-akhlāq.

AL-TAḤTĀNĪ

Persian philosopher and theologian writing in Arabic (d. 1365).

Quṭb al-dīn Muḥammad ibn Muḥammad al-Rāzī al-Taḥtanī came from his native

[92] The word mawqif, plural mawāqif, translated by "stations," has a philosophical sense and also a religious one (EI 3, 417), as in our expressions "station days," "stations of the cross," stations or "reposoirs" in a pilgrimage.

[93] I am much puzzled by the wazīr Ghiyāth al-dīn, who appears twice in this article, the first time as the patron of Al-fawā'id al-Ghiyāthīya, and the second time now. Apropos of the first occasion, Brockelmann (2, 209) states that Ghiyāth al-dīn was wazīr to the sulṭān Muḥammad Khudābanda. If so, the book is apocryphal or there is another error, for that Il-khān ruled from 1304 to 1316. Apropos of the second, he calls him (suppt. 2, 291) Ghiyāth al-dīn ibn Rashīd al-dīn. This is equally inconsistent, for this son of Rashīd al-dīn was put to death in 1336, and hence no treatise could be dedicated to him in 1368. The date 1368 may be wrong, but the reamplification of the summary of the Mawāqif could hardly have been composed before 1337. Many wuzarā' were probably called Ghiyāth-al-dīn (helper of the faith).

country (Persia) to Damascus in 1362, and he died there on July 25, 1365, being then over 70 years of age.

I had occasion to refer before (Introd. 2, 1019) to one of his works, the Muḥākamāt, wherein he discussed the differences of opinion between Fakhr al-dīn al-Rāzī (XII-2) and Nāṣir al-dīn al-Ṭūsī (XIII-2) with regard to the Kitāb al-ishārāt wal-tanbīhāt of Ibn Sīnā (XI-1).

He wrote commentaries on the famous Qur'ānic work Kitāb al-kashshāf 'an ḥaqā'iq al-tanzīl of Maḥmūd ibn 'Umar al-Zamakhsharī (XII-1), and on two logical treatises, the Risāla al-shamsīya fī-l-qawā'id al-manṭiqīya of 'Alī ibn 'Umar al-Kātibī al-Qazwīnī (XIII-2) and the Maṭāli' al-anwār fī-l-manṭiq of Maḥmūd ibn abī Bakr al-Urmawī (d. Qunya 1283).

Criticism. Ḥājjī Khalīfa (1, 301–3, 1835). Brockelmann (2, 209, 1902; suppt. 2, 293, 1938).

ḤAMDALLĀH MUSTAWFĪ

Persian historian and encyclopaedist writing in Persian (b. c. 1281, still living in 1340).

Ḥamdallāh ibn Abī Bakr Mustawfī al-Qazwīnī[94] was born in Qazwīn and was of Arabian and Shī'a ancestry. Indeed, he claimed descent from Ḥurr al Riyāḥī, who died for the imām Ḥusain ibn 'Alī at the battle of Kerbelā' (680). He himself was a convinced Shī'a. His great-grandfather, Amīn al-dīn Naṣr, was mustawfī, that is, accountant, of 'Irāq, and the name as well as the profession remained in the family. At any rate, both Ḥamdallāh and his brother Zain al-dīn Muḥammad were state accountants appointed by Rashīd al-dīn during the rule of the īl-khān Uljāi'tū (1304–16). Ḥamdallāh belonged to the literary circle of that great wazīr and hence had unusual opportunities of meeting the learned men of his time and obtaining valuable information. It is not known when he was born and died, but one can deduce from his writings that his birth occurred c. 1281 and that he was still living in 1340.

Three of his works have come down to us, Ta'rīkh i-guzīda (1330), Ẓafar-nāma (1335), and Nuzhat al-qulūb (1340), which I shall now describe, especially the last one, of greater interest to the historian of science.

1. Ta'rīkh i-guzīda (Select history) was completed in 1329/30 and dedicated to Rashīd al-dīn's son Ghiyāth al-dīn Muḥammad (put to death in 1336). It begins with an enumeration of 23 Arabic and Persian sources, and a discussion of the different eras and the conflicting views on the creation (or noncreation) of the world. After that introduction (fātiḥa), the history is divided into 6 chapters (bāb): (1) major and minor prophets; (2) pre-Islamic kings of Persia; (3) the Prophet, his companions and descendants; (4) post-Islamic kings of Persia; (5) biographies of pious and learned men (about 490; no scientists except a few physicians); (6) account of Qazwīn and its notable people. A tree of dynasties is sometimes added at the end of the MSS.

[94] He is often called al-Qazwīnī, but it is better to avoid that because it is misleading. I have already dealt with two important al-Qazwīnī (XIII-2; Introd. 2, 868), the better-known one being the cosmographer Zakarīyā ibn Muḥammad, a kind of Muslim Pliny, the other the astronomer and philosopher 'Alī ibn 'Umar, who flourished at the observatory of Marāgha. There were many other "al-Qazwīnī," for Qazwīn, in 'Irāq 'Ajamī, was one of the important centers of mediaeval Persia. The name Qazwīnī alone would generally be understood as referring to Zakarīyā ibn Muḥammad.

The whole text includes c. 170,000 words, which is relatively little considering the scope of the undertaking. Hence the account is generally swift, yet there are novelties in it, especially in the contemporary period.

2. Ẓafar-nāma (Book of victory). This is a historical poem of 75,000 couplets. It was meant as a continuation to the Shāh-nāma of Firdawsī (XI-1) down to c. 1331, and the only known MS of it (British Museum Or. 2833) contains also a text of the Shāh-nāma, to the revision of which Ḥamdallāh had devoted six years. He completed the Ẓafar-nāma in 735 H. = 1334/35 after having worked 15 years at it, and he was 40 years old when he began, whence we conclude that he was born in 680 H. = 1281/82.

The enormous poem (it is one-quarter longer than Firdawsī's) begins with the life of the Prophet and extends to 1331/32. Its chronological distribution is very regular, some 10,000 couplets being devoted to each century; or 25,000 couplets to the Arabs (first part), 20,000 to the Persians, 30,000 to the Mongols.

3. The Nuzhat al-qulūb (Delight of the hearts) was completed by him in 1340, at the request of friends who felt the need of a work of this kind—cosmography and scientific encyclopaedia—in Persian. He used a good many Arabic books, which are duly mentioned (full list in Rieu: Catalogue of Persian MSS in British Museum 1, 418–19, 1879). It is divided into five parts: introduction, three main parts, and appendix, as follows:

Fātiḥa. Account of the spheres, heavenly bodies, and elements. Inhabited quarter of the globe, longitude, latitude, climates.

Maqāla I. Mineralogy, botany, zoology. The purpose is largely medical. For example, the zoological section contains descriptions of 228 animals, and accounts of their medical and magical virtues. About a hundred diseases are mentioned. The animals are divided into three groups according to their habitat, land, sea, or air, and those of the first group are subdivided into five sections, to wit, domestic animals, wild animals, beasts of prey, poisonous animals and creeping things, animals certain of whose members resemble those of man. In each section the animals are introduced in the alphabetic order of their Arabic names. Arabic synonyms are mentioned, and the names are translated into Persian, and sometimes into Turkish and Mongolian. Many superstitions are recorded in the book, mixed with scientific information. The zoological section is different from other Arabic and Persian treatises on the subject in that the scientific information, scanty as it is, is not entirely submerged by literary and philological considerations. This may be due to the fact that the author was not primarily a literary man or theologian, but a state accountant having to deal exactly with hard realities. The main sources of the zoology are Muḥammad al-Awfī (XIII-1) and Zakarīyā al-Qazwīnī (XIII-2), but a good many others are duly quoted.

Maqāla II. Man. His bodily structure, faculties, moral qualities.

Maqāla III. Geography. Divided into 4 parts: (1) the two holy cities and the temple of Jerusalem; (2) description of Īrān, province by province, then account of its roads, distances, mountains, mines and minerals, rivers, seas and lakes (this fills two-thirds of this maqāla); (3) other countries bordering on Īrān and sometimes included in it; (4) countries which were never part of Īrān.

Khātima. Wonders and curiosities of Īrān and of other countries.

Endless remarks could be made about the geography, especially by scholars interested in this or that region. It is especially valuable, of course, for the study of Asiatic geography and of the customs of Mesopotamia, Persian and Turkish lands,

Central Asia. Ḥamdallāh quotes many literary sources, but it is highly probable that he was able to make use also of official documents, such as lists of post offices and taxation lists.

He reproduces a table drawn by 'Abd al-Raḥmān al-Khāzinī (XII-1) which enables one to determine the qibla (direction of Mecca) at any point the coordinates of which are known. In this table the latitudes and longitudes are given by means of letters, not of numerals (p. 26 of Le Strange's Persian text).

The geography relates many superstitions, e.g., that concerning the existence in the desert of the Maghrib of a city of women who reproduce themselves parthenogenetically (same text p. 272), being impregnated by water.

Text. Ta'rīkh i-guzīda. The first edition, a facsimile edition of "a fairly accurate and ancient MS" (dated 1453), was published in the Gibb memorial series (vol. 14, part 1, 1910). Abridged English version with full indexes by E. G. Browne and R. A. Nicholson (ibid. part 2, 1913).

Three partial editions had appeared before, to wit: ch. 4, dealing with post-Islamic dynasties of Persia, was edited in Persian and French by Jules Gantin (632 p., Paris 1903); ch. 6, dealing with Qazwīn, was translated into French by Barbier de Meynard (Journal asiatique 10, 257 f., 1857); ch. 5, section on Persian poets, was Englished by E. G. Browne (Journal of the Royal Asiatic Society, 1900–1).

Nuzhat al-qulūb. Lithographed edition, complete but poor (Bombay 1893/94).

There are critical editions and English translations of two important parts, the geography and zoology, in the Gibb memorial series. The geography, by Guy Le Strange, Persian text (vol. 23, part 1, 1915), English translation with notes (vol. 23, part 2, 1919). The zoology, in Persian and English, by John Stephenson (vol. 30, 1928; Isis 13, 435). It is hoped that the rest of the work will be edited and translated in the same style, preferably in the same series.

Criticism. J. T. Reinaud: Géographie d'Aboulféda (1, 155, 1848). G. Le Strange: Mesopotamia and Persia under the Mongols (134 p., London 1903); Lands of the Eastern caliphate (1905). Ferrand (p. 405–7, 1914). Browne (3, 87–100, 1920). V. F. Büchner (EI 2, 844–45, 1925). J. Stephenson: The zoological section of the Nuzhatu-l-qulūb (Isis 11, 285–315, 1928), elaborate analysis of that section, comparisons with similar works, extracts translated, Arabic index of about a hundred diseases. Paul Pelliot: Les formes turques et mongoles dans la nomenclature zoologique du Nuzhatu-l-qulūb (Bull. School of Oriental Studies 6, 555–80, London 1931). Conway Zirkle: Animals impregnated by the wind (Isis 25, 95–130, 1936; p. 121), apropos of women impregnated by water. Sir Jivanji Jamshedji Modi: References to ancient Iran in the Nuzhat al-qulūb (Journal of the Cama Society no. 31, 128–31, Bombay 1937).

MUḤAMMAD IBN MAḤMŪD AL-ĀMILĪ

Persian philosopher and encyclopaedist who wrote in Persian and died c. 1352.

We do not know when and where he was born, but he was a teacher (mudarris) in Sulṭānīyah, Jibāl, during the rule of the Mongol īl-khān Uljāi'tū (1304–16), and his main work, the Nafā'is al-funūn, was composed in 1335 but not completed before 1342.

In addition to the Nafā'is al-funūn, he wrote commentaries upon the kullīyāt of the Qānūn of Ibn Sīnā (XI-1), upon the kullīyāt of the Qānūn of Sharaf al-dīn al-Īlāqī,[95] upon the Mukhtaṣar fī-l-uṣūl of Ibn al-Ḥājib (XIII-1). This last-named

[95] Sharaf al-dīn Abū 'Abdallāh al-Sayyid Muḥammad ibn Yūsuf al-Īlāqī. His death year is unknown, but he is mentioned by Ḥājjī Khalīfa (1, 269; 4, 434, 494) as a disciple of Ibn Sīnā,

commentary (quoted by Rieu) seems strange to me, for Ibn al-Ḥājib's book dealt with Mālikī law, and al-Āmilī was a Shī'a, who engaged in controversies with the great Sunnī theologian 'Aḍud al-dīn al-Ījī. According to Ḥājjī Khalīfa (4, 500), the commentary on the Qānūn of Ibn Sīnā was completed in 1352–53; if that date is correct, al-Āmilī lived at least until that time.

In 1334–42 he compiled the Nafā'is al-funūn fī 'arā'is al-'uyūn, a large encyclopaedia of all the sciences (in one MS there are more than 12,000 lines). It was dedicated to a wazīr of the amīr Jamāl al-dīn Shaikh Abū Isḥāq ibn Maḥmūdshāh, ruler of Shīrāz from 1341–42 to 1353–54. In order to prepare himself for it, he traveled considerably and visited all the leading scholars of his time (statement made in his preface). It is divided into two main parts, dealing respectively with the modern or Muslim sciences, and with the ancient or pre-Muslim ones. Qism I is divided into 36 groups, to wit, 15 literary groups, 9 legal ones, 5 mystical (ṣūfī) ones, 7 conversational ones. Qism II (ancient sciences) deals with practical philosophy (ethics, domestic economy, government), speculative philosophy (logic, introduction to metaphysics, metaphysics, physics), mathematics (geometry, astronomy, arithmetic, music), branches of physics (medicine, alchemy, magic, oneiromancy, physiognomy, astrology, properties of natural objects, physical crafts as veterinary art, agriculture, falconry; art of holding the breath and other yoga practices), branches of mathematics (spherics, optics, 'ilm al-mutawassiṭāt,[96] practical arithmetic, algebra, surveying, constellations, making almanacs and using astrolabes, geography, numerical diagrams, mechanics, divination, games). In all, 160 arts or sciences are distinguished. My description is based upon the British Museum Persian MS Add 16,827 (Rieu 2, 435). Other MSS are arranged somewhat differently, and many MSS are incomplete.

Text. Nafā'is al-funūn. Lithographic edition (2 vols., 512 p., Teheran 1898–99).

Criticism. Charles Rieu: Catalogue of the Persian MSS in British Museum (2, 435–38, London 1881). Hermann Ethé: Catalogue of Persian MSS in the Bodleian (1, 909–13, Oxford 1889); Catalogue of Persian MSS in the India Office (1, 1212–16, Oxford 1903).

Plessner (p. 119–23, 1928). Dwight M. Donaldson: The qualities of the planets, astrology in Islam (Moslem world 29, 151–57, 1939), extract translated from the Teheran edition, 2, 176 ff.

D6. Muslim India

AL-MULTĀNĪ

Hindu theologian (Ḥanafī) and commentator on the Qur'ān, writing in Arabic and Persian (fl. 1317–33).

Isḥāq ibn Tāj al-dīn al-Multānī al-Ṣūfī al-Ḥanafī, called Ibn al-Tāj, is mentioned here chiefly to illustrate Persian influences in India. He flourished c. 1317 in al-Multān in the Punjab; there were ancient ṣūfī traditions in that city, witness the monumental tomb of Shams-i-Tabrīzī (d. c. 1247; Introd. 2, 874).

He wrote (1) an Arabic book on the ceremonies (or stations) of the Pilgrimage

---

which would place him in the second quarter of the eleventh century. The book referred to (after Rieu) is presumably the so-called Al-fuṣūl al-īlāqīya, collection of aphorisms derived from Ibn Sīnā's Qānūn.

[96] That is, intermediate knowledge between Euclid's Elements and the Almagest. See Introd. 2, 1001.

(manāsik al-ḥajj); (2) an Arabic treatise on theology and jurisprudence, Khulāṣat al-aḥkām bi-sharā'iṭ al-imām wal-islām; (3, 4) Arabic and Persian abridgments of 2; (5) Khulāṣat jawāhir al-Qur'ān fī bayān ma'ānī lughāt al-furqān, Persian explanations of terms occurring in the Qur'ān, one for each sūra, beginning with the first sūra, then the last, the last but one, etc. to the second. This last item was composed at Multān in 1317, but there is also an autograph MS written in Cairo 1333/34.

Criticism. Brockelmann (2, 220, 1902; suppt. 2, 310, 1938). Storey (sec. 1, 36, 1927).

E. HINDU INDIA

MEDHAṂKARA

Medhaṃkara, also called Nava-Medhaṃkara (meaning M. the younger). Burmese writer in Pāli. He was educated in Ceylon, then came to Martaban, southeast Burma, where he was tutor to queen Bhaddā, mother of Setibhinda (king of Martaban from 1348 on).

He composed the Lokadīpasāra, which is a collection of chapters dealing with different stages of existence—in hell, among animals, among ghosts, etc., each subject being illustrated with legends.

Criticism. Mabel Haynes Bode: The Pāli literature of Burma (p. 35, Royal Asiatic Society, London 1909).

RAṬṬA-KAVI

Raṭṭa-kavi, who flourished c. 1300, was the lord of a Jaina town in the Canarese country (southwest India). He wrote a popular scientific work in Canarese, entitled Raṭṭa-mata or Raṭṭa-sūtra; it deals with such phaenomena as rain, earthquakes, thunder and lightning, planets, and omina connected therewith. It was translated into Telugu by Bhāskara, a Telugu poet of the fourteenth century.

Text. No edition known to me of either the Canarese or the Telugu text.
Criticism. Edward P. Rice: History of Kanarese literature (Heritage of India series, p. 45, Calcutta 1921).

F. CHINA

WU CH'ÊNG

Chinese Confucianist and Taoist (1247–1331).

Wu Ch'êng was born in Ch'ung-jen, Kiangsi. He was styled Yu ch'ing, also Po ch'ing; nicknamed Lin Ch'uan, and canonized Wên Chêng. He lived in a thatched hut (tsao lu), and therefore was popularly known as Tsao lu hsien shêng. Though he devoted much time to study, he failed to obtain the chin shih degree. Yet his editions of the classics were brought to the attention of Kublai Khān (XIII-2); after having attained many offices, he was finally appointed in 1321 secretary of the Han-lin yüan. A few years later he retired into the country. He wrote a commentary on the Book of history, Shu ching or Shang shu, entitled Shang shu tsuan yen. He prepared annotated editions of the Tao tê ching of Lao Tzŭ (VI B.C.) and of the Nan Hua chên ching of Chuang Tzŭ (III-1 B.C.).

Criticism. Giles (no. 2316, 1898). Wieger (1, nos. 698, 735, 1911); (p. 377, 1920).

HSÜ CH'IEN

Chinese Confucianist (1270–1337).

He was styled I chih, was popularly known as Pai yün hsien shêng, and was canonized as Wên i. His tablet was placed in the Confucian temple in 1734.

He was born in Chin-hua, Chekiang, in 1270; and devoted himself so successfully to the study of philosophy and letters that he soon became famous. He refused to serve under the Yüan dynasty.

He wrote various commentaries on the Confucian canon, chiefly one on the Shih ching or Book of poetry, the second of the Five Classics, entitled Shih chi ch'uan ming wu ch'ao. He also composed a commentary on the Four Books, Tu ssŭ shu ts'ung shuo, in 4 chüan, and the Tu shu ts'ung shuo, in 6 chüan.

Criticism. Giles (no. 764, 1898). Wieger (p. 316, 1920).

CH'ÊN HAO

Chinese Confucianist (1261–1341).

Ch'ên Hao's style name (tzŭ) was K'o Ta and his nicknames (hao) were Yün Chuang and Ching Kuei. He was born in 1261 in Tu-ch'ang, Kiangsi, hence his name Tung Hui Tsê; his father was an official in Hupeh.

He wrote an elaborate commentary on the Li chi or Book of rites, one of the Five Classics, dating probably in its present form from the second century. This commentary, called Li chi chi shuo, was completed in 1322. He was canonized in 1724, and his commentary remained a standard textbook until very recent times.

Criticism. Giles (no. 218, 1898). Wieger (p. 420, 1920).

KOREA

LI CH'I-HSIEN

Korean Confucianist (1287–1367).

Li Ch'i-hsien is quoted here as one of the leading Confucianists of the last period of the Koryu dynasty (ending in 1392), who prepared the great Confucian revival of the Li dynasty in the following century.

In order to appreciate this, it is necessary to retrospect Korean Confucianism. As Korean culture was deeply influenced by China, it is not surprising that the Five Classics and the Four Books were fully appreciated by Korean scholars. As early as 1045 two of the Classics, Shih ching and Li chi, were reprinted from wooden blocks in Korea, and in 1056 a more ambitious series of reprints was begun. By 1091 Korean editions were already so well spoken of that the Sung emperor Chê Tsung sent an envoy to Korea to obtain copies of them.

Among the Four Books, the one most popular in Korea was the Great learning, Ta hsüeh, compiled by Confucius' disciple Ts'êng Tzŭ; among the Five Classics, the I ching, Ch'un ch'iu, and above all the Li chi, for the Korean scholar was a born ritualist.

Between 1020 and 1883, eighteen Korean scholars received the supreme honor of having their tablets enshrined in the Confucian temple. Two-thirds of these canonizations took place in the seventeenth and eighteenth centuries and do not concern us. Four only are anterior to the seventeenth century, two of them taking place in 1020 and 1022, Hsieh ts'ung (fl. c. 700) and Ts'ui Chih yüan (858–910); one in 1319, An Yü; and the last in 1517, Chêng mêng-chou (XIV-2).

An Yü[97] was perhaps the main instrument in teaching the new Confucianism of Chu Hsi, which proved to be so well adapted to the Korean temperament and conquered their minds completely. I say "perhaps" because there is a possibility that the neo-Confucian works did not reach many Korean scholars before 1313. At any rate, they certainly did reach them in that year, when Koreans bought in Nanking a considerable number of books which had belonged to the Sung dynasty (fallen in 1279). After 1313 Confucianism made enormous progress in Korea, and its triumph, prepared by great scholars such as Li Ch'i-hsien and Chêng mêng-chou (XIV-2), received its final official consecration in 1392 and following years from the new Li dynasty. That triumph unfortunately implied persecution and ostracism of the rival philosophies, Buddhism and Taoism. The obliteration of Taoism was relatively easy, for Taoism never flourished in Korea, but Buddhism was almost as important with them for close to a thousand years (c. 394–1392) as the Christian church is with us. Buddhism was mercilessly persecuted and reviled, but continued a secret life in the hearts of mountain hermits and of women.[98]

Criticism. Courant (p. cxxvii, 1894). Trollope (1932 passim), giving a list of the eighteen Confucian sages of Korea on p. 44. Youn (1939).

G. JAPAN

GEN-E

Japanese Buddhist and Confucianist (1269–1352).

Gen-e was born in Kyōto in 1269; he studied the Tendai doctrines at Mt. Hiei, out later joined the Rinzai-shū, and belonged to the Myōshin-ji, which became the principal monastery of that sect. He took part in the popular movement against the tyrannical rule of the Kamakura Hōjō (the Hōjō family had ruled Japan from 1200 to 1338, its head being called the shikken or regent of Kamakura), which led to the establishment of the Ashikaga shogunate. He died in 1352 (or 1350).

He was the leading Japanese exponent of the Sung Confucianism which had been initiated in China by Chou Tun-i (XI-2) and had been developed to its perfection by Chu Hsi (XII-2). He was invited to the imperial court and appointed reader or tutor to the emperor Go-Daigo (ruled 1319–38). He read the Buddhist scriptures to the emperor and explained to him and his entourage the hsing-li (the neo-Confucian natural philosophy). Thereafter that philosophy was taught in the "five temples" (go-zan) of Kyōto,[99] and thus became the official doctrine of the Zen-shū and more particularly of the Rinzai-shū.

It is said that he helped to compile the Kemmu shikimoku, but this is not clear to me, for that code of laws was compiled during the Kemmu era, in 1336; that is,

[97] 1243–1306. See Trollope (p. 18, 1932), with portrait.

[98] Right up to 1894 the law forbidding any Buddhist monk or nun to enter Seoul or any other city on pain of death still held good (Trollope p. 31, 1932).

[99] The five leading temples, determined by the authorities in imitation of Hindu and Chinese usage. Under the Kamakura, the go-zan were Enkaku-ji, Kenchō-ji, Jufuku-ji in Kamakura, and Kennin-ji, Tōfuku-ji in Kyōto. Under the Ashikaga, the go-zan were Tenryū-ji, Shōkoku-ji, Kennin-ji, Tōfuku-ji, and Manju-ji; and above them all was the Nanzen-ji, all these in Kyōto.

it was promulgated before the end of the Kamakura regime. We should perhaps understand that Gen-e, as adviser to the first Ashikaga shōgun Takauji (ruled 1338–58), was responsible for the preservation of the Kemmu code. Indeed, that code remained in force throughout the Ashikaga shogunate (i.e., until 1597).

The ascription to him of the Taihei-ki is open to similar objections. Of course he could only have written a part of that history, dealing with the years 1318–68. There is documentary evidence that a part at least of the text was written or revised by Gen-e.

He was certainly, however, the author of the Teikin ōrai, a course of morality and etiquette in the form of twenty-five epistles. A revised edition of the Teikin ōrai remained in use until the Meiji period (begun 1868).

Criticism. Papinot (p. 115, 1909). Brinkley and Kikuchi (p. 447, 454, 1914). Nihon bungaku dai-jiten (1935).

EARLY PRINTING IN JAPAN

I have spoken in volume 1 (p. 529) of the million Buddhist charms which were printed c. 770 by order of the empress Shōtoku-tennō. We have but very little information on the printing done after that date. However, the Tripiṭaka (the Buddhist library) was printed in Japan between 1278 and 1288. Soon afterward the Zen monasteries throughout the country began to print their favorite sūtra and commentaries. Some 181 editions of various works are known to have been printed in Japan in the fourteenth century; and many more were probably printed which are lost today or unidentified.

With the inauguration of the Ashikaga regime in 1338, the second great influx of Chinese culture began and soon flooded the country. This movement was largely restricted to the Sung culture, which had been stopped in China after 1279 by the Mongol conquest (the Yüan dynasty). It began a little before the Ashikaga "new deal," for one of its characteristics was the printing of secular (vs. Buddhist) books, and the earliest Chinese classic printed in Japan is the Kobun shōsho kōshi den, a documented biography of Confucius in 13 books, printed as early as 1322. This was followed by the Rongo shūkai, or Confucian analects (Lun yü) with commentary, in 10 books, printed in 1364.

Buddhist works continued to be printed for the sake of merit or in the form of ex voto, but by the second half of the fourteenth century the commercial side of printing and publishing was very well developed. For example, a Zen priest, Gidō Shūshin (1325–88), compiled an anthology of a thousand Chinese poems which obtained much popularity and was printed in Kyōto. Shūshin, having found in 1375 a copy full of errors, prepared a new edition which was published in the year of his death.

Yasuhiko Kimiya: Nihon ko insatsu bunka shi (History of early printing in Japan) (p. 208–314, 1932), in Japanese.

CHAPTER VI

MATHEMATICS AND ASTRONOMY

(First Half of the Fourteenth Century)

N.B. Only the main notes are published in this chapter. The mathematical and astronomical contributions of many other men, whose main work was done in other fields, are discussed in other chapters. For a general survey of mathematics and astronomy in the first half of the fourteenth century, see section VI of chapter I. More information on the men referred to in that survey may then easily be obtained by means of the index.

A. WESTERN CHRISTENDOM

A1. ITALY

JACOB OF FLORENCE

Florentine mathematician, who is unknown except as the author of a MS Tractatus algorismi . . . compilatus a Magistro Jacobo de Florentia apud montem Phesulanum, dated September 1307. I do not know whether one is allowed to deduce from the title that the treatise was compiled in Fiesole.

This treatise, represented by two MSS (Vatican and Riccardiana, Florence) is written in Italian. It continues feebly the traditions introduced by Leonardo da Pisa (XIII-1), with the best Leonardian material omitted and no novelty of importance. The same traditions may be followed in Italy down to the sixteenth century.

Jacob explains the fundamental operations of arithmetic in the Boetian manner; then he explains the new numbers and the zero (per se solo non significa nulla ma bene a potentia di fare significare) in the manner of Sacrobosco. He shows correctly how to multiply fractions, but does not know how to divide them except in a roundabout way (he reduces them to a common denominator and divides the numerators). Then follow the rule of three and various traditional problems. The algebraical part, which begins abruptly without definitions, contains six types of quadratic and linear equations as given by al-Khwārizmī (IX-1), but with numerical examples different from those of al-Khwārizmī, Abū Kāmil (X-1), and Leonardo of Pisa. Jacob deals also with fourteen other types of equations. There are added the usual problems on exchange, interest, and partnership, one of which at least is exactly the same (with other numbers) as one given by the Jaina mathematician Mahāvīra (IX-1).

It is remarkable that in the arithmetic published by the Florentine mathematician Filippo Calandri (Florence 1491),[1] the treatment of the multiplication table, the form of the illustrations, and many problems are the same as in Jacob's MS treatise of 1307. Calandri used that treatise, or both he and Jacob used the same sources. The comparative study of Leonardo da Pisa, Jacob of Florence, and Calandri shows how slowly arithmetic and algebra developed in three centuries.

Criticism. Louis C. Karpinski: The Italian arithmetic and algebra of master Jacob of Florence (Archeion 11, 170–77, 2 pl., 1929; Isis 14, 481).

[1] D. E. Smith (p. 47–49, 1908). Calandri dedicated his treatise to Julianus Laurentii Medices, whom I take to be Giuliano II de' Medici (1479–1516), 12 years old at the time of printing.

PAOLO DAGOMARI

Paolo dell'Abbaco, dell'Astrologo, Paolo Geometra, Paolo Arismetra. Italian mathematician, astronomer, astrologer, and poet. Born at Prato c. 1281, died sometime between 1365 and 1372. His family name may have been Ficozzi instead of Dagomari.

Paolo was highly spoken of by a number of Florentine writers, none of whom, it should be noted, was a mathematician or astronomer. Thus, Boccaccio praised him several times in the De genealogiis deorum (book 8, ch. 2; book 15, ch. 6, etc.) for his mathematical and astronomical knowledge, saying that Paolo had observed the astronomical facts himself by means of instruments built with his own hands. Coluccio Salutati applauded his astrological ability in a letter to Luigi dei Gianfigliazzi (Epistolario, edited by F. Novati, 1, 15, Rome 1891). Filippo Villani included Paolo's biography in his lives of the illustrious Florentines, and praised him as a mathematician and astronomer, but not as an astrologer. Villani was influenced by Boccaccio, and one suspects that the whole tradition of praise was largely of the same origin, that is, of very little weight for the historian of science.

According to Loria (1, 407), Paolo bequeathed his books and instruments to a Florentine student to be selected as the most deserving by four professors. The bequest was awarded to one Antonio de' Mazzinghi da Peretola, who obtained much renown on that account though he died at the early age of 30.

Paolo's most important work is the Trattato d'abbaco, d'astronomie e di segreti naturali e medicinali, written in 1339; it often appears under shorter titles and varies considerably in different manuscripts. The longest redaction contains sections on arithmetic, astronomical chronology, judicial astrology, medical recipes and secrets. The mathematical section contains problems in commercial arithmetic, some based on those in the Liber abaci of Leonardo of Pisa (XIII-1), tables of weights and measures and coinage. In the astrological section he discusses the properties of planets, their influences, the signs of the zodiac, etc., the text being illustrated by means of a number of astrological diagrams. The medical sections contain many charms and incantations as well as more rational discussions of drugs.

His mathematical knowledge may be appraised from the following examples. He dealt with equations of the first and second degree, and with third-degree equations having only two terms. His commercial arithmetic includes the undetermined problem: to find an integer x such that $x^2(x^2 - 36)$ be a square number. The Regoluzze are a collection of 52 short rules on arithmetic, geometry, and the calendar, in very poor order. The first explains how to divide large numbers beginning from the right in groups of three digits separated by dots, in order to facilitate their reading.[2] In rule 12 there is mention of continued fractions (rotti infilzati), but these had already been derived from Arabic sources by Leonardo of Pisa. In order to obtain the area of a circle, multiply the diameter by 22 and divide by 7 (rule 32). Rules 42 to 45 are devoted to the calendar.

$$\sqrt{A} \sim a + \frac{A - a^2}{2a} \text{ (rule 47).}$$

Paolo composed a taccuino or tacuinum, that is, an almanac, including predictions. He is said to have been the first Christian to do so. That statement may

[2] The idea was not new. It goes back at least to a Liber algorismi of c. 1200, and to Leonardo of Pisa. See Florian Cajori: History of mathematical notations (1, 57, 1928; Isis 12, 332–336).

rest on some misunderstanding. At any rate, he was one of the first compilers of a work of that kind, and both names, tacuinum (Ar., taqwīm) and almanac (Ar., manākh), point to the same Arabic origin.[3]

In another brief work, Operatio cylindri, he describes a cylinder which was a combined astrolabe, calendar, and gnomon. This instrument may be the continuation of a tradition, "the cylinder called horologe of travelers," which has been traced back to Hermann the Lame (XI-2).

Various poems have been attributed to Paolo, at least one of which deals with astrology.

Text. Le regoluzze, edited by Libri (3, 296–301, 1840); also by C. G., A. D. C. (Della miscellanea pratese no. 1, 16 p., Prato 1860); and again by Giacomo Frizzo (Verona 1883).

Operatio cilindri denovo composita anno Christi 1365, edited by B. Boncompagni: Intorno ad alcune opere di Leonardo Pisano (p. 380–83, Rome 1854). New edition with facsimiles, edited by Giuseppe Boffito: Il primo compasso proporzionale costruito da Fabrizio Mordente[4] e la Operatio cilindri di Paolo dell' Abbaco (p. 18–27, Florence 1931; Isis 26, 503), with biographical introduction.

Sonnet addressed to Jacopo Alighieri, edited by Giovanni M. Crescimbeni: Comentari intorno alla sua istoria della volgar poesia (3, 80, Rome 1711). Another sonnet, "d'argomento astrologico," edited by Giovanni Lami: Novelle letterarie (9, 348–49, Florence 1748).

It has been reported by a number of writers that a collection of Paolo's writings was printed in Basel in 1532 by Giovanni Ervagio with a commentary by Iacopo Micillo. No one, however, has ever been able to locate this work. It has been suggested by Boffito (Il primo compasso . . . , p. 16) that Domenico Maria Manni, the first one to mention it (Istoria del Decamerone p. 69, Florence 1742), had in mind the edition of the De genealogiis deorum of Boccaccio printed in Basel in 1532 by Giovanni Ervagio with a commentary by Iacopo Micillo. Paolo Dagomari is mentioned in this work of Boccaccio, but his own works are not included in the edition.

Criticism. G. Tiraboschi: Storia della letteratura italiana (5, 323–28, 1823). Libri (2, 205–7, 526, 1838). Baldassarre Boncompagni: Intorno ad alcune opere di Leonardo Pisano (p. 353–400, Rome 1854). Cantor (2d ed., 2, 164, 1899). D. E. Smith (p. 435–440, 1908). Enrico Massini: Maestro Paolo dell' Abbaco dei Ficozzi erroneamente creduto dei Dagomari (Rassegna nazionale 22, 215–25, 1919). Gino Loria: Storia delle matematiche (1, 407, Torino 1929; Isis 13, 228). Lynn Thorndike: Of the cylinder called the horologe of travelers (Isis 13, 51–52, 1929); History of magic (3, 205–12, 1934).

For comparison see Quido Vetter: Note sulle equazioni di grado superiore in due manoscritti anonimi del secolo XIV pubblicati da Libri (Archeion 9, 175–76, 1928).

COMMERCIAL ARITHMETIC IN ITALY IN THE FIRST HALF OF THE FOURTEENTH CENTURY

The Columbia University MS X511 A13, formerly in the library of prince Baldassare Boncompagni, is an interesting arithmetical document in the Italian language. In addition to 9 fragments written in different scripts, it may be divided into 141 chapters; it is illustrated with 42 crude drawings, some in colors. The treatment is unsystematic. The four fundamental operations are explained early

[3] Lynn Thorndike and G. Sarton: Tacuinum, taqwīm. With a digression on the word almanac (Isis 10, 489–93, 1928).

[4] Fabrizio Mordente of Salerno flourished in the second half of the sixteenth century and was mathematician to Rodolph II (emperor 1576–1612).

in the MS though in a curious order. There are many problems illustrating social and economic conditions. More than a hundred chapters begin with the phrase "Fammi questa rascione"; almost every chapter contains "a rule and a statement in which the reader is assured that that is the correct rule that should be applied in all similar cases." There is a long table (fol. 66r–70v) giving the relative values of coins of many places.

The text was probably written (in Florence?) for commercial apprentices having no interest in theory, but needing sets of handy rules for the solution of practical problems.

Analysis by Elizabeth Buchanan Cowley: An Italian mathematical MS (Vassar mediaeval studies, edited by Christabel Forsyth Fiske, p. 379–405, Yale Univ. Press 1923).

JOHN OF GENOA

Joannes de Janua. Genoese astronomer (fl. 1332–37).

He compiled tables for the computation of eclipses (Canones eclipsium) in 1332, derived from the Almagest, al-Battānī, John of Sicily (XIII-2), and John of Linières. He wrote also an Investigatio eclipsis Solis anno Christi 1337, and an undated Tabula ad sciendum motum Solis in una hora et semydiametros luminarium.

John may be identical with another John of Genoa who was surgeon and physician to Clement VI in 1348. That is not impossible, but we must remember that there were many Johns of Genoa in the fourteenth century, for John was a very common name and Genoa a great city.

Criticism. Duhem: Système (4, 74–75, 1916). Wickersheimer (p. 424, 1936).

HUGH OF CITTÀ DI CASTELLO

Italian (Umbrian) Dominican and astrologer (fl. c. 1337). Ugo de Castello, Hugo de Civitate Castellis, that is, Hugh of Città di Castello (a place in Umbria on the upper Tevere, Tifernum Tiberinum).

He studied at the Dominican convent of St. Honoré in Paris and began there a commentary on the Sphere of Sacrobosco, which he completed at Florence in 1337. He also wrote in 1358 (1338?) at Perugia a treatise on medical astrology (De diebus criticis secundum astrologos). In the contemporary MS (Vatic. Barb. 178) that text is dated 1358 and ascribed to one Hugo de Civitate Castellis, Dominican and bishop. According to Thorndike, the only bishop with a similar name is Hugues de Châtillon, bishop of Comminges in Gascony from 1335 to his death in 1352. Therefore, Thorndike proposes to change the date of the text from 1358 to 1338. This is not quite convincing. Note that Città di Castello is not very far (24 miles) from Perugia.

Text. Unpublished.

Criticism. Lynn Thorndike: Vatican Latin MSS (Isis 13, 53–102, 1929; no. 46); History of magic (3, 217, 1934).

DOMINICUS DE CLAVASIO

Italian mathematician and astrologer (fl. 1346).

Life. He was probably born in Chivasso (Piemonte) near Torino. His name is written also Dominicus de Clavisio, or Clavagio, and Dominicus Parisiensis (Dominic of Chivasso or of Paris). His main work was written in Paris in 1346.

He was a member of the faculty of arts in Paris 1349–50, and a member of the medical faculty in 1356–57. It is said that in 1349 he was teaching philosophy at the College of Constantinople in Paris. He was a court astrologer before 1368, that is, either to John II the Good (1350–64) or to Charles V the Wise (1364–80). If he died between 1357 and 1362 (Tannery), he was astrologer to John the Good.

Writings. His main work, the Practica geometriae, was written in Paris 1346. In addition he wrote Quaestiones super perspectiuam (Codex S. Marci florent 202), a question on the Sphere of John of Sacrobosco (Erfurt MS), a commentary on the De coelo et mundo (Vatican 2185), and he was planning to write a Tractatus de umbris et radiis.

Geometry. The Practica geometriae is a treatise on measurements divided into three books dealing with the measurements respectively of lengths, areas, and volumes. Judging by the number of MSS, this treatise attained some popularity, yet it remained unprinted. It includes trigonometrical notions to be considered in the next paragraph. In contradistinction to most mediaeval mathematicians, including even such men as John Campano and John of Saxony, Dominicus realized that $3\frac{1}{7}$ is only approximately equal to the ratio of circumference to diameter.

The Practica geometriae was the archetype of the so-called Geometria culmensis,[5] a geometrical treatise written for Conrad von Jungingen, grand master of the Teutonic Knights from 1393 to 1407. It was written in Latin (Liber geometrie practice usualis manualis), and also in German (probably at the same time). It is divided into five parts, dealing with measurements (1) and (2) of triangles, (3) of rectangles, (4) and (5) of other surfaces. The purpose is practical, errors being generally avoided. The German edition of the Geometria culmensis should not be confused with the Geometria deutsch, a different text, very short and perhaps of earlier origin (twelfth or thirteenth century), which was printed in 1489.

Trigonometry. Dominicus had a good elementary knowledge of trigonometry. He was acquainted with the sinus, sinus versus, cosinus, umbra versa, and umbra recta. He realized the practical value of the tangent. It is not known whether he was able to write his Tractatus de umbris et radiis, but he used trigometrical measurements in his Practica.

Text. The Practica geometriae is still unpublished. The edition had been undertaken by Maximilian Curtze, but was interrupted by his death in 1903; then Paul Tannery took it up, but died himself soon afterward, in 1904.

H. Mendthal: Geometria culmensis. Ein agronomischer Tractat aus der Zeit des Hochmeisters Conrad von Jungingen, 1393–1407 (76 p., Leipzig 1886), Latin and German texts edited in parallel columns.

The Geometria deutsch was printed anonymously in Nürnberg (quarto, 6 fol., 1489). According to Cantor (p. 450), 1487 is the upper limit of the date of publication, but Klebs says 1489 (p. 153, 1938). It was reprinted by Siegmund Günther: Zur Geschichte der deutschen Mathematik im 15. Jahrhundert (Zeitschrift für Mathematik und Physik, hist.-lit. Abt., 20, 5–7, 1875).

The other writings of Dominicus are unpublished.

Criticism. Maximilian Curtze: Über den Dominicus parisiensis der Geometria culmensis (BM 9, 107–10, 1895, including a list of MSS); Über die im Mittelalter zur Feldmessung benutzten Instrumente (BM 10, 69–72, 1896). Cantor (2, 127,

[5] Name given by the editor, Mendthal (1886), though found in only one MS. The text, however, mentions measures of Kulm (p. 21, duo pedes faciunt ulnam colmensem). A German writer flourishing in Kulm on the Vistula or in the Kulmerland east of that river might easily think of dedicating his work to the grand master of the Teutonic Knights.

150–54, 450–52, 1899). Braunmühl (1, 107, 110, 1900). Tannery (5, 329, 357, 1922), two short notes dating from 1900 and 1904. Gustav Eneström: Über zwei angebliche mathematische Schulen im christlichen Mittelalter (BM 7, 252–62, 1907). Axel Anthon Björnbo: Die mathematischen S. Marcohandschriften in Florenz (BM 12, 203, 218, 1912). Zinner (p. 75, 406, 1925). Michalski (p. 149–50, 1927). Lynn Thorndike: Vatican Latin MSS (Isis 13, 69, 1929); History of magic (3, 587, 1934). Wickersheimer (p. 121, 1936).

CECCO D'ASCOLI

Italian astrologer (1269–1327).

Life. Francesco degli Stabili. Cicchus Esculanus, Franciscus de Esculo. Born in the district of Ascoli (Ascoli Piceno nelle Marche) in 1269; his life is very little known, but he taught astrology in various Italian cities, finally in Bologna 1322–24. On December 16, 1324 the inquisitor Lamberto da Cingoli condemned him for heresy and forbade him to teach. Cecco went to Florence, and in 1326 was appointed physician and astrologer to Carlo duke of Calabria (son of Robert of Anjou). However, he aroused the enmity of some Florentines, chiefly Dino del Garbo, was again tried for heresy, was condemned by the Minorite fra Accursio, and was burned at the stake, he and his writings, in Florence on September 16, 1327.

Writings. Cecco wrote an obscure didactic poem in Italian, entitled L'acerba. There is no agreement upon the meaning of that title (acerbus? liber acerbae actatis? la cerva?). It is in terzetti and contains 4,867 lines, divided into five books: (I) description of heavens, elements and their order, eclipses, comets, meteorology; (II) fortune, man's birth and astrological influences, physiognomy, virtues and vices; (III) love, symbolical psychology, properties and symbols of animals and plants; (IV) movements of planets, occult sciences, problems of physics, meteorology, alchemy, anatomy, optics, biology, morality, etc.; (V, unfinished) continued creation of souls, transience of material world.

The scope of the poem is encyclopaedic, but the spirit informing it is astrological. The scientific knowledge explained is neither high nor new; much of it is to be classified as folklore.

Half a dozen Italian sonnets are ascribed to Cecco, one of them dealing with a tenebrous kind of alchemy (La pietra filosofale), the others being addressed to Cino da Pistoia, Dante, and Petrarca. He believed himself far superior in scientific knowledge to Dante.

He wrote a number of treatises in Latin:

1. Commentary on the Sphaera mundi of John of Sacrobosco, before 1322. The commentary is decidedly astrological.

2. Commentary on the astrological introduction of al-Qabīṣī (X-2), the very work to which John of Saxony devoted another commentary a few years later (1331). Cecco's commentaries on Sacrobosco and al-Qabīṣī have much in common and refer to the same authorities: Hippocrates, Hipparchos, Theodosios of Bithynia, Ptolemy, Abū Ma'shar, al-Farghānī, Thābit ibn Qurra, Ibn Sīnā, Albert the Great, etc.

3. De eccentricis et epicyclis. Lecture delivered at Bologna in 1322.

Other works ascribed to Cecco: De morbis cognoscendis ex aspectu astrorum; Epistola de qualitate planetarum; De quodam modo physionomiae; Liber de ascensione signorum (de ascensionibus). The last-named treatise deals also with arithmetical progressions.

Astronomical knowledge. Cecco's astronomy was not on a high level. For example, in his commentary on Sacrobosco, discussing the movement of the eighth sphere, he concluded that the precession is not continuous and does not exceed a total amount of 10°, then each star comes back to its initial location in a circular way. Cecco was primarily an astrologer; for him astronomy was only a means for astrological purposes.

Cecco's condemnation. His writings, Latin as well as Italian, are generally mediocre. It is probable that they owe their relative popularity, as witnessed by early editions (12 incunabula of the Acerba), to Cecco's martyrdom. It is difficult to account for the latter, for there is little if anything in his writings which could not be found as well in contemporary writings which were not condemned. Was he guilty of insisting too much on astrological fatalism? or of attaching too much importance to the horoscopes of individuals or of cities? All the astrologers did that, and every one of them had to find some means of reconciling astrological fatalism with Christian freedom. Cecco claimed that there were two universal causes, God being the first, the heavens being the second, duly subordinated to the first. Such doctrine was orthodox enough. While condemning magic, Cecco entertained a number of magical ideas; his contemporaries, however, were as muddleheaded as himself on the subject. It is probable that his condemnation was partly due to his polemical attitude, e.g. against Dante, to his Ghibellinism, and to the hostility which he had managed to arouse against himself. It may have been due to imprudent sayings or doings, rather than to his writings.

Text. 1. The Commentarius in Sphaeram is appended to several editions of Sacrobosco: Venice 1499, 1518 (twice). The edition of 1499 is entitled, Sphera mundi cum tribus commentis nuper editis, videlicet Cicchi Esculani, Francisci Capuani de Manfredonia, Jacobi Fabri Stapulensis. . . . The two Venetian editions of 1518 are included in rival editions of the Sphere with commentaries and related treatises (full titles in Duhem 3, 246). As to the two commentators above mentioned, Franciscus de Manfredonia was a doctor of arts and medicine who gave astronomical lectures at the University of Padua 1494–95; Jacobus Faber Stapulensis was the French humanist and mathematician Jacques Lefèvre d'Etaples (1455–1537).

2. The commentary on al-Qabīṣī, De principiis astrologiae, was first edited by Giuseppe Boffito (Giornale storico della letteratura italiana, 1903, suppt. no. 6; also Firenze 1905, 64 p., ill.). In appendix, texts of the Liber Esculei de ascensionibus, and of the De quodam modo physionomiae.

3. De eccentricis et epicyclis. Edited by Giuseppe Boffito (Pubblicazioni dell' Osservatorio del Collegio alle Querce, quarto ser., no. 7, Florence 1905).

First edition of the Acerba, Brescia c. 1473. Then: Venice 1476, 1478, 1481; Rome 1483, Milano 1484, Venice 1484/85, Bologna 1485, Venice 1487, 1492, Bologna 1496, Venice 1500. These twelve incunabula are described in GW (6, 356–60, 1934). There were at least 14 more editions in the first half of the sixteenth century, and another in Venice 1820. New edition by Pasquale Rosario, with introduction and bibliography (160 p., Lanciano 1916); this includes the six sonnets ascribed to Cecco. Critical edition by Achille Crespi (492 p., Ascoli Piceno 1927). This edition was published in Cecco's native town for the sixth centenary of his death; text with abundant notes and documents. The editor's mediaeval and scientific knowledge was insufficient for his task; some of the notes are childish, others are wrong.

The alchemical sonnet was reprinted in Mario Mazzoni: Sonetti alchemici-ermetici di Frate Elia e Cecco d'Ascoli (40 p., San Gimignano, Siena 1930). Uncritical. Frate Elia is Elia da Cortona, successor to St. Francis of Assisi and general of the Franciscans in 1232.

Criticism. Riccardi (p. 472–74; suppt. 1, 70; 3, 188; 5, 155; 1887–93). Giuseppe Castelli: La vita e le opere di Cecco d'Ascoli (Bologna 1892). Vincenzo Paoletti: Cecco d'Ascoli (182 p., Bologna 1905). Augusto Beccaria: La redazione in volgare della sentenza di Frate Accursio contra M. Cecco d'Ascoli (Atti dell' Accad. di Torino vol. 41, 30 p., 1906); I biografi di Cecco d'Ascoli e le fonti per la sua storia e la sua leggenda (Memorie dell' Accad. di Torino, ser. 2, vol. 58, 94 p. folio, 1908). Duhem: Système (4, 263–66, 1916). Thorndike: History of magic (2, 948–68, 1923); Relations of the inquisition to Peter of Abano and Cecco d'Ascoli (Speculum 1, 338–43, 1926). Giuseppe Boffito: La circolazione del sangue secondo Cecco d'Ascoli e Dante Alighieri (Pubblicazioni del Collegio alle Querce di Firenze, 20 p., 1932). Adalberto Pazzini: Il dottrinale medico nell' Acerba (Bolletino del Istituto storico italiano dell' arte sanitaria 14, 230–49, 274–92, 1934). Hiram Pflaum: L'Acerba di Cecco d'Ascoli, saggio d'interpretazione (70 p., Firenze 1939; Isis 33, 94), with critical edition of the contemporary Latin commentary on ch. I.

RUBERTIS

Dionysius de Rubertis de Burgo Sancti Sepulchri. Italian Augustinian, humanist and astrologer (d. 1339).

Friend and correspondent of Petrarca, who admired him (as an astronomer and astrologer!) and lamented his death. He was called to Naples by Robert (king 1309–43) for astrological advice. He wrote commentaries on Aristotle's Poetics, Rhetoric, and Politics, on Vergil, on the Metamorphoses of Ovid (43 B.C.–A.D. 18), on the De factis dictisque memorabilibus of Valerius Maximus (fl. under Tiberius, emp. 14–37), on the tragedies of Seneca (I-2), and on the epistle which St. Paul wrote to the Romans in 56 or 57.

Criticism. Thorndike (3, 219, 1934).

PAGANICA

Niccolò di Paganica (or di Aquila). Italian astrologer (fl. 1330).

Nicolaus de Paganica (near Aquila degli Abruzzi) was a Dominican who in 1330 dedicated a treatise on medical astrology, Compendium medicinalis astrologiae, to three physicians, Roger of Manfredonia, Nucio of Ascoli, and Raynald of Adria; in another MS it is dedicated to Giovanni da Oleggio (of the Milanese Visconti, d. 1366). Paganica was still living in 1371, if he is identical with the astrologer who drew the horoscope of the future John the Fearless, duke of Burgundy (b. 1371, d. 1419).

The Compendium medicinalis astrologiae is divided into 15 chapters, dealing in the conventional way with astrological generalities and their applications to physiology and medicine, e.g., with regard to the crises and their prognosis, or to the determination of auspicious times for bloodletting or the taking of physic.

Criticism. Thorndike (3, 213–17, 698, 1934). Wickersheimer (p. 574, 1936).

ANDALÒ DI NEGRO

Andalus de Negro, Andalius de Nigro de Ianua, Andalone del Nero. Italian astrologer and astronomer. Born of a noble Genoese family not later than 1260, died c. 1340. The famous Genoese sailor Carlotto di Negro was probably his brother. In 1314 Andalò was sent by the signoria of Genoa as ambassador to Alexios II Comnenos, emperor of Trebizond (1297–1330).

The details of Andalò's life are very uncertain. According to Boccaccio, he traveled all over the world; we may assume that he had traveled far and wide. He lived for some time in Rome, Naples, and Florence. He was Boccaccio's teacher in astronomy while the latter was in Naples (c. 1331–39), and owes his fame to the latter's enthusiastic, incompetent, and uncritical praise.[6]

Andalò was a prolific writer, but as only one of his works can be approximately dated (the Canones, c. 1323), it is not possible to examine them in chronological order. It will be convenient to classify them in three groups: theoretical astronomy, practical astronomy, astrology. We shall consider them in that order.

Theoretical astronomy. (1) Tractatus sphaerae (Novus spere tractatus), (2) Theorica planetarum, (3) Theorica distantiarum omnium sperarum et planetarum a terra et magnitudinem [sic] eorum.

The most ambitious of these treatises seems to be the last named, wherein Andalò claimed to have improved the knowledge of the dimensions of the celestial spheres as transmitted by al-Farghānī (IX-1), al-Battānī (IX-2), and Ibn Rusta (X-1). According to him, the results of his predecessors were incorrect because they had failed to add or subtract the radius of each planet. He took that radius into consideration each time and thus obtained the maximal and minimal distances of each planet from the center of the earth. These distances are expressed in function of the earth's own radius and its sexagesimal subdivisions. Thus (Duhem 4, 273), the distance of the moon (or radius of the first sphere) is 33 15′28″, the distance of Mercury (or radius of the second sphere) is 64 27′32″, the distance of Venus (or radius of the third sphere) is 178 30′8″, the distance of the sun (or radius of the fourth sphere) is 1,199 28′58″. It is not clear from what source Andalò obtained these figures; his own mathematical equipment was insufficient to develop a new method, and the improvement introduced by him was specious.

According to him, the movement of the eighth sphere implied not only the Ptolemaic precession but also the trepidation, that false notion reintroduced by Thābit ibn Qurra (IX-2) and later by al-Biṭrūjī (XII-2). In extenuation of this we should remember that the Thābitian trepidation was still accepted by Copernicus.

In his Tractatus spere (ch. IX) Andalò compared the value of the obliquity of the ecliptic as given in the Toledo tables (23°30′30″) with the Ptolemaic value (23°51′ 20″), but did not conclude that there was a secular variation.

On the other hand, in the same treatise (ch. III) he discussed the theory according to which the land sphere and the water sphere (in the earth) have not the same center, and concluded correctly against it. A similar conclusion was reached at about the same time by the author of the Quaestio de aqua et terra (1320), for which see my note on Dante, §9.

One of the MSS of treatises 1 and 2 (now in the Laurentiana, Firenze) was formerly owned by Boccaccio.[7] This fact tends to confirm the latter's claim that he had studied them, but he had no means of appreciating their value; to his untrained mind they represented the climax of astronomical knowledge!

Practical astronomy. Under this heading may be put together on the one hand a treatise on tables, and on the other a series of treatises on the astrolabe.

Andalò's (4) Canones super Almanach Profatii were written c. 1323. They deal

[6] Boccaccio went so far as to say that Andalò deserved the same authority in astronomy as Cicero in eloquence and Virgil in poetry! (De genealogiis deorum, book 15, ch. 6, p. 389, Basel 1532). There are many other references to him in that same work and in other writings of Boccaccio.

[7] Henri Hauvette: Notes sur des manuscrits autographes de Boccace à la bibliothèque laurentienne (Mélanges de l'Ecole française de Rome 14, 87–145, 1894; p. 102).

with the very popular tables compiled by Jacob ben Maḥir ibn Tibbon (XIII-2; Montpellier 1300). Andalò states that Jacob used the Alfonsine tables, i.e., the newer tables of Toledo, and not the older ones computed by al-Zarqālī (XI-2); he also correctly notes that the Alfonsine tables were drawn up in 1272 and not in 1252, a date frequently given by later writers.

His writings on the astrolabe are (5) Opus preclarissimum astrolabii, (6) Practica astrolabii, (7) De operationibus scale quadrantis in astrolabio scripte, (8) De compositione astrolabii, (9) Tractatus quadrantis. The first three were printed together at Ferrara 1475, and are the only writings of his thus far published, a fact which suggests that Boccaccio's enthusiasm was not shared by many people. The treatises 8 and 9 are sometimes considered as variants of 5 and 7; according to Boncompagni, there are considerable differences between the printed and unprinted texts.

Astrology. Andalò's astrological ideas are explained in a voluminous treatise entitled (10) Introductorium ad iudicia astrologie, the MSS of which include colored charts, the different colors having symbolic meanings (e.g., masculine vs. feminine, lucky vs. unlucky).[8] He probably took a number of his astrological theories from Peter of Abano's writings (though he might have found them elsewhere), for example, the contingency of astrological judgments, the astrological implications of correspondence or divergence between the zodiac of the eighth sphere and that of the ninth. Civilization grows as these zodiacs come closer together; it tends to decline as they separate. Andalò admits that astrological judgments are often erroneous, and unavoidably so, because of the infinite complexity of causes (e.g., one can only consider a few stars among a great many) and the equal complexity of materials (human and nonhuman) upon which these causes operate. These restrictions gave the astrologer convenient alibis but undermined his authority.

Andalò applied astrology to physiology in two treatises, (11) De infusione spermatis and (12) Ratio diversitatis partus, both of which deal with procreation, and to medicine in two or three others, (13) Liber iudiciorum infirmitatum, (14) Astrologia de urina non visa, (15) Canones modernorum astrologorum de infirmitatibus. Items 13 and 15 may be two variants of a single work. These treatises (11 to 15) are of the very kind which Petrarca criticized so furiously in his letters to Giovanni de' Dondi (1370); Petrarca, however, does not refer to them nor to their author, though he must have known of him through Boccaccio.

Text. Opus preclarissimum astrolabii. Practica astrolabii. De operationibus scale quadrantis in astrolabio scripte; all three printed together in Ferrara 1475 (only 20 leaves).

G. Bertolotto: Il Trattato sull'astrolabio riprodotto dall'edizione ferrarese del 1475 (Atti della Società ligure di storia patria 25, 51–144, 1892); not seen.

Criticism. Libri (2, 200–2, 1838). The early biography by Bernardino Baldi of Urbino (1553–1617), written in 1588, was first published in Boncompagni's Bullettino di bibliografia e di storia delle scienze (7, 337–38, 1874). Cornelio de Simoni: Intorno alla vita ed ai lavori di Andalò di Negro (ibid. p. 313–36). Baldassare Boncompagni: Catalogo de' lavori di Andalò (ibid. p. 339–76), very elaborate bibliography of MSS and editions. Antonio Favaro: Intorno al probabile autore di una predizione di terremoto riferita da Petrarca (Atti del R. Istituto veneto di

[8] For a discussion of these colored diagrams see Thorndike (3, 191) and the publications referred to in his footnote 3.

scienze, lettere ed arti 2, 545–58, 1876). Duhem: Système (4, 266–78, 1916). Lynn Thorndike: Andalò di Negro, Profacius Judaeus, and the Alphonsine tables (Isis 10, 52–56, 1928), correcting Duhem's erroneous statements; History of magic (3, 191–204, 692–94, 1934). Millás Vallicrosa (MS xxxvii, p. 154, 1942).

AUGUSTINE OF TRENT

Augustinus de Tridento. Italian Augustinian, medical astrologer (fl. 1340).

Augustine was born in Brescia, assumed the Augustinian habit, lectured at the University of Perugia. On July 12, 1340 he dedicated to Nicholas Abrein of Brünn, Moravia, then bishop (1336–47) of Trent in the March of Verona, a Latin treatise on the pestilence of 1340, which is of special interest because it is anterior to the Black Death and its abundant literature, yet is not essentially different from that literature.

The pestilence of 1340 was very severe in Florence, where it destroyed about one-sixth of the population. See account of it in the Istorie fiorentine of Giovanni Villani.

Augustine's treatise is divided into six parts: (I) Astrological causes and conditions of the pestilence of 1340. For example, he determines astrologically the territory of that pestilence as one would determine the territory of an eclipse. The pestilence may be caused partly by other circumstances, such as the failure of crops, heavy rains (though the exceptional rains of 1338 and 1339 did not cause sicknesses comparable with those of 1340), but the fundamental causes are astrological. Each planet affects certain organs of the body more than others. Remarks on the difficulty of diagnosing death and the possibility of burying people alive. (II) Regimen to avoid the plague, including astrological precautions. (III) Diet. (IV) Bloodletting, purgation, etc., and their astrological conditions. (V, VI) Astrological lord of the year (Saturn, then Jupiter, etc.).

Augustine was acquainted with various Aristotelian books and with Greek and Arabic medicine, as available in Latin, and he quotes repeatedly two contemporary physicians, Odoric and Jordan (qui experti sunt in astronomia et in medicina), presumably two colleagues of his or local worthies. His main astrological authorities were Hermes, the pseudo-Hippocratic treatise on the influence of the moon in the signs,[9] Ptolemy; Māshāllāh (VIII-2), al-Kindī (IX-1), Abū Ma'shar (IX-1), al-Qabīṣī (X-2), 'Alī ibn abī-l-Rijāl (XI-1), etc.; John of Seville (XII-1), John of Vicenza (XIII-1), Michael Scot (XIII-1), Guido Bonatti (XIII-2), and the Alphonsine tables, named after Alfonso X el Sabio (XIII-2).

Criticism. Thorndike (3, 222, 224–32, 699–707, 1934), including extracts from the Latin text.

THADDEUS OF PARMA

Italian astrologer and occultist (d. before 1341).

Thaddeus is said to have written questions on the De anima of Aristotle, but his main work is a commentary on the theory of planets of Gherardo da Sabbioneta (XIII-2), which he completed on July 12, 1318, Expositio theorice planetarum. This is a treatise on astrological medicine, but it contains a fantastic classification of the occult sciences. These are first divided into mantica and mathesis; mantica is subdivided into four parts corresponding to the four elements, geomancy, aeri-

[9] For that treatise, Astrologia Hippocratis sive De luna in signis, etc., see my note on Pietro d'Abano.

mancy, hydromancy, pyromancy; mathesis is subdivided into theurgy and altimancy; the major theurgy is subdivided into cathademonica, agathomantica, cacomantia; and so on. There are a great many subdivisions, each of which has a forbidding name (scenobathica, aliptica, illemantia, homosmantia, salisaliptitas, etc.), and for each an inventor is named! For example, the inventor of the major theurgy and of the minor one are respectively Nectanebus and Avenderich. Thaddeus was apparently as learned as he was unbalanced. His strange book is one of the pathological curiosities of mediaeval literature.

Criticism. Thorndike (3, 12–17, 649, 1934), including analysis and list of MSS.

A2. France

JEAN DE LINIÈRES

French (Picard) astronomer and mathematician, one of the greatest of the fourteenth century (d. c. 1350–55).

Contents: (1) Life. (2) Writings. (3) Astronomy. (4) Astronomical instruments. (5) Arithmetic. (6) Trigonometry.
(7) Text. (8) Criticism.

1. *Life*

Jean de (des) Linières (or Lignières), Joannes de Lineriis (Liveriis, Liverius) Ambianensis (i.e., of Amiens). Born in the diocese of Amiens, Picardy, place and time unknown. There are at least two places in that diocese called Lignières. In an early printed edition he is named Joannes de Lineriis Siculus, but that is probably an error. He may have been confused with a John of Sicily, e.g., the astronomer (XIII-2) who flourished in Paris c. 1290.

Jean de Linières flourished in Paris c. 1320–35; he was still living in 1350 and died before 1355. The German humanist Joannes Trithemius (1462–1516) in his Liber de scriptoribus ecclesiasticis (no. 580, Basel 1494) described him as "philosophus et astronomus omnium suo tempore celeberrimus," and named as his collaborators Bernard (this being very probably Bernard of Verdun, XIII-2), John of Meurs, and John of Saxony.

2. *Writings*

John de Linières wrote astronomical works which were very widely used in mediaeval times, witness the large number of MSS. The bibliography of these writings is made very difficult because the same works appear in various MSS under different titles or in separate parts, which have been considered as separate works.

In 1320 he compiled canons derived from the Alfonsine tables for the meridian of Paris, Canones super tabulas magnas. His tables begin with the year 1320 (hence the dating) and are dedicated to Robert of Florence (i.e., Roberto de' Bardi).[10] In his dedication he explains the difference between theoretical astronomy and observational astronomy. The observers need tables and instruments. The Canones contain the necessary tables with explanations of their use,

[10] This Roberto de' Bardi is not included in DNB, but I found two references to him in Robert Renwick and John Lindsay: History of Glasgow (1, 148, 151, Glasgow 1921), according to which Robertus de Bardis or de Florencia was dean of Glasgow in 1325. He was chancellor of the University of Paris in 1336, and died in 1339.

and descriptions of instruments, especially of the universal astrolabe; there is also included an arithmetical introduction, to which I shall come back presently.

In 1322 he completed new canons, Canones tabularum astronomie (Alfonsii), which are different from the earlier ones but serve the same purpose, i.e., to answer the needs of the practical astronomer. They include trigonometrical and astronomical tables.

A copy of these Canones (with or without the commentary of John of Saxony) was taken to Marsiglio of Padua in Milano 1327, and communicated by him to Simeone de Moronis, and others. This illustrates the eagerness of their reception by John's contemporaries.

In 1335, he wrote a book on theoretical astronomy, Theorica planetarum. Finally, he compiled a catalogue of 48 stars, giving their positions, based on personal observations, for the vernal equinox of 1350. A few smaller works are also ascribed to him, which are sometimes difficult to distinguish from parts of the larger ones.

3. *Astronomy*

John's catalogue of stars was based on personal observations at the time of the vernal equinox 1350; in 1364 their new positions were calculated by an anonymous Provençal, and some of the positions for 1350 and 1364 were copied by one John of Spires (Speier, near Mannheim). This was one of the earliest Western (non-Muslim) attempts to correct the data of Hipparchos. John had determined the distance of the tropics (he calls it the declination) for 1332, 47°3′30″. This gives for the obliquity of the ecliptic (half of the distance) 23°31′45″, a result remarkably close to that which could be deduced from Le Verrier's tables for that year (23°31′38″). John de Linières might have obtained it, however, not from his own observations but from those of William of Saint Cloud (XIII-2) for 1290. The main point is that accurate astronomical observations were made at that time in Paris, and their value was appreciated.

Though John de Linières was primarily interested in observations, he had his own views on theoretical astronomy, which he set forth in his Theorica planetarum (1335). These views were decidedly Ptolemaic, that is, he accepted without question the eccentrics and epicycles and rejected the homocentric spheres. He expressed doubts with regard to the motion[11] of the fixed stars and of the apogees of the planets, being satisfied, however, that the Alphonsine tables gave a better approximation of it than those of al-Zarqālī. This attitude is characteristic and illustrates a real scientific progress. John was fully aware of theoretical difficulties, but did not try to solve them recklessly; he realized the fundamental importance of making correct observations and of reducing the discordance between calculated and observed positions.

The Alphonsine tables in their printed form (Venice 1483) represent a modification of the original tables, made at Paris by John de Linières and his pupil John of Saxony (q.v.).

4. *Astronomical instruments*

The Canones of 1320 were partly devoted to the description of John's universal astrolabe, and that part was published separately under various titles: Abbreviatio instrumenti Campani, sive aequatorium; Instrumentum saphee; Canon saphee;

[11] That is, the trepidation reintroduced by Thābit ibn Qurra (IX-2); not, of course, the precession. The Thābitian trepidation, he concluded, was wrong (see Duhem: Système 4, 67).

Equatorium planetarum. It is possible that some of these MSS contain new materials; this can only be established by a comparative study of them. It is unlikely that his aequatorium or directorium was a novel instrument, or that the novelty was important. Similar instruments, differing only in small details, were invented by almost every astronomer of note, e.g., Jacob ben Maḥir ibn Tibbon (Prophatius), John Campanus, William of Saint Cloud, Richard Wallingford.

5. *Arithmetic*

The mathematical introduction to the Canones of 1320 dealt with the arithmetic of sexagesimal fractions, Modum additionis integrorum et minutiarum physicarum cum integris et minutiis physicis proponere. There are a great many MSS, with such titles as "algorismus de minutiis," which are either copies of that introduction or elaborations of it. Some of these MS texts deal not only with physical (sexagesimal) fractions, but also with vulgar ones, de minutiis physicis et vulgaribus. A comparative study of all these texts is badly needed. It is only when that study is completed that it will be possible to decide whether the Algorismus de minutiis (printed Padua 1483) bearing the name of Joannes de Lineriis Siculus is entirely the work of John de Lineriis, or an elaboration of it. I shall assume tentatively that it is an authentic work.

The subject of "physical fractions" was then a popular one. Cantor refers (2, 127, 1899) to a fourteenth-century MS, Cod. LXXVII in the library of Seitenstetten, lower Austria, wherein it is remarked that the characteristic value of sexagesimal fractions lies in their systematic arrangement, not in the number 60, which might be replaced by 10 or 12, except that 60 has more factors.

6. *Trigonometry*

Parts of John's second Canones (1322) dealing with trigonometry have also been copied separately under such titles as Tabule sinus, Tabule declinationum . . . et sinuum, Tractatus de sinibus et cordis, etc. John gave tables of sines for each half-degree, the radius (sinus totus, sinus perfectus) being counted as 60°, and tables of tangents for every degree, the radius being counted as 12. These tables are of Arabic origin, but the derivation is not clear (al-Zarqālī?). John added a tabula proportionis to facilitate interpolations.

7. *Text*

The treatise De minutiis was printed twice together with, and after, the Algorismus de integris of Prosdocimo de' Beldomandi (c. 1375–1428). First edition Padua 1483; second, Venice 1540.

Maximilian Curtze: Die Canones tabularum primi mobilis des Johannes de Lineriis (BM 1, 390–413, 1900). This is a part of the Canones of 1322, edited by Curtze, as one of his "Urkunden zur Geschichte der Trigonometrie im christlichen Mittelalter."

8. *Criticism*

Moritz Steinschneider: Intorno a Johannes de Liveriis et Johannes Siculus (Boncompagni's Bullettino di bibliografia e di storia delle scienze 12, 345–51, 1879). B. Boncompagni: Intorno alle vite di tre matematici, Giovanni Danck di Sassonia, Giovanni de Lineriis e Fra Luca Pacioli da Borgo San Sepolcro, scritte da Bernardino Baldi (1553–1617) (ibid. p. 352–427); Baldi's biography of John de Lineriis, dated 1588, is very brief (p. 420) and inaccurate; Baldi called John a "tedesco."

C. Le Paige: Notice historique sur la détermination des coordonnées géographiques de Liége (Mémoires de la Société royale des sciences de Liége vol. 15, 1888). Moritz Steinschneider: Johannes de Ligneriis (BM 3, 37–38, 1889). Maximilian Curtze: War Johannes de Lineriis ein Deutscher, ein Italiener oder ein Franzose? (BM 9, 105–6, 1895). Cantor (2, 126, 152, 207, 1899). D. E. Smith (p. 13, 1908). Guillaume Bigourdan: Sur l'astronome oublié Jean de Lignières (Comptes rendus de l'Académie des sciences 161, 714–17, 753–58, 1915; 162, 18–23, 61–67, 1916), four notes with slightly different titles; they include a list of all the Linières MSS. Tropfke (5, 26, 177, 1923). R. T. Gunther (2, 31, 234, 1923). Zinner (1925). Thorndike (3, 253–67, 1934).

JEAN DE MEURS

French author of popular textbooks on mathematics and music, astrologer (d. after 1350).

Contents: (1) Life. (2) Mathematics. (3) Mechanics. (4) Astronomy. (5) Astrology. (6) Music.
(7) Text. (8) Criticism (except music). (9) Musical criticism. (10) Jacobus of Liége.

1. *Life*

John of Murs (or Meurs), Jean de Meurs or Murs, Joannes de Muris, de Morys. John was born in the diocese of Lisieux, Normandy, at an unknown date (the date 1310 is certainly too late). There are various places called Murs (or Meures) in France, but I do not know of any in Normandy. In 1313 John was temporarily in Evreux, Normandy, but he seems to have spent the best part of his active life in Paris. He was connected with the Sorbonne at least from 1321 to 1339. He was still living in 1350.

We shall consider his writings in the order of their subject matter.

2. *Mathematics*

His main work (outside the musical field) was the Opus quadripartitum numerorum sive de mensurandi ratione, completed on November 13, 1343. The Quadripartitum numerorum (alias, rimatum) consists of a metrical text with a prose commentary; it is divided into four books and a semiliber, books I to III and the semiliber being devoted to arithmetic and algebra, book IV to various mathematical applications. Book IV includes six treatises: (1, 2) on mechanics (to be discussed in another section); (3) De monetis, scilicet de arte consolandi; (4) De sonis musicis; (5) Quaedam quaestiones delectabiles; (6) De arte delendi. Added to this is an arithmetical treatise in verse in the form of a letter to Philip of Vitry, bishop of Meaux.[12] The arithmetical and algebraical parts contain nothing new; they are derived mainly from al-Khwārizmī (IX-1) and from Leonardo of Pisa (XIII-1), also from John of Sacrobosco (XIII-1). The dependence on al-Khwārizmī is slavish; it extends in some cases to numerical illustrations. Much of al-Khwārizmī's algebra had already been incorporated in the works of Leonardo of Pisa, but John of Meurs was directly acquainted with al-Khwārizmī through the translation

[12] If John of Meurs called his friend bishop of Meaux (i.e., if that title is not a later interpolation), then John was still living in 1351, for Philip of Vitry was bishop of Meaux from 1351 to 1361. See note devoted to him.

by Robert of Chester (XII-1; 1145), and he occasionally quotes al-Khwārizmian examples not used by Leonardo of Pisa. The subjects dealt with include such as arithmetical computations, the six types of quadratic equations, solution of problems by the rule of double false position (regula augmenti et diminutionis, regula elchatayn, i.e., al-khaṭ'ain = duorum falsorum), the transformation of fractions into simplices fractiones (unit fractions) and philosophicas (sexagesimal). Arithmetic is called ars minor (which suggests the term ars maior used by Renaissance mathematicians for algebra, or ars magna by Cardan, 1545, etc.), algebra is called de censibus et re (cf. Regiomontanus, ars rei et census). Judging from the MSS, the Quadripartitum was much used in the fifteenth century; it and its influence can be traced in later works, such as those of Regiomontanus and Adam Riese (c. 1489–1559).

At an unknown date John wrote an arithmetic of the Boetian type, Arithmetica communis. It was printed in Vienna 1515, as if it were simply extracted from Boetius; it is more original than that title suggests, without containing anything intrinsically new. John's Arithmetica was a popular textbook for a considerable time (at least in the German countries).

In 1321 he composed tables relative to the use of sexagesimal and ordinary fractions, Canones tabule minutiarum philosophicarum (i.e., sexagesimal) et vulgarium, or Canones tabule tabularum. In Paris 1324, he composed another treatise on fractions, ending with the words Haec est arbor Boetii de arte numerorum sumpta et ordinata . . . .

To return to his main mathematical treatise, the Quadripartitum numerorum, it is important in the history of mathematical teaching and diffusion, but it is almost negligible in the history of mathematical discovery. The word "almost" must be added because of an extraordinary anticipation which occurs in book II, ch. 22. Having extracted the root of 2 as follows,

$$\sqrt{2} = \frac{1}{1.000}\sqrt{2.000.000} = \frac{1}{1.000}\,1414,$$

he gives the result in sexagesimals, $1°24'50''24'''$, then adds that if we say that 1414 is the root of 2, the first unit of that number is to be regarded as an integer, the following 4 as tenths, etc. This is the clearest anticipation of the idea of decimal fractions until Stevin's own (1585), almost two centuries and a half later.

Finally, John wrote a little tract explaining the computation of sines, Figura inveniendi sinus kardagarum et aliarum circuli porcionum . . . . In this text a kardaga is an arc of 15°. His method was derived from al-Zarqālī's.

A few other mathematical works are ascribed to him.

3. *Mechanics*

Of the six treatises which constitute the fourth part of John's Quadripartitum numerorum, the first two deal with mechanics. (1) The De moventibus et motis is a development of the fundamental (wrong) principle of Aristotelian dynamics, "every moving body submitted to a constant power and encountering a constant resistance moves with a uniform speed proportional to the power and inversely proportional to the resistance." (2) The De ponderibus et metallis deals with the properties of floating bodies and the determination of specific weights; it is derived from the pseudo-Archimedean treatise Liber de ponderibus. He was acquainted with Bradwardine's works or with some of their sources.

4. *Astronomy*

John was sufficiently influenced by Parisian astronomers such as William of Saint Cloud (XIII-2) to appreciate the value of careful observations and of adequate instruments. He admired the determination of the obliquity of the ecliptic made by William in 1290 (Introd. 2, 990) and instituted similar observations in Evreux 1318, but he was a little too boastful about them to inspire much confidence. His observations were made with a kardaja (?) the radius of which was 15 feet and the arc 15°, but there is little to conclude from that except that he was anxious to reach a greater precision (did he reach it?).

He compiled various astronomical tables: in Paris 1321, the Tabula tabularum et Canones tabularum Alfonsii, that is, canons for the use of the Alphonsine tables; and in Paris 1339, the Canones de eclipsi lunae. Other tables are in the form of calendars, e.g., a calendar for 1317, based on the tables of Toulouse rather than on the Alphonsine tables (the Toulouse tables had been used also by his master, William of Saint Cloud); a calendar and patefit for 1321 with tables for the period 1321–96, these being based upon the Alphonsine tables (the title "patefit" is the first word of the incipit Patefit ex Ptholomei disciplinis in libro suo qui dicitur Almagestis . . .); still another one compiled for Clement VI in 1346–47. The purpose of these calendars was probably astrological, yet their compilation may be considered astronomical work.

For the work concerning the reform of the calendar which he undertook with Firmin de Beauval in 1344 at the request of Clement VI, see my note on Firmin, for the respective contributions of John and Firmin cannot be dissociated. Both should be named among the forerunners of the Gregorian reform (1582), but their joint contribution was not important. It is said that John had already proposed in 1337 to correct the Julian calendar by omitting leap years for the next forty years (Cantor 2, 125). However that may be, that palliative was not adopted.

Thorndike has observed (3, 267, 298) that John used sexagesimal divisions of the day as well as of the hour. This illustrates the fact that before the invention of decimal fractions, sexagesimal fractions were considered the most rational. John divided the astronomical day into 24 hours, the hour into 1080 puncta, the punctum into 10 momenta. The division of the day was the occasion of various singularities in mediaeval times;[13] it still is now.

5. *Astrology*

John wrote various prognostications wherein he described with the usual concreteness and assurance the foreign wars and other evils which were bound to occur because of the simultaneous presence of two or more planets in the same zodiacal signs. One of his prognostications was devoted in 1341 to the famous conjunction of the three superior planets in 1345 (see note on Firmin de Beauval). He addressed to Clement VI (i.e., between 1342 and 1352) other prognostications concerning the conjunction of Jupiter and Mars in Cancer, 1357, and that of Jupiter and Saturn in Scorpio, 1365.

He may be the author of a treatise on the astrological determination of the most auspicious times for medical intervention (Liber de electionibus medicine) written in Paris 1344, of a treatise on geomancy (S. Marco VIII, 44) definitely ascribed to him, and of Aphorisms conforming to Ptolemy's Judgments (Amphorismi isti conveniunt Ptholomeo in suis iudiciis) ascribed to one John Morey.

[13] For example, P. Tannery: Sur la division du temps en instants au Moyen âge (BM 6, 111, 1905; Mémoires 5, 346–47, 1922; Isis 6, 434).

6. *Music*

John's mediaeval fame was based on his musical writings even more than on his mathematical ones. Musical treatises of his were used as obligatory textbooks in universities, e.g., in Leipzig and Louvain. Many musical treatises bear his name, the first two (in my list) being the most important.

1. Musica speculativa secundum Boetium abbreviata Parisiis in Sorbona 1323. A popular treatise which was commented upon eighty years later (1404) by Prosdocimo de' Beldomandi (c. 1375–1428), and was printed before the end of the fifteenth century.

2. Speculum musice. Sometimes dated 1321 and thus anterior to no. 1. There are good reasons for believing that this treatise was written later. According to W. Grossmann (1924), the Speculum musice was not written by John of Meurs, but by one Jacobus of Liége, who studied in Paris, where he was influenced by Pierre de la Croix,[14] then returned to Liége and wrote the Speculum there in old age c. 1330. However that may be, the treatise is divided into seven books, of which the first five deal with theory and the two others with practice. The theoretical books, discussing such notions as intervals and ratios, consonances, proportions, scales, tetrachords, are largely and professedly derived from Boetius. Book 6 is devoted to church music, explaining the ideas of Boetius, then those of Guido of Arezzo (XI-1) and his school, finally those of the "moderns." John was obviously out of sympathy with the latter, and opposed innovations, such as the exaggerations of descant, the excessive use of embellishments and of discords, the abandonment of the old organum and conductus in favor of the motet and cantilena. It has been claimed (and that claim has been repeated for centuries) that John invented the musical notes (long, breve, etc.)—he himself ascribed that invention correctly to Guido —and that he improved the musical notation, and various other inventions have been unwarrantedly ascribed to him. It would seem that the author of the Speculum invented nothing, that he was essentially a conservative, that his influence was restraining rather than progressive. He criticized the innovations of the ars nova, e.g., those of Philip of Vitry, and would gladly have taken the musicians back to Franco of Cologne (XII-2), the first exponent of mensural music in Christian Europe.

Other musical treatises are ascribed to John of Meurs (it will scarcely be possible to determine their genuineness until we have a critical comparative edition of them), as follows:

3. Summa magistri Johannis de Muris.

4. Ars (summaria) contrapuncti secundum Johannem de Muris.

5. Libellus (Tractatus) practice cantus mensurabilis. Nos. 4 and 5 were commented upon by Prosdocimo de' Beldomandi.

6. Ars discantus.

7. Quaestiones super partes musicae.

8. De sonis musicis (in book IV of the Quadripartitum).

John recommended the use of an instrument with four strings, and had one with nineteen strings. The strings were vibrated by means of keys; these instruments may thus be considered the ancestors of the clavichord.

7. *Text*

Arithmetica communis ex Boetii arithmetica per M. Joannem de Muris compendiose excerpta. Printed in a mathematical collection without title (Vienna

[14] Petrus de Cruce of Amiens, praised in the Speculum as a composer who followed Franco's rules. Reese (p. 318, 331, 340, 1940).

1515), containing also writings by Bradwardine, Oresme, Georg Peurbach, and Johann von Gemunden. Second edition entitled Arithmetica speculativa (Mainz 1538), more complete than the first but without marginal references to Boetius.

Prognostication relative to the conjunction of 1345, edited by H. Pruckner 1933; see below.

Two chapters of the Quadripartitum (ch. 11, 14 of book II) were edited by Alfred Nagl in his paper of 1890 cited below. They are entitled Theoremata multiplicacionis and De tabula abaci subtilis computacionis.

Epitoma quadrivii practici (Cologne 1500?). Cited by Klebs (p. 185, 1938).

Figura inveniendi sinus kardagarum et aliarum circuli porcionum demonstracione ordinata breviori modo et faciliori quo potest tradi. Edited by Maximilian Curtze: Urkunden zur Geschichte der Trigonometrie im christlichen Mittelalter (BM 1, 413–16, 1900).

The Musica speculativa secundum Boetium was first printed under the title Musica manuscripta et composita (Leipzig 1496), then again under the title Epytoma Johannis de Muris in Musica Boecii (Francfort 1508). The Musica speculativa, and two other musical treatises ascribed to John, the Summa and the Quaestiones, are included in Gerbert (3, 256, 189, 301, 1784). The Speculum musice, being very long, has never been entirely printed; books 6 and 7 and the chapter headings of books 1–5 are included in Coussemaker (2, 193–433, 1867). Book 1 (chs. 1–19) was edited by Walter Grossmann (Leipzig 1924). Coussemaker also edited the Libellus practice cantus mensurabilis, the Ars contrapuncti, the Ars discantus (3, 46–59, 59–68, 68–113, 1869).

8. *Criticism (except music)*

Alfred Nagl: Das Quadripartitum des Ioannes de Muris und das praktische Rechnen im 14. Jahrhundert (Zeitschrift für Mathematik und Physik 34, suppt. 137–46, 1890). Steinschneider (p. 622, 1893). Cantor (2, 123–25, passim, 1899). D. E. Smith (p. 117, 1908). Gustav Eneström: Über das Quadripartitum numerorum (BM 8, 216, 1908). L. C. Karpinski: The Quadripartitum numerorum (BM 13, 99–114, 1913), analysis of the work with extracts. Duhem: Etudes (3, 47, 300, 1913); Système (4, 30–38, 1916). L. C. Karpinski: The decimal point (Science 45, 663–65, 1917), apropos of John's anticipation of decimal fractions. Zinner (p. 231–32, 475–76, 1925). Lynn Thorndike and George Sarton: On the use of the word kardaga (Isis 14, 420–22, 1930). Hubert Pruckner: Studien zu den astrologischen Schriften des Heinrich von Langenstein (p. 80 ff., Leipzig 1933; Isis 23, 452–54). Thorndike (3, 294–324, 1934). George Sarton: The first explanation of decimal fractions, 1585 (Isis 23, 169, 174, 1935). Solomon Gandz: The invention of decimal fractions (Isis 25, 25, 1936).

9. *Musical criticism*

Robert Hirschfeld: Johann de Muris, seine Werke und seine Bedeutung als Verfechter des Classischen in der Tonkunst (68 p., Leipzig 1884). Walter Grossmann: Die einleitenden Kapitel des Speculum musicae (100 p., Leipzig 1924). J. F. R. Stainer in Grove (3, 581–84, 1927). Gerhard Pietzsch: Die Klassifikation der Musik von Boetius bis Ugolino von Orvieto[14a] (Freiburg i.B. Diss., 125 p., Halle 1929). H. G. Farmer: Legacy of Islam (p. 372, 1931), unexplained reference to John's use of the word alentrade, pointing to an Arabic source. Gérold (p. 364, 408, 1936). Reese (p. 331, 346, 358, 383, 1940).

[14a] Ugolino da Orvieto, author of a treatise De musica mensurata, flourished toward the end of the fourteenth century. François Joseph Fétis: Biographie des musiciens (2d ed., 8, 281, Paris 1870). Reese (p. 381, 1940).

10. *Jacobus of Liége*

Antoine Auda: La musique et les musiciens de l'ancien pays de Liége (p. 64, Liége 1930).

PIERRE VIDAL

Provençal Dominican, astronomer (fl. 1311–18).

There were living at about the same time three Dominican Pierre Vidal (Petrus Vitalis), one from Montpellier, the second from Cahors (in Quercy, dépt. Lot), the third from Carcassonne. The one in whom we are especially interested dedicated in 1318 to John XXII a Novum kalendarium, in the preface of which he shows the need of reforming the calendar. This calendar was computed for Montpellier and for three cycles of 19 years, from 1311 to 1368; Pierre showed how the calendar could easily be made perpetual. The idea of revision of the calendar was then in the air; compare the treatise written by Firmin de Beauval and John of Meurs for Clement VI in 1345.

Our astronomer is possibly identical with a Dominican P. Vitalis who studied the naturalia in Perpignan 1281, taught logic in Marseille 1282 and in Tarascon 1283, was again studying naturalia in Béziers 1284, being then called P. Vitalis de Montepessulano (of Montpellier). He studied theology in Montpellier 1287–89, and taught it in various places 1299–1302. No more is heard of him after 1302, simply because the proceedings of the Dominican province of Provence, created in 1303 and including Montpellier, have not come down to us.

Text. Novum kalendarium in Latin MS 7420 A of Bibliothèque nationale, Paris. Extracts given by Meyer and by Thomas.

Criticism. Paul Meyer: Traités en vers provençaux sur l'astrologie et la géomancie (Romania 26, 225–75, 1897; only p. 236–37). Duhem: Système (4, 38–60, 1916). Antoine Thomas (HL 35, 624–27, 1921).

Thomas speaks also (ibid. p. 627–29) of two other contemporary astronomers, probably both connected with Toulouse. The first is the Franciscan Raimond Bancal, who wrote a calendar for 1310. The second is magister Etienne Arblant, who used Bancal's calendar and wrote, probably in Latin, a treatise quoted in 1335 by an unknown Toulousain commentator in French, "C'est la Roe (roue, wheel?) à savoir la conjonction et la distance du soleil et de la lune." The commentator also refers to the kalendrier la Royne, the Latin calendar which Guillaume de Saint Cloud dedicated in 1296 to queen Marie (i.e., the queen mother, Marie de Brabant, widow of Philippe le Hardi) and of which he then made a French version for the other queen Marie (i.e., Marie de Champagne, d. 1305, wife of Philippe le Bel). The French version must have been made between 1296 and 1305.[15]

FIRMIN DE BEAUVAL

Firmin de Beauval (or Belleval) in the diocese of Amiens. Firminus de Bellavalle. French (Picard) astrologer (fl. 1338–45).

He wrote three treatises:

1. In 1338, the De mutatione (or De impressionibus) aëris, dealing with the influence of planets on meteorological phenomena (I prefer Thorndike's dating 1338 to Duhem's 1320).

The De mutatione aëris is divided into seven parts: (I) introduction, dealing with the nature of different parts of the sky and of the stars, the seasons and climates; (II) global changes due to great conjunctions and eclipses, and the entries

[15] This is an addition to my note on William of Saint Cloud (Introd. 2, 990).

of the sun into the solstices or equinoxes or other signs of the zodiac; (III) global changes due to conjunctions and opposition of sun and moon; (IV) particular judgments determined by such conjunctions and oppositions and others; (V) particular judgments determined by the relative position of the moon and stars, with reference to zodiacal signs; (VI) predictions concerning rain (de hora pluviae et ubi et quando fortior et debilior fuerit et quae sint loca apta ad hoc et de duratione eiusdem); (VII) other meteorological predictions derived from science or folklore. This work might be called a treatise on astrological meteorology. It is a compilation derived from many sources, chiefly Ptolemy, Pliny,[16] al-Kindī and Abū Ma'shar (IX-1), 'Alī ibn abī-l-Rijāl and 'Alī ibn Riḍwān (XI-1), John of Seville and Abraham ben Ezra (XII-1), Albert the Great and Leopold of Austria (XIII-2), not to speak of popular knowledge partly transmitted by oral tradition.

The book seems to have obtained some popularity; it was printed in 1485. There are many MSS, one of which is entitled Colliget astrologiae (with reference to the Colliget of Averroes, al-kullīyāt li ibn Rushd, Introd. 2, 356).

2. A prognostication from the conjunction of the three superior planets (Mars, Jupiter, Saturn) in 1345. Astrologers would naturally attach great importance to the conjunction of these three planets (the "milicia superiorum," as Firmin called them). Another prognostication relative to the same conjunction was made by John of Meurs.

3. A treatise on the reform of the calendar was written by him and John of Meurs (not John de Linières) in answer to a request of Clement VI. The request was dated September 25, 1344; the treatise was prepared in Avignon 1345. Firmin realized that the Julian calendar was no longer in step with the phaenomena of the solar year. The pope, however, was mainly concerned with the lunar calendar, the ecclesiastical calendar, the rectification of the golden number. Firmin and John's treatise was thus naturally devoted to these ecclesiastical problems rather than to the reform of the civil calendar.

Text. Opusculum repertorii pronosticon in mutatione aeris tam via astrologica quam metheorologica . . . (Ratdolt, Venice 1485). The author's name did not appear in this first edition. Second edition, Firmini repertorium de mutatione aeris, with notes and with a preface by Philippus Iollainus Blereicus (addressed to Jean Robert, abbot of St. Julien of Tours) (Paris 1539).

The prognostication relative to the conjunction of 1345 was edited by H. Pruckner in his book of 1933 cited below.

The third writing is unpublished.

Criticism. Eugène Déprez: Une tentative de réforme du calendrier sous Clément VI (Ecole française de Rome, Mélanges d'archéologie et d'histoire 19, 131–43, 1899). Duhem: Système (4, 38–60, 1916). Gustav Hellmann: Die Wettervorhersagen im ausgehenden Mittelalter (Beiträge zur Geschichte der Meteorologie 2, 189–92, 1917; Isis 4, 185). Zinner (p. 53, 400, 1925). Hubert Pruckner: Studien zu den astrologischen Schriften des Heinrich von Langenstein (p. 80–85, Berlin 1933; Isis 23, 452–54). Thorndike (3, 268–80, 1934).

Contemporary instruments. Jules Sottas: L'astrolabe quadrant du musée de Rouen (L'astronomie 26, 422–29, 4 ill., 1912), not included in Gunther (1932). Instrument made after 1310 probably in Rouen; not essentially different from the

[16] The anonymous Liber de presagiis tempestatum often quoted by Firmin and edited by Thorndike (3, 273, 708–14, 1934) has been identified by Miss Pearl Kibre as equivalent to Pliny's Natural history (book 18, ch. 35 or 78–90). See Lynn Thorndike: Pliny and Liber de presagiis tempestatum (Isis 34, 28, 1942).

instruments of the end of the thirteenth century. It may have been used by one of the early Norman navigators, e.g., Jean de Béthencourt, who conquered the Canary Islands in 1402–4. J. de Rey Pailhade: L'horloge solaire médiévale de Dijon (Société française de physique, séance du 17 mai 1918; Revue générale des sciences pures et appliquées 29, 381), dated 1310 or later.

JOHN OF BASSIGNY

Unknown French astrologer. Bassigny (pagus bassiniacensis) is an old "pays" of France, divided between Champagne and Lorraine (dépts. Haute-Marne, Aube, Meuse). John of Bassigny made astrological prophecies based on the positions of the stars, the Bible, and general information obtained during his extensive travels. He claimed to have discussed these matters beyond the seas with a Syrian and a Chaldaean c. 1336 and with a Jew c. 1342. He talked with them through an interpreter, and stayed with them for two continuous years (? when? c. 1336? c. 1342?). These statements do not inspire confidence, but whether they are true or not, John's prophecies are typical.

John is one of the astrologers who predicted the Black Death, but he predicted it for the year 1352. All kinds of calamities would begin in that ill-starred year or in the conjunction year 1345 and would continue until 1373. The plague itself would be universal, it would last for thirty-five years or more, and destroy from one-half to two-thirds of the population. He prophesied wars, revolutions, floods, earthquakes.

The MSS wherein these predictions are preserved date from the fifteenth century and include interpolations. It must have been very tempting to astrological quacks to produce false predictions written, or at least revised, after the events supposed to be predicted had actually occurred.

My knowledge of John of Bassigny is derived exclusively from Thorndike (3, 312–15, 1934), where more details may be found.

GEOFFROI OF MEAUX

Galfredus de Meldis. French astrologer and physician (fl. 1310–48). The name Geoffroi has many variants (Geoffroy; Geoffrey or Godfrey in English; Gaufredus, Gamfredus in Latin, etc.). There are many places called Meaux in France. This Geoffroi flourished mainly in Paris. In Paris 1310 he was one of the masters and bachelors who were charged to examine the Ars brevis of Ramon Lull. He had apparently taken degrees in arts and in medicine. In 1322 he was one of the six royal physicians witnessing the coronation of Charles IV. He may have been teaching astrology in Paris, and perhaps also in Oxford (1325, 1345).

He wrote in Latin at least half a dozen astrological tracts, which I shall consider in chronological order. These tracts have no scientific importance, but they are valuable documents illustrating the astrological knowledge of those days, and the tenacity of astrological convictions.

1. On the comet of 1315 (De stellis comatis). The tract opens with a defense of astrology from the point of view of Christian orthodoxy. His main authorities are Aristotle, Ptolemy, John of Damascus, and Abū Ma'shar. Discussion of the nature of comets. Are they sublunar and made of base substances? or new divine creations? or caused by extraordinary planetary conjunctions? Geoffroi had apparently made many observations of the comet of 1315, and of its passage across

the stars. He concluded that its virtue would continue at least for two years. It would cause all kinds of diseases and evils.

2. Calendar of 1320. Covering the period 1321–40, and derived from the tables of al-Zarqālī (XI-2), which he preferred to the Alfonsine tables.

3. On the conjunctions of 1325. Apropos of a conjunction of Saturn and Jupiter, and later of Mars, calculated to occur in May 1325. Geoffroi insists on the enormous and all-pervading influence of such conjunctions, an influence which will continue for two years. It is clear that for him these planetary influences were absolutely certain, the only doubts being due to differences of interpretation.

4. On the comet of 1337. Similar to the tract on the comet of 1315, and based like it on observations of the comet's trajectory. The comet was preceded by a solar eclipse (there was a solar eclipse on March 3, 1337, but it was visible only in eastern Europe), which would increase its influence. The comet itself may have been caused by the conjunction of the eclipse, Mars, and Saturn. Cometary influences must be interpreted in terms of their zodiacal relations. The comet of 1337 will cause plagues, wars, etc. Its virtue will last about two years (Geoffroi had a predilection for that period).

5. On the conjunction of 1345 (Super coniunctione Saturni et Iovis anno Christi 1345). Tract written soon before May 12, 1345 (Erfurt MS).

5 bis. On the causes of the Black Death (Rogatus a quibusdam amicis meis ut de causa huius generalis pestilentie aliquid scriberem . . .). Geoffroi's thesis is that the Black Death was caused mainly by the total lunar eclipse of March 18, 1345, the influence of which was intensified by a conjunction of Saturn and Jupiter. On that account the tract is sometimes entitled or described as Iudicium magne coniunctionis Saturni et Iovis anno 1345. The eclipse above mentioned lasted 3 hours, 29 minutes, 54 seconds (such precision, far exceeding his experimental possibilities, increases the reader's impression of unreality and his distrust); according to Oppolzer's Canon (Wien 1887) the eclipse lasted 3 hours 38 minutes. How is it possible to avoid the evil influences? Geoffroi gives prophylactic advice, the best of which is to shun causes of contagion.

6. Undated treatise on judicial astrology, Totius astronomie iudicialis compendium ex omnibus libris . . . . The zodiacal influences are as fundamental and all-pervading as if they issued from the ninth sphere (the primum mobile); special planetary influences issue from the respective spheres of each planet. Each planet is considered in turn, the qualities and influences of each being described. The bulk of the treatise is devoted to astrological medicine, i.e., the application of astrological theories to medical practice (determination of proper times for medical intervention, etc.).

Text. No text has been published, except the prognostication relative to the conjunction of 1345, included in Pruckner's book of 1933 cited below.

Criticism. Duhem: Système (4, 69–74, 1916). Zinner (p. 227, 473, 1925). Hubert Pruckner: Studien zu den astrologischen Schriften des Heinrich von Langenstein (p. 78 f., 84, 1933; Isis 23, 452–54). Thorndike (3, 281–93, 715–17, 1934). C. Doris Hellman: The comet of 1577 (p. 57–60, etc., Columbia University, New York 1944; Isis 36, 266–70).

A3. England

MAUDUITH

English mathematician and astronomer (fl. 1310). One of the founders of Western trigonometry.

John Mauduith (or Manduth, Mauduit, etc.) was a fellow in Merton College, elected c. 1305; he was teaching in Oxford in 1340 and seems to have been still alive in 1346. Richard de Bury (d. 1345) was a patron of his.

Whatever were the dates of his birth and death, which are unknown, 1310 was his golden year. His scientific writings bear that date, to wit, (1) Tabule facte in Oxon 1310, (2) Tabula ascensionis signorum in arco obliquo Oxon cujus latitudo est 51 grad. et 50 min. verificata Oxon 1310 (the correct latitude is 51°45′), (3) Parvus tractatus editus a magistro Johanne Mauduth super quattuor tabulis mirabiliter inventis in civitate Oxon 1310.

The Parvus tractatus is especially important, as it was a source of Wallingford's Quadripartitum. Mauduith was apparently the real initiator of Western trigonometry, preceding both Levi ben Gerson and Wallingford; unfortunately his energy seems to have flagged after the year 1310 or 1316. The four tables included in the Parvus tractatus are: (I) De chorda et arcu recto et verso et umbris, (II) De arcu aequinoctiali elevato et horis et arcu diei, (III) De altitudine stellarum et arcu diurno stellae et distantia ab aequinoctio, (IV) De ascensionibus regionis triae.

The umbrae, umbra recta and umbra versa, were respectively the cotangent and the tangent, introduced by the Arabs in the first half of the ninth century, al-Khwārizmī or Ḥabash al-Ḥāsib, if not before.

The only writing of Mauduith posterior to 1310 is a list of the names of fixed stars for 1316, "Nomina stellarum fixarum extractarum secundum M. J. Mandith in Oxonie pro anno Christi 1316 per additionem 36 grad. 40 min. super stellas Almagesti, et fuit motus octave spere 9 g. 23 m. 10 2°."

A treatise De doctrina theologica is also ascribed to him.

According to the antiquary John Leland (1506?–52), who studied in Cambridge, not in Oxford, Mauduith's tables were still used in his time. This is confirmed by the fact that a copy of them was included in the library of the famous mathematician Robert Recorde (1510?–58).

Text. One of the Tabule facte in Oxon 1310, to wit, the Tabula augmenti logissimi diei supra diem equinoctii pro omni terra habitabili, is reproduced in facsimile in Gunther (2, 49, 1923).

Criticism. C. L. Kingsford (DNB 37, 84, 1894). R. T. Gunther (1, 108, 336; 2, 48–49, 1923). John David Bond: Wallingford's Quadripartitum (Isis 5, 339–63, 1923; p. 361). Zinner (p. 224, 1925). Thorndike (3, 121, 1934).

ODINGTON

Walter Odington. English musician, mathematician, astronomer, and alchemist (fl. 1301–30).

In 1301, Walter Odington was a monk in the Benedictine abbey of Evesham. Hence, he is sometimes called Walter of Evesham. His name Odington is probably derived from that of a village in northern Oxfordshire, or in Gloucestershire; Evesham on the Avon is in Worcestershire. His places and dates of birth and death are unknown.

(Walter of Evesham should not be confused with Walter of Einesham, monk of Canterbury, chosen by the monks archbishop of Canterbury in 1228 but not appointed.)

In 1301 Walter compiled a calendar for Evesham abbey. In 1316 he was making astronomical observations in Oxford, and about that time he wrote his Declaratio de motu octave spere. In 1330 he was mentioned in an account of Merton College. He could not be a fellow of that college, being a Benedictine, not a secular.

His two main writings are a treatise on music, De speculatione musices, and an alchemical treatise, Icocedron. Before dealing with them at greater length, let us mention rapidly his other writings, to wit, Tractatus de multiplicatione specierum in visu secundum omnem modum, Ars metrica, Liber quintus geometrie per numeros loco quantitatum, De proprietatibus numerorum secundum Boetium et Euclidem, De mortibus planetarum (?), De aetate mundi (?), De mutatione aeris (?). Thorndike suggests that this last item might be an alternative title for the Exafrenon pronosticorum temporis, which treatise might possibly be ascribed to Walter instead of to Richard Wallingford.

The De speculatione musices is one of the earliest Latin treatises explaining mensural music. It is divided into six books, as follows: (I–III) acoustics, division of the monochord; (IV) musical notation; (V) plain song; (VI) mensural music. Walter was the earliest theorist "who plainly argued in favor of the consonance of thirds (major or minor), maintaining that the entire common chord, with doublings in the octave, should be considered consonant" (in the Pythagorean scale adopted by Boetius, thirds were dissonant). Walter's Speculatio was a distinct step forward, though it was only partially successful; for a more complete realization of his views we have to wait until the time of John Dunstable (d. 1453).

Walter was apparently a good practical musician as well as a good theorist. His treatise contains many examples of his own compositions. It is possible that his musical activity was anterior to his scientific one, and that the floruit date 1280 quoted by the early antiquary John Leland (1506?–52) refers to the former. In that case the De speculatione musices would be a work of the thirteenth century.

The Icocedron, or Ycocedron (derived from εἰκοσάεδρον, icosahedron, twenty-faced), so named with reference to the 20 chapters into which it is divided, is a treatise on alchemy, beginning with an attack on the "alchemists of modern times," who are described as humbugs. It seems independent of the writings of Arnold of Villanova and Raymond Lull, but Geber is quoted. It explains the different chemical processes (calcination, solution, sublimation, congelation) in the usual manner, and discusses the separation of the four elements. In ch. 15 and following, a remarkable attempt is made to measure the virtues (heat, dryness, etc.) quantitatively, in degrees. Walter's excellent intention was defeated by the lack of experimental definition. In the last chapter, a new approach is made, the "intentions" and "remissions" of qualities being compounded graphically. All this is very unclear, and one can but guess that his purpose was to introduce somehow quantitative precision instead of qualitative looseness.

Text. De speculatione musices, edited by Coussemaker (1, 182–250, 1864).

The Icocedron is unpublished but for a short fragment in Thorndike (3, 683–84, 1934).

Criticism. Henry Davey (DNB 59, 245–46, 1899). A. Hughes-Hughes in Grove (3, 679, 1927). Thorndike (3, 127–40, 682–84, 1934), dealing mainly with the Icocedron and contemporary writings of the same kind. Gérold (p. 333, 346–47, 1936). Reese (1940, passim).

WALLINGFORD

Richard Wallingford (c. 1292–1335). The greatest English mathematician of his time, one of the introducers of trigonometry into Christian Western Europe.

Contents: (1) Life. (2) His clocks and instruments and writings ad haec. (3)

FIG. 10. Portrait (?) of Richard Wallingford in MS Cotton. Claud. E iv. He is seen measuring a circular instrument with a pair of compasses; his abbot's miter is on the floor. The spots on his face may be due to the leprosy which afflicted him early in life and caused his death at the age of 43. This portrait was first published in color by R. T. Gunther: Early science in Oxford (vol. 1, Oxford 1923); see also Gunther's article in Nature (118, 773–74, 1926). Courtesy of Clarendon Press, Oxford.

His other writings. (4) Trigonometry. (5) Importance and influence of the Quadripartitum.
(6) Text. (7) Criticism.

1. *Life*

Richard, born c. 1292, was the son of William, a blacksmith of Wallingford (in Berkshire, on the Thames, in the diocese of Oxford) and the latter's wife Isabella. He lost his father when scarcely ten years old, was adopted by William de Kirkeby, prior of Wallingford, and sent by him to Oxford. He spent six years in Oxford and graduated as A.B. at the age of 23 (c. 1315). He then assumed the Benedictine habit at St. Albans (Hertfordshire, on the Ver,[17] 21 miles north-northwest of London). Later he returned to Oxford for nine years of graduate studies in philosophy and theology, received his degree of bachelor of divinity and the license to lecture on the Sentences. On October 29, 1326, he was elected abbot. This was a very high position, seldom attained, I imagine, by so young a man; indeed, from c. 1154 to 1396 the mitered abbot of St. Albans was the premier abbot of England. Richard traveled to Avignon to be inducted into office by the pope. At that time he was already afflicted with leprosy; he soon lost one eye, and by 1332 was almost bereft of the power of speech. He took considerable pains with the material administration of his abbey, the purging of its finances, jeopardized by previous abbots, the stopping of leakages and rascalities, and the increase of revenues. Thus, much of his time and energy was wasted in quarrels with his monks and litigations with the townsmen. The opposition to him within his own monastery and without grew to such an extent that the curia ordered an investigation, following which his prior, Nicholas Flamstede, was appointed his coadjutor (1333). Richard died on May 23, 1335, at the age of 43. His tomb is in the abbey church near the altar.

While in Oxford he was a student in the Benedictine house, Gloucester College. On some MSS he is entitled a fellow of Merton College (founded 1264; see Introd. 2, 863); this is not confirmed, however, by the Merton records. Moreover, Merton fellowships were granted only to "seculars," not to "regulars." It is very probable, however, that he was in touch with that college, which was then the only scientific center in Oxford, and remained supreme in scientific matters at least until the middle of the fifteenth century.[18] Among his teachers were Bradwardine and Mauduith. In all probability Richard's scientific work was done before his election to the abbacy of St. Albans, hence before 1327. Indeed, it was said (in Gesta abbatum S. Albini, ed. Riley, 2, 182) that in later years he regretted that he had spent so much time on arithmetic, geography, astronomy, and music, and had not spent his whole time on theology.

2. *His clock and instruments and writings ad here*

He constructed a complicated astronomical clock for St. Albans about 1320 (Gunther 2, 49) or 1326. It showed the motions of the sun and moon, and the ebb and flow of the tides. It was considered the most elaborate apparatus and the greatest curiosity of that time anywhere. It had been built magno labore, maiore sumptu, arte vero maxima (John Bale). Edward III (king of England 1327–77)

[17] Hence the ancient name Verulam.

[18] It may be that Richard was in Merton during his first Oxford stay, before he had assumed the Benedictine habit. This seems confirmed by the old list of Merton's learned men compiled by John Bale (1495–1563), given by Gunther (2, 43, 1923), where Wallingford is quoted among the Merton worthies of the time of Edward I (king 1272–1307).

blamed Richard for spending more money on that clock than on the church itself; Richard answered that others could build churches, but not clocks.

In 1326 Richard wrote (1) Canones de instrumento . . . Albion dicto, beginning "Albion est geometricum instrumentum." Is this the description of his clock, and rules for its construction and use? It is difficult to say, because the clock itself is lost. The name Albion (all-by-one) suggests a comprehensive instrument, such as the clock described above. The words "geometricum instrumentum" might be applied to a clock. Though the exact mechanism of the clock is unknown, it is probable that one of its features was a visible dial, as is suggested by a figure in a MS (British Museum, Nero D VII, reproduced by Gunther 1, 233).

There is no mention in Albion, however, of cogwheels, pulleys, and weights such as would be indispensable in a clock, and hence Albion was probably a geometrical instrument without motion of its own, a complicated aequatorium or volvelle, made up of many dials each relative to one of the planets.

Simon Tunsted (d. 1369) improved the instrument Albion and Richard's description of it.

There are many MSS of the Albion in German libraries, in some of which the text is elaborated by Johann von Gemunden (c. 1380–1442). This would suggest a link between the mathematical schools of Oxford and Vienna; but the German mathematicians do not seem to have been acquainted with the Quadripartitum.

In the same year 1326, a third instrument, the rectangulus, was created by Richard and its construction and use were described by him in (2) De arte componendi rectangulum and (3) Ars operandi cum rectangulo (in 10 chapters).

The rectangulus consisted "of three superposed limbs or rules connected by hinges in such a manner that each limb may not only be opened out at varying angles like the blade of a pocket knife, but may also be rotated round a peg-pivot below its hinge. Above all is an alidade, or rule with perforated sight-vanes, which is so hinged to the third limb that it can be either elevated above it or moved parallel with it. The hinges may all be clamped more or less tightly by wedges driven through slots in the pegs, like those used in astrolabes.

"To complete the instrument six scales of bronze were prepared and graduated. Three of these are fixed to the sides of the three limbs; the other three are movable, being pivoted on the pegs under the limbs. The lowest scale was divided along the edges into 60 equal divisions called degrees or parts of chords, *gradus seu partes cordarum*, each of which might, in the case of a large instrument, be further subdivided into 60 parts, while the middle or intervening band was divided by a table of right and versed chords, *corde recte et verse*. This middle divided band is omitted in the five other scales. The divisions of the upper scale of chords, which are called right chords, are numbered from the peg to the end of the scale; the lower scale, called verse chord, is numbered from the end of the rule to the peg. The ends of the alidade and upper limbs are provided with plumb-lines" (Gunther, in Nature 118, 774).

This geometrical instrument was used (as explained in item 3) to solve various simple trigonometrical and astronomical problems.

3. *His other writings*

Wallingford's writings are differently quoted by Fabricius (6, 250, 1746; 6, 88, 1754; 6, 389, 1859), Suter (1887), and Kingsford (1896), and a complete study of the MSS is not yet available.

His main writings can be divided into four groups:

A. Descriptions of instruments: that is, nos. 1 to 3 already quoted.

B. Trigonometry: (4) Quadripartitum de sinibus demonstratis. That is, his masterpiece, to which we shall return presently. (5) De sinibus et arcubus in circulo inveniendis. Of course no. 3 also deals indirectly with trigonometry.

C. Astrology: (6) Exafrenon pronosticorum temporis, or De judiciis astronomicis. The ascription of this work to Wallingford is doubtful; as its title suggests—ἕξ φρὴν ἑνός, six in one?—it is a composite work; its component parts are of different dates and authorship; Wallingford may have collected them. It is a collection of astrological rules and recipes, including (in the last and sixth chapter) astrological meteorology. The Exafrenon was soon translated into English (c. 1385?). (7) De eclipsibus solis et lunae.

This list is probably incomplete—to begin with, it does not include various writings (forming the fourth group) ascribed to him in his capacity of abbot in the Gesta abbatum S. Albani—but it is sufficient to give an idea of Wallingford's activities. We may now turn to the examination of his main work.

4. *Trigonometry*

The Quadripartitum de sinibus demonstratis is the first original Latin treatise on trigonometry. By original we simply mean that it is not a translation; it was derived from Greek and Arabic geometry and astronomy. Richard was acquainted with Euclid, probably in the translation of Giovanni Campano da Novara; with the Almagest and al-Zarqālī's Toledan tables, these two as translated by Gerard of Cremona, also with al-Battānī's astronomy as translated by Plato of Tivoli, wherein the trigonometrical term sinus occurred for the first time; and with contemporary works, especially those of his guides Bradwardine and John Mauduith.

The Quadripartitum contains a good account in Euclidean manner of the fundamental theorems of plane trigonometry. To be sure, it is clumsy as compared with modern trigonometry, but the essential is given. For a clear summary of it in the form of a series of formulas (which of course do not occur at all in the text), see Isis 5, 362–63..

5. *Importance and influence of the Quadripartitum*

The fact that Wallingford did not invent trigonometry does not detract from his merit as the first Latin exponent of it. If it could be shown that the Quadripartitum was the foundation of European trigonometry, his fame could not be exaggerated. Unfortunately this cannot be shown and is improbable. He influenced the Merton school, and may have influenced indirectly other English mathematicians, but the fountain spring of European trigonometry was not the Quadripartitum, but the great treatise of Regiomontanus, De triangulis omni modis, completed more than a century later (Venice 1464; first printed Nürnberg 1533). Now the source of Regiomontanus was not Wallingford,[19] but Levi ben Gerson. Levi wrote a trigonometrical treatise in Hebrew, and this was translated into Latin, De sinibus, chordis et arcubus, by Peter of Alexandria for Clement VI in 1342. It is interesting to note that Levi and Richard worked independently at about the same time; the points of contact between their two treatises are natural enough, inasmuch as they were both building on the same Greco-Arabic foundations.

[19] Zinner enumerates 20 Wallingford MSS in German libraries, but all of the Albion, none of the Quadripartitum (p. 356, 1925).

Levi and Richard must share the fame of having been the first to explain Arabic trigonometry to Western Europe; it was Levi, however, not Richard, who inspired Regiomontanus and hence determined future developments.

Richard Wallingford should not be confused with another abbot of St. Albans bearing almost the same name, William Wallingford, whose whole life was spent in the abbey. He was elected abbot in 1476 and died c. 1488. It was during his abbacy that printing was introduced in St. Albans, eight works being printed (the first six in Latin, the last two in English) between 1480 and 1486. The very last was the famous Boke of St. Albans, a treatise on hawking, hunting, and heraldry ascribed to the mysterious Dame Juliana Berners (born c. 1388), prioress of the Sopwell nunnery near St. Albans. See, for William, Mrs. Tout (DNB 59, 136–38, 1899), and for Juliana, M. G. Watkins (DNB 4, 390–92, 1885).

6. *Text*

Quadripartitum edited by John David Bond (Isis 5, 99–115, 1923); English translation by same (Isis 5, 339–63, 1923).

The Rectangulus and the Albion both edited by Rev. H. Salter in R. T. Gunther's work cited below (2, 337–70, 1923).

7. *Criticism*

Brian Twyne: Antiquitatis academiae Oxon. apologia (p. 216–21, Oxford 1608). Henry Thomas Riley: Gesta abbatum monasterii Sancti Albani (Rolls series no. 28, vol. 2, 183–299, London 1867). Heinrich Suter: Die Mathematik auf den Universitäten des Mittelalters (Festschrift der Kantonschule in Zürich p. 83, 1887). A. G. Little: Grey friars at Oxford (p. 241, 1892). Maximilian Curtze: Über die im Mittelalter zur Feldmessung benutzten Instrumente (BM 10, 70, 1896). C. L. Kingsford (DNB 48, 205–7, 1896). Gustav Hellmann: Die Wettervorhersage im ausgehenden Mittelalter (p. 182, Berlin 1917; Isis 4, 185). John David Bond: Wallingford (Isis 4, 459–65, 1922). R. T. Gunther (vols. 1, 2, by index, 1923). Vol. 1 contains, after p. 92, a portrait of Wallingford in color which we reproduce with the permission of the author and publisher; there is still another portrait of him (p. 233). Zinner (p. 356, 529, 1925). The sixth centenary of Wallingford's elevation to the abbacy of St. Albans was celebrated in that town on November 27, 1926 (Nature 118, 741, 1926). R. T. Gunther: Wallingford and his rectangulus (Nature 118, 773–74, 1926). Zinner (1931). Thorndike (3, 119–27, 1934), dealing mainly with Exafrenon.

BRADWARDINE

English mathematician, mechanician, and theologian (c. 1290–1349).

Contents: (1) Life. (2) Mathematics. (3) Mechanics. (4) Philosophy and theology.
(5) Text. (6) Criticism. (7) Scientific criticism.

1. *Life*

Thomas Bradwardine (Bragwardin, Bredwardyn, etc., de Bradwardina, de Bredewardina) was born c. 1290, in or near Chichester, Sussex; was educated in Merton College, Oxford, was a proctor there in 1325, and a lecturer from 1325 to 1335 (these ten years were probably his years of maximum scientific activity). In 1335 he was called to London by Richard of Bury, bishop of Durham, whose chaplain he became; in 1337 he was chancellor of St. Paul's cathedral; later, a canon in Lincoln; chaplain to Edward III, whom he accompanied in 1338 to Flanders, Cologne, etc.; he was apparently present at the battle of Crécy (1346) and the capture of Calais (1347). He was consecrated archbishop of Canterbury at Avignon July 19, 1349, and died of the plague at Lambeth, a little more than a month later, August 26, 1349.

2. *Mathematics*

Many of his writings deal with mathematics; namely, the Tractatus proportionum (to which we shall come back presently), a treatise De quadratura circuli (identical with that of Campanus?), the Arithmetica speculativa, the Geometria speculativa, and the treatise De continuo.

The arithmetic is, as the title indicates, of the Boetian type (vs. the practical one), that is, it deals with ratios, properties of numbers, figurative numbers, and similar topics. The large number of editions (1495, etc.) witnesses to its great popularity in the fifteenth and sixteenth centuries.

The Geometria speculativa is divided into four parts, dealing respectively with the following:

(1) Stellated polygons (de figuris angulorum egredientibus). Such a polygon may be drawn by extending the sides of a regular convex polygon; one thus obtains a stellated polygon of the first order; in the same way the latter can be transformed into a stellated polygon of the second order, etc. The stellated pentagon is the first stellated polygon of the first order, and the sum of its angles equals $2R$ (R = right angle); for each additional apex, the sum of the angles increases by $2R$, hence the sum is $(2n - 8)R$ for the stellated polygon of n sides (Bradwardine does not give explicitly that general rule). The first stellated polygon of the second order is a heptagon; and, more generally, the first stellated polygon of the mth order is derived from the third stellated polygon of the $(m - 1)$th order. A part of this is already in Campanus (XIII-2).

(2) Isoperimetric figures. Bradwardine shows (a) that isoperimetric figures increase in area with the number of sides, (b) that for an equal number of sides, the equality of angles gives the maximal area, (c) that for an equal number of sides and equal angles, the regular polygon has the maximal area, (d) that the circle has the maximal area of every isoperimetric figure. Bradwardine's source was in all probability Zenodoros (II-1 B.C.), who is not named; the Zenodoros tradition is still very imperfectly known (see my query in Isis 28, 461).

(3) Theory of proportions. Rational and irrational quantities (here called communicantes and incommunicantes, also commensurabiles and irrationales, assimetri). Acquaintance with the Archimedean value of π, 22/7.

(4) Solid geometry. Solid angles, five regular solids; sphere and circles on its surface. The last propositions are derived from the Spherics of Theodosios of Bithynia (I-1 B.C.).

The treatise de continuo deals with mathematical and physical continuity, with what the author calls the structure of continuity (de compositione continui quantum ad sua essentialia). It concludes that continuity can be decomposed only into continuities similar to itself, not into atoms (nullum continuum ex athomis integrari). Distinction between actual and potential infinity (infinitum cathetice et syncathetice); distinction between continuum permanens (e.g., surface, line) and continuum successivum (e.g., time, motion). Discussion of gravity; the free surface of a liquid in static equilibrium is a sphere concentric with the earth and the universe; hence a cup brimful of water contains the more water, the closer it is to the center of the earth.

A Vatican MS (Cod. Vatic. 3102) of the Perspectiva communis of John Peckham (XIII-2) contains four propositions added by Bradwardine, which show that the latter was familiar with umbra recta and umbra versa (i.e., cotangent and tangent) and their reciprocal relation. He was one of the earliest Western writers on trigonometry, but of course these notions were found in Arabic writings of a much earlier date, e.g., in those of Abū-l-Wafā' (X-2).

3. *Mechanics*

The Tractatus proportionum (or de proportionibus), dated 1328, deals with arithmetical proportions, but also with mechanics, and is far more important from the mechanical than from the purely mathematical point of view. Bradwardine was acquainted with the views of Jordanus Nemorarius or pseudo-Jordanus (XIII-1; Introd. 2, 614–15; Isis 25, 341–62) and with those of Gerard of Brussels (XIII-1). The tractatus is divided into four parts, dealing respectively (I) with arithmetical ratios, (II, III) with dynamics, (IV) with cinematics. In part III he explains the wrong law according to which speed is proportional to the ratio of power to resistance. In part IV he tries to define the velocity of rotation, but fails because he is not yet able to conceive what we call angular velocity.

In the last chapter of the tractatus (in the edition of 1505, not in that of 1515) he discusses the distribution of the four elements in the universe. These are all within the moon's orbit. He assumes that the volumes of the spheres limiting respectively earth, water, air, and fire form a geometric progression, and computes the ratios of these volumes and of the radii. That fantastic theory attracted much attention and was frequently repeated down to the middle of the sixteenth century.

In spite of his lack of positive achievement, Bradwardine's mechanical speculations are noteworthy; they represent a phase in the development of unclear ideas out of which clearer ideas would finally crystallize in the fullness of time. Bradwardine influenced Walter Burley, John of Meurs, and Buridan.

4. *Philosophy and theology*

By far his longest work was the treatise De causa Dei contra Pelagium[20] et de virtute causarum ad suos Mertonenses, composed between 1338 and 1346, wherein he develops the idea that the will of God is the source of every essence or existence (Non est ratio nec ulla lex necessaria in Deo prior eius voluntate). Hence God is the necessitating cause of every contingent activity, of every human volition. This is a kind of divine determinism the consequences of which were (or might become) disastrous for orthodox scholasticism.

Bradwardine was well acquainted with patristic and mediaeval literature (even with the main Arabic philosophers and the Jewish Ibn Gabirol). His favorite authors were St. Augustine, Boetius, St. Anselm, perhaps also Robert Grosseteste, Roger Bacon. He knew the Timaeus of Plato, the main Aristotelian books, and the pseudo-Aristotelian De mundo and De bona fortuna. There is no evidence that he had read Occam, but some of his ideas might be called Occamist, this being probably due to common origins.

[20] About Pelagius (V-1) and Pelagianism, see Introd. 1, 382. Pelagius is the man who said "If I ought, I can." The struggle between Bradwardine and the Pelagians is but one incident in the eternal struggle between the defenders of predestination on the one hand, and the defenders of free will on the other. ERE (9, 703–11, 1917).

The De causa Dei exerted a deep influence, the popular side of which is illustrated by Chaucer's bracketing him, in the "Nun's priest's tale," together with St. Augustine and Boetius. He was called Doctor profundus and magnus logicus. His influence was felt by such men as Wycliffe, Huss, Luther, Calvin.

It will suffice to mention his other philosophical writings: a commentary on the Sentences of Peter the Lombard, a Summa theologica (or Summa scientiarum), and questiones, etc.

His Ars memorativa is a treatise on mnemonics.

5. *Text*

De quadratura circuli, Paris 1495, 1502? (is not this Campanus' treatise?).

Arithmetica speculativa, Paris 1495/96, 1498, c. 1500, 1502, Valencia 1503, Paris 1504, 1505, c. 1510, 1512, 1530, Wittenberg 1534, 1536 (after D. E. Smith, 1908).

Geometria speculativa, Paris 1495, 1516, 1530.

Tractatus de continuo, critical edition by Edward Stamm (announced 1936).

For the trigonometrical propositions, see M. Curtze: Reliquiae copernicanae (Zeitschrift für Mathematik und Physik 20, 224, 1875).

Tractatus proportionum (or, de proportionibus), c. 1495, Paris c. 1500, Venice 1505, Vienna 1515. This last-named edition is an abbreviated one, Tractatus breuis proportionum abbreviatus ex libro de proportionibus; it covers 10 folios of an omnibus mathematical volume without general title.

The De causa Dei was very well edited by Sir Henry Savile (1549–1622) (folio, 910 p., London 1618); it includes all the biographical material then available.

Bartomeu Ma. Xiberta (O. Carm.): Fragments d'una qüestió inèdita de Tomàs Bradwardine (Martin Grabmann Festschrift p. 1169–80, Münster i.W. 1935). This is the incomplete text of one of the questiones "utrum Deus habeat praescientiam futurorum contingentium ad utrumlibet," with Catalan introduction and German summary.

6. *Criticism*

W. R. W. Stephens (DNB 6, 188–90, 1886). Sebastian Hahn: Bradwardinus und seine Lehre von der menschlichen Willensfreiheit (Beiträge zur Geschichte des Mittelalters vol. 5, no. 2, 55 p., Münster i.W. 1905). Michalski (p. 68–70, 1920; p. 233 f., 1937). De Wulf (2, 235–37, 1926).

7. *Scientific criticism*

Cantor (2, 113–20, 1899). Braunmühl (1, 57, 109, 1900). D. E. Smith (p. 61, 1908). Duhem: Origines (2, 323–25, 1906); Etudes (3, 295–301, 1913), on mechanics. Gustav Eneström: Sur l'auteur d'un traité de motu auquel Bradwardine a fait allusion en 1328 (Archivio di storia della scienza 2, 133–36, 1921). Edward Stamm: Tractatus de continuo von Thomas Bradwardina (Isis 26, 13–32, 1936; 27, 368).

POPULAR GEOMETRY IN ENGLAND IN THE FOURTEENTH CENTURY

We are given a glimpse into the knowledge of geometry attained in educated but nontechnical circles of England by means of a fourteenth-century MS (British Museum, Sloane 213, XIV fol. 120), "Tretis of geometri wherby you may knowe the heghte, depnes and the brede of most what erthely thynges" edited by Halliwell (p. 56–71, 1839).

The text is more interesting for the study of English terminology than for other historical purposes. It is divided into three parts, dealing with the measurement of heights, distances, and depths. I have no means of criticizing Halliwell's dating of it, nor of making it more precise.

ASHENDON

John of Ashendon. English astrologer (still living in 1368).

John of Ashendon (or Ashenden, Eschenden, Eschuid, Estwood, Eastwood, etc.). He probably hailed from Ashendon in Buckinghamshire. He is said to have become a fellow of Merton College, Oxford, in 1338. He was probably connected with Merton, though the incomplete records of that college do not mention him.

His main work is an astrological compilation entitled Summa iudicialis de accidentibus mundi, better known under the title Summa anglicana, which he completed in 1348. He was also the author of many prognostications, based on eclipses and conjunctions. He neglected the art of interrogations, elections, and horoscopes, and made a special study of eclipses and conjunctions of the planets and their influence on great catastrophes, such as earthquakes, floods, plagues, famines, wars, and conflagrations.

The Summa iudicialis is divided into two books, the second almost twice as long as the first, each divided into 12 distinctions and the distinctions subdivided into chapters. Book I was completed at Oxford on July 20, 1347, book II on December 18, 1348. Book I deals with preliminary matters, such as the age of the world and the position of the planets at the beginning, the natures of the planets, stars, and signs. In book II, dist. 1–7 deal with astrological meteorology; dist. 8–11, with the great catastrophes; dist. 12, with general rules of prediction and various conclusions. A great number of ancient and mediaeval authorities are quoted, often with accurate references to them. This very prolix treatise was abbreviated to half its size by John de Ponte of Lyon in 1379.

Historians of medicine will be specially interested in distinction 9 of book II, dealing with pestilences, their astrological generation, their transmission by air corruption, and the methods of prophylaxis and treatment. Ashendon quotes from all the ancient and mediaeval authors available to him, but refers also to a relatively recent author, Bernard of Gordon (d. c. 1320), and even to a recipe used by Oxford doctors during the plague of the very year of his writing.

Ashendon's earliest prognostication was made in 1345, and later (in his Summa) he claimed to have then foretold the calamities of the Black Death (1348 ff.), but no prophecy of his was sufficiently clear and specific to be identifiable without ambiguity with the terrible events of those years. He made other prognostications in 1349, 1357, 1365, 1368–74. Some of that work was done in collaboration with a younger Mertonian, William Rede.

These compositions, which are all of the same kind, do not deserve to be analyzed. The basis of each is the determination of the time when an eclipse or conjunction of planets will occur and exactly how long it will last. This is done with precision, or, at any rate, can be done with precision. Then the astrologer determines the time which will elapse after the phaenomenon has occurred before its effects will begin to be felt (that "lag" may extend to many years), how long these effects will last, and their precise nature (whether pestilence, or war, or rival popes, or what not). This is all done with great apparent precision, but is fantastic. The apparent precision throughout the prognostication, combined with the fact that some of it was (or could be) real precision, gave the astrologer considerable authority over other people. It is possible that he was not deliberately deceiving them, but was self-deceived. The precision of his purely astronomical predictions, which could be verified, gave him confidence in other predictions. The ready credulity of other people increased his self-deception, and the latter increased his assurance and his power of deceiving others.

The Summa iudicialis was so much appreciated, and considered so learned and so deep, that even the medical part of it (book II, dist. 9) obtained some influence. A century later the astrologer Nicolaus de Comitibus (Niccolò Conti) of Padua (fl. 1450–56) was still praising the recipes, and Pico della Mirandola was still quoting from the Summa with deference. Furthermore, the Oxford antiquary Anthony à Wood (1632–95) spoke of Ashendon as the greatest mathematician and astronomer ever produced by Merton College, and the founder of the Merton school, which, according to him, lasted a century and a half. Unfortunately (said Wood), many of the Merton books and records were stupidly destroyed under Edward VI (king 1547–53).

Text. Summa astrologiae iudicialis de accidentibus mundi quae anglicana vulgo nuncupatur. Printed by Johann Lucilius Santritter, Venice 1489 (Klebs no. 381).

Professor Francis J. Carmody called my attention (Oct. 23, 1941) to the fact that in this edition book 8, cap. I, 'Alī ibn abī-l-Rijāl (XI-1) is quoted verbatim from the Latin princeps (Ratdolt, Venice 1485), e.g., all the almost nonsensical transliterations of Arabic place names are identical; but Abū Ma'shar (IX-1), the Latin first editions of whom had been printed by Ratdolt in 1488 and 1489, was not exploited in the same way.

Criticism. Gustav Hellmann: Die Wettervorhersage im ausgehenden Mittelalter (p. 185–89, 1917; Isis 4, 185). John David Bond: Wallingford (Isis 4, 462, 1922). R. T. Gunther (1, 96, 107; 2, 43, 55, 58, 1923). Thorndike (3, 325–46, 717–21, 1934), elaborate account.

BREDON

Simon Bredon. English mathematician, astronomer, and physician (d. after 1368).

Simon Bredon, or Biridanus, born in Winchecombe, Gloucestershire. Educated in Oxford, M.D. in 1330, fellow of Balliol, later of Merton. He wrote his will in 1368, bequeathing his books and instruments to six Oxford colleges, to wit, University, Balliol, Merton, Exeter, Oriel, and Queen's, and to sundry friends.

Bredon is the author of various mathematical and astronomical treatises. For example, two trigonometrical ones continuing the Merton tradition, (1) Tabulae chordarum and (2) Calculationes chordarum. Then (3) an Arithmetica theoretica and (4) an Expositio in quaedam capita Almagesti, copies of which were included in the library of Robert Recorde (d. 1558). Finally, (5) Tabula declinationis solis, (6) Theoretica planetarum (also ascribed to Walter Bryte), (7) Oxford almanack for 1344, (8) a note on the eclipse of 1345, (9) Conclusiones quinque de numero quadrato, dealing with the quadrature of the circle. It is possible that 7 and 8 are the same item.

Bredon's will of 1368, including a list of his books and instruments, is a very interesting document. It helps us to visualize the library of an English physician and mathematician in the third quarter of the fourteenth century.

He had two astrolabes, the smaller of which, astrolabium minus, he bequeathed to William Rede; the larger, astrolabium maius, to Merton College. This second instrument may be identified with one of c. 1350 still kept in Merton, or with one of c. 1340 kept in Oriel.

Text. Facsimile of the Oxford almanack for 1344 in Gunther (2, 52, 1923). Catalogue of Bredon's library (ibid. p. 53–54).

Criticism. Steinschneider (p. 76, 1904), quoting Bredon as possible translator of Ptolemy's Quadripartitum (?). That translation was mentioned in Introd.

(2, 178) with the date c. 1305 instead of c. 1350. Savage (p. 146, 148, 271, 1911). R. T. Gunther: Early science in Oxford (vols. 1, 2, 1923; chiefly 2, 52–54, 208); Astrolabes (2, 473, 1932). Gunther's dates are confusing; in two places he gives as date of Bredon's floruit c. 1380 (1, 96, 336), then elsewhere he states that Bredon died in 1372 (2, 208). Frederick Maurice Powicke: Medieval books in Merton (300 p., Oxford 1931). Margaret Münsterberg: An unpublished mathematical treatise by Simon Bredon (More books p. 411, Boston Dec. 1944), apropos of a fifteenth-century MS of the Arithmetica theoretica recently acquired by the Boston Public Library.

Bredon is not dealt with in DNB, neither in the Athenae Oxonienses of Anthony à Wood, himself a Mertonian, for the latter begins his account with the year 1500.

MERLE

William Merle (or Merlee, Morley). English meteorologist (d. 1347).

William son of William Merle. Said to have been connected with Merton College, Oxford, though his name does not appear in the (incomplete) records of that college. He became rector of Driby, near Alford, Lincolnshire, in 1331, and died in 1347.

Merle has the distinction of being the first known man to keep a journal of the weather, Temperies aeris oxoniae pro septennio. His journal extends from January 1337 to January 10, 1344 (seven years). Of course, isolated meteorological observations are found in many chronicles and other writings, ancient and mediaeval, but Merle's journal was the first systematic and regular weather record.[21] In spite of the title, the observations are not restricted to Oxford weather, some being made in Lincolnshire, some in both places. For example, he refers to an earthquake on March 28, 1343, which brought down chimney stones in Lindsey (a district of Lincolnshire) and lasted long enough for the salutatio angelica to be said distinctly, but was not felt at Oxford.[21a]

He wrote in Oxford 1340 a treatise on weather forecasting entitled De futura aeris intemperie (with variant titles, De pronosticatione aeris, Regule ad futuram aeris pronosticanda, etc.; one title, Tractatus phisicus de secundis stellis, is very misleading). William's main sources were Aristotle's Meteorology and Problems, Vergil's Georgics, Pliny, Ptolemy's Quadripartitum, and English weather lore. In fact, there are fewer astrological prognostications in the treatise than popular premonitions such as are familiar to the farmers of every country. The treatise is divided into 12 chapters: (1) relations between different states of the weather; (2) signs in the air; (3, 4) signs of coming and past humidity; (5, 6) signs of coming and past wind; (7, 8) signs of coming and past frost; (9, 10) signs of coming and past hot weather; (11) qualities needed for weather forecasting; (12) causes of crop failures, especially in England. This treatise is as remarkable as Merle's meteorological diary, because of its matter-of-factness, and what might be called its scientific spirit (vs. astrological or other superstitions).

Text. Facsimile edition of the Digby MS 176 (Bodleian) containing Merle's journal, Consideraciones temperiei pro 7 annis, edited by George James Symons (folio, London 1891). The 10 pages of Digby 176 are beautifully reproduced, and

[21] Robert Steele has called attention to an earlier record, but much shorter and anonymous, extending over seven months 1269–70, and particularly full for three months, December to February. See Thorndike (3, 141).

[21a] That earthquake is not listed in Davison's catalogue. Charles Davison: History of British earthquakes (p. 14, Cambridge 1924).

Englished by Miss Parker, with an introduction of 2 p. and a few notes. A hundred copies were printed, one of which was made available to me by the courtesy of the U. S. Weather Bureau, Washington.

Latin text for the years 1337 and 1343 only in Gustav Hellmann: Neudrucke von Schriften und Karten über Meteorologie (no. 13, p. 1–5, Berlin 1901).

Criticism. C. L. Kingsford (DNB 37, 285, 1894). Gustav Hellmann: Die Wettervorhersage im ausgehenden Mittelalter (p. 183–85, 1917; Isis 4, 185). R. T. Gunther (1, 315–17; 2, 58, 1923). Thorndike (3, 141–45, 1934). Britton (1937), see years 1331, 1333, 1337, 1344. For the sake of comparison, see Lynn Thorndike: A weather record for 1399–1406 (Isis 32).

ROBERT OF YORK

Robertus Eboracensis, nicknamed Perscrutator. English Dominican, meteorologist (fl. York 1313–25).

The DNB names him Robert the Englishman, but such vague names should be avoided as much as possible. We have already dealt in volume 2 with two other Robert the Englishman, namely, Robert of Chester (XII-1), and the astronomer who flourished in Montpellier c. 1271–76.

Robertus Perscrutator was a physician, astrologer, meteorologist, and perhaps also an alchemist. His main work, De impressionibus aeris, was written in York 1325. It deals with meteorology (in the ancient acceptance of that term), but is mainly of an astrological nature. The author states that more importance should be attached to experiment than to the writings of the ancients, but in spite of his claim to originality, his work contains very few original observations. He tries to account for weather variations by the theory of elements, and by the influences of the seven planets. He discusses the effect of the moon on tides, and remarks on the dephasage of that effect in various places, e.g., up a river; Bede had already made similar remarks concerning what we call today the establishment of a port. He speaks of a comet, stella cum cauda multa, observed by him in York in 1313 (not 1323), portending a defeat of the English by the Scotch.

Robert's meteorological treatise was largely incorporated in the Summa iudicialis of John of Ashendon (1348), who had the effrontery to disparage his stolen goods! It was translated into German (MS of 1485). It was used by the Flemish diplomat Corneille Duplicius De Schepper,[22] in the latter's Assertionis fidei adversus astrologos . . . libri sex (Antwerp 1523; Cologne 1547).

Robert wrote various other treatises: De magia caeremoniali, De moralibus elementarum, De elementorum mixtione musica, De mysteriis secretorum. The De astrolabio canones ascribed to him is the work of the Robertus anglicus (XIII-2) dealt with in volume 2.

Another book ascribed to him but of doubtful genuineness is the Correctorium alchimiae, or Corruptorium alchimiae. It is probably a composition of a somewhat later time. It is divided into 18 chapters, and deals with such topics as these: art may improve nature, witness glassmaking; metals differ from minerals because they include mercury; metals also contain sulphur, but sulphur is an impediment to their purity, whereas mercury is their essence; different kinds of sulphur; live sulphur needed for transmutation exists only in gold and silver. The author criticizes ignorant chemists who lack fundamental knowledge and experience, hence the

[22] Cornelius Scepperus. Born in Nieuwpoort 1500, died in Antwerp 1555. J. J. De Smet (Biographie nationale de Belgique 5, 709–18, 1876); Krones (DNB 31, 93–97, 1890). (Isis 33, 559, n. 7.)

alternative title of his book in some MSS, Correctio fatuorum, ascribed to one master Bernard.[23]

Text. The apocryphal Correctorium alchimiae was included in the alchemical collections edited by Zetzner (2, 385–406, 1659) and by Manget (2, 165–71, 266–75, 1702).

Criticism. C. L. Kingsford (DNB 48, 371, 1896), less than half a page. Gustav Hellmann: Die Wettervorhersage im ausgehenden Mittelalter (p. 181, Berlin 1917; Isis 4, 185). Zinner (nos. 11767–72, 1925). Thorndike (3, 103–18, 1934). C. Doris Hellman: The comet of 1577 (p. 56, New York 1944; Isis 36, 266–70).

A4. Germany

JOHN OF SAXONY

German (Saxon) astronomer (fl. c. 1323–61).

Joannes de Saxonia, Danko nationis saxonicae. Danck, Dancko, Danckow, Danekotte Saxo, Joannes de Madenburch (= Magdeburg), etc. German astronomer whose main activities took place in Paris. In 1323 he was already there, a disciple of John de Linières. He was probably in Paris c. 1323–36; in 1339–48 in Magdeburg; he may have been in Prague in 1360; he was still alive in 1361.

It may be considered proved now (in spite of Duhem's statements to the contrary) that this John of Saxonia and John Danko are the same person, but there was more than one John in Saxony, and one must be careful not to confuse the one described above with others, e.g., with Joannes de Saxonia or de Erfordia, also called Alamannus, a Minorite canonist and legist who lived in Erfurt, Thuringia and wrote a Summa casuum and a Tabula iuris canonici et civilis (in Italy?, c. 1310–17) giving the opinions of jurists from the ancients down to John Andreae (c. 1270–1348) and John the Monk (French Cistercian, cardinal, d. Avignon 1313); see brief note by von Schulte (ADB 14, 454, 1881); he is not dealt with by Savigny. Or with the physician Joannes de Saxonia who flourished in Strassburg c. 1409 (Wickersheimer p. 475, 1936).

An Erfurt MS (quarto 365) contains "Notule Iohannis Danko super compotum" with the explicit "notule supra comp. mag. Ioh. de Saxonia, extracte a scriptis eiusdem completis a.D. 1297" (Schum p. 611). This is very puzzling, for our Danko could not have completed his writings so early.

To return to the Paris astronomer, he was the most famous disciple of John de Linières, and it was they who were largely responsible for the introduction of the Alphonsine tables in Paris, and subsequently in the main centers of Western Europe. The Tables began to be known in Paris c. 1292 (Introd. 2, 838), but in their Spanish form they could not exert much influence outside the Hispanic peninsula. They owed their immense popularity to the Latin versions, especially to the elaborations prepared by John of Saxony.

John wrote his first canons on these Tables in 1327 (incipit, Tempus est mensura motus); they include rules of eclipses and recognize the author's indebtedness to his teacher John de Linières.

In these tables John of Saxony divided the day (not the hour) into 60 equal parts of 60 seconds each (Thorndike 3, 266). It should be noted apropos of this that the mediaeval division of time (i.e., days and hours) is still very imperfectly known; the question is far more complicated than is generally realized. See P. Tannery:

[23] Perhaps Bernhardus Trevirensis or Trevisanus, Bernard of Treves or Bernard of Trevigo, enigmatic personality for whom see Ferguson (1, 100–4, 1906).

Sur la division du temps en instants au Moyen âge (BM 6, 111, 1905; Mémoires 5, 346–47; Isis 6, 434).

The Alphonsine tables were translated into Hebrew, together with John of Saxony's commentary, by Moses ben Abraham of Nîmes (Avignon 1460).

John compiled, presumably in 1335, an Almanach temporale for the years 1336 to 1380, derived from the Alphonsine tables and adapted to the longitude of Paris. These tables, made for astrological use, were very popular. They give the positions of the sun and moon for every day, of Saturn for every tenth day, of Jupiter for every eighth, of Mars for every sixth, of Venus and Mercury for every fourth. In 1355 he wrote a commentary on his teacher's canons (Exempla super tabulas primi mobilis et canones Ioannis de Lineriis), including praise of his teacher, tables of the primum mobile, of the planets, and of the eclipses.

Another well known work of John of Saxony, completed by him in Paris 1331, was his commentary on the Libellus isagogicus of Alcabitius, that is, the Kitāb al-madkhal ilā ṣinā'at aḥkām al-nujūm of al-Qabīṣī (X-2) as translated by John of Seville (XII-1). That Arabic astrological treatise was often printed with John of Saxony's commentary. John's commentary contains new materials derived from the Alphonsine tables, and from his own observations with the directorium (see note on John de Linières for that instrument). He repeats the defense of astrology against ten kinds of opponents given by Abū Ma'shar (IX-1) and adds that astrology does not conflict with the Christian faith.

In 1348 John of Saxony wrote to a friend in Lübeck of the great plague which occurred in Magdeburg, ascribing it to the lunar eclipse of 1345. His determination of the latitude and longitude[24] of Magdeburg was perhaps the first of its kind concerning a German city; the example was promptly followed, and before 1360 the coordinates of Mayence, Cologne, and possibly Braunschweig and Würzburg were known.

Text. The first printed edition of the Alphonsine tables included Danko's commentary, Tabulae astronomicae, Joannes Danck: Canones in tabulas Alphonsi (Ratdolt, Venice 1483). The second edition apparently does not contain Danko's commentary, but another one by Joannes Lucilius Santritter[25] of Heilbronn (Hamann, Venice 1492). Both editions are described in GW (2, 1–3, 1926). Other editions (1487, 1488, 1490) listed by Wegener (1905) are ghosts.

The Libellus isagogicus of Alcabitius (Introductorium ad scientiam iudicialem astronomie), translated by John of Seville, was first printed in Mantua 1473, then in Venice 1482. The third and fourth editions (Venice 1485, 1491) include the commentary by Joannes de Saxonia. See description of these four incunabula in GW (1, 416–19, 1925). John of Saxony's commentary was reprinted in Venice 1502, 1503, 1512, 1513, 1521 (twice), Lyon 1506?, Paris 1520, 1521.

Criticism. See the references in my note on John de Linières, and add the following: Wilhelm Schum: Beschreibendes Verzeichniss der amplonianischen Handschriften-Sammlung zu Erfurt (Berlin 1887). Moritz Steinschneider: Der Commentar des Johannes de Saxonia zur Introductio Alcabitii (BM 5, 114–16, 1891); Hebraeische Übersetzungen (p. 619, 637, 1893). Hermann Grauert: Meister Johann von Toledo (Sitzungsberichte der Kgl. bayerischen Akad. der Wissenschaften, phil. Cl., 1901, 111–325; p. 275). Alfred Wegener: Die astronomischen Werke Alfons X (BM 6, 129–85, 1905). Duhem: Système (4, 74–90, 581, 1916). Zinner (p. 78–82, 407–10, 1925). Thorndike (3, 253–67, 1934).

[24] With reference to Jerusalem and Toledo.

[25] German humanist, printer, editor who flourished in Venice c. 1488–92 (ADB 53, 711–12, 1907).

A5. Netherlands

HENRY OF BRUXELLES

Henri de Bruxelles, Henry of Brussels. Astronomer, computist and philosopher (fl. 1310).

Born in Brussels, he was a monk in the Benedictine abbey of Affighem, in the diocese of Malines.

He wrote a Calendarium pro accensionibus lunae ad punctum investigandis (lost), a Liber de ratione computi ecclesiastici (not identified), De compositione astrolabii (?), De usu et utilitate astrolabii (?), Quodlibeta, Quaestiones super libris Posteriorum, beginning Sicut scripsit Algazel (al-Ghazzālī, XI-2).

The Quodlibeta occur in a MS (Bibliothèque nationale, Paris) together with quodlibeta by Henry the German (Henricus Alamanni). The quodlibeta of Henry of Brussels contain questions on minerals and animals revealing a satirical and salacious mind, e.g., Utrum magnes suppositus capiti mulieris dormitantis caste moveat ipsam ad amplectendum virum suum proprium? . . . Utrum monachi debeant esse pinguiores quam alii?

Criticism. Barthélemy Hauréau (HL 27, 105–8, 1877). Emile Van Arenbergh (Biographie nationale de Belgique 9, 187, 1886).

NOTE ON CIVIL CALENDARS IN HAINAUT

A strange calendar is found in the accounts of Jeanne de Valois[26] from 1319 to 1336. Gobert the Clerk used a financial year of thirteen months of four weeks, the year beginning about Twelfth-night (fête des Rois, Epiphany). Another clerk, Jehan de Thuin, accountant to her son Guillaume (the future ruler of Hainaut, Guillaume II), began his accounts in 1332 in a very modern manner, dividing the year into two semesters beginning respectively on January 1 and July 1. This is of interest for the history of accounting as well as for the history of the calendar. This note is exemplative; I assume that the study of chronicles and accounts in other countries would lead to similar observations. A comparative study of all the calendars used for civil and financial purposes during the fourteenth century would be worth while.

Jules Dewert: Calendrier hennuyer au XIVe siècle (Le folklore brabançon 17, 77–81, 1937).

A6. Scandinavia

HAUKR ERLENDSSON

Norwegian, Icelandic historian, scholar, scientist (b. c. 1264, d. 1334).

Haukr was a judge in Norway and in Iceland; he produced the most detailed edition of the Landnámabók of Ari Fróthi Thorgilsson (XII-1). This edition is a part of the Hauksbók compiled by him (c. 1320), which contains also historical and geographical works, an algorismus, a pronostica temporum, an elucidarius, etc., all in Icelandic. Haukr knew Latin and French, and perhaps a little Hebrew.

The algorismus, Her byriar algorismum, is a translation of the Carmen de algorismo of Alexandre de Villedieu (XIII-1), which was one of the most popular works of its kind in the Middle Ages. It is about 2,700 words long. It includes

[26] Wife of Guillaume I (or III) the Good, count of Hainaut, Holland, etc. He died in 1337, she in 1342. He was succeeded by their son Guillaume II (or IV), who ruled from 1337 to 1345.

at the end the first nine square and cubic numbers, and Platonic considerations on the relations of the four elements to the numbers 8, 12, 18, 27.

At about the same time, in 1340, we hear of another Scandinavian mathematician, a certain Swedish magister Sven (better than Sunon), who obtained from the University of Paris the permission to lecture on spherics in his own house on feast days. Does this suggest that spherics was not taught in the university itself? The Swede Sven was then a kind of pioneer.

Text. First edition of the algorismus by P. A. Munch: Algorismus, eller Anviisning til af kjende og anvende de saakaldte arabiske Tal, efter Hr. Hauk Erlendssöns Codex meddeelt og ledsaget med oversaettelse (Annaler for nordisk oldkyndighed og historie p. 353–75, Kjöbenhavn 1848).

Complete edition of the Hauksbók by E. Jónsson and F. Jónsson: Hauksbók udgiven efter de Arnamagnaeanske håndskrifter (702 p., 2 facs., København 1892–96), with a long introduction in Danish (140 p.) by Finnur Jónsson, dated 1894. For the algorismus see p. 417–24.

Criticism. Cantor (2, 126, 1899). Benedict (1914).

For Sven, see Charles Thurot: De l'organisation et de l'enseignement dans l'université de Paris au Moyen âge (Paris 1850). Günther (p. 206, 1887).

Gustav Eneström: Sur quelques propositions de planimétrie énoncées dans un MS norvégien du XIVe siècle (BM 1898, p. 19–22; 1899, p. 64). Apropos of a Norwegian text dated c. 1320 inserted in a chronicle Annales islandicae ad annum 1313, published in Scriptores rerum danicarum (2, 177–99, 192, 1773), with a Latin translation; Eneström gives a French translation of that text. It is stated incidentally in it that the diameters of sun and earth measure respectively $225° \frac{2}{12}$ and $114° \frac{1}{2} \frac{1}{12}$. This may be derived from Macrobius (V-1)?

B. EASTERN CHRISTENDOM

MOSCHOPULOS

Manuel Moschopulos, Μανουὴλ ὁ Μοσχόπουλος. Byzantine humanist and mathematician who flourished during the rule of Andronicos II Palaeologos (emperor 1282–1328); there are many letters of his dated 1295 to 1316.

He was a nephew of Nicephoros Moschopulos, archbishop (μητροπολίτης) of Crete, and a disciple and friend of Maximos Planudes (XIII-2), who died in 1310.

He was the outstanding philologist of his time, and indirectly one of the founders of Western humanism. His best-known work is a grammatical catechism, Ἐρωτήματα γραμματικά, derived from an anonymous grammar, Ἐπιτομὴ νέα γραμματικῆς. The περὶ τρόπων (on tropes) is but a chapter of the Ἐρωτήματα, and the περὶ σχεδῶν an appendix to it. The σχεδογραφία or writing of σχέδη was a kind of simple grammatical exercise, τὸ σχέδος (scheda or scida) being a piece of paper upon which was written a passage to be parsed and interpreted. He compiled a classical dictionary, Συλλογὴ ὀνομάτων ἀττικῶν, and wrote elementary scholia (grammatical analyses and paraphrases, τεχνολογία) to the first two books of the Iliad, to Hesiodos (VIII B.C.), Pindaros, Euripides, perhaps Aristophanes, Theocritos, Philostratos Flavios (III-1), Paulos Silentiarios, silentiary (σιλεντιάριος) under Justinian (VI-1), and Nicetas David (d. c. 890).[27]

His most interesting work for our readers is a treatise written at the request of Nicolaos Rhabdas on the invention of magic squares, Παράδοσις εἰς τὴν εὕρεσιν τῶν τετραγώνων ἀριθμῶν, that is, a means of arranging the numbers 1 to n^2 in a square

[27] Νικήτας Δαυὶδ Παφλαγών, bishop of Dadybra in Paphlagonia, the most important writer of the late ninth century next to Photios. Krumbacher (p. 167).

so that the sum of the numbers in each row, column, or diagonal equals $\frac{1}{2}n(n^2 + 1)$. He explains how to do that when $n = 2m + 1$ and $n = 4m$; he was planning to deal also with the case when $n = 4m + 2$, but failed to do so. That knowledge was not entirely new, for magic squares were already known to Theon of Smyrna (II-1), to the Ikhwān al-ṣafā' (X-2), to Abraham ben Ezra (XII-1), not to speak of the undatable Chinese tradition,[28] yet Moschopulos' is the earliest Greek treatise on the subject and reveals no Arabic influence. It is perhaps the earliest treatise in any language, except perhaps[29] those of Aḥmad ibn 'Alī al-Būnī and of Ibn al-Lubūdī (XIII-1)? The earlier Greek and Arabic texts contain magic squares, and such are often found on talismans, but the mathematical properties of those squares are not explained, nor the manner of building them. There is no magic whatsoever in Moschopulos' treatise, not even in the terms, for he speaks of the invention of "square numbers," not of magic squares.

Text. Ἐρωτήματα, first edited by Demetrios Chalcondyles (1424–1511) together with the latter's work on the same subject (Milano 1493). Second edition together with the treatise of Theodoros Gaza (c. 1400–c. 1475), Grammaticae artis graecae methodus Manuele Moschopulo authore, eiusdem artis Theodori Gazae libri II (Basel 1540). Many later editions.

Περὶ σχεδῶν. De ratione examinandae orationis libellus (268 p., Paris 1545), Greek text only with elaborate index. Second edition, Vienna 1773.

Opuscula grammatica, edited by Franz Nicolas Titze, together with the anonymous ἐπιτομὴ νέα γραμματικῆς, the apocryphal περὶ μέτρων, and alia (Leipzig 1822).

Συλλογὴ ὀνομάτων, edited by Francescus Asulanus[29a] (Venice 1524). Second edition with the Ἐκλογή of Thomas Magister (Paris 1532).

For the editions of the scholia, a subject which implies a discussion of the editions of the authors commented upon by Moschopulos, see Krumbacher (p. 548).

The treatise on the construction of magic squares was first known through an analysis published by Philippe de La Hire (1640–1718) in the Mémoires de mathématiques et de physique de l'Académie des sciences (1705, p. 162). The Greek text was first edited by Siegmund Günther: Vermischte Untersuchungen zur Geschichte der mathematischen Wissenschaften (p. 195–203, 267–68, Leipzig 1876). Corrections by Alfred Eberhard (Hermes 11, 434–42, 1876). Improved text and French translation by Paul Tannery (Annuaire de l'Association pour l'encouragement des études grecques, 1886, p. 88–118; reprinted in Mémoires 4, 27–60, 1920). Tannery did not take Eberhard's remarks into account. Uncritical English version of the French one by John Calvin McCoy (Scripta mathematica 8, 15–26, 1941).

Criticism. P. Tannery: Moschopoulos et Rhabdas (Bulletin des sciences mathématiques 8, 263–77, 1884; reprinted in Mémoires 4, 1–19, 1920). Krumbacher (p. 546–48, 1897). Theodor Hopfner: Thomas Magister, Demetrios Triklinios, Manuel Moschopulos. Eine Studie über ihren Sprachgebrauch in den Scholien zu

[28] See Introd. vols. 1, 2, index s.v. "magic squares."

[29] I say "perhaps" because I do not know at all what Ibn al-Lubūdī's "essay" on magic squares (mentioned in Introd. 2, 624) amounts to. As to al-Būnī's Shams al-ma'ārif (Introd. 2, 596), I have a Cairene edition of it which I have not read (it is very bulky). A superficial examination shows that it is full of magic, but it may include hidden somewhere a method of building magic squares.

[29a] Giovanni Francesco di Asola (prov. Mantua), son of Andrea Torresano "l'Asolano" (1451–1529). Andrea bought in 1479 the printing shop of Nicholas Jenson in Venice; the great humanist Aldo Manuzio (1450–1515), founder of the Aldine press (1490) in the same city, married Andrea's daughter Maria and from 1508 was associated with him, their books bearing the imprint "in aedibus Aldi et Andreae Asulani soceri." Andrea's business was continued by his sons and grandsons. The Torresani and the Manuzzi played a very important role in Venetian typography and humanism during the sixteenth century.

Aischylos, Sophokles, Euripides, Aristophanes, Hesiod, Pindar und Theokrit (Sitzungsberichte der Kais. Akad. der Wissenschaften, phil. Kl., vol. 172, 74 p., Wien 1912). Heath (2, 549, 1921).

RHABDAS

Nicolaos Artabasdos Rhabdas. Νικόλαος Ἀρτάβασδος ὁ Ῥαβδᾶς. Byzantine mathematician (fl. 1341).

We know practically nothing of his life. The floruit 1341 is derived from a calendar in one of his writings. He originated in Smyrna and lived in Constantinople, being styled "arithmetician and geometer." It would seem that Manuel Moschopulos wrote his treatise on magic squares for Rhabdas; that is not quite certain, however, for that statement was made on the title of Moschopulos' treatise posthumously by another person. The statement, however, is plausible.

Rhabdas prepared a new edition of the arithmetic after the Hindu method, Ψηφοφορία κατ' Ἰνδούς, of Maximos Planudes (XIII-2), and he composed a short grammar for his son Paul. He wrote two arithmetical letters which are not very original but are very interesting for various reasons. Strangely enough, the first paragraph of each letter is copied verbatim from the beginning of Diophantos' preface to his Arithmetica; at any rate, this indicates some familiarity with Diophantos.

The first letter, entitled Brief and very clear explanation of the science of computation, Παράδοσις σύντομος καὶ σαφεστάτη τῆς ψηφοφορικῆς ἐπιστήμης, was written for the master of requests Georgios Chatzyces (ὁ τῶν δεήσεων κύριος Γεώργιος ὁ Χατζύκης). It explains the use of Greek letters to designate numbers, including a way of representing myriads of different orders. Then finger notation (ἔκφρασις τοῦ δακτυλικοῦ μέτρου) up to 9,999; this is of particular interest as being the earliest Greek account in writing; of course finger symbolism had been used by the Greeks for a long time before that (Aristophanes alluded to it c. 420 B.C.), but it had been transmitted only by oral tradition. For comparison, I recall a similar account given in the West by venerable Bede (VIII-1). The Παράδοσις ends with an explanation of the four operations, the approximate extraction of square roots, the progression of decimal numbers (how one passes from one order 10^n to the following 10^{n+1}), and computation tables for alphabetic numbers, this being given as an invention of Palamedes (ψηφοφορικόν, εὕρεμα Παλαμήδους). Palamedes is the name of a mythical hero who joined the Greeks in the expedition against Troy and to whom many inventions (lighthouses, weights and measures, scales, dice, alphabet) were traditionally credited.

The second letter, dated like the first from Constantinople, and having no title except the dedication to his dear friend Theodoros Tzabuches of Clazomenai near Smyrna, Θεόδωρος Τζαβούχης ὁ Κλαζομένιος, deals with more difficult problems. He explains more in detail the approximate extraction of square roots, which is essentially the Heronian method. The same method was also explained by Barlaam, who was aware that it could be continued indefinitely, and we find it in two anonymous Byzantine documents of about the same time. Then multiplication and division of fractionary numbers of the type $N \frac{2}{3} \frac{1}{k} \frac{1}{m} \frac{1}{r} \frac{1}{z} \ldots$ (that is, the Egyptian type), which he reduces to common denominators. Rule-of-three problems, μέθοδος πολιτικῶν λογαριασμῶν (first use of the term political arithmetic, with reference here to problems of daily life); these practical problems give incidentally some information on contemporary metrology and trade. Determination of the Orthodox Easter without reference to the Jewish Passover. This table refers to the current year 6849 Byz. = A.D. 1341/42. Problems leading to equations of the types

$$(1) \quad \frac{x}{m} + \frac{x}{n} + \cdots = a$$

$$(2) \quad x + y = a \qquad mx = ny$$

$$(3) \quad x + \frac{y}{m} = y + \frac{x}{n} = a$$

In short, Rhabdas' letters are less interesting from the point of view of invention than from that of tradition. They reveal the continuation of tradition which can be traced back to early Greek days and even to Egyptian methods. It is remarkable that Rhabdas had not been more influenced by the "new" Hindu (Arabic) arithmetic, with which he was well acquainted. In one of the contemporary anonymous documents above mentioned we find the use of a strange compromise, Greek alphabetic numerals being used but with place value, thus $\alpha\eta = 18$, $\frac{\alpha\gamma}{\beta\eta} = \frac{13}{28}$, etc. All of which illustrates the slowness of the introduction of the simplest idea if it conflicts with immemorial traditions.

Text. The two letters have been very well edited by Paul Tannery (Notices et extraits des MSS 32 (1), 121–252, 1886; reprinted in Mémoires 4, 61–198, 1920), with French translation, notes, and valuable glossary and indexes.

The Greek edition of Maximos Planudes' Ψηφοφορία by C. J. Gerhardt does not include Rhabdas' additions, which are still unpublished.

Rhabdas' grammar is also unpublished.

The anonymous Byzantine documents on square roots have been edited by J. L. Heiberg: Byzantinische Analecten (Abhandlungen zur Geschichte der Mathemathik part 9, 163 ff., Leipzig 1889).

Criticism. P. Tannery: Moschopoulos et Rhabdas (Bulletin des sciences mathématiques 8, 263–77, 1884; reprinted in Mémoires 4, 1–19, 1920); Le Vaticanus graecus 1411 et les MSS de Rhabdas (Archives et missions scientifiques vol. 13, 1888; Mémoires 2, 310–19, 1912). Krumbacher (p. 624, 1897), only a few lines. Cantor (3d ed., 1, 513–15, 1907). D. Cauer (PW, 2d ser., 1, 11–13, 1914). Heath (2, 550–54, 1921).

PEDIASIMOS

Joannes Pediasimos, Ἰωάννης ὁ Πεδιάσιμος. Byzantine mathematician, commentator on Aristotle, rhetorician (fl. end of thirteenth cent. and first half of fourteenth).

Dates and places of birth and death are unknown. He was already middle-aged about the turn of the century, for he was one of the correspondents of Gregorios of Cyprus (patriarch 1283–89). He was deacon and archivist (χαρτοφύλαξ) of Bulgaria under Andronicos II (1282–1328) and Andronicos III (1328–41). He was sometimes called Galenos (γαληνός = serene, a title).

He wrote many works, the most important from our point of view being a treatise on geometry and surveying, Γεωμετρία, σύνοψις περὶ μετρήσεως καὶ μερισμοῦ γῆς, which is closely dependent on Heron of Alexandria (it may be used for the elucidation of

Heron's text). In fact, in the preface, he declares that he will give an account of Heron's lines, angles, and surfaces (γραμμαί, γωνίαι, ἐμβαδά)[30] and complete Heron's views.

Another treatise of his deals with music, Ἐπιστασίαι μερικαί, observations concerning musical points which require arithmetical explanation, e.g., the reason why certain intervals, as the fourth and fifth, have numerical names.

His most curious composition is a mathematical-physiological-mystical treatise on the viability of seven-month and nine-month foetuses, Περὶ ἑπταμήνων καὶ ἐννεαμήνων or Περὶ τοῦ πῶς ἑπτάμηνος καὶ ἐννεάμηνος τόκος σώζεται, wherein he discusses the old superstition, why are foetuses of seven and nine months viable but not the eight-month ones! That concept can be traced back to the Pythagoreans, or at least to Plato's strange calculation concerning the creation of the soul (ψυχογονία) in Timaeos. Plato's views were commented upon by Posidonios (I-1 B.C.), and through him reached Varro (I-2 B.C.), Plutarch (I-2), Quintilian (I-2), Censorinus (III-1), Iamblichos (IV-1), Macrobius (V-1), Proclos (V-2). In his discussion Pediasimos considers physical, astrological, and mathematical arguments, but above all harmonical ones! It is a remarkable example of fantastic reasoning kept alive throughout two millenia. The superstition itself is still alive in a humbler form in the folklore of our own times.

Pediasimos wrote scholia on Hesiod, Aristotle, Theocritos, and on the astronomy of Cleomedes (I-1 B.C.). The Aristotelian scholia relate to the Analytica, but he was well acquainted also with the περὶ ἑρμηνείας. Finally, rhetorical exercises on the twelve labors of Heracles, derived from Apollodoros' Library, and on the nine Musae, and a double poem on the goodness of women and their badness, entitled Πόθος (desire, regret), περὶ γυναικὸς κακῆς, περὶ γυναικὸς ἀγαθῆς, which is a good example of Byzantine argument and refutation (κατασκευή, ἀνασκευή).

Text. The geometry was edited by Gottfried Friedlein in a Programm of the Studienanstalt Ansbach (Ansbach 1866); also Jahns Neue Jahrbücher für Philologie (92, 366–83, 1865).

Vittorio de Falco: In Aristotelis Analytica scholia selecta (200 p., Naples 1926), with elaborate indexes; long review by Karl Praechter (Byzantinische Zeitschrift 27, 105–13, 1927). Vittorio de Falco: Altri scolii di Giovanni Pediasimo agli Analitici (Byzantinische Zeitschrift 28, 251–69, 1928).

For other scholia see Krumbacher. The scholia on Cleomedes are unpublished.

Franz Cumont: L'opuscule περὶ ἑπταμήνων καὶ ἐννεαμήνων (Revue belge de philologie 2, 5–21, 1923; Isis 24, 204).

Ἐπιστασίαι μερικαί, edited by H. Vincent (Notices et extraits 16 (2), 289–315, 1847).

Περὶ τῶν δώδεκα ἄθλων τοῦ Ἡρακλέους, edited by Richard Wagner: Mytographi graeci, volumen 1. Apollodori Bibliotheca (p. 247–59, Leipzig 1894).

Πόθος, edited by Lucas Holstenius in Demophili, Democratis et Secundi sententiae morales, in Greek and Latin (120 p., Rome 1638; Leiden 1639). I have seen only the so-called second edition (p. 32–35, Cambridge 1670). New edition by Emmanuel Miller: Catalogue des MSS de l'Escurial (p. 75–82, 1848), including a translation in French verse dated 1797.

Criticism. Gottfried Friedlein: Pauca de Pediasimi geometria (Boncompagni's Bulletino di bibliografia e di storia delle scienze 3, 303, 1870). Krumbacher (p. 556–58, 1897). Cantor (3d ed., 1, 510, 1907).

[30] Historians of mathematics will remember the Liber embadorum of Abraham bar Ḥiyya (XII-1), translated from Hebrew into Latin in 1145 by Plato of Tivoli (XII-1).

THEODOROS METOCHITES

Theodoros Metochites or Metochita (Θεόδωρος ὁ Μετοχίτης). Byzantine humanist, philosopher, astronomer (d. 1332).

The place and date of his birth are unknown, but he was the son of Georgios Metochites, archdeacon of Hagia Sophia, who died in prison after 1308. Georgios Metochites was a partisan of Joannes Beccos (Ἰωάννης Βέκκος or Βέκος, Βέκων), patriarch from 1275 to 1282, who defended the union of the Eastern and Western churches and justified the Latin dogmas; Joannes XI (Beccos) was deposed, disgraced, exiled, and died in prison in 1293. Joannes XI and Georgios Metochites may be called martyrs of the cause of religious unity.

To return to Theodoros, he entered the service of Andronicos II in 1290 and had reached the high office of grand chancellor (μέγας λογοθέτης)[31] or treasurer (λογοθέτης τοῦ γενικοῦ), when he was unfortunately involved in the feud between Andronicos II and the latter's grandson (Andronicos III). The deposition of Andronicos II in 1328 caused Theodoros' own fall. When Andronicos III entered the capital and established himself at the palace of the Porphyrogénnetos (Tekfour serai), his soldiery sacked the house of Metochites, who was banished to Didymotica for two years. Upon his return, in 1330, Theodoros withdrew to the monastery of St. Saviour in Chora, which he had restored and decorated in his prosperous days. Yet his miseries were not over; he suffered from a very painful illness; his sons were implicated in a political plot and thrown into prison. He died in the monastery in 1332, probably in March, for it is said that he died one month later than Andronicos II, whose death occurred on February 13, 1332.

Before 1328 his days were devoted to his state and court duties, and part of his nights to philosophy and science. He was a humanist, a student of Aristotle, and a great admirer of Plato. He was a very learned man in many fields and an abundant writer, who reminds us of Photios (IX-2) and of Michael Psellos (XI-2) and anticipates Gemistos Plethon (Γεώργιος Γεμιστὸς Πλήθων, c. 1356-1450) and the Platonic revival of Florence.

Astronomy. His most important work for us is probably his commentary on Ptolemy or astronomical introduction, Στοιχείωσις ἐπὶ τῇ ἀστρονομικῇ ἐπιστήμῃ, a treatise which is still hardly known. He was the astronomical tutor of Nicephoros Gregoras, to whom we owe an enthusiastic account of his life and deeds. He was apparently well acquainted with ancient mathematics, e.g., with Euclid, Apollonios, Nicomachos.

Commentaries on, or paraphrases of, Aristotle. Theodoros wrote a long series of such explanatory paraphrases, περὶ φυσικῆς ἀκροάσεως, περὶ ψυχῆς, περὶ οὐρανοῦ, περὶ γενέσεως καὶ φθορᾶς, περὶ μνήμης καὶ ἀναμνήσεως, περὶ ὕπνου καὶ ἐγρηγόρσεως, περὶ τῶν ἐνυπνίων, περὶ τῆς καθ' ὕπνον μαντικῆς, περὶ ζῴων κινήσεως, περὶ βραχυβιότητος καὶ μακροβιότητος, περὶ γήρως καὶ νεότητος καὶ ζωῆς καὶ θανάτου, περὶ ζῴων πορείας, περὶ ζῴων μορίων, περὶ ζῴων γενέσεως, περὶ τῶν μετεωρολογικῶν, περὶ αἰσθήσεως καὶ αἰσθητῶν.[32]

Theodoros' Miscellany. His most ambitious literary work is a collection of some 120 essays on historical, literary, and philosophical subjects, which has come down

[31] The logothetes was a ratiocinator, that is, an accountant, but the office of μέγας λογοθέτης or of λογοθέτης τῶν σεκρέτων, existing anteriorly (1081-1204), had other implications. See Charles Diehl: Un haut fonctionnaire byzantin, le logothète (Mélanges offerts à Nicolas Jorga par ses amis de France p. 217-27, Paris 1933; Byzantinische Zeitschrift 34, 373-79, 1934).

[32] List taken from Sathas (1, πγ', 1872).

Fig. 11. Mosaic portrait of Theodoros Metochites in the church of St. Saviour in the Fields (now Kahrie jami). He is seen offering to Christ that very church, which he had restored and embellished. The portrait was made c. 1303–21, within Metochites' lifetime. Photograph by Sébah and Joaillier, Constantinople. Courtesy of Fogg Museum, Cambridge, Massachusetts.

FIG. 12. Mosaic in Kahrie jami, Constantinople, representing the marriage of Cana, bearing the Byzantine date 6811 (= A.D. 1303) in Arabic numerals. This is the earliest monumental use of such numerals in Europe. The date is written above the circular arch, above and to the left of the jug carried by the man on the right. Photograph reproduced from the Kahrie jami album, by Th. I. Schmitt (Bull. Russian Archaeological Institute in Constantinople, vol. 11, Sofia 1906; album of 92 plates, Munich 1906). Courtesy of Dumbarton Oaks Library, Washington.

to us under the Greek title, Ὑπομνηματισμοὶ καὶ σημειώσεις γνωμικαί (Records and opinions), and the Latin one, Miscellanea philosophica et historica. These essays discuss many ethical problems such as λάθε βιώσας, is marriage better than celibacy? is life in the cloister better than in the world?, etc., and also the literary, artistic, historical questions which would arrest the attention of educated people of his time and of all times. He seems to have considered an ideal of constitutional monarchy.

His sources were exclusively Greek, but abundant, some 70 authors being quoted, most of them ancient; his main authority was, strangely enough, Synesios of Cyrene (V-1), bishop of Ptolemaïs.

He wrote a few other literary works of less importance, in prose and verse. His poems (20 in number, a total of 9,188 lines) contain autobiographical and historical information. One of them deals with his monastery (μονὴ τῆς χώρας), another is a didactic poem on the mathematical species or aspect of philosophy, and especially the harmonic aspect, περὶ τοῦ μαθηματικοῦ εἴδους τῆς φιλοσοφίας καὶ μάλιστα περὶ τοῦ ἁρμονικοῦ.

Most poems of that time were written in political verse (that is, a type of accentual verse, chiefly fifteen-syllabled iambic lines). All of Theodoros' poetry, however, is in classical hexameters, for he was making a great effort to restore the ancient language. In this also he proves himself to be a forerunner of the Western humanists.

The mosaics of St. Saviour in Chora. In the eyes of posterity, Theodoros' greatest achievement was in a very different field. We remember him now chiefly because he restored the church of St. Saviour in the Fields (τῆς χώρας), which had been plundered and almost completely destroyed by the Latins in 1204 and left in a ruinous state. It is one of the oldest churches in Constantinople, dating back to the days of Justinian (VI-1); a domed basilica, the only one of its type in the city; located near the north end of the landward wall not far from the palace of the Blachernae (ἐν Βλαχέρναις, the 14th ward of the city). It was close to the Gate of Charisios (Edirné kapoussi),[32a] through which the Muslim conquerors entered the city in 1453, and hence was the first Christian sanctuary to fall into their hands. It was turned into a mosque about the end of the fifteenth century, and called Kahrie jami, under which name it is now generally known. It disappeared from general view until 1860, when it was discovered by the Greek architect Pelopidas D. Kouppas. It is now one of the main treasures of Constantinople; I shall never forget my joyful surprise and wonder when I visited it in May 1932, just six centuries after the death of its restorer.

To return to the latter, he spent a fortune for the renovation of the dilapidated church and the decoration of the two narthexes and of the parecclesion (the central part had suffered less damage). The narthexes were decorated with a series of 48 mosaics representing the life of Christ according to the canonical and apocryphal Gospels, figures of saints, etc. There are 38 frescoes in the parecclesion. The mosaics are particularly impressive. To appreciate their importance in the history of art, it will suffice to recall that they are contemporary with Giotto (1276–1337) and even with Giotto's youth. Indeed, one of them (the marriage of Cana, central bay of the exonarthex) bears the Byzantine date 6811 = A.D. 1303. That date is written in Arabic numerals and is the earliest example of the monumental use of

[32a] The Turkish name, meaning the Gate of Adrianople, is here spelled as in Van Millingen (p. 265, 290, 304, 1912). In that spelling, as in that of the word tekfour above, the ou is the French (and Greek) u.

such numerals known to me (Isis 22, 224). It proves that the decoration was begun before 1303; we know that it was completed in 1321 (see fig. 12).

Another mosaic (in third bay of inner narthex) is historically important. It represents Theodoros in the dress of a grand logothete offering his church to Christ. It bears the inscription, not legible in our reproduction (fig. 11), ὁ κτήτωρ λογοθέτης τοῦ γενικοῦ Θεόδωρος ὁ Μετοχίτης. The strange headdress was given Theodoros by Andronicos II as a special distinction (Van Millingen p. 325, 1912).

Text. The astronomical treatise is still unpublished, except for extracts and introduction quoted by Sathas (vol. 1, πδ' to ριη', Venice 1872).

The Aristotelian paraphrases were printed in Latin, Basel 1559, again 1562; Ravenna 1614.

Miscellanea. First partial edition by Janus Bloch (Copenhagen 1790). Many other partial editions. First and only complete edition by M. Chr. G. Müller and M. Th. Kiessling (Leipzig 1821).

Criticism. Constantinos N. Sathas: Μεσαιωνικὴ βιβλιοθήκη (vol. 1, οζ to ριη', p. 139–95, Venice 1872). Henri Omont: Projet de réunion des églises grecque et latine sous Charles le Bel en 1327 (Bibliothèque de l'Ecole des chartes 53, 254–57, 1892), letters from Andronicos and Theodoros Metochites to Charles le Bel and to the Dominican Benedict of Assinago (bishop of Como 1328–38). Krumbacher (p. 550–54, 623, 1897). Charles Diehl: Etudes byzantines (Paris 1905). Van Millingen (p. 288–331, ill., 1912). Eleutheroudakis encyclopaedia (9, 385, 1930). G. Sarton: Earliest monumental use of Arabic numerals (Isis 22, 224, 1934); The astronomical summary of Theodoros Metochites (query no. 89, Isis 32, 120).

There has been considerable discussion about the mosaics of Kahrie jami. Are they purely Oriental, or were they submitted to some Western Giottesque or pre-Giottesque influence? See histories of Byzantine art, for example, Charles Diehl (2, 799, 1926), or Diehl's article Les mosaïques de Kahrié-djami (Gazette des Beaux-Arts, nov. 1904, janv. 1905; reprinted in his Etudes byzantines p. 392–431, Paris 1905).

CHRYSOCOCCES

Georgios Chrysococces, Γεώργιος ὁ Χρυσοκόκκης. Byzantine astronomer and geographer who flourished at Trebizond c. 1335–46.

It is not known when or where he was born. He may have been born in Trebizond or have been attracted there by the fame of that city as a center of physical and mathematical studies. There was a kind of academy in Trebizond, made illustrious by Gregorios Chioniades, the attraction of which was felt even in Constantinople.

Chrysococces was educated by a priest named Manuel who was himself a disciple of Chioniades and had succeeded him in the academy. This Manuel introduced him to the study of the books which Chioniades had brought back from Persia, and thus enabled him to write in 1346, for one Joannes Charsanites, a treatise on the astronomy of the Persians, including tables, Τοῦ σοφωτάτου ἰατροῦ κυροῦ Γεωργίου τοῦ Χρυσοκόκκη ἐξήγησις εἰς τὴν σύνταξιν τῶν Περσῶν ἐκτεθεῖσα πρὸς τὸν αὐτοῦ ἀδελφὸν κυρὸν Ἰωάννην τὸν Χαρσανίτην.

These Persian tables are sometimes misleadingly called Tables of Yazdigird (Yezdikerti, Yazdegerd). Their epoch is the first year of Yazdigird III, A.D. 632 June 16. There were three Sāsānian kings of that name; Yazdigird III, the last of his dynasty, ruled from 632 to 651.

The tables were translated into Hebrew (or a Hebrew adaptation was composed) in Salonica 1374, by Solomon ben Elijah, alias Sharbiṭ ha-zahab (XIV-2), under the title Mahalak ha-kokabim. In 1425, Mordecai ben Eliezer Comtino (d. Constantinople c. 1485–90) wrote a Hebrew commentary upon them, entitled Perush luḥot. The tables were not much known in the West. Mordecai ben Abraham Finzi (fl. Mantua 1441–73) mentioned them, and so did Joseph del Medigo (1591–1655), but the latter was a Cretan (that is, an Easterner), and these mentions are exceptional.

In addition to his treatise of 1346, Chrysococces wrote other astronomical treatises, to wit, Πρόχειρος παράδοσις εἰς τοὺς Περσικοὺς κανόνες τῆς ἀστρονομίας (or is this simply another title of the first work, or a part of it?);[33] Πῶς ὁ τῆς σελήνης εὑρίσκεται κύκλος (Determination of the moon's orbit), dated 1335; Πῶς ὁ τοῦ ἡλίου εὑρίσκεται κύκλος (Determination of the sun's orbit); Κανόνιον τοῦ ἡμεροευρεσίου. He also wrote geographical treatises, Περὶ ἐπωνυμίας πόλεων καὶ τόπων (The naming of towns and places), very short; Κανόνια τοῦ μήκους καὶ τοῦ πλάτους τῶν ἐπισήμων . . . πόλεων (Table of longitudes and latitudes of remarkable cities).

In the MSS, Georgios Chrysococces is often called physician (ἰατρός). Thus we may assume that he practiced medicine in Trebizond. No medical writings, however, are ascribed to him.

The astronomical tables of Immanuel Bonfils (XIV-2), Shesh kenafayim (Six wings), completed at Tarascon in 1365 (radix 1340), were commented upon in Greek, Ἔκδοσις γεγονυῖα εἰς τὸ ἰουδαϊκὸν ἑξαπτρέρυγον κατὰ τὸ ,ϛπμγ'[34] ἀπὸ τῆς ἀρχῆς τοῦ παντός, by one Chrysococces, not by Georgios, however (as has been mistakenly said and repeated), but by Michael Chrysococces, who was notary (νοτάριος) of the great church of Trebizond in 1435. How did Michael know of the Hebrew tables and become interested in them? Could he read them in Hebrew, or were they translated for him into Greek, or did he use the Latin translation of 1406?

Another Georgios Chrysococces, who was a deacon and schoolmaster in Constantinople, has some importance in the history of humanism, for he counted among his disciples Francesco Filelfo (1398–1481) and Bessarion of Trebizond (c. 1400–72). He copied many MSS for Filelfo and others, dated 1420 to 1428.[35] In short, we should distinguish between:

Georgios Chrysococces, astronomer, fl. Trebizond 1346.
Georgios Chrysococces, copyist, fl. Constantinople 1420–28.
Michael Chrysococces, astronomer, fl. Trebizond 1435.

Text. Ismael Boulliau (Bullialdus, 1605–94): Synopsis tabularum persicarum ex syntaxi Persarum Georgii medici Chrysococcae . . . excerpta et nunc primum in lucem edita (folio, 232 p., appended to his Astronomia philolaica, Paris 1645). Extracts in John Hudson: Geographiae veteris scriptores graeci minores (vol. 3, Oxford 1712), Greek and Latin with notes.

Hermann Usener: Ad historiam astronomiae symbola (Programm, Bonn 1876); reprinted in his Kleine Schriften (3, 323–71, 1914).

Criticism. Friedrich Schoell: Histoire de la littérature grecque profane (2d ed., 7, 66, Paris 1825), only a few lines. Krumbacher (p. 622, 1897), only a few lines. Steinschneider (p. 629, 1893); (p. 15, 1904). Louis H. Gray: Zu den byzantinischen Angaben über den altiranischen Kalender (Byzantinische Zeitschrift 11, 468–72, 1902). Paul Tannery: Les éphémérides chez les Byzantins (Bulletin des sciences

[33] Or a confusion with the treatise of same title ascribed to Isaac Argyros (XIV-2)?

[34] 6943 = A.D. 1434–35. The first two letters are not sigma and pi, but stigma and sampi.

[35] According to the recent Greek encyclopaedia, Ἐγκυκλοπαιδικὸν λεξικὸν Ἐλευθερουδάκη (12, 972, Athens 1931)—a very fine work, by the way—he is said to have been a friend of Theodoros Gaza (c. 1400–c. 1475) and to have worked with him in the Vatican library (??). The copy of the Odyssey (Vaticanus Palatinus 7) dated 1336 (not 1436) was probably made by the elder Georgios Chrysococces, not by the younger.

mathématiques 30, 59, 1906; Mémoires 4, 289–93, 1920). O. Schissel: Note sur un catalogus codicum chronologorum graecorum (Byzantion 9, 269–95, 1934), only brief reference to Chrysococces, p. 288. U. Lampsides: Georges Chrysococcis, le médecin et son oeuvre (Byzantinische Zeitschrift 38, 312–22, 1938), containing text of Περὶ ἐπωνυμίας πόλεων καὶ τόπων.

CATRARIOS

Joannes Catrarios (or Catrares), Ἰωάννης Κατράριος (or ὁ Κατράρης). Byzantine astrologer (fl. 1322).

He is known as a copyist of Greek MSS and author of a satirical poem (219 lines) written against a "philosopher and rhetorician" called Neophytos (Νεόφυτος). In 1322 he wrote a dialogue concerning astrology, Ἕρμιππος ἢ περὶ ἀστρολογίας (two books of 20 and 21 chapters), which is a clever attempt to reconcile astrology with Christian teachings. This could be done only by sacrificing the astrological ideas conflicting with those teachings, especially astrological fatalism. It is done well, though Neoplatonic conceptions are not always completely concealed. In order to reinforce the argument the writer introduces various Christian miracles or legends susceptible of an astrological slant, i.e., the star guiding the Magi, the darkness occurring at the time of Christ's death. The main source is the treatise De revolutionibus nativitatum of Abū Ma'shar (IX-1), available in a Greek translation, some passages of which are copied verbatim.

Text. Hermippos was first edited by O. D. Bloch (Copenhagen 1830). New edition by Wilhelm Kroll and Paul Viereck: Anonymi christiani Hermippus. De astrologia dialogus (102 p., Leipzig 1895), with glossary.

Criticism. Krumbacher (p. 627, 780, 1897), considering Hermippos to be a product of the fifth or sixth century, a hypothesis which has become untenable since the derivation from Abū Ma'shar has been proved. W. Kroll (PW 15, 854–57, 1912). Franz Boll: Eine arabische-byzantinische Quelle des Dialogo Hermippos (Sitzungsberichte der Heidelberger Akad. der Wissenschaften, phil. Kl., Abh. 18, 28 p., 1912), containing Arabic text edited by Carl Bezold, early Greek version, early Latin version taken from Hermetis philosophi de revolutionibus nativitatum I, cap. VII (as edited by Hieronymus Wolf in appendix to an anonymous commentary to Ptolemy's Tetrabiblos and to Porphyry's astrological isagoge, Basel 1559, p. 214–16), De eo quod debet astrologus praescire aetatem eius cuius est revolutio, German translation of the Arabic text and notes. Honigmann (p. 94, 100, 189, 1929).

C. ISRAEL

C1. Provençal Jews

ABBA MARI BEN ELIGDOR

Also called Sen Astruc (Asṭruq) de Noves (or de San Nagri, Negre?). Judeo-Provençal exegete and mathematician. Born at Noves, near Avignon; flourished at Salon near Aix in Provence c. 1322; he was still living at the end of 1335, but was then very old. He taught Samuel ben Judah of Marseille astronomy in Salon.

He wrote an introduction to the first book of Euclid, and commentaries on Job and the Song of songs and the Pirqe de Rabbi Eliezer.[36] His commentary on Job

[36] The Pirqe (or Baraita) de Rabbi Eliezer is a mystico-astronomical commentary on the Torah, traditionally but wrongly ascribed to Eliezer ben Hyrcanus ha-gadol, a tanna of the second generation (second half of first cent.). It is certainly post-Talmudic.

is a discussion of the problem of evil. His views are largely Maimonidean. He criticized adversely the Ṭirat kesef (a commentary on the Torah) of Joseph ben Abba Mari Kaspi.

Criticism. Steinschneider (p. 508, 1893), doubting the ascription to Abba Mari of the commentary on Euclid. H. Gross (p. 389, 1897). Neubauer-Renan (p. 548–52, 1893). Louis Ginzberg (JE 1, 32, 1901). J. N. Simchoni (EJ 1, 152, 1928).

C2. Spanish Jews

ISAAC ISRAELI THE YOUNGER

Not to be confused with Isaac Israeli the Elder (X-1), Egyptian physician and philosopher. These two men have nothing in common, "Isaac the Jew" being a name which could be applied to thousands of individuals.

Isaac ben Joseph ben Israel of Toledo. Judeo-Spanish astronomer (fl. Toledo 1310; d. after 1330).

He wrote three astronomical works, Sha'ar ha-shamayim (Gate of heaven), Sha'ar ha-melle'im (Gate of space), Yesod 'olam (Foundation of the world). The first two are unpublished and practically unknown. The third was written at Toledo in 1310 at the invitation of his master, Asher ben Jehiel (XIII-2), and represents the climax of mediaeval Jewish astronomy.

The Yesod 'olam is divided into five parts: (I) Geometrical and trigonometrical introduction; this includes a complete solution of right-angled spherical triangles. (II) System of the world according to the Ptolemaic views as revised by al-Biṭrūjī (XII-2); astronomical summary. (III) Motions of sun and moon. (IV) Elaborate and clear account of the Jewish calendar, with Maimonides' calculation of the new moons (in the latter's Hilkot qiddush ha-ḥodesh; Introd. 2, 373); chronologies of foreign nations; Jewish chronology to the end of the Gaonic period after the Sefer ha-qabbalah of Abraham ben David ha-Levi (XII-2). At the end of part IV there is an appendix dealing with a dispute with a convert about a point of chronology; the dispute occurred in 1334; hence this appendix is an interpolation. (V) Tables and their explanations.

The author's son, Joseph ben Isaac Israeli, began an abridgment of the Yesod 'olam in Arabic, in Toledo c. 1324–31, but left it incomplete because of his death in 1331. The Arabic text is lost, but there is a Hebrew translation of it, Qiẓẓur yesod 'olam, by a member of the same family, Isaac ben Solomon ben Israel (perhaps identical with the man who completed in 1367 at the age of 28 a commentary on the treatise Abot[37]). There are also various Hebrew commentaries on and references to Yesod 'olam, proving its popularity, e.g. in Elijah ben Abraham Mizraḥi (of Constantinople, c. 1455–1525/26).

Isaac's brother, Israel ben Joseph, who died in 1326[38] in Toledo, was a favorite pupil of Asher ben Jehiel, and translated for him various texts from the Arabic into Hebrew. He was a Talmudist and exegete, and wrote preferably in Arabic. For example, he wrote in Arabic a liturgical treatise which was translated into Hebrew, Miẓwot zemaniyot, by Shem-ṭob ben Isaac ibn Ardotial (Arduṭil) in Sòria, Old Castile, c. 1345; and he wrote also in Arabic a commentary on Abot.

The fact that two Jewish writers, Joseph ben Isaac Israeli and Israel ben Joseph

[37] A part of the Babylonian Talmud.
[38] End of 1316 (?) (EJ 8, 659).

Israeli (it is true, of the same family), and probably others, continued to write in Arabic in Toledo in the fourteenth century is significant. It cannot be accounted for save by the scientific prestige of the Arabic language, even as some authors continued to write in Latin when that language had been generally displaced by various vernaculars. Isaac Israeli himself also wrote in Arabic, for he refers in his Yesod 'olam (IV, 14) to an Arabic epistle (iggeret) which he addressed to his brother Israel.

Text. An extract from the Yesod 'olam (IV, 18) was included in the second edition of Sefer yuḥassin of Abraham Zacuto, edited by Moses Isserls (Cracow 1580). Editio princeps of the Yesod 'olam, incomplete however and insufficient, by Baruch ben Jacob of Sklov, with an introduction by Naphtali Hartwig Wessely (Berlin 1777). Liber Jesod olam seu Fundamentum mundi, edited by Berl Goldberg and L. Rosenkranz, with German analysis by David Cassel (Berlin 1846–48). This valuable edition was published in two installments, the first (1846) containing parts IV and V together with the German summaries, the second (1848), parts I to III with their summaries. As the second installment includes the beginning and main substance of the Yesod 'olam, it is easily mistaken for the whole work. I used first an incomplete copy of this edition, then a complete one, and publish this note as a warning. The German analysis is very elaborate.

Criticism. Steinschneider: Die Mathematik bei den Juden (BM 11, 39, 1897); Hebraeische Übersetzungen (p. 596, 912, 1893); Arabische Literatur der Juden (p. 164, 1902). Isaac Broydé (JE 6, 670, 1904). Josef Heller (EJ 8, 648, 658, 1931). W. M. Feldman: Rabbinical mathematics and astronomy (p. 111, 1931; Isis 19, 208–12). Alexander Marx: The scientific work of some outstanding mediaeval Jewish scholars (Essays in memory of Linda R. Miller p. 149–50, New York 1938).

SOLOMON BEN ABRAHAM CORCOS

Judeo-Spanish astronomer, who flourished c. 1331 in Avila. In that year and place he wrote a commentary on the astronomical treatise Yesod 'olam which Isaac Israeli had composed some twenty years earlier in Toledo. He was a pupil of Judah ben Asher (Introd. 2, 889).

He was one of the earliest known members of a distinguished Sephardic family which is still represented today in Gibraltar and Morocco. The Hebrew name is written Qorqos, generally with final samek (sometimes with final sin).

Criticism. Louis Ginzberg (JE 4, 265, 1903). Genealogical table of the Corcos family (ibid. p. 263). Similar note by J. Heller (EJ 5, 658, 1930).

JOSEPH BEN JOSEPH NAḤMIAS

Joseph ben Joseph Naḥmias of Toledo. Member of a prominent Jewish family of Toledo which can be traced back to the beginning of the twelfth century. He flourished in the second quarter of the fourteenth century.

He was a disciple of rabbi Asher ben Jehiel (XIII-2), and wrote commentaries on the Torah, Proverbs, Esther (1326–27), Pirqe abot. He wrote in Arabic, c. 1330–50, an astronomical treatise entitled Nūr al-'ālam (Light of the world). This was put into Hebrew, Or 'olam, within the same century by an unknown translator, but a critical note by Profiaṭ Duran (XIV-2) follows the translation (MS Bodl. Canon. 334). In the Nūr al-'ālam Joseph discussed the value of epicycles and eccentrics vs. homocentric spheres; he reviewed astronomical theories in general and particularly those of al-Biṭrūjī and Maimonides; he asked himself whether opposite circular motions could be admitted on logical grounds, and finally rejected the system of al-Biṭrūjī.

He may be identical with the contemporary Joseph ben Abraham Naḥmias, who transliterated from Arabic into Hebrew script at least a part of the commentary on Ibn Sīnā's Qānūn composed in Arabic by Solomon ibn Ya'īsh.

Criticism. Steinschneider: Hebraeische Übersetzungen (p. 597, 686, 1893); Die Mathematik bei den Juden (BM 11, 38, 1897); Arabische Literatur der Juden (p. 166, 1902). Meyer Kayserling (JE 9, 145, 1905).

ISAAC BEN PULQAR

Isaac ben Joseph ben Pulgar (Pulqar, Pulkar, Polkar). Hispano-Jewish philosopher and translator from Arabic into Hebrew (fl. 1307-30).

He completed in 1307 the translation of al-Ghazzālī's Maqāṣid al-falāsifa, begun by Isaac Albalag (XIII-2) under the title Tiqqun ha-filusufim. Albalag had translated the first two parts (logic, metaphysics) and begun the third (physics); Isaac ben Pulqar completed the translation of the third part.

He wrote a refutation of astrology in Spanish, and another in Hebrew directed against the Minḥat qanaot of Abner of Burgos and entitled Iggeret ha-ḥarfah (Letter of reproach).

His most important work is a treatise in defense of Judaism, called 'Ezer ha-dat (Support of law), written c. 1330. It consists of five dramatic dialogues against (1) apostates, Christians, and ignorant Jews, (2) skeptics, (3) those who believe in astrology, (4) Biblical literalists and those who try to explain everything by means of allegories; qabbalists and sorcerers, (5) those who do not believe in the immortality of the soul.

Judging from his discussion with Abner of Burgos, his own views on immortality were remarkable, for he believed in the immortality of a universal soul, not of a personal one. The reward of duty is its very observance; the punishment of sin, its very commission.

Isaac's uncompromising attacks on astrology are almost unique in Hebrew literature; in this respect he was almost the only mediaeval Jew who dared follow the lead so boldly taken by Maimonides. I write "almost," because I am thinking of the Eben boḥan of his contemporary Qalonymos ben Qalonymos, and there may be other examples, but they are certainly very rare.

Text. The second dialogue has been edited in Eliezer Ashkenazi II: Ṭa'am zeqenim (Francfort a.M. 1854). 'Ezer ha-dat, edited by George S. (Gershon ben Joseph) Belasco (London 1906).

Criticism. Isidore Loeb: Polémistes chrétiens et juifs en France et en Espagne (Revue des études juives 18, 63-70, 1889), analysis of the 'Ezer ha-dat and two curious extracts against qabbalists and sorcerers. Steinschneider (p. 299, 1893). Max Seligsohn (JE 6, 539, 1904). Alexander Marx: The correspondence between the rabbis of southern France and Maimonides about astrology (Hebrew Union College annual 3, 311-58, 1926, p. 18 of reprint; Isis 11, 172), important paper but mainly devoted to Maimonides. Duncan Black Macdonald: The meanings of the philosophers by al-Ghazzālī (Isis 25, 9-15, 1936).

C3. Eastern Jews

See summary in section VI of chapter I.

D. ISLAM

D1. Maghrib

MUḤAMMAD IBN IBRĀHĪM AL-ABULĪ

Abū 'Abdallāh Muḥammad ibn Ibrāhīm al-Abulī.[39] Algerian mathematician, philosopher, and scientist, teacher of Ibn Khaldūn; died after 1347.

Al-Abulī was born in Tlemcen toward the end of the thirteenth century. At the time of the first siege of that city (1299–1307) by the Marīnī sulṭān Yūsuf ibn Ya'-qūb, he left it to accomplish the Pilgrimage and travel in the East. After his return he continued his studies in Tunis, Tlemcen, and Marrākush (1310), where he sat at the feet of Ibn al-Bannā' (XIII-2).[40] After the death of Ibn al-Bannā', in 1321, he spent some time as tutor and shaykh to a Berber chieftain, first in the Atlas mountains, then in Fās al-Jadīd. He was thus brought to the attention of the Marīnī sulṭān Abū-l-Ḥasan 'Alī (ruled 1331–48). After the Marīnī conquest of Tunis (1347) he went to Tunis with that sulṭān, and it was then that Ibn Khaldūn became one of his disciples. Ibn Khaldūn speaks warmly of him ("our shaykh") in his autobiography, and relates anecdotes concerning him in the Muqaddama; he does not mention the date of his death, though he certainly survived him. Suter says al-Abulī died c. 1368/69 (?).

Al-Abulī transmitted to Ibn Khaldūn the knowledge he had obtained from Ibn al-Bannā' and others; in other words, he was the great historian's scientific instructor, and as such deserves to be remembered in spite of his having left no writings. He was probably responsible for the scientific tendencies which are apparent in Ibn Khaldūn's works.

The only sources for his life are Ibn Khaldūn's autobiography and Muqaddama (Prolégomènes 1, xxiv–vi; 2, 202, 351). Suter (no. 414, 1900).

'ABD AL-'AZĪZ IBN 'ALĪ AL-HUWĀRI

Moroccan mathematician of Berber origin; his nisba refers to the Huwāra, one of the most important Berber tribes (EI 2, 349). He was a disciple of Ibn al-Bannā' (XIII-2), and wrote a commentary, Ghāyat al-kuttāb (or al-lubāb), on the latter's arithmetical treatise, Talkhīṣ fī a'māl al-ḥisāb (Summary of the operation of calculation).

The Talkhīṣ was a popular textbook, which was commented upon not only by this 'Abd al-'Azīz, but also by the Egyptian Ibn al-Majdī (XIV-2), by the Spaniards Abu Zakarīyā Muḥammad al-Ishbīlī (fl. probably in second half of fourteenth cent. or beginning of fifteenth) and al-Qalaṣādī (d. 1486), etc.

Criticism. Hājjī Khalīfa (vol. 2, no. 3532, 1837). Suter (no. 415, 1900). H. P. J. Renaud: Additions à Suter (Isis 18, 173, 1932).

[39] M. G. de Slane (Prolégomènes d'Ibn Khaldoun 1, xxiv) reads Abbeli, which he connects with Abbela in Spain (Avila?). If so, Muḥammad's family originated in Spain. As the Christian reconquest proceeded, many Spanish-Muslim families fled to North Africa. For criticism of de Slane's data see Renaud (p. 18, 1938).

[40] Dealt with in Introd. 2, 998–1000. Since then H. P. J. Renaud has devoted to him an elaborate study, "Ibn al-Bannā' ṣūfī et mathématicien" (Hespéris, 1938, 30 p.). He confirms and precises my dates (birth, December 29, 1256; death, August 1, 1321) against Suter, who defended a later date of death (1339) because of an error of de Slane. We must bear in mind, however, that Ibn al-Bannā' may have done a considerable part of his work in the fourteenth century.

MUḤAMMAD IBN AL-JAZŪLĪ

Shams al-dīn Muḥammad ibn al-Jazūlī. Moroccan astronomer (fl. 1344).

His nisba refers to the Berber tribe Jazūla in the Moroccan Sūs (al-Sūs al-aqṣā, a triangular district bounded on the west by the Atlantic, on the north by the Great Atlas, on the south by the Anti-Atlas). He wrote treatises relative to the use of astrolabes, (1) Risāla fī-l-'amal bil-isṭarlāb, (2) R. fī-l-'amal bil jaib al-ghaib (use of the quadrant with the hidden sine), (3) R. fī thumn al-dā'ira (on the octant), etc.

Criticism. Suter (no. 412, 1900). Brockelmann (2, 255, 1902; suppt. 2, 364, 1938). Schmalzl (p. 108, 1929).

With regard to the contemporary use of astrolabes in Morocco see Georges S. Colin: Un Juif marocain du XIVe siècle, constructeur d'astrolabes (Hespéris 22, 183–84, 1936), apropos of an astrolabe made by a Jew of Fās called Jacob ben Moses Ṭāfīruh and dated 1316. A. Maitrot de la Motte: Un astrolabe shakaziyi (Bulletin de la Société de géographie d'Alger et de l'Afrique du Nord, 2e sem. 1940, p. 108–32), reviewed by H. P. J. Renaud (Hespéris, 1941, p. 109–12). According to Renaud, this astrolabe is probably not to be identified with the kind discussed by Ibn al-Bannā' (XIII-2) in his Risālat al-'amal bi-l-ṣafīḥat al-shakārīya (or shakkāzīya), a lost treatise listed by Renaud (nos. 40–41, in Hespéris 25, 40, 1938).

ABŪ MUQRI'

Abū Muqri' (or Miqra') Muḥammad ibn 'Alī al-Baṭṭiwī. Moroccan astronomer (fl. 1331).

His nisba refers to the tribe Baṭṭiwa in the Rīf. He is probably identical with the general sent to Algeria c. 1331 by Abū-l-Ḥasan 'Alī (Marīnī sulṭān 1331–48). He wrote a poem (arjūza) on the calendar and astrology, which has been commented upon many times, notably by al-Jādarī (XIV-2) and al-Qalaṣādī (d. 1486).

Text. Les mansions lunaires des Arabes, publié, traduit et annoté par Gustave Adolphe de Calassanti Motylinski (Alger 1899); not available to me, published by the Algerian government.

Criticism. Brockelmann (2, 255, 1902; suppt. 2, 364, 1938). H. P. J. Renaud: Additions à Suter (Isis 18, 178, 1932); MSS arabes (p. 106, 1941).

D2. Spanish Muslims

IBN AL-RAQQĀM

Abū 'Abdallāh Muḥammad ibn Ibrāhīm Ibn al-Raqqām al-Awsī al-Mursī. Spanish Muslim physician, mathematician, astronomer (d. 1315).

The nisba Awsī refers probably to the Medīna tribe Aws; one of his distant ancestors may have belonged to that tribe; the second nisba shows that he was connected with Murcia. Ibn al-Raqqām might be translated son of the embroiderer (Dozy 1, 549), or of the arithmetician? (raqm hindī means Hindu numeral). He practiced medicine for many years in Granada, and died in that city in old age, May 27, 1315.

Various writings are ascribed to him dealing with scientific instruments, astronomical tables for Andalusia, etc. A single one has come down to us. It discusses sundials, fī 'ilm al-ẓilāl.

Criticism. Suter (nos. 388, 417, 1900). H. P. J. Renaud: Additions à Suter (Isis 18, 173, 1932). Brockelmann (suppt. 2, 378, 1938).

IBN BĀṢA

Abū 'Alī al-Ḥasan ibn Muḥammad ibn Bāṣa. Spanish Muslim maker of astronomical instruments (d. 1316).

The name Bāṣa (also read Māṣ?) suggests a Jewish origin. This al-Ḥasan came from eastern Andalusia, was a theologian, mathematician, astronomer, and chiefly a maker of astronomical instruments, such as sundials and astrolabes. He was chief time computer (mu'addil) in the great mosque of Granada, that is, he was holding a position of great liturgical responsibility. He died in that city in 1316-17.

His son Abū Ja'far Aḥmad ibn al-Ḥasan succeeded him as mu'addil and also as a maker of astronomical instruments, and the instruments made by him were much praised. He was considered a great master in that art.

Renaud has suggested that the father, al-Ḥasan ibn Muḥammad, may be identical with Ḥusain ibn Aḥmad ibn Bāṣa al-Islamī, who wrote a treatise on the astrolabe, al-ṣafīḥa al-jāmi'a li-jamī'a al-'urūd, in 160 or 161 chapters, completed in 1274. This does not seem plausible to me, though all these men belonged probably to the same Andalusian family, Ibn Bāṣa, already made famous in the second half of the twelfth century by the architect Aḥmad ibn Bāṣa, who directed building operations in Gibraltar 1160, then in Cordova, and became in 1172 the chief architect of the great mosque of Seville.

Criticism. Suter (no. 381b, p. 157, 1900). H. P. J. Renaud: Additions à Suter (Isis 18, 172, 183, 1932); Les Ibn Bāṣo (Hespéris, 1937, 12 p.), elaborate article illustrating the difficulties of the subject and the main problems remaining unsolved; Quelques constructeurs d'astrolabes en occident musulman (Isis 34, 20-23, 1 fig., 1943).

D3. MAMLŪK

MUḤAMMAD IBN SAM'ŪN

Nāṣir al-dīn Muḥammad ibn Sam'ūn[41] al-Muwaqqit (d. 1336/37).

Egyptian or Syrian astronomer, or rather timekeeper (muwaqqit) in a mosque. He wrote a treatise dealing with various astronomical questions, Al-tuḥfa al-malikīya fī-l-as'ila wal-ajwiba al-falakīya, and another on the use of the astrolabe, Kanz al-ṭullāb (Treasure of the students), derived from Abū-l-Ṣalt Umaiya (XII-1).

Criticism. Suter (no. 398, p. 162, 1900). Brockelmann (2, 126, 1902).

AL-MIZZĪ

Abū 'Abdallāh Muḥammad ibn Aḥmad al-Mizzī al-Ḥanafī. Muslim Egyptian astronomer (d. 1349).

He was born in 1291, studied in Cairo, and flourished in Damascus, where he was muezzin (mu'adhdhin) in the great mosque. He constructed astrolabes and quadrants. For example, there is in the national library of Leningrad a quadrant made by him in Damascus 1333/34 for Nāṣir al-dīn Muḥammad ibn 'Abdallāh ibn 'Abd al-raḥīm[42] (according to an inscription on the instrument). He wrote various treatises dealing with the construction and use of such instruments. Judging from

[41] This is the same name as the Biblical Simeon.

[42] This is not, I think, the Baḥrī Mamlūk sulṭān Nāṣir al-dīn Muḥammad (who is chronologically possible, for his third rule lasted from 1309 to 1340); the latter's father was named Qalā'ūn, not 'Abdallāh.

the number of MSS scattered in many libraries (every large Arabic library has at least one of them), these treatises enjoyed much popularity.

I quote these treatises in the same order as Brockelmann:

1. Al-risāla al-iṣṭarlābīya (On the astrolabe).
2. Kashf al-raib fī-l-'amal bil-jaib (The removal of doubt concerning the use of sines); this may refer to the sine quadrant or to the sine calculations implied.
3. Al-rauḍāt al-muzhirāt fī-l-'amal bi rub' al-muqanṭarāt (The flowering gardens concerning the use of the quadrant with parallel circles).
4. Al-risāla fī-l- ('amal bil) mujannaḥa, on the "winged" astrolabe, which may be a special kind introduced by the author.
5. Naẓm al-lu'lu' al-muhadhdhab fī-l'amal bil-rub' al-mujaiyab (String of golden pearls concerning the use of the sine quadrant), 20 chapters in verse (arjūza) with an introduction.
6. Risāla fī-l-'amal bil-rub' al-musattar (On the use of the precious or mysterious quadrant).
7. Mukhtaṣar fī-l-'amal bil-rub' al-dā'ira (Summary concerning the use of the quadrant of the circle).

The titles, all of which except one contain the words fī-l-'amal (concerning the use of . . .), suggest that these treatises are all dealing with very similar subjects, the use of various instruments. Suter mentions two other treatises, the one on the folded quadrant (al-muqanṭarāt al-maṭwīya), perhaps identical with no. 3, and the other a table for the latitude of Damascus (Jadāwil al-ḥiṣaṣ).

Text. None of these texts has been published.

Criticism. Bernhard Dorn: Drei in der K. Bibliothek zu St. Petersburg befindliche astronomische Instrumente mit arabischen Inschriften (Mémoires de l'Académie de St. Pétersbourg, 7th ser., vol. 9, no. 1, 150 p., 2 pl., 1865), important study. Suter (p. 165, 227, 1900). Brockelmann (2, 126, 1902; suppt. 2, 156, 1938). H. P. J. Renaud: Additions et corrections à Suter (Isis 28, 173, 1932). Philip K. Hitti: Catalog of the Garrett collection of Arabic MSS (nos. 2040, 2182, Princeton 1938; Isis 31, 558), MSS of nos. 3 and 2, one of them unmentioned by Brockelmann.

AL-KARAKĪ

Abū Bakr ibn Muḥammad ibn Ayyūb al-Tamīmī al-Karakī (fl. first half of fourteenth cent.).

The nisba Tamīmī refers to the Arabic tribe Tamīm ibn Murr (EI 4, 643–46); Karakī, probably to the place al-Kerak, east of the Dead Sea, in the land of Moab. Al-Karakī was a disciple, probably in Damascus, of al-Mizzī. He was timekeeper (muwaqqit) in a mosque in Jerusalem, and compiled astronomical tables.

Criticism. Not in Suter. Brockelmann (suppt. 2, 156, 1938).

D4. Persia

AL-ABHARĪ

Amīn al-dīn al-Abharī. Persian mathematician writing in Arabic (d. 1332/33).

He wrote an arithmetical treatise, Fuṣūl kāfiya fī ḥisāb al-takht wal mīl (Sufficient chapters concerning computation with table and needle). The word translated needle (mīl, pl. muyūl or amyāl) is the name of the needle used by women to put collyrium (eye salve) on the eyelids; the word translated by table (takht) may refer to a tablet for writing or to a table covered with sand (takht raml) or simply to a surface of sand used by the geomancer (rammāl). See Introd. 2, 175. Thus this treatise probably deals with written computations, as opposed to mental or mechanical ones, but it might refer to geomancy?

It is better to read Abharī than Abahrī. We have dealt with another Abharī, named al-Mufaḍḍal ibn 'Umar (XIII-2), also a mathematician and far more important than Amīn al-dīn. The nisba in both cases refers to the place Abhar in Jibāl.

Criticism. Suter (no. 393, 1900). Brockelmann (2, 211, 1902).

AL-KĀSHĀNĪ

'Imād al-dīn Ya'qūb ibn Aḥmad al-Kāshānī. Persian mathematician and rhetorician writing in Arabic (fl. 1343).

The nisba al-Kāshānī (or Kāshī) refers to the city of Kāshān in Jibāl; Jamshīd ibn Maḥmūd (d. 1436/37), first director of Ulūgh Beg's observatory in Samarqand, was connected with the same city.

This al-Kāshānī flourished in Iṣfahān in 1343 and was a qāḍī. He wrote a book on arithmetic, Lubāb al-ḥisāb, and commentaries on the famous rhetorical or dialectical treatise Miftāḥ al-'ulūm of al-Sakkākī (XIII-1) and on the similar treatise Risāla fī ādāb al-baḥth of Muhammad ibn Ashraf al-Samarqandī (XIII-2).

Criticism. Brockelmann (suppt. 2, 295, 1938).

NIẒĀM AL-A'RAJ

Persian mathematician and astronomer, who flourished at the end of the thirteenth century and the beginning of the fourteenth, in Qumm (Jibāl) and Nīsābūr or Nīshāpūr (Khurāsān).

Niẓām al-a'raj (or Niẓām al-dīn, al-a'raj)[42a] al-Ḥasan ibn Muḥammad al-Qummī al-Nīsābūrī was a pupil of Nāṣir al-dīn al-Ṭūsī (XIII-2), possibly a direct one; if so, he was a man of 40 at least by the end of the thirteenth century. Some of his works, however, are dated 1305, 1311/12, and none bears an earlier date.

He wrote a large commentary on the Qur'ān, entitled Gharā'ib al-Qur'ān wa raghā'ib al-furqān, derived from the Kashshāf of al-Zamakhsharī (XII-1) and from the Mafātīḥ al-ghaib of Fakhr al-dīn al-Rāzī (XII-2); and also a commentary on the short Arabic grammar, al-shāfīya, of Ibn al-Ḥājib (XIII-1). We are more interested, however, in his mathematical works, which may be divided into three groups:

1. A treatise on arithmetic, Al-risāla al-shamsīya fī-l-ḥisāb.
2. A commentary on the Almagest as edited by Nāṣir al-dīn, Sharḥ taḥrīr al-Mijisṭī, completed in March 1305.
3. Commentaries on various works of Nāṣir al-dīn, primarily on the Tadhkira fī 'ilm al-hai'a, his most famous astronomical work. That commentary, Tawḍīḥ al-tadhkira, was completed in 1311/12. The other commentaries refer to the ilkhanic tables, Al-zīj al-īlkhānī, and to the Risāla-i-sī faṣl (Treatise on the calendar in thirty chapters).

Text. The works are unpublished except the Gharā'ib al-Qur'ān, printed at least twice in the margins of the Tafsīr of al-Ṭabarī (X-1) (Ṭihrān 1864, Delhī 1864).

Criticism. Suter (p. 161, 1900; p. 177, 1902). Brockelmann (2, 211, 1902; suppt. 2, 273, 1938).

[42a] Al-a'raj means the lame (boiteux), but it does not follow that Niẓām himself was lame.

SHAMS AL-DĪN MĪRAK

Persian philosopher and astronomer writing in Arabic (d. c. 1339).

Muḥammad ibn Mubārakshāh Shams al-dīn Mīrak (this word, meaning "little lord," is sometimes omitted) al-Bukhārī al-Ḥarawī. Little is known about him except that he came from or flourished in Bukhārā (and Herāt) and died c. 1339.

He wrote commentaries on philosophical and astronomical works, to wit:

1. Tabṣira fī 'ilm al-hai'a, astronomical treatise, by Muḥammad ibn Aḥmad al-Kharaqī (XII-1); this commentary was written in 1332/33.

2. Hidāyat al-ḥikma (Guide to wisdom), an encyclopaedia of logic, physics, and theology, by al-Mufaḍḍal ibn 'Umar al-Abharī (XIII-2).

3. Ḥikmat al-'ain, encyclopaedia of logic, science, and philosophy, by 'Alī ibn 'Umar al-Kātibī (XIII-2).

4. Manār al-anwār fi uṣūl al-fiqh of 'Abdallāh ibn Aḥmad al-Nasafī (XIII-2).

He may be identical with the Shams al-dunīya wal-dīn Muḥammad ibn Mubārakshāh to whom a contemporary, 'Alī shāh ibn Muḥammad al-Khwārizmī,[43] dedicated c. 1300/1 an astrological treatise, Ashjār wa athmār (Trees and fruits).

He may be the Σάμψ μπουχαρῆς (obviously a transcription of Shams Bukhārī) of the Greek text (Florence, Cod. Laurent. plutei XXVIII, 17) dated 1323 which is an elaboration of notes taken in Persian. That is, the author of that Greek astronomical text sat at the feet of a teacher Shams Bukhārī, who may be identical with Shams al-dīn Mīrak, though we have already mentioned other possibilities (Introd. 2, 1020). Shams al-dīn was not an uncommon title, and Bukhārā was a great center.

There is in Constantinople a Persian MS entitled Zīj Shams al-munajjim (astronomical tables of Shams the astrologer) which may be the work of one of the three (two or one?) contemporary astronomers mentioned in this note.

Shams al-dīn Mīrak may be the author of the very elaborate commentary on the Kitāb al-adwār (Musical modes) of Ṣafī al-dīn (XIII-2) edited by R. d'Erlanger.

Rathgen (p. 704, 1928) mentions an Arabic MS dated 1311 by one Shams al-dīn Muḥammad, containing powder recipes for the midfa'u (pl. madāfi'u, war engine), for incendiary arrows, and for rockets. The composition of the powder is 74:10:15. This Shams al-dīn may be our Mīrak or the one dealt with in Introd. 2, 1020, or another still.

Text. Baron Rodolphe d'Erlanger: Les commentaires de Mawlānā Mubārak Shāh sur le Kitāb al-adwār, in his treatise La musique arabe (3, 185–609, Paris 1938; Isis 30, 334); French translation with notes.

Criticism. Hermann Usener: Ad historiam astronomiae symbola (Programm, Bonn, 1876), reprinted in his Kleine Schriften (3, 323–71, 1914). Steinschneider (p. 630, 1893). Krumbacher (p. 622, 1897). Suter (p. 161, 219, 1900; p. 177, 1902). Cantor (3d ed., 1, 508, 1907). Brockelmann (1, 466, 1898; 2, 196, 1902; suppt. 1, 847, 1937). Sarkis (col. 1632, 1930).

AL-JAGHMĪNĪ

Maḥmūd ibn Muḥammad ibn 'Umar al-Jaghmīnī. Persian astronomer and physician writing in Arabic (d. 1344/45?).

[43] Also called 'Alā al-munajjim (the astrologer) al-Bukhārī. I have referred to him in Introd. 2, 1006, as the author of the 'Umdat al-īlkhānīya, a commentary on the astronomical table of Nāṣir al-dīn al-Ṭūsī (XIII-2). According to Suter (p. 161, 228, 1900), he wrote another astrological treatise, Aḥkām al-a'wām (Judgments of the years).

The nisba Jaghmīnī (or Čaghmīnī) refers to the place Jaghmīn (or Čaghmīn) in Khwārizm. The following works are ascribed to him:

1. Al-mulakhkhaṣ fī-l-hai'a (Quintessence of astronomy), which was very popular in Islām judging by the number of MSS and commentaries on it, e.g., by Mūsā ibn Maḥmūd Qāḍīzāde al-Rūmī (d. 1436–46) and by 'Alī ibn Muḥammad al-Jurjānī (XIV-2). It was translated into Persian.

2. Qiwā al-kawākib wa ḍa'afhā (The strong and weak influences of the stars), on astrology.

3. Qānūnče (The small qānūn), an extract or abridgment of the Qānūn of Ibn Sīnā. This was translated into Persian, under the rule of the Tīmūrī ruler of Transoxiana, Shāhrukh (ruled 1404–47), the immediate predecessor of Ulūgh Beg.

The data given above are those accepted by Suter, but according to Brockelmann, there were two men bearing the same name, the earlier of whom, astronomer and author of no. 1, died in 1221/22; the other, physician and author of no. 3, died in 1344/45. Brockelmann does not mention the astrological treatise (our no. 2), but ascribes to the astronomer two arithmetical treatises, the Risāla fi ḥisāb al-tis'a (which I assume deals with the casting out of nines), and the Sharḥ ṭuruq al-ḥisāb fī masā'il al-waṣāya (or al-qīwāmī fī-l-ḥisāb), on arithmetical methods.

Text. German translation of the Mulakhkhaṣ by G. Rudloff and Ad. Hochheim (Zeitschrift der Deutschen morgenländischen Gesellschaft 47, 213–75, 1893).

Lithographed editions of the Qānūnče, Lucknow 1868, Lahore 1908, Delhi 1908, Lucknow 1909. The Persian version was published in Calcutta 1782.

Criticism. Brockelmann (1, 473, 1898; 2, 213, 1902; suppt. 1, 865, 1937). C. A. Nallino's edition of al-Battānī (1899–1907, by index). Suter (p. 164, 1900; p. 177, 1902); EI (1, 996, 1912). Honigmann (p. 163, 1929). Renaud (p. 75, 1941).

D5. 'Irāq

See summary in section VI of chapter I.

D6. Tūrān

al-Jūzjānī

Aḥmad ibn 'Uthmān al-Jūzjānī, Turcoman theologian and astronomer writing in Arabic (1282–1343).

He hailed from Jūzjān (Persian, Gōzgān), district of Khurāsān between the Murghāb and the Amū Daryā (or, to put it otherwise, between Marv al-Rūd and Balkh). He was born in 1282/83 and died in Cairo in 1343/44. He wrote a commentary on the shorter astronomical treatise, Kitāb al-tabṣira fī 'ilm al-hai'a, of Muḥammad ibn Aḥmad al-Kharaqī (XII-1).

The same commentary is also ascribed to his brother 'Ali ibn 'Uthmān al-Māridīnī, called Ibn al-Turkumānī, distinguished theologian (d. 1349).

We came across another Jūzjānī, Abū 'Ubaid 'Abd al-Wāhib ibn Muḥammad, who was the favorite disciple of Ibn Sīnā (XI-1) and completed the latter's autobiography.

Criticism. Suter (nos. 401, 405, 1900).

E. India

See summary in section VI of chapter I.

F. CHINA

CHU SHIH-CHIEH

Chinese mathematician, one of the greatest mathematicians of his race, of his time, and indeed of all times (fl. 1280–1303).

Chu Shih-chieh was styled Han Ch'ing and nicknamed Sung T'ing. His life is very little known; we do not even know the dates of his birth and death. He was born in Yenshan, traveled considerably in China from c. 1280 to c. 1303, earning his livelihood as a teacher of mathematics. He finally settled in Kuanglin, where many pupils gathered "from the four directions" to study under him or to consult him.

He wrote two mathematical works, which we shall examine presently: (1) in 1299, the Suan-hsüeh ch'i-mêng (Introduction to mathematical studies), (2) in 1303 the Ssŭ-yüan yü-chien (Precious mirror of the four elements).

The first work is an elementary treatise on arithmetic and algebra divided into 3 chüan and 20 mên or chapters. It includes some 259 problems, explaining addition, subtraction, multiplication, division, mensuration of various areas and solids, method of excess and deficiency, solution of simple equations. It gives the rules of signs for algebraical addition and multiplication, already implied in earlier works.

It contains hardly any novelty, yet is very important because it was the main vehicle by means of which Chinese algebra reached Japan, and it deeply influenced Japanese mathematics. It was first brought over to Japan from Korea by Toyotomi Hideyoshi's expeditionary force of 1597–98. Some Japanese historians believe that it was known in Japan before through Chinese editions, but so far no edition earlier than the Korean one mentioned below has been discovered.

The Precious mirror of the four elements is intrinsically far more important. We find in it, illustrated by 288 problems, some of which are very complex, the earliest explanation of the art (or method) of four elements, ssŭ yüan shu. In other words, Chu was the first to apply the method of the celestial element, t'ien yüan—in Japanese, tengen jutsu—to a system of linear equations with as many as four unknown quantities or elements, these four being characteristically called jen, man; ti, earth, mater terra; t'ien, heaven, pater aether; wu, things or matter.[44] His method of solving such a system is probably the greatest achievement of Chinese mathematics. He also used a method of solving numerical equations of any degree, like the ling lung k'ai fang or harmoniously alternating evolution, anticipating to some extent the Ruffini-Horner procedure (Introd. 2, 626).

Strangely enough, he does not mention his great predecessors Ch'in Chiu-shao (XIII-1), Li Yeh[45] (XIII-1), and Yang Hui[46] (XIII-2), but he speaks of various other mathematicians of whom nothing is known. I made a similar remark apropos of Yang Hui. This suggests that the history of mediaeval Chinese mathematics is far more complex than we realize, or that we are acquainted with only a small part of it.

[44] I think it is a mistake to compare the use of wu for an unknown to that of res and cosa in the West, as is done by Smith and Mikami (p. 51, 1914). The origin of the European term is less likely to be Chinese than Egyptian (Rhind mathematical papyrus, Isis 14, 251–55).

[45] The name Li Yeh, to which I gave the preference (Introd. 2, 627), is wrong. The correct name is Li Chih. The mistake was first made in the Yüan shih, as the two words yeh and chih are very similar. See the history of Chinese mathematics by Ch'ien Pao-tsung (part 1, 116, Academia sinica 1932), in Chinese.

[46] Yet the Precious mirror contains a biquadratic equation identical with one of Yang's.

The same treatise contains a diagram for the eighth and lower powers, which is an arithmetical triangle giving easily the binomial coefficients up to the eighth power —the so-called Pascal's triangle.[47]

It also includes a discussion of the summation of integral finite series, some results of which are truly remarkable. For example, if we write

$$r^{|p|} = r(r + 1) \cdots (r + p - 1),$$

r and p being positive integers, Chu obtained the relations

$$\sum_{r=1}^{n} \frac{r^{|p|}}{1^{|p|}} = \frac{n^{|p+1|}}{1^{|p+1|}}$$

$$\sum_{n=1}^{n} \frac{n^{|p|}}{1^{|p|}} \cdot \frac{(n + 1 - r)^{|q|}}{1^{|q|}} = \sum_{n=1}^{n} \frac{n^{|p+q|}}{1^{|p+q|}}$$

and many other relations of a similar nature, but he gave no proofs.

Chu's method of solving simultaneous equations of less than five variables is practically the method of elimination and substitution; in some points his reasoning is very similar to Sylvester's dialytic elimination, except that he did not use determinants.[48]

His method of representing equations is really very natural and convenient, but it cannot be extended to more than four variables. Perhaps that is the main reason why he did not study the mirror of five or more elements.

Text. The Suan-hsüeh ch'i-mêng was believed to be lost, but a Korean reprint made in 1660 was discovered by Lo Shih-lin and published in Yangchow 1829. The Library of Congress has an annotated edition entitled Suan-hsüeh ch'i-mêng shu i. An edition was prepared and prefaced by Chao Ch'êng, styled Yüan Chên. For Lo Shih-lin, styled Ming-hsiang (d. 1853), see Hummel (p. 538–40, 1943).

A Japanese edition based on the Korean one, entitled Sangaku keimō kunten (or Punctuated edition of the mathematical introduction) was printed in Japan in 1658. The first annotated edition appeared in 1672, entitled Sangaku keimō chūkai (chūkai means commentary), by Sanenori Hoshino, of whom little is known. It is in four volumes. The most extensive and scholarly commentary appeared in 1690, entitled Sangaku keimō genkai, by Katahiro Takebe (1664–1739), astronomer of the Shōgun. It is in seven volumes, and within the following three or four years it went through at least four editions. There are several abridgments of Takebe's work printed in one or two volumes, and several other minor commentaries.[49]

[47] The expression is misleading, for there are examples of it in various forms anterior to Pascal's own (c. 1654): Apianus 1527, Michael Stifel 1544, Tartaglia 1556–60, etc. Tropfke (6^2, 34–38, 1924). It should be noted that Chu speaks of this as an "ancient" method. It may be of Muslim origin; 'Umar al-Khayyâm (XI-2) may have known of it. Dickson (vol. 2, p. 4, 1920).

[48] The determinant is a Japanese development of Chinese mathematics. The first inventor was the great Japanese mathematician Seki Kowa (1642–1708), who explained determinants more completely in his Kai fukudai no hō, dated as revised in 1683, than did Leibniz ten years later in his letter to the Marquis de l'Hospital (April 28, 1693). The first to give a connected exposition of the theory, that is, the real founder of the theory, was Alexandre Vandermonde in his Mémoire sur l'élimination, read on January 12, 1771 (Histoire de l'Académie des sciences, 1772, part 2, 516–32). The term determinant was first used by Gauss in his Disquisitiones arithmeticae (XV, 2, Leipzig 1801).

For the Japanese discovery see Yoshio Mikami: The Japanese theory of determinants (Isis 2, 9–36, 1914); see also Mikami (p. 191–99, 1913), Smith and Mikami (p. 91–127, 1914). For the Western development see Thomas Muir: The theory of determinants in the historical order of development (vol. 1, London 1906).

[49] Information kindly given by Dr. Shio Sakanishi (letter dated Washington May 18, 1940).

The Ssŭ-yüan yü-chien was lost for a considerable time. When Juan Yüan[50] published his biographies of mathematicians in 1799 he had not yet found it. In 1802 Lo Shih-lin discovered a copy of it. In 1836 he edited it under Juan's patronage under the title Ssŭ-yüan yü-chien hsi-ts'ao, or Explanations and rules of quadriliteral algebra. Though Chu was extremely reticent about his method and hence very hard to understand, Lo gave detailed explanations; but whether Lo's interpretation of Chu's secret method is correct or not, no one knows. The text was included by Ting Ch'ü-chung in his mathematical collection published in 1876, together with a brief commentary.[51] It was also edited by Chao Ch'êng, styled Yüan Chên, with a preface by Mo Jo of Lin Ch'uan and a preface by Tsu I.

The Library of Congress has the text of Ssŭ-yüan in the Pai fu t'ang suan hsüeh ts'ung shu, vols. 33–35.

Ch'ên Tsai Hsin: The precious mirror of the four elements. A Chinese algebra published by Chu Shih Chieh in 1303. A translation with explanatory notes (typescript, v + 211 p., dated Peking June 22, 1927). Elaborate English translation prepared by the head of the department of mathematics, Yenching University, Peking. I examined it twice, first in March 1929, when it was submitted to me by the Harvard-Yenching Institute for advice on publication. I concluded that it should be published with a few changes necessary chiefly from the philological point of view; I also recommended the reprinting of the Chinese text (letter to R. P. Blake, Mar. 6, 1929). Thanks to the courtesy of my colleague Sergei Grigorevich Eliseev, I was able to examine the MS again in May 1940. I hope that it will be possible to publish this Chinese text with English translation in the Harvard-Yenching series. It is the most important Chinese book of its kind, and one of the outstanding mathematical books of mediaeval times.

Criticism. Wylie (1867, p. 117 of reprint 1922). Mikami (p. 89–98, 1913). Smith and Mikami (p. 48, 51, 56, 1914). Wieger (p. 518, 522, 1920). Mikami, in Scientific Japan (p. 186, 1926). L. Van Hée: Le précieux miroir des quatre éléments (Asia major 7, 242–70, Leipzig 1931; Isis 21, 365), the best analysis of that work, with technical terms in Chinese characters.

CHAO YU-CH'IN

Chinese mathematician and astronomer who flourished in the first half of the fourteenth century.

Chao Yu-ch'in was styled Yüan Tu. We do not know the circumstances of his life, not even the dates and places of his death and birth. We know him only as the author of a treatise on astronomy, Ko hsiang hsin shu, in 5 chüan. That book was written after 1281, and it has a preface by Sung Lien (1310–81), hence we may assume that it belongs to the fourteenth century, perhaps to the first half. There is also a revised and abridged edition, Chung hsiu ko hsiang hsin shu, in 2 chüan, prepared by Wang Wei (1311–72).

In the Ko hsiang hsin shu, Chao obtained the value of π as 3.1415926+ by inscribing a regular polygon of 16,384 sides in a circle.

Text. Both editions of the treatise are included in the Ssŭ k'u ch'üan shu. See note on the alchemist Ch'ên Kuan-wu.

[50] On this famous viceroy and scholar (1764–1849), styled Po yüan, see Giles (no. 2573, 1898); Hummel (p. 399–402, 1943); and father Louis Van Hée: The Ch'ou-jen chuan (Isis 8, 103–18, 1926), including Juan's portrait.

[51] L. Van Hée: Bibliotheca mathematica sinensis Pé-fou (T'oung pao 15, 111–64, 1914).

CHAPTER VII

PHYSICS, TECHNOLOGY, AND MUSIC

(First Half of the Fourteenth Century)

N.B. Only the main notes are published in this chapter. The physical, technical, or musical contributions of many other men, whose main work was done in other fields, are discussed in other chapters. For a general survey of physics, technology, and the theory of music in the first half of the fourteenth century, see section VII of chapter I. More information on the men referred to in that survey may then easily be obtained by means of the index.

1. OPTICS AND OPTICAL METEOROLOGY

DIETRICH OF FREIBERG

German Dominican, optician, meteorologist, philosopher (d. 1311 or soon after).

Theodoricus Teutonicus de Vriberg. It is probable but not certain that he originated in Freiberg in Saxony rather than Freiburg im Breisgau. Hence it would be more correct to call him simply Theodoricus magister in theologia, or Dietrich. He was a Dominican of the German province, and was elected provincial in Strassburg 1293; he remained the master of that large province (including then Germany, Austria, the Low Countries) until 1296. He graduated as master of theology in Paris probably in 1297. Later he was prior of the Würzburg monastery. He attended the general chapter of his order held in Toulouse 1304 and was then instructed by the Dominican general Aimerich (1303–12) to publish his optical theories. In 1310 he was appointed vicarius of his province. He died in 1311 or soon after.

It is remarkable that the facts of his life are not better known (e.g., the place and time of his death). This may be due to his scientific and philosophic activities, which kept him in the background. He wrote many treatises (Krebs enumerates 35 plus 2 letters), most of which deal with philosophy and theology.

Our account must be largely restricted to the three optical treatises upon which his scientific fame is based:

1. De luce et eius origine (De causa luminis in diaphano; De generatione lucis). Divided into 19 chapters. Much of this is philosophical or theological. The author quotes St. Augustine, Aristotle, and Averroes.

2. De coloribus. Divided into 16 chapters. Partly derived from Aristotle and Averroes. Dietrich tries to find a middle path between the explanation of color given by Avicenna and the one given by Averroes. He gives a theory of what might be called inner total reflection in transparent bodies, using it to explain colors; he claims that because of refraction and inner reflection, even the most transparent bodies can act as mirrors.

3. De iride et radialibus impressionibus. This is a much longer treatise, as well as the most important. It was written between 1304 and 1310, and deals with optical meteorology with special reference to the rainbow. It is about 57,000 words long and is divided into four parts and 103 chapters. The first part is devoted to generalities, parts II and III to the main and secondary rainbows, part IV to other optical phaenomena. In part I (17 chapters), optical phaenomena of the

sky are divided into two classes, naturales (such as comets, ignes volantes, clouds, mist) and radiales (radiations of luminous bodies, haloes). The author is especially interested in the second kind, the radiations, of which "light" is the "form." How do these radiations affect us (radiales impressiones), how do they reach the eye? Enumeration of fifteen optical meteorological phaenomena. The discussion of rainbows (parts II and III) covers no less than 60 chapters. Part IV (26 chapters) deals largely with haloes, but also with mist rainbows. The authors quoted are Aristotle, the Elements of Euclid, the Sphaera of Theodosios, the Almagest, Boetius' Consolatio, and the Perspectiva of Alhacen (Ibn al-Haitham).

The main optical source stricto sensu was Ibn al-Haitham's great treatise, Kitāb al-manāẓir (Opticae thesaurus), which influenced many Western writers from Roger Bacon down to Kepler. Another treatise of Ibn al-Haitham's, the De crepusculis et nubium ascensionibus, was translated by Gerard of Cremona (XII-2), and the Opticae thesaurus was probably translated at the same time or not much later.

The most original part of Dietrich's optics is his theory of the rainbow, derived from Aristotle's Meteorology and commentaries upon it and from Ibn al-Haitham's secondary writings, for there is no discussion of the rainbow in Ibn al-Haitham's main work. According to Dietrich's explanation, the sunrays undergo in the drops of water two refractions and one reflection (that is, for the primary rainbow; for the secondary one it is necessary to postulate—and he does so—a second internal reflection; that second reflection accounts for the lesser intensity of the secondary bow; see De iride, part III, ch. 9). Witelo had pointed out, c. 1275, the necessity of refraction as well as reflection, but had not developed the idea (see Risner's edition, Basel 1572, part 2, p. 457); Witelo was not quoted by Dietrich, but Dietrich's reference to the "liber perspectivae" or the "auctor perspectivae" might be construed perhaps as applying not only to Ibn al-Haitham, but also to the latter's commentator Witelo? At any rate, the idea of introducing refraction, even if Witelo was the first to express it explicitly, was already implied in earlier attempts to account for colors (e.g., Ibn Rushd; see Krebs p. 35).

It is remarkable that Dietrich's theory of the rainbow was proposed at about the same time independently by a Persian, Quṭb al-dīn al-Shīrāzī (XIII-2; d. Tabrīz 1311). Quṭb al-dīn's undated work is certainly anterior to Dietrich's, for it had already been commented upon by another Persian, Kamāl al-dīn al-Fārisī, at the very time when Dietrich was writing (Dietrich wrote c. 1304–10, Kamāl al-dīn c. 1302–11).

Dietrich's views on the rainbow were known to Regiomontanus (1436–76), who even thought of publishing Dietrich's book; and they were taught in the University of Erfurt (and probably in others) at the beginning of the sixteenth century. Moreover, they were hardly improved upon until the publication of Marco Antonio de Dominis' treatise (Venice 1611)[1] and the discovery of the law of refraction by Willebrord Snel (1618) and Descartes (1637). A complete explanation of the main rainbows could be given only after the genesis of colors had been correctly explained by Newton (1672),[2] and this was done by Newton himself in his Opticks (1704). To put it otherwise, Dietrich (and Quṭb al-dīn) went just as far as it was possible

[1] The progress made by M. A. de Dominis was very small, much smaller than most people imagine. R. E. Ockenden: Marco Antonio de Dominis and his explanation of the rainbow (Isis 26, 40–49, 1936).

[2] G. Sarton: Discovery of the dispersion of light and of the nature of color (Isis 14, 326–41, 1930), including facsimile of Newton's paper of 1672.

to go without knowledge of the exact law of refraction and of the dispersion of light. Indeed, Dietrich had made simple experiments on the dispersion of light by crystals (Würschmidt p. 14, 94, 1914) some 362 years before Newton. These experiments, rudimentary as they are, are among the most remarkable of mediaeval times.[3]

Dietrich was a philosopher of some originality. He was eclectic, defending Thomist as well as Augustinian ideas, but the main sources of his thought were Aristotle, St. Augustine, and above all Proclos (Elementa theologiae).[4] As a consequence his conclusions are sometimes very close to those of Meister Eckhart. His Neoplatonism is deeper than Witelo's; for example, he entertains the ideas of emanation and intermediate creations. The world may be eternal, but God is super-eternal.

His philosophical writings are too many to be enumerated (see complete list in Krebs 1906). The most important is said to be the De intellectu et intelligibili. We may mention also the De esse et essentia, De habitibus, finally De intelligentiis et motoribus coelorum. In the last-named treatise, derived from Aristotle, Ptolemy, Ibn Rushd, Thomas Aquinas, he considers how many intelligences are needed to move the celestial spheres. This implies a discussion of astronomical theories. He concludes that the phaenomena cannot be accounted for except by the theory of eccentrics and epicycles, but realizes the supremacy of the experimental method.

Text. Long extracts from the De iride were first published by Giovanni Battista Venturi (1746–1822): Commentari sopra la storia e la teoria dell' ottica (vol. 1, Bologna 1814), not seen. First complete edition by Joseph Würschmidt: Über den Regenbogen und die durch Strahlen erzeugten Eindrücke (Beiträge zur Geschichte der Philosophie des Mittelalters vol. 12, parts 5, 6, 220 p., Münster i.W. 1914). Complete Latin text with German summary and introduction.

De intellectu et intelligibili and De habitibus, edited by Engelbert Krebs in his general study of 1906 (p. 124*–206*, 207*–215*).

De esse et essentia, edited by Engelbert Krebs: Le traité de esse et essentia de Thierry de Fribourg. Contribution à l'histoire des luttes engagées dans l'ordre des frères prêcheurs au sujet de la doctrine thomiste (Revue néoscolastique 18, 516–36, 1911).

Criticism. Barthélemy Hauréau: Thierri de Fribourg (HL 27, 74–79, 1877). Gustav Hellmann: Meteorologische Optik, 1000–1836 (Neudrucke von Schriften und Karten über Meteorologie no. 14, Berlin 1902). Engelbert Krebs: Meister Dietrich. Sein Leben, seine Werke, seine Wissenschaft (Beiträge zur Geschichte der Philosophie des Mittelalters vol. 5, part 5, 400 p., Münster i.W. 1906), capital study more than half of which is devoted to an analysis of Dietrich's writings with copious extracts. L. Gautier: Un psychologue de la fin du XIIIe siècle, Thierry de Fribourg (Revue augustinienne, Paris 1909, p. 657–70; 1910, p. 178–206, 541–66). Duhem: Système (3, 383–96, 1915). Alexander Birkenmajer: Drei neue Handschriften der Werke Meister Dietrichs (Beiträge zur Geschichte der Philosophie des Mittelalters vol. 20, part 5, p. 70–90, 213–16, 1922). De Wulf (2, 120–25, 1926). G. Sarton: The tradition of the optics of Ibn al-Haitham (Isis 29, 403–6, 1938).

[3] Thanks to Aydin M. Sayili for drawing my attention to them (Nov. 1942).

[4] In my article on Proclos (V-2) in Introd. 1, 402–5, I did not speak of the Elementa theologiae (στοιχείωσις θεολογική), except indirectly apropos of the Liber de causis. I did not then realize its importance for the understanding of mediaeval thought. It is not a book of "theology," in the modern acceptance of that word, but rather of metaphysics. A good and convenient edition of it has been provided by E. R. Dodds: Proclus. The elements of theology, a revised text with translation, introduction and commentary (390 p., Oxford 1933; Isis 29, 423–28).

KAMĀL AL-DĪN AL-FĀRISĪ

Kamāl al-dīn Abū-l-Ḥasan (or Ḥusein) Muḥammad ibn al-Ḥasan al-Fārisī. Persian mathematician and physicist writing in Arabic (d. c. 1320).

He wrote the Tadhkira al-aḥbāb (Remembrance of friends) on amicable numbers, and the Asās al-qawā'id fī uṣūl al-fawā'id, which is a commentary on the Kitāb al-fawā'id al-Bahā'īya fī-l-qawā'id al-ḥisābīya, a treatise on arithmetic, geometry, determination of areas, volumes, and inheritance by Ibn al-Khaddām.[5] His main work, however, is the Tanqīḥ al-manāẓir (Correction of the optics), which is an elaborate and original commentary on the optics, or Kitāb al-manāẓir, of Ibn al-Haitham. Kamāl al-dīn had been studying Ibn al-Haitham's work under the direction of his teacher Quṭb al-dīn al-Shīrāzī (XIII-2).

Considering the encyclopaedic nature of mediaeval optics (it covers not only physical and physiological optics, but also meteorology, perspective, and many odd subjects), a complete analysis of the Tanqīḥ would be too long. It will suffice to note the main points.

The Tanqīh includes fine remarks on aerial perspective, color effects, etc., reminding one of some of the ideas expressed by Leonardo da Vinci in his notebooks.

Kamāl's theory of the rainbow is comparable to that explained by his contemporary Dietrich of Freiberg, yet better. That coincidence is not very surprising, for both authors, Dietrich and Kamāl al-dīn, were building upon the same foundations, mainly Aristotle and Ibn al-Haitham. The intermediate transmitters in the second half of the thirteenth century were, in the West, Witelo (d. c. 1278), Roger Bacon (d. c. 1292), John Peckham (d. 1292), and John of Paris (d. 1306, dealt with below in chapter XIII); and in the East, Nāṣir al-dīn al-Ṭūsī (d. 1274), Zakarīya ibn Muḥammad al-Qazwīnī (d. 1283), al-Qarāfī (d. 1285),[6] and Quṭb al-dīn al-Shīrāzī (d. 1311). For a summary of Arabic views on the rainbow, in addition to the publications quoted below under "Criticism," consult Hughes (p. 533, 1885), and E. Wiedemann's article in EI (2, 833–84, 1925). In the Kashf al-ẓunūn of Hājjī Khalīfa (4, 581, no. 9640, 1845) a special science of the rainbow ('ilm qaws quzaḥ) is recognized.

Kamāl al-dīn suggested the use of hyperboloidal lenses in order to avoid spherical aberration.

He gave an account of the refraction of light (Tanqīḥ 2, 130–32) which implies recognition of the following facts: the speed of light is finite but very great, indeed so great that it is often thought to be infinite; the speed of light in different media is inversely proportional to the optical density (not the same as material density). The second of these facts might be said to be an adumbration of the wave theory of light as against the corpuscular theory. Kamāl al-dīn applied the principle of the composition of forces.

The use of a camera obscura, initiated by Ibn al-Haitham, was much improved by Kamāl al-dīn, who showed that images obtained in a dark place are independent of the shape of the hole through which the rays penetrate, and that the smaller the hole, the sharper the images. By such means he observed eclipses and the move-

[5] 'Imād al-dīn 'Abdallāh ibn Muḥammad Ibn al-Khaddām al-'Irāqī al-Baghdādī, born 1245/46, died (?). Iraqian physician and mathematician, pupil of Nāṣir al-dīn al-Ṭūsī (XIII-2), teacher of Shāfi'ī law, head physician and leader of the Mashyakhat al-ribāṭ in Baghdād (Brockelmann 2, 167; suppt. 2, 215). 'Abdallāh's book Fawā'id Bahā'īya was thus called because it was dedicated to one Bahā' al-dīn Muḥammad ibn Muḥammad al-Juwainī.

[6] See note on him below.

ments of clouds and birds, noting that the images and directions were reversed. Astronomical use of the camera obscura was made also by Kamāl's younger contemporary, the Provençal Jew Levi ben Gerson (d. 1344). This coincidence can be accounted for in the same way as the simultaneous rainbow theories; the Kitāb al-manāẓir was causing similar fermentations of ideas, East and West.

It should be noted that according to mediaeval usage the Tanqīḥ contains, or is supposed to contain, the whole text of the Kitāb al-manāẓir. Every statement of Ibn al-Haitham is preceded by the word qāla (dixit), and every statement of Kamāl al-dīn's commentary by the word aqūlu (dico). However, in his recent work on Ibn al-Haitham (1942), Muṣṭafā Naẓīf bey remarks that the original text cannot always be disengaged from the Tanqīḥ.

Kamāl al-dīn did not restrict his commentary to the Kitāb al-manāẓir, but extended it to half a dozen smaller treatises of Ibn al-Haitham, whose texts he thus helped to preserve or to correct.

Text. The Tanqīḥ al-manāẓir has been printed completely at Haidarābād in the Deccan (2 vols., 1022 p., abundant figs., 1928–30). Many short extracts are translated into German in the Wiedemann papers of 1912 cited below.

Criticism. E. Wiedemann (Annalen für Physik 7, 679, 1879; 21, 541–44, 1884); Über die Brechung des Lichtes nach Ibn al-Haitham und Kamāl al-dīn (Beitr. 19, Sitzungsberichte der Physikalisch-medizinischen Sozietät in Erlangen 42, 15–58, 1910); Zu Ibn al-Haithams Optik (Archiv für die Geschichte der Naturwissenschaften 3, 1–53, 1912); Zur Optik von Kamāl al-dīn (ibid. 3, 161–77, 1912); Arabische Studien über den Regenbogen (ibid. 4, 453–60, 1913); Über die Camera obscura bei Ibn al-Haitham (Beitr. 39, Erlangen Sitzungsberichte 46, 155–71, 1914); Kamāl al-dīn (EI 2, 704, 1924). Other articles by Wiedemann on Arabic optics, which should be considered by the thorough student of the Tanqīḥ al-manāẓir, are cited in my notes on the other Arabic opticians.

Suter (p. 159, 1900). Joseph Würschmidt: Über die Brennkugel (Monatshefte für den naturwissenschaftlichen Unterricht 4, 98–113, 1911); Dietrich von Freiberg, Über den Regenbogen (Beiträge zur Geschichte der Philosophie des Mittelalters vol. 12, parts 5, 6, Münster i.W. 1914). Carra de Vaux (2, 246–49, 1921). F. M. Shuja: Cause of refraction as explained by the Moslem scientists (16 p., Delhi 1936; Isis 29, 487). G. Sarton: The tradition of the optics of Ibn al-Haitham (Isis 29, 403–6, 2 fig., 1938). Brockelmann (suppt. 2, 295, 1938).

Muṣṭafā Naẓīf bey: Al-Ḥasan ibn al-Haitham. His optical studies and discoveries (514 p., in Arabic, Cairo 1942; Isis 34, 217–18), elaborate study based on the Arabic MSS of Ibn al-Haitham and the Haidarābad edition of the Tanqīḥ.

NOTE ON AL-QARĀFĪ (XIII-2)

Inasmuch as al-Qarāfī was not dealt with in volume 2, I add the following note to correct my omission.

Shihāb al-dīn Abū-l-'Abbās Aḥmad ibn Idrīs al-Ṣanhājī al-Bahnasī al-Qarāfī. Egyptian theologian of Berber origin. The nisba Ṣanhājī refers to the Berber tribe Ṣanhāja (G. Marçais in EI 4, 152, 1925); the nisba Qarāfī, to Qarāfa, a cemetery in Cairo (Ḥājjī Khalīfa 1, 158, 1835). He was born in Bahnasā (ancient Oxyrhynchos, on the edge of the Libyan desert, district of Banī Mazār, c. 28°30′N.); he became the most famous Mālikī jurist of his time in Cairo, and died in Dair al-ṭīn[7] in August

[7] As this fact, the death of a Muslim apologist in a Christian convent, intrigued me, I wrote for information to my friend Dr. Max Meyerhof, who kindly replied (Cairo, Oct. 20, 1939): "The Coptic monastery Dair al-tīn exists still today on the right bank of the Nile near the ruins of Fusṭāṭ and the village of Basātīn just south of Cairo. The name dair may refer to

1285. He wrote various treatises on mālikī fiqh, defenses of Islām against the Jews and the Christians, notably one addressed to Paul al-Rāhib, Melkite bishop of Sidon,[8] which has been called the best apologetical effort of Islām. We are interested mainly in a scientific treatise, the Kitāb al-istibṣār fī mā tudrikuhu-l-abṣār,[9] which he had been moved to write by the questions submitted before 1239 by the emperor Frederick II to the Ayyūbī sulṭān al-Kāmil (Introd. 2, 600). This includes his explanation of the rainbow.

Criticism. E. Wiedemann (Jahrbuch für Photographie und Reproduktionstechnik, 1913). Brockelmann (1, 385, 1898; suppt. 1, 665, 1937). Sarkis (col. 1501, 1930). Aydin M. Sayili: Al-Qarāfī and his explanation of the rainbow (Isis 32, 16–26).

EARLY OBSERVATIONS OF AURORA BOREALIS

In my previous volumes I have referred but once to northern lights, apropos of the Norwegian encyclopaedia Konungs skuggsjá (XIII-1), wherein they are briefly described and discussed. More references would have been possible if I had been more alert, for we have elaborate catalogues of auroras going back to A.D. 502.[10] I cannot help being very skeptical, however, about the accounts of auroras anterior to the sixteenth or even the seventeenth century. If it were possible to analyze their contents, most of them, I am afraid, would be found to be as intangible as the *χάσματα, βόθυνοι καὶ αἱματώδη χρώματα* of Aristotle (Meteor. 342a, 35). For one thing, the majority of these ancient observations were made in relatively low latitudes, where auroras are much rarer and more difficult to distinguish. Even the most experienced observers today cannot always decide whether a luminosity seen in the northern sky is an aurora or something else; it is true that by means of a small pocket spectroscope they can easily resolve their doubts, for in the case of an aurora the green auroral line will be readily detected,[11] but the spectroscope is a fairly recent instrument and the earliest spectroscopic observations of auroras were made only in or about 1867 by Anders Jonas Ångström.

---

the village adjoining the monastery as well as to the monastery itself. But in this case I think that al-Qarāfī really passed his last days or months in the monastery under the care of the Coptic monks, who sometimes assumed the role of physicians or male nurses. You must consider that, except for periods of fanaticism, the relations between Copts and Muslims were rather friendly, that some physicians and all the accountants and administrators of domains and so on were always Copts. . . . According to the Dībāj of Ibn Farḥūn (d. 1396) al-Qarāfī died at Dair al-tīn, but nothing is said of his last days."

[8] Cheikho (p. 69, no. 242, 1924). No date given except thirteenth century.

[9] I owe to the kindness of my friend Max Meyerhof, of Cairo, a copy of the Cairene MS of it (no. VI, 88; 61 p.).

[10] Jean Jacques Dortous de Mairan (1678–1771): Traité physique et historique de l'aurore boréale (Mémoires de l'Acad. royale des sciences, 1731, 281 p. quarto, Paris 1733). Reprinted in small size (Amsterdam 1735). Second edition, much enlarged (602 p. quarto, Paris 1754). The catalogue of 1731 contained 229 auroras, from 502 to 1731; the catalogue of 1754 listed 2,137 auroras, 1,441 of them being independent of one another. These auroras were incorporated in the catalogue published by Joseph Lovering: On the periodicity of the aurora borealis (Memoirs of the American Academy of Arts and Sciences 10, 9–356, Boston 1868), extending from 502 to 1868 and referring to nearly 12,000 independent auroras. See also Hermann Fritz: Verzeichniss beobachteter Polarlichter (255 p., Wien 1873), northern lights from 503 B.C. to 1872 and southern lights from 1640 to 1872. Sophus Tromholt: Catalog der in Norwegen beobachteten Nordlichter (445 p., Kristiania 1902), from 1594 to 1878.

[11] Carl Størmer: Photographic atlas of auroral forms and scheme for visual observations of auroras, published by the International Geodetic and Geophysical Union (p. 19, Oslo 1930).

Magnificent and unambiguous auroras, such as may be seen in high latitudes, could not pass unnoticed, yet mediaeval observations properly dated are very rare. The best account is that of the Konungs skuggsjá,[12] referring to the beautiful northern lights which could be seen in Greenland (no dates given). Russian chronicles mention many definite auroras, appearing in 919, 922, 1016, 1111, 1259, 1292. In the fourteenth century (1335, 1397) and later, when the Russian government intensified the colonization of northern regions, auroras of exceptional beauty were interpreted by the clergy as divine commands to erect churches and monasteries.[13]

In Lovering's catalogue (1868), northern lights are listed for the following fourteenth-century dates: 1307, March 6; 1309?; 1325, May 30; 1351 (or 1352), December; 1352, October 30; 1353, August 19; 1354, March 9; 1361, December 12; 1375; 1399. That is a total of ten auroras, represented by some thirty-seven observations. As some of them were noticed by many independent observers, we may assume that they were real auroras of considerable magnitude.

The earliest *printed* descriptions of auroras occurred in 1527, three publications of that year referring to the aurora of October 11, 1527, which was thought to be a comet. Two of these publications were by Peter Creutzer, unknown man calling himself the disciple of the astrologer Johann Lichtenberger, author of the famous prognosticatio of 1488 (Klebs no. 606); the third, derivative from the earlier ones, was by Gerhard Geldenhauer of Nymegen. Gustav Hellmann: Die älteste gedruckte Nordlichtbeschreibung (Beiträge zur Geschichte der Meteorologie no. 3, 107–13, 3 facsim., Berlin 1914; Isis 4, 144). C. Doris Hellman: The comet of 1577 (p. 99, 101, New York 1944).

This note is published in the optical section, for until relatively late the aurora was considered simply as an optical phaenomenon. Edmond Halley was the first to suggest, in 1714, that it was really a magnetic phaenomenon, and this suggestion was confirmed in 1741 by Olaf Peter Hjörter, who noticed that magnetic needles were disturbed during its occurrence. In the meanwhile Jean Jacques de Mairan had suggested a relation between the frequency of sunspots and that of auroras (his book of 1733, cited above, p. 250). The nature of auroras was better understood when spectroscopic observations began (1867), and better still after the discovery of cathodic rays (Adam Paulsen's theory of 1894).

Our best information concerning auroras always came from the northern regions, where they are more frequent and more impressive. Indeed, auroras as seen in high latitudes[14] constitute one of the most beautiful and marvelous spectacles which may be man's privilege to behold. It is not surprising that European poets (except Scandinavian and Russian ones) did not celebrate that awful wonder; the silence of American poets[15] is perhaps a little more difficult to account for. The only symphonic poem devoted to the auroras which I know of was written, properly enough, by a Russian. I am referring to the "Ode or meditation at night on the majesty of

[12] Chiefly end of ch. 19. Oscar Brenner's edition (p. 54–56, München 1881). See English translation by Laurence Marcellus Larson: The king's mirror (p. 18–19, 101, 146, 149–52, New York 1917).

[13] Daniil Osipovich Sviatskii: Aurora borealis in Russian literature from the tenth to the eighteenth century (Archives of history of science 4, 47–67, 2 pl., 1 fig., Leningrad 1934), in Russian (Isis 24, 282).

[14] Whether north or south, aurora borealis or australis, but in the Middle Ages only northern lights are in question.

[15] However, read Robert Hillyer's Northern lights, in his Pattern of a day (p. 38, New York 1940).

God as revealed by the aurora borealis," composed by Nicolas Nabokoff in 1928.[16] To complete this little excursus on the influence of auroras on the arts, I may mention the beautiful paintings by Howard Russell Butler and Leonard M. Davis kept in the American Museum of Natural History, New York.[17]

The best discussion of ancient observations we owe to Sigmund Günther: Das Polarlicht im Altertum (Beiträge zur Geophysik, Zeitschrift für physikalische Erdkunde 6, 98–107, Leipzig 1904). For later history, Gustav Hellmann: Die Entwicklung unserer Kenntnisse vom Nordlicht (Beiträge zur Geschichte der Meteorologie no. 13, 47–58, Berlin 1922).

Some of the information collected in this note was kindly given to us by Dr. John Adam Fleming, director of the Department of Terrestrial Magnetism, Carnegie Institution, in Washington (letter dated Mar. 21, 1941).

2. WEIGHTS AND MEASURES

It might be argued that weights and measures are outside the field of physics, or at least remained outside it until the committee appointed by the Academy of Sciences of France in 1789 investigated the possibility of connecting them with physical constants. To which one could answer that the ideas materialized during the French Revolution were not completely new and may even be traced back to Babylonian days, and, more to the point, that the determination of a system of weights and measures is always a physical problem, irrespective of the rationality or nonrationality of its solution, and that the practice of measurement, e.g., the weighing by means of scales, is a physical practice. Indeed, measurement of distances, weights, etc. is one of the roots, as well as one of the fundamental operations, of physical science.

It remains true that the study of the innumerable kinds of weights and measures used in any one time, such as the fourteenth century, is a branch of archaeology rather than of the history of science. In order to complete it, it would be necessary to explore the files of many numismatic and archaeological serials and periodicals, and this I have neither the time nor the inclination to do. The determination of all the coins, weights, and measures used in various parts of the world during the fourteenth century would be interesting, and would be valuable, e.g. for the interpretation of texts, but it would add little if anything to our understanding of contemporary knowledge.

It will thus suffice here to indicate that that archaeological problem exists and to suggest various means of solving it. Where shall we look for information on weights and measures?

To begin with, Biblical commentators, especially those who were archaeologically minded, found it necessary to discuss the weights and measures referred to in the Old Testament, and also, if they were Christians, in the New Testament, or, if they

[16] I am not familiar with that score, but I heard Nabokoff's Sinfonia biblica at Carnegie Hall, New York, January 2, 1941. Nabokoff was born in St. Petersburg 1903, and lives, as behooves the first composer of aurora music, in Aurora, New York. Judging from its title, his "ode" was inspired by the famous "spiritual ode" composed in 1743 by the great Russian scientist and man of letters Mikhail Vasilievich Lomonosov (1711–65). Text and German translation in Lomonosov's works (edition of the Imperial Academy, vol. 1, St. Petersburg 1891).

[17] Both artists died within the past few years (letter from Clyde Fischer, dated Jan. 27, 1941).

were Jews, in the Talmud. The characterization and determination of the Biblical measures implied comparisons with those familiar to the commentators themselves and to their immediate audience. Hence these Biblical commentaries are (or may be) a source for the study of contemporary weights and measures.[18]

In the second place, medical books often included a study of the weights and measures used by doctors. The best example of this class is the De ponderibus et mensuris of Dino del Garbo (d. 1327). It is more elaborate than other studies appearing in medical treatises, and is valuable for comparative purposes, for it includes Greek, Hebrew, and Arabic terms as well as Latin ones. Dino's main authority was the Qānūn of Ibn Sīnā (XI-1), but he quotes from many other authors, ancient and mediaeval. Elementary notions on medicinal weights were often inculcated in metrical form. For an example (dating from the end of the century, 'tis true, but that does not matter) see Karl Sudhoff: Merkverse über Medizinalgewichte und -Masse aus dem Ende des 14. Jahrh. (Mitt. 13, 159, 308, 1914).

A third source of information, restricted to Arabic literature (from the eleventh century on), is the kind of books written for the guidance of the muḥtasib, an officer in charge of markets in Muslim towns. The regular inspection of weights and measures was one of his duties. In the Ma'ālim al-qurba fī aḥkām al-ḥisba of Ibn al-Ukhuwwa (d. 1329), two chapters (9, 10) are devoted to weights and measures, but remarks concerning them are also found in other chapters (e.g., 11). The inspection of scales is explained in detail; Ibn al-Ukhuwwa warned inspectors that the so-called "Coptic steelyard" (al-qabbān al-qubṭī) could be easily falsified, and showed how to test it. His treatise reveals that the weights and measures used in the Muslim world were as numerous as the Christian ones. For example, he speaks of seven kinds of cubit (dhirā', pl. adhru'). It is not possible to deduce their exact lengths from his text, but the muḥtasib was provided with a standard cubit in wood or iron (EI 1, 959) as well as with standard weights. In some cases the unit of length was engraved on a wall near the marketplace; I saw such a one in a North African town, I think it was in Tlemcen.

Finally, information on weights and measures could probably be culled from treatises on geography and history, e.g., those written for the guidance of Mamlūk state secretaries, also from the annals of various nations, and from administrative regulations and codes of laws.

It might be worth while to put together the data collected from all these sources, and from the archaeological monuments (existing weights and measures), but that would be a considerable task, and conclusions should be suspended until it is accomplished.

Metrological bibliography. The study of mediaeval metrology cannot be separated from that of ancient metrology, hence, in spite of rigorous selection, this list includes a few titles relative to the latter rather than to the former.

Alexis Jean Pierre Paucton (1732–98): Métrologie, ou Traité des mesures, poids et monnoies des anciens peuples et des modernes (quarto, 972 p., Paris 1780).

[18] My colleague H. A. Wolfson has serious doubts on this subject, at least so far as the Jewish commentators are concerned. He does not wish to generalize, but states that in the commentaries known to him there is no reference to contemporary measures. The old Jewish commentators were satisfied to explain the Biblical or Talmudic system as it was, without reference to its origins (Babylonian and Egyptian) or to its later vicissitudes. For example, they showed the relation of the cubit of Ezekiel's temple to other Biblical or Talmudic units, but did not try to express its exact length.

Vicente Vazquez Queipo: Essai sur les systèmes métriques et monétaires des anciens peuples depuis les premiers temps historiques jusqu'à la fin du khalifat d'Orient (3 vols., Paris 1859); vol. 3 is a collection of tables; the Muslim measures are discussed in vol. 2, p. 87–279.

B. Zuckermann: Über talmudische Gewichte und Münzen (Breslau 1862); Das jüdische Mass-System und seine Beziehungen zum griechischen und römischen (Jahrbuch des Jüdischen theologischen Seminärs Fraenkel, Breslau 1867). Friedrich Hultsch (1833–1906): Griechische und römische Metrologie (340 p., Berlin 1862; 2d ed., 760 p., Berlin 1882). Henri Joseph Sauvaire: La numismatique et la métrologie musulmane (Journal asiatique vols. 3–8, 1884–86). Jacob Zallel Lauterbach: Weights and measures (JE 12, 483–90, 1906). Paul Guilhiermoz: Notes sur les poids au Moyen âge (Bibliothèque de l'Ecole des chartes 67, 161–233, 402–50, 1906; 80, 5–100, 1919).

Sir Flinders Petrie (1853–1942): Ancient weights and measures, illustrated by the Egyptian collection in University College, London (folio, 58 p., 54 pl., London 1926); Glass stamps and weights, illustrated from the same collection (folio, 30 p., 26 pl., London 1926). Both volumes belong to the same series, published by the British School of Archaeology in Egypt. The first is a fundamental study which is not restricted to ancient Egypt, but deals also with mediaeval Arabic items; the second is devoted to a purely Egyptian tradition which began in Roman times, and was continued by the Muslim rulers at least until the second half of the thirteenth century; it thus stops short of our period, yet may serve in elucidating its metrology.

Paul Burguburu: Essai de bibliographie métrologique universelle (327 p., Paris 1932). Reprinted from Bibliographe moderne 1926–32. Uncritical list of 4,206 titles, stupidly arranged, yet useful.

See also indexes of previous volumes s.v. metrology, weights and measures.

METROLOGY IN THE FAR EAST

In my previous remarks I had in mind the Western and Islamic cultures, with which I am more familiar, but the same remarks would apply mutatis mutandis to conditions in the Far East. Information on metrology may be found in the "memoirs" (chih) or more technical parts of the Chinese dynastic histories, and probably also in some writings of the Buddhist[19] and Taoist (?) patrologies. Occasional data might be culled from the examples quoted in arithmetical treatises. That is actually the case for the ancient classic Sun Tzŭ suan ching (III-1?), and applies presumably to later works of the same kind. I do not remember any Chinese or Japanese treatise of this period specifically devoted to metrology.

These matters have been investigated by modern Chinese and Japanese scholars. Dr. A. W. Hummel kindly wrote me (Mar. 25, 1941):

"As to Chinese foot measures, you will find a long article with illustrations in the Journal of the North China Branch of the Royal Asiatic Society, 1928, pp. 111–23. This is a translation which I made of a study by the celebrated Chinese scholar Wang Kuo-wei (1877–1927).[20] This shows the development of foot measures in China in the last two thousand years.

"As for weights, I know of no study in English, but here too Wang Kuo-wei made some studies which are mentioned briefly by Pelliot in the T'oung Pao, 1928–29, p. 132, bottom. Pelliot there analyzes a ts'ung-shu by Wang Kuo-wei and summarizes the results of Wang's studies. In the T'oung Pao, 1932, p. 219, Pelliot

[19] McGovern (p. 41, 1923).

[20] Paul Pelliot: L'édition collective des oeuvres de Wang Kouo-wei (T'oung Pao 26, 113–82, 1929).

summarizes a book in Russian by A. V. Marakuev on weights and measures in China (152 p., Vladivostok 1930).

"Also, if you look at the index to Sir Aurel Stein's Serindia (Oxford 1921) you will find numerous references to measures found by him and probably also to weights. These are the only sources that I regard as reliable treatments of these subjects."

Dr. Shio Sakanishi wrote me on the same day and with equal kindness:

"There are two authoritative histories of weights and measures in the Japanese language. The first and most important of the two is Honchō do-ryō-kenkō kō [Treatise on weights and measures in Japan], by Kariya, Ekisai (1775–1835).

"Kariya, Ekisai was a famous bibliographer and a scholar in Japanese and Chinese classics. The present work is in four volumes. It remained in manuscript till 1912, when Dr. Tokuzō Fukuda edited and annotated it and included it in the Nihon keizai sôsho [Japanese economic series]. Honchō do-ryō-kenkō kō is not only a history of Japanese weights and measures, but it is also a comparative study of the problems throughout the Far Eastern countries. It traces the Japanese terms to the Chinese sources, and through early Buddhistic and other works, to Hindu and sometimes Arabic origins. The Nihon koten zenshū kankō-kai reprinted the work in two small volumes for students in 1927.

"The second work is by Hirata, Atsutane (1776–1843), one of the most distinguished classical scholars and an authority on Shintō: Kōkoku do sei kō [System of measures in the Empire], in two volumes. It was completed and printed during the Tempō period (1830–43). Hirata, Atsutane examined the ancient records, culled all the references to numbers, and examined them. He brings the data to the end of the fourteenth century. Hirata's work is not so scientific, because, as an ardent Shintoist, he was hampered by certain religious conceptions of these numbers."

3. MAGNETISM

THE DISCOVERY OF THE COMPASS

The early history of the compass has been discussed in volumes 1 and 2 (passim).[21] It will suffice to recall that although the attractive property of the loadstone was soon discovered, namely by Thales (VI B.C.), its directive property was far more difficult to recognize, for it implied the existence of an elongated loadstone or needle, free to turn without resistance. The Chinese discovered that property and made use of it at an early time for geomantic purposes.

Muslim sailors, who monopolized the trade of the eastern seas, were perhaps the first to use the magnetic needle for navigation.

References to the compass and its use may be found in Berakya ha-Naqdan (XII-2), Alexander Neckam (XII-2), who speaks already of a pivoted needle, Guiot of Provins (XIII-1), Thomas of Cantimpré (XIII-1), James of Vitry (XIII-1), Bailak al-Qabajaqī (XIII-2),[21a] and in Peter the Stranger (XIII-2). The latter's epistola of 1269 contains a description of two kinds of compass, a dry kind with divisions marked off on the box, and a floating one with a reference scale divided into 360 degrees. Thus it is clear that by 1269 an elaborate compass placed in a

[21] Summaries in 1, 764; 2, 24, 509, 629–31.

[21a] Addition to note in Introd. (2, 1072): Bailak ibn Muḥammad al-Qabajaqī (or Qybčāqī) flourished in the second quarter of the century under the Ayyūbī sulṭān al-Muẓaffar II Taqī al-dīn Maḥmūd (ruler of Ḥamāh 1229–44). See Brockelmann (suppt. 2, 904, 1938).

box (bòssolo, bùssola) and properly graduated was already available. The early portolani give further evidence of the mariner's use of compasses (Introd. 2, 1048).

To these data should be added one which I overlooked. Ari Fróthi Thorgilsson (XII-1), speaking of the discovery of Iceland in 874 by Floki Vilgerdarson (Introd. 1, 605), says that Floki took with him ravens from the direction of whose flight he might determine the lie of the land. A later gloss (c. 1225) runs, "In northern lands those who sailed the sea had not the loadstone." This implies that by 1225 they did have it. The sagas contain many references to the leidarstein (German, Leitstein), and the early maritime discoveries of the Vikings make plausible the assumption that they already had technical means of navigation at their disposal.[22]

This Scandinavian account is especially interesting because it proves that knowledge of the compass was not restricted to the Mediterranean, and thus helps to disprove the traditional story ascribing its discovery to one Flavio Gioja of Amalfi (c. 1302). We have seen that a fairly elaborate compass was described in 1269. Of course, it was still capable of many improvements (it is still being improved upon in our own days). It is possible that the amalgation of the compass card[23] with the magnetic needle, a great step forward, was accomplished in the fourteenth century, and such an invention might have been made by the Amalfi mariners, who sailed from the Gulf of Salerno to the eastern end of the Mediterranean Sea; but there is nothing to prove that it was made by them, and Flavio Gioja is a ghost whom Italian archaeologists have been thus far unable to substantiate. The Gioja legend originated with Antonio Beccadelli of Palermo (1393–1471) "il Panormita," was given currency by Flavio Biondo of Forlì (1388–1463) in the latter's Italia illustrata (1451), and then was copied from one book to another by many others. Thus endless testimonies may be quoted in its support, but all these testimonies are but the reflections of a single original error.

The main purpose of this note is to lay the ghost of Flavio Gioja, but, alas! uncritical people will resurrect him from time to time.

The development of the compass in the fourteenth and fifteenth centuries was very slow. Many separate improvements were probably restricted for a considerable time to few specimens, or even to single ones; indeed, these improvements were in the nature of trade secrets which a family or guild (e.g., the sailors belonging to a definite harbor) would not wish to share with strangers. The oldest compass known to me is preserved in the Ferdinandeum, Innsbruck. It dates from 1451 and indicates a declination of 11°E. It is described and reproduced by Gustav Hellmann (Meteorologische Zeitschrift 23, 146, 1906). By the way, it is possible that the declination was known long before the time of Columbus, and perhaps as early as the thirteenth century (?). Some of the windroses on portolani may be interpreted in that light (?). It has been claimed that Chaucer had some knowledge of it in 1380 (?).

To pass to another fact of a more tangible kind, the Cardan's suspension (suspension in gimbals) was introduced only in the sixteenth century. That device is much older than Gerolamo Cardano (1501–76), for it was described by Philon of Byzantium (II-2 B.C.?) and in the Mappae clavicula (VIII-2), and was known to

[22] My attention was drawn to Ari's account by professor Lloyd William Taylor, of Oberlin College, Oberlin, Ohio, who has shown his deep interest in the history of physics in his book Physics, the pioneer science (910 p., ill., Boston 1941; Isis 34, 378).

[23] The windrose represented on the card is much older than the compass itself; it goes back to Greek times. For the related question of "wind-blowers" on maps, see Isis 19, 503; 23, 253.

the Chinese[24] as early as the Han dynasty, but the earliest description of a compass thus suspended occurs in Martin Cortez: Breve compendio de la esfera y de la arte de navegar (Cadiz 1546, 1551; Sevilla 1556). The description may not occur in the first edition, nor in the second, but it occurs in the third, which deals with magnetic declination.

The slowness of further evolution of the compass may be appreciated from the fact that until the nineteenth century these instruments remained very imperfect.

Bibliography. See Introd. 2, 630. Johann Christian Poggendorff: Geschichte der Physik (p. 98, Leipzig 1879). Albert Schück: Der Kompass (folio, 3 vols., Hamburg 1911–18; Isis 4, 438); this is the fundamental work on the subject; vol. 1 is a collection of plates representing the principal documents and monuments with very brief explanations, but vol. 2, 1915, contains elaborate studies on the legendary history of the compass, the Chinese, Muslim, and Amalfian claims being discussed very fully. Additional information on the Chinese case fills the greater part of vol. 3. Feldhaus (1914; 1931). Mottelay (1922, passim). Heinrich Winter: Who invented the compass? (Mariner's mirror 23, 95–102, 1937); Die Nautik der Wikinger und ihre Bedeutung für die Entwicklung der europäischen Seefahrt (Hansische Geschichtsblätter 62, 173–84, Weimar 1938; Isis 30, 165); Die Erkenntnis der magnetischen Missweisung und ihr Einfluss auf die Kartographie (Congrès international de géographie 2, 55–80, 4 pl., Amsterdam 1938; Isis 31, 242).

4. EARLY MECHANICAL CLOCKS

MEASUREMENT OF TIME IN MEDIAEVAL EUROPE

Before examining the obscure problems connected with the discovery and early development of mechanical clocks (vs. clepsydrae and sundials), it is well to explain the horological needs of the time. This will help us to understand why early clocks began to be used in the fourteenth century.

The spiritual needs of the Christian communities were largely dominated by the church, and thus the divisions of the day were determined to a large extent with reference to canonical and liturgical rules. In particular, monastic discipline made it necessary to fix times for masses, work, meals, sleep. These times had to be clearly announced, but need not be exactly the same from day to day. According to Jewish traditions, the day began at dusk and the night was divided into three watches. Monastic life began during the third watch, called (1) matins (matutina); this was followed by (2) prima at sunrise, (3) tertia halfway between sunrise and noon, (4) sexta at noon (hence the word siesta = midday rest), (5) nona in midafternoon, (6) vespers (vesperae) an hour before sunset, and finally (7) compline (completa) at sunset. These hours, or at any rate the middle ones, were relatively mobile. For example, in the course of time tertia (mass time) was immediately followed by the office of sexta and breakfast, then nona became the "noon" hour (our word noon is really derived from nona). But even if these changes be overlooked, it is clear that the divisions depended on the variable length of daylight (as opposed to nychthemeron). In addition, sunrises and sunsets were not always easy to determine, especially in high latitudes. Finally, the time and duration of religious services varied from day to day according to the liturgy. Thus a clock running regularly and dividing the day into periods of equal duration would have been, at first, more disturbing than useful. For monastic purposes a human vari-

[24] Berthold Laufer: Cardan's suspension in China (Holmes anniversary vol., p. 288–92, 1 pl., Washington 1916).

able clock (e.g., a bell rung by a monk or lay brother at the needed irregular intervals) was more practical than an automatic one.

The end of the thirteenth century and the whole of the fourteenth, however, witness a gradual laicization of life proceeding with increasing speed. Power and initiative were passing from the hands of the clerics to those of the laymen; the main centers of activity were no longer the monasteries, large or small, but the market towns. Civil life called for increasing regularity, equal hours, standards of broadening application. It is not strange, therefore, that better timepieces were created at this age.

When automatic clocks and equal hours were introduced, the day was first divided into 24 hours from sunset to sunset, the completion of the day being indicated by 24 strokes of the bell (this was still the case in some places as late as 1370). In the course of time (the dates varying somewhat from one country to another) the day was divided into two halves of 12 hours each, beginning respectively at midnight and high noon. The division of the day into two halves was a practical one, to avoid the necessity of striking bells more than twelve times in close succession; its beginning at midnight was a rational necessity, for the time from sunset to sunset varied a little from day to day.

It is difficult to say when these changes were introduced. To conclude from the chronicles is hazardous, for it is quite possible that monastic diarists continued to speak of canonical hours after the establishment of the newfangled clocks[25] even in their own monasteries. When, however, a chronicler says "circa horam septimam post horam nonam," as an English one did in 1377 (meaning 7 P.M.), we may be sure that the reform was already accomplished at that date. From many other examples of the same kind we may conclude that it was generally accomplished in the last quarter of the century. For further details on such matters see Bilfinger (1892).[26]

EARLY CLOCKS

In the following pages I have collected all the evidence available to me. It should be noted that in many cases it is not possible to be certain that the reference is to a mechanical clock, as distinguished from a water clock. The word horologium and its variants in Latin, English (20 listed in the Oxford English Dictionary), and other languages are full of ambiguities. They may mean sundial, clepsydra, (mechanical) clock.

In the rule of Cîteaux (c. 1120) the sacristan is given the responsibility of adjusting the monastery's horologe in order that it may awake the monks for matins. This was an alarm clock which might be of different kinds, perhaps a primitive clock, perhaps a clepsydra releasing the alarm mechanism. The sacristan was thus awakened, and proceeded to ring the bells in order to awaken his brethren.

In certain cases the meaning of horologium was almost certainly sundial, e.g., the horologium viatorum discussed by Lynn Thorndike (Isis 13, 51–52, 1929) and Ernst Zinner (Isis 14, 385–87, 1930); Thorndike (3, 211, 1934).

Early clocks were often diversified and embellished with jacks[27] and other autom-

[25] Even as pious people today may speak of matins or vespers or the angelus time.

[26] Some of the references in this chapter are to the general bibliography, others to the special bibliography below.

[27] Derived from the proper name Jack (James) or from the French jacquemart, Latin jaccomarchiadus, a man in a suit of armor. The word jacquemart (or jaquemart) is used in French to designate the automatic personages standing around ancient clocks.

ata. These were luxuries, but they helped to draw the people's attention to the clocks and to educate their sense of regularity. It took an exceedingly long time to do so, and in some countries the education is hardly begun.

In our discussion of mechanical clocks one should always bear in mind that the essential points in their creation were, first, the introduction of a weight drive,[28] setting a train of wheels in motion; and second, more important still, the introduction of an oscillatory escapement stopping the weight regularly at short intervals. The earliest known escapement is the foliot balance, which is perhaps represented in a drawing of Villard de Honnecourt (XIII-2).

Methods of dating clocks

Clocks may be dated by means of texts or drawings, or by means of monuments. As to the monuments, the mechanical parts may be considered, or the dial and astronomical representations, or the jacks and other ornamental parts. Howgrave-Graham (p. 274–80, 1927) has suggested the following approaches: (1) material used for the mechanism (the earliest material is iron, brass parts are later); (2) evidence of conversion from the use of the foliot balance (the foliot continued to be used, however, until the middle of the seventeenth century, long after the introduction of the pendulum; the wheel balance was used in domestic clocks only); (3) general arrangement of frame; (4) use of lantern pinions; (5) number of arms or spokes in train wheels; (6) method of welding cross to rim; (7) sectional shape of arbors or spindles; (8) design of locking plates in strike mechanism; (9) use of spokes for winding drums; (10) use of spokes as detent ratchets; (11) number of wheels in going train; (12) presence of screws (screws do not appear before the fifteenth century); (13) design of corner standards and ornamental detail.

This enumeration has been given to indicate the complexity and difficulty of the problems. For many of the earliest clocks, however, we have nothing but literary evidence, generally too scanty and vague to enable us to determine the existence of mechanism, let alone its nature.

Chronological summary

c. 1257. Villard de Honnecourt (XIII-2). Fl. 1235–57. Perhaps inventor of the foliot escapement? See Fremont (p. 4–8, figs., 1915). Howgrave-Graham (p. 260, 265, 1927; hereafter cited as HG).

c. 1271. Robert the Englishman (XIII-2). In his commentary on the Sphere of John of Sacrobosco (XIII-1), composed c. 1271, Robert describes a kind of mechanical horologium driven by a weight indicating 24 equal hours from sunrise to sunrise. Latin text edited by Lynn Thorndike (Speculum 16, 242–43, 1941).

c. 1277. Five books on clocks in the Libros del saber translated from the Arabic into Castilian by order of Alfonso el Sabio (XIII-2) c. 1276–77. Describing a sundial, a water clock, a mercury clock, and a candle clock, all of them for inside use. No trace of escapement (Baillie p. 43).

c. 1285. John of Meung (XIII-2). Roman de la rose, completed c. 1268–85. Reference to "orloges" (Langlois ed., l. 21,033), maybe the bells of an alarm clock, but more probably a musical instrument, i.e., a carillon of small bells.

1284, Exeter. Grant of a tenement to Roger de Ropford, the bell founder (campistarius), and others for the repair of organa and orologium. That horloge

[28] There was already a kind of weight drive in water clocks of the falling-drum type. Hermann Diels: Antike Technik (p. 204–19, Leipzig 1920; Isis 3, 433).

was probably a bell for announcing the canonical hours. It became a clock in the course of time, and was moved to a specially made clock chamber in 1376–77. It underwent a series of repairs and changes until 1423–24, when it was entirely renewed. The existing remains are probably posterior to the last-named date (HG p. 268, 295–301).

1286, St. Paul's, London. An account of that year mentions allowances made to one Bartholomaeus Orologiarius, who was a timekeeper of some kind (HG p. 268).

1288, Westminster. The chief justice Ralph of Hingham (d. 1311) was condemned to pay an enormous fine (8,000 l.), which is said to have been used for the building of a tower in Palace Yard, opposite the entrance to Westminster Hall, with a clock striking the hours. There is no contemporary evidence to substantiate that anecdote; the earliest reference to it dates from 1329. By 1365/66, however, such a clock tower did exist at Westminster (HG p. 268, 273) (DNB 25, 410–11). Radulphi de Hengham Summae, edited by William Huse Dunham, jr. (p. lv, Cambridge 1932).

1288, Merton College, Oxford. Payment of 4s. 4d. ad opus horologii. The horologium was removed from the Hall in 1327. Various expenditures were made for it in 1387 (HG p. 268).

1292, Christ Church cathedral, Canterbury. Novum orologium magnum in Ecclesia xxx l. (HG p. 268).

1306, Sant' Eustorgio, Milano. According to the Dominican Galvaneus Flamma (d. after 1344), who wrote a chronicle of Milano to 1333 (Chronica de antiquitatibus civitatis mediolanensis, Cronaca Galvagnana), under date 1306 "Benignus tercia vice prior efficitur. Iste fecit ampliari celles infirmatorii et cameras, stella aurea super campanile ponitur, horologium ferreum fabricatur." This is the first record of a public clock in Italy, but it was probably a sundial; otherwise, the chronicler would have qualified the term horologium with an adjective expressing its novelty. That clock was restored in 1333, 1555, 1572 (Baillie p. 28; Robertson p. 31, where the initial date is wrongly given, 1309 instead of 1306).

1314 or before. In an inventory of the possessions of Charles V of France, dated 1380, there is mentioned "un reloge d'argent tout entièrement, sans fer, qui fut du roy Philippe le Bel, avec deux contrepoix d'argent empliz de plomb." Philip the Fair died in 1314. As this clock was made of silver, it was probably small; it is the oldest chamber clock about which we have definite information (Baillie p. 44; Robertson p. 45).

1314, Caen. Clock erected upon the bridge, bearing the inscription (Robertson p. 34; Ungerer p. 71–72):

Puisque la ville me loge
Sur ce pont pour servir d'orloge
Je ferai les heures ouir
Pour le commun peuple réjouir.

c. 1320, Wimborne, Dorsetshire. "The existing remains of the Wimborne clock, persistently assigned until a year ago to Peter Lightfoot, have a feebler claim to high antiquity than any other member of the west-country group, though the date, c. 1320, is still a matter of belief with many persons" (HG p. 303–7). Follows a discussion of the records, the mechanism, the dial and dial case, and the jack.

1320, cathedral of Peterborough, Northamptonshire. Traditional but unsupported date. Only the striking part of the older mechanism remains; it is of primitive workmanship. The clock never had a dial, which is a sign of antiquity (HG p. 286–87).

1316–21. Two references to clock and clockwork in Dante's Paradiso (X, 139; XXIV, 13), composed c. 1316–21:

> Indi, come orologio, che ne chiami
> Nell'ora che la sposa di Dio surge
> A mattinar lo Sposo perchè l'ami . . .
>
> E come cerchi in tempra d'oriuoli
> Si giran sì, che'l primo, a chi pon mente,
> Quieto pare, e l'ultimo che voli . . .

The first quotation may refer to a primitive alarm clock of any kind; the second may have been suggested by the striking train of a clock, with the slow movement of the great wheel and the rapid revolution of the fly. Or "l'ultimo che voli" may be an allusion to the swinging foliot, which in early clocks was in a prominent position at the top (HG p. 260; Baillie p. 42; Robertson p. 29–31).

1322–25, Norwich cathedral. Records of material needed in the building of it (HG p. 269).

1323–34, Glastonbury abbey, Somerset. There was a clock there which, like the Wimborne one (c. 1320), was ascribed to the monk Peter Lightfoot, who is practically unknown but for the reference by John Leland (1506?–52) in his Itinerary (1st ed., 3, 83, Oxford 1710): "In transepto Eccl. in merid. parte . . . Horologium. Petrus Lightfote monachus fecit hoc opus." In his chronicle to 1493 John of Glaston says that the abbot Adam of Sodbury (1323–34) "magnum horologium, processionibus et spectaculis insignitum et organa mirae magnitudinis in eadem construxit" (1726 ed., p. 263). It was related that this Glastonbury clock was removed to Wells when the former abbey was suppressed, in 1539. The Wells clock is certainly a later one (c. 1392).

For the Lightfoot legend and other legends which clustered around it, see R. P. Howgrave-Graham: Peter Lightfoot and the old clock at Wells. A poem with an illustrated account of the same (56 p., 7 pl., 3 fig., Glastonbury 1922), and the same author's more critical account in his paper of 1927 (p. 288–89).

1326–35, St. Albans abbey, Hertfordshire. The discussion of this item is centered on the personality of one of the abbots, Richard Wallingford, who was dealt with in chapter VI. Our information is derived from the Gesta abbatum monasterii Sancti Albini, and from Leland, writing two centuries later. In the account of Richard's abbacy it is said that he built the instrument called Albion (a kind of orrery?), "Fecit quoque et illud nobile opus horologii in ecclesia, magnis sumptibus et industria." When Edward III visited St. Albans he rebuked the abbot Richard for wasting so much money and work on that irrelevant horologium when the church was still in a ruinous state and necessary things remained undone. The horologium was still incomplete at the time of Richard's death (1335); it was completed toward the end of the rule of the next abbot but one, Thomas de la Mare (ruled 1349–96), i.e., c. 1390. The work was done by the horologiarius Lawrence of Stokes, helped by the monk William Walsham, both of them superior craftsmen; on account of its size and complexity, the cost was very high, being estimated at a hundred marks and over. From this we must conclude that the Albion or horologium (perhaps both terms designate the same object) was a very complicated instrument, whatever it was (HG p. 269; Baillie p. 29).

1335, church of Beate Vergine (San Gottardo), Milano. According to the chronicler Galvaneus Flamma or Fiamma (mentioned above under 1306), there was established in 1335 a clock which struck the hour every hour of the day: "Est ibi unum horologium admirabile, quia est unum tintinabulum grossum valde, quod percutit unam campanam vigintiquatuor vicibus, secundum numerum XXIV horarum diei et noctis, ita quod in prima hora noctis dat unum tonum, in secunda duos ictus, in tertia tres, et in quarta quatuor; et sic distinguit horas ab horis quod est summe necessarium pro omni statu hominum" (Baillie p. 32; Robertson p. 32).

1343, Modena. Public clock (Baillie p. 41).

1343, Avignon. Chamber clock with bell for the pope's garderobe; the pope's reader took care of it and a specialist was in charge of repairs. In an account of 1353 there is mention of an elaborate domus horologii. In 1363, 20 florins were paid to brother John of Venice (Joannes de Venetiis) for the building of a clock in the pope's back room. In 1374–75, we find mention of a magister magni orologii domini nostri pape, magister orologiorum Petrus de Sancta Beata. He was clockmaker to Charles V and had been called from Paris to Avignon by Gregory XI. In 1391, the clockmaker of the antipope Clement VII (1378–94) was Jacobus Pavieta. These data show that from 1343 on there were clocks and clockmakers in the court of Avignon.

Robert Michel: Les premières horloges du palais pontifical d'Avignon (Ecole française de Rome, Mélanges d'archéologie 29, 213–19, 1909).

1344, Padua. Mechanical clock designed by Giacomo de' Dondi for the Carrara tower in Padua. For that achievement Giacomo was called horologius or dall' Orologio, a title transmitted to his descendants. Giacomo's clock was destroyed by the Milanese in 1390, but a clock in the Piazza dei Signori finished in 1434 was probably a copy of it. A more elaborate clock was constructed by Giacomo's son, Giovanni, from 1348 to 1364. The second clock will be discussed in our chapter XXI; it was necessary to mention it here because the two clocks are repeatedly confused. For example, the claim that the Dondi clock is the first about which we have definite knowledge does not refer to Giacomo's clock of 1344, about which we know little, but to the clock of 1364.

The information given by Baillie (p. 36, 41) and Robertson (p. 33) is incorrect. Lynn Thorndike: The clocks of Jacopo and Giovanni de' Dondi (Isis 10, 360–62, 1928). See my notes on the two Dondi farther on.

1347, Monza, near Milano (Baillie p. 41).

1348, Dover castle. This is one of the earliest clocks in existence. Its mechanism is exhibited in the Science Museum, London. It is the oldest known specimen of verge escapement with the "foliot" or crossbar balance (see fig. 13). The specifications are:

Going Train	Striking Train
Great wheel 96, pinion 7	Great wheel 72, pinion 9
Crown wheel 33	Second wheel 72, pinion 8
Foliot 28 inches long	Fly

This clock would be the earliest one in existence if its traditional date 1348 were correct. That dating, however, is due to a misunderstanding. In 1345–48, new bells were installed in the tower of the castle, but the earliest reference to a clock is in an exchequer account of 3–6 Henry V (= 1415–18). The clock was probably made about the end of the fourteenth century, say 1390–1400, but it may be later still. It was removed from Dover Castle in 1872 (HG p. 281; Baillie p. 33–35; Robertson p. 69–73).

The upshot of this long enumeration is not very satisfying. It is clear that mechanical clocks were devised and used in the first half of the fourteenth century if not a little before, but it is impossible to point to a concrete case for which the literary and archaeological evidence is complete. We might perhaps say that the Milano clock of 1335 is the first real striking clock, but it is lost; the Dover clock has been preserved, but it is certainly of a later date than was traditionally believed, perhaps even posterior to the fourteenth century.

Bibliography. Gustav Bilfinger: Die mittelalterlichen Horen und die modernen Stunden (290 p., Stuttgart 1892). Feldhaus (col. 1199–1239, 1914). Charles Fremont: Origine de l'horloge à poids (quarto, 28 p., Paris 1915; Isis 27, 482). Frederick James Britten (1843–1913): Old clocks and watches and their makers (5th enlarged ed., by his daughter Annie, 834 p., London 1922; 1st ed. 1899). Willis Isbister Milham: Time and timekeepers (629 p., New York 1923). J. Eric Haswell: Horology. The science of time measurement and the construction of clocks, watches and chronometers (284 p., London 1928). Howgrave-Graham (1927). G. H. Baillie (1929). Usher (p. 146–71, 1929). J. D. Robertson (1931). Alfred Ungerer: Les horloges astronomiques et monumentales les plus remarquables de l'antiquité à nos jours (quarto, 514 p., 458 fig., Strasbourg, chez l'auteur 1931). John James Hall: Iron work fastenings of the fourteenth century and the method of their conversion in modern times (Transactions Newcomen Society 16, 129–39, 1935/36). Lynn Thorndike: Invention of the mechanical clock about 1271 (Speculum 16, 242–43, 1941), forecast made by Robert the Englishman (XIII-2) in his commentary on Sacrobosco's Sphere.

5. ARMS AND ARMOR

THE INVENTION OF FIREARMS

At the end of my note on saltpeter and the invention of gunpowder (Introd. 2, 1036–38) I remarked, "It is very probable that gunpowder was invented before the end of the thirteenth century; but even so, it is certain that nobody understood as yet the implications of that invention." The main implication, the explosive and propulsive power of gunpowder, was discovered in the first half of the fourteenth century, but it is impossible to say exactly when and where.[29]

The invention of firearms, that is, of cannon or guns, implied not only the discovery of that quality of gunpowder, a task for the alchemist, but also the making of guns, a task for the armorer, blacksmith, and founder. The great progress made in the thirteenth and fourteenth centuries by the workers in brass and bronze was thus timely. The art of the founder is a very subtle one, full of pitfalls and of secrets.

The discussion is obscured by verbal ambiguities; references in chronicles to

[29] Roger Bacon (XIII-2) had already suggested that the explosive power of gunpowder would be increased if the powder were enclosed in a solid cavity (Opus tertium, Little p. 51, 1912).

FIG. 13. Earliest clock movement, from Dover Castle. This illustration is placed here because that clock is traditionally dated 1348; it was made probably about the end of the century. The original is kept in the Science Museum, South Kensington, London. British Crown copyright. Courtesy of Science Museum.

FIG. 14. Earliest type of cannon, in a MS dated 1327 (Christ Church, Oxford). From Henry W. L. Hime: The origin of artillery (Longmans, Green, London 1915), with kind permission.

siege engines or even to artillery or to cannon do not necessarily mean that those engines were firearms. A number of engines were used for throwing stones or other projectiles, or even for throwing "Greek fire" (Introd. 1, 494) or other inflammable substances. They were called catapults, trebuchets, ballista, ribaudequins, mangonels, etc., and some of them were of unwieldy size. The main weapons used in the field, for fighting at a distance, were longbows and crossbows, which had become arms of remarkable power and precision. Note that the names used for the new arms were old names, as mortar, a chemist's tool; cannon, meaning canna (κάννα), a reed or tube also used for Greek fire; gun, from engine or canna, or short for mangonel?

Scholars have accumulated long lists of references extracted from local chronicles, accounts, etc., each of which would require a long investigation out of place in this volume. Such lists may be found in Feldhaus (1914) and in Rathgen (p. 703–10, 1928); iconographical documents have been collected by Essenwein (1877) and Guttmann (1906). The earliest representation of a cannon is probably the one included in a MS of the De officiis regum dedicated by its author, Walter de Milemete, to Edward III in 1327[30] (see our fig. 14). It represents the earliest kind of cannon, called vasi and pots de fer by the Italians and the French.

Were firearms already used in 1319 at the siege of Berwick, as John Barbour (XIV-2) suggests? He speaks of gynis for crakkis[31] (Deters p. 145, 1913). Were they used at the siege of Metz in 1324? (Oman 2, 212, 1924). Were they used by Moors in Andalusia, at Baza 1325, Martos 1326, Alicante 1331? (Rathgen p. 704, 1928). Were they used by Edward III in his war against the Scots in 1327 (crakys of war)? (Oman 2, 213). Were they used in 1331 by German knights in the siege of Cividale del Friuli (Udine)? Were cannon made at Cambrai in 1339? Were they used in the capture of Algeziras by Alfonso XI of Castile in 1342? In 1345 Edward III ordered the keeper of the Tower wardrobe (in London) to repair and ship guns and pellets for the king's expedition of that year (Tout p. 238, 1934). Other items of the same kind give color to the argument that cannon were used in 1346 at Crécy-en-Ponthieu, near Abbeville (Picardie). The battle of Crécy is often interpreted as a victory of the English longbowmen over the undisciplined crossbowmen of France. Did the English use cannon too? This cannot be proved, but by this time they had already used them. Cannon were used by the English at the siege and capture of Calais in 1347.

According to a document in the archives of Tournai, a gun was cast in 1346 in that city by Peter of Bruges, pewterer. He was invited by the councilmen to test the gun (conoille); after having passed through a wall and a house, the projectile, weighing two pounds, killed a man. This is said to have been the first gun made in the Low Countries. See note by Fréd. Alvin in Biographie nationale de Belgique (17, 430, 1903).

To turn to another kind of argument, there are references to firearms in the Buch der Natur written by Conrad von Megenberg (Pfeiffer's ed., p. 91, 274) and in the De remediis utriusque fortunae of Petrarca (1, 99), both works dating from the middle of the century.

Our conclusion is curiously the same as for clocks. We are tolerably certain that firearms, that is, small cannon, were used in the second quarter of the century, but

[30] MS in Christ Church, Oxford. Walter de Milemete, prebendary of the collegiate church of Glaseney, Cornwall, was chaplain to Edward III (Hime p. 122, 1915).

[31] Cf. Shakespeare, Macbeth 1, 2, "Cannons overcharged with double cracks."

we cannot completely prove it in any one of almost innumerable cases. The abundance of references to cannon in accounts of various sorts is very remarkable. They are mentioned in the archives and chronicles of England, France, Spain, Italy, Germany, Flanders, etc. Those early firearms were very inefficient and did not make much impression, either military or psychological. The revolution brought about by their use was very gradual; it was not fully realized until the sixteenth century. Indirect evidence of that slowness is provided by the continued popularity of armor. The day would come when armor would no longer protect the bodies of men and horses, but that day was still very distant, and the period 1400-1550 was the golden age of armor.

Bibliography on firearms. Napoleon III: Etudes sur le passé et l'avenir de l'artillerie (6 vols., Paris 1846-71), written with the cooperation of Ildefonse Favé. August Essenwein: Quellen zur Geschichte der Feuerwaffen, hrg. vom Germanischen Museum (small folio, 178 p., large collection of plates, Leipzig 1877). Max Jähns: Geschichte der Kriegswissenschaften vornehmlich in Deutschland (vol. 1, München 1889). S. J. von Romocki: Geschichte der Explosivstoffe (vol. 1, Berlin 1895). Wirt Gerrare (= William Greener): Bibliography of guns and shooting (216 p., Westminster 1896), of little use for the study of origins. Oscar Guttmann: Monumenta pulveris pyrii (50 p., 67 pl., London 1906), collection of iconographic documents. Charles Henry Ashdown: British and foreign arms and armour (400 p., 450 fig., 42 pl., London 1909), only the last chapter (p. 360-70) deals with firearms. Rudolf Schneider: Die Artillerie des Mittelalters nach den Angaben der Zeitgenossen (193 p., 8 pl., Berlin 1910), no firearms. Thomas Frederick Tout: Firearms in England in the fourteenth century (English historical review 26, 666-702, 1911; reprinted in Collected papers 2, 233-75, Manchester 1934). Friedrich Deters: Die Englischen Angriffswaffen zur Zeit der Einführung der Feuerwaffen, 1300-50 (Anglistische Forschungen no. 38, 164 p., Heidelberg 1913). Feldhaus (col. 408-17, 1914). Hime (p. 119-33, 1915), many errors. Bernhard Rathgen: Feuer- und Fernwaffen des 14. Jahrh. in Flandern (Zeitschrift für historische Waffenkunde 7, 1-32, 1917). Johann Ottsen: Über den derzeitigen Stand unserer Kenntnisse von den Anfängen der Pulverwaffen (Beiträge zur Geschichte der Technik 13, 1-9, 1923), based upon Rathgen's abundant investigations, published, like the one quoted above, in the Zeitschrift für historische Waffenkunde and in local antiquarian journals. Charles Oman: History of the art of war in the Middle Ages (2, 205-29, 1924; first published in 1 vol., 1898). Major H. B. C. Pollard: History of firearms (London 1926), only ch. 1. Rathgen (1928). W. W. Arendt: History of artillery in mediaeval times (Archives on the history of science 7, 297-323, Leningrad 1935; Isis 26, 268), in Russian. Charles ffoulkes: The gunfounders of England with a list of English and continental gunfounders from the XIV to the XIXth centuries (quarto, 150 p., 15 pl., 38 ill., Cambridge 1937).

Some books primarily devoted to armor may also be consulted. Wendelin Boeheim: Meister der Waffenschmiedekunst vom XIV. bis ins XVIII. Jahrh. (258 p., 20 pl., 159 fig., Berlin 1897). Jacob Heinrich von Hefner-Alteneck: Waffen. Ein Beitrag zur historischen Waffenkunde vom Beginn des Mittelalters bis gegen Ende des 17. Jahrh. (folio, 58 p., 100 pl., Frankfurt a.M. 1903). See also the catalogues and publications of the collections of arms and armor, e.g., those of London, Paris, Vienna, Madrid, New York—though they contain but very few documents anterior to the fifteenth century, and even to the sixteenth. See also the very abundant literature concerning monumental brasses.

Edmund O. von Lippmann: Zur Geschichte des Schiesspulvers und des Salpeters (Chemiker-Zeitung 1928; Isis 11, 429; 18, 1911).

NOTE ON DINANDERIE

In the fourteenth century the art of making objects in copper, brass, and bronze reached a high level of popularity and quality. It was not by any means new, for bronze work goes back to prehistoric days. The mediaeval craft derived from Roman and Scandinavian examples, and received a Byzantine stimulus at the time of the marriage of princess Theophano with the emperor Otto II in 972 (Introd. 1, 655). It was described with many technical details by Theophile the Priest (XII-1); Theophile also gave the first European account of bell founding.[32]

The art experienced a new efflorescence in Theophile's time, especially in the town of Dinant on the Meuse. Hence the name "dinanderie."[33] Among the earliest monuments of true "dinanderie" are the font of St. Bartholomew in Liége and the so-called censer of Lille, both of which are ascribed to the aurifaber Regnier of Huy (beginning of twelfth cent.). By the middle of the thirteenth century the superiority of the Dinant craftsmen was already proverbial;[34] their alliance with the Hanseatic League (Introd. 2, 1063) made it possible for the Dinantais to procure copper and tin more easily and to distribute their own wares. There was no copper and tin in their immediate neighborhood, but an abundance of calamine (a hydrous zinc silicate), which proved very handy for the making of brass. Unfortunately the "war of the cow" which broke out in 1273 between Namur and Liége, and the savage rivalry between Dinant and Bouvigne[35] (their neighbor across the Meuse), jeopardized the leadership of Dinant. By the end of the fourteenth century, it was over; the craft was already developed in many other places, but the name dinanderie immortalized the city where it had reached a new climax.

Here are a few examples illustrating the diffusion of the art in various countries. Consider bronze doors.[36] There were built in 1300 the outside gates of San Marco, Venice, by Bertuccio; in 1330 the wonderful southern door of the baptistery of Florence, by Andrea Pisano; in 1335 the door of Hagia Sophia cathedral of Nov-

[32] I leave out of account in this chapter the independent tradition of similar arts in the Far East, but I may recall the gigantic Daibutsu or statue of Buddha Dainichi-nyorai (Birushana-butsu), 16 m. high, erected at Nara in 750 (Introd. 1, 515), and another one, 15 m. high, erected at Kamakura in 1252. There was nothing comparable in Western countries. William Gowland: The art of casting bronze in Japan (Smithsonian Report for 1894, p. 609–51, 7 pl.). Papinot (p. 62, 1909). A. Lloyd (ERE 4, 388–90, 1912).

For Korean bells, see E. M. Cable (Transactions Korea branch, Royal Asiatic Society, 16, 1–45, 53, 1925), with map.

[33] Our language testifies to the excellence of other wares of the southern Netherlands: arras (Italian, arazzo) for tapestries from Arras; cambric for finely woven linen from Cambrai.

[34] Yet even then admirable monuments had already been produced in other places. Let me cite only the magnificent lion in the Burg Platz of Brunswick. It is said to have been erected in 1166 by Henry the Lion (restored 1616, 1858). It was probably made by Saxon craftsmen. A copy of it may be seen in the courtyard of the Germanic Museum, Cambridge, Mass. Ancient bronzes are not in question.

[35] Bouvigne controlled the production of derle, a kind of clay, which the brass potters (potiers d'airain) needed.

[36] The inclusion of bronze doors in this chapter may be objected to, the word "dinanderie" being generally restricted to movable objects. If so, doors and also bells would be excluded. Moreover, there is a continuous tradition of bronze doors throughout the Middle Ages, going back to prototypes in the Pantheon of Rome (27 B.C.) and Hagia Sophia in Constantinople (early sixth cent.). No harm is done, however, in enumerating here the outstanding bronze doors of the fourteenth century.

gorod;[37] in 1337 the door of the cathedral of Toledo; in 1377 the door of Cordova, and probably before the end of the century the Puerta del perdon of Seville.

Bells of large size began to be made in the thirteenth century, and in the following century they became very numerous. Every parish church had one or two, and every cathedral at least six; moreover, cities of importance had their own bells, sometimes very large, hanging in a church tower or in a special belfry. Unfortunately, very few of those early bells have escaped the vicissitudes of time. Their metal was often used for the casting of new bells or of guns.

Monumental brasses, that is, brass sheets placed over tombs or against the walls of churches, date back to the thirteenth century, but they remain very exceptional in that century. Many more were made in the fourteenth century, and they continued to be made in the fifteenth and sixteenth; then the decadence set in. The golden age is the fourteenth century. They were exceedingly numerous in England, where some 4,000 exist to this day plus about as many matrices (i.e., hollows cut in a stone to receive the plate); a large number were lost in the great fire of London. The language used on the English brasses was first Norman French; later, Latin.

The earliest brass in England was to the memory of Simon de Beauchamp, earl of Bedford (d. c. 1208); it still existed in the sixteenth century, for John Leland (d. 1552) saw and described it. The oldest English brass in existence is that of Sir John d'Aubernon (1277) at Stoke Dabernon, Surrey; the oldest brass of a woman is that of Margarete de Camoys (1310) at Trotton, Sussex. The oldest continental brasses known to me are those of bishop Ysowilpe (1231) in Verden and of Otto of Brunswick (1279) in Hildesheim, both in Hannover. A number of very beautiful fourteenth-century brasses are illustrated by Creeny and in the other books cited below. The art began in Flanders and Germany, and many of the English brasses were of foreign origin, or else brass sheets were imported and engraved by English artists. Some of the best English brasses of the fourteenth century were made abroad (Macklin p. 84, 1907); the art was given international scope by the Hanseatic League, for many of the brasses (e.g., those dating from 1356 to 1361) represent Hanseatic merchants; these brasses come probably from the same workshop, yet are dispersed in England and the continent.

Select bibliography concerning monumental brasses. Charles Boutell: Monumental brasses and slabs (252 p., ill., London 1847). W. F. Creeny: Book of facsimiles of monumental brasses of the continent of Europe (large folio, London 1884), examples dating from 1231 to the end of the sixteenth century; there are 2 examples of the thirteenth century (1231, 1279), 22 of the fourteenth century. Herbert W. Macklin: The brasses of England (356 p., ill., London 1907); Monumental brasses (6th ed., 194 p., ill., London 1913; first published in 1890). Edward T. Beaumont: Ancient memorial brasses (214 p., ill., London 1913). Mill Ste-

[37] As no information about that beautiful door is available except in Russian books, the following details may be welcome. It was ordered by the archbishop St. Basil of Novgorod and bears the date 6844 (= 1335) on itself; it is mentioned in the Novgorod letopis under 6844 (= 1336). It was moved in 1570 by order of Ivan the Terrible to Aleksandrovskaya Sloboda (now Aleksandrov, govt. of Vladimir, c. 50 miles northeast of Moscow), where it was placed in the Trinity Cathedral, Ouspenskii convent. The images on the panels of the door are in the Novgorod style, similar to that of Ignatios the Greek (fl. 1338), a Novgorod iconographer. The door is reproduced as no. 33 in section VI of the atlas of Drevnosti rossiiskago gosudarstva (Antiquities of the Russian empire) and described as no. 32 in section VI of the text volume (p. 72–84, Moscow 1853).

phenson: List of monumental brasses in the British Isles (734 p., London 1926), very elaborate list arranged by counties but without chronological summaries.

Many woolmen of the Cotswold (in Gloucestershire; the most important wool district in the fifteenth century) are commemorated by beautiful and typical brasses which testify to the importance of the mediaeval wool trade in England. Power (p. 49–51, 1941).

For dinanderies in general, I have used chiefly J. Tavenor-Perry: Dinanderie, a history and description of mediaeval art work in copper, brass and bronze (quarto, 250 p., 48 pl., 71 drawings, London 1910).

6. DEVELOPMENT OF PRINTING IN THE EAST

BLOCK PRINTING IN THE FAR EAST AND CENTRAL ASIA

It may seem strange to devote a special section to the art of printing, considering that that art was already so old in the fourteenth century that the appearance of new printed books was taken for granted all over Buddhist Asia (a very large part of the world) and was mentioned without surprise and without comment.

Block printing began in China perhaps as early as the sixth century; it was certainly established there by the middle of the eighth century, for by the end of that century it had already been spread on the wings of Buddhism as far as Japan. The earliest printed documents in existence (outside of textiles) are Buddhist charms printed c. 770 by order of the empress Shōtoku. The intimate connection[38] of printing with Buddhism is proved by the fact that the earliest printed books extant or definitely known are various Chinese translations of the Prajñāpāramitā (or Diamond sūtra)—the earliest of all dated May 11, 868, the second printed in 1016, others in 1157 and 1189. The edition of 1157 was one of the earliest books printed in Japan, but not (as was said by Carter, p. 207, 1925) the earliest. After the empress Shōtoku's Dharani of 770, the earliest printed work is Bussetsu rokuji shinju ōkyō, printed before 1053. A chapter of the Lotus sūtra was printed before 1080. The first dated Buddhist work in Chinese translation printed in Japan is the Jyō-yuishiki ron,[39] as translated by Hsüan Tsang (VII-1); it was in ten volumes and the printing was completed in 1088. Copies of vols. 1, 2, 5–10 are preserved in the Shōsō-in of Nara; the purpose of the edition, its date, the names of the sponsor and wood engraver are given in the postscript. The earliest edition extant in Japan of the Diamond sūtra is dated eleventh month of 1247.

Books were probably printed in Buddhist monasteries in the way that is still practiced in Tibetan lamaseries; that is, every year, or more often if necessary, as many impressions are taken from the blocks as have been ordered or may be needed in the near future. In other words, books were printed in the same manner that positives are taken from photographic films today.

The Buddhists were not alone in using the new art for the diffusion of their philosophy. The Confucians and Taoists imitated their example. For example, in 932 the prime minister Fêng Tao (X-1) had ordered the preparation of a standard

[38] That connection was very close but not exclusive, not even in the beginning. As early as 835 an imperial edict ordered that the private printing of calendars be stopped. Two dictionaries, the T'ang yün (or Kuang yün) and the Yü p'ien, were printed in 865, that is, three years before the Diamond sūtra (Peake p. 15, 1935). For the history of printed herbals or pên ts'ao, the earliest of which was dated 973, see chapter X. (Isis 33, 439–42.) It is possible that the Buddhist examples of early printing were the only ones to survive because they were more abundant.

[39] That is, the Vidyāmātrasiddhi (Nanjio no. 1197), called in Chinese Ch'êng wei shih lun.

edition of the Classics; that edition, including text and commentary, was completed in 130 volumes in 953.[40] A rival edition was printed at about the same time in Ssŭch'uan. Collections of the dynastic histories were also issued. The Buddhist patrology (1,521 works covering some 5,000 chüan, 130,000 pages) was printed c. 972; the Taoist patrology appeared only c. 1016.

The edition of the Classics printed in 953 was prepared under the auspices of the Han-lin yüan, the academy which had preserved Chinese traditions since the days of Ming Huang (VIII-1) in spite of every vicissitude.

A government printing press was established during the southern Sung dynasty (c. 1236), and that institution was improved under the Mongols, especially by order of Kublai Khān (XIII-2). Kublai reorganized the government press in Khānbaliq, and in 1293 he integrated its activities with those of the Han-lin yüan. Perhaps I should say "he perfected the integration," for the edition of the Classics of 953, above mentioned, suggests that the press and the academy were then already cooperating. Thanks to Kublai's interest in printing, all the blocks obtained in Kiangsi or in Hangchow after the defeat of the Sung rulers were taken to Khānbaliq and the potential stock of books was thus considerably increased. Moreover, Kublai ordered the printing of books in Mongolian as well as in Chinese. Thus before the end of the thirteenth century printing not only was practiced, it was practiced on a gigantic scale, and had been thus practiced for centuries under the auspices of religious and also of civil authorities.

Similar remarks apply to Korea, where printing began about the middle of the tenth century and where the Chinese classics were issued in such beautiful editions as to awaken the covetousness of the Sung emperors; they apply even more to Japan, where the printing art was very quickly and energetically consecrated to the diffusion of Confucian and Buddhist ideals. The immense Tripiṭaka was already printed in Japan by 1288. It is typical of the derivative nature of Japanese civilization that the early Japanese printing was exclusively in Chinese, and we have to wait until 1321 for a text including a Japanese syllabary.

To return to the mainland, by the beginning of the fourteenth century some scientific books were already printed, for example, an edition of the Ching shih chêng lei ta kuan pên ts'ao in 1302.[41] Moreover, the new art had been applied for a considerable time to a lay, commercial purpose, namely the issuance of bank notes. The earliest Chinese reference to paper money goes back to 807, but it is not clear whether that money was printed; by the tenth century, however, that is, by Fêng Tao's time, we are practically sure that it was actually printed, and by the end of the same century the amount of paper money in circulation was already enormous. From 1035 on, paper money was printed from metal blocks (Lo Chên-yü, 1914; Peake p. 60, 1939). In 1068, we hear for the first time of counterfeit bills. By that time the circulation of paper money was so large that it was difficult to keep it at par. Wang An-shih (XI-2) revised the financial system and began the fight against inflation which exercised the mind of so many Chinese statesmen after him. In 1294, the Chinese invention was for the first time used in a foreign country,

[40] The printing of the Classics by private parties was prohibited until 1064 (Peake p. 13, 1935). This suggests that the Chinese were from the first as anxious to standardize these canonic texts as to diffuse them. It also suggests that private editions had been either published or attempted.

[41] For which see Introd. 2, 248. The edition of 1302 is Chinese, not Korean, but it was reprinted at least twice in Korea, and the Korean editions have been mistaken for the Chinese one from which they are derived. Courant (3, nos. 2494, 2495, 1896).

when paper money (ch'ao) was printed in Tabrīz;[42] this being the first occurrence of printing in Islām. There are various references to Chinese paper money in Western writings by William de Rubruquis (XIII-2), Roger Bacon (XIII-2), Marco Polo (XIII-2), Hayton the Monk, Odoric of Pordenone, Pegolotti (the last three of XIV-1), Ibn Baṭṭūṭa (XIV-2), but the references are not clear with regard to printing, as distinguished from the use of seals. Even those who saw and handled that money (e.g., Marco Polo) did not notice its most important characteristic from the technical point of view. (We never see but what we know.) It is strange that the earliest extant specimens of Chinese paper money date only from the rule of the first Ming emperor, Hung Wu (1366–99), i.e., probably from the year 1375, date of the only recorded issue of paper money during that rule.[43]

Issues of paper money occurred in Japan in 1319, 1327 (Carter p. 77).

Though the Western writers, whether Christian or Muslim, failed to give a clear account of printing, such an account was given by two Eastern historians of our period, both writing in Persian. The first was Rashīd al-dīn (d. 1318) and the second was Dā'ūd al-Banākatī (d. 1329). As the latter copied from the former, these two accounts are but a single one; it is so remarkable that we beg leave to reproduce it here (after Browne 3, 102, 1920). Al-Banākatī, having explained the care with which the Chinese compile their annals, added:

"Then, according to a custom which they have, they were wont and still continue to make copies from that book in such wise that no change or alteration can find its way into the text. And therefore when they desire that any book containing matter of value to them should be well written and should remain correct, authentic and unaltered, they order a skilful calligraphist to copy a page of that book on a tablet in a fair hand. Then all the men of learning carefully correct it, and inscribe their names on the back of the tablet. Then skilled and expert engravers are ordered to cut out the letters. And when they have thus taken a copy of all the pages of the book, numbering all [the blocks] consecutively, they place these tablets in sealed bags, like the dies in a mint, and entrust them to reliable persons appointed for this purpose, keeping them securely in offices specially set apart to this end on which they set a particular and definite seal. Then when anyone wants a copy of this book he goes before this committee and pays the dues and charges fixed by the Government. Then they bring out these tablets, impose them on leaves of paper like the dies used in minting gold, and deliver the sheets to him. Thus it is impossible that there should be any addition or omission in any of their books, on which, therefore, they place complete reliance; and thus is the transmission of their histories effected."

This description is significant not only because of its clearness, but also because it confirms our remarks concerning the printing business in Tibet, and above all because the value of printing as a means of standardization of a text is so well understood. We might assume that in the East just as later in the West, the practical value of the art, as a means of producing more copies with less time and effort than is otherwise possible, a wholesale method, would have been perceived long

[42] Tabrīz was then under Mongol rule. It is not surprising that the provincial khān (īl-khān) ruling Persia imitated the great khān ruling China.

[43] Illustrated in Carter (p. 73, 1925). Carter's ch. 11 (p. 70–81) is entirely devoted to the printing of paper money. Specimens of these ch'ao of c. 1375 are in the British Museum and in the Society of Numismatics, New York.

before its spiritual value, as a means of preserving the integrity of a text. Yet Rashīd al-dīn and al-Banākatī emphasize standardization rather than diffusion. It is true that printing as practiced then and there did not reveal its economical feature at once. The engraving of the blocks (in reverse) must have cost a large amount of skilled labor; the identity of the copies struck from those blocks must have been immediately apparent, but the economy of time would begin only when and if a sufficient number of copies were gradually required. This may help us to understand why Rashīd al-dīn did not use the Chinese method which he knew so well for the diffusion of his own writings. He was perhaps too much in a hurry; he was aware that scribes could work considerably faster than wood engravers, and he was perhaps too trustful in their accuracy.[44]

BLOCK PRINTING IN EGYPT

About the year 1880, excavations made in al-Madīna (Madīnat al-Faiyūm, ancient Arsinoë or Crocodilopolis) brought to light a great many documents (more than 100,000 sheets and fragments of papyrus, parchment, and paper) which now constitute the Archduke Rainer Collection in the National Library of Vienna. These documents, written in ten languages, date from the fourteenth century B.C. to the fourteenth century after Christ. The paper documents date from c. 796 to 1388; the last papyrus document dates from 936.

Some 50 fragments of the Rainer Collection show evidence of block printing. Similar fragments are available in the museums of Heidelberg, Berlin, and Cairo. One of the Heidelberg block prints is on parchment; all the other Egyptian block prints are on paper. All are written in the Arabic language and in the Arabic script (except for a single Arabic prayer transliterated in the Coptic alphabet). They can be dated on epigraphic grounds from 900 to 1350, most of them belonging to the latter part of that period. The printing technique appears to be similar to that of China and Central Asia. That is, these documents were probably printed not by means of a press, but by being laid on the block and rubbed with a brush or pad.

The contents of all are religious (verses from the Qur'ān, prayers, 99 names of God, charms); in this respect the Egyptian block prints are similar to the earliest Asiatic ones. Buddhism brought the latter, and Islām the former, into existence. The Egyptian printing art stopped, however, in the fourteenth century, and, the Islamic attitude toward printing having in the meanwhile become inimical (Isis 33, 561), no more printing was done by Muslims (except in China) until 1825, and the printing of the Qur'ān was frowned upon until our own days. The whole period of Egyptian block printing was anterior to the Western one. It may have been due to Turkish influences, for there were many Turks in Central Asia familiar with printing, and there were also many Turks in Egypt, the Mamlūk dynasty being Turkish.

Carter (p. 133–38, 240–41, 1925). Giorgio Levi Della Vida: An Arabic block print (Scientific monthly 59, 473–74, 1944), apropos of his discovery of a fourteenth-century block print in the Museum of the University of Pennsylvania.

[44] As Oriental secretaries were trained to copy line for line and page for page, they were less inaccurate than we would imagine. On the other hand, the engraving of the text in reverse was simpler than we would think. It was probably done in this way. The text was written by a good calligraphist on a sheet of thin paper, which was then pasted face down on a block of wood. The engraver would see the text in reverse and his knife would follow the lines as he saw them.

DEVELOPMENT OF TYPOGRAPHY IN CHINA

Western scholars inclined to belittle Eastern achievements may object that hitherto we have spoken only of block printing (chiefly xylography), not of printing as that art has generally been understood since the middle of the fifteenth century. To this we may answer, first, that block printing was not developed in Western lands until the second half of the fourteenth century, that is, at least six centuries and perhaps eight centuries later than in China. And second, that typography, i.e., printing with movable type, though not quite as old as block printing, was invented in China as early as the eleventh century. That invention is ascribed to Pi Shêng (XI-1), and we have an accurate description of it by his younger contemporary Shên Kua (XI-2). The text as translated by Carter (p. 160) is worth reproducing:[45]

"During the period Ch'ing-li (1041–1049) Pi Shêng, a man in cotton cloth (i.e., a man of the common people), made also movable type. His method was as follows: He took sticky clay and cut in it characters as thin as the edge of a cash. Each character formed as it were a single type. He baked them in the fire to make them hard. He had previously prepared an iron plate and he had covered this plate with a mixture of pine resin, wax and paper ashes. When he wished to print, he took an iron frame and set it on the iron plate. In this he placed the type, set close together. When the frame was full, the whole made one solid block of type. He then placed it near the fire to warm it. When the paste [at the back] was slightly melted, he took a perfectly smooth board and rubbed over the surface, so that the block of type became as even as a whetstone.

"If one were to print only two or three copies this method would be neither convenient nor quick. But for printing hundreds or thousands of copies, it was marvellously (lit. 'divinely') quick. As a rule he kept two forms going. While the impression was being made from the one form, the type were being put in place on the other. When the printing of the one form was finished, the other was all ready. In this way the two forms alternated and the printing was done with great rapidity.

"For each character there were several type, and for certain common characters there were twenty or more type each, in order to be prepared for the repetition of characters on the same page. When the characters were not in use, he had them arranged with paper labels, one label for each rhyme, and thus kept them in wooden cases. If any rare character appeared that had not been prepared in advance, it was cut as needed and baked with [a fire of] straw. In a moment it was finished.

"The reason why he did not use wood is because the tissue of wood is sometimes coarse and sometimes fine, and wood also absorbs moisture, so that the form when set up would be uneven. Also the wood would have stuck in the paste and could not readily have been pulled out. So it was better to use burnt earthenware. When the printing was finished, the form was again brought near the fire to allow the paste to melt, and then brushed with the hand, so that the type fell of themselves and were not in the least soiled with clay.

"When Pi Shêng died, his font of type passed into the possession of my followers, and up to this time it has been kept as a precious possession."

We have no record of comparable clearness explaining the first experiments made by Western typographers four centuries later.

After these experiments with clay and wood, an unknown Chinese inventor used

[45] For annotations to the text see Carter (p. 251–52).

type of tin, perforated and held in place by a wire; then these investigations were apparently abandoned. One should bear in mind that a language like Chinese, the writing of which necessitates many thousands of different characters, lends itself much less to typography than a language like Latin, the printing of which required only about one hundred and fifty characters.[46] Chinese typography would need considerable technical elaboration before it would be able to supersede xylography. It is thus not so surprising that nothing more is heard of the typographical art until c. 1314, when Wang Chên experimented again with metal and wooden type and devised a system of revolving type cases to contain, within easy reach of the typesetter, the innumerable characters which might be needed (see fig. 20). His great work on agriculture, Nung shu, was actually printed in 1314 with wooden movable type, but Wang Chên had already printed another work before that date. The revolving type case was a natural development of a much earlier Chinese invention, the lun tsang[47] (Japanese, rin-zō) or revolving repository, a kind of revolving library said to have been invented in 544 by Fu hsi (497–569). It is an eight-angled bookcase revolving around a vertical axis.

The reality of Wang Chên's invention, or reinvention, of typography has been proved by Pelliot's discovery of just such wooden type dating from c. 1300 in one of the caves of Tun-huang. Pelliot found hundreds of them, most of them in perfect condition, made of hard wood, of exactly the same height and depth. That type answers Wang's description in every particular, except one: it does not reproduce Chinese characters, but Uighūr *words*. This last detail is interesting; the Uighūr printer who had adapted the Chinese invention had not thought of extending it to the new possibilities of his own (alphabetic) language and of using it for the printing of separate letters, not simply of separate words as is unavoidable in Chinese.

As to the books printed with movable type, Wang's own treatise on agriculture, printed in 1314, has already been mentioned. There is also a Korean edition of Confucius' domestic talk (the title reads in Chinese Piao t'i yüan ping shih), said to have been printed with movable type in 1317–24. Courant, however (1, no. 229, 1894) maintains that that book was engraved, not set in type, and that the date is not trustworthy, Koreans having often reprinted Chinese books exactly as they were, i.e., with the original Chinese date, the reprint itself being undated. The evidence given by the books themselves is thus insufficient.

Nevertheless the accumulated evidence converging from the literary, archaeological, and bibliographical angles leads to the conclusion that typography was reinvented in China in the first quarter of the fourteenth century, and that it was practiced during that period, in China and also perhaps in Korea.[48]

[46] That is, about 150 for each size, because the early printers inherited from the scribes all kinds of ligatures, and did not think of using the same letter in every combination of letters (as we do) until much later! This story is well told by Pierce Butler: The origin of printing in Europe (p. 55–57, Chicago 1940; Isis 33, 95). The same aberration continues to this day in Arabic printing. It is one of the merits of the late Aḥmad Zakī pāshā (1867–1934) to have reduced considerably the Arabic font; he more than halved it. See article by Joseph Schacht on him (Al-mustami' al-'arabī vol. 4, no. 23, March 7, 1944).

[47] The name lun tsang is given to the building containing the revolving bookcase as well as to the bookcase itself. Nanjio (p. xxv, 1883).

[48] The first mention of movable type in the Korean annals, Kao-li-shih, refers to the year 1392. A library bureau was established in that year in Seoul and an officer appointed in charge of casting metal type and printing. Unfortunately these efforts were interrupted and the organization of printing with movable type was completed only in the second month of 1403. See chapter XXI.

Carter (1925). Carter's account was excellent, but new knowledge has accumulated since 1925 (the edition of 1931 was hardly more than a reprint). Cyrus H. Peake: The origin and development of printing in China in the light of recent research (Gutenberg Jahrbuch, 1935, p. 9–17); Additional notes (ibid. 1939, p. 57–61). Judson Daland: The evolution of modern printing and the discovery of movable metal type by the Chinese and the Koreans in the fourteenth century (Journal of the Franklin Institute vol. 212, p. 209–34, 1931; T'oung Pao 29, 164).

K. Kawase: Ko katsuji-bon no kenkyu (2 vols., Tokyo 1937), in Japanese. Vol. 1, 800 p., discusses the history of printing in China, Korea, Japan, special attention being paid to Japanese typography; vol. 2 reproduces early printed pages, mainly Japanese.

T'ieh chin tung chien lou Sung Chin Yüan pen shu ying (9 vols., Ch'angshu, Kiangsu 1922), in Chinese. Facsimiles of Sung, Chin, and Yüan printing (960–1361).

Lo Chên-yü (1866–1940): Szŭ-ch'ao ch'ao-pi t'u-lu (s.l., 1914), in Chinese, history of printed bank notes from 1213 to 1911, with many illustrations.

7. HYDROSTATICS

DE INSIDENTIBUS AQUAE

A short text bearing this title is included in a MS of the beginning of the fourteenth century belonging to the Dresden library (Cod. Dresd. Db 86, fol. 272–74). Starting from the Archimedean principle, it deals with the possibility of determining the proportions of the different constituents of an alloy or mixture by means of specific gravity measurements. It is derived from the περὶ ὀχουμένων of Archimedes (Isis 22, 325), known to the author in the Latin translation made by William of Moerbeke (XIII-2) in 1269. No source is indicated, however. It is divided into ten propositions.

Text. Edited by Maximilian Curtze: Ein Beitrag zur Geschichte der Physik im 14. Jahrh. (BM 1896, p. 43–49).

8. CANALS

The history of canals has never been written with any attempt at completeness, and information concerning the canals of the Old World must be hunted for in local histories and annals, or in archives. Some canals go back to ancient times; e.g., the one connecting the Red Sea with an eastern branch of the Nile may be traced back to the sixth century B.C. (Introd. 1, 78, 571), a canal across the Athos peninsula to the fifth century B.C. (1, 95), a Chinese canal to the second half of the third century B.C. (1, 168), the canal of Corinth to the second half of the first century (1, 247). The thirteenth century was as great an age from the point of view of canals and waterworks as from many others; e.g., the Naviglio Grande of Milano and the mole and aqueduct of Genoa belong to that century (Introd. 2, 299, 406), and the Grand Canal of China, reaching a total length of 1,200 miles, was completed by the end of it (2, 765, 981, 1058). I do not know of any canal which was built in the fourteenth century, but it is improbable that that tradition was completely interrupted during that period.

Locks and sluices have also a very long history. Some may go back to antiquity. It is probable, however, that as long as ships were relatively small and light it was often easier to move them from one water level to another by dragging them along an inclined plane. An example is the δίολκος, slipway for passage of ships across the isthmus of Corinth, thrice mentioned by Strabo (I-2 B.C.) in his Geography.[49] According to Feldhaus (col. 962, 1914) some Dutch sluices were built in the thirteenth century; he refers to one established near Amsterdam in 1220, and another, a "Kammerschleuse" or lock, built at Spaarndam, near Haarlem, in 1253 by Willem II, count of Holland (1228–56). It is curious that locks bring us back to the thirteenth century, not the fourteenth. The next mentions of them belong to the fifteenth century, that is, the locks (sostegni, conche) built near Bologna in 1439 by Fioravante of Bologna and Filippo degli Organi of Modena, and the description given by Leon Battista Alberti (1404–72). The conche of Fioravante are the earliest locks about which we have definite if slight information; and Alberti gave the first clear description of locks. On that account Alberti has sometimes been called their inventor; the invention is certainly anterior to him, perhaps much so.

9. MECHANICAL THEORIES

CEFFONS

Pierre Ceffons (de Ceffona). Cistercian monk in Clairvaux (d. 1351?). Author of a commentary on the Sentences.

That commentary is interesting from the mechanical and the astronomical point of view. In book II, query 4, he questions commonly accepted opinions, such as the finity and uniqueness of the world, and the rotation of celestial spheres by intelligences, and ends by denying them. So far as the motion of the spheres is concerned, he finds it easier to account for it by means of a material motor, or a force inherent in the spheres, than by means of intelligences (Octava conclusio: non est naturali ratione convincente omnem protervum sufficienter probatum, quod alica intelligentia moveat orbes). In the following query, Ceffons gathers all the objections to the diurnal motion of the earth and refutes them (even as Oresme, XIV-2). He concludes that the theory of the diurnal motion of the earth is not true, though the opposite theory is unproved (!?).

Criticism. I know of him only through a brief reference in Chevalier (col. 3701, 1907) and a single page in Michalski (p. 155, 1927). His name puzzles me. There is a place called Ceffonds in Haute-Marne.

SWINESHEAD

Richard Swineshead. English mathematician, physicist, and philosopher (fl. 1337–48).

Richard (not Roger) Swineshead, or Swinshed, Suisset, Suicet, Suiseth, etc. The form Ricardus de Ghlymi Eshedi found by Duhem in a single MS is very probably a corruption of the same name. He was often called Calculator, from the title of his main work.

Probably born in Glastonbury, Somersetshire; educated at Merton College, Oxford, where he took part in a riot in 1348. Later he assumed the Cistercian habit in Swineshead, Lincolnshire.

He wrote Quaestiones in Sententias; commentaries on the Ethics of Aristotle and on the De coelo et mundo; Descriptiones motuum (De motu coeli et similibus;

[49] VIII, 2, 1; VIII, 6, 4; VIII, 6, 22 (Loeb ed., by Horace Leonard Jones, 4, 13, 155, 197, 1927). In the first passage, Strabo states that the isthmus measured 40 stadia along the diolkos: ὁ δ'ἰσθμὸς κατὰ τὸν διολκόν, δι' οὗ τὰ πορθμεῖα ὑπερνεωλκοῦσιν ἀπὸ τῆς ἑτέρας εἰς τὴν ἑτέραν θάλατταν, εἴρηται ὅτι τετταράκοντα σταδίων ἐστίν.

De motibus naturalibus et annexis, Erfurt MS dated 1337); De insolubilibus; etc.; and Calculationes (Calculator). His fame was based almost exclusively on this last-named work, which was printed as early as 1477, many times reprinted and commented upon.

Calculator is not at all a book of calculations, astronomical or otherwise; it deals with the increase and decrease of forms and connected subjects. We may find in it vague anticipations of the graphical representation of functions. Many mathematicians are quoted, the latest being Bradwardine. In spite of Duhem's efforts to give the precedence to Oresme (see Thorndike 3, 374, 1934), it is more probable that Oresme was posterior. A critical edition of the text (which varies in the MSS and printed editions) is much to be desired. Some of the subjects dealt with are: intention or remission of qualities, intentions in difform things, functions of different qualities, rarefaction and density and their variations (what happens if the object considered is infinite?), how are qualities affected by the speed of change? what is the nature of force, resistance, reaction? does force vary with the amount of form in matter or with its intension or extension? maxima and minima of various kinds, natural position of elements, quantity and intensity of light, local motion, medium without resistance, "inductio gradus summi," etc. In short, Swineshead tackled awkwardly many of the fundamental questions of mechanics and physics, introducing new abstractions, which were not very fertile yet stimulated thought.

One of the problems discussed by him may be taken to be comparable to the summation of the infinite series

$$\frac{1}{2} + \frac{2}{4} + \frac{3}{8} + \cdots + \frac{n}{2^n} + \cdots = 2$$

and his argument about it is a kind of adumbration of the proof of the convergence[50] of an infinite series.

It is interesting to note that the terms fluxus and fluens used by the Calculator (and other fourteenth- and fifteenth-century writers) are the prototypes of the terms used more than three centuries later by Newton (1655) in his theory of fluxions (the fluxion being the rate of change of the fluent).[50a]

The interest aroused by Swineshead's discussions is proved by a whole series of other writings of the same kind, as well as by the reactions of many later writers. For example, Pico della Mirandola spoke of the quisquiliae Suiceticae (S.'s rubbish), and most humanists, if they read him at all, disposed of his difficulties in the same easy manner.[51] On the other hand, Bassanus Politus published in Venice 1505 a Tractatus proportionum introductorius ad Calculationes Suiset; Alvarus Thomas of Lisbon published in Paris 1509 a Liber de triplici motu proportionibus annexis Suiseth Calculationes ex parte declarans; in Bologna 1514, Pietro Pomponazzi of Mantua (1462–1525) published his De intensione et remissione formarum, criticizing Swineshead, and he aggravated his criticism in the following year in his De reactione (Bologna 1515); about 1520, Raggio of Florence wrote another treatise

[50] The notions of convergence and divergence of series were introduced only in 1667 by James Gregory (Osiris 1, 531, 563, 1936).

[50a] I am not sure that Newton obtained those terms from Swineshead or from other mediaeval writers. He, or his teacher Isaac Barrow before him, might have obtained them directly from the Greek. Fluxio is the same as ῥύσις, used as a mathematical term by Iamblichos (IV-1) and Proclos (V-2).

[51] E.g., Juan Luis Vives (1492–1540), for whom see Duhem: Etudes (3, 170, 1913).

with the same purpose. The great mathematician Gerolamo Cardano (1501–76) included Swineshead among the twelve greatest thinkers of all time.[52] That accidental praise affected many later writers of the seventeenth century and even of the eighteenth. The most astounding echo of it is found in Leibniz' letter to Thomas Smith (1696), "Vellem etiam edi scripta Suisseti vulgo dicti Calculatoris qui mathesin in philosophiam scholasticam introduxit."[53] In the absence of any positive and tangible achievement, it is impossible to estimate the value of Swineshead's gropings in the dark. One might give him unlimited credit or none at all. To those who would object that it is meritorious to raise questions, even if one cannot answer them, we must answer that Swineshead's questions were not well put; they lacked precision and missed the point.

Text. The Calculations were first edited by John of Cyprus (Padua s.a., probably 1477, not 1485). Later editions: Pavia 1498, Venice 1520. See Klebs (no. 943).
Criticism. Prantl (4, 90, 1870), simple reference. C. L. Kingsford (DNB 55, 231, 1898). Cantor (2, 122, 1899). J. Timtchenko: Sur un point du Tractatus de latitudinibus formarum de Nicolas Oresme (BM 1, 515, 1900; also p. 503, 504). Duhem: Etudes (vol. 3, 1913). Adolf Krazer: Zur Geschichte der graphischen Darstellung von Funktionen (Jahresbericht der deutschen Mathematiker-Vereinigung 24, 340–63, Leipzig 1915 [1916]; Isis 4, 138). Michalski (p. 47, 79, 1925a). Thorndike (3, 370–85, 1934). Carl B. Boyer: The concepts of the calculus (New York 1939; Isis 32, 205–10). Marshall Clagett: Note on the Tractatus physici falsely ascribed to Giovanni Marliani (Isis 34, 168, 1942); this is really a copy of Swineshead's Liber calculationum; professor Marliani, commentator on Ibn Sīnā, physician and physicist, died in Milano 1483. Klebs (nos. 664–66).

FRANCIS OF MARCHIA

Francisco da Pignano (in the Marche), Franciscus Picenus. Italian Franciscan, theologian and physicist (fl. 1320).

He lectured on the Sentences in Paris 1320. In the first quaestio of book IV, under the misleading title "Utrum in sacramentis est aliqua virtus supernaturalis . . . eis formaliter inhaerens," he devotes two articles to the discussion of impetus or impulsus (which he calls virtus motiva). The virtus motiva of a projectile, he claims, is caused, not by the airy medium, but by the initial impulsion (e.g., of the hand which has thrown it); yet he concedes that the medium may help somehow in maintaining the motion. Marsilius of Inghen (XIV-2), though more radical than Francis, was still willing to make the same concession. Francis had reached that conclusion (against the Aristotelians) because his theory was simpler, more economical, and the only one adequate to explain why the motion of a projectile can be sometimes independent of the air and why a heavy body moves more strongly than a light one; he concludes that it is more correct to say that the air is moved by the projectile than that the projectile is moved by the air.

What is even more remarkable, he extends that theory to the celestial bodies, which move because of the initial impulsion which God gave them. Since then they have continued to move without cease, because of a kind of inertia. In this,

[52] The others being (in chronological order) Archytas of Tarentum, Aristotle, Euclid, Archimedes, Apollonios, Vitruvius, Galen, al-Khwārizmī, al-Kindī, Jābir ibn Aflaḥ, Duns Scotus; that is, six Greeks, one Roman, three Arabs, and two Latins, including Swineshead (De subtilitate XVI, 568–71, Lyon 1580).

[53] As quoted by Thorndike (3, 370, 1934).

the extension of sublunar mechanics to the heavenly regions, Francis anticipated Buridan.

Francis and Buridan also agree in considering the initial impulsion as a distinct quality (or accidental form) different from the ensuing motion. Occam did not share that opinion.

Criticism. Michalski (p. 140–42, 1927).

GIOVANNI DA CASALE

Joannes de Casali. Italian Franciscan, physicist (fl. 1346–75).

Little is known about this John. He was a native of Montferrat, which may probably be identified with Casale Monferrato in the province of Alexandria, Piedmont. He entered the Franciscan order and became doctor in theology. In 1375, Gregory XI (pope 1370–78) sent him on an embassy to Frederick king of Trinacria (Frederick III of Aragon, king of Sicily 1355–77).[54]

We quote him here simply as the author of a query on the velocity of the motion of alteration dated 1346, in a Riccardian MS of Florence, "Utrum in mobilibus (moventibus) ad qualitatem id semper velocius moveatur quod in equali tempore acquirit maiorem latitudinem qualitatis . . . ," which was printed in Venice 1505 together with similar treatises on "modes," "proportions," "latitudes" by Bassanus Politus, Richard Swineshead, Thomas Bradwardine, Nicolas Oresme (XIV-2), and Biagio Pelacani (XIV-2). That question would deserve to be analyzed in relation to the other treatises.

Text. As indicated above, the Quaestio subtilis de velocitate motus alterationis was printed in Venice 1505, by Scotus. The whole book contains 73 folii; Casali's treatise covers fol. 57–70.

Criticism. Duhem: Etudes (3, 492, 1913). Lynn Thorndike: Vatican Latin MSS in the history of science (Isis 13, 77, no. 50, 1929). Thorndike and Kibre (p. 756, 1937). G. Sarton: John de Casali (query no. 82, Isis 30, 509, 1939). L. Thorndike: Answer to that query (Isis 34, 214, 1943).

JOHN THE CANON

English Franciscan, commentator on Aristotelian physics (fl. 1329).

Joannes Canonicus flourished in Oxford. He is said to have attended lectures of Duns Scot in Paris (that would be before 1308), then to have returned to Oxford, where he became a doctor in divinity.

He wrote quaestiones disputatae, a commentary on the Sentences, and another on Aristotle's Physics. This last work obtained some amount of popularity, witness the number of MSS and at least 8 early printed editions (1475 to 1520).

Discussing the question of vacuum (Quaestiones super Phys. Arist. IV, 4; fol. 42, Venice 1520), he introduces the following argument: If water put in a metal container is allowed to freeze, the frozen water will occupy less space, and hence there will be a vacuum around it. This is denied, not on the ground that water expands instead of contracting when it freezes, but on the ground that such a vacuum could not exist, the container being immediately broken by the strength (the horror vacui) of the whole universe.

Text. John the Canon's questions on Aristotle's Physica were printed together with the questions of John of Jandun (Klebs 553) in Padua 1475, Venice 1481, St.

[54] L. Wadding: Annales minorum (8, 323, xxxvi, 1932).

Albans 1481, Venice 1487, 1492. They are not printed with Jandun's questions in the edition of Venice 1488.

Later editions of John the Canon's questions: Venice 1505, 1516, 1520.

Criticism. R. L. Poole (DNB 8, 445, 1886), giving the floruit date 1329 which I have reproduced, for it is plausible, without justifying it. De Waard (p. 16, 1936).

11. VARIOUS TECHNICAL IMPROVEMENTS AND THEIR SOCIAL IMPORT

See chapter I, p. 150–58.

12. MUSICAL THEORIES

A. In the Latin West

MARCHETTUS

Marchetto of Padua. Italian theorist of music who flourished at Cesena and Verona about the beginning of the fourteenth century. He was for a time in the service of Rainier II Grimaldi, lord of Monaco from 1300 to 1330. He wrote two important musical treatises, the Lucidarium and the Pomerium.

The Lucidarium in arte musicae planae was written in 1274, but revised in or after 1309, being dedicated to Rainier II after the death of Charles II of Anjou in 1309. It is divided into 16 tractatus of very unequal length, and treats the theory of music in general, with special reference to the innovations.

The Pomerium in arte musicae mensuratae is a further treatise on the same subject, a little longer, dedicated to Robert of Anjou, king of Jerusalem and of Naples (1309–43). It often refers to the Lucidarium.

In the Lucidarium the whole tone is divided either into three-fifths and two-fifths (diatonic and enharmonic semitones) or into four-fifths and one-fifth (chromatic semitone and diesis). The Pomerium marks the transition between the Franconian notation (see my note on Franco of Cologne, XII-2, Introd. 2, 406) and the ars nova as explained by Philip of Vitry (d. 1361), wherein the minim and semiminim were differentiated. In the Franconian notation, the shortest musical note was the semibreve (= one-third of a breve). Marchetto introduced various kinds of semibreves, from two to twelve to the breve. His system of notation, being far too complicated, failed to be accepted and was superseded by the simpler method of the traditional ars nova.

He must, however, have attained a modicum of success, because as late as 1425 (rather than 1410) another Paduan, the mathematician and musician Prosdocimo de' Beldomandi (d. 1428), found it necessary to launch a violent attack against him in his Tractatus musice speculative. According to Beldomandi, Marchetto was simply a practician, not a theorist, "Fuit enim vir iste in scientia musice simplex practicus sed a theoria sive speculativa omnino vacuus."

Text. The Lucidarium and Pomerium are both included in Gerbert (3, 64–121, 121–88, 1784).

A summary of the Pomerium, entitled Brevis compilatio magistri Marchetti musici de Padua in arte musica mensurate pro rudibus et modernis, was made in the fourteenth century. It is included in Coussemaker (vol. 3, 1869).

Beldomandi's treatise was edited by D. Raffaello Baralli, with introduction by Luigi Torri (Rivista musicale italiana 20, 707–62, 1913).

Criticism. Giosue Carducci: Musica e poesia nel mondo elegante italiano del secolo XIV (Nuova antologia, 1870; reprinted in Opere, ediz. naz., 9, 295–391, 1936). Melchiorre Balbi: Marchetti de Padua, studio bibliografico analitico (35 p., 1 pl., Padua 1878). Torri's introduction to Beldomandi (1913). J. F. R. Stainer in Grove (3, 320, 1927). Reese (p. 157, 340 f., 371, 381, 1940).

HANDLO

Robert de Handlo. English musician (fl. 1326).

The name is probably derived from the manor of Handlo, now Hadlow, near Tonbridge, Kent. Nothing whatever is known about Robert, except that he wrote in 1326 a commentary on the musical theories of Franco of Cologne (XII-2), entitled Regulae cum maximis magistri Franconis cum additionibus aliorum musicorum, the "other musicians" quoted by him being Petrus de Cruce, Petrus le Viser, John of Garland, Admetus de Aureliana, and Jacobus de Navernia. His quotations are always preceded by the author's name, his own additions by his own. He seems to have borrowed largely from John of Garland (XIII-1; Introd. 2, 695–97), for example the idea of truncation or hocket (ochetus), which, Richard says, is a "combination of notes and pauses"; the name ochetus, derived from the Arabic īqā'āt, suggests the origin of these notions.

Robert's Regulae constitutes an elementary treatise dealing with notation, time values, and the modes of rhythm. It illustrates the unsettled state of the musical notation of that time for notes of less value than the brève. E.g., he follows John of Garland in describing four kinds of semibreves: the major and minor, which are respectively two-thirds and one-third of a perfect breve, and the minorata and minima, which are respectively two-thirds and one-third of the minor. The notations representing these four kinds were rather confusing.

Robert de Handlo was quoted by Thomas Morley (1557–1604?) in the latter's Plaine and easie introduction to practicall musicke (London 1597).

Text. The Regulae were edited by Coussemaker (1, 383–403, 1864).
Criticism. W. Barclay Squire (DNB 24, 291, 1890). J. F. R. Stainer in Grove (2, 518, 1927). H. G. Farmer: Music (Legacy of Islam p. 372, 1931). Reese (p. 289, 331, 414, 1940).

SPECHTSHART

Hugo Spechtshart of Reutlingen. German musician, grammarian, and chronicler (1285–c. 1359).

Hugo Spechtshart or Hugo of Reutlingen (Hugo de Rütlinga) was born in Reutlingen, near Tübingen, Württemberg, in 1285, was educated in Prague (?), and became a priest in his native city. In 1324 and 1338 he continued to sing the mass in spite of the interdict, and was therefore anathematized, but in 1348 bishop Friedrich of Bamberg rehabilitated him together with many others. He made his will in Reutlingen in 1359; the exact date of his death is unknown.

In 1330 he wrote a poem on grammar, Speculum grammaticale metricum; in 1332, a musical treatise; and about 1350, a chronicle in verse.

The musical treatise, Flores musice omnis cantus gregoriani, is a paraphrase of the teachings of Guido of Arezzo (XI-1) in 635 lines of leonine verse. It is divided into four parts, (I) De tribus alphabetis, (II) De monochordo, (III) De modis, (IV) De tonis. It was commented upon by Hugo's nephew, the schoolteacher Conrad

Spechtshart (d. 1395). Judging by the number of MSS and early editions, the Flores musice enjoyed some popularity; it was one of the earliest musical books printed in Germany. The first edition (Strassburg 1488) and presumably the later ones contain a woodcut illustrating the manus guidonica, "Guido's hand," a mnemonic device to aid in remembering the notes of the scale indicated by syllables (Guido's solmization).

The Cronica metrificata is a summary in verse of the history of the Roman emperors from Augustus to Charles IV, divided into two parts. Most of it was completed in 1347, the rest added in 1350. As usual it is worthless, except the end, dealing with contemporary events, and the value even of that part is very small. The Cronica was an easy crambook for clerks, nothing more. Early glosses for the years 1218–1348 have been preserved. The Leningrad MS of the chronicle is very valuable, because it contains songs of the flagellants (Geisslerlieder). Hugo describes the ceremonies upon the flagellants' arrival in a town, their penitential rites, and the farewell procession, each of these ceremonies including songs in the vernacular. In melodic outline these songs or laude foreshadow the Lutheran chorale.

Text. Flores musice (Klebs no. 525), Strassburg 1488, 1490, 1492. Modern edition with German translation by Carl Beck, dean of Reutlingen (Litteratischer Verein, Tübingen 1868).

Cronica first edited by Karl Gillert (Forschungen zur deutschen Geschichte vol. 21, p. 21–65, Göttingen 1881). A. Huber: Excerpta ex expositione Hugonis de Reutlinga in chronicam metricam, in Joh. Friedr. Böhmer: Fontes rerum germanicarum (4, 128–37, 1868).

Criticism. Th. Schön (ADB 35, 77, 1893). Potthast (p. 625, 1896). Zoltán Haraszti (More books 4, 370–71, Boston 1929), describing the first edition of Flores musice, 1488, with Guido's hand. Reese (p. 239, 1940). S. H. Steinberg: The Forma scribendi of Hugo Spechtshart (The Library 21, 264–78, 1941; Isis 35, 227).

VITRY

Philip of Vitry. Philippus de Vitriaco. French theorist of music (1291–1361).

Philip was born at Vitry in Champagne on October 31, 1291. He was secretary to Charles IV le Bel (king of France 1322–28), to Philip VI of Valois (king 1328–50), and to the latter's son John, duke of Normandy, later John II the Good (king 1350–64). He represented the king in various missions, and in 1350 arranged for an interview between him and Clement VI in Avignon. A bishopric was his reward. He was bishop of Meaux from 1351 to his death, in Paris, June 9, 1361.

Philip was a poet, a composer, and a musical theorist. We have only a few lines of his poetry, his compositions are lost, and thus his fame is based almost exclusively on the musical treatises, four of which are ascribed to him: Ars nova, Ars contrapunctus, Ars perfecta, and Liber musicalium. The second and third of these are probably apocryphal.

He was apparently the main theorist of the "ars nova," as the new music was called. This does not mean that the new art was invented by him, or even that he contributed much to its development. It is probable that the influence of contemporary musicians, like the poet Guillaume de Machaut, was greater. And there were other contemporary theorists, but Vitry was perhaps the most famous. He was praised by Petrarca in 1350, who teased him for his love of Paris, by the Champenois poet Eustache Deschamps (XIV-2), and, what is more to the point, by Simon Tunsted (XIV-2), not to speak of later writers who may have been simply repeating the eulogies of their predecessors.

The "ars nova" had enough importance and popularity to cause the issuance of a denunciatory bull by John XXII in 1322.[55] This shows that the "ars nova," opposed to the "ars antiqua," was already sufficiently developed in 1322 to alarm the friends of the traditional "plain song." Without going into technicalities, we might say that the general tendency of the age was to introduce shorter and shorter notes, and this implied the necessity of establishing relations between the notes of various lengths and of inventing symbols for their representation. The ars nova or mensurable music took into account five lengths of notes: large, long, breve, semibreve, and minim, each of which equaled thrice the following (this being called perfect time, probably with reference to the Holy Trinity) or twice the following (imperfect time). The division of the large into longs was called major mode; that of the long into breves, minor mode; that of the breve into semibreves, time; that of the semibreve into minims, prolation. In each case the division could be perfect or imperfect (alias, misleadingly, major or minor). We cannot explain other improvements or complications which the musical historian will recognize under the technical terms augmentation, diminution, alteration, proportion, ligatures.

The result of this overwhelming tendency, which different musicians satisfied in various manner, was the existence by the end of the century of a very intricate notation, new musical subtleties, and corresponding difficulties, in short, of a very confusing situation, out of which would gradually emerge, in the fullness of time, the art of counterpoint and our own musical notation.

During four centuries, Philip's fame as a poet was based on an enormously long French poem, Ovide moralisé (Ovid moralized), which is certainly apocryphal. The real author was still another Champenois, Chrétien Legouais of Sainte More, near Troyes, who composed it, it is believed, for queen Jeanne, wife of Philippe le Bel (king 1285–1314; he married Jeanne de Navarre in 1284; she died in 1305). Though Ovid's Metamorphoses are hardly more than 10,000 lines long, the Ovide moralisé extended to 62,000 lines, the additional material being in the form of symbolic and allegoric interpretations and Christian justifications. This was the last effort on a grand scale to Christianize pagan literature. After this time the new humanistic tendency was more and more to preserve the pagan masterpieces in their original beauty without moralization or Christian whitewashing.

The only poem of Vitry's that has come down to us, Les dicts du Franc-Gontier, is only 32 lines long. The theme of it is the happiness of humble people, like the poor woodman Franc-Gontier. This poem was translated into Latin by the humanist Nicolas de Clamanges (or Clémanges, 1360–c. 1440), and it was refuted by François Villon (d. c. 1489).

Text. The four musical treatises have been edited by Coussemaker (3, 13–46, 1869).

Prosper Tarbé: Les oeuvres de Philippe de Vitry (Collection des poètes de Champagne antérieurs au XVIe siècle vol. 8, 222 p., Reims 1850). Only one page of this is Vitry's, the rest being extracts from the apocryphal Ovide moralisé.

Criticism. Petit de Julleville (2, 343, 1896). Johannes Wolf: Geschichte der Mensural-Notation von 1250 bis 1460 (3 vols., Leipzig 1904). Combarieu (1, 385 ff., 1913). Barbara Smythe in Grove (5, 555, 1926). Heinrich Besseler: Studien zur Musik des Mittelalters. I, Neue Quellen des 14. und beginnenden 15. Jahrhunderts. II, Die Motette von Franko von Köln bis Philipp von Vitry (Archiv für Musikwissenschaft 7, 167–252, 1925; 8, 131–258, 1926). Marius Schneider: Die Ars nova

[55] See part of text in Combarieu (1, 383, 1913).

des 14. Jahrhunderts in Frankreich und Italien (Berlin thesis, 92 p., 1930). Gérold (1936). Reese (1940).

GUILLAUME DE MACHAUT

French poet and musician (d. 1377). So great a poet that the French compared him to Petrarca, and the outstanding musician of his time. Though he did not write on the theory of music, he exerted so deep an influence on the ars nova that he must be dealt with here.

Machaut is also spelled Machau and Machault. In Latin, Guilielmus de Mascaudio; Italians called him Guglielmo de Francia. He was born c. 1300 in the diocese of Reims. There is a place called Machault in Champagne (southern part of Ardennes dépt.), not very far from Reims. He took holy orders and c. 1323 became secretary to John of Luxemburg, king of Bohemia. He stayed with that king in Bohemia and accompanied him on his expeditions to Poland, Lithuania, Italy, France, until the king's death at the battle of Crécy (1346). He then entered the service of John's daughter, Bonne of Luxemburg, who had married in 1332 John, duke of Normandy. Bonne died in 1349 and Guillaume remained attached to her husband when the latter became king of France (Jean II le Bon, 1350–64). After the latter's death he continued in office under the next king, Charles V the Wise. He had become a canon of Reims cathedral in 1333, and spent much of his time in that city, where he died in 1377.

He wrote in French a great many poems which are valuable for the study of contemporary conditions, and even, some of them, as historical documents. For example, he wrote in 1365 or later a chronicle of the capture of Alexandria and of Peter I of Lusignan (d. 1369); Machaut is repeatedly quoted by historians of that crusade. The same poem and another, Remède de Fortune, contain the names of many musical instruments. For example, in the Prise d'Alexandrie he speaks of the eschaquier d'Engleterre (the English chessboard), which was an early attempt to apply a keyboard to a stringed instrument (Reese p. 383).

Far more important than his poems are his musical compositions, many of which have come down to us (some in splendid MSS, e.g., the one written for the brother of Charles V, the great collector, duke Jean de Berry). These compositions illustrate almost every musical form of that time, to wit, rondeaux, motets, lais, virelais, ballades, some of which are very sophisticated—polyphonic, examples of coloratura passages, ritardandi, rubati, musica falsa (or ficta), etc. He used binary rhythm and the minim. In short, he was the first interpreter or realizer in France of the ars nova which was so well explained by his older contemporary Philippe de Vitry.

His masterpiece is the mass in four voices said to have been composed by him for the coronation of Charles V at Reims in 1364. There is no documentary evidence for the date of that mass; but the date is plausible. The coronation mass, as we may call it, is the earliest known polyphonic setting of the ordinary of the mass by one man. The anonymous Messe de Tournai is not much older as a unit (first half of the fourteenth century), and it is far from homogeneous; indeed, it is a collection of various compositions written by different hands at different times. Machaut's mass was the climax of a long series of efforts and experiments to enhance the beauty of the ordinary with organum and descant; it was also the beginning of a new series leading to the polyphonic masses of Josquin des Prés (d. 1521), Roland de Lassus, and Palestrina (both of the latter d. 1594).

Guillaume's motets, in three or four parts, were religious or secular; in the first case the words were in Latin, in the second case they were in French. At least two of his motets are bilingual (Latin words in motetus, French words in triplum).

The most precious MSS of his musical compositions are in the Bibliothèque nationale, Paris. Two of them are so early that they were probably edited under his direction. There is a beautifully illustrated MS of Machaut's poems in the Pierpont Morgan Library, New York. That MS (no. 396) includes many unpublished poems, and with it are bound portions of Jacques Bruyant's Le chemin de pauvreté et de richesse, Alain Chartier's La belle dame sans merci, and Boetius' Consolation in French. It is a MS on vellum, written and illuminated in eastern France, probably in Burgundy, in the second quarter of the fifteenth century (La belle dame sans merci was composed in 1424); there are 126 colored wash drawings scattered in the text. Information kindly given me by Miss Belle da Costa Greene (letter dated New York, June 3, 1941). Ricci and Wilson (p. 1440, 1937).

Text. Ernest Hoepffner: Oeuvres de Guillaume de Machaut (Société des anciens textes français, 3 vols., 1908-21).

Paulin Paris: Le livre du Voir-dit où sont contées les amours de messire Guillaume de Machaut et de Peronnelle dame d'Armentières (Bibliophiles français, 444 p., Paris 1875).

L. de Mas Latrie: La prise d'Alexandrie ou Chronique du roi Pierre I de Lusignan (368 p., Genève 1877).

V. Chichmaref (i.e., Vladimir Fedorovich Shishmarev): Poésies lyriques (2 vols., Paris 1909), also published by the University of St. Petersburg.

Musical examples have been repeatedly printed, in both ancient and modern notation, but the first collected edition was initiated by Friedrich Ludwig: Musikalische Werke (Publikationen älterer Musik vols. 1-3; folio, 3 vols., Leipzig 1926-29). Vol. 1, ballads, rondeaux, virelais; vol. 2, introduction; vol. 3, motets.

The so-called Mass for the coronation of Charles V has not yet been completely published. It is available on records of L'anthologie sonore (nos. 31, 32), sung without words by the Paraphonistes of St. Jean des Matines, choir and brasses conducted by Guillaume De Van. The mass as recorded is very beautiful, but I have no time for investigating how close it comes to the original score.

Criticism. Every history of music deals with him. For early accounts see Chevalier (col. 1956, 1905). Elaborate biographies in the editions of Hoepffner and Chichmaref. George Lyman Kittredge: Machaut and the book of the duchess (Modern Language Association 30, 1-24, 1915). Grove (3, 268-69, 1927). Reese (1940, passim).

B. Byzantine Music

MANUEL BRYENNIOS

Μανουὴλ Βρυέννιος. Byzantine musicologist who flourished under Michael IX Palaeologos (emperor 1295-1320). The circumstances of his life are unknown, except that he composed a treatise on music (Ἁρμονικά) in three books, which is the latest Byzantine treatise on the subject. It is very elaborate but seems to be essentially a compilation derived from the ancient writers, as Aristoxenos (IV-2 B.C.), Euclid (III-1 B.C.), Nicomachos (I-2), Adrastos of Aphrodisias (II-1), Theon of Smyrna (II-1), but also from a recent one like Georgios Pachymeres (XIII-2), who died c. 1310 (Introd. 2, 972). The compilation is uncritical because the author had but little historical sense. For example, he divided the history of music into three periods, pre-Pythagoraean, Pythagoraean, and later; hence Byzantine music was confused with practically the whole of the extant music of ancient times.

Theory and practice are not always clearly divided. For all that, Bryennios' work is very valuable, a mine of musicological information (e.g., on the ancient Greek melopoeia) which has not yet been properly exploited. It is probably of great importance from the special point of view of liturgic music, and the more so that the Byzantine traditions go deeper than the Catholic ones, which cannot be traced farther back than the Harmonica institutio of Hucbald of St. Amand (c. 840–930)[56] and Guido of Arezzo (XI-1).

Judging from the number of MSS—Wallis could make use of four Oxford MSS and there are others—the work enjoyed some popularity.

The Harmonica (in Wallis' edition) is divided into three books, subdivided respectively into 9, 15, and 11 sections. The text is extremely technical and is illustrated with elaborate diagrams, of which we reproduce two (figs. 15, 16); similar diagrams were already used by Georgios Pachymeres and may probably be traced farther back. The first section of book I is introductory and historical; the constant mixture of musical with astronomical ideas is remarkable. This was a Pythagoraean and Platonic tradition which permeated astronomical and musical thought until the seventeenth century (cf. Kepler).

The name Bryennios was not uncommon in the mediaeval Greek world (is it connected with the French crusader family Brienne, which originated in Brienne in Aube?). We have dealt previously (Introd. 2, 250) with Nicephoros Bryennios (XII-1), who wrote a biography of his father-in-law Alexios Comnenos (emperor 1081–1118). It is possible that Manuel Bryennios was related to the more famous and later Bryennios, Joseph Bryennios, theologian, teacher, and court preacher, who was himself taught and patronized by Demetrios Cydones, Theodoros Meliteniotes, and the great archivist (χαρτοφύλαξ) Joannes Holobolos. In 1381 Neilos (patriarch 1380–88) sent Joseph to Crete, which was then under Venetian, i.e. Catholic, power. In 1405, Joseph was patriarchal vicary (τοποτηρητής) in Cyprus. He was strongly anti-Latin. He bequeathed his library to Hagia Sophia.[57]

Text. The first edition of the Harmonica is due to no less a person than the great mathematician John Wallis (1616–1703) and is included by him in his Opera mathematica (folio, 3, 359–508, Oxford 1699), together with Latin translation, notes, and diagrams.

Criticism. François Joseph Fétis: Biographie universelle des musiciens (2, 100, 1861). Vetter (PW 28, 1362–66, 1930).

C. Muslim Music

AL-KHAṬĪB AL-IRBILĪ

Muḥammad ibn 'Alī al-Khaṭīb al-Irbilī. Iraqian theorist of music (fl. 1329–37).

The nisba Irbilī refers to the town of Irbil (ancient Arbela) in the plain between the upper and lower Zāb rivers, east of the Tigris. He wrote in 1329 a treatise on music, Jawāhir al-niẓām fī ma'rifat al-anghām (Jewels of arrangement concerning the knowledge of notes). It is divided into sections in the manner of Kitāb al-adwār of Ṣafī al-dīn 'Abd al-Mu'min (XIII-2). It is written in verse (rajaz meter)

[56] For Hucbald of St. Amand (in the diocese of Tournay) see Max Manitius: Geschichte der lateinischen Literatur des Mittelalters (1, 588–94, München 1911).

[57] Krumbacher (p. 113, 1897). A. Palmieri (DTC 2, 1156–61, 1905; third printing 1923), including long list of Joseph's writings, relatively little known because they failed to be included in Migne's Greek patrology. They had been edited, however, by Eugenios Bulgaris (vols. 1, 2, Leipzig 1768; vol. 3, 1784). J. W. Thompson (p. 328, 1939).

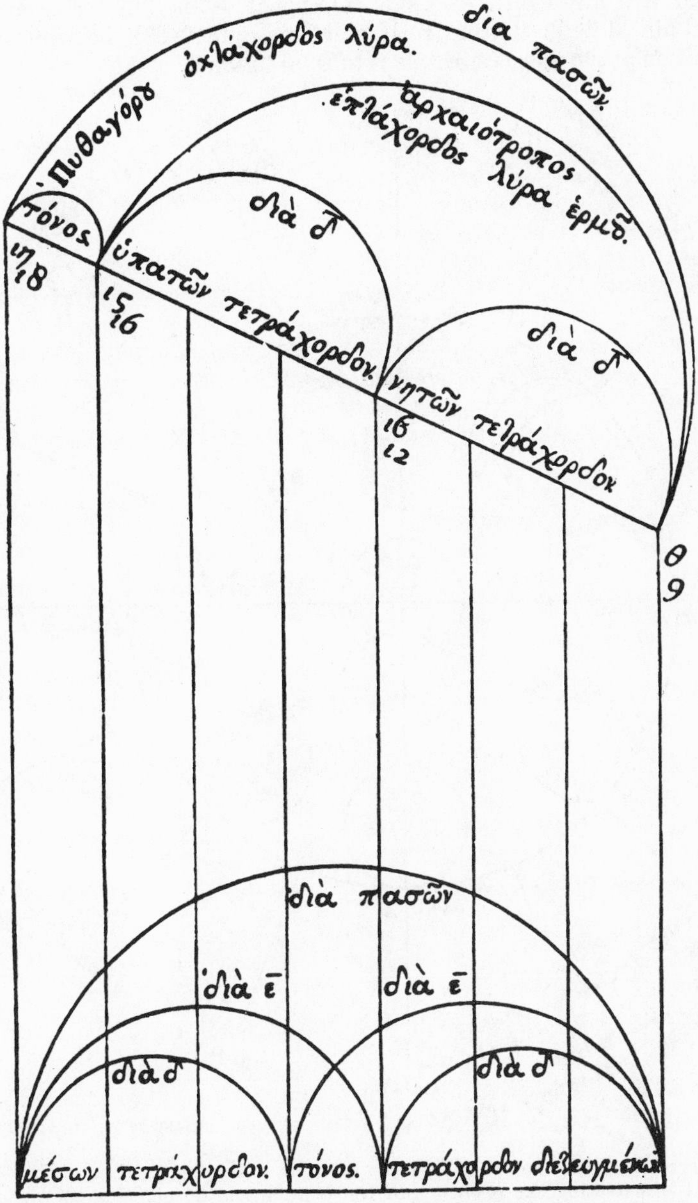

FIG. 15. Bryennios' Harmonica. Diagram occurring in the first section of the work (Wallis 3, 366). It illustrates the Pythagoraean eight-stringed lyre in two ways. Above, two tetrachords joined together, which constitute the ancient seven-stringed lyre of Mercury and a preceding tone; from the note "proslambanomenon" to the note "meson," the intervals following in this order: tone; semitone, tone, tone; semitone, tone, tone. Below, two tetrachords separated by an intermediary tone, from the note "hypate-meson" to the note "neten-diezeugmenon," the intervals following in this order: semitone, tone, tone; tone; semitone, tone, tone.

and therefore it is also called Al-qaṣīda fī-l-anghām. In 1337, being at the court of Shams al-dīn al-Ṣāliḥ (Urtuqī ruler of Māridīn 1312–63), he wrote a treatise on the definition of the sciences, Risāla fī ta'rīf al-'ulūm.

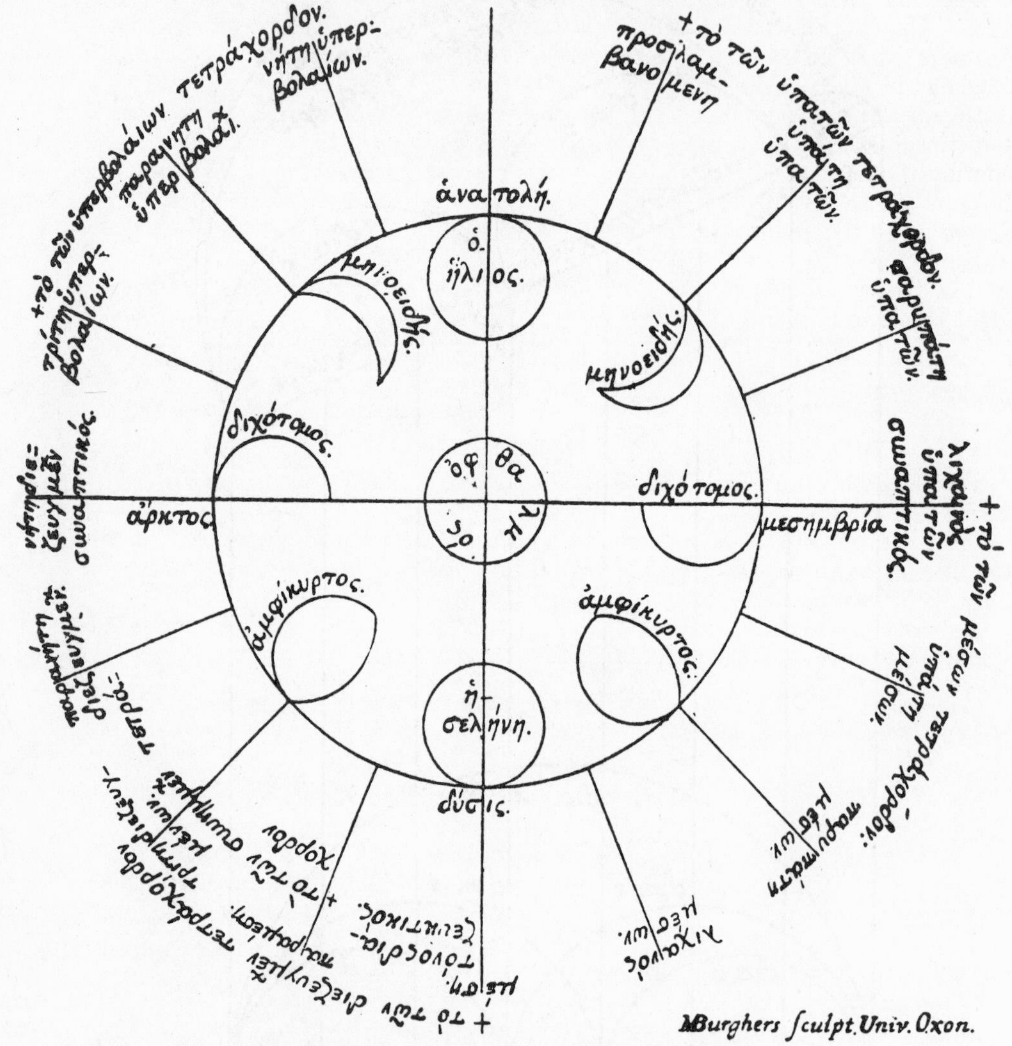

FIG. 16. Bryennios' Harmonica. Diagram occurring in the final section of the work, book III, section 11, illustrating the positions of the tetrachords terminating the melody. The combination of geographical and astronomical ideas with musical ones is curious. Note that the east (ἀνατολή) is at the top, as was the case in the majority of Christian mappae mundi (Andrews 1926), whereas Muslim maps were generally oriented south up (Isis 34, p. 32). For explanation of the diagram, reference must be made to the Greek-Latin text in Wallis (3, 507).

Text. Jawāhir edited by father Cheikho in Al-mashriq (p. 895–901, Beirūt 1913).
Criticism. Brockelmann (2, 169, 1902; suppt. 2, 218, 1938). Farmer (p. 51, no. 211, 1940).

'ABD AL-'AZĪZ IBN SARĀYĀ AL-ḤILLĪ

Ṣafī al-dīn 'Abd al-'Azīz ibn Sarāyā al-Ḥillī. Iranian poet and musician (1278–1349).

His nisba refers to Ḥilla in 'Irāq (same site as Babylon). He was born in August 1278. He was poet at the Urtuqī court in Māridīn (Jazīra); in 1326 he visited the Mamlūk court in Cairo, but returned soon afterward to Māridīn. He died in Baghdād in March 1349.

He was a famous poet who is still a favorite among young Arabic literati of today, but we speak of him here only because of a treatise on musical composition which continued a curious Arabic tradition. It is entitled Fā'ida fī tawallud al-anghām ba'ḍaha 'an ba'ḍ wa tartībihā 'alā-l-burūj (The advantage of composing melodies according to the zodiac). This kind of musical astrology can be traced back to al-Kindī (IX-1).

It is better not to call him Ṣafī al-dīn al-Ḥillī, to avoid confusion with the great musician Ṣafī al-dīn 'Abd al-Mu'mīn (XIII-2).

Criticism. Brockelmann (2, 159, 1902; suppt. 2, 199, 1938). Farmer (p. 53, no. 223, 1940).

IBN KARĀ

Shams al-dīn Muḥammad ibn 'Īsā Ibn Karā al-Ḥanbalī. Egyptian theorist of music (1282–1358).

Ibn Karā was said to be a descendant of Marwān II ibn Muḥammad (d. 750), the last of the Omayyad caliphs in Damascus. He was born in Cairo in June or July 1282; became a ṣūfī; died in 1358.

He wrote a treatise on music, Ghāyat al-maṭlūb fī fann al-anghām wal-ḍurūb (Goal of desire in the art of melodies and rhythms).

Criticism. Ḥājjī Khalīfa (4, 304, no. 8543, 1845). Brockelmann (suppt. 2, 173, 1938). Farmer (p. 53, no. 224, 1940).

CHAPTER VIII

CHEMISTRY

(First Half of the Fourteenth Century)

N.B. Only the main notes are published in this chapter. The chemical contributions of many other men, whose main work was done in other fields, are discussed in other chapters. For a general survey of chemistry in the first half of the fourteenth century, see section VIII of chapter I. More information on the men referred to in that survey may then easily be found by means of the index.

6. ALCHEMISTS IN THE LATIN WEST

BUONO

Pietro Buono. Italian alchemist (fl. 1330).

Pietro Buono (or Petrus Bonus Lombardus) is supposed to have been a physician of Ferrara. In 1323 he was in Traú, Dalmatia, and in 1330 (rather than 1338–39) in Pola d'Istria, where he composed his Pretiosa margarita novella.

These data are not certain, but they are on the whole plausible, and it seems clear that the author of the Precious pearl should not be confused with Petrus Bonus Advogarius (Avogario), a Ferrarese astrologer of incunabula times whose astrological predictions were printed 29 times in Italian and Latin from 1477 to 1501 (Klebs no. 138; Sarton p. 183, 190, 213, 1938), or with the physician Pietro Antonio Boni, who is said (by Mazzuchelli 1762) to have flourished in 1494, or with various other Petri Boni; the name "good Peter" was of course a very common one.

The Pretiosa margarita novella is a very prolix treatise in defense of alchemy, derived from Aristotle or pseudo-Aristotelian literature and from all the classical and Arabic treatises available in Latin. As far as internal evidence is concerned, that treatise may well have been written, as it claims to be, in 1330. It does not refer to Albert the Great, Thomas Aquinas, Roger Bacon, Arnold Villanova, and Raymond Lull; but most of the alchemical books ascribed to those authors are apocryphal publications which did not yet exist in 1330 or were hardly anterior to that date.

It is clear enough that the author had received a medical education, for he shows repeatedly his familiarity with Aristotelian zoology, with Galen, and with the Qānūn of Ibn Sīnā. What is more remarkable, he was well acquainted with the mining practices of his time. For example, he explains that in Constantinople one calcines certain rocks, then dissolves them, in order to extract the alum of Edessa and Aleppo (de rocha et de alap). Certain mines of lead and tin produce pure silver; certain lodes of silver contain gold as well, which may be separated from the silver by means of sulphur. These facts suggest that natural transmutations are going on all the time, though it is objected that no intermediate substances are ever found.

The Precious pearl is a very long treatise (covering 158 closely printed folio columns in Manget's edition). It begins with an introduction dealing with generalities relative (1) to speculative alchemy, and (2) to practical alchemy. The treatise proper is divided into 26 chapters. The first three discuss the arguments against and for alchemy; the question is not whether alchemy is possible or not, but whether it is true or not. The discussion is based on Aristotelian physics and metaphysics and on a mass of other writings used without any attempt at criticism. The contents of the other chapters may be indicated briefly as follows: (4) Difficulties of the art. (5) Its unity and wholeness in spite of redundant terminology. (6) The art is at once natural and divine, which enabled ancient philosophers to prophesy future miracles. The author refers to the stone impregnating and reproducing itself, comparing it to the Holy Virgin and the immaculate conception (Manget 2, 30, 1702). (7) The main difficulty concerns the composition of the elements. (8) History of the art; why some people understand it and others not; why philosophers speak of it obscurely; if it were open to all, that would be the end of the world. (9) The philosopher's stone and the many names given to it in order to put off the ignorant. Opinions of ancient philosophers and Aristotle's reprobation of them. (10) Against sophists, deceivers, and contradictors; brevity (?), nobility, and verity of the art. (11) The first name given to the philosopher's stone is that of ferment. This chapter is devoted to the study of that aspect throughout alchemical literature. The philosopher's stone acts like leaven in bread, but it is intangible, like the soul in the body; its action is spiritual. (12) Elements of the philosopher's stone; it cannot be derived from animal or vegetable substances. (13) Discussion of theriaca and poison. (14) Coagulum (like rennet) and lac (milk); male and female in the elixir. (15) Truth of the art proved in a threefold manner, by the authorities, by reasoning, by experiment. (16) Discussion of objections. (17) Metals. (18, 19) Sulphur. (20) Action and potentiality, perfection and imperfection. (21) Bronze and iron (there are no means of transmuting them into gold or silver). (22) Nature does not convert imperfect metals into gold. (23, 24) Principles, generation and transmutation of metals; the art can and must imitate nature. (25) The generation of gold out of sulphur, mercury, and elixir compared to the generation of the embryo out of sperm and menstrual blood, and to the generation of the bird out of the egg. (26) Truth of the art reasserted.

I have indicated the main contents, but the book defies analysis, for each chapter is an endless farrago of quotations, the order of which is not by any means clear. The author tried to develop his argument in the scholastic manner, explaining, discussing, refuting the objections one by one, proving the possibility, reality, and truth of the art, examining every aspect of the philosopher's stone, indicating the main possibilities, rejecting the impossibilities, etc., but he was overwhelmed by the mass of his authorities, and the result is a hopeless compilation containing innumerable reiterations and not a few contradictions.

His authorities are all the ancient and mediaeval writers available in Latin, not only the regular alchemists, and standard authorities like Hermes, Pythagoras, Democritos, Plato, Aristotle, but also Homer, Virgil, Ovid. Among the Arabic alchemists Rāzī is the one whom he quotes from most frequently, but he refers only to apocryphal writings; the same remark applies to Geber, whom he uses with a complete absence of discrimination. The Summa perfectionis (Introd. 2, 1043) and the Turba philosophorum (Isis 20, 302–5) are quoted repeatedly.

I do not know how Pietro Buono composed his Precious pearl, but if he had written out all the Latin alchemical, philosophical, and mystical books available to him, cut the copies into small pieces, classified the innumerable fragments as plausibly as possible, and finally edited them in the new order thus obtained, editorial remarks being inserted here and there to increase the cohesion of the fragments or decrease their incoherence, the final result would not have been very different from his compilation.

Buono was the first (?) to speak of a ceramical glaze, a combination of calcined lead and tin. "Videmus quod cum plumbum et stannum fuerunt calcinata et combusta, quod post ad ignem congruum convertuntur in vitrum, sicut faciunt qui vitrificant vasa figuli."[1]

Text. Condensed edition of Pretiosa margarita novella in the alchemical collection bearing that very title put together by the Calabrian Franciscan Giano Lacinio or Janus Lacinius (Venice 1546). Reprinted Nürnberg 1554, etc.

More complete edition under the title Introductio in divinam chemiae artem integra magistri Boni Lombardi Ferrariensis physici (286 p., Basel 1572), including preface by the editor, Michael Toxites, addressed to the duke of Bavaria. Reprinted by Jacques Foillet (432 p., Montbéliard 1602), again by Lazarus Zetzner (420 p., Strassburg 1608). Included in Zetzner (5, 507–713, 1660) and in Manget (2, 1–80, 1702).

German translation of the Lacinius text by Wolffgang Georg Stollen (Leipzig 1714), and English paraphrase of it by Arthur Edward Waite: The new pearl of great price (432 p., London 1894).

Criticism. Hoefer (1, 436–37, 1869). Ferguson (1, 115–16; 2, 2–3, 1906). John Maxson Stillman: Petrus Bonus and supposed chemical forgeries (Scientific monthly 17, 318–25, 1923); (277, 285, 287, 293–96, 1924). Thorndike (3, 147–62, 1934), summary of the Precious pearl, very different from my own and completing it. Julius Ruska: L'alchimie à l'époque du Dante (Annales Guébhard-Séverine 10, 411–17, Neuchâtel 1934).

DASTIN

John Dastin. English (?) alchemist who flourished during the pontificate of John XXII (1316–34).

His personality is very obscure, the very name being uncertain, Dastin, Daustin, Daustyn. The only facts helping us to fix him in time are the letters addressed by him to John XXII and to Napoleone Orsini, cardinal deacon of St. Adrian from 1288 to 1342; and to fix him in space, the abundance of MSS bearing his name in England.

Many alchemical writings are ascribed to him:

1. To begin with, his letter to John XXII, Epistola de alkimia, which is probably anterior to that pope's decretal Spondent quas non exhibent against alchemists (undated), or his bull Super illius specula (1326–27) against magicians. That letter, beginning Hoc est secretum secretorum impretiabile pretium, is in fact an alchemical treatise. By means of mercury and a little gold or silver, acting as a ferment, one can obtain the elixir. The elixir will enable one to make gold or else to accelerate the cure of diseases.

2. Libellus aureus. Explaining ideas similar to those in the letter to John XXII.

3. Rosarius or Rosarium (including Desiderabile desiderium). Ascribed to John Dastin but also to John Hastiri (misreading?), John Tyrus of Toledo, and Arnold of Villanova. There are some 22 MSS of it anterior to 1500 in England alone (D. W. Singer, 1928–31). Repeats the theory that the art of transmutation consists essentially in combining quicksilver with gold or silver. Sulphur is not

[1] Quoted by Hoefer but without reference to chapter or page of the Margarita.

needed, except the traces contained in the noble metals. To that theory are added many other philosophical and mystical conceptions. Various alchemical operations are described. Comparison of human generation with alchemical transmutation. Numerical and geometrical fancies. The only authors quoted are Aristotle and Geber.

Two other Rosarius (3 bis, ter) are ascribed to Dastin, the texts of both differing from our no. 3. In one of them sulphur (called kybrit)[2] is called the father of mercury and of liquefiable bodies, which does not tally very well with the conception of sulphur in nos. 1, 2, 3. It is vain to try to find much consistency or any clearness in the writings of the alchemists. Their experimentation was so gross that they could not handle pure elements, nor reckon how impure they were. They could only repeat very gross reactions, yet all their arguments implied purifications hopelessly beyond their reach, and reactions of metaphysical subtlety.

4. Verbum abbreviatum (Liber de cognitione; De transmutatione metallorum; Speculum secretorum alkimiae).

5. Sapientum aurinum (Liber philosophiae). Both 4 and 5 are addressed to cardinal Orsini. They contain references to Hermes, Aristotle, Plato, Geber, al-Rāzī, Ibn Sīnā, and many other standard authorities, the references being far more abundant in these treatises 4 and 5 than in 3. The theories seem to be the same, so far as can be judged, in texts wherein the fundamental terms—such as sulphur, mercury—change their meaning according to convenience.

6. Super arte alchemistica. Very brief.

7. Visio super artem alchemicam. Beginning Cum omnium in natura constantium (s. consistentium) certus sit effectus generationis et augmenti. Short treatise describing an astrological alchemical vision. Complicated allegories mixed with Gospel language concerning the passion and atonement; the same mixture occurred in treatises ascribed to Arnold of Villanova (see Introd. 2, 896, no. 63).

8. Donum Dei. Also ascribed to Raymond Lull and to John of Damascus, unless different texts bearing the same tempting title have been confused.

This list might possibly be extended, or further analysis might drive out one or two items. This would not affect materially our general impression of the Dastin alchemical writings.

Text. 2. Libellus aureus, edited by Zetzner (3, 659–65, 1659).

3. Rosarium secretissimum philosophorum arcanum comprehendens. First printed in Hofgeismar (Hesse-Nassau) 1647, German translation in Alchymistisch Sieben-Gestirn (Hamburg 1675; again Frankfurt 1772). Latin text reprinted by Manget (2, 119–33, 309–24, 1702).

7. Visio super artem alchemicam. First printed in Harmoniae chymico-philosophicae (2, 301–8, Frankfurt 1625). Reprinted with no. 3 (Hofgeismar 1647) in the Ginaeceum chimicum (Lyon 1679), and in Manget (2, 324–26, 1702). German translation in the same collections as no. 3, 1675, 1772.

Criticism. Alsager Vian (DNB 14, 89, 1888). Ferguson (1, 199–200, 1906). D. W. Singer (1928–31). Thorndike (3, 85–102, 676–78, 1934).

7. BYZANTINE ALCHEMY

A number of Greek MSS enable us to form a very definite idea of Greek alchemy in the fourteenth century. Many of them date from that century, and hence the texts which they carry cannot be later. Some of them are even exactly dated; for

[2] Cf. Arabic kibrīt. Gold is sometimes called al-kibrīt al-aḥmar (red sulphur); pure gold, dhahab kibrīt; pure silver, fiḍḍat kibrīt. These ambiguities are significant.

example, a composite Cod. Paris gr. 2286 (Catalogue 1, 180–91, 1924) was written c. 1353 by the monk Neophytos; the Cod. Vatic. gr. 984 was written in 1354 (Catalogue 2, 329–30, 1927); the Cod. Venetus Marcianus inter Nanianos 247 was written in 1376. These three fall into the category of libri Koeranidum or Cyranides, compendia of ancient lore on the virtues of animals, stones, and plants (Introd. 2, 347). Then there is the very technical Cod. Vatic. gr. 1134, written in Reggio di Calabria 1376 (Catalogue 2, 153–92, 1927). Many more alchemical MSS of the fourteenth century, or later MSS containing texts dating from that century, could be found by examining thoroughly the eight published parts of the Catalogue of Greek alchemical MSS published by the Union académique internationale (1924–32).

One of them was discussed in our note on Petros Theoctonicos (XIII-2), the otherwise unknown translator into Greek of the Semita recta ascribed to Albert the Great. The most important of all these MSS is probably the Περὶ μεταλλικῆς τέχνης ἢ περὶ μετάλλων συστροφῆς εἰς χρυσὸν καὶ ἄργυρον, written in southern Italy about the beginning of the fourteenth century or perhaps later, but certainly before 1378. It is a very long treatise, divided into 100 chapters, and covering almost 200 printed pages. The sources are Latin; e.g., Arnold of Villanova (Ῥινάλδος τῆς Βιλανόβα) is quoted. The main authority is Hermes. Much of it is esoteric, yet other parts have a clearer meaning. It deals with metals, the substances needed for their transmutation, methods, and instruments. All substances are made of sulphur and mercury, but common metals include so many impurities that they are ill, leprous (λεπρός); yet by means of the "art" it is possible to cure them, that is, by the proper use of fire, the four spirits, the elixir, or by the use of tinctures.[3] Sexual distinctions are emphasized. For example, the four spirits (sulphur, quicksilver, arsenic, salmiac)[4] are supposed to be active and male, whereas the substances are passive and female; sometimes mercury is held to be female, though iron and tin are always counted as male. The elixir or philosopher's stone or ferment (ζύμη) is an embodied spirit or a spiritual body, it is active in very small doses (like leaven). Pure gold may be used itself as a ferment to cure other metals. It is called ὄβρυζον (cf. Arabic abrīz or ibrīz); the impure gold is strangely called ἄσημον (uncoined gold or silver). Metals are connected with the planets: quicksilver with Hermes (Mercury), iron with Ares (Mars), copper with Aphrodite (Venus), etc. Arsenic is the best intermediary between males and females. Many operations and instruments are described, e.g., an apparatus for distillation (ὄργανον).

This anonymous Greek text has many points of contact with the Sedacina totius alchimiae or Summa sedacina, composed c. 1378 by the Catalan Carmelite Guillem Sedacer (XIV-2). Many more authorities are quoted in the Sedacina than in the Greek text. It is not suggested that Sedacer used the latter, but rather that both authors exploited the same Latin sources. Southern Italy was of course the country where such amalgamation of Greek and Latin knowledge could occur as nowhere else, for its main language was Greek, yet Latindom was near enough, and the use of Latin and Italian must have increased considerably by this time.

[3] This reminds me of the enormous (excessive) importance which Arthur John Hopkins (1864–1939) gave to tincturing and coloring of metals in the old alchemical methods. See his book Alchemy, child of Greek philosophy (274 p., Columbia Univ. Press, New York 1934; Isis 24, 174–77) and his articles in Isis (7, 58–76, 1925; 28, 424–31, 1938; 29, 326–54, 1938).

[4] This enumeration varies, for sometimes quicksilver is counted among the common metals and salmiac among the salts, and spirits are sometimes derived from such animal substances as blood, urine, hair, and egg.

Text. Excellent Greek-Latin edition by C. O. Zuretti: Anonymi de arte metallica seu de metallorum conversione in aurum et argentum, forming vol. 7 of the Catalogue of Greek alchemical MSS (526 p., 1930; Isis 15, 410), with elaborate glossary.
Criticism. Edmund O. von Lippmann: Ein neues alchemistisches Handbuch aus der Zeit um 1300 (Chemiker-Zeitung, 1930, p. 869–71).

Another Greek MS of this period deserving special attention is the Cod. gr. Holkham Hall 290. It is a composite MS dealing with astronomy, astrology, and alchemy. It will eventually be discussed in volume 9 of the Catalogue of Greek astrological MSS. The chemical part has been edited by Otto Lagercrantz in the Catalogue of Greek alchemical MSS (3, 29–82, 1924).

This suggests that other MSS not specifically alchemical may contain alchemical portions. Consider, for example, the anonymous manual of cosmology and geography edited by Delatte (1930), which, judging from the number of MSS (at least eight), enjoyed some popularity. The MSS are mostly of the fifteenth century, but the text may be somewhat earlier; it contains references to John of Damascus (VIII-1). The last part of it discusses the four elements, *περὶ τῶν τεσσάρων στοιχείων τοῦ οὐρανοῦ*, but contains nothing which is not already in Aristotelian physics, in the Christian fathers, or in Byzantine authors such as Michael Psellos (XI-2) or Nicephoros Blemmydes (XIII-2). This reminds us of the very ancient roots (Ionian philosophy) of the idea of transmutation.

Text. Armand Delatte: Geographica (Byzantinische Ztschr. 30, 511–18, 1930).
Criticism. Delatte (1932).

8. MUSLIM ALCHEMY

'ABDALLĀH IBN 'ALĪ AL-KĀSHĀNĪ

Abū-l-Qāsim 'Abdallāh ibn 'Alī ibn Muḥammad ibn abī Ṭāhir al-Kāshānī. Persian author of a unique (Persian) account of the technique of glazing earthenware, as this was done in his own native place, Kāshān, in 'Irāq 'Ajamī (or Jibāl) between Kumm and Isfahān. (Arabic writers, as distinguished from Persian ones, often write Qāshān.) 'Abdallāh al-Kāshānī wrote that account in Tabrīz 1300.

It was found recently by Hellmut Ritter in two Hagia Sophia Persian MSS (nos. 3614 and 3613) of a treatise on precious stones and perfumes, Kitāb jawāhir al-'arā'is wa aṭā'ib al-nafā'is, composed by our 'Abdallāh. This treatise is similar to various other treatises on precious stones in Arabic and Persian but for the final chapter, dealing with the art of enameled pottery (or ghaḍārah, faïence), an art which is, as is stated at the beginning of the text, a kind of iksīr (elixir, philosopher's stone). The first of these MSS was written by the author himself (who spells his nisba Qāshānī) in Tabrīz 1300, and dedicated to Rashīd al-dīn Faḍl Allāh or to the latter's colleague (as wazīr) Tāj al-dīn al-Tabrīzī. The second MS is much younger (1583). The first MS may have been carried to Istanbul after the battle of Chaldirān (August 23, 1514), for after that battle the victorious Ottoman sulṭān Selīm I took away from Tabrīz several hundreds of artisans.

The chapter on the making of faïence is very precious because it is the only document of its kind in Islamic literature, and I know nothing equivalent to it in earlier or contemporary Asiatic[5] or in European literature before the Arte del vasaio

[5] For Asiatic literature I have applied to Dr. Shio Sakanishi and Dr. A. W. Hummel. The former knows of no early treatise of that kind in Japanese. The latter knows of none in Chinese. He wrote to me (Sept. 21, 1939):

"The references in Chinese literature are rather numerous, though we can find no treatise on the subject as such earlier than the Persian one you mention. Glazing is mixed up with the

written by Cipriano Piccolpasso between 1556 and 1559.[6] Moreover, it was written by an expert, who belonged to a family of potters in Kāshān. The maker of the beautiful luster miḥrāb of the tomb of the imām Yaḥyā (now in the Hermitage, Leningrad), dated 1305, Yūsuf ibn 'Alī ibn Muḥammad, was possibly a brother of our 'Abdallāh ibn 'Alī ibn Muḥammad.

It discusses the ingredients needed for faïence, their mixtures or combinations, kiln processes and implements, the methods of glazing and decorating. Many of the ingredients, such as clay, borax (?), feldspar (?), cobalt, were available near Kāshān, a fact which explains how that town became a center of the Persian ceramic industry. Other ingredients needed were lapis lazuli, copper ores, lead, tin, special varieties of clay. Some of them had to be imported from Kirmān or Khurāsān, from Yazd or Isfahān, even from Asia Minor, China, and the land of the Franks. From the last-named country came cobalt-manganese and tin, the latter being marketed in snake-shaped pieces duly stamped. An especially fine clay was brought from Isfahān. The author describes the technique of glazing with two fires (luster), leaf gilding, overglaze decoration fired in a muffle kiln (i.e., separated from the flames, the source of heat being outside), "haft rang" (Persian term referring to the seven colors of the planets); this may be a reference to the polychrome overglaze technique, the so-called mīnā'ī ware (another Persian term; mīnā wash means luster; mīnā'ī, colored enamel). The author indicates differences between the art as practiced in Kāshān and in Baghdād and Tabrīz, no other places being mentioned. In Baghdād and Tabrīz other kinds of firewood and potash were used.

The discovery and publication of this text, unique in mediaeval literature, has drawn connoisseurs' attention to the Kāshān wares, which were far less known than the wares of other places like Rayy. It is certain that Kāshān was the main center of ceramics production in mediaeval Persia. This is proved (1) by frequent references in Arabic literature, that is, in the writings of al-Muqaddasī (X-2), Yāqūt (XIII-1), Abū-l-Fidā', and Ibn Baṭṭūṭa (XIV-2); (2) by the tradition exemplified in the use of the Persian words kāshī or kāshānī (or the same words written in

---

subject of glass and the two terms have to be studied together in Chinese. The term for glass, po-li, is of Western origin (see Giles' Glossary of reference on the Far East, p. 105). The term for glaze, liu-li, appears in a slightly variant form for the first time in the Former Han history (Ch'ien Han-shu 96/24b, see ed. of Wang Hsien-ch'ien) as coming from the West. Liu-li is also a foreign word derived from the Sanskrit (see T'oung Pao 1927–28, p. 456, for derivation); see also T'oung Pao 1925–26, p. 356; 1923, p. 3, 268 note, for important conclusions. The Chinese encyclopaedia, Ku-chin t'u-shu chi-ch'êng, section 334, has many references to liu-li and many concerning glass. For example, it cites Li Shih-chên (author of the herbal Pên-ts'ao kang-mu, 1590) as quoting the Wei-lüeh, a history of the third century, now lost, to the effect that Syria (Ta-ch'in kuo) produced gold, silver, and liu-li (glaze or glass?). You see that the references in encyclopaedias and poetry before 1300 are very numerous, but we cannot point to a separate treatise on the subject in Chinese prior to that date. Later references in Chinese are also numerous, but it is not easy to distinguish whether glaze or glass is meant." See additional note below.

[6] The cavaliere Cipriano Piccolpasso of Castel Durante (1524–79) belonged to an old Bolognese family. Li tre libri dell' Arte del vasaio were first edited by Mgr. A. Cajani (Rome 1857). I have used the Italian-English edition by Bernard Rackham and Albert Van de Put (folio, 110 p., 80 pl., Victoria and Albert Museum, London 1934). Most of Piccolpasso's account is devoted, like that of his Persian predecessors, to what "is variously known as maiolica, faïence or delft, that is, earthenware coated with a glaze or enamel rendered opaque and white by the inclusion of tin in its composition." That art had been introduced into Italy from the Near East, perhaps via Spain, in the fourteenth century. Piccolpasso's account is more elaborate than the Persian one, but it is younger by more than two centuries and a half!

Arabic with qāf) to refer to colored wall tiles;[7] (3) by the existence of a few splendid luster maḥārīb made in Kāshān in the thirteenth and fourteenth centuries; (4) by the recent discovery in Kāshān of many kilns and wasters. "Wasters" are imperfect specimens thrown away by the potter, and one may generally assume that they were made where found. In Kāshān were made not only wall tiles, but all kinds of objects covered with opaque or translucent glazes, also the mīnā'ī wares generally ascribed to Rayy. It may be that the mīnā'ī technique originated in Kāshān rather than in Rayy, where it was considerably developed. It should be noted that with the exception of a few Kāshān tiles, there are no dated and signed specimens of Persian faïence anterior to the Ṣafawī dynasty (1502–1736) which can be assigned to a definite place of manufacture; even when the potter's name is written, this gives generally no clue to the place of origin (Pope p. 1461).

It is interesting to note in this connection that the art of making glazed earthenware (setomono) was introduced into Japan from China only c. 1228 by Katō Shunkei (XIII-1). Did the Persian art of faïence come also from China? Not necessarily.

Text. Hellmut Ritter, Julius Ruska, F. Sarre, R. Winderlich: Orientalische Steinbücher und persische Fayencetechnik (Istanbuler Mitteilungen no. 3, 70 p., 4 pl., Istanbul 1935; Isis 24, 480), includes Persian text of both MSS, German translation, notes, and discussion. Reviewed by Richard Ettinghausen (Bulletin American Institute for Iranian Art and Archaeology 4, 46–49, 1935).

Criticism. Cl. Huart: Kāshī (EI 2, 788, 1925). Kurt Röder: Zur Technik der persischen Fayence im 13. und 14. Jahrhundert (Zeitschrift der Deutschen morgenländischen Gesellschaft 89, 225–42, 1935). Arthur Upham Pope: Survey of Persian art (vol. 2, text; vol. 5, plates, Oxford 1938–39), including an elaborate discussion of all the problems relative to Persian pottery. For Kāshān ware see p. 1574.

For the sake of comparison see Armand Abel: Gaibī et les grands faïenciers égyptiens d'époque mamlouke. Avec un catalogue de leurs oeuvres conservées au Musée d'art arabe du Caire (quarto, 115 p., 31 pl., Le Caire 1930). Richard Ettinghausen: Evidence for the identification of Kāshān pottery (Ars islamica 3, 44–70, 36 fig., Ann Arbor, Mich. 1936).

ADDITIONAL NOTES ON MESOPOTAMIAN AND CHINESE DOCUMENTS CONCERNING THE MANUFACTURE OF GLAZES AND CERAMICS

1. For Mesopotamian glazes, see the Assyrian cuneiform texts of the seventh century B.C., and long ahead of them the extraordinary Babylonian tablet (BM no. 120960) of the time of Gulkishar (1690–36 B.C.), sixth king of the first dynasty of the Sea-Land. That Babylonian text was edited and translated by C. J. Gadd and R. Campbell Thompson: A middle Babylonian chemical text (Iraq 3, 87–96, 1 pl., 1936; Isis 26, 538). R. C. Thompson: A dictionary of Assyrian chemistry and geology (Oxford 1936; Isis 26, 477–80).

2. Chinese manufacture of ceramics. An interview with the late Mr. John Ellerton Lodge, director of the Freer Gallery in Washington, on January 7, 1941, and a letter from him written the following day, enable me to add that the earliest

[7] E.g., see Ibn Baṭṭūṭa (Defrémery's ed. 1, 415; 2, 46, 130, 225). He writes qāshānī and compares the word thrice with the Maghribī term zulaij, designating colored wall tiles. According to Dozy's Supplément (1, 598, 1881), zulaij (Spanish azulejo) is itself derived from the Persian-Arabic lāzhuward, lapis lazuli. In Persian, a potter is called kāshī-paz, and the manufacture of tiles, kāshī-sāzī or kāshī-kārī.

technical information available in Chinese concerns the I-hsing (alias Yi-hsing, Ihing) yao or pottery, so called after a place on the western shore of Lake T'ai Hu, some miles west of Shanghai. The typical I-hsing ware is dark and plain, or decorated with applied, molded, or incised designs; much of it is tea ware or writers' ware (brush stands and brush pots); it was made from the sixteenth century on; many specimens are dated and signed by known craftsmen. On its first arrival in Europe it was confused with the American Indian bucaro! The I-hsing teapots exported to Europe in the middle of the seventeenth century are historically important for another reason; as they arrived with the first consignments of tea, they served as models for the first European teapots. Augustus II, elector of Saxony (1670–1733), formed a collection of I-hsing ware in Dresden; this inspired Böttger,[7a] and the latter's creations were copied in Holland, Staffordshire, and Fulham.

Oku Saburōbei: Ming hu t'u lu (2 vols., Tokyo 1878), illustrated account of I-hsing pottery, in Japanese. P'ang Yüan-chi: Hsü chai ming t'ao t'u lu (2 vols., s.a.), catalogue of the Chinese pottery in the collections of P'ang Yüan-chi. Geoffrey Hedley: Yi-hsing ware (Transactions of the Oriental Ceramic Society 14, 70–86, 8 pl., London 1937). R. L. Hobson: Handbook of the pottery and porcelain of the Far East (p. 42–44, British Museum 1937).

To avoid misunderstandings it should be observed that this note concerns the earliest technical description of the making of glazed pottery. The history of the manufacture itself is a different matter. Glazed pottery, faïence, glass were first made in Egypt, the Near East, the Mesopotamian region, about the beginning of the second millennium B.C. if not earlier. Chinese manufacture is certainly much later. Laufer (p. 120, 1917) stated that glazed pottery first appeared during the Han period (206 B.C.–A.D. 221), and was unknown before. Since then, specimens of Chinese glass have been discovered dating from the middle of the sixth century B.C. In any case the question remains, Was the glazing rediscovered by the Chinese or was it derived by them from the Mediterranean or Mesopotamian region, or from Īrān? Laufer concluded that the second alternative was the true one.

See my very incomplete account of ancient glass (Introd. 1, 389). Berthold Laufer: The beginnings of porcelain in China (Chicago 1917; Isis 3, 131). William Charles White: Tombs of old Lo-yang (Shanghai 1934). G. Sarton: Chinese glass of the beginning of the Confucian age (Isis 25, 73–79, 2 fig., 1936).

One of the best-known Chinese scholars writing about porcelain was Lang T'ing-chi (1663–1715), himself a porcelain maker; but he dealt mainly with a much later period, K'ang hsi (Hummel p. 441, 1943).

AL-JILDAKĪ

'Izz al-dīn 'Alī ibn Aidamur ibn 'Alī al-Jildakī. Muslim alchemist (fl. Cairo and Damascus c. 1339–42). The date of his death is uncertain, 1342/43 or 1360/61?; he died in Cairo.

He is the last important Arabic writer on alchemy, but he came too late to influence Western science. Some twenty treatises are ascribed to him; I shall mention only those about which I have some information to communicate. I quote them in alphabetic order.

1. Al-badr al-munīr fī asrār al-iksīr (The brilliant moon on the secrets of elixir).

[7a] Johann Friedrich Böttger (or Böttiger, 1682–1719), alchemist and so-called inventor of porcelain.

This is one of the author's commentaries on the Shudhūr al-dhahab[8] fī fann al-salāmāt of the Spaniard 'Alī ibn Mūsā Ibn Arfa' ra'sahu (XII-2). Another commentary of his on the same book is entitled Ghāyat al-surūr; judging from its preface, it is philosophical rather than technical.

2. Bughyat al-khabīr fī qānūn ṭalab al-iksīr (The wish of the expert . . .), composed at Damascus 1339/40.

3. Al-burhān fī asrār 'ilm al-mīzān. Elaborate work divided into four parts and dealing not only with alchemy ('ilm al-mīzān, or 'ilm al-mawāzīn, science of scales, title of one of the Jābir books), but with natural history, physics, and metaphysics. It includes commentaries on a treatise of Balīnās or Balīnūs[9] on the seven bodies (planets and metals), and on the treatises on the seven bodies and on the balances ascribed to Jābir ibn Ḥaiyān (VIII-2).

4. Al-durr al-manthūr (The scattered pearls). Another commentary on the Shudhūr al-dhahab, composed in 1342/43, mentioned by Leclerc (1876).

5. Al-durr al-maknūn fī sharḥ qaṣīdat Dhī-l-Nūn (Hidden pearls). Commentary on an alchemical (mystical) treatise by the Egyptian Dhū-l-Nūn (IX-2), written in Cairo 1342.

6. Ghāyat al-surūr (Limit of joy). See no. 1. Mentioned by the author in the preface to his Miṣbāḥ (no. 9).

7. Al-ikhtiṣāṣ wa-durrat al-ghawwāṣ fī asrār al-khawāṣṣ. Natural and occult properties of animals and stones.

8. Kashf al-sutūr (Removing of the veils). Another commentary on the Shudhūr al-dhahab, quoted by Leclerc (1876).

9. Al-miṣbāḥ fī asrār 'ilm al-miftāḥ (The lamp on the secrets of alchemy). 'Ilm al-miftāḥ is another of the many names of alchemy. In the preface the author gives a brief history of Arabic alchemy, speaking of his own works on the subject (nos. 3, 6) and of his seven main authorities, who are, in chronological order, the amīr Khālid ibn Yazīd (VII-2), Jābir ibn Ḥaiyān (VIII-2), Muḥammad ibn Umail al-Tamīmī, Maslama ibn Aḥmad al-Majrīṭī (X-2), al-Ḥusain ibn 'Alī al-Tughrā'ī (XII-1), 'Alī ibn Mūsā Ibn Arfa' ra'sahu (XII-2), Abū-l-Qāsim al-'Irāqī (XIII-2).[10]

10. Mukhammas al-mā' al-waraqī. Quintessence of the Kitāb al-mā' al-waraqī wal-arḍ al-najmīya (Silvery water and starry earth) of Muḥammad ibn Umail al-Tamīmī. The Quintessence was composed in Damascus 1340.

11. Natā'ij al-fikar fī aḥwāl al-ḥajar.

12. Nihāyat al-ṭalab (End of the search) fī sharḥ al-muktasab. Extensive commentary on the Kitāb al-'ilm al-muktasab fī zirā'at al-dhahab (Knowledge acquired concerning the cultivation of gold) of Abū-l-Qāsim al-'Irāqī (XIII-2). This commentary on one of the most important books of Arabic alchemy seems to be itself quite important. It contains many quotations from earlier works, e.g., from

[8] With regard to the Shudhūr al-dhahab, see my note on Abū Ḥaiyān. Of course, this same title (or beginning of title) may have been given and was actually given to different works. For example, one of the grammatical treatises of Ibn Hishām is called Shudhūr al-dhahab (Brockelmann 2, 24, 1902); it was often printed in Būlāq and Cairo.

[9] That is, Apollonios of Tyana, who flourished in the first century (Isis 3, 319; Introd. 1, 320). See Carra de Vaux: Balīnūs (EI 1, 620, 1911).

[10] All of whom have been dealt with at their proper places in my Introduction, except Muḥammad ibn Umail al-Tamīmī, who flourished at the end of the ninth century and the beginning of the tenth. Brockelmann (1, 241, 1898; suppt. 1, 429, 1937). M. Turāb 'Alī, H. E. Stapleton, M. Hidāyat Ḥusain: Three Arabic treatises on alchemy by Muḥammad bin Umail (Memoirs of the Asiatic Society of Bengal 12, 1–213, Calcutta 1933; Isis 24, 310–42, J. Ruska). This al-Tamīmī should not be confused with Muḥammad ibn Aḥmad al-Tamīmī (X-2), Palestinian physician.

those ascribed to Jābir ibn Ḥaiyān, and some novelties, as the use of nitric acid to extract silver out of gold-silver alloy. Al-Jildakī remarked that substances do not react except by definite weights.

13. Sharḥ qaṣīdat abī-l-Aṣba'. Commentary on an alchemical poem of Abū-l-Aṣba' 'Abd al-'Azīz ibn Tammām al-'Irāqī, who flourished in Maiyāfāriqīn (northeast of Diyārbakr, upper Tigris) in the tenth century. That commentary is also called Kashf al-asrār (Brockelmann 1, 524, 1898).

14. Sharḥ al-shams al-akbar li Balīnās. Commentary on the greater sun of Apollonios of Tyana (see no. 3).

15. Al-taqrīb fī-l-asrār al-kīmiyā' (or, fī asrār al-tarkīb) (Introduction to the secrets of alchemy).

This list, which is incomplete, is sufficient to show al-Jildakī's great activity as an alchemical writer. It is interesting to note that all his writings dealt almost exclusively with alchemy. A study of them is as desirable as difficult, for to assess their value it would be necessary to know very well the contents of the vast alchemical literature used by him. That examination has been begun by such men as Ruska, Stapleton, Holmyard, and their disciples, but much remains to be done, and relatively few of the texts are available in critical editions; many are known only in MS.

Text. 1. Shudhūr al-dhahab, with al-Jildakī's commentary (152 p., lithog., Bombay 1881).

9. Misbāḥ (160 p., lithog., Cairo 1884).

11. Natā'ij. Undated edition, Būlāq.

12. Nihāya. Persian edition together with Jābir ibn Ḥaiyān (151 p., lithog., Bombay 1890).

There is not a single critical edition, nor any translation.

Criticism. Wüstenfeld (p. 150, 1840). Leclerc (2, 280–82, 1876). Brockelmann (2, 138, 1902; suppt. 2, 171, 1938). Eilhard Wiedemann: Zur Alchemie bei den Arabern (Abhandlungen zur Geschichte der Wissenschaften no. 5, p. 21–24, Erlangen 1922; Isis 5, 534); Beiträge zur Mineralogie usw. bei den Arabern (Lippmann Festschrift p. 48–51, Berlin 1927). E. J. Holmyard: Chemistry to the time of Dalton (p. 29, London 1925; Isis 8, 616); Aidamir al-Jildaki (Iraq 4, 47–53, 1937; Isis 35, 226), important study seen too late to be incorporated in this note.

9. ALCHEMY IN BUDDHIST ASIA

LU YU

Chinese author of a history of ink manufacturers[11] (fl. c. 1329).

Lu Yu, style Yu Jên, also Chai Chih, was a native of P'ing Chiang. His book entitled Mo shih, in 3 chüan, deals with 130 ink manufacturers from the Wei dynasty to the Sung dynasty.

Another work of his, a collection of miscellaneous essays entitled Yen pei tsa chih, has a preface by himself dated 1329. This establishes his floruit.

CH'ÊN KUAN-WU

Chinese alchemist and Taoist (fl. c. 1331).

Ch'ên Kuan-wu, alias Shang-yăng-tzŭ, alias Chih hsü. His dates and place of birth and death are unknown to me. Various alchemical writings are ascribed to him, to wit:

[11] Real black ink (lamp black) had been reinvented in China in the fourth or fifth century. Red ink (cinnabar) was already used in the Han dynasty if not before. Egyptians knew both inks, black and red, long before the Chinese (Introd. 1, 369).

1. A commentary on the Ts'an t'ung ch'i written by Wei Po-yang, Taoist and alchemist of the second century (Giles no. 2287, 1898).

2. A short preface ($1\frac{1}{2}$ p. in the original) to the Hsien fo t'ung yüan lun (The Taoist immortals and Buddha are of the same origin), by the mathematician Chao Yu-ch'in.

3. A song on an idea ($2\frac{1}{2}$ p. in original).

4. Chin tan ta yao (Essentials of the gold medicine), in 10 chüan.

The last item is the most important; it deals with theoretical alchemy and the tao, and contains a number of pictures and diagrams. At least that is the case in the Ming edition of the alchemical collection called Chin tan chêng li ta ch'üan, in 24 chüan, the title of which might be translated, Comprehensive account of the genuine preparation of the gold medicine. That collection contains the four items above mentioned; according to its editor, the main treatise, Chin tan ta yao, was written during the Chih Shun years (1330–32) of the rule of Wên Ti (Yüan emperor 1329–32). We may thus date it c. 1331.

Text. The Ming edition cited above was printed during the first rule of the emperor Ying Tsung (1436–50). It was a reprint from a Yüan edition.

Criticism. Wieger (no. 1053, 1911). William H. Barnes: Diagrams of Chinese alchemical apparatus (Journal of chemical education 13, 453–57, 11 fig., 1936). Tenney L. Davis: Pictorial representations of alchemical theory (Isis 28, 73–86, 9 fig., 1938). T. L. Davis and Chao Yün-ts'ung (Proceedings of the American Academy of Arts and Sciences 73, 371–99, Boston 1940; Isis 33, 90, 95), including a description and table of contents of the Chin tan chêng li ta ch'üan (p. 391–99). William Jerome Wilson: Alchemy in China (Ciba symposia 2, 594–624, 1940). T. L. Davis and Ch'ên Kuo-fu: Shang-yang tzŭ (Harvard journal of Asiatic studies 7, 126–29, 4 pl., 1942).

This note was largely written on the basis of a letter kindly written to me by professor T. L. Davis (Cambridge, Mass., May 15, 1940) before his papers of 1940 were available.

CH'ÊN CH'UN

Chinese commissioner of the salt gabelle at Shanghai (fl. c. 1334).

Ch'ên Ch'un was a native of T'ient'ai. The dates of his birth and death are unknown. During the period Yüan-t'ung (1333–35) of the Yüan dynasty he was commissioner of the salt gabelle in Hsia sha ch'ang, at that time under the jurisdiction of Shanghai. On the basis of earlier works and of his own experience he wrote the book Ao po t'u, dealing with the manufacture of salt, with a set of 47 figures drawn by the Ch'ü (?) brothers: Shou-jên (H., Lo-shan) and Shou-i (H., Ho-shan). These figures were beautifully drawn and were entrusted to him by Ho-shan's son, T'ien-hsi (H., Ching-chai). The book was included in the Yung Lo ta tien, but with only 42 figures, 5 being lost.

Text. The Harvard-Yenching library has a rare manuscript of the Ao po t'u, whence the information given above was derived. This manuscript, completed in 1781 by a court artist and a scribe under the order of emperor Ch'ien-lung (ruled 1736–1796), was redrawn from the copy in the Yung Lo ta tien and was a first draft intended for inclusion in the Ssŭ k'u ch'üan shu.

Since the Ming manuscript was lost to the world with the partial destruction of the Yung Lo ta tien in 1860, and since no printed editions have ever been discovered in China or in Japan, the Harvard manuscript is now the earliest extant copy of this important work.

This note was kindly revised and amplified by Dr. A. Kaiming Chiu, librarian of the Harvard-Yenching Institute, on May 8, 1945.

CHAPTER IX

GEOGRAPHY

(First Half of the Fourteenth Century)

N.B. Only the main notes are published in this chapter. The geographical contributions of many other men, whose main work was done in other fields, are related in other chapters. For a general survey of geography in the first half of the fourteenth century see section IX of chapter I. More information on the men referred to in that survey may then easily be found by means of the index.

A. LATIN WEST

A1. Italy

VESCONTE

Pietro Vesconte (or Visconte). Genoese cartographer who flourished 1311–20; in 1318 he was in Venice.

We owe him a number of portolani, which deserve to be considered one by one:

1. The first is dated 1311, this being the earliest dated portolano. It is worth noting that that earliest dated map is Italian. It measures 48 by 62 cm., was discovered in 1880, and is now preserved in the state archives of Florence.

It deals mainly with the eastern Mediterranean and the Black Sea, but it extends westward far enough to include Corsica and Sardinia. The northern coast of Africa is indicated as far as Ras Hadid in Algeria. Only the coasts and islands are dealt with, the hinterland being entirely neglected. Scales are indicated in the upper and lower margins.

2. Atlas of 1313. This atlas includes six leaves of parchment 50 by 31 cm. It formerly belonged to prince Roland Bonaparte and is now in the Bibliothèque nationale, Paris. The first leaf contains a calendary, an Easter table, and the author's name, Petrus Vesconte de Janua, and date 1313. Leaf 2, Black Sea to the Dardanelles. Leaf 3, Greek archipelago to southern Candia (Crete). Leaf 4, eastern Mediterranean from Asia Minor to Egypt. Leaf 5, Tyrrhenian Sea with Corsica, Sardinia, Sicily, and North Africa. Leaf 6, western Mediterranean with northwest coast of Africa and Atlantic coast upward to England and the Netherlands.

3. Atlas of 1318. Atlas of seven leaves 25 by 15 cm., now in the Museo civico, Venice. Contents: (1) astronomical table, (2) Black Sea, (3) Aegean Sea, (4) Adriatic, (5) Tyrrhenian Sea and North Africa, (6) western Mediterranean with Spain and North Africa, (7) Northwestern Europe. The last map bears the author's name and date, Venice 1318.

4. Second atlas of 1318. By calling it "second" we do not mean to imply that it is necessarily posterior to the "first" atlas. Both atlases bear the same date, 1318, without further precision; the "first" atlas is dated Venice 1318, the "second" 1318, without mention of place. Contents: (1) eastern Mediterranean to Candia, (2) middle part between North Africa, southern Italy, and Sicily, (3) part between Italy, Sicily, and the Balearic Islands, (4) east and south coasts of Spain, North Africa, (5) Adriatic, (6) Archipelago, (7) French, Spanish, Portuguese Atlantic

coast from Ouessant (near Brest) to the Berlengas (or Burlings) Islands (39°25′N.), (8) northwest European coast to England and Denmark, (9) Black Sea. A tenth leaf bears the author's name and date, 1318. The leaves measure 19 by 18.5 cm. and are now in the National Library in Vienna.

5. Atlas of 1320. Atlas of ten leaves discovered by Kretschmer in the Vatican library (Cod. Palatinus 1362), containing eight maps: (1) round planisphere, (2) Black Sea, (3) Greece and the Archipelago, (4) eastern Mediterranean, (5) Adriatic; southeastern Spain, North Africa, (6) western Europe, (7) Palestine, (8) Jerusalem and Ptolemais (Acre). Leaf 9 bears a synchronic table of patriarchs, counts, and princes of the Crusaders' states. The atlas is signed and dated 1320, but without indication of place.

6. Atlas of 1320 or 1321 attached to the Liber secretorum fidelium crucis written by Marino Sanudo il Vecchio and presented by him to John XXII in Avignon 1321 (see my note on Sanudo). There are nine MSS of this atlas, which differ somewhat, in the number and choice of maps, from each other as well as from the Cod. Palatinus 1362, dealt with in our no. 5. The Cod. Vaticanus 2972 seems to be the very copy offered to the pope. It is almost certain that the maps attached to Sanudo's project were made by Pietro Vesconte or under the latter's immediate supervision. The Cod. Palatinus 1362 and Cod. Vaticanus 2972 tally completely, except that the maps of Palestine, Jerusalem, and Ptolemais are lacking in the latter.

7, 8. To these maps and atlases may still be added an atlas and a map made by one Perrinus Vesconte de Janua in Venice, in 1321 and 1327. Is Perrinus Vesconte identical with Petrus Vesconte? Note that both are Genoese, live in Venice, and flourish at about the same time. Perrinus might be a copyist's error for Petrus, or Perrinus might be a son or brother or other relative? In the second case, would he not have revealed his relationship rather than hidden it? Or he might be an imitator and plagiarist? The first hypothesis (copyist's error, identity of Perrinus and Petrus) seems more plausible to me.

7. Atlas of Perrinus Vesconte, Venice 1321. Now preserved in the library of Zürich. Beautiful atlas illustrated with miniatures: (1) British Isles; western coast of Europe from Denmark on; Spanish peninsula to the Gulf of Lions and the Baleares, and North Africa down to Mogador (31°32′N.); (2) the middle Mediterranean, including the Baleares, Corsica, Sardinia, Sicily, and mouth of the Adriatic to Durazzo; (3) the Archipelago and the surrounding coasts to the Dardanelles; (4) Black Sea; (5) calendarial tables.

8. Map made by Perrinus Vesconte in Venice 1327. Size 94 by 58 cm. Preserved in the Laurentiana, Florence. Map of Europe and North Africa as far as Mogador, showing the coasts only. Two compass roses extend over the map, and there is also a scale.

Text. Facsimile della carta nautica di Pietro Vesconte dell' anno 1311 (Venezia 1881). Facsimile del portolano dell'anno 1318 (7 pl., Venezia 1875). Both facsimiles are also included in Theobald Fischer's Raccolta (1871–81; nos. 2, 4). There are other reproductions in collections like Nordenskiöld's Periplus (1897), etc.

Criticism. Kretschmer (p. 110–17, 1909), including bibliography relative to each map or atlas. R. D. Oldham: The portolan maps of the Rhône delta (Geographical journal 65, 403–28, 1925; Isis 8, 746). Oldham's paper deals with Vesconte's maps only incidentally, but it is an important contribution to the comparative study of portolani.

CARIGNANO

Giovanni di Carignano. Genoese cartographer (d. 1344).

Giovanni di Carignano, alias Presbiter Joannes, rector Marci de portu Janue, was rector of St. Mark's in Genoa from c. 1306 to 1344. He was author of one of the oldest portolani, in fact of the fourth oldest, if we call the Carte pisane (end of thirteenth century) the first, the Tammar Luxoro atlas (see note below) the second, and Pietro Vesconte's (1311) the third. Carignano's map dates from about 1320; it is very superior in scope and technique to the earlier maps. It measures 92 by 62 cm., and is now preserved in the archives of Florence.

It represents not only the Mediterranean world, but the whole of Europe, Western Asia, North Africa (to Cape Nun). It includes the whole of the Black Sea, Ireland, the Scandinavian peninsula (thus represented for the first time), the first representation of the Sahara. With regard to the latter Giovanni had obtained his information from a Genoese merchant established in Sijilmāsa in the Tāfīlālt (Sijilmāsa, some 200 miles south-southeast of Fez, is an ancient Roman settlement, and the Muslims were well acquainted with it;[1] Ibn Baṭṭūṭa visited it in 1351–52. But its mention in Giovanni's map was its first appearance in the Western Christian tradition.) In a note to his map Giovanni describes the Berber traffic across the Sahara. It took them forty days to cross the forbidding desert from Sijilmāsa to the Walata (Biru) oasis and to Guinea.

One of the most curious features of this map is the relative positions and sizes of the seas; for example, the Baltic is very large, almost parallel to the Mediterranean, and its eastern end comes very close to the Black Sea. This proves that the map was not based on the astronomical determination of a number of points, but was rather drawn step by step on the basis of sailing directions.

A remark made in Introd. 2 (p. 1049) concerning the existence of a decimal scale in the Moorish chart of the Ambrogiana (Milano) and in Carignano's chart is misleading and needs correction. There are mile scales on both sides of Carignano's chart, and the scales are explained, but unfortunately the explanation is almost illegible. One can barely read the words ". . . miliaria decem maius spacium denotat miliaria quinquaginta. . . ." The indications of lengths corresponding to 10 miles and to 50 miles do not constitute a decimal scale; the most that we can say is that it is a scale the unit of which represents 10 miles.

Text. Facsimile del planisfero di prete Giovanni da Carignano di Genova (Venice 1881).

Criticism. Beazley (3, 513, 518, 1906). Kretschmer (p. 109–10, 1909). La Roncière (1, 113, pl. vi, ix, 1925), with good facsimile. Kimble (p. 192, 1938).

NOTE ON THE SO-CALLED TAMMAR LUXORO ATLAS

I should have spoken of this little but important atlas in my volume 2, p. 1047–50, when I dealt with the earliest portolani, but it is not too late to do it here and now. It is supposed to be the second in date of portolani, the first being the Carte pisane, and to be anterior to the fourteenth century (though this cannot be proved); it is almost certainly anterior to Carignano's map.

It is called after the name of its owner, the Genoese landscape painter Tammar Luxoro (1824–99), and still belongs, I believe, to Luxoro's family. It includes eight maps, very small (15 by 11 cm.), but prepared with great care and consid-

[1] EI 4, 404–5, 603, 1927–28.

erable minuteness: (1) western coast of Europe from Holland on, French and Spanish coasts down to Finisterre, Galicia; parts of England and Ireland; (2) continuation of Spanish coast, southern coast of France, Baleares, North Africa; (3) part of the Mediterranean between the Baleares and central Italy, containing Corsica, Sardinia, and part of the North African coast; (4) next part of the Mediterranean, extending eastward to the Greek-Albanian coast, with the relevant slice of the African coast; (5) Adriatic; (6) Archipelago and surrounding coasts in Europe, Asia, and Africa; (7) Levantine and Egyptian coasts; (8) Black Sea.

Cornelio Desimoni and Luigi Tommaso Belgrano: Atlante idrografico del medio evo posseduto dal prof. Tammar Luxoro pubblicato a facsimile ed annotato (168 p., 8 facs., Genova 1867); this includes facsimiles, complete nomenclature with modern equivalents, fully indexed. Kretschmer (p. 108, 1909).

DALORTO AND DULCERT

Angellino (or Angelino) de Dalorto (or dell' Orto) is the author of a mappemonde dated 1325 (or 1330). He belonged probably to a Genoese family. The reading Dalorco (or dal'Orco, related to Orca Peligno in the Ligurian Apennines) is less plausible.

Dalorto's map reproduces Europe, North Africa, and Western Asia in the portolan style. It measures 107 by 66 cm. and is owned by prince Tommaso Corsini of Florence. It bears the title "Hoc opus fecit Angellinus de Dalorto ano domini MCCCXXV [or XXX?] de mense martii composuit hoc." As in the portolani, the main emphasis is on the shore lines of the Mediterranean and the northeast Atlantic, yet the map contains much information concerning the hinterlands. In fact, it is one of the first maps on which enough information of that kind is given, e.g., concerning rivers and towns.

There is in the Bibliothèque nationale, Paris, another map obviously derived from the first, but larger (145 by 75 cm.) and more detailed, made in the city of Majorca (Palma de Mallorca) in 1339. It bears the inscription "Hoc opus fecit Angellino Dulcert anno MCCCXXXVIIII de mense Augusti in civitate maioricarum." According to experienced cartographers, both maps must have been made originally by the same man. On that basis we should assume that the name Dulcert on the second is a copyist's error, or that Dalorto changed his name and Catalanized it when he moved to Majorca. This assumption (the identity of Dalorto and Dulcert) is extremely plausible but not certain. It remains possible that a Catalan cartographer called Angellino Dulcert flourished at about the same time as the Genoese Angellino Dalorto and copied the latter's work, improving it.

The map of 1339 is more extensive toward the east than the earlier one, including the western shore of the Caspian and the Persian Gulf. Many significant details are common to the two maps, e.g., various islands north of the British Isles, which are lacking in the Catalan map of 1375 and the Soleri map of 1385. The map of 1339 illustrates the recent discoveries of the Genoese in the Canaries. The first map knows of the North African Sahara only Sijilmāsa (like Giovanni di Carignano, c. 1320); the map of 1339 indicates the road leading across the Atlas Mountains to the king of the gold mines (rex melli), this being the earliest cartographical reference to Mali. Each map is built on a rectangular canvas made of equal squares, as if the separating lines were meridians and parallels.

E. T. Hamy: La mappemonde d'Angelino Dulcert de Majorque 1339 (Bulletin de géographie historique et descriptive no. 6, 15 p., Paris 1887). Alberto Magnaghi: Angellinus de Dalorco (Rivista geografica italiana 4, 282–94, 361–69, 1897); La carta nautica costruita nel 1325 (folio, 15 p., with full-sized facsimile, Firenze 1898). Beazley (3, 522–23, 1906). Kretschmer (p. 117–19, 1909). La Roncière (1, 122, pl. vii, 1925). R. D. Oldham: The portolan maps of the Rhône delta (Geographical journal 65, 403–28, ill., 1925; Isis 8, 746). Bovill (p. 74, 1933). Kimble (p. 114, 1938).

A colored facsimile reproduction of the Dalorto map of 1325 was published by the Royal Geographical Society (London before 1929). I have not seen it, but it is referred to by Edward Heawood: Reproductions of notable early maps (Geographical journal 76, 240–48, 1930).

OPICINUS DE CANISTRIS

Opicinus de Canistris, Opicius de Papia. Priest and author. Born on December 24, 1296, in Lomello, district of Pavia, he considered Pavia his native city. He belonged to a Guelph family and had to suffer from the vicissitudes of political struggles, especially after 1315, when Pavia had fallen into the hands of the Ghibelline leader Galeazzo Visconti of Milano, and was ruled by the Pavian-Ghibelline family Beccaria. Opicinus' family was impoverished, his education interrupted, and he was obliged to support himself in various ways. In 1315, his family fled to Genoa, where he earned a living as a limner of manuscripts. In 1318, he returned to Pavia with his widowed mother and sisters; in 1323, he became curate of Santa Maria Capella. In 1327, he was again obliged to leave the city; he went to Tortona, Alessandria, Valenza; finally, in the spring of 1329, he established himself in Avignon, where he spent the remainder of his life, in exile.

Sometime after his arrival in Avignon, poor in health and poorer still in money, he was appointed by John XXII (pope 1316–1334) a clerk (scriptor) in the poenitentiaria (the penitentiary tribunal of the curia). He held that position at least until 1348. He was still living in 1350, and died probably in 1352.

He had obtained a good education; his Latin was correct but colorless, he had a sufficient knowledge of the Bible, the canons, the compotus, and was very well acquainted with the geography of northern Italy.

The most important of his writings are:

1. Tractatus de preeminentia spiritualis imperii (Avignon 1329). Mediocre treatise in defense of the church against the empire, dedicated to John XXII.

2. Liber de laudibus civitatis Ticinensis, or Libellus de descriptione Papie (Avignon 1330; not 1318–21, as in Muratori). A charming book in praise of his native city, representing a type of literature not uncommon in those days, when local patriotism was extremely intensified.

3. An astonishing collection of drawings with text, including maps and schemas of various kinds. This, being his most original production, and the raison d'être of his inclusion in our Introduction, will be described at greater length.

This collection, forming Codex Palatinus latinus 1993 (Vatican), contains 27 sheets of parchment of unequal sizes, 70 to 97 cm. in length and 50 (or less) to 72 cm. in breadth. All these sheets except two are used on both sides; there are thus 52 pages covered with drawings, charts, and notices. Every composition is posterior to February 1335; sheet 20 (a graphical autobiography, 1296–1336) is dated June 3, 1336; the majority of the other drawings were completed by 1336. Hence the date of the album is 1335–36, with perhaps a few later additions.

Many of the compositions are maps, and almost all of them (not only the maps) indicate the cardinal points, this being done in the mediaeval manner (east at the top). The directions of the compass are given moral as well as geographical meanings: east, origin of light; north, region of sin, etc. Some of his maps are remarkably accurate, e.g., those relative to northern Italy. The form of these maps, and their purely geographical contents, are comparable to the best cartographical work of that time, but the spirit is vastly different. It is intellectual rather than practical, synthetic rather than analytic. Opicinus' main interests are theological; he tries to bring out the symbolic truth hidden behind the geographical facts; and introduces various occult comparisons (e.g., Europe to a man, Africa to a woman). About the Mediterranean (table 41 right), he remarks: "Hoc mare non est peccatum, sed testimonium peccati. Similiter terra non est peccatrix, sed testificatio peccatoris." Everything is given a deeper, symbolic, interpretation. Thus, though his maps are comparable in form to the contemporary portolani or topographical maps, in substance they go back to the earliest mappae mundi, the Beatus maps and wheel maps. His moralizing tendencies are always to the fore (e.g., see table 34), and hence his maps are good examples of the "cartes moralisées."

Many tables are decorated with calendrical borders (the letters a b c d e f g repeated 52 times, plus a), which were probably imitated from contemporary portolani, e.g., one of those of Petrus Visconte. There are other calendrical particularities, often as ingenious as they are futile. Opicinus also liked to replace the common designations of days by new ones more cryptic (e.g., for March 21, instead of "Benedicti," "benedictio patris"; for September 12, instead of "adventus Syri et Yventii in Papiam," "seminatio fidei super terram"). Thus his calendar becomes a "calendrier moralisé" completing the "carte moralisée."

Above all, he reveled in complicated tabular combinations, cross-shaped or arranged in other symbolic forms involving all kinds of parallelisms. This was but a personal amplification of a general characteristic of mediaeval thought, East and West.

These tables contain naturally many references to the zodiac, though here too the author cannot resist the temptation of replacing common designations by cryptic ones, and writing, e.g., instead of aries, agnus, or oves gregis, or agni novelli; instead of virgo, filia virginis, or filie Babylonis, or virginibus proxime.

The most curious of all these tables is table 20, which is a unique document in mediaeval literature: Opicinus' autobiography in schematic arrangement. Around a circular center containing the Virgin and Child are drawn 40 concentric circles, each of which is divided into 366 parts; thus every day of his first 40 years is represented by a definite point. The circles bear autobiographical data, each in its proper chronological space. On account of their necessary terseness and of their candor, these data constitute a very remarkable confession, almost without equivalent in mediaeval times. Compare the autobiographical remarks included in the chronicle of Thietmar of Merseburg (XI-1; see Introd. 1, 733). Opicinus was dangerously self-centered, pessimistic, humble, pedantic, an astrological dilettante with occult and apocalyptic tendencies. Such qualities were probably not uncommon among the learned and the half-learned men of his time. His originality consists rather in his mode of expression, in his graphical and schematic habits.

Text. Tractatus de preeminentia spiritualis imperii. Partly edited by Richard Scholz: Unbekannte kirchenpolitische Streitschriften aus der Zeit Ludwigs des Bayern, 1327–1354, Analysen und Texte (Bibliothek des Kgl. Preussischen historischen Instituts in Rom vols. 9, 10, 1911–14).

Liber de laudibus civitatis Ticinensis. Edited by Muratori in the Rerum italicarum scriptores (vol. 11, 1728).

Criticism. Faustino Gianani: Opicino de Canistris l'anonimo ticinese (163 p., 6 pl., Pavia 1927). Reviewed by Richard Salomon (Göttingische gelehrte Anzeigen, July 1928, p. 305–31).

Richard Salomon: Opicinus de Canistris. Weltbild und Bekenntnisse eines Avignonesischen Klerikers des 14. Jahrhunderts (Studies of the Warburg Institute vol. 1A, text, 348 p., vol. 1B, 45 pl., folio, London 1936; Isis 26, 460–63, 1 pl.).

NICOLOSO DA RECCO

Genoese navigator who sailed from Lisbon on July 1, 1341, in command of one of two ships, for an Atlantic expedition under the patronage of Affonso IV, king of Portugal (1325–57). A Florentine resident in Seville, Angelino del Tegghia de' Corbizzi, was a member of the expedition.

After five days of navigation they made a landfall in one of the Fortunate Islands (Canary Islands). These islands had been reached c. 1270–75 by another Genoese, Lanzarote Malocello, who probably discovered Lanzarote (named after him) and Fuerteventura (marked on the Dulcert map of 1339). Nicoloso reached first Fuerteventura (?), then "Çanaria" (Grand Canary), Ferro (?), Gomera (?), Teneriffe (?) or Palma (?). The question marks are added because it is impossible to identify the islands discovered without ambiguity, the description of them being insufficient. It is certain that Nicoloso and his men discovered many of the Canaries, where they spent all together four months. They brought back to Lisbon in November a diversified cargo, an idol, and prisoners.

An account of the expedition based upon information received from Nicoloso da Recco and other Seville merchants was written by Boccaccio under the title: De Canaria et de insulis reliquis ultra Hispaniam in Oceano noviter repertis. This is the first description of those islands.

Text. First edition by Sebastiano Ciampi: Monumenti d'un manoscritto autografo di messer Giovanni Boccacci (112 p., Firenze 1827). Second edition revised and enlarged (660 p., Milano 1830). In the second edition (I have not seen the first), the text covers p. 55–63, and is followed by an Italian translation. German translation in Hennig (3, 206–20, 1938).

Criticism. Gregorio Chil y Naranjo: Estudios históricos, climatológicos y patológicos de las Islas Canarias (1, 258–67, Las Palmas de Gran-Canaria 1879), includes the Latin text and a Spanish translation. Beazley (3, 424–27, 1906). La Roncière (2, 4–6, 1925).

JAMES OF VERONA

Fra Giacomo da Verona. Augustinian monk born at the end of the thirteenth century; pilgrim to the Holy Land in 1335.

Giacomo and a few companions left Verona on May 7, 1335, sailed from Venice to Otranto, then to Crete (which he confused with Malta), Cyprus, where he witnessed the arrival of a fleet from Ayās (on the coast of Cilicia) with thousands of Armenian refugees fleeing from the Muslims. He continued his journey to Jaffa, Jerusalem, Bethlehem, Ghaza, Mt. Sinai, the Red Sea, Cairo, Damietta, Hebron, Jerusalem, Nazareth, Damascus, Baalbek, Beirūt, Sidon, Tyre, Acca, back to Beirūt, whence he returned home in October 1335.

He wrote a fairly long (140 printed pages) account of his journey, Liber peregrinationis, preceded by a prooemium including a pilgrim's guide, Peregrinationes et indulgentie Terre Sancte, Conductus de via, Benedictio vini in amorem S. Johannis Baptiste. The account itself, divided into 14 chapters, does not simply describe the journey, but gives much incidental information on the Mamlūk citadels and army, chiefly their large cavalry force (many Greek and Latin slaves incorporated in it),[2] the beautiful Mamlūk tombs, the Egyptian and Syrian harbors blocked by huge boulders to prevent the entry of hostile fleets, the Muslim religion and manners, their fanaticism. He obtained some of his information from earlier works, as Burchard of Mount Sion (XIII-2), but most of it from his own observations and interviews with Muslims, Greeks, Latins, and Jews. He praises the topographical knowledge of the last named. Apparently his text was illustrated with sketches, one of which has survived; it indicates the topography around the St. Catherine monastery in Sinai (p. 235 in Röhricht's edition). Giacomo's purpose was double: he wanted to provide a guide for pilgrims and to promote a new crusade.

The text was translated into German before the end of the fifteenth century.

Text. The Liber peregrinationis Fratis Jacobi de Verona was edited by Reinhold Röhricht (Revue de l'Orient latin 3, 155–302, 1895).
Criticism. Golubovich (4, 235–41, 1923). Atiya (p. 165–68, 1938).

MARINO SANUDO IL VECCHIO

Venetian traveler, geographer, publicist, promoter of a new crusade which never materialized (c. 1260 to c. 1337).

Marinus Sanutus Torsellus. Marino Sanudo (or Sanuto) Torsello; Marin Tourxelle. He is called il Vecchio (the Elder) to distinguish him from another great Venetian, Marino Sanudo Torsello il Giovine (1466–1535), who wrote Diari relative to the period 1496–1533.

Marino was born c. 1260 in Venice, the son of Marco Sanudo, a Venetian senator. The name Torsello or Torcello was acquired by some of his ancestors who had lived on the famous Torcello island in the Laguna Veneta. Some members of this Sanudo family, famous throughout the thirteenth and fourteenth centuries, were merchants and traders, others were governors of various Aegean islands. Marino speaks of many visits made to his cousin duke Marco II on the islands of Naxos, Andros, and Amorgos; he accompanied Marco to Negropont.

Marino's early years were spent in Venice and Rome, but the rest of his life was passed mainly in the Near East: in Greece, Cyprus, Rhodes, Armenia, and Alexandria. He made, in all, five trips to the Near East, the last one in 1333. In 1334 he was again in Venice, where he died c. 1337. He also traveled in France, Flanders, Holstein, and visited many cities in Germany and along the shores of the Baltic Sea, trying to arouse enthusiasm for a new crusade.

His Liber secretorum fidelium crucis super Terrae Sanctae recuperatione et conservatione (Secreta . . . , Historia Hierosolymitana, Liber de expeditione Terrae Sanctae, Opus Terrae Sanctae) was begun in 1306, and the final redaction, finished in 1313, was presented to John XXII (pope 1316–34) in 1321 at the papal court in Avignon. A copy was also presented to Philip V (1316–22). The first part of the Secreta, dealing with Biblical history, the Roman conquest, and a history of the

[2] This is confirmed from many sources. Genoese traders were commissioned by the Mamlūk government to obtain slaves from Caffa, and were many times reproved and excommunicated by the popes for doing so (Atiya p. 199, 433, 1938).

Crusades, depends in large part upon the works of Vincent of Beauvais (XIII-2), Jacques de Vitry (XIII-1), and William of Tyre (XII-2).

The most important part of the work is that which deals with his plan for recapturing the Holy Land, which had been completely lost when the Mamelukes had captured Acre in 1291. First, he said, the power of the sulṭān should be destroyed in Egypt; this could be accomplished by forbidding trade between Christians and all subjects of the sulṭān, by forbidding any ships to stop in Egypt, and by establishing a fleet to patrol the Mediterranean. Marino's plan was very similar to that proposed by Ramon Lull in his Liber de fine (Montpellier 1305) and even as early as 1288, but he was able to work it out in more detail because of his greater practical knowledge. After three years of this blockade, the sulṭān could easily be subdued by a concerted attack upon Egypt and Syria, if possible, with the help of the Tatars. In one of his letters, written at a much later date, Marino admits that this theory of trade suspension was impossible of execution. He also advocated the union of the Greek and Latin churches.

The purpose of the Secreta was political, but the book is of great importance for the student of economic and geographic history. It contains more abundant and more detailed information on trade roads and trade conditions than any other mediaeval writing, and in that respect may be considered the pioneer of the kind of statistical works (in the old sense) represented in the sixteenth century by the Cosmographia of Sebastian Münster (1537) and the Relationi universali of Giovanni Botero (1593).[3] It is also very valuable for the history of navigation and shipbuilding, for it explains for the use of the crusaders the best methods of equipping and manning their ships and the best itineraries. It contains no mention of gunpowder or firearms.

Sanudo had added maps to his treatise, e.g., in the copy presented to the pope in 1321. These maps are similar to those of Pietro Vesconte, author of the earliest dated portolan (1311; Introd. 2, 1048, and note above); they must be based upon them, or derived from common (Arabic?) sources. There are all together, at the end of the Secreta, three plans (of Jerusalem, Antioch, and Acre) and seven maps, dealing with the world (mappe mundi), the Mediterranean, the Black Sea, the west coast of Europe (these being regular portolani), Palestine, and Egypt. The map of Palestine is divided into spatia (squares used on maps for reference in locating cities), a system followed by other fourteenth-century writers. Marino probably was never in Palestine itself, except in Acre (c. 1282–86), so for the topography of that region he depended chiefly on James of Vitry (XIII-1) and Burchard of Mount Sion (XIII-2).

The Historia de regno de Romania, once thought to be apocryphal, has now been definitely identified as Marino's second and best work. It was written between 1328 and 1333, not long after the Chronicle of Morea (q.v.). Marino's work is of much more historical value than that chronicle, since he was able to acquire valuable first-hand information from his cousin Marco Sanudo II, duke of Naxos, and a number of other eyewitnesses of the most important events.

His letters are as valuable as his chronicles for the history of this period; they deal with the following subjects: new crusades to the Holy Land; the proposed alliance between the Tatars and the papacy; literary, artistic, and economic activities in Venice and Flanders; Venetian trade with Hamburg, Lübeck, Wismar, and other Hanseatic towns.

[3] For the appreciation of Sanudo as a statistician and economist, see Heyd (vol. 2, 1886).

Sanudo's influence continued much longer than one would expect. For example, Leibniz was acquainted with the Secreta fidelium crucis through the princeps, edited in Hanover 1611 by the French Calvinist Jacques Bongars (1554–1612), and Sanudo's treatise suggested his own De expeditione aegyptica, addressed to Louis XIV in 1671, wherein he advised the king to conquer Egypt and destroy the Turkish empire instead of undertaking a campaign against Holland (Leibniz' autograph MS in the Hanover library). Leibniz' proposal was not presented to the king; it had no chance of being considered, for Louis XIV was then negotiating a new treaty of commerce and amity with the Sublime Porte! On the other hand, Bonaparte's expedition to Egypt was undertaken without knowledge of Leibniz' views, and presumably without knowledge of Sanudo's.

Text. Liber secretorum fidelium crucis super Terrae Sanctae recuperatione, edited by Jacques Bongars: Gesta Dei per Francos (2, 1–288, Hanover 1611), a poor edition, parts of the manuscript are omitted. Book III, part XI, ch. 6–9, edited by Reinhold Röhricht: Testimonia minora de quinto bello sacro (p. 252–58, Geneva 1882). An English translation of book III, part XIV by Aubrey Stewart (Palestine Pilgrims' Text Society 29, 1–73, 3 maps, London 1896).

Epistolae (23), edited by Jacques Bongars: Gesta Dei (2, 289–316, Hanover 1611). Friedrich Kunstmann: Studien über Marino Sanudo den Aelteren mit einem Anhange seiner ungedruckten Briefe (Abhandlungen der Kgl. Bayerischen Akad. der Wissenschaften, hist. Cl., 7, 695–819, 1855). Charles de La Roncière and L. Rorez: Lettres inédites et mémoires de Marino Sanudo l'ancien 1334–1337 (Bibliothèque de l'Ecole des chartes 56, 21–44, Paris 1895), 9 letters with an interesting introduction. Fragmentum, probably part of a letter, edited by Karl Hopf: Chroniques gréco-romanes (p. 171–74, Berlin 1873).

Historia del regno di Romania, edited by Karl Hopf: Chroniques gréco-romanes (p. 99–170, Berlin 1873), a fourteenth-century Italian translation of the Latin original, which is now lost.

A collection of fragments of unedited works of Marino Sanudo, edited by R. Fulin (Archivio veneto 22, 1–154, 1881).

Criticism. Friedrich Kunstmann: Studien über Marino Sanudo den Aelteren (Abhlandlungen der Kgl. Bayerischen Akad. der Wissenschaften, hist. Cl., 7, 695–819, Munich 1855). A. Postansque: De Marini Sanuti vita et scriptis (Paris thesis, 102 p., Montpellier 1855). E. H. F. Meyer (4, 113–14, 1857). H. Simonsfeld: Intorno a Marino Sanuto il Vecchio (Archivio veneto 24, 251–79, Venice 1882). Maurice Faucon: Marino Sanudo à Avignon (Mélanges d'archéologie et d'histoire 2, 222–23, Paris 1882). Röhricht (p. 67–68, 1890). Konrad Kretschmer: Marino Sanudo der Aeltere und die Karten des Petrus Vesconte (Zeitschrift der Gesellschaft für Erdkunde zu Berlin 26, 352–70, Berlin 1891). Cornelio Desimoni: Una carta della Terra Santa del secolo XIV . . . Marino Sanuto e Pietro Visconte (Archivio storico italiano 11, 241–58, 1893). Arturo Magnocavallo: Marin Sanudo il vecchio e il suo progetto di crociata (154 p., Bergamo 1901); La carta "de mari mediterraneo" di Marin Sanudo il Vecchio (Bollettino della Società geografica italiana 3, 438–49, 9 pl., 1902); Di alcuni codici del Liber secretorum (Nuovo archivio veneto 6, 174–80, 1903). Beazley (3, 309–19, 520–21, map, 1906). J. H. Kramers: Geography and commerce (Legacy of Islam p. 92, Oxford 1931). Atiya (p. 114–27, 1938).

PEGOLOTTI

Francesco Balducci Pegolotti: Florentine author of an Italian textbook on commercial practice and economic geography (fl. c. 1340).

Francesco was the son of Balduccio Pegolotti, who was a man of some importance in Florence, for he represented the city in Siena for the negotiation and ratification of the treaty of 1311. We do not know when Francesco was born, but it must have been in the thirteenth century, for in 1310 he already had a position of some responsibility in the Bardi banking house. In 1315 he was in Antwerp conducting negotiations for the Bardi; in 1317–21 he was in England, being from 1318 on a director of his firm in London. In 1321 he returned to Tuscany. The crucial years of his life, perhaps, were the years 1324–29, spent in Cyprus, chiefly in Famagusta,[4] where he obtained direct and abundant knowledge of the Oriental trade and in addition received the full impact of Oriental life and manners. In 1331 he was back in Florence and was then elected for the first time gonfaloniere di compagnia, a post of importance in the city administration; as Evans put it (p. xxii of his introduction), it involved the combined duties of a city councilor and ward boss. He returned to Cyprus somewhat later and was there in 1336, when he obtained for the Bardi a charter from the king of Armenia, giving his company various advantages. It is not certain whether he was himself in Armenia (that is, of course, Lesser Armenia); but a trip from Famagusta to Ayās would have been easy enough. On the other hand, he certainly did not go to Cathay; his Chinese information was obtained in Cyprus, where all kinds of Oriental travelers met. In 1340 he was again in Florence, and was reappointed gonfaloniere in the following year. In 1346 he was vessillifero di giustizia (banner bearer of justice), and as such president of the priors, the highest position in the commune. At about that time the Bardi company was forced to declare bankruptcy, and Pegolotti was engaged in administering the bankruptcy proceedings against it; these proceedings ended in a liquidation at 48 per cent with all creditors except those of England and Naples. Strangely enough, the death of Pegolotti is not recorded.

It was possibly during his first stay in Cyprus that he conceived the idea of writing his commercial treatise. At any rate, the endless complexities of international trade in the Near East would naturally have suggested such a plan to him, if only for his own use and convenience. The bulk of the treatise was actually put together between 1335 and 1343, probably c. 1340; the treatise may be safely dated c. 1340, if one bears in mind that such composition admits, and even invites, interpolations and additions.

Before speaking of the treatise, in order to underline its importance, it is well to recall that Florence was then one of the greatest commercial centers of the world, a center of international trade and banking, and that Cyprus under the dynasty Antioche-Lusignan was one of the greatest trade centers of the Near East.[5] Furthermore, the Bardi company of Florence, of which Pegolotti was a distinguished servant for 36 years or more, was one of the greatest banking organizations of that time. It had branches in Antwerp, Bruges, Paris, London, Avignon, in many Italian cities, in Majorca, Rhodes, Cyprus, Constantinople; it dealt with kings and popes and enjoyed all kinds of privileges. Thus Pegolotti was truly at one of the

[4] May I be permitted to recall that it was my privilege to visit Famagusta in September 1931. I was deeply impressed by the ruins of that city, especially those of the magnificent Gothic cathedral, now a mosque. Thus I can fully appreciate what it meant to spend five years in that city, at the time of its glory.

[5] The real center was Famagusta, where Pegolotti spent many years. The first blow to the prosperity of that city occurred about half a century later, when the Genoese occupied it, in 1373.

main centers of affairs; he had the means of obtaining the best information available anywhere.

His treatise, Libro di divisamenti di paesi e di misure di mercatantie (called more simply by Pagnini, Practica della mercatura), was meant to be a handbook of reference for international merchants. It describes trade roads and markets, the main articles imported by various countries, their tariffs, their means of packing various articles of merchandise, their moneys, weights and measures, business methods, etc.

The first chapters are devoted to China. The long road from Tana (the Genoese factory on the Sea of Azov) to Cathay is described as being perfectly safe day and night. There were then many European merchants in Cambaluc (Khānbaliq, Peking), also Hindus and Persians. The Italians imported cloth and exported silk. Pegolotti refers to the Chinese paper money (moneta di pappiero, Evans p. 23), which had already been described by Marco Polo.

The Practica della mercatura includes a number of tables, e.g., dates of Easter from 1340 to 1465, dates of Sundays, moon table, table of alloys, table of interest. The latter was the earliest of its kind, though not the first to appear in print (the first to appear in print was Simon Stevin's, printed more than two centuries later, Antwerp 1582; Isis 21, 247–48, 207–9, 1934).[5a]

The value of Pegolotti's treatise is not due only to the abundance of information which it contains, but also to its genuineness. Pegolotti had had considerable experience in the international trade which he was describing; in the eastern bazaars he had met all those merchants whom he refers to, Florentine like himself, or Genoese, Venetian, Pisan, Anconese, Provençal, Catalan, Sicilian, "e tutti altri strani." His Chinese information was secondhand, to be sure, but obtained from experts.

Pegolotti made use of a number of original documents (tariffs, regulations), which were available to him in his quality of merchant and representative of a great and privileged banking organization. Some of these documents have been identified and discovered; it would seem that Pegolotti's quotations from them were not always accurate. However, our only MS (copied in Florence 1472 by Filippo di Niccolaio Frescobaldi) being twice removed from the original text, the discrepancies between it and the documents may be due to the carelessness of copyists.

The influence of that "bahnbrechend" work was great, but before speaking of it we must mention another work of the same kind, almost contemporary (after 1345), that is, the Venetian Tarifa zoè noticia dy pexi e mexure di luogi e tere che s'adovra marcadantia per el mondo. The Tarifa was partly if not completely independent of Pegolotti's book; resemblances between the two texts may be accounted for by derivation from the same sources.

Pegolotti's book was used by Giovanni di Antonio da Uzzano in his Practica della mercatura, compiled in 1442, and again by Giorgio di Lorenzo Chiarini, in the latter's Libro che tracta di mercatantie et usanze de paesi (printed soon after its composition, Florence 1481). Chiarini's book was incorporated in Luca Pacioli's

[5a] As admitted by Stevin himself, a specimen of table of interest was already included in the Arithmétique of Jean Trenchant, first printed in Lyon 1558 and often reprinted; 6 editions of it appeared before the publication of Stevin's book (Isis 21, 207–9). Cornelis Marius Waller Zeper: De oudste intresttafels in Italië, Frankrijk en Nederland met een herdruk van Stevins Tafelen van interest (Amsterdam 1937; Isis 36, 185).

Summa de arithmetica, etc. (Venice 1494). It is interesting to note that Pegolotti (fl. 1340), Uzzano (fl. 1442), Chiarini (fl. 1481), and Pacioli (d. after 1509) were all Tuscans. Pacioli's publication completed the introduction of this new kind of book, the commercial treatise, into the world's literature.

Text. Pegolotti's treatise was first published by the economist Gian Francesco Pagnini of Volterra (1715–1789) in his Della decima e di varie gravezze imposte dal Comune di Firenze, della moneta e della mercatura de' Fiorentini fino al secolo XVI (4 vols., Lisbon and Lucca 1765–66; the work was really published at Florence). Pegolotti's Practica is in vol. 3. English translation of extracts dealing with China in Yule's Cathay (3, 137–73, 1914).

Allan Evans: Francesco Balducci Pegolotti, La Practica della mercatura (498 p., 4 pl., Mediaeval Academy, Cambridge, Mass. 1936). This is a critical edition, with introduction, notes, and glossaries of toll stations on the road from Ayās to Tabrīz, of English religious houses, of place names, coins, weights and measures, etc. The same author is preparing a complete English translation.

The Venetian Tarifa was published by the R. istituto superiore di scienze economiche e commerciali di Venezia (Venezia 1925).

Uzzano's Practica della mercatura was published by Pagnini, in vol. 4 of his Della decima (1766).

Chiarini's Libro che tracta di mercatantie was printed separately thrice in the fifteenth century: Florence 1481, 1497, Parma 1497?, then again in Pacioli's Summa, Venice 1494 (Klebs 271.1–3, 718.1). The Summa was reprinted in Toscolano 1523. Sixth edition by Franco Borlandi: El libro di mercatantie et usanze de' paesi (266 p., Torino 1936), with introduction, notes, and glossaries. Borlandi's work was done at the same time as Evans' and independently; there is a blind reference to Evans in the preface.

Criticism. Heinrich Kiepert: Über Pegolotti's vorderasiatisches Itinerar (Monatsbericht der K. preussischen Akad. p. 901–13, Berlin 1881). Heyd (1885–86). Beazley (vol. 3, 1906). Hennig (3, 177–86, 1938).

Note on Francesco Datini (d. 1410). The archives of the Bardi bank have disappeared except, I believe, a few ledgers, but we have other documents concerning contemporary organizations. For example, soon after the Bardi bankruptcy there arose in Florence another financial wizard, Francesco di Marco Datini, born in Prato (near Florence) c. 1335, died in Prato August 10, 1410. Francesco directed a number of commercial affairs from his house in Prato and his office in Florence, and he had branches in Avignon, Barcelona, Majorca, Valencia, Genoa, and Pisa. His archives have been preserved, classified, and investigated.

Enrico Bensa: Francesco di Marco da Prato. Notizie e documenti sulla mercatura italiana del secolo XIV (512 p., 7 ill., Milano 1928). Léon Mirot: Une entreprise commerciale à la fin du XIVe siècle et ses archives (Journal des savants, 1935, p. 200–13). Raymond de Roover: Early accounting problems of foreign exchange (Accounting review 19, 381–407, 1944; Isis 36, 42).

NICCOLÒ DA POGGIBONSI

Nicola di Corbico da Poggibonici, Niccolò Corbizo da Poggibonsi, Poggibonizi, Poggibonizio, Pocibonici.

Italian traveler, Franciscan monk. Born in the first quarter of the fourteenth century in Poggibonsi, a small town on the River Elsa, just north of Siena. In March 1345, Niccolò set forth to visit the Holy Land, Syria, and Egypt, a trip which took about four years to complete. His account of his travels, entitled Libro d'oltramare and written in Italian, is in the form of a diary and is very detailed.

He spent about a year traveling in Italy, from Poggibonsi to Florence, Bologna, Ferrara, Chioggia, and then by ship to Venice, where he spent some time; he described in detail the customs of the people, their economic condition, the "streets" of water, and the leaning towers. In April 1346 Niccolò left for the East, but after reaching Pola the party was turned back to the Gulf of Venice by a bad storm. Finally, however, they succeeded in reaching Candia on the island of Crete, then went on to Cyprus, where Niccolò spent a month. Included in these first chapters of his book are excellent descriptions of storms at sea, pirates, various kinds of vessels used in the Mediterranean, as well as descriptions of places, and often bits of their ancient history. In the Holy Land and Egypt he visited all the Christian shrines and described them in minute detail. His description of Jerusalem is particularly good—he seemed to be interested in the real beauty of the city as well as in the religious significance of the Holy Places. Niccolò also visited Alexandria, Cairo, Sinai, Giza, Damietta, and finally Cyprus, whence he returned to Italy by sea. Although Niccolò refers to strange animals (elephants, giraffes, ostriches, camels, etc.), his descriptions of them are not as accurate and valuable as the ones given by Ludolf of Suchem and other contemporaries.

Text. Extract edited by Carlo della Volpe: Viaggio da Venezia a Gerusalem, testo inedito del secolo XIV (Per la nozze Casoni-Nardozzi, 16 p., Imola 1872). Libro d'oltramare, edited by Alberto Bacchi della Lega: Libro d'oltramare (Scelta di curiosità letterarie nos. 182/183, 2 vols., 633 p., Bologna 1881).

Criticism. Cornelio Desimoni: Libro di oltramare di Fra Nicolò da Poggibonsi (Giornale ligustico 9, 130–50, Genoa 1882). Röhricht (p. 86, 1890). Augusto Franco: Cenni su Niccola da Poggibonsi (Esercitazioni sulla letteratura religiosa in Italia, edited by Guido Mazzoni, p. 298–300, Firenze 1905). Beazley (3, 392, 484, 1906).

JOHN OF CORA

Born probably in Cora (or Cori), a town of the Roman Campagna about 6 miles from Velletri. Dominican (d. 1346?).

On August 9, 1329, John succeeded William Adam as archbishop of Sulṭānīyah, in Jibāl (Persian 'Irāq).[6]

John of Cora has been mentioned as the possible author of the Directorium ad faciendum passagium which has likewise been ascribed to William Adam, and to Brocard.

He probably wrote the Livre de l'Estat du Grant Caan, at the command of John XXII, between 1328 and 1334. The original Latin text is lost, but the work has been preserved in the French translation made by Long John of Ypres c. 1351.

It has not been proved that John was ever in Cathay; he may have merely compiled this account from reports and letters from other travelers.

He depicts the great power of the khān, and describes Cathay; its peoples, customs, foods, trade, and so on. Many of his stories have their counterpart in the Travels of Marco Polo and other contemporary authors; for instance, his festival of the New Year, paper money, the alms-giving of the khān, etc. He adds some new details to these accounts, however, especially about the red and black letter-

[6] Soltania, Tigranocerta, Mesopotamia.

ing on the paper money, the Franciscan missions, the Nestorian church in Cathay, the work of John de Monte Corvino, the trade relations between China and the West, etc.

Text. Le Livre du Grant Caan, Paris 1529 (Cordier 2, col. 1930–35, 1906). Also in E. Jacquet (Nouveau journal asiatique, 6, 57–72, Paris 1830); and in Louis de Baecker: L'extrême orient au moyen âge (p. 335–46, Paris 1877), poor edition.

The book of the estate of the Great Caan, set forth by the Archbishop of Soltania, circa 1330, translated into English from the edition of E. Jacquet by Yule (3, 89–103, 1914).

Criticism. Cordier: Bibliotheca sinica (2, col. 940, 1885). Beazley (3, 98, 207–12, 221, 1906). Moule (p. 196, 249–51, 1930). Pouzyna (p. 24, 35, 1935).

PEREGRINE OF CASTELLO

Peregrinus de Castello (there are many localities called Castello in Italy, and it is impossible to say which was his birthplace). Italian Franciscan who traveled to China and died, presumably in Zaiton, in 1322 or 1323.

Nothing is known about Peregrine until his appointment by Clement V in 1307 as suffragan to Giovanni di Montecorvino (XIII-2), created at the same time archbishop of Khānbaliq (Introd. 2, 1055). Peregrine started in that year with his brother Franciscan and suffragan Andrew of Perugia, and they reached Khānbaliq c. 1309–10. Peregrine remained there until the death of brother Gerard, first bishop of Zaiton (from c. 1313), whom he succeeded. In 1318, being already in Zaiton, he wrote an account of the Franciscan mission. He spoke of the construction of a new church in Khānbaliq for the Armenians and of the eagerness of the Alans[7] to be converted. These Alans were probably Nestorians; and it should be noted that most of the men "converted" by the Franciscans were in all probability of the same kind; the conversion was not from non-Christianity to Christianity, but rather from Nestorianism to Latin Christianity. In Zaiton, as in Khānbaliq, the mission received help from the Armenian colony. The Franciscans were allowed to preach to the Muslims ("in moscheta Saracenorum") and to the idolaters, but Peregrine complained of the fewness of the laborers and of their linguistic difficulties, "Vere credimus quod si linguas eorum haberemus mirabilia Dei apparerent. Messis multa valde sed operarii pauci et sine falce . . ." (Sinica franciscana 1, 366). In Zaiton there were only three Franciscan fathers in addition to the bishop, to wit, Giovanni Grimaldi, Emmanuel de Monticulo, and Ventura de Sarezana. The last named was originally a merchant, who assumed the Franciscan habit in China.

The authenticity of this letter has been questioned by Jerome Golubovich and Paul Pelliot, the unique MS of it (Vatican library) being considered a forgery made by the genealogist and falsifier Alfonso Ceccarelli of Bevagna (1532–83).

A. C. Moule: The Minor Friars in China (Journal of the Royal Asiatic Society, 1921, p. 83–115); Christians in China (1930).

Streit (p. 49, 1928). Van den Wyngaert (vol. 1, 1929), includes text of the letter, p. 365–68.

[7] The Alans, or Alains, Alani, in Chinese A su, were Caucasians imported into China in Mangū's time (1248-59). See Introd. 2, 982; Couling (p. 9, 1917); Grousset (p. 215, 303, 422, 466, 500, 1929).

ODORIC OF PORDENONE

Italian Franciscan, traveler to the Far East (d. 1331).

Odorico da Pordenone (or del Friuli), Odoricus de Portu Naonis, sive de Foro Julii. The Christian name Odoric is the same as Ulric, Udalric, Vodaric, etc.

He was born at an unknown date between 1274 and 1286 in Villanova, a village near Pordenone, Valle Noncello, in the March of Friuli, just north of the head of the Adriatic. The family name was probably Mattiussi, and some of his ancestors may have come originally from Bohemia.

At an early age Odoric joined the Franciscan order, and soon became known for his asceticism and humility. In 1314 he set forth on his travels to the East. Odoric spent sixteen years in the East and returned to Padua in 1330. At the request of Guidotto, a priest in the parish of St. Anthony of Padua, Odoric dictated an account of his travels to a brother Franciscan, Guglielmo da Solagna. After this, Odoric started for the papal court at Avignon, but became ill in Pisa and turned back to Udine, in his own "paese" of Friuli, where he died on January 14, 1331. He was beatified by Benedict XIV in 1755.

The account of his travels attracted immediate attention. In 1340 another redaction was made in Avignon by Heinrich von Glatz, a Silesian Franciscan, and in 1351 it was translated into French by Long John of Ypres (XIV-2).

Although Odoric was an uneducated person and had no scientific curiosity, his descriptions are valuable as those of a fairly accurate observer; he was not always correct in his deductions, but always of good faith; in spite of its brevity, his chronicle contains many interesting facts not recorded by his contemporaries, or facts which the great Marco Polo had failed to observe. He must be considered one of the greatest travelers of the Middle Ages, and the best historian of the Catholic missions in China.

His itinerary was as follows. He went to Trebizond, then to Erzerum, Tabrīz, Sulṭānīyah. He spent five or six years sharing the apostolic work of his brethren in that region. When he left Sulṭānīyah, he proceeded to Kāshān and Yazd, Persepolis (Iṣṭakhr), Shīrāz, Baghdād, Hurmuz (Ormuz), a harbor in the eastern part of the Persian Gulf (the order is not quite clear and seems strange). He sailed from Ormuz to Tana, near Bombay, in 28 days, landing there soon after April 3, 1321. He then traveled down the Malabar coast, stopping at many places including Ceylon, then up the coast of Coromandel as far as Maịlāpur, where he took ship for the Malay peninsula. He landed in Sumatra, Java, Borneo, on the coast of Champa, and finally reached Canton. He then continued to Chang Chou (Zaiton; Introd. 2, 1055), Fuchow, Hangchow, Nanking, Yangchow, whence he sailed on the Grand Canal (Introd. 2, 981) to the Mongol capital Khānbaliq (Cambaluc, Peking). He remained three years in Khānbaliq, then returned more rapidly overland, via the provinces of Shansi, Shensi, Ssŭch'uan, and farther on by an unknown road, with brother James of Ireland (Jacobus de Hibernia); it is not clear to me whether brother James was with him all the time or only on the return journey.

The best way of giving the reader some idea of the contents of Odoric's account is to select a few samples. In Chaldaea he saw the tower of Babel, or rather the Birs-i-Nimrūd (a part of the ruins of the great temple of Nabū at Borsippa), which he mistook for that tower. The same mistake was made by other mediaeval travelers, such as Benjamin of Tudela (XII-2). Indeed, the true tower of Babel was already in ruins when Alexander the Great arrived in Babylon (324 B.C.); Alexander gave orders to rebuild it, but died (323 B.C.) before their complete execution; a partial execution was evidenced in the course of Robert Koldewey's (1855–1925) excavations at the beginning of this century.

A great part of his description of India is devoted to the martyrdom of four Franciscans by Muslims sometime before his arrival at Tana (see note on Jordan Catala). He described the customs of the Hindus, but not always clearly, e.g., his account of the marriage ceremonies is hardly intelligible. He observed that the Hindus cultivated a sacred herb (the tulasī or tulsi, holy basil). He observed the worship of cows, the ceremonial use of the cow's urine and cow dung, the custom of suttee (cremation of living widows on their husband's funeral pile). In Coromandel he observed something like the Juggernaut chariot (though he did not visit Jagannāth) and other evidences of religious frenzy.

He was the first European to speak of Sumatra, unless Marco Polo's Samara is identical with Sumatra. His mention of "another realm called Resengo" (Yule-Cordier 2, 150) may be a reference to the territory of the Rejang, a very civilized people of Sumatra, who remained otherwise unknown to Europeans for several centuries after Odoric's time.

He has left us a detailed picture of the court and government of the Great Khān, of the pax mongolica, and of the splendid organization of travel in the empire, e.g., of the inns established at suitable intervals along the main roads where travelers were fed twice a day at the khān's expense (that description is confirmed by Ibn Baṭṭūṭā, c. 1347). He greatly admired Chinese architecture, and the perfection of their arts and crafts, a perfection which he ascribed to their hereditary devotion to the same craft generation after generation. He noticed the custom of letting the fingernails grow very long, the binding of the women's feet (unnoticed by Marco Polo). He gave the first European description of cormorant fishing (a matter also curiously neglected by Marco Polo). In some MSS (and in the Ramusio edition of 1583) cormorant fishing is replaced by otter fishing; the other variation was given wide circulation by Sir John Mandeville (XIV-2). Otter fishing was already practiced in China in the seventh and eighth centuries and probably long before; it is practiced to this day on the Yangtze-kiang and particularly near the Ichang gorge. E. W. Gudger: Fishing with the otter (American naturalist 61, 193–225, 1927; Isis 12, 425; 35, 178).

To return for a moment to cormorant fishing, the domestication of cormorants for fishing originated probably in Japan; at any rate, the earliest records concern Japan. It is probable that the same discovery was made independently in China (for the Chinese methods are very different from the Japanese ones), but Chinese mentions of cormorant fishing are surprisingly late, not before the tenth century. It is significant that cormorant fishing is unknown in Korea, the natural bridge of almost every Sino-Japanese transmission. This confirms the theory of convergence (vs. imitation) with regard to that discovery; the fact that the discovery was made independently in Japan and China and nowhere else remains very puzzling. E. W. Gudger: Fishing with the cormorant. I. In China (American naturalist 60, 5–41, 16 fig., 1926; Isis 10; 277); II. In Japan (Scientific monthly 29, 5–38, 31 fig., 1929). Berthold Laufer: The domestication of the cormorant in China and Japan (Field Museum, Anthropological series, 18, 201–62, 4 pl., Chicago 1931; Isis 24, 254), a masterly study.

Finally, he gave a good account of the Catholic missions in Khānbaliq and of the great number of converts in the Mongol court. He also spoke of many Franciscan monasteries in other cities, and how pagans came to them from long distances to be delivered from their devils and receive baptism.

One of the last chapters (35) deals with the Old man of the mountain (senex de monte) and the Assassins (Introd. 1, 752; 2, passim).

It has been claimed that Odoric reached Tibet and was the first European to visit Lhasa. That could only have been done on his return journey, and the claim is now disproved. His account of Tibet (ch. 33) is incorrect; he probably referred to Ladakh in Kashmir, not Tibet.[8]

Other works have been erroneously ascribed to him, such as sermons, letters, and a chronicle (Liber de aetatibus) dealing with events from the beginning of the world up to the death of John XXII. Another work entitled De Terra Sancta, edited by J. C. M. Laurent: Peregrinatores medii aevi quatuor (p. 146-48), under the name of Odoric, is most probably not by him.

Text. De rebus incognitis, first edition, Latin title but Italian text, Pesaro 1513. Reprinted in Ramusio: Navigatione e viaggi (2, 245v-253r, Venice 1574, 1583, 1606). These editions are based on the version of Guglielmo da Solagna. Another edition (in Latin) of this Solagna version was edited by Giuseppe Venni: Elogio storico alle gesta del Beato Odorico (152 p., Venice 1761).

A shorter version in Ramusio (ibid. 253v-256r).

An edition of the version made by Heinrich von Glatz in 1340 is in the Acta sanctorum, Jan. 14 (1, 983-92, Antwerp 1643); and another is edited by Marcellino la Civezza (Storia universale delle missioni francescane 3, 739-81, Rome 1859). A better edition of the Glatz version is in Teofilo Domenichelli: Sopra la vita e i viaggi del Beato Odorico da Pordenone (Latin p. 153-200, Italian p. 201-55, Prato 1881).

Later editions: Latin, by Van den Wyngaert (1, 412-95, 1929), with a long introduction, p. 381-412 (J. R. A. S., 1930, 209-10). This text is translated by Giorgio Pullè: Viaggio del Beato Odorico da Pordenone (vol. 17 of the collection Viaggi e scoperte, 255 p., Milan 1931; Isis 19, 534).

A French translation made by Long John of Ypres in 1351, printed Paris 1529. Edited by Henri Cordier: Les voyages en Asie au XIVe siècle du bienheureux frère Odoric de Pordenone (Recueil de voyages et de documents pour servir à l'histoire de la géographie vol. 10, 760 p., Paris 1891), long introduction.

Journall of Frier Odoricus edited by Richard Hakluyt: Principal navigations (2, Latin 39-53, English [incomplete] 53-67, London 1599, 1809, etc.).

An English translation by John Aston (London 1887), very poor.

English versions also found in various editions of the Travels of Sir John Mandeville, cf. A. W. Pollard's edition of 1900.

Yule (1, 1-162, London 1866); Odoric's account was the original nucleus of Yule's great work. It forms the whole of vol. 2 (380 p., London 1913) of the new edition, revised and enlarged by Cordier (English text p. 97-277, Latin p. 278-336, Italian p. 337-67), long introduction and bibliography.

Another English text based on the Hakluyt and the Yule-Cordier texts, edited by Manuel Komroff: Contemporaries of Marco Polo (p. 213-50, New York 1928).

Criticism. The earliest life of Odoric, written before 1369, was printed in the Analecta franciscana (vol. 3, Quaracchi 1897); translated by A. C. Moule (T'oung Pao 20, 278-85, 1921). The two most elaborate biographies are in Cordier's and Yule's editions. See also Teofilo Domenichelli: Vita e viaggi del beato Odorico

[8] Yet a very careful writer, Reginald Fleming Johnston, observed in his book From Peking to Mandalay (p. 225, London 1908), "It is interesting to note that Friar Odoric's account of 'Tebek' is almost literally true, if we except the remark about the tusked ladies."

(410 p., Prato 1881). Heyd (2, 132, 151, 220 ff., 246, 1886). Röhricht (p. 69–71, 1890). Cordier: Bibliotheca sinica (2, col. 937–40, 1885; suppt. col. 1920, 1895). V. Savi: Della patria e della nazionalità del Beato Odorico da Pordenone (Nuovo archivio veneto 301–25, 1896). Beazley (3, 251–87, 321–23, passim, 1906). Berthold Laufer: Was Odoric ever in Tibet? (T'oung Pao 15, 405–18, 1914); the answer is no (Isis 3, 100). Girolamo Golubovich: Il B. Fr. Odorico da Pordenone (Archivum franciscanum historicum 10, 17–46, Ad Claras Aquas 1917); reprinted in Golubovich (3, 374–94, 1919). A. C. Moule: A life of Odoric of Pordenone (T'oung Pao 20, 275–90, 1921); A small contribution to the study of the bibliography of Odoric (ibid. p. 301–22, 1921); Bibliographical notes (ibid. 21, 387–93, 1922); Christians in China (p. 241–48, passim, 1930).

Sir E. A. Wallis Budge: The rise and progress of Assyriology (p. 59, London 1925; Isis 9, 547). Streit (p. 56, 66–69, 109, 1928). Jarl Charpentier: The Livro da seita dos Indios orientais (p. xvii, Uppsala 1933; Isis 25, 564). Pouzyna (p. 20, 25, 99, 1935). Hennig (3, 153–60, 1938).

ANDREW OF PERUGIA

Andreas de Perusio. Italian Franciscan who traveled to China and died, presumably in Zaiton, sometime between 1326 and 1335.

Andrew was ordered by Clement V to go to China with Peregrine, both as suffragans to Giovanni de Montecorvino (XIII-2). They left Italy in 1307; the date of their arrival in Khānbaliq is uncertain (1309–10?). Later Andrew proceeded to Zaiton (Chang Chọu), and after Peregrine's death, in 1322 or 1323, succeeded him as bishop of that see. In 1326 he addressed a letter to the warden of the convent of Perugia, which is one of the most impressive documents of that age. In his book written before 1335 John of Cora states that the bishop of Zaiton is Peter of Florence.[9] Hence Andrew died before 1335.

Andrew's letter of 1326 is an additional witness to the greatness and wealth of the Mongol empire and to the spirit of toleration which obtained there. "Truly in that vast empire there are people of every nation under the heaven, and of every sect. And it is permitted to each and all to live according to his religion. Indeed they share the opinion, or rather the error, that every one can obtain salvation in his own faith. We are allowed to preach freely and safely, but no Jew or Muslim is ever converted; a great many idolaters are converted but they do not keep to the straight Christian path" (Sinica franciscana 1, 376). Andrew had built a new church and monastery in a grove near Zaiton. He refers to the Franciscan brethren who had been lynched by Muslims in India (in Tana, before 1321; see note on Odoric of Pordenone).

Text. A. C. Moule: Documents relating to the mission of the Minor Friars in China in the thirteenth and fourteenth centuries (Journal of the Royal Asiatic Society, 1914, p. 533–99), texts in Latin and English; Christians in China (1930).

Criticism. Streit (p. 58, 1928). Van den Wyngaert (1, 368–77, 1929). Sarton: Introduction (2, 1055).

SAVIGNONE

Andalò da Savignone (a place not far from Genoa). Genoese traveler to China. While in that country he obtained the confidence of the Great Khān, probably

[9] According to Gams (p. 126, 1873), the successor of Andrew of Perugia was James (not Peter) of Florence, Jacobus de Florentia, fourth and last bishop of Zaiton, who died a martyr in 1362.

Tughān Tīmūr (i.e., Shun Ti or Hui Tsung, the last Yüan emperor, 1333-68),[10] and came back to Europe as his representative. In 1338 he took advantage of the departure of a Venetian fleet to return to China, probably via Tana (now Azov), the Genoese harbor at the mouth of the Don. He took with him a cargo of "jocalia de cristallo," that is, glass beads and glass imitations of precious stones, which was then a specialty of the Venetian trade (says Marin, "jocalia de cristallo, cioè bagatelle o bisutterie di quel genere da' mille sino a diecimille fiorini d'oro").

Carlo Antonio Marin: Storia civile e politica del commercio de' Veneziani (5, 261, Venice 1800). Heyd (2, 218, 711, 1886).

MARIGNOLLI

Giovanni de' Marignolli. Italian Franciscan, traveler to China (d. c. 1358).

Giovanni de' Marignolli, Giovanni Marignola, John of Florence. A member of a noble Florentine family, born in Florence toward the end of the thirteenth century; he assumed the Franciscan habit in Santa Croce, Florence. He lectured for a time at the University of Bologna.

A Mongol embassy had reached Avignon early in 1338 bringing to Benedict XII messages from the Great Khān and from the Christian Alans.[11] In return the pope sent a large embassy including Marignolli, Nicholas Boneti, Nicholas of Molano, Gregory of Hungary, and many more (the party still numbered 32 persons at the time of its arrival in Khānbaliq c. 1342). The ambassadors were accredited not only to the Great Khān, but also to the Chagatāy Khān in Central Asia. They left Avignon in December 1338, and went to Naples, where they waited for the Mongol envoys until Easter 1339. Soon afterward they sailed to Constantinople, then to Caffa (Sea of Azov), where the land journey began. They spent some time (1339-40) at the court of Ūzbeg, khān (1312-40) of the Blue Horde of western Qipčāq, then continued toward Almāligh[11a] (where many Franciscans had been put to death the year before, 1339) and stayed there about a year, 1340-41. They then proceeded eastward via the northern route of the Thian Shan Mts., Kamul (or Hami), the Gobi Desert, reaching Khānbaliq in 1342, where they were the honored guests of the last Yüan emperor, Shun Ti (or Hui Tsung, Tughān Tīmūr, ruled 1333-68). The Catholic embassy remained more than three years in the Mongol capital, where it was not only royally entertained, but permitted to proselytize. According to Marignolli there were then some 30,000 Alans in the Mongol service, some of them very high up, most of them Christians. In 1345-46 the ambassadors went to Zaiton, where they admired the Italian warehouse (depositorium omnium mercatorum) and the many churches. They sailed from Zaiton on December 26, 1346, to Columbum (Kulam or Kawlam on the coast of Malabar; Koilum of Marco Polo; modern Quilon in Travancore), the great pepper market ("ubi nascitur piper totius orbis"). From Malabar Marignolli sailed

[10] Giles (p. 741, 1898).

[11] For the Alans, see my note on Peregrine of Castello. The embassy sent by Tughān Tīmūr (Hui Tsung, last Yüan emperor, 1333-68) to Benedict XII in 1336 included two Frenchmen named Guillaume de Noix and André, and an Alan called Togaï; all of them were Christians, and the first two were merchants established in Peking. They arrived in Avignon early in 1338 and left in May (Pouzyna p. 25, 1935).

[11a] Almāligh in the upper Ili valley, Transoxiana, was a Mongol capital under Chagatāy, son of Chingiz Khān (XIII-1), and later. Its ruins exist near the city of Qulja (or Kulja, Ghulja). Le Strange (p. 487, 1905). EI (2, 468, 1919; 1113, 1927). Moule (p. 197, 255, 1930).

back to the Madras or St. Thomas country on the other coast of India, then to Saba (?) and Ceylon, where he stayed four months. From Ceylon he sailed to Ormuz and the Persian Gulf, then visited Babylon, Baghdād, Mosul, and Nineveh, Edessa, Aleppo, Damascus, Jerusalem, Cyprus (?) on his way to Italy.

His reminiscences include accounts of the pepper culture in Malabar and Madras, the unique vineyards of the Thomas district, etc. His descriptions (e.g., of Saba) are often unintelligible and fantastic. Adam's Peak in Ceylon, he says, should not be foolishly confused with Paradise, yet he believes it is very close to it, witness Adam's footprint. He mistakes statues of Buddhas for patriarchs, but gives an ingenuous and impressive account of Singhalese (Buddhist) ascetics. He makes a reference to the Abascy, where "the Christians of St. Matthew" live, far up the Nile; the sulṭān of Egypt pays a tribute to them lest they dam the river and ruin Egypt. This is obviously an allusion to the Abyssinia of Prester John (ḥabasha in Arabic). Marignolli's anthropology was very crude and full of fables, yet he refused to accept the notion of people living at the antipodes, for the greatest part of the ocean cannot be navigated, and God did not intend men to live on the other side of the globe (this is the Augustinian point of view, Introd. 2, 45).

Marignolli brought back various souvenirs from his journey, notably a piece of brick of the tower of Babel found in Baghdād, an Indian garment of camall-cloth or coconut fiber (which he deposited in the sacristy of the Franciscan church of Florence), an Eastern umbrella.

He was back in Avignon in 1352–53 after an absence of 13 years. In 1354 he was elected bishop of Bisignano in Calabria, and proceeded to Florence. At that time Charles IV of Luxemburg was traveling to Rome to be crowned emperor; he appointed Marignolli his chaplain, secretary, and historiographer. After that Marignolli was employed on various diplomatic and political missions. He died probably in 1358; certainly before March 22, 1359. A monument was built to his memory in Santa Croce, Florence 1898.

The Chronicle of Bohemia which he wrote upon the emperor's order was a very poor work, sometimes to the point of incoherence, but he managed to insert into it reminiscences of his Oriental journey (ut ex visis aliqua breviter inseramus) which are very valuable, the more so because soon after his visit to China, the Mongol (Yüan) dynasty came to an end (1368); it was replaced by a purely Chinese xenophobic dynasty (Ming), the Christian missions were suppressed and relations with Europe almost completely interrupted.

The text of his chronicle was not printed until 1768, and even then its peculiar value was not realized. This happened only in 1820, when Joseph George Meinert edited separately the geographical interpolations. The main facts of Marignolli's journey are confirmed by Franciscan and Yüan annals.

Text. Editio princeps of the chronicle by Gelasius Dobner: Monumenta historica Bohemiae nusquam antehac edita (2, 68–282, Prague 1768). Josef Emler: Fontes rerum bohemicarum (3, 487–604, Prague 1882).

J. G. Meinert: Johannes von Marignola Reise in das Morgenland 1339–1353 (Abhandlungen der Kgl. böhmischen Gesellschaft der Wissenschaften vol. 2, 108 p., Prague 1820), geographical extracts in Latin and German with notes. English translation of the Asiatic items in Yule (3, 177–269, 1914), with copious introduction and notes.

Van den Wyngaert (1, 515–60, 1929), Chinese fragments reprinted from Emler's edition.

Criticism. Meinert (1820). Friedrich Kunstmann: Der Reisebericht des Joh. Marignola (Historisch-politische Blätter 38, 701–19, 793–813, München 1859). Beazley (3, 288–309, 1906). Streit (p. 80–81, 1928). Moule (p. 254–60, 1930). Hennig (3, 191–205, 1938).

A2. France

JORDAN CATALA DE SÉVÉRAC

Jourdain Cathala, Jourdain de Sévérac. French Dominican, missionary to Persia and India (d. after 1330).

Jordan was born in one of the villages called Sévérac, probably Sévérac-le-Château, in Rouergue, now department of Aveyron. It is not certain when he started for the East, but the first definite notice concerning him is in 1320 in Persia. But as he knew the language fairly well by then, it is presumed that he arrived there some time before 1320. From France he had followed the regular trade route via Messina, Negropont, Greater Armenia, and finally reached Tabrīz in Persia during the year 1320. There he joined four Franciscan missionaries, and in 1321 they all set out from Ormuz for China. But contrary winds blew them to Tana[11b] near the island of Salsette, not far from Bombay.

While Jordan was on a missionary trip to Parocco (modern Broach), north of Tana, and Supara (near the present Surat), the four Franciscans were put to death in Tana.[12] Jordan himself mentions this affair in many of the letters he wrote during this period. The first letter was written in Caga (the modern Gogha, across the Gulf of Cambay from Broach), and is dated October 12, 1321. In this letter he also describes his missionary work in Broach, his preparations for establishing a church there, his wish to have other friars come to Supara, Columbum (Quilon, in Travancore), and Broach. The second letter was written in Tana and was dated January 24, 1323 (probably our 1324). In this one he describes his sufferings and trials, and the difficulties of his work. He suggests that the pope establish a fleet in the Indian Ocean; it would be a blow to the sulṭān, and would help the friars spread the Christian religion through India. Jordan says that the Indians were longing for the coming of the European Christians. Extracts from other letters deal with the affair at Tana and with missionary work in India.

During the period from 1324 to 1327 Jordan probably visited Malabar, Travancore, and part of the Coromandel coast. By 1328 or 1329 he was in Avignon, and it was probably during this time that he wrote the Mirabilia descripta. In 1329 John XXII created the new bishopric of Columbum for Jordan, and by 1330 Jordan was again in that city. After this date nothing is known about his life.

His Mirabilia descripta contains a great deal of firsthand information on Asiatic lands, races, products, from Chios and Chaldaea to the extreme south of the Deccan. Jordan shows great interest in geographical affairs; he describes first the Mediterranean region, then Armenia and Persia. Naturally the discussion of India, especially the districts of Gujarāt, Malabar, and Travancore, occupies the

[11b] Tana is the mediaeval spelling; it would be better perhaps to use the modern spelling Thana, as does Moule (1930). Salsette Island is in the Thana district of Bombay. The spelling Thana would avoid confusion with the other Tana, mentioned above, located near the mouth of the Don River in the Sea of Azov, one of the main terminals of the caravan roads from Central Asia and Cathay. The words Tana and Don are both transcriptions of the Greek Τάναϊς. Tanais was already an important Greco-Scythian market in ancient times.

[12] The story of this martyrdom of the Franciscans has been told by a number of other writers; see Odoric da Pordenone.

largest part of the book. He includes briefer sketches of Arabia and the Caucasus, Georgia, and various parts of Asia Minor. He had evidently visited these places and also had access to good secondhand information. His description of Tartary is interesting, but not so accurate as the one of India. To him as well as to Marignolli we owe a renewal of interest in Abyssinia.

His description of India, the first contributed by a Frenchman, is more elaborate than those given by other early writers, and sometimes more accurate; in many cases, however, his observations are uncritical and senseless. He goes into great detail concerning the natural products of India, its birds, animals, fruits, and the manners of the various peoples. Jordan was not as intelligent, however, as Pian del Càrpine (XIII-1) or William of Rubruquis (XIII-2), and he was not as good an observer as Marco Polo (XIII-2). He witnessed various cases of suttee (not by any means a novelty, for that practice was known even to the ancients). He gave a brief but essentially correct description of the Parsees; this being probably the earliest European description of them. He spoke of the Dōms, one of the lowest classes of Hindus, as scavengers and eaters of carcasses. He was aware that many Hindu shrines had been polluted and ruined by Muslims. He knew that the Hindus were monotheists and worshiped cows; his account of Hindu sacrifices, however, was grotesque. According to him, the Hindu considered the world to be 28,000 years old. In southern India he observed the practice of inheritance in the female line.

Text. Mirabilia descripta, edited by Eugène Coquebert de Montbret: Description des merveilles d'une partie de l'Asie (Recueil de voyages et de mémoires, Soc. de géographie, 4, 1-68, Paris 1839). Text of Coquebert de Montbret translated into English by Henry Yule: Mirabilia descripta. The wonders of the East (Hakluyt Society Publications vol. 31, 86 p., London 1863); notes and corrections to this translation in Cathay (1, 192-96, 1866). Henri Cordier: Les merveilles de l'Asie (French text p. 47-103, Latin text 109-24, 19 pl. of facsimiles of the Latin text, Paris 1925; Isis 10, 131); for criticism of this edition see A. C. Moule: Brother Jordan of Sévérac (Journal of the Royal Asiatic Society, 1928, p. 348).

The Caga letter, dated October 12, 1321, first printed by Quétif and Echard (1, 549-50, 1719). Translated into English by Yule (1, 225-28, 1866), and in the edition revised by Cordier (3, 75-78, 1914). Also edited by Golubovich (2, 69, 70, 113, 1913). Translated into French by François Balme (Année dominicaine, 1886, p. 24-25). Other editions by Henri Cordier: Odoric de Pordenone (p. 94-95, Paris 1891), and in Les merveilles de l'Asie (p. 19-21, 1925).

The Tana letter, dated January 20, 1323 (probably 1324 according to our reckoning), first printed by Luke Wadding: Annales Minorum (6, 359-61, Rome 1733). Translated into English by Yule (1, 228-30, 1866), and into French by F. Balme (Année dominicaine, 1886, p. 26-27). Later edition by Cordier: Les merveilles de l'Asie (p. 25-28, 1925).

Criticism. Friedrich Kunstmann: Die Missionen in Indien und China im vierzehnten Jahrhundert. Die Mission in Meliapor und Tana (Historisch-politische Blätter 37, 25-38, 1856). François Balme: Le vénérable père Jourdain Cathala de Sévérac evêque de Coulam (Quilon) sur la côte de Malabar, aux Indes Orientales, 1306-1336 (Année dominicaine, 46 p., 1886). Beazley (3, 215-35, passim, 1906). Charles V. Langlois: Jordan Catala, missionnaire (HL 35, 260-77, 1921). Streit (1928, passim). A. C. Moule: Brother Jordan of Sévérac (Journal of the Royal Asiatic Society, 1928, p. 349-76). Jarl Charpentier: The Livro da seita dos Indios orientais of Jacobo Fenicio, S.J. (p. xvi, Uppsala 1933; Isis 25, 564). Pouzyna (p. 21, 35, 1935). Haroutiun Kurdian: A correction to Mirabilia descripta by

Friar Jordanus (Journal of the Royal Asiatic Society, 1937, p. 480–81), footnote to the Armenian section.

A3. Spain

PASCAL OF VITORIA

Pascal of Vitoria (or Vittoria, presumably the capital of Alava, one of the Basque provinces of Spain). Spanish Franciscan, traveler to Central Asia (d. 1339).

Paschalis de Victoria assumed the Franciscan habit in his country, which he left c. 1333 (nothing is known of his earlier life) with his brother in Christ Gonsalvo Transtorna. He went to Avignon to report to the pope and to his general, Geraldus Odonis; then to Assisi and Venice, whence he sailed to the Sea of Azov. He landed at Tana, then proceeded through the steppes of the Golden Horde. He spent a year in Sarai on the lower Volga, where he studied the Cumanic (Kumān) language and the Uighūr script and prepared himself for predication among those people. Then he visited Urganj (in Khwārizm, on the lower Āmū-Daryā) and Almāligh (i.e., Qulja) in the upper Ili valley, then the capital of the Chagatāy Khānate (Transoxiana).

While he was in Almāligh in 1338 he wrote a short account of his journey and of the Franciscan mission, addressing it to the warden of his monastery in Vitoria. He died a martyr of his faith in 1339.

Text. L. Wadding: Annales Minorum (7, 256–57, 1733). English translation by Yule (3, 81–88, 1914). Van den Wyngaert (1, 499–506, 1929). See also Martyrium fr. minorum Almaligh an. 1339 (ibid. p. 508–11).
Criticism. Beazley (3, 235–50, 1906). Streit (p. 76, 1928).

JAIME FERRER

Catalan (Majorcan) explorer (fl. 1346).

Jaime, Jacme, or Jaume Ferrer is practically unknown but for his great exploit recorded in the Medicean atlas of 1351 and in the Catalan map of 1375, and again (less well) in the account of the Genoese sailor Uso di Mare (1455). He left Majorca in 1346 and undertook an expedition along the Guinea coast, and on August 10 of that year he rounded Cape Bojador (lat. 26°7′N.), reaching the territory called Rio de Oro (see also the Venetian map of 1367). The Rio de Oro, or Rivaura, was also called Vedamel, conjectured to be derived from the Arabic Wādī Nīl;[13] it is true that the early explorers dreamed of a western African "river of gold," which they assumed was connected with the Nile.

This Jaime Ferrer should not be confused with two namesakes, both Catalan, who may belong to the same family. The first of these, whom I shall call Jaime Ferrer II, was a Majorcan who was appointed by the infante Enrique o Navegador, c. 1438, a professor in the naval academy founded by the latter at Sagres. The second, who may be called Jaime Ferrer III or better Jaime Ferrer de Blanes, was a cosmographer who flourished in Blanes (Gerona, Catalonia) about the end of the fifteenth century.

Criticism. Ferdinand Denis (NBG 17, 537, 1856). EUI (23, 920, 1924). Beazley (3, 429–30, 526, 1906). Errera (p. 211, 216, 1926). Hennig (3, 237–40, 1938). Kimble (p. 109, 113, 1938).

[13] I have never come across that Arabic term. The Nile is called Nīl Miṣr, or Baḥr Miṣr, or al-Baḥr, or Baḥr al-Nīl.

LIBRO DEL CONOSÇIMIENTO

The "Book of knowledge," the full title of which will be found below, is a geographical treatise—a description of the world—composed in 1348 (or later, but before 1375) by a Spanish Franciscan, born in Castille in 1305. It contains a description of all the countries in the following order (roughly): Spain, Portugal, France, Germany, Denmark, Bohemia, Poland, Galicia, Sweden, Norway, Scotland, Northern Isles, France, Italy, Dalmatia, Hungary, Asia Minor, Cyprus, Egypt, Barbary coast, Majorca, Morocco, West African coast, Atlantic Isles, Central Africa, Egypt, Aethiopia, Red Sea, Mesopotamia, Arabia, Persian Gulf, India, Malay Archipelago, China, Mongolia, Tibet, the Indies, back to Constantinople via Persia, Greek dominions, Caspian, Russia, finally back to Seville whence he had started.

If we were to believe his statements, he himself had traveled in those countries. This is incredible, yet he is not a blatant liar like Mandeville (XIV-2); he gives sometimes an impression of ingenuity. Perhaps he had traveled much, so much that he felt justified in adding to the account of his own travels that of other travels of which he had heard or read. Many travelers have done that, especially in the Middle Ages, and their innocence or guilt depends on the proportion of the mixture. If they made a clear distinction between their own experiences and those of other people, no objection could be raised; but unfortunately they generally forgot to make that distinction, even as they forgot to mention their sources. We should bear in mind that that neglect was not so grave to them as it is to us, and judge them more leniently.

The Libro del conosçimiento was first known through the use made of it by Pierre Bontier and Jean le Verrier, chaplains to Jean de Bethencourt, in their account of his conquest of the Canaries (1402–22).[14]

The Franciscan geographer was the first to mention and give the names of most of the Canaries, Madeiras, and Azores. He gave information concerning Sorleone Vivaldo's search for his father and uncle, the brothers Vivaldi (XIII-2). He seems to have been well acquainted with the West African coast to Cape Bojador and even—but this is doubtful—as far as the Guinea coast and Sierra Leone (c. 8°N.). He had practically no knowledge of the interior of West Africa. Maybe all his West African knowledge had been obtained from Genoese and Venetian traders? He was the first to place the mythical Prester John (Introd. 2, 416–17) in Abyssinia instead of India. The original text was illustrated with the arms, flags, or devices of all the countries, in colors. This is the first collection of its kind. These illustrations were deemed an essential part of the text, for they are found in the three MSS extant, all in Madrid, dating from the last third of the fifteenth century.

The Este world map (c. 1450), preserved in the Biblioteca estense, Modena, was largely derived from the Libro del conosçimiento, and was thus a tribute to the latter's continued influence. Irrespective of the Franciscan's sources, direct, indirect, or imaginary, his Libro was an appreciated geographical treatise, completing in written form the synthesis accomplished in the portolani. It is an interest-

[14] Richard Henry Major: The Canarian, or Book of the conquest and conversion of the Canarians in 1402 by Jean de Bethencourt (Hakluyt Society, 286 p., London 1872). Gabriel Gravier: Le Canarien (Société de l'histoire de Normandie, 342 p., Rouen 1874). Gravier edited the French original text, Major an English translation of it. Chs. 55–58 are explicitly derived from the Spanish Libro.

ing mise au point of the geographical knowledge available by the middle of the fourteenth century.

Text. Márcos Jiménez de la Espada: Libro del conosçimiento de todos los reynos y tierras y señoríos que son por el mundo y de las señales y armas que han cada tierra y señorío por sy y de los reyes y señores que los proueen, escrito por un franciscano español á mediados del siglo XIV y publicado ahora por primera vez (318 p., Madrid 1877). Sir Clements Markham: Book of the knowledge of all the kingdoms, lands, and lordships that are in the world, and the arms and devices of each land and lordship, or of the kings and lords who possess them (Hakluyt Society, 100 p., London 1912), English translation, with notes most of them derived from the Spanish edition.

Criticism. Beazley (3, 416, 1906). La Roncière (1, 117–19, 1925). Hennig (3, 221–36, 241–55, 1938). Kimble (p. 109–13, 1938). Beazley, La Roncière, and Hennig are skeptical, Kimble more indulgent.

A4. Western Isles

SYMON SIMEONIS

Simon the son of Simon, or Simon Fitzsimon, was an Irish Franciscan, who left Clane, Kildare county, in October 1322 with another Franciscan, Hugo Illuminator, Hugh the Limner, for a pilgrimage to the Holy Land. Their itinerary was as follows: Wales, London, Beauvais, Paris, Troyes; by ship down the Saône and Rhône to Arles, by land to Venice; by ship to Alexandria (where they stayed in October 1323 at the Marseille fondaco in preference to the Genoese, Venetian, and Catalan houses), and up the Nile to Cairo, where Hugh died. Symon continued to Jerusalem, but we do not know whether he really entered the Holy City, or what happened to him after his arrival outside its walls.

The account written by Symon is generally brief, except with regard to Egypt, which is described with more detail. Symon even characterizes the manners and religion of the Egyptians. The account ends abruptly with a description of the outside of Jerusalem.

Text. James Nasmith: Itineraria Symonis Simeonis et Willelmi de Worcestre[15] (p. 1–73, Cambridge 1778). Golubovich (3, 237–82, 1919).

Criticism. DNB (52, 258, 1897). Beazley (3, 484, 491, 1906).

A5. Germany

WILLIAM OF BOLDENSELE

German traveler to the Near East (d. Cologne c. 1337–38). His real name was Otto von Nienhues (Rienhuzz), or Otto de Nygenhus. Nothing is known of his family except that it was a noble one.

He entered the Dominican monastery of St. Paul at Minden, in Westphalia, but deserted it in 1330. After obtaining an indulgence in Rome, he joined the Knights of St. John, and took the name of William of Boldensele.

The exact year in which he made his journey to the Holy Land is not known, but it must have been made c. 1332–33, and his account of the trip, Tractatus de quibusdam ultramarinis partibus (also called Hodoeporicon ad Terram Sanctam),

[15] William of Worcester or Botoner (1415–82?) traveled in England c. 1478–80 and left a detailed itinerary (DNB 62, 441–43, 1900). This has nothing to do with either Palestine or the fourteenth century.

was written probably in 1336, the same year in which Benedict XII (pope 1334-42) preached a new crusade.

William made the journey at the request of cardinal Hélie de Talleyrand-Périgord (1301-64, cardinal from 1331), probably for political reasons. He went through Lombardy to Noli, thence to Constantinople, Crete, Cyprus, Phoenicia, Tyre, and Acre to Egypt, then returned by way of Sinai, Damascus, Beirut, and thence to Germany.

In spite of the privileges which he enjoyed because of his rank and recommendations, he has little to tell which is new or important. His description of the Holy Land is commonplace; that of other countries of the Near East is a little more interesting. On the whole this work is better than the accounts of other pilgrims. It was very popular in his own century, and by 1351 was translated into French by Long John of Ypres. Many parts of it were borrowed by Sir John Mandeville (XIV-2).

Boldensele was a very skeptical person, refusing to believe the old miracles of the travelers' tales. He gives a very sensible explanation of the weeping marble pillars, also a good description of the Red Sea, and refutes the stories of its red water, red shores, and red bottom. There are also interesting bits of information on the Beduins, and the "camels called dromedaries."

Text. Tractatus de quibusdam ultramarinis partibus, or Hodoeporicon ad Terram Sanctam, or Itinerarius in Terram Sanctam. First edition of the Latin text by Henricus Canisius: Antiquae lectionis tomus V (p. 95 f., Ingolstadt bef. 1604); reprinted in Jacques Basnage: Thesaurus monumentorum (4, 331-57, Antwerp 1725).

Modern edition by Carl Ludwig Grotefend in Zeitschrift des historischen Vereins für Niedersachsen (vol. of 1852, p. 237-86, Hanover 1855).

The French translation was printed by Jehan de St. Denys: L'hystoire merveilleuse . . . du grand empereur de Tartarie (Paris 1529). This was the earliest printed edition.

A German translation was edited by K. Khull: Zweier deutschen Ordensleute Pilgerfahrten (Gaben des katholischen Pressvereins, p. 1-46, Graz 1895).

The edition purporting to be in J. H. Jäck: Taschenbibliothek (2, 109-62, Nürnberg 1827) is not there.

Criticism. Baron de Reiffenberg: Le chevalier au cygne et Godefroid de Bouillon (4, 277-80, Brussels 1846). C. L. Grotefend: Wilhelm von Boldensele (Zeitschrift der Deutschen morgenländischen Gesellschaft 16, 710-13, Leipzig 1862). D. von Alten: War Otto von Nienhus wirklich der letzte Sprosse der Grafen von Wölpe? (Zeitschrift des historischen Vereins für Niedersachsen, vol. of 1861, p. 219-37, Hanover 1862). Röhricht (p. 73, 1890). Beazley (3, 322-23, 393-98, 1906).

LUDOLF OF SUDHEIM

Suthem, Suchem, Suchen. Sometimes called Peter instead of Ludolf. Suthem or Sudheim was once a small village near Lichtenau, in the diocese of Paderborn, East Westphalia.

Westphalian parish priest and pilgrim to the Holy Land. Ludolf spent the years 1336-41 visiting various islands in the Mediterranean, Constantinople, Egypt, and Syria. After his return to Paderborn he wrote, c. 1350, a description of his travels entitled De Terra Sancta et itinere iherosolimitano, and dedicated it to Baldwin of Steinfurth, bishop of Paderborn 1340-61. Although Ludolf copied verbatim many of the facts concerning the Holy Land from the Hodoeporicon ad Terram Sanctam written in 1336 by William of Boldensele, he nevertheless adds a great many interesting as well as fantastic details to his own text. From a geographical viewpoint his text is practically worthless, but he does give some valuable bits of information concerning the ordinary and extraordinary winds over the Mediterranean, curious descriptions of Mt. Etna and its eruptions, of the migration of birds, accounts of contemporary historical events.

It is very probable that Ludolf wrote a second account of his travels, this time in German. The original redaction is lost, but a Latin translation of it was incorporated in the second part of a work on the Holy Land (Notabilia de Terra Sancta) compiled in the latter part of the fourteenth century by Nicholas of Hude,[16] a Cistercian monk; the first part being a redaction of Ludolf's Latin treatise. Ludolf's German work is more systematic than the Latin one, the fanciful stories are omitted, and in general this second account is much better and more scientific than the first. It was written about 1360.

Text. There are a number of incunabula editions in Latin and German without place or date. Libellus de Terra Sancta et itinere iherosolimitano, Esslingen, C. Fynor, no date, c. 1470; Antwerp c. 1485.

Thomas Philipps, London 1825; later edition by Ferdinand Deycks (104 p., Stuttgart 1851); latest by Ivar von Stapelmohr (170 p., Lund 1937; Isis 31, 152).

German translations: edited by S. Sorg, Augsburg? 1475?; by G. Zainer, Augsburg c. 1477; by Sigmund Feyerabend: Reyssbuch dess heyligen Lands (p. 433–54, Frankfurt-am-Main 1584, 1609, 1659); by J. G. L. Kosegarten: Ludolf von Suchen Reisebuch (88 p., Greifswald 1861). Partial edition, F. W. E. Roth (Zeitschrift der Deutschen morgenländischen Gesellschaft 42, 421–40, 1888).

English translation: Aubrey Stewart (Palestine Pilgrims' Text Society no. 27, 142 p., London 1895).

De itinere Terre Sancte et Descriptio Terrae Sanctae [sic], the Latin translation of Ludolf's second work, edited by G. A. Neumann (Archives de l'Orient latin 2, B, 305–77, 1884); long critical introduction.

Criticism. Ferdinand Deycks: Über ältere Pilgerfahrten nach Jerusalem mit besonderer Rücksicht auf Ludolfs von Suchen Reisebuch (64 p., Münster 1848). Von Evelt: Ludolf von Suthem, Pfarrer im Hochstift Paderborn (Zeitschrift für vaterländische Geschichte und Alterthumskunde Westfalens 20, 1–22, Münster 1859). R. Röhricht, H. Meisner: Deutsche Pilgerreisen nach dem Heiligen Lande (p. 46, 466, 564, 647, Berlin 1880). Röhricht (p. 76–79, 87, 1890). Beazley (3, 398–402, 1906). H. Kurdian: A note on the "Description of the Holy Land and of the way thither" by Ludolph von Suchem 1350 (Journal of the American Oriental Society 55, 102–4, 1935), poor attempt to give Ludolf's work an earlier date. Atiya (p. 168–171, 1938).

RUDOLF OF FRAMEINSBERG

Rudolphus, or Ludolf, von Frameynsberg.

Nothing is known about his early life except that he was a Bavarian knight. In 1346 he traveled from Landshut (on the Isar, in lower Bavaria) to Jerusalem and back again. He ascended Mt. Sinai. He wrote an account of his journey wherein he drew many comparisons between places in the Near East and in Germany, between Gaza and Landshut, Alexandria and Ratisbon, Mt. Sinai and Mt. Pogen (?), the Nile and the Danube, etc. He has quite a little to say concerning the increasing importance of Venice in the Near East, and economic conditions in general;

[16] There was a Cistercian monastery in Hude between Bremen and Oldenburg.

he kept a careful list of his own expenditures, which amounted to 346 florins, just 4 less than he took with him. His descriptions of places do not contain any unusual or important details.

Text. Itinerarium in Palaestinam ad montem Sinai et in Aegyptum anno 1346. A fragment of this is published by Henricus Canisius: Antiqua lectio (6, 323–27, Ingolstadt 1601–4). Reprinted by Jacques Basnage: Thesaurus monumentorum (4, 358–60, Antwerp 1725).

Criticism. Joseph Freiherrn von Hormayr: Taschenbuch für die vaterländische Geschichte (p. 119–20, München 1832). Röhricht (p. 87, 1890). Beazley (3, 398, 1906).

B. BYZANTINE GEOGRAPHY

ANDREAS LIBADENOS

Ἀνδρέας ὁ Λιβαδηνός. Prototabularios (chief recorder) and chartophylax (archivist) of the metropolitan church of Trebizond. Flourished under Basilios I and Alexios III, emperors of Trebizond 1333–40 and 1350–90. His main work is a geographical treatise, Περιηγητικὴ ἱστορία, in the form of a speech (a little rhetorical) to his friends, wherein he describes a journey from Constantinople to Egypt and Palestine, and the return to Constantinople and Trebizond.

It is not only of geographical but also of historical interest, for Libadenos wrote it during the troubled times which followed Basilios' death in 1340, and gives information concerning them. He pays tribute to the contemporary fame of Trebizond as a center of scientific studies (Paranikas' ed., p. 22).

In addition to his periegetic history, Libadenos wrote a confession of faith (ὁμολογία πίστεως), prayers, letters to Gerasimos, bishop of Cerasus,[17] religious poems, etc.

Text. The Περιήγησις was edited by Matthaios K. Paranikas (Constantinople 1874).

Criticism. M. K. Paranikas: Beiträge zur byzantinischen Litteratur (thesis, Sitzungsberichte der Kgl. bayerischen Akad. der Wissenschaften p. 23–43, Munich 1870), including analysis of text. Krumbacher (p. 422, 1897), abbreviating Paranikas. Philippidos Chrysanthos, metropolitan of Trebizond: Ἡ ἐκκλησία Τραπεζοῦντος (906 p., a great many pl., large maps; forming vols. 4, 5 of the collection Ἀρχεῖον Πόντου, Σύγγραμμα περιοδικὸν ἐκδιδόμενον ὑπὸ τῆς ἐπιτροπῆς Ποντιακῶν μελετῶν, Athens 1933–36). This book is richly documented, full advantage being taken of the works of Libadenos and Michael Panaretos,[18] and many other documents. Aleksandr Aleksandrovich Vasiliev: The empire of Trebizond in history and literature (Byzantion 15, 316–77, Boston 1941).

STEPHEN OF NOVGOROD

Russian pilgrim who traveled with eight companions from Great Novgorod (near Lake Ilmen) to Constantinople in the time of the patriarchate of Isidoros I (1347–49). They arrived in that city during Holy Week. Stephen gives an account (in Russian) of Hagia Sofia (which the human spirit, he remarks, cannot under-

[17] Κερασοῦς, a harbor on the south shore of the Black Sea, west of Trebizond. Original home of the cherry tree (?), whose name is derived from its own name.

[18] Μιχαὴλ ὁ Πανάρετος wrote a chronicle of Trebizond from 1204 to 1426; we may assume that he flourished in Trebizond c. 1426. Krumbacher (p. 393, 1897), Chrysanthos (p. 326, passim, 1933).

stand) and of the many churches and conventS which they visited. It ends with the words, "Having gone around all the holy places [of Constantinople] we started for Jerusalem." Did they reach the Holy Land?

Text. The Russian text was edited by J. P. Sakharov in his Narrations of the Russian people (2, 51–56, St. Petersburg 1849). French translation by Mme B. de Khitrovo: Itinéraires russes en Orient (p. 113–25, Genève 1889).

C. JEWISH GEOGRAPHY

ESTORI FARḤI

Estori ben Moses ha-Parḥi. Judeo-Languedocian physician, translator from Latin into Hebrew. First scientific topographer of Palestine since Eusebios (IV-1). He flourished c. 1306–22.

His family originated in Florenza, Andalusia, hence the name Farḥi or Parḥi, derived from feraḥ = flower. His father, maternal grandfather, and great-grandfather were learned men; the last named was rabbi in Carcassonne or in Trinquetaille (Arles). Estori was born in Languedoc. His dates of birth and death are unknown; he was certainly born in the last quarter of the thirteenth century, for in 1306 he called himself a youth (no'ar). He studied in Montpellier, his main teachers being his famous relative Jacob ben Maḥir ibn Tibbon and Asher ben Jehiel. He was in Montpellier when the Jews were expelled from France in 1306, and has given us a very vivid account of his own exile. He moved to Perpignan, then to Barcelona, Toledo, and finally to Egypt. In 1313, he was in Cairo, then he proceeded to Palestine and established himself in Beth-shean (Baisān, in the Jordan valley, c. 16 miles south of the Sea of Galilee). He spent some seven years studying Palestinian topography, devoting two years to Galilee, and five to the other districts.

His main work was completed in Palestine in 1322. It is entitled Kaftor u-feraḥ (Knop and flower; allusions to Exodus 25:33 and his own name), and is divided into 60 chapters. His purpose in writing it was to answer the queries: What would be the necessary rites and customs of his people if they were re-established in the Holy Land? What are the limits of that land and its peculiarities? He was the first to try to identify systematically Biblical, Talmudic (he identified only a portion of the sites mentioned in the Torah and Talmud), and Arabic place names; he listed the Jewish communities and discovered the ruins of a synagogue in Beth-shean. His work is valuable from the point of view not only of topography, but also of archaeology and natural history. For example, ch. 16 deals with Jewish numismatics and weights and measures. He gives a list of Hebrew plant names with their Arabic equivalents. Various details may interest botanists, zoologists, folklorists, and historians.

In order better to illustrate the relative importance of the Kaftor u-feraḥ, let me add a paragraph concerning the later development of Palestinian topography. Estori's book remained the main authority on the subject until 1714, when a new treatise appeared by the Dutch Hebraist Adriaan Reeland (1676–1718): Palestina ex monumentis veteribus illustrata (quarto, 2 vols., Utrecht 1714), or even until 1845, when the Bavarian Sephardi Joseph Schwarz (1804–65) published in Jerusalem his Tebu'ot ha-ereẓ, this being the second part of his Sefer debri Joseph, divided into four parts: (I) Tebu'ot ha-shemesh, on astronomy and chronology, (II) Tebu'ot ha-ereẓ, geography of the Holy Land, (III) its products, (IV) its history. Part II was re-edited by Joseph Kohen-Ẓedeq (Lemberg 1865) and a third time by Abraham Moses Luncz (Jerusalem 1900), with maps, index, and biography of Schwarz. Parts II–IV were Englished by Isaac Leeser: A descriptive geography of Palestine (Philadelphia 1850), with maps, illustrations, and additional materials. This was the largest Jewish book published in America down to that time. There is also a German translation of part II by Israel Schwarz: Das heilige Land (Frankfurt a.M. 1852). Still another book, Adolf Neubauer (1832–1907): La géographie du Talmud (468 p., Paris 1868), was largely derived from the Tebu'ot ha-ereẓ. Since that time many other topographical studies have appeared, too many to be mentioned, the latest being Paul Romanoff: Onomasticon of Palestine, a new method of post-Biblical topography (Proceedings of the American Academy for Jewish Research vol. 7, 100 p., New York 1937; Isis 28, 240), specimen restricted to the letter kâf.

To return to Estori Farḥi, while in Barcelona, i.e., c. 1306–7, he translated into Hebrew a medical treatise of Armengaud son of Blaise (XIII-2), Targum sefer refu'ot. The Latin text is lost; its title was probably De remediis. The Hebrew text is divided into 6 parts: (1) names of remedies, (2) their importance, (3) composition, (4) properties and indications as to their use, (5) posology, (6) times at which the medicines should be taken. He translated also, presumably from the Latin, an anonymous treatise on purgatives, in 7 chapters, Sefer ha-kibbussim. The author's name seems to be Elijah ben Judah of Montpellier.

Estori knew Arabic, for he had read Saadia Gaon ben Joseph (X-1) and Ibn Janāḥ (XI-1) in that language. This does not prove, however, that he knew Arabic before his arrival in the East; his translations from the Latin suggest that he did not know Arabic in his youth; on the other hand, during his long residence in the Holy Land he would necessarily learn it and learn it well.

His astronomical knowledge was derived from Abraham bar Ḥiyya and Jacob ben Maḥir. He was acquainted with Hippocrates, Aristotle, Ptolemy, Galen, Ibn Sīnā.

Text. The Kaftor u-feraḥ was first printed in Venice c. 1549, the text being wrongly ascribed to Isaac Kohen Sholal, nagid of Egypt, who had discovered the MS in 1515. Second edition by Ẓebi Hirsch Edelmann: Caftor wa-pherach auctore Pharchi, liber in quo de ritibus Terram Sanctam spectantibus nec non de geographia, antiquitatibus, nummis etc. eodem pertinentibus agitur. Denuo edidit, textum ex codicibus manuscr. Bibl. Bodl. emendavit, introductionem variique generis annotationes adjecit (Berlin 1852). Third edition by Abraham Moses Luncz (2 vols., Jerusalem 1897–98).

Partial German translation by Lazarus Grünhut: Die Geographie Palästinas von Estori haf-Farchi (Jerusalem 1912).

As the Kaftor remained until 1912 a secret book to non-Hebrew-reading scholars, it exerted but little influence and its importance was hardly realized. For example, there is no mention of it in Sir George Adam Smith: The historical geography of the Holy Land (London 1894), the classic book on Palestinian topography in the English-speaking world; at least, not in the early editions (mine is the 3d, 1895), I have not used later ones (25th, 1932).

A critical edition and English translation of the Kaftor are very desirable.

Criticism. A. Asher: The itinerary of R. Benjamin of Tudela (vol. 2, 1841, note by Yomṭob Lipmann Zunz). Neubauer-Renan (p. 403–9, 1893). Steinschneider (p. 778, 835, 1893). Israel Abrahams: Chapters on Jewish literature (p. 204–5, 1899). M. Franco (JE 5, 343, 1903), stating that Estori died in Palestine, probably in 1357 (?). S. Klein (EJ 6, 932–35, 1930).

ISAAC ḤELO

Isaac ben Joseph Ḥelo. Jewish pilgrim and qabbalist. Born in Catalonia toward the end of the thirteenth century. He left Lerida (Lleyda) with his family in 1333 to go and settle in Jerusalem. Perhaps he hoped to find qabbalistic secrets in the Holy Land? Soon after his establishment there in the same year, he wrote a letter to his father and friends. He explored the country, taking special pains to identify the tombs of prophets and saints. In 1334 he wrote a longer letter, entitled Shebile di Yerushalim (The roads from Jerusalem), divided into 7 chapters, each of which deals with a special road: Jerusalem to Arad, Jerusalem to Jaffa, Jerusalem to Shechem, Jerusalem to Acre, Jerusalem to Tiberias, Tiberias to Safed, Jerusalem to Banias (Dan). In Safed he found Jews from all over the world; in Seilun (Shiloh) he met or heard of an old German qabbalist living in the vicinity of a holy sepulcher and supporting himself by the copying of sacred books. The author's descriptions are somewhat impaired by his qabbalistic tendencies (love of miracles, of the number seven, etc.). He made use of the previous relations of Benjamin of Tudela (XII-2) and Estori Farḥi, but does not mention them.

Text. French translation with notes by Eliacin Carmoly: Itinéraires de la Terre sainte (p. 219–320, Bruxelles 1847). The Hebrew MS from which that text was edited was a part of a composite MS in the Bibliothèque nationale, Paris; it has since been lost or stolen. Carmoly's French version was retranslated into Hebrew by Israel Ze'eb Horowitz (Jerusalem Jahrbuch, edited by Abraham Moses Luncz, 13, 81–127, 1919). Horowitz' Hebrew version was reprinted in Judah David Eisenstein: Ozar massaoth (p. 71–79, New York 1926; Isis 11, 147–49). Carmoly's French version was Englished by Elkan Nathan Adler: Jewish travellers (p. 130–50, London 1930).
Criticism. Röhricht (p. 76, 1890). EJ (p. 504, 1931), 16 lines.

D. MUSLIM GEOGRAPHY

D1. Mamlūk

ABŪ-L-FIDĀ'

Syrian geographer and historian (1273–1331).

Abū-l-Fidā' Ismā'il ibn 'Alī, 'Imād al-dīn al-Aiyūbī. He belonged to the family of the princes of Ḥamāh on the Orontes, a branch of the Aiyūbī royal family created by Ṣalāḥ al-dīn (the famous Saladin, 1169–93). He was born in November 1273, not in Ḥamāh, but in Damascus, where his family had been obliged to take refuge from the Mongols. He received an elaborate education in spite of his being involved in all kinds of military campaigns throughout his youth. For example, at the age of 12 he took part in the conquest of the fortress al-Marqab from the Knights of St. John (1285).[19] In 1299 he entered the service of the Mamlūk sulṭān al-Nāṣir Muḥammad, who appointed him governor of Ḥamāh in 1310. From that time on he continued to rule his hereditary principality, but as a fief of the Mamlūk empire. His loyalty to his liege lord was rewarded in 1312 with the rank of a prince and the title of al-Malik al-Ṣālih, and again in 1320 with the rank of sulṭān and the title of al-Malik al-Mu'ayyad. He died at Ḥamāh in October 1331, and was buried in the mausoleum he had built there for himself.

That mausoleum had gradually fallen into ruins, but in or after 1925 it was re-

[19] E. Honigmann: Marqab (EI 3, 294–96, 1930).

stored by the care of my friend Dr. Tawfīq al-Chīchaklī (or Shīshaklī) (d. 1940), and it was my privilege to visit the restored building on April 21, 1932 (figs. 17, 18).

Abū-l-Fidā's life was a long series of military campaigns and travels; he accomplished the great Pilgrimage at least thrice, and was often obliged to report to Cairo. In spite of these many activities and responsibilities, he was able to write considerably, and he devoted much of his time to the embellishment of his capital and the patronage of learned men who gathered at his court.

His main writings are the Mukhtaṣar ta'rīkh al-bashar and the Taqwīm al-buldān.

The Mukhtaṣar, written in 1315 but continued by the author to 1329, is a universal history dealing with pre-Islamic history and with the history of Islām down to 1329. It is largely based, except of course for the last century, on the Kāmil fī-l-ta'rīkh of Ibn al-Athīr (XIII-1), but the author used many other sources, having a rich library in his palace of Ḥamāh. The most valuable part of his work is the contemporary one, derived from his own political and military experience, which was considerable, and from the information collected during his travels in the Near East and Arabia. Looking at it from another angle, that part includes many data of autobiographical interest.

The importance of Abū-l-Fidā's chronicle was soon appreciated, witness the existence of many summaries, extracts, and continuations, e.g., by Ibn al-Wardī, who continued it to 1348; by Ibn Ḥabīb al-Dimashqī (XIV-2); by Ibn al-Shiḥna al-Ḥalabī (XIV-2), who continued it to 1403. It was also very much appreciated by the early Western Orientalists, partly because of the accident of its being known long before the works of al-Ṭabarī (X-1) and Ibn al-Athīr; in fact, it was the first large Arabic chronicle to be known in the West with the exception of that of Abū-l-Faraj or Barhebraeus (XIII-2).

The Taqwīm, begun in 1316 or before, was completed in 1321. Leyden University owns a MS of it corrected by the author. It is an elaborate treatise on geography, beginning with generalities on the shape of the earth, the seven climates, seas, lakes, rivers, and mountains. This is followed by chapters each dealing with a definite part of the world in the order indicated: (1) Arabia, (2) Egypt, (3) Maghrib, (4) equatorial Africa, (5) Spain, (6) islands of the Mediterranean and the Atlantic, (7) northern regions of Europe and Asia, (8) Syria, (9) Jazīrah, (10) 'Irāq 'arabī, (11) Khūzistān or Ahwāz, (12) Fārs, (13) Kirmān, (14) Sijistān, (15) Sind, (16) Hind (India), (17) China, (18) eastern islands, (19) Rūm (Asia Minor), (20) Armenia, Arrān, and Adharbāijān, (21) Jibāl or 'Irāq 'ajamī, (22) Daylam and Jīlān, (23) Ṭabaristān, Māzandarān, and Qūmis, (24) Khurāsān, (25) Zābulistān and Ghūr, (26) Ṭukhāristān and Badakhshān, (27) Khwārizm, (28) Mā warā-l-nahr (Transoxiana). This enumeration is interesting; it represents the 28 parts of the ancient world in the eyes of an Arabic geographer, and is very different from those which a modern geographer would mention.

The chapter on Transoxiana includes an account, unfortunately too meager, of the small but famous district of Sughd (ancient Sogdiana), traversed by the river Sughd (or Zarafshān), on which stood the cities of Bukhārā and Samarqand. Apropos of Sughd (or Ṣughd), see Le Strange (p. 460–73, 1905); V. V. Barthold (EI 4, 473, 1927); Richard N. Frye: Sughd and the Sogdians. A comparison of archaeological discoveries with Arabic sources (Journal of the American Oriental Society 63, 14–16, 1943; Isis 34, 444).

The 28 chapters are very unequal in length, but are arranged in the same order,

FIG. 17. Mosque of the snakes (Jāmi' al-ḥayyāt) in Ḥamāh (ancient Epiphania). In the foreground, the river Orontes (Nahr al-'āṣī). In the background, the mausoleum of Abū-l-Fidā', close to the square minaret. From Max van Berchem and Edmond Fatio: Voyage en Syrie (vol. 2, pl. xxii; Mémoires de l'Institut français d'archéologie orientale du Caire, vol. 38, Le Caire 1915).

FIG. 18. Mausoleum of Abū-l-Fidā' in Ḥamāh. Photograph by Mrs. G. Sarton (spring 1932).

that is, each is in two parts, the first of which is devoted to a general account of the country (its boundaries, physical peculiarities, political and ethnical divisions, manners and customs, monuments, main roads, etc.) and the second gives in tabular form a series of data concerning the main cities: name, sources of information, longitude, latitude, mathematical climate (as indicated by coordinates), physical climate or province, orthography, short description. Abū-l-Fidā' often quotes conflicting coordinates, stating his preference or not; these coordinates are often erroneous, sometimes grossly so. It is very remarkable that in his indications of geographical coordinates (degrees and minutes) he always uses the literal (abujad) numerals (e.g., lām for 30, sīn for 60), not "Arabic" numerals[20] (fig. 19).

The prolegomena contain two interesting remarks: first, with regard to the loss or gain of one day when traveling around the world (Arabic text, p. 3); second, about three-quarters of the earth's surface are covered by the seas (p. 19), renewing the ancient argument that this must be so because the four elements must balance each other and the earth crust is on the average thrice heavier than water. The treatise contains an abundance of miscellaneous information from which it is hardly possible to choose. For example, the excellent indexes of the Reinaud-Guyard edition will enable one to find many data concerning the mining of salt, bitumen, mercury, silver, and gold.

The tabular form as well as the title of the book had been suggested to the author by the Taqwīm al-abdān of Ibn Jazla (XI-2), he says so himself (p. 3). Abū-l-Fidā's purpose was encyclopaedic and scientific, and he realized that the tabular form, versus the purely literary one, not only is more concise and clearer, but tends to greater precision. He had studied previous publications carefully and quotes his sources at the beginning, then more specifically in each table. He took great pains to establish the orthography and orthophony of place names. His frequent quotation of divergent data (e.g., for coordinates) is typical of his honesty; this was due to his using different sources which he had no means of checking.

The longest chapters deal respectively with (I quote them in the order of decreasing length) the northern regions of Europe and Asia (but that is a large collection of countries), Syria (this being the largest chapter devoted to a single country and probably the most valuable, as the author knew that country best), Arabia, Maghrib, Egypt, equatorial Africa, Spain, Transoxiana, 'Irāq 'arabī, Jazīrah, western islands. Other chapters are very short, those on India and China absurdly so.

A Turkish abbreviated translation in alphabetical order was made by Muḥammad ibn 'Alī Sipāhīzāde (d. 1588/89), under the title Auḍaḥ al-masālik ilā ma'rifat al-buldān wal-mamālik. A part of the Taqwīm was edited in the West as early as 1650, and the author was thus known there by his Taqwīm before being known by his Mukhtaṣar (1723).

Abū-l-Fidā' was learned in many fields; for instance, he had a good knowledge of botany and materia medica. It is said (e.g., by Carra de Vaux 1, 146) that he wrote a work in many volumes on medicine, entitled Kunnāsh. I believe this is a confusion due to the fact that the word kunnāsh (of Aramaic origin), meaning collection, pandectae, was used chiefly for medical collections (see Dozy 2, 494), the best-known example being the Syriac kunnāsh of Yaḥyā ibn Sarāfyūn or Serapion

[20] Even so the compilers of the Alphonsine tables (c. 1272) used Roman numerals, not Arabic ones (Introd. 2, 5, 837). That is, the Arabic numerals were discarded in the very cases when they were most needed.

٢٩٤٦

سطر العدد	الاسمآء	اسماء المنقول عنهم	الطول درج	الطول دقائق	العرض درج	العرض دقائق	سادس الاقاليم العرفيــة وهــو بلاد الشام الاقليم الحقيقى	الاقليم العرفى	ضبط الاسمــآء
١٨	عمّان	اطوال	نو	ك	لا	ح	من الثالث	من البلقآء قال العزيزى وهى البلقآء اى قاعدتها	بفتح العين والميم المشدّدة والف ونون فى الآخر
١٩	الكرك	ابن سعيد قياس	نو نر	ن ل	لا لا	ل ل	من الثالث	من البلقآء ظنًا	بفتح الكاف والرآء المهملة ثم كاف ثانية فى الآخر
٢٠	ماب وهى الربّة	اطوال قياس	نو نر	ل ل	ل لا	له ل	من الثالث	من البلقآء العزيزى وهى ومدينة اذرح مدينتنا جبل الشراة	بفتح الميم والف وبآء موحدة فى الآخر والربّة بفتح الرآء المهملة وتشديد البآء الموحدة وهآء فى الآخر
٢١	الشوبك	ابن سعيد قياس	نو نر	ه ه	لا لا	ه ه	من الثالث	من الشراة	بفتح الشين المعجمة وسكون الواو وبآء موحدة مفتوحة وكاف فى الآخر
٢٢	بيروت	اطوال رسم وابن سعيد وقانون	نط نط	يه ل	ل لد	ك ه	من الثالث	من سواحل دمشق	بفتح البآء الموحدة وسكون المثناة التحتية وضم الرآء المهملة وواو وتآء مثناة من فوق فى آخرها

FIG. 19. A page from the Taqwīm al-buldān (Paris 1840), showing one of the tables concerning Syria. Note that the longitudes and latitudes are indicated by means of abujad (ḥurūf al-jumal), not Hindu numerals (arqām hindīya), the latter being used for the simpler task of numbering the items (in this case items 18 to 22). The places dealt with in this table are 'Ammān, al-Karak, Moab or al-Rabbah, al-Shaubak, Beirūt.

the Elder (IX-2), but the word was also used for other collections, and Abū-l-Fidā' wrote a grammatical kunnāsh, Al-kunnāsh fī-l-naḥw wal-ṣarf.

Text. The first complete edition of the Mukhtaṣar was published in Constantinople 1869–70 (2 vols.). Many partial editions had previously appeared in the West, the earliest being the biography of the Prophet edited in Arabic and Latin by John Gagnier (1670?–1740): De vita et rebus gestis Mohamedis (Oxford 1723); and the most important, the very erudite edition by Johann Jacob Reiske (1716–74) of the second (Muslim) part of the Chronicle, Annales muslemici arabice et latine, published posthumously by Jacob Georg Christian Adler (quarto, 5 vols., Copenhagen 1789–94) with Arabic and Latin indexes and abundant notes.

The first (pre-Islamic) part has been edited in Arabic and Latin by Heinrich Leberecht Fleischer (Leipzig 1831).

There are even more "partial editions" of the Taqwīm, as that work lends itself naturally to such treatment. Students of a particular country are interested only in the part of the Taqwīm relating to that country. The first partial edition was restricted to Khwārizm and Transoxiana and prepared by the English mathematician John Greaves or Gravius (1602–52) (London 1650). The Syrian part was edited in Arabic and Latin by Johann Bernhard Koehler, with very valuable Animadversiones ad Abulfedam et prodidagmata ad historiam et geographiam orientalem by Johann Jacob Reiske (240 p., Leipzig 1766, reprinted 1786). It is not necessary to mention other partial editions, all of which are superseded by the complete Arabic edition of the Société asiatique, prepared by Joseph Toussaint Reinaud and baron de Slane (590 p., Paris 1840), with French preface (47 p.), and by the French translation begun by Reinaud and completed by Stanislas Guyard. It appeared in three quarto parts, vol. 1 and vol. 2, part 1 by Reinaud (Paris 1848), vol. 2, part 2 by Guyard 35 years later (1883). Vol. 1 is a long introduction (464 p.) on Oriental geography which was very remarkable at the time of its appearance and is still valuable, though much of it is superseded because of the availability of many more Arabic texts. Vol. 2, part 1 contains the French translation of chapters 1–7 of the Taqwīm; vol. 2, part 2, the remaining 21 chapters and rich indexes.

The preparation of an English translation, taking into account another century of research work in Arabic and Oriental geography, is much to be desired.

For the sake of curiosity and because I have not seen it referred to anywhere else, I mention one more partial edition of the Taqwīm, an Arabic-Greek one prepared by Demetrios Alexandrides: Ἀμπουλφέδα Ἰσμαὴλ βασιλέως Ἀπαμείας ἐκ τῶν γεωγραφικῶν πινάκων περιγραφὴ Χορασμίας, Μαουαραλνάχρης ἤτοι τῶν πέραν τοῦ ποταμοῦ Ὤξου τόπων, Ἀραβίας, Αἰγύπτου, Περσίδος, ἔτι δὲ τῆς Περσικῆς καὶ Ἐρυθρᾶς θαλάσσης, published in Συλλογὴ τῶν ἐν ἐπιτομῇ τοῖς πάλαι γεωγραφηθέντων τύποις ἐκδοθέντων (vol. 2, 291 p., folding tables, Vienna 1807).

Criticism. Joseph Hammer-Purgstall: Über Reinaud's Übersetzung (Sitzungsber. Wiener Akad., phil.-hist. Cl., 1849, 42 p.). Paul Chaix: Etude sur Aboulféda (Nouvelles annales des voyages 1, 5–46, 1862). Wüstenfeld (no. 398, p. 161–66, 1881). Brockelmann (2, 44–46, 1902; suppt. 2, 44, 1938); EI (1, 85, 1908). Ferrand (2, 398–404, 1914). Carra de Vaux (1, 139–46; 2, 356, 1921). Sarton: Tacuinum, taqwīm (Isis 10, 490–93, 1928). R. Blachère: Extraits des géographes arabes (p. 290–98, Beyrouth 1932; Isis 24, 447–49).

AḤMAD AL-ṬĪNĪ (?)

Arabic (Egyptian?) geographer who is quoted many times in the Nukhbat al-dahr of al-Dimashqī, a work composed c. 1323. Al-Dimashqī quotes Aḥmad's works al-manāhij and al-mabāhij. Now, a cosmography entitled Manāhij al-fikar wa mabāhij al-'ibar (Means of thoughts and joys of examples) or Mabāhij al-fikar wa manāhij al-'ibar is ascribed to Muḥammad ibn Ibrāhīm al-Waṭwāṭ al-Anṣārī al-Warrāq (XIII-2), who died in 1318 (Introd. 2, 870). Is not that perhaps the same work? On the other hand, al-Dimashqī quotes one Aḥmad al-Miṣrī al-Warrāq,[21] who is probably the same as Aḥmad al-Ṭīnī. The nisba Ṭīnī is probably derived from al-Ṭīna on the Suez Canal. The outstanding difficulty is the name Aḥmad.

An edition of the Manāhij (or Mabāhij) al-fikar is desirable; it might help us to solve the problems indicated above. For MSS, see Brockelmann (2, 55, 1902; suppt. 2, 54, 1938); for other references see my note on al-Dimashqī.

AL-DIMASHQĪ

Shams al-dīn Abū 'Abdallāh Muḥammad ibn Ibrāhīm ibn abī Ṭālib al-Anṣārī al-Ṣūfī al-Dimashqī. Syrian cosmographer (d. 1326–27).

Al-Dimashqī was a descendant of the early helpers of the Prophet in Madīna. He was born in 1256–57, perhaps in Damascus. At any rate he spent a good part of his life in or near that city. He was imām in the village of al-Rabwa, on a hill overlooking Damascus. Toward the end of his life he retired to Ṣafad (near Mt. Tabor) in upper Galilee, and died there in 1326–27.

1. His main work, the one upon which his fame exclusively rests, is a cosmographical treatise, Kitāb nukhbat al-dahr fī 'ajā'ib al-barr wal-baḥr (Selection of the age on the wonders of land and sea). It was written in Rabwa and completed late in his life, for he mentions earthquakes which happened in 1319–20 and 1323. Before dealing more fully with the Nukhbat, I shall mention rapidly his other writings:

2. Kitāb al-siyāsa fī 'ilm al-firāsa (or al-firāsa li ajl al-siyāsa), on physiognomy in relation to government.

3. On the signs of death according to Hippocrates.

4. Jawāb risāla ahl jazīrat Qubrūṣ, a defense of Islām against the Christians of Cyprus.

5. Al-maqāmāt al-falsafīya wal-tarjamāt al-ṣūfīya, a treatise in 50 chapters on taṣawwuf, which explains his name al-ṣūfī.

To return to the Nukhbat, it is an elaborate cosmography, inferior to that of Abū-l-Fidā' from the point of view of mathematical geography, but containing considerably more information of many kinds. It is divided into nine parts and 75 chapters: (I) Configuration of the earth and opinions of the ancients on the subject (10 chapters). This includes a good deal of mathematical and general geography: size of the earth, longitude and latitude, seven climates (his views on the limits of each climate differ a little from those of earlier Arabic geographers), seasons, ancient monuments. The last chapter deals with the Sabians. (II) The seven metals (gold, silver, copper, iron, zinc, tin, and lead or quicksilver), their properties and influences. Precious stones. Formation of mountains (11 chapters). (III) Rivers, fountains, wells, and springs (6 chapters). (IV) The sea and its motions, how it covers the earth except the emerging parts. Cause of its saltness. Islands (6 chapters). (V) Description of the Mediterranean (6 chapters). The last 2 chapters deal more briefly with the Black, Caspian, and Aral seas. Tides. (VI) Indian Ocean, with the great gulf deriving from it (i.e., the western Pacific, the China Sea). Its islands (8 chapters). (VII) Eastern kingdoms. Provinces which are (or were) parts of the Dār al-Islām. Main cities and their marvels (13 chapters). (VIII) Western kingdoms, beginning with Egypt and ending with Spain (6 chapters). (IX) Various races of men, descendants of Sem, Ham, and Japheth.

[21] See p. 103, 163, 179 of Mehren's edition; the form Aḥmad al-Ṭīnī is found on p. 95, 97, 222.

Their respective qualities, vicissitudes, calendars, holidays. How they are influenced by their environment. The virtues of man (9 chapters).

This summary does not exhaust the rich contents of this work. It would take too long to do that, and it is better to draw attention to a few points. Though al-Dimashqī was especially interested in mineralogy, metals, geology, he gives much information also on plants and animals, on historical facts, arts and crafts. He observed earthquakes, which he ascribed to the explosion of imprisoned winds, and thought there was some connection between earthquakes and the formation of mountains and of springs. He described a subterranean grotto with stalactites, near Damascus. Though on the whole hostile to alchemy, he shared the Neoplatonic views on the growth and possible "education" or transformation of metals. In fact, he explains the formation of the seven metals out of mercury and sulphur; mercury itself being derived from sulphur and water, and sulphur from water. Though there are many ideas in his work which seem irrational to us, if one takes into account (as one should) the limitations of his time and environment, al-Dimashqī must be considered a man of unusual sense and freedom. He had added a colored map to his work, but the tradition of it is lost (at any rate it is not preserved in the printed Arabic and French editions).

The sources of the Nukhbat are easier to evaluate as a whole than in detail. It is clear that al-Dimashqī was very well acquainted with the Arabic literature on cosmography and geography, and with some Arabic standard books on tradition and history. As to ancient literature, he refers thrice to the Almagest and once to the Ḳitāb al-aḥjār of "Aristotle" (in reality an Arabic production; Isis 1, 266). The author most frequently mentioned or referred to is al-Mas'ūdī (X-1). Al-Dimashqī refers either directly or indirectly to al-Balkhī (X-1), Qudāma (X-1), Ibn Waḥshīya (X-1), al-Bakrī (XI-2), al-Idrīsī (XII-2), the historian 'Alī ibn Muḥammad Ibn al-Athīr (XIII-1) and his older brother the traditionist Majd al-dīn Abū-l-Sa'ādāt Ibn al-Athīr (1149–1209), Aḥmad al-Ṭīnī. Many other writers or books are mentioned only once or twice.

Al-Dimashqī's treatise on physiognomy mentioned above (no. 2) deserves to arrest our attention because it is the first Arabic treatise (according to Mourad p. 9, 1939) wherein that old science or art (a branch of physics, like medicine) is contaminated with astrological developments; the astrological part of the treatise, however, is separated from the rest, forming a kind of appendix at the end of it (p. 51–61 of the printed text). The main sources are Hippocrates, Aristotle, Polemon of Laodicea (II-1); the Sirr al-asrār ('ilm al-siyāsa fī tadbīr al-riyāsa, Introd. 1, 556); the Kitāb fī 'ilm al-qiyāfa ascribed to the imām al-Shāfi'ī (IX-1), founder of the Shāfi'ī school; the Kitāb al-ṭibb al-Manṣūrī of al-Rāzī (IX-2); the Kitāb al-firāsa of Fakhr al-dīn al-Rāzī (XII-2); and, finally, the great ṣūfī doctor Ibn 'Arabī (XIII-1), who was the first to introduce a new kind of firāsa, the mystical one.[22]

Al-Dimashqī's treatise on the signs of death according to Hippocrates (no. 3

[22] The oldest term seems to be qiyāfa, which occurs in the title of the book ascribed to al-Shāfi'ī. A qā'if (pl. qāfa) is a man who can deduce the interior of a thing from the exterior. The term firāsa means physiognomy as expanded by the Arabs on a Greek foundation, the application of the theory of humors, temperaments, and complexions to physical and psychological divination (of present circumstances and even of future ones). Ibn 'Arabī made a further distinction between natural physiognomy (firāsa ṭabī'īya or ḥikmīya) and divine physiognomy (firāsa ilāhīya), the mystical power given to some inspired men, which enables them to see far beyond appearances in space or time.

above) is also connected with the physiognomic tradition; this relation was explained in an apocryphal treatise ascribed to al-Jāḥiẓ (IX-2). That is, certain signs of the body represent not only actual conditions, but potential and future ones. The πρόσωπον νεκρώδης is a prefiguration of death visible to the experienced physician.

Text. The Arabic text of the Nukhbat al-dahr was edited by August Ferdinand Mehren (quarto, 375 p., St. Petersburg 1866). I have used a photographic reprint of that edition (Leipzig 1923), which includes a good index. Mehren published a French translation of the same work: Manuel de la cosmographie du Moyen âge (octavo, 463 p., Copenhagen 1874).

Kitāb siyāsa fī 'ilm al-firāsa (66 p., Cairo 1882).

Criticism. Reinaud (1, cl, 1848). Steinschneider (p. 132–34, 1877). Henri Dehérain: Quid Schemseddin al-Dimaschqui geographus de Africa cognitum habuerit (Paris 1897). Brockelmann (2, 130, 138, 1902; suppt. 2, 161, 1938); EI (1, 975, 1912). Ferrand (p. 363–93, 1914). Carra de Vaux (2, 35, 377, 390, 1921). Gaudefroy-Demombynes (p. 46, 1923), apropos of al-Rabwa. Honigmann (p. 180 and by index, 1929), valuable comparison of the extent of the climates according to al-Dimashqī and other geographers; see table p. 163. Enrico Cerulli: Noterelle somale ad al-Dimashqī ed Ibn 'Arabī (Orientalia 4, 335–43, Vatican 1935), notes concerning Somaliland. Mourad (p. 8, 31–34, 55, 1939).

IBN FAḌLALLĀH AL-'UMARĪ

Syrian historian, geographer, encyclopaedist, and man of letters (1301–49).

Shihāb al-dīn Abū-l-'Abbās Aḥmad ibn Yaḥyā ibn Faḍlallāh al-'Umarī al-Qurashī al-Shāfi'ī. Born in Damascus on June 11, 1301, in a distinguished family, the Banū Faḍlallāh, claiming to be descendants of the orthodox caliph 'Umar, hence their laqab 'Umarī. He studied in Damascus, Cairo, Alexandria, and the Ḥijāz, was qāḍī in Cairo, and later succeeded his father as chancellor to the Mamlūk government. His work as chancellor was done in Cairo and later in Damascus, where he died of the plague on February 28, 1349.

His literary activity seems to have been limited for the most part to the last ten years of his life, or maybe it blossomed then after years of preparation.

His two main works are the Masālik al-abṣār fī mamālik al-amṣār (Voyages of the eyes in the kingdoms of the main cities), composed c. 1342–49, and Al-ta'rīf bī-l-muṣṭalaḥ al-sharīf, composed in 1340/41.

The first is a very large and heterogeneous collection of data relative to geography and natural history, political history, history of Arabic poetry, biographies. It extended to 23 or 27 volumes. For example, vol. 1 deals with geography and natural history, vol. 14 with pre-Islamic Arabic poetry, vol. 15 with the poets of the first three Islamic centuries, vol. 16 with the western (Arabic) poets, vol. 17 with the poets of the fourth to seventh Islamic centuries, vol. 23 with political history from the middle of the twelfth century to the middle of the fourteenth (1146–1343). The work contains an elaborate description of the lands, institutions, and manners of India, and similar descriptions relative to other Muslim countries, which it is interesting to compare with the accounts of his contemporary Ibn Baṭṭūṭa (XIV-2). The author used literary sources, but also questioned living witnesses, whose statements he criticized carefully. His position of chancellor to the sulṭān gave him exceptional facilities for obtaining firsthand information from a number of diplomats, travelers, and merchants of various nationalities. For example, one of his informants concerning Turkish lands was the Genoese Balbān, whose original name was Domenico Doria, son of Taddeo Doria (Quatremère p. 338, 347).

One of the most valuable parts of al-'Umarī's geography is the one dealing with Abyssinia, the kingdoms of Fez, Tlemcen, and Tunis, and the Negro (Mandingo) empire of Mali in the western Sūdān. One of the kings of Mali, Kankan (or Gongo, or Mansa) Mūsā (d. 1332), had created a sensation in Cairo when he arrived there in 1324 on his way to the Pilgrimage, because of his magnificent caravan and his extravagant expenditures. He put so much gold into circulation that its value fell considerably in Egypt!

Mansa Mūsā's predecessor, Muḥammad Gao, had organized two expeditions to explore the Atlantic and lost his life during the second (c. 1307), and al-'Umarī mentions still another Atlantic adventure (Gaudefroy-Demombynes p. 74–82, 1927), all of which shows that the Mandingo people continued the Arabic traditions of Atlantic exploration, represented by Khashkhāsh of Cordova in al-Mas'ūdī (X-1) and the Maghrūrīn in al-Idrīsī (XII-2).[23]

Al-'Umarī's second work, Al-ta'rīf bi-l-muṣṭalaḥ al-sharīf, is a manual of chancellery or diplomatics, mainly a collection of models for official letters and documents, divided into 7 chapters: (1) letters to Muslim and non-Muslim princes and dignitaries, (2) formulas for decrees and diplomas, (3) oath formulas, (4) security letters and other contracts, (5) Mamlūk administration, political geography of the territories submitted to it, (6) means of information and communication, (7) alia. The Ta'rīf is an important source for the study of Mamlūk administration and institutions in Syria and Egypt.

A smaller work of his deserves mention, a collection of "winter" letters, al-shatawīyāt, addressed to various scholars, and their answers. They describe the hard winter and heavy snows experienced in Damascus in 1344.

Text. The Ta'rīf was printed in Cairo 1894/95. Analysis and partial German translation (chs. 5, 6) by Richard Hartmann: Politische Geographie des Mamlūkenreiches (Zeitschrift der Deutschen morgenländischen Gesellschaft 70, 1–40, 477–511, 1916), with abundant notes.

The late Aḥmad Zakī pāshā (1867–1934) had collected photographs of MSS of the Masālik al-abṣār and reconstructed a complete copy. He began a critical edition published by the National Library in Cairo, but only one volume has appeared (223 p., Cairo 1923/24).

The chapters of the Masālik relative to Asia were translated into French and discussed by Quatremère (Notices et extraits des MSS 13, 151–384, Paris 1838). French translation of the African part, less Egypt, by Maurice Gaudefroy-Demombynes (Bibliothèque des géographes arabes vol. 2, 354 p., 5 maps, Paris 1927; Isis 12, 358). Franz Taeschner: Bericht über Anatolien in al-'Umarī (part 1, Arabic text, 100 p., Leipzig 1929; Isis 24, 208). Otto Spies announced in 1936 the preparation of the text relative to India, in Arabic and English, with two Hindu collaborators.

Criticism. Reinaud (1, clii, 1848). Wüstenfeld (no. 411, p. 6–7, 1882). Louis Dussieux: Les grands faits de l'histoire de la géographie (1, 228–34, Paris 1882). Suter (p. 166, 1900). Henri Lammens: Relations officielles entre la cour romaine et les sultans mamlouks (Revue de l'orient chrétien 8, 101–10, 1903); Correspondances diplomatiques entre les sultans mamlouks et les puissances chrétiennes

[23] Introd. 2, 1062. Beazley (3, 532, 1906). For first orientation on Mandingo, see articles by Henri Labouret on Mali (EI 3, 203, 1929) and Mandingo (EI 3, 239–42, 1929), and by Maurice Delafosse on Sūdān (EI 4, 495–97, 1927).

(ibid. 9, 151–87, 359–92, 1904). Brockelmann (2, 141, 1902; suppt. 2, 175, 1938); EI (2, 37, 1913). Aḥmad Zakī pāshā: Une seconde tentative des Musulmans pour découvrir l'Amérique (Bulletin de l'Institut d'Egypte 2, 57–59, Cairo 1920; Isis 10, 133). Gaudefroy-Demombynes (p. 306, 1923). Ḥasan Ḥusnī 'Abdalwahhāb: Waṣf Ifrīqīya wal-Maghrib (50 p., reprinted from al-Badr, Tunis 1922–23), in Arabic, reviewed in Andalus (2, 436–38). Walther Björkman: Beiträge zur Geschichte der Staatskanzlei im islamischen Ägypten (p. 36, passim, Hamburg 1928). Gaudefroy-Demombynes: Quelques passages du Masālik el-abṣār relatifs au Maroc (Mémorial Henri Basset 1, 269–80, Paris 1928). Sarkis (col. 204–5, 1930). Blachère (p. 301–13, 1932). Bovill (p. 72, 1933). Hennig (3, 128–32, 1938), apropos of the Atlantic expedition referred to by al-'Umarī. L. A. Mayer: Some problems of Mamlūk coinage (Transactions of the International Numismatic Congress, London 1936, p. 439–41, London 1938).

IBN AL-FIRKĀḤ

Syrian author of a pilgrim book to Jerusalem (1262–1329).

Burhān al-dīn Abū Isḥāq Ibrāhīm ibn 'Abd al-Raḥmān Ibn al-Firkāḥ al-Shāfi'ī al-Badrī al-Fazārī (reference to Fazāra tribe) was born in 1262, became assistant to his father, Tāj al-dīn 'Abd al-Raḥmān ibn Ibrāhīm Ibn al-Firkāḥ (1227–91), professor of Shāfi'ī law in the Bādarā'īya madrasa in Damascus; he succeeded his father in that chair and became a preacher in the Umayya mosque; he died in 1329. In his long account of the jāmi' Banī Umayya, Ibn Baṭṭūṭa (XIV-2) refers to Ibn al-Firqāḥ as one of the teachers there (I, 213).

Ibn al-Firkāḥ wrote:

1. Bā'ith al-nufūs ilā ziyāra al-Quds al-maḥrūs, a guidebook for pilgrims to Jerusalem and also to Hebron (tombs of the patriarchs), Bethlehem, etc. It is derived from earlier texts, especially one by al-Qāsim ibn 'Asākir (d. 1203).
2. Al-i'lām bi-faḍā'il al-Shām, description of the beauties of Damascus, derived from an earlier work by 'Alī ibn Muḥammad al-Raba'ī (d. 1043).
3. Al-manā'iḥ li-ṭālib al-ṣaid wal-dhabā'iḥ, on the ritual slaughter of animals.
4. Ḥall al-qinā' 'an ḥall al-samā' (Loosening the veil concerning the solution of listening [to music]).

Text. No. 1 was edited by Charles D. Matthews (Journal of the Palestine Oriental Society, vol. 14–15, p. 284–93, plus 37 p. in Arabic, Jerusalem 1934–35; Isis 30, 334).

Criticism. Brockelmann (2, 130, 1902; suppt. 2, 161, 1938). Farmer (no. 212, p. 51, 1940).

D2. 'Iraq

IBN SHABĪB

Najm al-dīn Aḥmad ibn Ḥamdān ibn Shabīb al-Ḥarrānī al-Ḥanbalī. The nisba Ḥarrānī refers to the town Ḥarrān in Jazīrah, Mesopotamia. Iraqian cosmographer who flourished in Egypt c. 1332.[24]

He composed an encyclopaedia of geography, natural history, folklore, called Jāmi' al-funūn (or, al-'ulūm) wa salwat al-maḥzūn. As far as the wonders of Egypt are concerned, his main source was the Jawāhir al-buḥūr wa waqā'i' al-umūr wa

[24] According to Ḥājjī Khalīfa (2, nos. 3922, 3934, 1837), he died in 1295/96. That, says Brockelmann, is a mistake.

'ajā'ib al-duhūr wa akhbār al-diyār al-Miṣrīya, by the Egyptian Ibrāhīm ibn Waṣīf Shāh (uncertain date, before 1209).

A great part of the Jāmi' al-funūn (from section 4 on) was reproduced almost literally by Sirāj al-dīn 'Umar ibn Muḥammad Ibn al-Wardī (d. 1457) in the latter's encyclopaedia Kharīdat al-'ajā'ib wa farīdat al-gharā'ib. This Ibn al-Wardī should not be confused with the greater Zain al-dīn Ibn al-Wardī. The Kharīdat al-'ajā'ib was translated into Persian and into Turkish.

After an introduction wherein Ibn al-Wardī quotes his sources (but not Ibn Shabīb!) and generalities on the mappa mundi, measures, etc., the Kharīdat al-'ajā'ib is divided into 14 chapters: (1) large countries, (2) seas and straits, (3) islands, (4) marvels of those islands, (5) great rivers, (6) springs and wells, (7) high mountains, (8) stones and their properties, (9) mines and precious stones, (10–13) botany, (14) zoology. It ends with remarks on the day of the resurrection.

This book was probably one of the sources of the storytellers of the Arabian nights.

Text. The Jāmi' al-funūn is unpublished, but there are many Cairene editions of the Kharīdat al-'ajā'ib which include the greater part of the plagiarized work (1289 [1872/73], 1298 [1880/81], 1300 [1882/83], 1302 [1884/85], 1316 [1898/99], 1324 [1906/7] H.).

Some partial European editions of the Kharīdat al-'ajā'ib are in fact editions of the work of Ibn Shabīb. Thus, Excerptum geographicum de terra Syriae exponens ex Ibn ol Wardii geographia e historia naturali, edited by Johann Bernard Koehler in Arabic and Latin, and appended to Abū-l-Fidā': Tabula Syriae (p. 167–92, Leipzig 1766). Christian Martin Fraehn: Aegyptus (112 p., Halle 1804), in Arabic and Latin. Carl Johan Tornberg: Fragmentum libri Margarita mirabilium (2 parts, Uppsala 1835–39), in Arabic and Latin.

Criticism. Joseph de Guignes: Perle des merveilles (Notices et extraits des MSS 2, 19–59, 1789), analysis of the work wrongly ascribed to the elder and greater Ibn al-Wardī. Reinaud (1, 155, 1848). E. H. F. Meyer (3, 308–9, 1856). Wüstenfeld (no. 412, 1882). Edward William Lane: Arabian society (p. 99, 283, London 1883). Brockelmann (2, 130, 131, 1902; suppt. 2, 161, 162, 1938). Ferrand (p. 408–25, 1914). Moh. b. Cheneb (EI 2, 428, 1918), short note. Franz Taeschner: Bericht des Ibn al-Wardi über Konstantinopel (Beiträge zur historischen Geographie, etc., edited by Hans v. Mžik in honor of Eugen Oberhummer, p. 84–91, Leipzig 1929). Conway Zirkle: Animals impregnated by the wind (Isis 25, 121, 1936), apropos of the island of women where the latter are impregnated by the wind.

'ABD AL-MU'MIN IBN 'ABD AL-ḤAQQ

Arabic geographer (b. 1259–60, d. 1338–39).

Abū-l-Faḍā'il Ṣafī al-dīn 'Abd al-Mu'min ibn al-Khaṭīb 'Abd al-ḥaqq al-Baghdādī al-Ḥanbalī. Born in Baghdād 1259–60, his father, 'Abd al-ḥaqq ibn 'Abdallāh, being a preacher. Abd al-Mu'min studied ḥadīth, theology, arithmetic, algebra, geometry, and other sciences in Baghdād, Damascus, Mecca, also in Egypt. He belonged to the Ḥanbalī school of theology. He died in Baghdād 1338–39, and was buried in the cemetery of the imām Aḥmad.

'Abd al-Mu'min compiled a geographical dictionary entitled Marāṣid al-iṭṭilā' 'alā asmā' al-amkina wal-biqā', which, large as it is, is only a summary of the great dictionary of Yāqūt (XIII-1), the Mu'jam al-buldān. In Juynboll's edition the

Arabic text of the Marāṣid covers 1,410 pages. The arrangement of the place names is strictly alphabetical; but, whereas the Mu'jam contains not only geographical information, but also historical, biographical, astrological, and literary data and poetic quotations, the Marāṣid is restricted to geography. It includes additions to the Mu'jam.

The Marāṣid has been ascribed wrongly to the Egyptian polygraph al-Suyūṭī and to Yāqūt himself. The ascription to the latter is easy to understand and can be to some extent justified, 'Abd al-Mu'min being then considered as an editor and abstractor, not as an original author. It is impossible to say how much original material there is in the Marāṣid without making an elaborate comparison between it and the Mu'jam, and this would take considerable time.

Text. T. G. J. Juynboll: Lexicon geographicum cui titulus est Marāṣid (6 vols., Leiden 1850–64); vols. 1–3 contain the Arabic text; vols. 4–6, introduction, notes.

I recall that Yāqūt's Mu'jam was edited by Ferdinand Wüstenfeld: Jacuts geographisches Wörterbuch (6 vols., Leipzig 1866–71); and again by Muḥammad Amīn al-Khānajī with the help of Aḥmad ibn al-Amīn al-Shinqīṭī, together with a modern supplement relative to Europe, America, etc., compiled by the former (10 vols., Cairo 1906–7).

Criticism. Ḥājjī Khalīfa (5, 625, 1850). Brockelmann (1, 480, 1898; suppt. 1, 880, 1937). Sarkis (col. 160, 1930). The biographical information given above is derived from the author's name and beyond that from Sarkis' account, the source of which is not quoted.

D4. Maghrib

AL-TIJĀNĪ

Abū Muḥammad 'Abdallāh ibn Aḥmad al-Tijānī.[25] Tunisian traveler in North Africa, geographer (fl. 1306–11).

The dates and places of his birth and death are unknown. All we know is that he left Tunis in December 1306 with a prince of the Ḥafṣī dynasty, who became king later (1311–17) under the name Abū Yaḥyā Zakaryā; they intended to make the Pilgrimage, but illness obliged al-Tijānī to abandon the others soon after reaching Tripolis (June 1309). He returned to Tunis after an absence of 970 days. Abū Yaḥyā after his accession gave al-Tijānī a high position at his court; thus the latter lived at least until 1311.

The account of his journey written by al-Tijānī, entitled Riḥla, is far more than an itinerary. It contains a wealth of information, historical, archaeologic, and scientific, concerning the relatively small region traversed; also extracts from other books some of which are lost. It is the only riḥla covering the Ḥafṣī territory at that time.

The same author wrote a popular erotic work, called Tuḥfat al-'arūs wa-nuzhat al-nufūs (Gift of the bride and delight of the souls), in 25 chapters, giving advice on the choice of a wife, marks of beauty on different parts of the body, amatory recipes. This includes many quotations from earlier jurists, theologians, and poets.

Text. There is no complete edition or translation of the Riḥla. Parts of the text have been edited and translated by Michele Amari: Bibliotheca arabo-sicula (ch. 45, Leipzig 1857) and Alfred Bel: Les Benou Ghânya; derniers représentants de l'empire Almoravide et leur lutte contre l'empire Almohade (Publication de l'Ecole des lettres d'Alger vol. 27, 1903).

[25] Or Abū 'Abdallāh Muḥammad ibn Aḥmad (or ibn Ibrāhīm).

French extracts from the whole work in Alphonse Rousseau: Voyage du scheikh et-Tidjani (Journal asiatique 20, 57–208, 1852; 1, 101–68, 354–425, 1853), with brief notes but no index.

The Tuḥfat al-'arūs was printed in Cairo 1884 (210 p.), Fās 1900. Three chapters (i, vii, viii) translated into French (Alger 1848). R. P. A. Dozy: Loci de Abbadidis (2, 139–55, Leiden 1852), extract in Arabic and Latin, in a collection of texts concerning the 'Abbādī dynasty of Seville (1023–91).

Criticism. M. Plessner (EI 4, 745, 1929). Brockelmann (2, 257, 1902; suppt. 2, 368, 1938).

AL-BALAWĪ

Abū-l-Baqā' Khālid ibn 'Īsā. Hispano-Muslim traveler to the Near East in 1335–40.

Al-Balawī was born at Qanṭūriya near Granada. He left his native place in October 1335 to accomplish the Pilgrimage, traveling across Africa to Tunis, whence he sailed to Alexandria. He then went to Cairo and Jerusalem, Madīna, and Mekka. He returned by the same way to Alexandria, whence he sailed to Tripolis, but was obliged to come back to Alexandria. Later he managed to go to Tunis, where he spent a couple of years. He was back home in Qanṭūriya on May 29, 1340, where he was appointed qāḍī and spent presumably the rest of his life.

He wrote an account of his journey entitled Tāj al-mafriq fī taḥliyat 'ulamā al-mashriq (Crown of the vortex on the description of the learned men of the East). As the title indicates, it deals mainly with the men whom he met or heard of in various places. Much of the account was borrowed from other writings, especially Ibn Jubair (XII-2).

Criticism. Wüstenfeld (no. 438a, p. 17, 1882). Pons Boigues (p. 330, 1898). Brockelmann (2, 266, 1902; suppt. 2, 379, 1938). Henry de Castries: Relation d'une ambassade marocaine en Turquie (1589–91) traduite et annotée (146 p., Paris 1929; p. xiii–xvi; Isis 14, 487), apropos of Abū-l-Ḥasan 'Alī ibn Muḥammad of Tamgrūt in southern Morocco (c. 1560–1594/95), who copied parts of his account from the Kitāb al-'iqd al-farīd of Ibn 'Abd Rabbihi (d. 940; Introd. 1, 556; Isis 34, 43) and from al-Balawī.

E. GEOGRAPHY IN THE FAR EAST

CHU SSŬ-PÊN

Chinese cartographer (fl. 1311–20).

Chu Ssŭ-pên, styled Pên-ch'u, nicknamed Chên-i. He was born in 1273.

He compiled in 1311–20 an elaborate map of China entitled Yü-t'u or Yü ti-t'u. The original is lost, but the tradition was continued by Lo Hung-hsien, styled Ta-fu (b. 1504, chin shih 1529, d. 1564), in his atlas Kuang yü-t'u, the very title of which shows that it is an expansion of the Yü-t'u. In the preface to that atlas, Lo Hung-hsien declares that he had searched three years for a copy of Chu's Yü-t'u, until he found one seven feet square. He revised and expanded it, and for the sake of convenience divided it into smaller sections published in atlas form. The original Yüan map still existed at the end of the seventeenth century, for a copy of it was owned by the historian Yao Chi-hêng, styled Li Fang, born 1647, and listed by him in the catalogue of his library Hao-ku t'ang shu-mu, preface dated 1715.

According to the Ming editor Lo Hung-hsien, Chu Ssŭ-pên was the first to introduce the idea of dividing maps into squares to indicate distances, the side of each square representing a definite number of li.[26] Such division suggests that the difficulties of map projection had not even occurred to the Chinese cartographer. It was not new with Chu, but continued an old tradition represented by Pei Hsiu (III-2), by Chia Tan (VIII-2), and by the two oldest Chinese maps extant, both dated 1137 (Introd. 2, 225).

Though Chu's map is lost, some of his writings in prose and verse have been preserved.

The cartographic tradition of the Yü-t'u and Kuang yü-t'u remained supreme in China until the publication by the Jesuit father Matteo Ricci (1552–1610) of the map of the world K'un yü wan kuo ch'üan t'u, in 1584.[27]

Text. The Kuang yü-t'u was first printed c. 1550 (no copy of that princeps is known). Later editions bear prefaces dated 1551, 1566, 1579, 1615, etc.

The Library of Congress has a MS copy in 4 vols. (folio, 144 p., 40 maps), and editions of 1558, 1579. The one of 1558 was printed by order of the censorate at Nanking. The atlas consists of two folding albums, complete in 117 folio pages, each page 38½ by 41½ cm. The first album has 17 maps, the second 31. There are two undated prefaces, the first reprinted from the lost map of Chu Ssŭ-pên, the other, unsigned, by Lo Hung-hsien. Each map measures 32½ by 33½ cm. and is divided into squares, the sides of which measure 40, 100, 200, 400, or 500 li. Each map is followed with explanations concerning physical, agricultural, administrative, and economic geography, including various statistics.

Chu's prose and verse are available in the Shih yüan ts'ung shu, being entitled "Chên i chai tsa chu."

Criticism. Arthur W. Hummel: Report of the Library of Congress (p. 246, 1927; p. 174–76, 1937).

CHINESE CARTOGRAPHY

A map of Central Asia was included in the encyclopaedia Ching shih ta tien, meaning The great standard of administration. The compilation of this encyclopaedia was ordered in 1329; it was completed in 1331 and offered to the emperor in the following year. It dealt mainly with Mongol institutions. It is lost, but parts of it are extant in the annals of the Yüan dynasty, the Yüan shih hastily compiled in 1369, and in later encyclopaedias. For example, the map of Central Asia above mentioned is preserved in the Yung Lo ta tien (first half of fifteenth century), and it is from there that it has been derived by various modern editors: Wei Yüan in his Hai kuo t'u chih, a treatise on the historical geography of Asia, in 1842–44; the archimandrite Palladius, in Memoirs (Trudy) of the Russian Ecclesiastical Mission in Peking (vol. 4, 1886); etc.

A MS copy of one chapter of the Ching shih ta tien was in the Rumiantsev Museum, Moscow, in 1888. There is a copy of the map, made from the original in the Chinese Imperial Library, in the Archives of the Russian Ecclesiastical Mission in Peking.

Bretschneider (2, 3–136, 1888). Paul Pelliot: Note sur la carte des pays du Nord-Ouest dans le King che ta tien (T'oung Pao 25, 98–100, 1927).

[26] Li, equaling 1,800 ch'ih, Chinese feet, or about 1,894 English feet. The statute mile equals 5,280 feet, a little less than 3 li.

[27] There were probably eight editions of that map within Ricci's lifetime, the first in Chao-Ch'ing, Huangtung 1584, the last in Peking 1608. Henri Bernard: Ricci's scientific contributions to China (Peiping 1935; Isis 26, 164). Kenneth Ch'en: Matteo Ricci's contribution to, and influence on, geographical knowledge in China (Journal of the American Oriental Society 59, 325–59, 1939). Of modern editions I cite only the one by Yü kung hsüeh hui (Peiping 1936).

The Library of Congress has the Hai kuo t'u chih in an edition of 1852 in 100 chüan and twelve volumes; and in an edition of 1896 in 100 chüan and sixteen volumes. For Wei Yüan (1794–1856, historian and geographer, see Hummel (p. 850–52, 1944).

WANG HSI

Chinese geographer and cartographer (fl. about the middle of the century).

There are in Chinese a number of books dealing with the rivers and waterways of China, the most ancient being the so-called "Water classic," Shui ching. A work bearing that title and ascribed to Sang Ch'in cannot be much later than the beginning of our era, for it is quoted by the historian Pan Ku (I-2), but the book which has actually come to us under that title is probably somewhat later, say, from the time of the Three kingdoms (221–65); we have also a commentary on it by Li Tao-yüan, of the northern Wei dynasty (386–535). Other books of the kind were published during the Sung dynasty.

About the middle of the fourteenth century Wang Hsi wrote the Chih ho t'u lüeh, which is a treatise on the course of the Yellow River, called Huang-ho or simply the River, Ho. It includes six charts and gives an account of the overflowings and changes of course of the great river during the past centuries.

Another treatise, Ho fang t'ung i, explaining how to protect the banks of the Yellow River, was written during the same (Yüan) dynasty, by Sha K'o-shih. It includes much information concerning past and present conditions of that river.

Text. The Library of Congress has the Chih ho t'u lüeh in vol. 65 of the Mo hai chin hu.

Criticism. Wylie (p. 54, 1902).

Chinese writings on the conservancy of rivers. Studies on rivers and river conservancy constitute a typical Chinese "genre" throughout the centuries. The Shui ching and its commentaries were investigated and commented upon again and again, e.g., by Ch'üan Tsu-wang (1705–55), Chao I-ch'ing (1711–64), Tai Chên (1724–77), and Ch'ên Li (1810–82). Many Chinese officials were obliged to devote their attention to river conservancy, the prevention or cure of floods, etc., and they generally sought for wisdom in the Shui ching and its derivatives. For example, Chu Chih-hsi (d. 1666), Chin Fu (d. 1692), Chang P'êng-ko (d. 1725), Chang Po-hsing (d. 1725), Kao Pin (d. 1755), Fan Kuan-chêng (d. 1768), Ch'i Chao-nan (d. 1768), Kao Chin (d. 1779), Liu Ē (d. 1909)—the last named more famous as discoverer of the oracle bones and author of the novel Lao-ts'an yu-chi. See Hummel (1943–44), under the name of each,[28] critical study by Hu Shih (p. 970–82), and indexes (p. 1059, 1092).

HUANG CHIN

Huang Chin, Chinese man of letters and topographer (1274–1354).

He was styled Chin Ch'ing and was canonized as Wên Hsien. Born in 1274 at I-wu, Chehkiang; obtained in 1315 his "doctor's" degree, chin shih; served in the Han-lin yüan and as adviser to the emperor. He wrote a topography of his native country, and two collections of essays entitled respectively Jih sun chai pi chi and Jih sun chai kao.

Criticism. Giles (no. 849, 1898). Wieger (p. 312, 1920).

[28] Except that Ch'i Chao-nan will be found under Ch'i Shao-nan (Isis 34, 522).

WANG TA-YÜAN

Chinese geographer (fl. c. 1349).

Wang Ta-yüan, styled Han Chang, native of Nan-Ch'ang, Kiangsi, visited many countries of the Malay archipelago, traveling in a merchant ship, and wrote c. 1349 an account of those countries and peoples, entitled Tao i chih lüeh, meaning "A brief description of island 'barbarians.' "

Text. The Library of Congress has a copy of the Tao i printed in one volume in 1892. The text is included in Ssŭ k'u chüan shu, with two prefaces, the one by Chang Chu, the other by Wu Chien. Wu's preface is dated 1349.

Criticism. Wylie (p. 58, 1920). William Woodville Rockhill (1854–1914): Notes on the relations and trade of China with the eastern archipelago and the coasts of the Indian Ocean during the fourteenth century (T'oung Pao 14, 473–76, 1913; 15, 419–47, 1914; 16, 61–159, 236–71, 374–92, 435–67, 604–26, 1915), derived from the Yüan shih, the Tao i chih lüeh, and later writings. Obituary of the author (ibid. 16, 160–64).

CHAPTER X

NATURAL HISTORY

(First Half of the Fourteenth Century)

N.B. Only the main articles are grouped in this chapter. The contributions to natural history of many other men, whose main work was done in other fields, are related in other chapters. For a general survey of natural history in the first half of the fourteenth century, see section X of chapter I. More information on the men referred to in that section may then easily be found by means of the index.

A. LATIN WEST

A1. Italy

PIETRO DEI CRESCENZI

Petrus de Crescentiis. Pietro Crescenzio (many other variants in different languages). Italian writer on husbandry. Born in Bologna c. 1230–33, died in 1320 (or beginning of 1321).

His father, Giambonino dei Crescenzi, was a well-to-do landowner belonging to an old Ghibelline family. Pietro studied logic, medicine, natural sciences, and finally law at the University of Bologna, and was called a judge (giudice). He was not a senator (as he was called in the Basel edition of 1538), but from 1269 to 1299 he held various political and judicial offices as technical assessor to the podestà in Sinigaglia, Asti, Imola, Ferrara, Pisa, Brescia, and Piacenza. (These cities are distributed all over northern Italy; Pietro's peregrinations illustrate a political custom of the time: the cities would select their main public servants among outsiders, graduates of the law school of Bologna being especially in favor. Intense political unrest would cause frequent mutations.) He visited many other Italian cities and traveled probably also to Provence. In 1299, he withdrew from political activity and settled down on his estate, Villa d'Olmo in Urbizzano (now Rubizzano) near Bologna. He spent the rest of his life there, devoting himself to the management of his patrimony and the composition of the great book which immortalized his name.

That book was a treatise on husbandry entitled Liber cultus ruris or Ruralium commodorum libri XII. He completed it between 1304 and 1309 (say, c. 1306) and dedicated it to Charles II of Anjou (d. 1309), then the head and protector of the Guelph party, of which Bologna was a stronghold.

It should be noted that Pietro was really a man of the thirteenth century and contemporary with another great agricultural writer, Albert the Great of that century. At the time of Albert's death, in 1280, Pietro was at least 47 years old; at the end of the century he was almost an old man. We did not deal with him in our volume 2 because his work, though it was a fruit of the thirteenth century, was not completed by him until c. 1306. His case is very similar to that of another illustrious authority in his own field, Cato the Censor, who published his De agri cultura in the second century B.C., though he was to some extent a man of the previous century.

The Ruralia commoda was written in the barbaric and Italianate Latin of that time, and the text was revised by sundry Dominicans and scientists of Bologna before being printed. After the dedication and a preface explaining his purpose, the author divides his subject into twelve books, as follows:

I. De locis habitabilibus eligendis et de curiis et domibus, etc. Discusses the best location of the farm or manor, and its best arrangement; agricultural hygiene with regard to exposure and water supply; duties of the farmer and of the pater familias. All this is essentially Roman in inspiration.

II. De natura plantarum et rerum communium cultui cuiuslibet generis agrorum. Botany and agriculture. This botanical introduction to agriculture is similar to that given by Roman authors (Varro, Pliny), but there is added to it an Aristotelian biology of plants in the manner of Ibn Sīnā and Albert the Great. Discussion of manure, including the new Italian methods (e.g., sovèscio, ploughing in of tares or the like). The treatment of this agricultural problem and of others is largely derived from Albert, but reorganized. This was so good that Giovanni Battista della Porta (1540–1615) was hardly able to improve upon it in his Villa (1592) almost three centuries later.

III. De campestribus agris colendis. Construction of the threshing floor and the granary. Cultivation of cereals, and other grasses, fodder, peas, and beans.

IV. De vineis et vito. Nature of vines and their medical properties; 40 kinds of vines are individualized; elaborate viticulture; preservation of fresh and dried grapes; making of wine; diseases of wines and their remedies; correction of wines (how to change their taste and quality); their virtues. This is partly derived from Pietro's own observations in northern Italy, and is described by him with precision and clearness. He also describes some Provençal customs. This is perhaps the most important book.

V. De arboribus. Arboriculture. General considerations followed by special discussion of a number of fruit trees and other trees.

VI. De hortis. Horticulture. Cultivated and wild plants. Alimentary and medicinal plants. Special discussion of 131 species in alphabetical order, most of them medicinal; only a score being real vegetables or aromatics for kitchen use. This is the largest book.

VII. De pratis. On meadows and woods. Their nature. Amelioration of wild meadows and woods and cultivation of new ones.

VIII. De viridariis et rebus delectabilibus ex arboribus herbis et fructu ipsarum artificiose agendis. On gardens. Much of this book is original. Pietro explains how to combine utility with pleasure. This book is a forerunner of the treatises on gardening which appeared in the sixteenth and seventeenth centuries.

IX. De omnibus animalibus quae nutriuntur in villis. Dealing with horses and their ailments, mules, asses, cows, sheep, goats, pigs, dogs and shepherds, hares, peacocks, pheasants, geese, ducks, chickens, pigeons, doves, thrushes and partridges, bees.

X. De diversis ingeniis capiendi animalia fera. On hunting and fishing. Great variety of hunting methods; fishing in fresh water only.

XI. De regulis operationum ruris. General summary in the form of 52 rules.

XII. Commemoratio de his omnibus quae singulis mensibus sunt in rure agenda. Agricultural calendar. Recapitulation of main duties and tasks month by month.

The comprehensiveness of this plan is obvious, and it was worked out with an abundance of details well understood and clearly explained. It is true Crescenzio did not insist as much as Cato and Palladius on agricultural economy, or "the political and social aspects of estate management." He mentioned some 292 species of plants (about 350 varieties) and a number of domestic and wild animals. He took pains to prepare an encyclopaedic treatise on the subject, utilizing all the available sources of information, written and unwritten, and he accomplished his purpose so well that his treatise was one of the most important and popular books of the fourteenth century and even of the Middle Ages, and remained a standard book in its field for two and a half centuries.

Sources of the Ruralia commoda. The main sources were in the first place the Latin authors Cato the Censor, Varro, Pliny, Palladius. The last named is the author who is mentioned most often (103 references to him out of 387); then Varro (54 times). Columella he could only know indirectly.[1] He was not acquainted with the Georgics, nor with Gargilius Martialis. Of the Geoponica he knew only the part on viticulture translated by Burgundio of Pisa (XII-2).

His main mediaeval sources were Ibn Sīnā (quoted more than 50 times) and Albert the Great, whom he did not quote often but used extensively. Among other Christian sources were Isidore of Seville, Matthew Platearius, Nicholas of Salerno, and the horse doctor Giordano Ruffo (XIII-2), this last one being unquoted. His main Arabic sources were al-Rāzī, Isḥāq al-Isrā'īlī, Ibn Sīnā, and one Serapion. Unfortunately he was not acquainted with Arabic agriculture, the great book of Ibn al-'Awwām (XII-2) having remained untranslated.

Character of the book. To these personal sources should still be added impersonal ones, "agricultores experti Bononiae," and last but not least his own lifelong experience. His book was professedly a compilation, but one made critically by a man deeply versed in the subject. He tried to give the intelligent husbandman as comprehensive an account as possible, reconciling the agricultural point of view of the Romans with the botanical one of Albert the Great, and the practical one of contemporary Italian farming. His treatise might be considered a revision of the Roman ones adapted to the new vision and needs of his time.

The most original part perhaps is his elaborate discussion of the grafting of vines and trees. His account of apiculture (including a bee calendar) shows that the Roman tradition on the subject had not been discontinued. He also deals with insect larvae destroying plants, and how to fight them. He insists that such troubles are partly due to the physiological condition of the plants themselves, and that healthy plants are able to resist them to some extent.

Tradition of Crescenzio's work. The popularity of this work is proved by the number of MSS (at least 132), some of which may be found in almost every large European library and in a few American ones.[2] The first printed edition (Augsburg 1471) was followed by many others, at least 16 incunabula, some 36 more in the sixteenth century, a total of about 60. Crescenzio's book was the first printed book on the subject, except Pliny's Historia naturalis, which was printed in Venice 1469. The Scriptores rei rusticae, including the treatises of Cato, Varro, Columella, and Palladius, appeared a year later than Crescenzio (Venice 1472); there

[1] Columella's Res rustica was used by Pliny, Palladius, and others; Cassiodorus (VI-1) still knew of it, but direct acquaintance with it seems to have stopped with him. The text of Columella was hardly known to mediaeval writers until the discovery of a MS by Poggio Bracciolini sometime after 1415 (date and place uncertain).

[2] After Lodovico Frati (1933). He enumerates 94 Latin MSS, 23 Italian, 12 French, 2 German, 1 Latin-Italian. Many are illustrated with miniatures, and some bear a portrait of the author.

were only 7 incunabula of the Scriptores, but the total number of editions, most of them in Latin, was at least 80.

After the middle of the sixteenth century Crescenzio's influence began to wane. The latest Latin edition appeared in Basel 1548, the latest practical Italian edition in Venice 1564 (as distinguished from later Italian editions of philological interest). From that time on Crescenzio was displaced by Columella or by modern writers.

Translations. Crescenzio's book was promptly translated from the Latin into Italian. That translation was made in the first half of the fourteenth century, printed in Florence 1478, and often reprinted in Italy. In spite of its imperfections it is an important monument of the early Italian (Toscan) language. A French translation was made in 1373 by the Augustinian Jehan Corbechon for Charles V the Wise (king 1364–80); a second French translation was made in 1413 by the Dominican Nicholas of Dijon. The first French version was printed twice in Paris 1486. A German translation was printed in Speier 1493, if not before; a Polish edition, in Cracow 1549.

There is no Spanish translation, but the Obra de agricultura (Alcala de Henares 1513) composed by Gabriel Alonso de Herrera of Talavera by order of cardinal Ximenes (1436–1517) was an adaptation of Crescenzio and Columella (chiefly of the former). Herrera's book was printed at least 28 times.

The lack of any English translation[3] or adaptation, and of any edition published in England, is remarkable. It may be explained by the fact that the English were more interested in the pure Columellian or Roman tradition, and also by the success of Walter of Henley's Hosebondrie (XIII-1) and later of Sir Anthony Fitzherbert's[4] Husbandrie (1523).

A comparative study of the translations of the agriculturists confirms our conclusion from our comparative study of the early Latin editions. The Italian translation of Crescenzio was printed (1478) before the Italian translations of other texts except Pliny (1476); the French and German translations and the Spanish adaptations were much ahead of the translations of other texts.

This is very interesting. Crescenzio's work was very popular and influential because of (1) its comprehensiveness, many-sidedness, and relative up-to-dateness, and (2) its greater availability in the vernaculars. There was less temptation to translate the Scriptores rei rusticae, genuine Latin writings, than the Ruralia commoda, thought out in Italian and written in a somewhat artificial Latin. Of the 59 editions of the Ruralia commoda, only 12 are in Latin, 18 are in Italian, 15 in French, 12 in German, 2 in Polish. It is typical that none of the Latin editions appeared in Italy. In short, though there was not a great difference in substance between the Scriptores and Crescenzio, the former were regarded as classics, and the latter as a relatively modern author, and that impression was right.

Text. The following notes concerning the printed editions and translations of the Ruralia commoda are derived from the latest and very comprehensive investigations made by Albano Sorbelli (1933). I had previously accepted the results published by Luigi Savastano (1922). Sorbelli, being far more prudent, has retained fewer editions.

The princeps is the Latin edition of Augsburg 1471. Latin editions appeared in Louvain 1474, c. 1480 (two), Strassburg 1486, Speier? 1490/95 (Klebs nos. 310.1–6),

[3] Except the partial edition of 1924, which hardly counts.

[4] The author may have been Sir Anthony's brother John?

and finally two Basel editions, 1538 and 1548. There is no critical edition of the Latin text.

The first Italian edition appeared in Florence 1478. Others Vicenza 1490, Venice 1495 (Klebs 311.1-3). Last practical Italian edition, Venice 1564. A critical edition of the Italian text was prepared by Bastiano de' Rossi for the Accademia della Crusca (Florence 1605). The latest Italian edition was prepared by Bartolomeo Sorio (Verona 1851). It is linguistic but also agricultural. There are in all 18 Italian editions.

Two French editions appeared in Paris 1486 (Klebs 312), these being the only French incunabula, but the French text was very popular in the first half of the sixteenth century, no less than 13 editions being published between c. 1515 and 1540, when the latest French edition appeared. The earliest French translation of book IV was reprinted in the Annales de la viticulture française et étrangère (84 p., Paris 1863).

There are 2 German incunabula, one of which is dated Speier 1493, the other is Speier? 1495? (Klebs 313). At least 6 more editions appeared in the first half of the sixteenth century, 1 in the second half of the sixteenth century, and the final one in 1602.

Two Polish editions appeared in Cracow 1549 and 1571.

In 1933, the seventh centenary of Pier de' Crescenzi's birth was celebrated by the Società agraria di Bologna, with the publication of a beautiful volume: Pier de' Crescenzi. Studi e documenti (xxvii + 377 p., 16 fig., 25 pl., Bologna 1933; Isis 27, 126). That volume contains 6 biographical papers, contributed by Napoleone Passerini, Arturo Palmieri, Tommaso Alfonsi (O.P.), Giovanni Livi, Guido Zucchini, Lino Sighinolfi; then 5 others on the Ruralia commoda: Francesco Todaro on cereals, Gaspare Ungarelli on herbs, Roberto Bozzelli on book IX, Alessandro Ghigi on domestic animals, fishes, and bees, Dino Zucchini on rural architecture. In his edition of Giordano Ruffo (XIII-2) published at Padova in 1818, Gerolamo Molin had claimed that Crescenzi had plagiarized Ruffo; Bozzelli's paper is a defense of Crescenzi against that accusation. See the section wherein I discussed Crescenzi's sources. As the latter's purpose was to produce a work as comprehensive as possible, he was bound to utilize to the limit all the predecessors he knew of. However, he used Ruffo—his older contemporary—without quoting him. The Studi e documenti are completed with two very elaborate bibliographies, of the MSS by Lodovico Frati, and of the printed editions by Albano Sorbelli (p. 259-369, 16 fig., 25 pl.).

Chapters 1-3 of book VIII, on gardens, have been translated into English by Frank Crisp: Mediaeval gardens (1, 15-18, London 1924).

Criticism. Gaetano Lorenzo Monti, in the Italian edition published at Bologna 1784. E. H. F. Meyer (4, 138-59, 1857). L. Moulé (part 3, 51-55, 1900), to be used with caution. Paul Weise: Petrus de Crescentiis (Hamburg diss., 14 p., 1906). C. Frati: Pier de' Crescenzi e l'opera sua (Atti e memorie della R. deputazione di storia patria di Romagna 9, 146-64, Bologna 1919). Luigi Savastano: Contributo allo studio critico degli scrittori agrari italici—Pietro dei Crescenzi (Annali della R. stazione sperimentale di agrumicoltura e frutticoltura vol. 5, 132 p., 1919-21; separately printed 1922; Isis 6, 151), elaborate study. Luigi Savastano e Emilio Chiovenda: Di una rara edizione del Liber cultus ruris (Archivio di storia della scienza 3, 311-15, Rome 1923), apropos of the French princeps published by Antoine Verard, Paris 1486; unimportant. Anna Röding: Studier till Petrus de Crescentiis och hans antika källor (Göteborg diss., 121 p., 1927), gives a critical edition, in Latin, of book IX, chs. 85-105. Bodenheimer (1, 73, 184-86, 202-4, 1928). Hermann Fischer (p. 181-84, 1929), discusses Crescenzio's relation to Albert the Great.

MATTHAEUS SYLVATICUS

Mattheus Silvaticus. Italian lexicographer, botanist, and physician (d. c. 1342). Called "miles et regis physicus," nicknamed Pandectarius.

He was born either in Mantua or in Salerno in the latter part of the thirteenth century; flourished in Salerno and was already teaching there by 1297; practiced under the patronage of Robert, king of Sicily from 1309 to 1343; died c. 1342. He must not be confused with a contemporary physician of the same name who lived in Milan.

He kept a botanical garden in Salerno, which is the earliest garden of its kind known to us, if conventual herb gardens are not taken into account. In that garden he cultivated not only domestic but also foreign plants, such as Arum colocasia; he sowed in it seeds which he had obtained in Greece (see article Cantalides in his work). He seems to have traveled extensively, and to have observed plants in many localities and collected information on them (see articles Condros, Pusca).

He compiled a large materia medica entitled Pandectae (hence his nickname) or Liber (opus) pandectarum medicine omnia medicine simplicia continens quem ex omnibus antiquorum libris aggregavit. The work, begun c. 1297, was completed about 1317 and dedicated to king Robert (in 1337?).

It is a reference book on diseases and their remedies in the form of a dictionary of simples, divided into 724 chapters in the original edition (or 720 in other editions). It is arranged approximately in alphabetical order, the names of plants being given in Greek, Arabic, and Latin. His Arabic transcriptions are atrocious; it is clear that he had no knowledge of the language. The names are followed by descriptions of the simples and their properties according to the "authorities." In some instances he adds his own observations. Many erroneous statements are due to his ignorance of the true names of the plants he dealt with.

The Pandectae is much larger than the Synonyma of Simon of Genoa (XIII-2), but generally inferior, except from the purely botanical point of view. His descriptions of plants are more elaborate than Simon's and he could occasionally refer to his experience as a traveler and as a gardener. These genuine botanical observations redeem the Pandectae from Haller's severe judgment, "Auctori barbari opus chaoticum."

His main sources were the Synonyma medicinae of Simon of Genoa and the Aggregatus in medicinis simplicibus of Serapion the Younger (XII-1). Many other authorities are frequently mentioned by him, e.g. Hippocrates, Theophrastos, Celsus, Dioscorides, Pliny the Elder, Galen, Theodorus Priscianus, Cassius Felix, Alexander of Tralles, Ibn Sīnā, Platearius, Maimonides, Albert the Great, but it is probable that he knew them only through Simon.

According to Simon of Phares,[4a] he wrote an astrological treatise on particular judgments, but if this treatise ever existed, it is lost.

Text. Opus (or Liber) pandectarum medicinae. According to Klebs (no. 919), the princeps was published in Naples 1474, and was followed by 9 other incunabula, to wit, [Bologna] 1474, Lyon 1478, Vicenza [1480], Venice 1480, [Strassburg 1481], Venice 1488, 1492, 1498, 1499.

[4a] Ernest Wickersheimer: Recueil des plus célèbres astrologues et quelques hommes doctes faict par Symon de Phares du temps de Charles VIII (p. 215, passim, Paris 1929; Isis 13, 167). Simon de Phares flourished about the end of the fifteenth century. Wickersheimer (p. 743–44, 1936).

The princeps was enlarged and corrected by Angelus Cato Supinas (Angelo Catone da Sepino), physician to Ferdinand II of Aragon. Catone's preface is printed by Renzi (doc. 255, 1857). According to H. Fischer (p. 72, 1929), the Venice 1480 edition contains a colored portrait of Matthaeus sitting in a garden. The Harvard Library copy of this edition, however, does not have any portrait.

Criticism. Kurt Sprengel: Opuscula academica, edited by Julius Rosenbaum (p. 116–31, Leipzig 1844), the most extensive account, written from the early sources. A. W. E. Th. Henschel: Berühmte Wundärzte und Aerzte des XIII. und XIV. Jahrhunderts (Janus 2, 398–99, Leipzig 1853). Renzi (p. 527–50, doc. 253, 254, 1857). E. H. F. Meyer (4, 167–77, 1857). Haeser (1, 709–10, 1875). Julius Pagel: Geschichte der Medizin im Mittelalter (Puschmann's Handbuch der Medizin 1, 681, Jena 1902). Pierre Guigues: Les noms arabes dans Sérapion 'Liber de simplici medicina' (p. 5, Paris 1905). H. Fischer (p. 70–74, 152, 233, 1929). Thorndike (3, 233, 1934).

A4. Germany

CONRAD OF MEGENBERG

Conrad von Maidenberg (Meydenberg, Meydenburg). Conradus de Monte Puellarum. Southern German scientist, theologian, and historian (c. 1309–74).

He was born c. 1309, probably in Megenberg (or Mainberg), near Schweinfurt. His father was probably a bailiff or overseer in the old castle of Mainberg (Schloss Mainberg is extant). Conrad studied the liberal arts in Erfurt, and then went to Paris, where he became a magister and studied and taught philosophy and theology. He remained eight years in Paris (c. 1329–37), then went to Vienna, where he directed the St. Stephen school. Finally, in 1342 he moved to Ratisbon (Regensburg), where he became a parish priest, then a canon of the cathedral, and where he remained until his death, on April 14, 1374. He is buried in the Benedictine nunnery of Nieder-Münster, in Regensburg. In 1357 he traveled to Avignon to defend the rights of the Benedictine abbey of St. Emmeram before the curia.

The best part of his life was thus spent in Regensburg, and it is there that most of his works were written. Conrad was the first great scientific writer in German, and the fact that he worked in Regensburg is significant, for the same city had witnessed the activities of Otloh[5] in the eleventh century, and later of Albert the Great (XIII-2), who was bishop there from 1260 to 1262.

His most important works from our point of view are two scientific treatises written in German (Bavarian-Austrian dialect), both being free translations from the Latin, which he prepared in order to help educate the women and the common people, in the same spirit as this had been done almost a century earlier by the Fleming Jacob van Maerlant (XIII-2). We shall deal with these two works first.

The more famous of these works is Das Buch der Natur, composed by Conrad in 1349–51. It is a very free translation of the De natura rerum of Thomas of Cantimpré (XIII-1). Maerlant had translated it into Dutch (Flemish) c. 1264–69. Both Maerlant and Conrad ascribed the De natura rerum to Albert the Great; Conrad considered it a work of Albert's youth. The Latin text is reorganized in the German version, some sections being expanded and others contracted. A few original observations have been added here and there. Each of the eight books

[5] Not mentioned in volume 1, because he devoted himself only to classical and historical studies. Otloh was educated at Tegernsee and Hersfeld and assumed the Benedictine habit at St. Emmeram, Regensburg, in 1032. He died in that city after 1067 (ADB 24, 546, 1887, Wattenbach). Max Manitius: Geschichte der lateinischen Literatur des Mittelalters (vol. 2, Munich 1923).

into which Das Buch der Natur is divided is preceded by an introduction containing moralizations and theological ideas. Conrad's descriptions of natural phenomena are generally followed by theological or astrological explanations.

Das Buch der Natur was very popular, witness the number of MSS (17 in the Munich library alone, two of which are of the fourteenth century) and the 6 Augsburg incunabula. These 6 early editions are in folio, and each includes 12 plates of woodcuts representing animals. The first edition (1475) is the first book containing printed drawings of animals.

Das Buch der Natur is divided as follows:

I. Von dem Menschen in seiner gemainen Natur, 50 chapters. Anatomy, physiology; interpretation of character from physical signs and dreams.

II. Von den Himeln und von den siben Planêten, 33 chapters. Astronomy and meteorology. Description of the comet which he saw in Paris in 1337 (Pfeiffer ed. p. 75), and of the invasion of southern Germany by locusts, which he witnessed soon afterward, when he had just returned home (P., p. 75–76). Detailed description of a white rainbow which he saw on a May morning in Riez, near Nördlingen (P., p. 98); imperfect description of a colored rainbow. In ch. 33 (P., p. 107–13) he discusses earthquakes in general, and in particular the one which occurred at Villach, in Carinthia, in 1348, and describes the ravages of the plague in Austria and Bavaria in the following year; he explains that the plague was caused by the earthquake. According to him, the Black Death was also caused by earthquakes. Ch. 25, on thunder and lightning (as well as a later chapter in book III, see P., p. 91, 274), contains casual references to firearms, which prove that these were already known in Regensburg about the middle of the fourteenth century.

III. Von den Tiern in ainer Gemain (i.e., animals in general), 69 chapters on quadrupeds, 72 on birds, 20 on wonders of the sea (e.g., crocodile, seal, dolphin, hippopotamus, sirens; many of these wonders cannot be identified), 29 on fishes (including whales, crayfish, mussels, "shipholder," i.e. Echeneis;[6] at least four cannot be identified, others are doubtful), 37 on "snakes," 31 on "worms" (i.e., mainly insects, but also toads, frogs, snails, leeches, arachnids, earthworms, and at least one fabulous creature).

IV. Von den Paumen (trees), 84 chapters. Ch. 42, on the oak tree, contains a mention of galls, which are misunderstood; the worms found in them are used to prophesy the weather (P., p. 343).

V. Von den Kräutern (herbs), 89 chapters.

VI. Von den edlen Stainen (precious stones), 86 chapters. Ch. 3, on the "diamond," contains a reference to a floating needle, the point of which has been rubbed on a "diamond," used for navigation. Chapter 50, on the magnet, is full of superstitions. Conrad's confusion of diamond and loadstone, as well as his fantastic stories, illustrate his utter lack of criticism.

VII. Von dem Gesmaid (metals), 10 chapters. The seven metals: gold, silver, Gunderfai (electrum), copper, tin, lead, and iron, plus quicksilver, orpiment (arsenic trisulphide, yellow arsenic), sulphur.

VIII. Von den wunderleichen Prunnen. Dealing with wonderful properties of streams and waters and with human monstrosities.

In books IV to VII there are many references to the medicinal and other virtues of plants and stones. Conrad does not include as many items as Thomas, but some-

[6] E. W. Gudger: Some old time figures of the shipholder, Echeneis or Remora, holding the ship (Isis 13, 340–52, 9 fig., 1930).

times his discussions are more elaborate. The literary sources are apparently the same as those of the De natura rerum; divergences could only be established by a more meticulous comparison of the two texts.

The other scientific work of Conrad is his Deutsche Sphaera, a free version of the Sphaera mundi of Sacrobosco (XIII-1). He wrote it probably before the Buch der Natur, and even probably before he went to Regensburg. Sacrobosco's Sphaera was one of the most popular scientific textbooks of the Middle Ages; a popularity not undeserved, because it was a clear summary of Arabic astronomy (chiefly al-Farghānī), the shortest way then to astronomical knowledge. Conrad's Sphaera was the first astronomical and physical textbook in the German language, but it did not share the popularity of its model. It is represented by only three MSS, and was not printed until 1516. The reason is that Germans interested in astronomy preferred to read the Sphaera in Latin, and the non-Latin-speaking Germans were not interested in astronomy (however great their astrological curiosity might be). The Deutsche Sphaera was an abstract book which could not obtain in popular circles the popularity of the Buch der Natur, full of marvelous stories and edifying remarks.

Conrad's main writings in approximate chronological order:

Planctus ecclesiae in Germaniam, a poem written in Paris 1337. Bewailing the troubles between the pope Benedict XII and the emperor Ludwig IV of Bavaria, and also between regulars and seculars.[7]

Deutsche sphaera, before 1342. In Vienna? See above.

Speculum felicitatis humanae, dedicated in 1348 to Rudolph, duke of Austria.[8] In two books, the first dealing with passions and friendship, the second with moral and intellectual virtues.

Das Buch der Natur, 1349–51. See above.

Oeconomica, dedicated to Lupoldus de Bebenburg, bishop of Bamberg from 1352 to 1362. Probably written soon after 1352. Dealing with government, and defending the papal vs. the imperial point of view, against John of Jandun and Marsiglio of Padua.

Tractatus pro romana ecclesia et pontifice Joanne XXII contra Wilhelmum Occam. A book of the same kind as the preceding, written c. 1354, seven years after the death of the emperor Ludwig (d. 1347). (John XXII had been pope from 1316 to 1334.)

Statuta et consuetudines capituli ecclesiae ratisbonensis, c. 1355.

Vita sancti Erhardi, 1357–58.

Tractatus contra mendicantes ad papam Urbanum V (pope 1362–70).

De erroribus Begehardorum et Beginarum.

He wrote various other works, some of which are only known by title; the titles which I have quoted are sufficient to give an idea of his activities.

Text. Das Buch der Natur was first printed in Augsburg 1475. There are at least 5 other incunabula editions, all in Augsburg: 1478, 1481, 1482 (two), 1499. All folio editions, with woodcuts (see above). Klebs (nos. 300.1–6).

Critical edition by Franz Pfeiffer: Das Buch der Natur. Die erste Naturgeschichte

[7] Introd. 2, 712, 823; 3, 47.

[8] According to Pfeiffer (p. xxii), after the Regensburg MS dated 1348. Rudolph III died in 1307; Rudolph IV was born in 1339. The Speculum was probably dedicated to this child for the sake of his education.

in deutscher Sprache (870 p., Stuttgart 1861). Elaborate glossary (p. 553–807). My references above are to this edition, called P.

Hugo Schulz: Das Buch der Natur (455 p., Greifswald 1897). Translation in modern High German, with few notes but good index.

Otto Matthaei: Deutsche Sphaera (Deutsche Texte des Mittelalters vol. 23, 78 p., 2 pl., Berlin 1912). This is a critical edition, and strictly speaking the first edition. According to Pfeiffer in his edition of the Buch der Natur (p. xxi, 1861), the Deutsche Sphaera was first printed without author's name by Konrad Hainfogel in Nürnberg 1516; later editions, Cologne 1519, Strassburg 1533, 1539. See my query no. 63 (Isis 25, 455, 1936); and the answer by H. Noll-Husum (Isis 27, 324–25, 1937). The edition of 1516 has not yet been traced, and may be a ghost, though Gabriel Doppelmayr spoke of it very definitely in 1730, as well as of the editions of 1519 and 1533 (V. Zoubov in Isis 28, 92). In the edition of Cologne 1519 (title page in Isis 27, 325), Conradt Heynfogel used Megenberg's version, but with considerable independence, correcting it repeatedly after reference to Sacrobosco's Latin text. Thus these editions (or at any rate that of 1519) represent German versions of Sacrobosco's Sphaera, but are not editions of Megenberg's version. The matter is contentious, however: when does the edition of an old version become a new version? Where will the line be drawn?

Planctus ecclesiae in Germaniam: Flos et apex (poem), printed by Richard Scholz: Unbekannte kirchenpolitische Streitschriften aus der Zeit Ludwigs des Bayern (2, 188–248, Rome 1914).

Tractatus de electione Caroli IV, or Tractatus pro romana ecclesia et pontif. Johanne XXII contra Wilhelmum Occam (1354), printed by R. Scholz (ibid., p. 346–91).

Tractatus de translatione imperii (1355), printed by R. Scholz (ibid., p. 249–345).

Vita St. Erhard, in Acta Sanctorum, Januarius VIII (1, 541–44, Antwerp 1643).

Breve chronicon episcoporum ratisbonensium (to 1296), in J. G. Ecchard: Corpus historicum medii aevi (2, cols. 2243–52, Leipzig 1723).

De erroribus Begehardorum ex codice Conradi de Monte Puellarum contra Begehardos et Beginas, a fragment printed in Jacob Gretser: Opera omnia (12, part 2, 98–99, Regensburg 1738); and in Maxima bibliotheca patrum (25, 310, Lyon 1677).

Oeconomica, preface only in B. G. Struve: Acta litteraria (fasc. 4, p. 82–91, Jena 1706, and in his Collectanea 2, 82–91, Jena 1713).

Statuta et consuetudines capituli ecclesiae ratisbonensis, printed by A. Mayer: Thesaurus novus (2, 1–37), not seen.

Criticism. E. H. F. Meyer (4, 198–206, 1857). Haeser (3, 100, 139, 168, 1882). Riezler (ADB 16, 648–50, 1882). Gustav Hellmann: Meteorologische Volksbücher (p. 5–13, 1891; 2d ed., 68 p., Berlin 1895). Philipp Schneider: Der Traktat Konrads De limitibus parochiarum civitatis ratisbonensis (Historisches Jahrbuch 22, 609–30, Munich 1901). Hermann Grauert: Konrads Chronik und sein Planctus ecclesiae in Germaniam (Historisches Jahrbuch 22, 631–87, Munich 1901). Richard Scholz; Unbekannte kirchenpolitische Streitschriften aus der Zeit Ludwigs des Bayern (1, 79–140, 236–42, Rome 1911). Otto Matthaei: Konrads von Megenberg Deutsche Sphaera und die Uebersetzungstechnik seiner beiden deutschen Prosawerke (Berlin diss., 111 p., Gross-Lichterfelde 1912). Hermann Schöppler: Konrad von Megenberg über die Zähne (Deutsche zahnärztliche Zeitung, 3 p., Pössneck 1913). Richard Salomon: Zur Oeconomica des Konrad von Megenberg (Neues Archiv 39, 190–200, Hanover 1914). Hermann Meyer: Lacrima ecclesiae (Neues Archiv 39, 471–503, Hanover 1914). Hans Georg Kroschel: Diätetik und Therapie in Konrad von Megenberg's Buch der Natur (Greifswald diss., 1920). William A. Locy: The earliest printed illustrations of natural history (Scientific monthly 13, 238–58, 11 ill., 1921; Isis 5, 220). Rathgen (p. 9–10, 1928). Bodenheimer (vol. 2, 1929), includes Conrad's account of an invasion of locusts (p. 30), and a list of the insects known to him (p. 330). Konrad Böhner: Geschichte der Cecidologie (1, 158, 367, 1933; Isis 24, 180–83). Helmut Ibach: Leben und Schriften des Konrad von Megenberg (Neue deutsche Forschungen 210, 185 p., Berlin 1938; Isis 31, 151), elaborate study received after the completion of my note, and thus not used as completely as if it had reached me at an earlier time. The author gives a chronological list of 28 writings ascribed to Megenberg; the dates given by him are not always the same as mine. He lays special stress on Megenberg's conception of a Christian order which should be primarily a germanicus ordo. C. Doris Hellman: The comet of 1577 (p. 59, New York 1944).

A5. Flanders

BEUKELS

Willem Beukels. Dutch inventor of an improved method of preserving and packing herring, the application of which had great economic consequences and "changed the course of European history" (d. 1347).

This Willem Beukels is also called Beukelzoon or Beukelsen (and the same forms occur with ck instead of k and z instead of s), which all amounts to the same thing, for it means the son of Beukel. There was a man of that name, not a simple fisherman but a man of substance, who lived in the fourteenth century in Biervliet, then an important town of Dutch Zeeland, near Vlissingen (Flushing). In 1312 Willem and his sister Adelise appointed a chaplain to the church founded by their mother, Elizabeth, in 1308. According to investigations made by the archivist of Zeeland in 1875, Willem Beukels died in 1347, not in 1397 as is very often stated.[9] There is much confusion about this, for the same dates, 1347 and 1397, are also mentioned not as his death year, but as his birth year. If 1397 is taken as the birth year, the invention is postponed a full century. For example, in Darmstaedter's Handbuch (1908) the invention is arbitrarily dated 1420.

So much for the man; as to his invention, it did not consist only in salting the fish, for salting had been practiced for centuries, even perhaps in ancient times. There are archival documents of the eleventh and twelfth centuries referring to the salting of herrings. It is probable that other attempts to preserve and pack herrings were made before the fourteenth century. Beukels' invention consisted in preserving the herrings in a much better way by gutting them, throwing out the parts which would spoil, then salting the eviscerated fish and packing them in barrels, wherein they could be kept a long time in good condition and transported to distant places by land or water.

The Dutch technical term for the operation is kaken, hence the French caquer, which confirms the Dutch origin of the invention.

There are many sixteenth-century accounts of Beukels' invention, e.g., by the Florentine Francesco Guicciardini (1482–1540), by Marc Van Vaernewyck of Ghent (1518–69), by Jacques Marchant of Nieuport (1537–1609). In the latter's Flandria descripta (Antwerp 1596), under "Biervlietum," one may read, "domicilium hic fixit et morte refixit anno 1347 Guillelmus Bouclensis, inventor artis stipandi condiendique haleces in cadis salsamentariis" (after Raepsaet 1816, p. 14). That statement or a similar one was often repeated; e.g., we find it in a memoir of the Belgian archaeologist Pierre Joseph Heylen (1737–93), De inventis Belgarum (read at the

[9] Information kindly given to me by Dr. Cornelis De Waard, of Vlissingen, in his letter of Oct. 2, 1938.

Brussels Academy in 1786, p. 93). Heylen refers to a curious remark made by the German Benedictine Odilo Schreger in the latter's Studiosus jovialis (Munich 1749),[10] "Artem condiendi haleces et in tonnis conservandi primus excogitavit Wilhelmus Boeckel è Belgio piscator anno 1416; undè hi pisciculi vocantur Boekelheringe." This is a fanciful etymology; the words "Pökelhering" in German, "pekelharing" in Dutch, "pickled herring" in English are constructed from the verbs pökeln, pekelen, or to pickle, derived from the same root, which must be an ancient one. It is a strange coincidence that the name Beukels seems to belong to the same root!

To return to the invention, it was a complex one, for it implied many operations, gutting, eviscerating, salting, packing, each of which could be done in many ways, and was susceptible of gradual improvements. To measure Beukels' achievements one should know more exactly what he did, and that is impossible. Moreover, the invention may have occurred partly or completely to many men engaged in the herring industry. Finally, it is always difficult to distinguish between an invention and the industrial and commercial exploitation of it. Was Beukels the inventor of a new method or the creator of a new industry?

It is certain that a great improvement occurred in that industry in the fourteenth century, an improvement which revolutionized the economic condition of Holland, and indeed of Europe; we may give credit for it to Willem Beukels, as no other contemporary names have ever been mentioned in competition with his. The invention was very probably Dutch, and it is certain that the Dutch were the main gainers by it.[11] The industry developed astoundingly well in Zeeland and became a source of prosperity for that country. Much information about that development is available in the books dealing with the history of the Netherlands, especially with economic history or with legal history, for the herring industry became rapidly of such fundamental importance that it entailed abundant and minute regulations and restrictions. The most comprehensive edict was promulgated by Charles V in 1519 (see Jenkins p. 68 ff., 1927).

It would seem that Beukels' merits were soon appreciated, and his tomb was honored by his countrymen. It is said that Charles V visited that tomb on August 30, 1556, together with his two sisters, Eleanor, dowager queen of France, and Mary, dowager queen of Hungary, governess of the Netherlands. I have found no documentary evidence for this, but the story is plausible, for we know that soon after his imperial abdication Charles Quint and his two sisters visited Ghent, then proceeded to Zeeland. He sailed from Flushing on September 17, 1556 for his final voyage to Spain. The magistrates of Flushing would certainly have drawn their august visitor's attention to the main industry of Zeeland and its founder. Beukels' tomb still existed at the end of the seventeenth century (Raepsaet p. 18, 1816). It has now disappeared, together with a good part of the town, gradually reconquered by the sea.

Final correction: After this article had already been written and rewritten, more information received from Dr. De Waard and from professor G. G. Dept, of Ghent, obliges me to add the following note. The new information is derived primarily from a study by R. Degryse: Oorsprong van het haringkaken in Vlaanderen (Nederlandsche historiebladen 1, 201–19, 1938), a copy of which was kindly sent me by

[10] Not available to me. My quotation is taken from Heylen's memoir (p. 93). Heylen refers to the edition of Augsburg (p. 489, 1773).

[11] Note that the Russian name "gollandskiya seledki" (Dutch herrings) also suggests a Dutch origin, though it may refer only to the modern source of importation.

professor Dept; Degryse's views have been summarized and made more accessible in the Geschiedenis van Vlaanderen edited by Rob. Van Roosbroeck (3, 317, Amsterdam 1938). According to Degryse, the new industry originated in Scania (the southernmost district of Sweden, then in Danish hands). The "Oosterlingen" (or "Easterners," as the Hansa merchants were called)[12] brought the industry to the Zwin near Bruges. Thus the herring industry was established in Flanders before 1375. Gillis Beukels of Hugevliet (near Biervliet) took a leading share in it. He died in 1397. The Flemish authorities discouraged the new industry at first (1395–98) and began to encourage it only c. 1419.

Criticism. Pierre Joseph Heylen: De inventis Belgarum (Nouveaux mémoires de l'Académie impériale et royale de Bruxelles, hist., 1, 74–122, Bruxelles 1788; bound in Mémoires de l'Académie vol. 5, 1788). Jean Joseph Raepsaet: Note sur la découverte de caquer le hareng, faite par Guillaume Beukels, pilote de Biervliet en Flandre, lue à l'Académie de Bruxelles 1816 (18 p., Gand 1816). There is a second note by Raepsaet: Réponse aux observations de Noël de la Morinière sur l'invention de caquer le hareng (Gand 1819), which I have not seen.

I owe to Mr. C. De Waard the following references, which I was not able to check: H. M. C. Van Oosterzee: Over W. Beukelsz van Biervliet (Zeeuwsche Volksalmanak, 1844, p. 131). J. Egberts Risseeuw: Iets over W. Beukelsz (Bijdragen tot de Oudheidkunde en Geschiedenis, inzonderheid van Zeeuwsch-Vlaanderen, part 4, p. 200). J. Ter Gouw: Karel V bij het graf van Willem Beukelszoon te Biervliet (Nederlandsch Geschiedenis 1, 175). Frederik Nagtglas: Zelandia illustrata. Verzameling van kaarten, portretten, platen, enz., betreffende de oudheid en geschiedenis van Zeeland (2, 589–90, Middelburg 1880).

There is an abundant "herring" literature, and every history of the herring industry refers to Beukels. I have consulted only the three following books: John M. Mitchell: The herring, its natural history and national importance (384 p., 7 pl., Edinburgh 1864; p. 134). Arthur Michael Samuel: The herring, its effect on the history of Britain (220 p., many ill., London 1918; p. 101). James Travis Jenkins: The herring and the herring fisheries (186 p., 13 ill., London 1927; p. 68). Jenkins refers to Kurt Jagow: Kulturgeschichte des Herings (p. 151–55, Langensalza 1920), stating that it includes a long Beukels bibliography.

One of the earliest accounts of herring fisheries occurs in book 6 of he De natura rerum of Thomas of Cantimpré (XIII-1).

B. BYZANTIUM

THE PULOLOGOS

In this section we shall consider briefly a few popular Byzantine writings of the fourteenth century (or perhaps a bit later) which deal with animal and plant stories and may interest indirectly the student of natural history in those days.

1. Perhaps the earliest in its final form is the Πουλολόγος, which has been dated back to the first half of the fourteenth century. It is a poem of 650 political verses, developing the following story: King Eagle has invited all the birds to attend his son's wedding. They all eat and drink and have a good time until they begin to quarrel. The author was a Greek writer who had some contact with the Franks or at least with Western literature. So many different birds are involved that the poem is like a manual of ornithology. There is a didactic intention, and even more clearly a satirical one. The various birds are made to represent different types of human weaknesses and to ridicule the political, ecclesiastical, and ethnographical

[12] Indeed, the Baltic was called Oostzee (Eastern Sea).

conditions of the Byzantine empire. There is a mention of the compass (l. 531, *τὸν πούσουλα*).

The title Πουλολόγος, meaning bird student, is in all probability an imitation of the term *φυσιολόγος*, designating a Christian bestiary of Alexandrian origin which enjoyed a tremendous popularity throughout the Middle Ages, being translated from the Greek into many Western and Eastern languages. See my Introduction (1, 300). In the same way, the term volucraire is an imitation of bestiaire.

2. The children's story of the four-footed animals (*Διήγησις παιδιόφραστος τῶν τετραπόδων ζῴων*) is a poem of 1,082 lines, similar to the preceding one, but dealing with quadrupeds instead of birds. King Lion sits on the throne with the Elephant, the Panther and Leopard stand near them, and the other court officers are the Wolf, the Dog, and the Fox. King Lion decides to establish eternal peace. All kinds of trouble follow, until the Lion is obliged to recognize the impossibility of peace. Since that time animals have continued their natural warfare.

It is impossible to read that blunt and humorous text without thinking of the Western cycle of Reynard the Fox (Introd. 2, 393), and yet the Greek text has the appearance of being an original creation. We must not forget that by this time (the fourteenth century) there was a well established animal folklore extending with sundry variations over a great part of the world. The roots are neither Latin nor Byzantine, but much deeper; and many of the animal stories can be traced back through the Physiologos and Aesop to Persian and Sanskrit sources.

To illustrate the utterly uncritical nature of the traditions, it will suffice to refer to the description of the elephant (l. 19–20),

καὶ συγκαθήμενον ἐλεφάντα τὸν μέγαν,
τὸν μηδ' ἁρμοὺς, μὴ γόνατα, μηδ' ἀστραγάλους ἔχων,

as an animal without articulations, knees, and ankle joints; a description which the simplest observation disproves.[13]

According to the poem (l. 10), the meeting of the animals took place in 1365, and that may well be the date of the poem itself. The date is plausible.

3. The ritual of the honorable ass (*Συναξάριον τοῦ τιμημένου γαδάρου*) and The beautiful story of the ass, the wolf, and the fox (*Γαδάρου, λύκου, καὶ ἀλουποῦς διήγησις ὡραία*). Two poems, of 393 and 540 political verses, which are later than the preceding ones. They date from the middle of the fifteenth century, and were expanded at the end of the same century or the beginning of the sixteenth century. The connection of these stories with the Reynard cycle is clear, yet there are many Byzantine deviations. The wolf and fox are represented as gossips, the wolf being a monk and the fox, a nun. The pilgrimage of the animals takes place by sea, not by land, and of course they go to the Holy Mountain. The fox is described as a pupil of the wise lion (allusion to Leon VI the Wise, emperor 886–911).

4. *Διήγησις τοῦ πωρικολόγου* (Story of the fruits). Story in prose and verse built on the same pattern as the preceding ones, but the actors this time are fruit trees, impersonating various dignitaries. The quince tree is king; the pomegranate tree, lord high steward; the pear tree, protonotarios; the apple tree, logothetes, that is, chancellor; the orange tree, protobestiarios; the peach tree, protostator; the lemon, great drungarios (*δρουγγάριος*, a military title). The wine grape accuses many officers of treason, etc.; in the end, the wine grape is condemned. The pur-

[13] The same stupid error is found in contemporary Arabic and Persian literature (Isis 11, 291), and yet Oriental writers had many opportunities of watching elephants walk and kneel.

pose of the story is to describe the dangerous properties of wine; at the same time there is a satirical intention in the parody of Byzantine offices and titles.

The date of this text is unknown; it may go back to as early as the twelfth century, and therefore I spoke of it in volume 2, 426. It has been transmitted to us not only in Greek, but also in Serbian-Slovenian and Turkish translations or adaptations.

Two of these five texts belong probably to the fourteenth century; the others appear to be later or earlier and hence are outside the chronological boundaries of this volume. I thought it worth while, however, to speak of all of them, as they should be considered together. It would be worth while to prepare a complete edition of them with sufficient notes from the point of view of natural history, as well as of philology.

Text. All these texts have been edited by Wilhelm Wagner: Carmina graeca medii aevi (p. 112–202, Leipzig 1874). For other editions, see Krumbacher.

Criticism. Krumbacher (p. 873–84, 1897).

PHILES

Manuel Philes, Μανουὴλ Φιλῆς. Byzantine poet (fl. c. 1275 to c. 1345).

Philes originated in Ephesos, but spent most of his life in Constantinople, being a kind of court poet, as good a representative of that type and of the time of the Palaeologoi as Theodoros Prodromos "Ptochoprodromos" (XII-1) had been of the same type and the time of the Comnenoi two centuries earlier. We might call him Ptochophiles, the poor Philes! He was a friend of Georgios Pachymeres (XIII-2; Introd. 2, 972) and of Maximos Planudes (XIII-2), both of whom died c. 1310.

He wrote a large number of poems on many subjects, a total of about 20,000 lines, most of these dodecasyllabic iambic trimeters; he used only rarely the fifteen-syllable political verses which became the favorite meter of late Byzantine literature.

One of his poems is a dialogue between man and his soul, Ἄνθρωπος διαλεγόμενος μετὰ ψυχῆς, but we are especially interested in a few poems dealing with natural history. The main one, on the qualities of animals (περὶ ζῴων ἰδιότητος), 119 sections, 2,015 lines, describes many kinds of birds, quadrupeds, and fishes, also fantastic ones such as the unicorn and the onocentauros (ὀνοκένταυρος), a sort of tailless ape. His main sources were in all probability the Physiologos (for which see Introd. 1, 300), the Περὶ ζῴων of Aelianos (III-1), and the folklore of his own time. Many other sources would be brought to light by closer investigations. For example, Philes tells the story of vultures (γύψ) which are only of the female sex and are impregnated by the wind. That story is, as he reveals himself, of Egyptian origin, and can be traced in the writings (I mention only Greek ones) of Plutarch (I-2), Origen (III-1), who used it to refute Celsos (II-2) and defend the miracle of Christ's parthenogenetic birth, Eusebios (IV-1), Horapollon (IV-1), St. Basil the Great (IV-2), Cassianos Bassos (VI-2), Theophylactos Simocattes (VII-1), Joannes Tzetzes (XII-1), Michael Glycas (XII-1).

Another poem is a description of the elephant, in 381 lines, Σύντομος ἔκφρασις ἐλέφαντος, and others still are devoted to various plants, roses, grapes, pomegranates.

Text. First collected edition of poems, by Gottlieb Wernsdorf: Carmina graeca omnia nunc in unum, excepto poemate de animalibus, collecta, emendata, latine interpretata et annotationibus illustrata (Leipzig 1768). All the poems on natural history were edited by Friedrich Dübner in the Poetae bucolici et didactici of the Didot collection, Philes' poems in Greek and Latin covering 70 p. (Paris 1851).

Other poems were edited by Emmanuel Miller: Carmina . . . nunc primum edita (2 vols., Paris 1855–57), and by Emidio Martini (Rendiconti del R. Istituto lombardo ser. 2, vol. 29, 1896), also Carmina inedita (Naples 1900).

The first edition of the poem on the particularities of animals was prepared by Arsenios, bishop of Monemvasia in southeastern Morea: *Στίχοι ἰαμβικοὶ περὶ ζῴων ἰδιότητος* (84 p., St. Sabios 1533). Latin translation in verse (Cologne 1575). Greek and Latin edition by Gregor Bersman of Annaberg (1538–1611) with a supplement by Joachim Camerarius (1500–74) of Bamberg (Leipzig [1575]). Greek and Latin edition by Joannes Cornelius de Pauw (Utrecht 1730).

Criticism. Krumbacher (p. 774–80, 1897). Conway Zirkle: Animals impregnated by the wind (Isis 25, 95–130, 110, 1936). D'Arcy Wentworth Thompson: Glossary of Greek birds (first published 1895; new ed. Oxford 1936, p. 83; Isis 29, 135–38). Conway Zirkle: The jumar (Isis 33, 487, 1941).

NEOPHYTOS PRODROMENOS

Νεόφυτος Προδρομηνός. Byzantine monk, theologian, and botanist who flourished at an unknown time in the fourteenth century.

I place him tentatively in the first half of the century because he wrote a treatise against the Latinizing theologians Barlaam and Acindynos, *'Αντιλογία πρὸς τὸν Βαρλαὰμ καὶ 'Ακίνδυνον*, though that treatise might have been written after their deaths (examination of this unpublished text would probably show whether or not this was the case).

Our readers will be more interested in another work of his, a botanical glossary, *Πρόχειρος καὶ χρήσιμος σαφήνεια καὶ συλλογὴ κατὰ στοιχεῖον περὶ βοτανῶν καὶ ἄλλων παντοίων εἰδῶν θεραπευτικῶν.* This text is represented by at least seven MSS, two or three of which belong to the fourteenth century, and none of which is later than the sixteenth century. There are unusually large variations between some of these MSS, and it is difficult to determine the exact nature of the original text. Though it is relatively short, a large number of plants are enumerated and briefly defined.

Text. The text of the *Πρόχειρος* was first published by Delatte (2, 273–302, 1939). This text is followed by 14 other botanical glossaries (p. 302–454) of uncertain times and mostly anonymous. One of them is ascribed to a physician Nicomedes, another to Galen, a third to a physician of the eighteenth century Nicolaos Hieropais of Agrapha. A comparative study of these glossaries would be useful.

Criticism. Krumbacher (p. 105, 632, 1897), only a few lines without importance. For comparison, see Bernhard Langkavel: Botanik der spaeteren Griechen vom 3. bis 13. Jahrhunderte (232 p., Berlin 1866); Beiträge zur Geschichte der Botanik aus Du Cange Griech. Glossar (Programm, 24 p., Berlin 1866). This second publication is quoted only for its elimination; it is entirely included in the first and is but a small part of it.

C. ARMENIA

THOMAS OF CILICIA

Armenian naturalist (fl. in the fourteenth century?).

According to Torkomian, there is in the Mekhitarist library in S. Lazzaro, Venice, a MS treatise on the botany and zoology of Cilicia, very full in spite of its brevity. It is said to belong to the time of Nerses Balì.

This note is inserted here tentatively. We have thus far very little information on Armenian writings of this kind. To be sure, they are relatively rare, but the few which exist should be investigated. Apropos of this we may recall that king Hetūm, probably not Hayton the Elder (XIII-2), but Hetūm II (or Hayton II, king 1289–97), ordered the translation of three treatises on hippology and hippiatrics from Arabic into Armenian. The Arabic treatises ad hoc of the Mamlūk age were justly famous.

Text. Hippiatric fragments have been published by the Mekhitarists of Venice in their monthly Bazmavep (1867).

Criticism. V. Torkomian: Coup d'oeil sur l'histoire de la médecine en Arméno-Cilicie (Revue des études arméniennes 6, 19–26, 25, Paris 1926).

Some miniatures of Armenian MSS include animal and floral decorations which might deserve investigation from our special point of view. The following book is a good introduction to an abundant literature in Armenian and Western languages: Sirarpie der Nersessian: Manuscrits arméniens illustrées des XIIe, XIIIe et XIVe siècles de la Bibliothèque des pères Mekhitharistes de Venise (Paris thesis, folio, 214 p., plus album 102 pl., 1936–37; p. 148–50).

E. ISLAM

IBN LUYŪN

Abū 'Uthmān Sa'd ibn Aḥmad Ibn Luyūn al-Tujībī. Spanish Muslim writer on agriculture and many other subjects (d. 1349).

The nisba Tujībī shows that he was a member of the Banū Tujīb, a famous Arabic family of Spain dating back to the Muslim conquest. A branch of it was established in Almería. Ibn Luyūn was probably born in that city, but he flourished for a time in Granada, for Ibn al-Khaṭīb (XIV-2) was one of his pupils. He died of the plague in Almería, August 30, 1349.

His most interesting work is a poem (rajaz) of about 1,500 lines on agriculture and horticulture, entitled Ibdā' al-malāḥa wa inhā' al-rajāḥa fi uṣūl ṣinā'at al-filāḥa, wherein various Arabic agricultural writers are quoted, Easterners as well as Westerners. It has attracted the attention of philologists because it includes many Latin-Spanish terms.

Text. In 1940 Señorita Joaquina Eguarás was preparing in Granada an edition and Spanish translation of the Ibdā' al-malāḥa under the direction of professor Alois Richard Nykl. Its future publication is announced in Al-Andalus (9, 266, 1944). Many excerpts from that text had been published by José Lerchundi and F. J. Simonet in their Crestomatia arábigo-española (Granada 1881).

Criticism. Francisco Javier Simonet: Glosario de voces ibéricas y latinas usadas entre los Mozárabes (p. lxxxviii, clii, Madrid 1888). Antonio Almagro y Cárdenas: Catálogo de los manuscritos árabes de Granada (XI Congrès des orientalistes, sec. 3, p. 47, Paris 1899). Brockelmann (suppt. 2, 380, 1938).

AL-MUJĀHID 'ALĪ AL-RASŪLĪ

Al-Malik al-Mujāhid 'Alī ibn Dā'ūd was the fifth sulṭān of the learned Rasūlī dynasty of Yaman. He ruled from 1321 to 1362, and wrote an important treatise on the breeding of horses and other animals.

That work, entitled Kitāb al-aqwāl al-kāfīya wal-fuṣūl al-shāfīya fī 'ilm al-baiṭara, is divided into six parts, dealing with the breeding, upkeep, and training of domestic animals, such as horses, mules, asses, camels, elephants, buffaloes, sheep, and cattle. It includes data of interest to zoologists, breeders, and veterinarians. It is especially valuable with regard to camels and elephants, as the great treatise of Ibn al-Mundhir deals more exclusively with horses. It includes an account of a terrible plague which decimated the horses of Yaman c. 1327. It is derived from Arabic literature, but also largely from the author's personal experience.

It was translated into Persian in 1837 by Fakhr al-dīn ibn Aḥmad ibn Mawlā Khiḍr al-Rūdbārī for the governor of Kurdistān.

Text. Extracts concerning mules, asses, camels, elephants, and cattle translated into French by A. Perron: Le Nācérī (3, 348–424, Paris 1860).

Criticism. Charles Rieu: Supplement to the catalogue of Arabic MSS in British Museum (no. 816, p. 553, 1894); Supplement to the catalogue of Persian MSS in British Museum (no. 161, p. 114, 1895). L. Moulé (part 2, 38, 1896). Brockelmann (2, 190, 1902; suppt. 2, 252, 1938).

IBN AL-MUNDHIR

Abū Bakr ibn Badr al-dīn Ibn al-Mundhir al-Baiṭār. Muslim veterinarian who flourished under the Mamlūk sulṭān al-Nāṣir Nāṣir al-dīn Muḥammad ibn Qalā'ūn, who ruled Egypt and Syria in (1293–94), 1298–1308, and 1309–40.[14]

We know nothing of his life except that his father, Badr al-dīn, was an experienced veterinarian in whose footsteps he followed. It is probable that both were employed by the sulṭān, which would give them endless opportunities of increasing their knowledge.[15]

Ibn al-Mundhir wrote an elaborate treatise on hippology and hippiatry entitled Kāshif (or Kashf) al-wail fī ma'rifat amrāḍ al-khail, or also Kāmil al-sinā'atain al-baiṭara wal-zarṭafa,[16] meaning the perfection of the two arts, the veterinary art and hippology. However, the treatise is more often called for short Kitāb al-Nāṣirī, after the sultan al-Nāṣir to whom it was dedicated.

It is the best-ordered and most complete book on both subjects, hippology and hippiatry, written in mediaeval times. The sources are Greek (indirectly) and Arabic. The author quotes Hermes, Hippocrates, Aristotle, Galen, one Abū Yūsuf (?), and Muḥammad ibn Aqī Ḥizām al-Jabalī (quoted apropos of castration, Perron 3, 240), who flourished in the middle of the ninth century. He was probably acquainted with the Arabic books on horses, equitation, medicine, and farriery, but depended largely upon the rich experience of his father Badr al-dīn and his own.

The Kitāb al-Nāṣiri is divided into nine sections (maqālāt), the first four of which cover hippology, the others hippiatry. I shall try to give some idea of their contents, but these are so rich and varied that my account is necessarily very incomplete.

[14] He was born in December 1285; hence his first rule was as a child. We may thus assume that he employed Ibn al-Mundhir in the period 1298–1340, which we may call the beginning of the fourteenth century. That sulṭān completed the great hospital (bīmāristān) begun by his father; he was a great builder and a great lover of horses. K. V. Zettersteen (EI 3, 864–66, 1934). For the bīmāristān al-Manṣūrī (or al-Qalā'ūn) founded by al-Manṣūr al-Qalā'ūn (ruled 1279–90), see Introd. 2, 246.

[15] People of our time can hardly realize the extent of royal stables in earlier days, especially in Muslim lands. That extent was brought home to me a few years ago when I visited the old stables of Meknès in Morocco, built for Mūlāy Ismā'īl (sulṭān 1672–1727) to accommodate, it is said, 12,000 horses! The buildings which remain are so enormous (and it was so hot) that I drove inside them in a taxi!

[16] According to the Gotha MS zarṭaqa, which I don't understand and which is probably a mistake for zarṭafa (f and q can be very easily confused in Arabic script) meaning equitation, art of breeding and training horses, hippology. The origin of the word is unknown (Perron 1, 428–30).

I (20 chapters). Holy war, different races of horses, analogies and differences between horses and men, breeding of horses, their longevity and teeth, blood vessels and bloodletting, skeleton, articulations, instincts and vicious inclinations, racing horses, training of horses, proportions of their body, food and upkeep, harness and saddlery, natural signs and marks of coat, white stockings (balzanes), paces, brands used to designate ownership.

II (10 chapters). Various coats of horses and their names; coats of mules and donkeys.

III (10 chapters). Reserves of horses for war needs; horses which should not be reserved; "molettes" and "épis,"[17] thoroughbreds, differences between stallion and mares; whinnying, neighing, and other noises; various anatomical abnormalities, various breeds, foals, offspring of common horses and donkeys, various kinds of mules and asses.

IV (12 chapters). Signs of good (or poor) health to guide buyers.

V (34 chapters). This is the beginning of the hippiatry. The 34 chapters deal with the causes and symptoms of all the diseases affecting horses.

Parts VI to VIII contain a great many chapters, each of which treats a separate disease or complaint. In Perron's translation, parts V to VIII have been combined in a single order, putting together the theoretical and practical considerations relative to each disease. The original Arabic text has been completely preserved, but the elements of it are reshuffled. Thus the text of these four parts is divided into 34 chapters, preceded by general remarks on different manners of bloodletting and rules of conduct for farriers.

Part IX (12 chapters) is the formulary, wherein the drugs or remedies are classified according to their kinds (collyria, powders, unguents, etc.) or properties (purgatives, styptics, etc.).

Text. A. Perron: Le Nācérī, La perfection des deux arts ou Traité complet d'hippologie et d'hippiatrie arabes (3 vols., Paris 1852–60). Vol. 1 is a long introduction, vols. 2, 3 contain a French translation of the Nāṣiri together with fragments translated from an earlier Arabic text of the same kind (acephalous anonymous MS of a text composed in Baghdād 1208/9), from a contemporary one, the Kitāb al-aqwāl al-kāfīya fī-l-uṣūl al-shāfīya composed by the Rasūlī sulṭān of Yaman, al-Mujāhid 'Alī, etc. The author has added many notes of value from the veterinarian point of view. In spite of some disorder, use of poor Arabic sources, and occasional carelessness, his work is very important; it is the source of all later Western commentaries. A critical edition of the Arabic text is much to be desired.

Perron's three volumes are apparently rare; I had great difficulty in obtaining them. A copy was finally loaned to me by the Cleveland Public Library, to which I express my gratitude. It is a part of the John Griswold White Collection of Folklore and Orientalia.

Criticism. Josef von Hammer-Purgstall: Das Pferd bei den Arabern (Denkschriften der Kais. Akad. der Wissenschaften, phil. Cl., vols. 6–7; reprint 96 p. quarto, 1 pl., Wien 1856), including severe unfair criticism of Perron's first volume. Leclerc (2, 224, 1876). L. Moulé (part 2, 32–37, 1896). Brockelmann (2, 136, 1902; suppt. 2, 169, 1938). J. Ruska (EI 2, 405, 1918). Reinhard Froehner: Das Nacerische Buch (Archiv. für Tierheilkunde 60, 362–75, 1929); Die Tierheilkunde des Abu Bekr ibn Bedr (Abhandlungen aus der Geschichte der Veterinärmedizin no. 23, 150 p., 7 fig., Leipzig 1931; Isis 20, 523); this is the only important

[17] I quote these words in French after Perron, as I do not know with sufficient certainty the equivalent terms in English.

study since 1856, yet is very largely derived from Perron; the author has no knowledge of Arabic, but is one of the leading historians of the veterinary art today. Leclainche (p. 112, 116, 1936), insignificant.

IBN ARQĀM

Abū Yaḥyā Muḥammad ibn Riḍwān Ibn Arqām. Spanish-Arabic astronomer and writer on horses (d. 1356).

He originated in Cadiz, and according to the Iḥāṭa of Ibn al-Khaṭīb (XIV-2) obtained considerable learning, especially in mathematics and astronomy.

He wrote an astronomical poem, Manẓūm fī 'ilm al-nujūm, treatises on the astrolabe, Risāla fīl-istarlāb (sic), and on Arabic genealogy, Shajara fī ansāb al-'Arab. He composed for the amīr al-muslimīn Abū 'Abdallāh Ibn Naṣr, probably the third Naṣrī, Muḥammad III (ruled Granada 1301–9), a treatise on horses, Kitāb al-iḥtifāl fī istīfā' taṣnīf mā lil-khail. According to the MS of the last-named work in the Escorial (902, only vol. 2 of it), it is a "synopsis equitandi disciplinae" containing many verse quotations.

Criticism. Pons Boigues (no. 286, 1898). Renaud (no. 902, 1941).

This note having been inserted after the writing of chapter I, Ibn Arqām is not referred to in that chapter.

F. CHINA

WANG CHÊN

Chinese agriculturist and inventor (fl. 1314).

Wang Chên, or Chêng, wrote a treatise on agriculture, called Nung shu, the preface of which is dated 1314. The first six books contain general rules on agriculture, then follow four books on cereals and twelve books of illustrations representing agricultural implements.

Wang Chên improved the invention of movable type first made by Pi Shêng (XI-1); he cast type in metal, but, noticing that they did not take ink readily and that they rapidly deteriorated, he used wooden type, and he devised revolving type cases with a great many "boxes" to contain the different characters within easy reach of the typesetter. The Nung shu was printed in 1314 with wooden movable type, but Wang Chên had printed previously with such type (c. 60,000 pieces of it or more) a gazetteer of the district for which he was magistrate. The Nung shu contains an elaborate account of the invention of movable type and of the author's share in it. It would seem that type of clay and of tin was not used a great deal, but Wang's wooden type may have been used to a larger extent.

The reality of this invention has been put beyond doubt by the discovery of a set of wooden type, dating from c. 1300, on the floor of one of the caves of Tun-huang. That discovery was made by Paul Pelliot. He found several hundred pieces of wooden type, most of them in perfect condition, and even as Wang had described them, except that it is Uighūr instead of Chinese script. Uighūr is an alphabetic writing, but the type is word type, in slavish imitation of the Chinese model (see illustrations in Carter 1925, facing p. 163).

Text. The text of the Nung shu was incorporated, chapter by chapter and paragraph by paragraph, in the Yung Lo ta tien,[18] that is, the immense encyclopaedia compiled by order of Yung Lo (third Ming emperor, 1403–24).

[18] This is the largest encyclopaedia ever compiled anywhere. It comprised originally 22,937 chüan, forming 11,095 volumes. "The 11,095 volumes standing nearly two feet high and one

The Ch'ing emperor Ch'ien Lung (ruled 1736–96) caused the text of the Nung shu to be extracted from the Yung Lo ta tien and reconstructed. The Library of Congress has a copy of that edition (22 chüan, 8 volumes); it contains an illustration, here reproduced (fig. 20), showing Wang Chên's revolving table. The same library has a Ming edition (36 chüan bound in 12 volumes) and a third edition in the Kuangtung printing of the Wu ying tien chü chên pan ts'ung shu. It has recently obtained a copy of the earliest extant edition, dated 1530, in 10 volumes with several hundred woodcuts illustrating agricultural tools and methods. That edition is divided into 36 chapters, which Wang called chi (collection) instead of

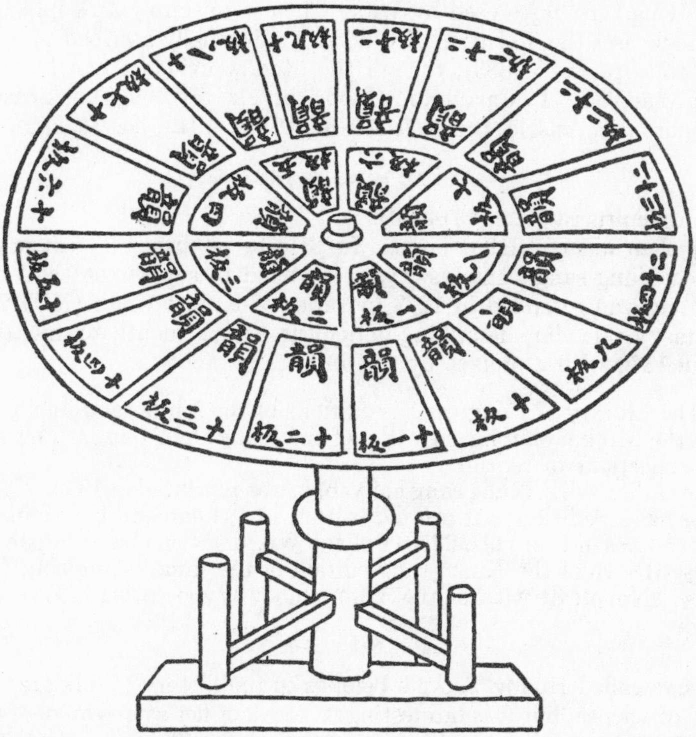

FIG. 20. Revolving type cases invented by Wang Chên (fl. 1314). From Carter (p. 162, 1925), with kind permission of Columbia University Press. It is taken from the Ch'ien Lung edition of Wang Chên's Nung shu.

foot deep would occupy one seventh of a mile of shelf-space" (Swingle). It remained in MS and only one part of it is extant. The main editor was Hsieh Chin (b. Kiangsi 1369; d. 1415; Giles no. 727, 1898). Hsieh Chin was helped at first by 148 scholars, later by 2 associate editors, 20 subeditors, and no fewer than 2,069 assistants. The whole work was completed in 1409. A new copy was made in 1562–67 and kept in the Han-lin library, Peking; many of the volumes were gradually lost in various ways. The enormous bulk of that work is explained by the fact that it was to a large extent a ts'ung shu, that is, a collection of most of the Chinese writings reprinted verbatim, though a single work was often cut in parts, each part being copied under a different heading and included in a different chüan. Mediaeval encyclopaedists like Vincent of Beauvais (XIII-2) proceeded in the same way but more sparingly, and the Yung Lo ta tien therefore is enormously vaster than the Speculum maius. Modern scholars like Chu Yün (d. 1781) and Ma Kuo-han (d. 1857) have reconstructed ancient books from the fragments quoted in the Yung Lo ta tien and other encyclopaedias (Hummel p. 198, 557, 1943).

chüan; he explained his reason for doing so at the beginning of the table of contents. Chüan, he said, is the old term referring to a roll, and should not be used when rolls are disused (it is as if we objected to the term volume instead of book).

Criticism. Wylie (p. 94, 1902). Courant (1, xliv–ix, 1894; suppt. p. ix, 1901), for the history of printing with movable type in Korea. Wieger (p. 463, 512, 1920). Walter T. Swingle: Reports of the Librarian of Congress (p. 184–86, 1922; p. 274, 1925; p. 261, 1927). Carter (p. 161–68, 253, 1925), contains a translation of the Chinese text relative to printing. Arthur W. Hummel: Report of the Librarian of Congress for 1941 (p. 128–29).

The revolving type cases used by Wang Chên were simply an application of the revolving bookcases the invention of which is traditionally ascribed to Fu hsi (497–569, see Nanjio p. xxvi, 1883), though the literary evidence can be traced back only to the year 955. L. Carrington Goodrich: The revolving book-case in China (Harvard journal of Asiatic studies 7, 130–61, 10 fig., 1942; Isis 34, 265).

LU MING-SHAN

Chinese agriculturist (fl. c. 1314–30).

Lu Ming-shan was of Uighūr birth. In 1314 he published a treatise on agriculture entitled Nung sang i shih ts'o yao, intended to supplement and correct the Nung sang chi yao compiled in 1273 by order of Kublai Khān (XIII-2). It is a sort of farmer's calendar, describing agricultural work month by month. It was reprinted in 1330 with a preface by the author.

Text. The Library of Congress has editions of the Nung sang i shih ts'o yao in vol. 108 of the Mo hai chin hu, in vol. 4 of the Kung shun t'ang ts'ung shu, and in two other collections of reprints.

As to the earlier work, Nung sang chi yao, it was reprinted in 1330. The Library of Congress has an edition of it printed in 1895 in 7 chüan and bound in 2 volumes. It has other copies of it in vols. 235–41 of the Wu ying tien chü chên pan ts'ung shu and in vols. 518–19 of the Kuangtung edition of the same ts'ung shu.

Criticism. Not dealt with in the Yüan shih. Wylie (p. 94, 1902).

HUANG TAO-P'O

The woman called Huang Tao-p'o belongs to the history of folklore rather than the history of science, but it is interesting to speak of her as a symbol of cotton, the use of which was generalized in China in this period. This note should have been included in the preceding volume, because the most important dates of her life (see below) are 1295–97. My note had been partly derived from Giles, who says that she flourished about the beginning of the fourteenth century (this may be true) and adds downright errors; I have rewritten it completely on the basis of Goodrich's study.

Huang Tao-p'o hailed from Yai-chou, Kuangtung; or else she came from Wu-ni-ching, near Shanghai, but found herself stranded in Yai-chou, and learned there, where cotton was cultivated, methods of spinning and weaving its fibers. By that time cotton was already known to the people of the lower Yangtze region, but their methods of using it were crude. When Huang came (or returned) to Wu-ni-ching in 1295–97, she taught the people of that district the southern ways of spinning and weaving cotton. She was thus the introducer of the cotton industry into Kiangsu, whence it spread to other parts of northern China. Her merit was recognized early, for a shrine was put up to her memory in 1337 (date uncertain); it was destroyed during the disturbances which occurred toward the end of the Yüan dynasty (before 1368), then rebuilt in 1483–86; a shrine to the lady Huang was still standing near Shanghai a few years ago.

This story assumes the existence of a cotton culture in the southern province of Kuangtung before Huang's time, but it is quite true that the use of cotton did not become extensive in China before the thirteenth and fourteenth centuries, and Huang may have been one of the originators of that extension.

It is not out of place to remark here that the Chinese had been acquainted with cotton and cotton goods at least since the fifth century. Fa-hsien (V-1) noticed the plant in India; Shên Huai-yüan (fifth century) saw a cotton-like plant in southwest China; in 430 Java sent cottons, fine and coarse (po-tieh, ku-pei), to China; a king of India of the Gupta dynasty sent cotton (chi-pei) in the period 502–19; in 523 cotton reached Nanking from Sumatra or other Malay regions; according to Annamese accounts, cotton was exported from Annam to China c. 679.

Specimens of early cotton have rarely been found in China. The late Sir Aurel Stein discovered a few of them, the most remarkable being a cotton shroud, dated 706, used to cover a coffin at Astāna near Kara-khōja.[19] The tradition according to which the early Chinese paper included cotton fibers is very doubtful; the statement in Introd. (2, 1054) that Arghūn's famous letter of 1289 was written on cotton paper is probably wrong.

In 1077 some cotton was imported from the Coromandel coast. The seventy pioneer Jewish families who established themselves in K'ai-fêng fu, capital of the northern Sung dynasty (960–1126), brought with them five kinds of cotton, presumably from India.[20] The Taoist traveler Ch'iu Ch'ang-ch'un (XIII-1) observed the culture of cotton in 1221 in Almāligh (near Kulja, Dzungaria, Central Asia).

Marco Polo (XIII-2) described the abundant manufacture of cotton goods in Fuhkien (a southern province), but does not speak of cotton in north and central China. There is a full account of cotton cultivation and manufacture in the Nung shu of Wang Chên. Polo was in China from 1275 to 1292, and Wang Chên flourished c. 1314; they embrace the period wherein the Huang episode is placed, and we shall not be far wrong if we consider that period as the one during which cotton husbandry and industry were finally established on a national basis, and cotton goods began to be used throughout China.

Criticism. Giles (no. 870, 1898). Couling (p. 134, 1917). Berthold Laufer: Sino-Iranica (p. 490–91, 574, Chicago 1919; Isis 3, 299–302). L. Carrington Goodrich: Cotton in China (Isis 34, 408–10, 1943).

For cotton literature in China see the article on Fang kuan-ch'êng (1698–1768) in Hummel (1, 233–35, 1943).

[19] Sir Aurel Stein (1862–1943): Innermost Asia (2, 708, 1044, pl. 127, Oxford 1928; Isis 14, 522).
[20] William Charles White: Chinese Jews (1, 115, Toronto 1942; Isis 35, 257).

CHAPTER XI

MEDICINE

(First Half of the Fourteenth Century)

N.B. Only the main articles are grouped in this chapter. The medical contributions of many other men, whose main work was done in another field, are related in other chapters. For a general survey of medicine in the first half of the fourteenth century, see section XI in chapter I. More information on the men referred to in that section may then easily be found by means of the index.

A: LATIN WEST

A1. Italy

MAINO DE MAINERI

Italian (Milanese) astrologer and physician (d. c. 1364).

Maynus de Mayneriis, Magninus or Magnus Mediolanensis, Magninus de Magnis de Mediolano. He studied medicine in Paris, and was a master regent of the faculty of medicine there in 1326; on the occasion of his marriage, in 1331, he obtained a papal license which allowed him to continue as regent. In 1346 he was a physician to the Visconti in Milano; in 1364, he was still in the service of Barnabò Visconti.

His son Pietro, like himself a clerk in the diocese of Milano and also physician to the Visconti rulers, is said to have taught medicine in Pavia 1382–83, and died in 1404, being then bishop of Piacenza.

To return to Maino, many writings are ascribed to him. The best known is the Regimen sanitatis which is also ascribed to Arnold de Villanova (Introd. 2, 434, 894, 898, and by index). Some copies are dedicated to Andrea Ghini dei Malpighi, then bishop of Arras (1331–33, later cardinal, d. 1343), whose physician he was and whom he may have followed to Tournai (1333–42). Some references in the text of the Regimen sanitatis tend to show that its author was Milanese.

Maino in 1329/30 wrote a philosophical treatise entitled De intentionibus secundis.

His De saporibus, a brief work dealing with sauces, may be merely a chapter from another work, such as the Regimen sanitatis, or the enlargement of such a chapter. He discusses all kinds of sauces and warns his readers that under certain circumstances they are good for one but in other cases they are harmful. The subject of sauces is treated from a medical, not a culinary, point of view.

In 1358 he wrote the Theoria corporum celestium, and in 1360, a plague tract entitled Libellus de preservatione ab epydimia. This tract is more astrological than medical in its treatment of the subject.

The Dialogus creaturarum moralizatus, a collection of fables, was perhaps written by Maino, and not by the unknown "Nicolaus Pergamenus" to whom it is usually credited.

While he was in the Visconti service, i.e., sometime after 1346 (in 1360?), Maino composed the Liber medicinalis octo tractatuum. The first of these eight treatises deals with medicinal waters. This first treatise, if not the eight, was translated into Hebrew.

Various other works are ascribed to him, e.g., a book on chiromancy (palmistry) available in an early French version, Livre de cyromancie (MS Grenoble no. 813); Contemptus sublimitatis; De regimine sterilitatis, De emoptoica passione et ptisi, Liber memorialis de cura egritudinum, Opusculum de flebotomia. The ascription to Maino of the four medical treatises just mentioned is sometimes based on nothing but their being copied or printed together with the Regimen sanitatis.

Text. Regimen sanitatis, printed under his name, Louvain 1482, 1486, Paris 1483, 1524, Basel 1493, Strassburg 1503. Printed under the name of Arnold of Villanova in the Lyon 1504 edition of the Opera and in later editions.

For the complicated bibliography of early editions of the Regimen sanitatis see Klebs (nos. 828–32, 1938).

Opusculum de saporibus, edited by Lynn Thorndike: A mediaeval sauce-book (Speculum 9, 183–90, 1934).

Libellus de praeservatione ab epydimia (written 1360), edited by R. Simonini: Maino de Maineri ed il suo Libellus (48 p., 1 pl., Modena 1923).

Dyalogus creaturarum moralizatus. First printed Gouda 1480. Again Cologne 1481, Gouda 1481, 1482, Stockholm 1483, Gouda 1484, Antwerp 1486, 1493, Paris 1511, Lyon 1511 (different title).

Dutch editions, Gouda 1480?, 1481, 1482, 1484, Delft 1488, Antwerp s.a.

French edition, Gouda 1482.

Early English editions, s.a.l., London 1530?, Antwerp 1535. Reprinted by Joseph Haslewood: The dialogues of creatures moralised, appliable and edifying to every merry and jocund matter, and right profitable to the governance of men (294 p., London 1816). This is the only edition I have seen; it contains 122 dialogues or fables.

Dialogus creaturarum. Die Zwiesprach der Tiere. Das erste Tierbuch. 75 S., 38 Holzschnitte mit dazugehörigem Text (Gouda 1480). Verlag der Münchner Drucke, München 1926.

Criticism. Pio Rajna: Intorno al cosiddetto Dialogus creaturarum ed al suo autore (Giornale storico della letteratura italiana 3, 1–26; 4, 337–60; 10, 42–113; 11, 41–73, 1884–88). Steinschneider (p. 809, 1893). Karl Sudhoff: Pestschriften nach der Epidemie des "schwarzen Todes" 1348 (AGM 16, 115–16, 1925). Thorndike (3, 220, 235, 520–21, 1934). Wickersheimer (p. 533–34, 1936).

FRANCESCO DI PIEDIMONTE

Francescus de Pedemontium. Italian physician (d. 1319).

He was born in the second half of the thirteenth century, but the place of his birth is uncertain. According to early authorities he was born in the city of Piedimonte near Alife in the Terra di Lavoro, near the modern city of Capua. De Renzi says that according to the documents which he has found, Francesco was born in the Terra di Piedimonte near San Germano, the modern Frosinone, which is southeast of Rome. F. Pellegrini claims that this Francesco is the same as a Francesco Pindemonte who was born in Verona, but De Renzi says that Francesco Piedimonte and Francesco Pindemonte are two distinct authors.

Francesco probably studied in Salerno, then became a professor in the University of Naples. Not much is known about his life except that he was a very popular physician at the court of Robert of Naples (king 1309–43) and his son the duke of Calabria. In his Complementum he speaks of his extensive practice in Naples. He died in 1319.

The only work ascribed to him is the Complementum written as a continuation to the Grabadin[1] medicinarum compositorum of Mesuë the Younger (XI-1), and usually published with it. It is one of the most complete compendia of practical medicine of the Middle Ages, and the most scholastic in tone of those written in the fourteenth century.

In this work he tries to reconcile the Arabic and Greek doctrines with those of his own day; it helped to stimulate the interest of his contemporaries in medical writings of the classical period.

In spite of his prolixity, he adds very few new ideas. The sections dealing with gynaecology and midwifery were of considerable importance to the doctors of his time, and for several succeeding generations, as his account is one of the most complete composed in the Middle Ages. These too, however, are mainly a compendium of the writings of Hippocrates, Galen, Ibn Sīnā, and other Arabic writers. He insists that in normal deliveries the midwife should not try to anticipate nature.

His work deals primarily with therapeutics, and is divided into the following sections: De egritudinibus cordis, mamillarum, meri, stomachi, epatis, splenis, intestorum, ani, renum et vesice, testiculorum et virge, matricis, ventris, juncturarum; De medicinis egritudinum universalium ad omnes febres; De apostematibus sanguineis, cholericis, melancholicis, et phlegmaticis.

In his first section, De egritudinibus cordis, he mentions his patron Robert, king of Naples and Sicily, and explains the plan and method of his work. First it is necessary to know what the disease is, as Galen says, then to know what medicine should be used, "Cura confestim sequitur cognitionem facientis cause et etiam substantie." When he discusses each part of the body, he proceeds in the same way; giving first the symptoms, usually according to Galen or Ibn Sīnā, and then all the prescriptions he could find which might effect a cure. He seldom gives his own opinion, but depends almost entirely upon the earlier "authorities." The work is well organized, however, and must have been very useful to the practicing physician.

He names hundreds of medicinal plants, and many unusual ones, but he does not describe them in as much detail as does Christophorus de Honestis (XIV-2).

Francesco, like the authors of the plague tracts, has much to say concerning the evil effects of pestilential air and advises his readers to build their homes in regions where the air is good.

He cites a great number of authorities, many of whom are well known, but some are difficult to identify probably because they were merely friends of his in Naples or Salerno, and not famous writers; for instance, his magister Arnaldus was an Arnold of Naples, and not Arnold of Villanova. His main authorities were Galen and Ibn Sīnā, but the following were mentioned many times: Hippocrates, Plato, Aristotle, Theophrastos, Asclepiades of Bithynia, Dioscorides, Oribasios, Paul of Aegina, Isidore of Seville, al-Kindī, al-Rāzī, Papias the Lombard, Nicholas of Salerno, Ibn Rushd, John of Procida, Simon of Genoa, Bernard of Gordon, and many others.

[1] When I first came across that strange word or its variants (Introd. 1, 608, 728), I should have explained it. It is derived from the Arabic (aqrābādhīn, and variants), and similar forms occur also in Hebrew. This Arabic word is obviously outlandish. Ḥājjī Khalīfa (1, 378, 1835) suggested that it was Greek and meant tarkīb, composition, i.e., the composition of drugs and their rules. But there is no word of that form or sound in Greek meaning composition. See M. Steinschneider in Z. d. m. G. (5, 90, 1851). The Greek term suggested, ἀκριβὴς δίαιτα (precise diet), is not very plausible. The word γραφίδιον is more plausible as to sound, but the meaning is different (little treatise).

Text. Complementum Mesuae (in the editions of Mesuë), Venice 1479, 1484, 1485, 1489–91, 1495, 1497, 1515, 1562, 1576, 1581, 1584, 1602, 1623, Lyon 1525.

The Tractatus de balneis, one of the chapters of the Complementum, was also published separately in the Collectio de balneis (Venice 1553).

Criticism. F. von Herff: Die Gynäkologie des Franz von Piedmont (Giessen 1843), not seen. Renzi: Collectio (2, 784, 1853); Storia (p. 546–50, cxv, 1857). Haeser (1, 706–7, 805, 1875). Giliberti: Un celebre medico di Re Roberto d' Angiò, Maestro Francesco di Piedmonte (Rivista Campana, Maddaloni 1921), not seen. G. M. Monti: L'età angioina (Storia della università di Napoli, by F. Torraca and others, p. 76, 85, 92–93, Naples 1924). Francesco Pellegrini: Sulla patria di Francesco Pindemonte (Rivista di storia delle scienze mediche e naturali 13, 187–97, 1931).

DINO DEL GARBO

Dino is short for Aldobrandino (Hildebrand). Dinus de Florentia, Florentinus. Nicknamed Expositor (i.e., expositor Avicennae).

Dino was born in the last part of the thirteenth century, and died in Florence in 1327. He was the son of Buono (or Bruno) del Garbo, who was a brother-in-law of Taddeo Alderotti (XIII-2) and a surgeon in Florence. Dino's own son, Tommaso del Garbo (XIV-2), was also a physician. Dino studied both with his father and with Taddeo. He received his doctorate in Bologna about 1300, and then taught in Bologna, Siena, Padua, and Florence. He is mentioned among the physicians to John XXII (pope 1316–34).

Dino was a well beloved physician, and wrote a number of commentaries but few original works.

He was unjustly accused of plagiarizing the works of Pietro Torrigiano. He was supposed to have been an enemy of Cecco d'Ascoli and to have been instrumental in securing the latter's condemnation. His own death occurred on September 30, 1327, a few days after Cecco's.

Robert, king of Naples from 1309 to 1343, desiring to have all the untranslated works of the Arabs rendered into Latin and explained, urged Dino to write two great volumes of commentaries, one on medicine and one on surgery; hence Dino's treatises on the Qānūn of Ibn Sīnā (XI-1). The Super IV fen primi Canonis Avicennae, also called Dilucidatorium totius practice generalis medicinalis scientie, was written between 1311 and 1319. He wrote commentaries on two of Hippocrates' aphorisms, on his De natura foetus (περὶ φύσιος παιδίου), and on Galen's De malitia complexionis diversae.

His original writings include a valuable treatise on weights and measures in which he lists many of Arabic, Hebrew, Greek, Egyptian, and early Latin origin which were used by mediaeval doctors; and one on plasters and unguents. There is an anonymous partial Hebrew translation of the latter entitled Sefer ẓirugiah (i.e., chirurgia, probably from the incipit: Et sunt apte cyrurgie). In his Chirurgia Dino says that he wrote a book De ingenio sanitatis, otherwise unknown.

His writings are dominated by scholastic philosophy. He tried to prove by astrology that the germs of hereditary diseases reside in a sub-organ of the heart. All plants and animals which develop from seeds owe their birth to a kind of fermentation.

He wrote a commentary on the Canzone d'amore of the Florentine and Ghibelline poet Guido Cavalcanti (d. 1301), friend of Dante.

Text. Chirurgia, or Expositio super 3ª et 4ª et 5ª fen, quarti Canonis Avicennae, Ferrara 1489, Venice 1496, 1499, 1519, 1536, 1544. (Klebs no. 336.)

Super IV fen primi Avicennae praeclarissima commentaria, quae Dilucidatorium totius practicae generalis medicinalis scientiae nuncupantur, Venice 1514, 1522, 1594.

Expositio supra Canones generales de virtutibus medicamentorum simplicium secundi Canonis Avicennae, Venice 1499, 1514, 1522.

Expositio supra capitulum de generatione embrionis cum quaestionibus eiusdem, scriptum super libro De natura foetus Hippocratis, Venice 1502, 1518.

Commentum in duos Hippocratis Aphorismos. Puccinotti published the commentary on aphorism 12, part 1, but without Dino's introduction.

Commentum in librum Galeni De malitia complexionis diversae, in Puccinotti (2, part 1, CVII–CXII).

Enarratio cantionis Guidoni de Cavalcantibus De natura et motu amoris (Venice 1498). Rime di Guido Cavalcanti edite ed inedite. Aggiuntovi un volgarizzamento antico non mai pubblicato del commento di Dino del Garbo sulla canzone "Donna mi prega" fatto per ser Jacopo Mangiatroja. Per opera di Antonio Cicciaporci (186 p., Firenze 1813; p. 73–115).

De ponderibus et mensuris, Venice 1496, 1499, 1519, 1536, Florence 1544.

Compilatio emplastrorum et unguentorum, Ferrara 1489, Venice 1496, 1499, 1519, 1536, Florence 1544.

De coena et prandio, Rome 1545.

Criticism. Francesco Maria Colle: Storia scientifico-letteraria dello studio di Padova (3, 161–68, Padua 1824–25). Puccinotti (2, part 1, LXXXIX–CVI, CVII–CXII, 1855; 2, part 2, 344–46, 1859). Haeser (1, 701–2, 1875). Steinschneider (p. 790, 1893). Gurlt (1, 799, 1898). P. Pansier: Les médecins des papes d'Avignon 1308–1403 (Janus 14, 405, 1909). Mary Catherine Welborn: The De ponderibus et mensuris of Dino di Garbo (Isis 24, 15–36, 1935). Wickersheimer (p. 119, 1936). Otto Bird: The Canzone d'amore of Cavalcanti according to the commentary of Dino del Garbo (Mediaeval studies of Toronto 2, 150–203, 1940; 3, 117–60, 1941), text and commentary with introduction.

GUGLIELMO DA VARIGNANA

Italian physician, flourished in Bologna, where he died in 1339 (not 1330). Born about 1270, the son of Bartolommeo da Varignana. His own sons, Pietro and Matteo, likewise were medical teachers in Bologna.

Guglielmo studied under the direction of Taddeo Alderotti (XIII-2), and by 1302 was a professor in the medical school of Bologna. His father was probably a better physician, but was not so well known in the following centuries because his works were not printed.

At some time in his career he was at Zara in the service of Melandino, ban (governor) of Croatia and Bosnia, to whom he dedicated his Secreta sublimia medicinae ad varios curandos morbos, written in 1319.

His other treatise, the Opera medica, is similar to the Rose of John Gaddesden, but more empiric. Guglielmo took a great many of his facts from the Cyranides (Introd. 2, 347) and from Arabic writers. Most of his cures were effected by superstitious or ridiculous remedies.

(Sudhoff doubts the statement that he believed in the isolation of plague-stricken patients.)

Text. Secreta sublimia medicinae ad varios curandos morbos, Pavia 1519, Venice 1520, 1540, Lyon 1526, 1539, Basel 1597. (Also with the various editions of the Opera medica.)

Ad omnium interiorum et exteriorum partium morbos remediorum praesidia et ratio utendi eis pro circumstantiarum varietate, Basel 1531. (Also with the various editions of the Opera medica.)

Opera medica, De curandis morbis tam particularibus quam universalibus lib. XIX, De febrium curatione lib. II, De apostematum, ulcerumque differentia et cura lib. V, De venenis lib. III, De faciei, totiusque corporis, mundificationibus lib. VIII, Basel 1540?, 1545, 1595, Lyon 1560.

De cura variolarum et morbillorum, edited by C. G. Gruner: De variolis et morbillis fragmenta (Jena 1790).

De febrium dispositione tractatus duo, in G. M. Savonarola: Practica canonica (Lyon 1560).

Criticism. A. W. E. Th. Henschel: Berühmte Wundärzte und Aerzte des XIII. und XIV. Jahrhunderts (Janus 2, 390, Leipzig 1853). Mauro Sarti et Mauro Fattorini: De claris archigymnasii bononiensis professoribus (1, 571–72, Bologna 1888). Neuburger (2, 421, 425, 432, 483, 1911). Ludovico Frati: Guglielmo da Varignana (Rivista di storia delle scienze 1, 136–38, 1912). Karl Sudhoff: Pestschriften nach der Epidemie des "schwarzen Todes" 1348 (AGM 16, 122, 1925).

NICCOLÒ DA SANTA SOFIA

Italian physician (d. bet. 1350 and 1353).

The family probably originated in Constantinople. A certain Guglielmo moved to Venice in 1292, then to Padua. Niccolo was the first doctor, but was followed by many other members of the family who were also medical men. His son Giovanni (d. 1389) was a professor in Padua and Bologna, and his son Marsiglio (d. 1403/5) taught in Padua, Pavia, and Bologna.

Niccolò was a student and successor of Pietro d'Abano. He taught in the University of Padua between 1311 and 1350.

Although none of his writings remains, he is supposed to have written three books on diet; a commentary on Ibn Sīnā's Qānūn; two books on methods of curing acute fever in cases of the plague; and a book on snake bite.

Criticism. A. G. Tiraboschi: Storia della letteratura italiana (5, 266, Modena 1789). Francesco Maria Colle: Storia scientifico-letteraria dello studio di Padova (3, 170–71, Padua 1824–25). Andrea Gloria: Monumenti della università di Padova (1, 445–46, Padua 1888). Gustavo Tànfani: Una illustre famiglia di medici padovani nel medio evo (Rivista di storia delle scienze 15, 97–112, Siena 1933).

PIETRO TORRIGIANO DE' TORRIGIANI

Turrisanus, de Turrisoniis, Trusianus, Cruscianus, Drusianus Valorius, Pietro da Firenze, Torrigiano Rustichelli. Italian physician.

Born between 1270 and 1280 near Florence, a descendant of two famous families, the Valori and the Torrigiani.

He studied first in Bologna under the direction of Taddeo Alderotti (XIII-2) and became his most distinguished disciple; then he studied and taught in Paris between 1306 and 1311, after which he returned to Bologna. Toward the end of his life he became a Carthusian monk. Pietro died about the middle of the century. His main work is an elaborate commentary on the Microtegni (τέχνη ἰατρική) of Galen, which he proudly entitled Plusquam commentum, and which caused him to be nicknamed Plusquam commentator. That commentary, full of scholastic subtilities, attained much favor until the middle of the sixteenth century, witness the number of editions down to that time.

Pietro was a contemporary of Dino del Garbo, who was unjustly accused of plagiarizing his (Pietro's) work.

In his Plusquam commentum, he shows some originality by daring to contradict Aristotle, Galen, and Ibn Sīnā. Contrary to the opinion of Aristotle, Pietro said that the seat of the sensations is in the brain and not in the heart. He also said that it is not necessary to have two sets of nerves, one to control movements and the other to convey sensations, that one set is enough to take care of both functions. One especially noteworthy remark was to the effect that fevers are not produced by putrid humors. He claimed that medicines attract humors in the same way that a magnet attracts iron, by their specific forces.

Like his master Taddeo, he believed that anatomical demonstrations should be performed for the benefit of medical students; also that mathematics was a necessary preliminary discipline for medical students. On the other hand, his works contain much more speculative philosophy than do those of Taddeo. He refers frequently to the writings of Boetius, the masters of Salerno, and the favorite Greeks and Arabs.

Text. Plusquam commentum in Microtegni Galeni, Bologna 1489, 1498?, Venice 1498, 1504, 1512, 1517, 1527, 1543, 1557. (Klebs no. 983.)

Questiones de ypostasi (published with the Venice 1498, 1512, 1557 editions of the Plusquam commentum).

Canones balneandi LXXXI, selections from his Plusquam commentum, published in the Venetian Collectio de balneis (Venice 1553).

Criticism. Kurt Sprengel: Histoire de la médecine (trans. by A. J. L. Jourdan, 2, 444–45, Paris 1815). Puccinotti (2, part 2, 340–43, 1859). Neuburger (2, 484, 1911). Wickersheimer (p. 770, 1936).

MONDINO FRIULANO[2]

Mondino de Foro Julio, Mundinus Friuliensis, Giovanni Mondino da Cividale del Friuli (a district northeast of the March of Verona). (Mondino is the shortened form of Raimondo, Rimondo, or Rimondino.) Italian physician (d. c. 1340).

He is not to be confused with the anatomist Mondino de' Luzzi, nor with another Mondino Friulano, who was a physician in Padua in the second half of the fourteenth century.

Mondino was the son of William of Cividale del Friuli. Nothing is known about his early life. By 1307 he was a professor of medicine in Padua, where he was associated with Peter of Abano. He died about 1340, having spent his entire life in one university.

Mondino's principal work was the Abbreviatio synonymorum Simonis Januensis cum additionibus quibusdam, finished about 1321. It has never been printed, but there are a number of MS copies. It is based on the Synonyma of Simon of Genoa (XIII-2), contracting some parts of this work and expanding others. For instance, the list of weights and measures has been considerably increased.

Wickersheimer says that Mondino is the author of a MS in the Escurial entitled Expositio brevis super 2^{am}–4^{am} fen primi Canonis Avicenne, finished in 1316.

He may have written another work called the Physiognomia.

[2] Note contributed by M. C. Welborn.

Mazzucchelli attributes to this Mondino the commentary on the Canones universales of Mesuë the Younger (XI-1) which was really written by Mondino de' Luzzi.

Criticism. Francisco Maria Colle: Storia scientifico-letteraria dello studio de Padova (3, 156–61, Padua 1824–25). A. W. E. Th. Henschel: Berühmte Wundärzte und Aerzte des XIII. und XIV. Jahrhunderts (Janus 2, 391–92, Leipzig 1853). Giacosa (p. 503, 1901). Ernest Wickersheimer: Une liste, dressée au XVe siècle, des commentateurs du Ier livre du Canon d'Avicenne et du livre des Aphorismes d'Hippocrate (Janus 34, 33, 1930).

BARTOLOMMEO DA VARIGNANA[2a]

Italian physician (d. 1318).

Born in Bologna, the son of Giovanni da Varignana, a physician. (Varignana is the name of a place located between Bologna and Imola.) Studied medicine, first with his father and then with Taddeo Alderotti (XIII-2). Bartolommeo became a very irritating rival of Taddeo, with whom he had many quarrels.

He practiced medicine in Bologna, and soon became famous and wealthy. He was employed by the city to teach medicine and played an important part in municipal politics. In 1303 he was holding some municipal office, but three years later he was banished from the city for a while on account of his adherence to the Ghibelline party. During the years 1311–13 Bartolommeo was with Henry VII of Luxemburg (d. 1313) in Italy. Bartolommeo died in Bologna in 1318. His son Guglielmo was also a physician in Bologna.

The earliest post-mortem examination of which we have a formal record was made by him, assisted by another physician and three surgeons, in Bologna, February 1302. The record does not suggest that his was an unusual procedure.

Bartolommeo wrote commentaries on the works of Hippocrates, Galen, and Ibn Sīnā, which are very long and full of scholastic subtilities. Only one fragment of his works has been published, the rest is still in manuscript. The works not yet printed are: In librum Tegni, sive in artem parvam Galeni ampla commentaria, or Lectura optima super Tegni; Rationes super libro de Canonibus (Ibn Sīnā); Recollectiones in librum in interioribus; In librum de complexionibus Galeni; Liber de regimine sanitatis. (Is this last work the one ascribed to Taddeo? see Introd. 2, 1087.)

In the Experimenta of Taddeo there are some treatises which are ascribed to Bartolommeo: Aqua vitis ad calculum; and Tragea magistri Thaddaei et magistri Bartholomaei.

Text. Utrum medicina nutriat (a part of the Quaestiones super libro Galeni de complexionibus), printed by Puccinotti (2, part 1, CXIII–CXXIX, 1855).

Criticism. A. G. Tiraboschi: Storia della letteratura italiana (4, 233–34, Modena 1788). Puccinotti (2, part 1, CXIII–CXXIX, 1855; 2, part 2, 360–61, 1859). Haeser (1, 701, 1875). Mauro Sarti et Mauro Fattorini: De claris archigymnasii bononiensis professoribus (1, 568–72, Bologna 1888). Justus Niedling: Die mittelalterlichen und frühneuzeitlichen Kommentare zur Techne des Galenos (Leipzig diss., p. 13, Paderborn 1924; Isis 7, 181). C. Singer (p. 73, 83, 1926).

[2a] This note on Bartolommeo is preceded by that on his son Guglielmo because the latter was named with other "professors," whereas the former is included among the anatomists. It does not matter as long as one is aware of it.

MONDINO DE' LUZZI

Mondino dei Liucci, de' Luzzi, de' Liuzi; Mundinus Liucius de Lentiis, de Leutiis. Mondino is an endearing form of Raimondo. Italian anatomist (c. 1275–1326).

Of the famous Florentine family of Luzzi, who came to Bologna about 1270. His father, Nerino Franzoli de' Liucci, was an apothecary, and his uncle Liuccio taught medicine in Bologna about 1295.

Mondino was born in Bologna about the year 1275. He was first enrolled in the guild of apothecaries, then began the study of medicine in the University of Bologna, where he was a fellow student of Henry of Mondeville. They studied under the direction of Taddeo Alderotti (XIII-2). The scholastic method of writing medical works, as taught by Taddeo, is easily recognizable in the writings of Mondino. He received his doctor's degree in 1300, and from that time on practiced in Bologna and taught in the university until his death in 1326.

He was called the restorer of anatomy, and greatly honored until the time of the new (Vesalian) renaissance. In 1315 he dissected two females bodies, one of which had menstruated, and in 1316, a pregnant sow; he must have made many other dissections. Human bodies were occasionally (very rarely) dissected in the second half of the thirteenth century (Introd. 2, 72), but Mondino was apparently the first since the days of Erasistratos and Herophilos (III-1 B.C.) to use human cadavers in public lectures, and to apply to them the technique of demonstrative dissection. As contrasted with many of the anatomists who followed him, until Vesalius' time, Mondino did his own dissecting; but this was partly due to the fact that anatomical teaching was not yet deemed sufficiently important and the professor had to shift for himself without the assistants, *ostensor* and *demonstrator*, who were associated with him a little later.

His chief work was a compendium of anatomy (Anatomia Mundini), which he completed in 1316 and which enjoyed more than two centuries of popularity. It was first printed c. 1475, and there are about forty editions, some of them illustrated (the original text had no illustrations). The Anatomia's popularity was due to its simplicity and directness. Mondino was a restorer of anatomy in the sense that his popular textbook and his experimental teaching helped to prepare the anatomical revival. It cannot be said, however, that he added much to the Greek and Arabic knowledge already available in Latin versions; he repeated many of the old errors and thus gave them new currency.

The Anatomia Mundini contains surgical and pathological notes, yet as a whole—and for the first time—anatomy was almost completely dissociated from surgery. It still included much physiology, for physiology had not yet become a separate subject.

It is a practical textbook, arranged like a manual of dissection. After a general introduction, the organs are dealt with in the following order: (1) abdominal cavity (venter inferior); (2) thoracic cavity (medius venter); (3) head (venter superior); (4) bones, spinal column, extremities. The first three groups correspond to the old division of members into (1) natural, (2) spiritual, and (3) animal. The arrangement was imposed by circumstances; in the absence of good means of preservation, it was necessary to dissect first the most perishable organs, etc., and to complete the whole dissection within a few days. Yet Mondino used preparations dried in the sun to exhibit the general direction of tendons and ligaments; and he also examined macerated bodies to trace the nerves to their extremities.

In spite of his personal observations, Mondino was almost entirely dependent upon Galen and Theophilos (VII-1) and upon Arabic authorities. Through his master Taddeo Alderotti he had access to a direct translation of Aristotle's Parts of animals (dating from c. 1260); otherwise his knowledge of Greek anatomy was almost exclusively obtained through Arabic channels, that is, through Latin translations of Arabic works.

This explains the confusion of his terminology and the number of Arabic or Arabicized terms which it contains. Many of these terms were popularized by him. Here are a few examples: Mirach = abdominal wall, from A. maraqq, pl. marāqq, root raqqa. Siphach = peritoneum. Meri = oesophagus, A. marī'. Venae guidech (guidegi) = venae jugulares, A. wadaj, pl. awdāj; widāj, dual widājān. Vena chilis (coele) = vena cava, G. κοίλη. Caib = talus or astragalus, A. ka'b. He seems to have been responsible for the introduction of the words matrix and mesentery (mescrenium). These terms among others were used by him; I do not claim he was the first to use them. Such questions are very difficult to solve, because the same terms were introduced more than once with different meanings. Anatomical nomenclature did not begin to be stabilized until the middle of the sixteenth century. In the absence of a historical dictionary of Latin terms, and of a historical dictionary of Arabic, one can only guess. See Fonahn (1922); his study on "Arabic and Latin anatomical terminology" was a good beginning, but much work remains to be done.

The organs of the body are described in some detail, but the bones are only listed. The muscles are seldom mentioned, although a good description is given of those in the abdomen. Nerves or blood vessels are mentioned incidentally but are only briefly dealt with. It was almost impossible at that stage to analyze the texture of different tissues, but he made a brave attempt to solve those difficult problems. According to his own statement, "In setting forth the anatomy of the organic members I shall speak of the related parts according as each particular part is dominant in each organ: for example, I shall speak of the flesh in the anatomy of the hip, of the bones in the anatomy of the back and feet, and of the [anatomy of the] nerves in the anatomy of the cerebrum and back of the neck."

His physiology was largely derived from Theophilos Protospatharios (VII-1),[3] that is, it was essentially Galenic.

Some peculiarities of his anatomy and physiology must still be mentioned. According to him, the stomach is spherical, and the liver five-lobed like a pig's liver. This error goes back at least to the time of Rufus (II-1). He had made many observations of the womb, normal, after menstruation, during and after parturition, yet he continues to describe it as seven-chambered (see Michael Scot, XIII-1). He pays much attention to the gall bladder and the slipper-shaped spleen, which secrete two of the four humors, the yellow bile (choler) and the black bile (melancholia). His description of the caecum does not include the vermiform appendix, but he mentions the pancreatic duct.[4] He gives an interesting account of the sexual organs and tries to establish analogies between the male and female organs. He remarks that the abdomen is composed only of soft parts, so that it may expand to a great extent in cases of tympanites and dropsy. His description of the heart, derived from Ibn Sīnā, is very crude. Urine is ex-

[3] The mediaeval tradition of Theophilos is very complicated. See general indications in Introd. 2, 75.

[4] Which we call duct of Wirsung (ductus pancreaticus). The Bavarian Johann Georg Wirsung described it in 1642.

plained as a filtration from the blood by the kidneys. The brain is divided into three vesicles or ventricles as follows: the anterior part is the center of the senses, the sensus communis (hence our phrase, common sense); the middle and posterior parts are respectively the seats of imagination and memory; mental operations are controlled by the motions of a sort of "red worm" (the chorioid plexus of the third cerebral ventricle). To these functions of the brain, Mondino adds the old Aristotelian function of cooling the heart. This illustrates the lack of originality of his physiology; he is afraid of rejecting any authoritative statement and tries to reconcile all of them. A similar remark may be made with regard to his embryology: it is a compromise—a reasonable one—between the opinions of Galen and of Aristotle on the physiology of embryo formation (Needham).

Though his anatomy is remarkably independent of surgery, it contains some surgical items: operation of hernia with or without castration; lithotomy; abdominal paracentesis; treatment of cataract by couching; and he recommends an extraordinary way of closing an incised wound of the intestines: ants should be made to bite the edges and then their heads should be cut off.

His medical activity is witnessed by the existence of nineteen consilia which deal with such ailments as catarrh, fevers, stone, melancholic humors, and other similar subjects.

Mondino wrote a number of commentaries on that collection of classical writings known as the Ars medicinae or Articella; these commentaries are entitled, Super libro prognosticorum Hippocratis, Super Hippocratis de regimine acutorum, Annotata in Galeni de morbo et accidenti. Haller, in his Bibliotheca anatomica, mentions another commentary on the De pulsibus, probably the treatise by Theophilos Protospatharios (VII-1), which is also to be found in the Articella.

He also wrote a commentary called Lectura super primo, secundo et quarto de juvamentis. This De juvamentis, which he and other mediaeval writers (e.g., Barnabas of Reggio) ascribe to Galen, is probably the latter's De usu partium. His commentary on the Canones of Mesuë the Younger (XI-1) is very long and includes many remedies and names of medicinal drugs; and quite a little material from his Anatomia is added to the text of Mesuë.

Mondino also wrote treatises on weights and measures, human viscera, prescriptions and drugs, medical practice, and fevers.

Various commentaries have been written on Mondino's Anatomia, notably by Iacopo Berengario da Carpi (d. 1550), Commentaria cum amplissimis addictionibus super anatomiam Mundini (Bologna 1521); and by Matteo Corti (1475-1542), of Pavia, In Mundini anatomiam commentarius (Pavia 1550, Lyon 1551).

Text. There are about forty printed editions of the Anatomia; some of the most important ones are listed below:

Latin editions, Padua 1476, the editio princeps. Also Padua 1484, Pavia 1478, 1492, 1507, 1550, Bologna 1482, 1514, 1521, Leipzig 1493 (two), 1505, Venice 1494, 1498, 1507/8, 1512, 1521, 1538, 1580, Strassburg 1509, 1513, Paris 1527, Milan 1510, Geneva 1519, Rostock 1514, Lyon 1524, 1528, 1529, 1531, 1551, Marburg 1541. (Klebs nos. 573, 688.)

A number of these have one or more woodcuts, e.g. Venice 1494, Leipzig 1493, Strassburg 1513, Rostock 1514, Bologna 1521, and Marburg 1541.

A facsimile of the Pavia 1478 edition has been printed by Ernest Wickersheimer: Anatomies de Mondino dei Luzzi et de Guido de Vigevano (p. 1-65, Paris 1926), vol. 3 of the Documents scientifiques du XVe siècle; title pages and colophons of seven other editions are included.

There are at least two early French translations, one by Richard Roussat, a doctor and canon of Langres, printed at Paris in 1532; and another by an unknown translator, Paris 1541. Dr. Crummer claimed that this latter edition was the first French translation.

An Italian translation by Sebastian M. Romano was included in the 1493 edition of the Fasciculo di medicina; see Charles Singer's facsimile edition (vol. 2, Florence 1925). For another Italian translation see Lino Sighinolfi: Mondino de' Liucci Anatomia (Bologna 1930), a fifteenth-century Italian translation, and a photographic reproduction of a fourteenth-century MS of the Anatomia.

Dr. Singer has translated into English the 1493 Italian edition mentioned above, The Fasciculo di medicina (1925).

Consilia: seven are printed by Vonderlage (1922).

Domini Joannis Mesuë de consolatione medicinarum simplicium et correctione operationum earum, Canones cum expositione praeclarissimi medici Magistri Mondini de Lentiis feliciter incipiunt, Venice 1490, 1495, 1497, 1570, 1638, Lyon 1525. (Klebs nos. 880.13-15).

The following works of Mondino have not yet been printed:

Practica de accidentibus morborum secundum Magistrum Mundinum de Liucius de Bononia.

Tractatus de ponderibus secundum Magistrum Mundinum.

De visceribus humani corporis.

Super libro prognosticorum Hippocratis.

Mundinus super Hippocratis de regimine acutorum..

Annotata in Galeni de morbo et accidente.

Super libro de pulsibus.

Tractatus de dosi medicinae.

De medicinis simplicibus (probably the De arboribus omnibus et aromaticis).

Practicae medicinae libri X.

Consilia medicinalia.

Consilium ad retentionem menstruorum.

De accidentibus febrium.

Criticism. Giovanni Fantuzzi: Notizie degli scrittori bolognesi (6, 44-46, Bologna 1788). Haeser (1, 737-44, 1875). Mauro Sarti et Mauro Fattorini: De claris archigymnasii bononiensis professoribus (1, 551, 1888). Gurlt (1, 791-95, 1898). Weindler (1908). Giovanni Martinotti: L'insegnamento dell' anatomia in Bologna (Studi e memorie per la storia dell' università di Bologna 2, ser. 1, 1-146, Bologna 1911). Ludovico Frati: Ricerche sull' anatomico Mondino (Rivista di storia critica delle scienze 1, 156, Faenza 1912), brief note establishing the date of his death. Choulant-Frank (p. 88-96, 1920). F. Filippini: L'esodo degli studenti da Bologna nel 1321 (Studi e memorie per la storia dell' università di Bologna 6, ser. 2, 140, 183, Bologna 1921). Fonahn (1922). Balduin Vonderlage: Consilien des Mondino dei Luzzi aus Bologna (Leipzig diss., 52 p., 1922; Isis 6, 152). Charles Singer: Introduction to English edition above mentioned (Florence 1925); Evolution of anatomy (p. 74-85, 1925). Needham (p. 77, 1934). Le Roy Crummer: La première traduction française de l'Anatomie de Mondini (Aesculape 20, 204-7, 4 fig., 1930), translation discovered by the author, printed Paris 1541, containing interesting woodcuts. Vittorio Putti: Ignota e forse prima edizione dell' Anatomia di Mondino dei Liucci (La bibliofilia 33, 381, Florence 1931), apropos of the 1476 edition. Umberto Dallari: Due documenti inediti riguardanti Liuzzo e Mondino de' Luzzi (Rivista di storia delle scienze 14, 1-7, 1932; Isis 19, 261). Mary Catherine Welborn: Mondino de' Luzzi's commentary on the Canones generales of Mesuë the Younger (Isis 22, 8-11, 1934). Lynn Thorndike: Little known medical works in Basel MSS (Annals of medical history 2, 283, 1940).

GUIDO DA VIGEVANO

Guy de Vigevano, Guido de Papia. Italian anatomist and physician (c. 1280–after 1345).

Born in Pavia, not Vigevano, about 1280, a member of the noble family of Vigevano (in the diocese of Pavia). Guido studied medicine probably in Bologna. When he returned to Pavia, in addition to his medical practice, he took an active part in politics as an ardent Ghibelline. He joined the emperor Henry VII during the latter's expedition into Italy. After the death of Henry, in 1313, Guido returned to his medical practice in Pavia. Then, to get away from the struggles between Guelf and Ghibelline, he went to France, where he was royal physician to queen Marie of Luxemburg, wife of Charles IV; after the death of Marie he was one of the physicians of Jeanne of Burgundy, the wife of Philippe VI of Valois, king of France from 1328 to 1350.

In 1335, inspired by the plan of Philippe to lead an expedition to the Holy Land, Guido wrote the Tesaurus regis Francie acquisicionis Terre Sancte de ultra mare, necnon sanitatis corporis eius et vite ipsius prolongacionis ac etiam cum custodia propter venenum. The first part, Liber conservacionis sanitatis senis, is a health regime prepared especially for older men who were planning to go to the Holy Land (Philippe was then 42). The second part deals with military science; the methods of attacking fortified places, descriptions of battering rams and apparatus for scaling walls and crossing rivers. This book (MS 11015 fonds latin, Bibliothèque nationale, Paris) contains a number of valuable illustrations. It has not yet been edited.

In 1345 Guido wrote the Liber notabilium a libris Galieni extractus, which he dedicated to Philippe. The first part is a collection of extracts of Latin translations of the following works of Galen: De ingenio sanitatis, De interioribus, De accidenti et morbo, De crisi, De diebus criticis, De complexionibus, De malicia complexionis diverse, De simplicibus medicinis. These translations constitute the largest part of this whole work. The second part, Regimen sanitatis, is practically the same as the Liber conservacionis sanitatis mentioned above. This part is based not only on the works of Galen, but also on those of Hippocrates, Dioscorides, al-Rāzī, Ibn Sīnā, and others. The third part, the Anothomia, is a little treatise on human anatomy, based partly on his own dissections and partly on the work of Mondino de' Luzzi. Like Mondino, Guido omitted all discussion of osteology from this treatise. The introduction, in which Guido discusses the reasons why all doctors should know anatomy, is followed by a description of the veins and arteries (based largely on Ibn Sīnā). Next is a detailed explanation of 18 anatomical drawings. At the end is a short appendix on the tumefaction of the uvula and the palate. The Vigevano drawings witness considerable advance in the technique of dissection as compared with those of Henry of Mondeville. Although this Anothomia is very brief, it shows that Guido was not content merely to read and make abstracts of earlier writers, but that he frequently drew his own conclusions.

He made experiments on the properties of aconite, refuting a fanciful theory of Ibn Sīnā, and risked his life trying an antidote.

Text. Anothomia, edited by Ernest Wickersheimer: L'anatomia de Guido de Vigevano (AGM 7, 1–25, 18 fig., 1913). Edited from the Chantilly MS 569, which contains nine other medical treatises in Latin, eight being extracted from

Galen, and the ninth a Regimen sanitatis. The very interesting illustrations of Vigevano's Anothomia are reproduced. Facsimile edition, together with Mondino's Anatomy, edited by E. Wickersheimer (p. 72–85, Paris 1926).

Criticism. Carlo Promis: Gl'ingegneri militari (Miscellanea di storia italiana 12, 418–19, Turin 1871). Elie Berger: Guy de Vigevano et Philippe de Valois (Journal des savants 12, 5–14, Paris 1914). Karl Sudhoff: Weitere Beiträge zur Geschichte der Anatomie im Mittelalter, part IV (AGM 8, 133–35, 1914). G. Romano: Guido da Vigevano (Bollettino della Società pavese di storia patria 14, 353–61, 1914; 15, 282–92, Pavia 1915). L. Choulant (p. 60, 1920). C. Singer (p. 85, fig. 42, 1926). Alessandro Colombo: Il medico aulico Guido da Vigevano e la sua famiglia (Rivista di storia delle scienze 10, 255–75, 1928). Thorndike (3, 26–27, 544, 1934), apropos of the experiment on aconite. Wickersheimer (p. 216, 1936).

NICCOLÒ BERTRUCCIO

There are many variants of the name Bertruccio, a diminutive derived from Alberto: Bertucci, Bertuccio, Vertuzzo, Vertuccio, etc. Nicolaus Bertrucius.

Italian physician and anatomist, professor of logic and medicine in Bologna. Born in Lombardy, son of Rolandino of the noble Rolandi family. Died in 1347, a victim of a plague and famine which visited Bologna in the latter part of that year. He married Giacoma, daughter of a Giovanni of Parma, a doctor of medicine. Studied under Mondino de' Luzzi. Teacher of Guy de Chauliac (XIV-2).

He continued the practice of making human dissections in the classroom, originated by Mondino. His dissections were conducted in the following order: (1) nutritive organs, because they are the most perishable (abdomen); (2) spiritual organs (thorax); (3) animal organs (head); (4) extremities. The discussion of each organ was arranged in this order: positio, substantia, complexio, quantitas, numerus, figura, colligatio, actio et utilitas, aegritudines (which reminds one of the ten categories of Aristotle). He opposed surgical intervention unless it was unavoidable.

His main work is a general medical treatise called Compendium; he also wrote a commentary on Hippocrates' Aphorisms and on Galen's Tegni ("Tres sunt omnes doctrinae . . .").

He claimed to have included in his Compendium only those theories which he believed to be true. It is divided in the following way: (1) De regimine sanitatis, (2) De aegritudinibus particularibus quae sunt a capite usque ad pedes, (3) De aegritudinibus universalibus hoc est de febribus, (4) De crisi et de diebus criticis, (5) De venenis, (6) De decoratione. There is a single chapter on anatomy including a description of the brain. In discussing each disease he gives first the rational treatment, then the empiric, the treatment according to the Qānūn, and finally the principal symptoms. There are a few chapters on dentistry: De dolore dentium, De casu et mobilitate dentium, De corrosione dentium et gingivarum, De fluxu sanguinis ex gingivis, De ulceribus gingivarum.

Text. Nusquam antea impressum collectorium totius fere medicine, edited by Nicolaus de Landa, Lyon 1509, 1515, 1518; edited by D. Joannes Caesar, Cologne 1537.

Methodi cognoscendorum tam particularium quam universalium morborum, Mainz 1534, Lyon 1518.

In medicinam practicam introductio, Strassburg 1533, 1535.

Diaeta seu regimen sanitatis de rebus non naturalibus et advertendis morbis, Mainz 1534, Strassburg 1534.

Criticism. G. Mazzuchelli: Gli scrittori d'Italia (2, part 2, 1073, Brescia 1760). G. Fantuzzi: Notizie degli scrittori bolognesi (2, 154–58, Bologna 1782), good account of his life based on original documents. Justus Niedling: Die mittelalterlichen und frühneuzeitlichen Kommentare zur Techne des Galenos (Leipzig diss., p. 19, Paderborn 1924; Isis 7, 181). K. Sudhoff (Mitt. 24, 201, 1925), short note on the commentary on Tegni.

GENTILE DA FOLIGNO

Gentilis Fulginas, Fulgineus, de Fulgineo, de Gentilibus. Called Speculator and "L'anima di Avicenna." Italian physician (d. 1348).

Gentile was born in Foligno near Perugia, Umbria, in the latter part of the thirteenth century. His father may have been Gentile da Foligno, a physician who later moved from Foligno to Bologna.

Gentile studied probably in Bologna under Taddeo Alderotti (XIII-2) before 1303. Then he studied under the direction of Peter of Abano in Padua, before 1315. There is no evidence that he was ever a personal physician of John XXII. By 1325 he had begun to teach at the University of Perugia, and from 1337 to 1345 he lectured at the University of Padua. At this time he was also a personal physician of Ubertino da Carrara (ruler of Padua 1338–45). In 1345 he went to Perugia, where he died on June 18, 1348, of the plague. He was buried at Foligno.

He made a number of public dissections and autopsies; for instance, one at Padua in 1341. It was at this conference that he is supposed to have made the discovery of a gallstone. According to Marcello Donati (1538–1602),[5] Gentile described gallstones, and if this is true he was probably the first to do so.

He wrote many commentaries and consilia, but is chiefly famous for the latter, which we shall consider first.

Gentile wrote some 90 Consilia on general subjects such as fevers, various ailments a capite ad pedes, and other medical questions. They contain many practical remarks on diseases, and methods of treatment. His regimens are detailed, and many of his methods of treatment are based on practical experience rather than on theory or "authority." These Consilia were written for physicians as guides for their practice and so do not contain elaborate discussions of general theories, such as are found in his Commentaries. The Consilia show independence of thought and observation. They also show that the author was often impatient with the subtleties and fancies of his contemporaries, though capable of indulging in many subtleties of his own.

One of his most famous works was a Consilium addressed to the physicians in Genoa and Pisa on the occasion of the plague in Genoa in 1348. This must be one of the earliest plague treatises, for it was written at the request of the university and city of Perugia at the beginning of the plague, of which he was an early victim. It is divided into four parts, as follows: (1) causes of the pestilence; (2) a preservative regimen against it; (3) methods of curing those already afflicted; (4) 17 problems in connection with the plague for student discussion. Gentile says that the plague was brought to Italy by the ships trading with the Levant, appearing first in Genoa and then in Perugia, and later in many other towns, even so far south as Naples. His careful enumeration of the causes of the pestilence includes astrological causes, corruption of the air due to putrefactions, the opening of old wells and caverns, the evil smells arising from lakes and ponds; and infections (he

[5] De medica historia mirabili p. 197, Venice 1597 (first edition, Mantua 1586).

uses the words semina for what we would call the germs of the disease, and reliquiae to designate the vestiges of it left by patients). Death is caused by a putrid poison collecting around the heart and lungs. He gives elaborate directions concerning the proper food and drink, medicines, bloodletting, etc., during an epidemic.

While Cino da Pistoia was preparing some arguments on a certain paternity case, he came upon the Lex septimo mense. Before handing down his decision, he wrote to Gentile in order to obtain the best medical opinion of his time on this question. Gentile replied in a long letter, Tractatus super lege VII° mense, in which he discussed the various views of the philosophers and doctors, such as Hippocrates, Aristotle, Ibn Sīnā, al-Ghazzālī, Peter of Abano, and others, on this subject. He considers the three following points: (1) Why does the duration of pregnancy vary? (2) What are the limits of that duration? (seven to ten months, but Aristotle speaks of a birth in the eleventh month and Ibn Sīnā of one in the fourteenth); during the successive months of its life in the womb the unborn child is influenced by different planets. (3) Are these durations definitely fixed or changeable? Are fractions of months to be counted as whole months or not? Medical experts might determine the legitimacy of a child by comparing the complexions of mother and child. Some of this illustrates the weaker side of Gentile's mind, but the question was of the kind leading to intellectual extravagance.

Other discussions of his concerning such subjects as incubi, incantations, and demons would elicit similar remarks. He deals with incubi, however, simply from the medical point of view, and much of what he says on cures brought about by incantations might be endorsed by faith healers of today; it is neither much worse nor better. He justifies the possibility of the existence of demons by the old (Arabic) concept of intermediate beings.[6]

His medical theories were dominated by the theory of humors. His prescriptions reveal the same dominant thought; they also include various irrational remedies and recommendations, which the modern reader should not censure too severely.

Gentile wrote many commentaries on the works of such writers as Galen, Mesuë, Ibn Sīnā, and Giles of Corbeil (XII-2). These commentaries illustrate more completely even than the consilia the speculative and scholastic side of his character. They are well organized; he states the opinions of his authorities, giving brief details, sums up his own conclusions in clear, concise sentences, and then proceeds to elaborate his ideas. His commentary on the first fen of the fourth book of Ibn Sīnā's Qānūn, dealing with fevers, was composed in 1346.

Among the writings of his which have not yet been printed, we may still mention: De hernia intestinali; De ruptura sifac, i.e., rupture of the peritoneum (the Arabic word ṣifāq was used for peritoneum and other enclosing membranes); Commentarium super tractatum Mesues de venenis qui est VI^{a} VIII^{ti}; Quaestio de equali ad pondus disputata subtiliter; Rationes contra Galienum principem medicorum in quinto Afforismi secunde particule; Sermo de silva; Quaestio de saporibus.

Gentile understood the value of hot baths and mineral-water baths in the treatment of diseases. In his De balneis he speaks of three such baths near Lucca as well as of others.

Gentile's sources. Gentile was very well read and may be assumed to have been acquainted with most of the Greek and Arabic medical writings available in

[6] E.g., al-Mas'ūdī (X-1). See Introd. 1, 638. That concept might be compared with the modern theory of evolution, but it was highly speculative and vague.

Latin. He often quoted his sources: Galen, al-Rāzī, 'Alī bin 'Abbās, Ibn Sīnā, Ibn Zuhr, Maimonides, Peter of Abano, etc. In some cases he quoted his authorities (even Galen) in order to contradict them. It is highly probable that he knew Arabic medicine only through Latin translations, yet in his commentary on fevers he speaks of having translated a medical work by Maimonides from the Arabic (Thorndike 3, 236). Is there any other evidence that he knew Arabic? Even if he had some acquaintance with that language, it would remain true that most of his knowledge of Arabic medicine had reached him through Latin channels.

The tradition of his writings. The popularity of his writings is proved by the number of fifteenth- and sixteenth-century editions. There are incunabula of many of his books, the two earliest being the Tractatus de balneis and the Tractatus de utilitatibus aquae balnei de Porretta,[7] both printed in Padua 1473, unless the earliest edition of the Consilium contra pestilentiam be earlier still? His treatise De complexione, proportione et dosi medicinarum, first printed c. 1479, was many times reprinted, even as late as 1623.

One of his treatises was translated into Hebrew, that is, the plague consilium ('eẓah); his name being spelled Genṭil. He was quoted in various Hebrew works, e.g., by Judah ben Isaac ha-Kohen.

Text. Consilium contra pestilentiam (known as the long consilium), Padua 1475?, Colle 1478, Venice? c. 1500. (Klebs no. 445.)

Tractatus de pestilentia et causis eius et remediis, annotated edition in Karl Sudhoff: Betrachtungen über Pestaetiologie und Pestprophylaxe, geschrieben während der Pestepidemie von 1348 (AGM 5, 83–87, 1911).

Consilia (brief articles on the Black Death) printed by Karl Sudhoff (AGM 5, 332–40, 396, 1912).

Consilia (on various subjects, a capite ad pedes), Pavia 1488?, Venice 1502. (Klebs no. 453.)

Consilia peregregia ad quaevis morborum corpori humani genera, first edition undated; Pavia 1492, Venice 1503.

Tractatus super lege VII° mense, printed in Hermann U. Kantorowicz: Cino da Pistoia (Archivio storico italiano 37, 122, 128, 1906).

Quaestiones de febribus, Venice 1494, 1502. According to Klebs no. 448, De febre, Padua 1477?, 1486.

Expositio et quaestiones super primo libro Microtechni Galeni, Venice 1557, 1576.

Libellus de divisione librorum Galieni, Venice 1483, 1487.

Quaestiones subtilissimae in Artem parvam Galeni, Venice 1576.

Commentum super tractatu De uriniis et pulsibus (Giles of Corbeil), Venice 1514.

Commentum super Tractatu pulsuum Magistri Egidii (Giles of Corbeil), Padua 1484, Lyon 1505, Basel 1529.

Commentum super Carmina de urinarum judiciis Magistri Egidii, Padua 1479, 1483, Venice 1494, Lyon 1515, 1516, Basel 1529.

Mundinus Anatomia, Gentilis de Fulgineo reprobatio Mundini, Leipzig c. 1493.

Supplementum in secundum Librum compendii secretorum Ioannis Mesues, Venice 1623.

De complexione, proportione et dosi medicinarum, Pavia 1486, Venice 1549, 1575, 1602, 1623.

De balneis, Padua? 1473, Venice c. 1497, 1502, 1533.

De utilitatibus aquae balnei de Porretta, Padua 1473.

[7] Bagni della Porretta, 36½ miles from Bologna.

De dislocationibus et fracturis, Venice 1499.

Introductorium practice de febribus, Bologna 1517, Venice 1521.

De curandis febribus introductio, Venice 1575.

De variola, in Christian Gottfried Gruner: De variolis et morbillis fragmenta (Jena 1790).

Quaestiones et tractatus extravagantes, Venice 1520, Lyon 1529.

Quaestiones et consilia, Venice 1501–3 (includes Quaestio de febre, Quaestio de actuatione medicinarum, Quaestio de ptysi, Quaestio de maioritate morbi, Quaestio de proportionibus medicinarum, Consilia on many things).

Quaestio de maioritate morbi (1344), Padua 1476, Vicenza? 1477, Pavia 1486.

Quaestiones de prolongatione febris, Padua 1477?, 1486.

Expositiones in primum librum Avicenne, Venice 1501–3.

Expositio in secundum librum Canonis Avicenne, Pavia 1488?, Venice 1501–3.

Expositio in tertium librum Canonis Avicenne, Padua 1477, Pavia c. 1480, Venice 1501–3, 1520–22.

Expositio in primam fen quarti Canonis Avicenne (1346), Padua 1476, Vicenza? 1477, Pavia 1486.

Expositio super tractatu De lepra Avicenne, Venice 1499, 1519.

Expositio super quinto Canonis Avicenne, Pavia 1488?, Venice 1501–3.

De tempore partus, edited by Kurt Leonhardt: Eine Abhandlung des Gentile de' Gentili da Foligno über die Schwangerschaftsdauer (De tempore partus) c. 1330 (Leipzig diss., p. 12–20, 1917).

The Recepta printed under Gentile's name were compiled by his younger contemporary Bernard Alberti (XIV-2).

See Klebs nos. 444–53.

Criticism. A. Philippe: Histoire de la Peste Noire (Paris 1853), giving large portions of the long Consilium in Latin with French translation. Puccinotti (2, part 1, CXLII, 1855). Steinschneider (p. 791, 1893). Hermann U. Kantorowicz: Cino da Pistoia ed il primo trattato di medicina legale (Archivio storico italiano 37, 115–28, Florence 1906), apropos of the medical letter sent by Gentile to Cino da Pistoia. Ritter von Töply: Wann hat Gentile sein Introductorium practice de febribus verfasst? (Mitteilungen zur Geschichte der Medizin 6, 95, 1907), brief query. G. G. Perrando: Giovanni Filippo Ingrassia[7a] e le origini della medicina legale in Sicilia (Archivio storico per la Sicilia orientale 5, fasc. 1, 218–19, Catania 1908), refutes Kantorowicz' statement that Gentile's letter was the first medical legal document. Placido Lugano: Gentilis Fulginas Speculator e le sue ultime volontà (Bollettino della R. Deputazione di storia patria per l'Umbria 14, 195–260, Perugia 1908), including a biography and list of editions. P. Pansier: Les médecins des papes d'Avignon (Janus 14, 405, 1909). Karl Sudhoff: Pestschriften aus den ersten 150 Jahren nach der Epidemie des "schwarzen Todes" 1348, nos. 30, 31–34 (AGM 5, 83–87, 332–40, 396, 1911). Romanus Johannes Schaefer: Gentile da Foligno über die Zulässigkeit des artifiziellen Aborten, c. 1340 (AGM 6, 321–28, 1913). Kurt Leonhardt: Eine Abhandlung des Gentile de' Gentili da Foligno über die Schwangerschaftsdauer (De tempore partus) und ihre historischen Zusammenhänge c. 1330 (Leipzig diss., 36 p., 1917). Hans Eichler: Die allgemeine Therapie in den "Consilien" des Gentile da Foligno mit besonderer Berücksichtigung der Diätetik (4 p., Leipzig 1921; English trans. in Medical life 30, 21–25, 1923; Isis 5, 218). Osler (1923). Klebs and Sudhoff (p. 31, 86, 118–25, 1926). Campbell (1931). Thorndike (3, 233–52, passim, 1934). Wickersheimer (p. 175, 1936). G. Tanfani: Neurassite vaiolosa in un consilium di Gentile (Atti e memorie dell' Accad. di storia dell' arte sanitaria, Sept. 1938), known to me only through analysis in Rivista di storia delle scienze (p. 116, 1939).

[7a] Giovanni Filippo Ingrassia of Palermo (1510–80), the "Sicilian Hippocrates" (BL 3, 374, 1931).

Note on early plague treatises. As Gentile's Consilia contra pestilentiam was one of the earliest and best-known treatises concerning the Black Death of 1348–50, it may be expedient to give here a list of others. When these are dealt with in this work, I simply add (XIV-1) or (XIV-2); for a few anonymous treatises not dealt with, I give brief information derived from the book of Anna Montgomery Campbell (1931). The 16 treatises are cited in the order established by Miss Campbell; they are discussed in my own book in a different order because I deal not only with these treatises, but with all the activities of their authors. See also the list given in chapter XXV of this volume.

1. Master Jacques d'Agramont, April 24, 1348 (XIV-1).
2. Gentile da Foligno (XIV-1).
3. John of Penna (XIV-1).
4. Compendium de epidimia. Treatise compiled in October 1348 by the Parisian faculty of medicine, by order of Philippe VI le Bien Fortuné (king 1328–50). This is the oldest document of that medical faculty in existence. It is in tone academic and philosophical, and carried much authority. Its influence can be detected in many treatises published not only in France, but also in other countries. It was rewritten in various forms and translated, or summarized or plagiarized, in many languages—Italian, French, German, maybe others (Campbell p. 14–17).
5. Master Albert. Consilium ad pestilentiam in 1348. Brief collection of prophylactic and therapeutic prescriptions. Origin and time unknown; perhaps contemporary Italian (Campbell p. 17).
6. Alfonso of Cordova (XIV-1).
7. Ibn Khātimah (XIV-1).
8. Tractatus de epidemia written by an unknown physician at Montpellier, May 19, 1349 (Campbell p. 21).
9. Quaeritur primo quae sint aegritudines nunc currentes. Short tract in form of catechism. Place and date unknown, probably early spring 1349 (Campbell p. 22).
10. John Hake (XIV-1).
11. Schatz der Wijsheit und der Kunst, Treasure of wisdom and of art of five Strassburg physicians. German text written probably in Strassburg between July and October 1349. See my note on Albert of Parma (XIV-1).
12. Utrum mortalitas que fuit hiis annis fit ab ultione divina propter iniquitates hominum vel a cursu quodam naturali. Short text (295 lines), probably composed in Germany c. 1350 (Campbell p. 25).
13. Ibn al-Khaṭīb (XIV-2).
14. Dionisio II Colle (XIV-2).
15. Primo de epydimia, secundo de praeservatione eius et corruptione aeris circumstantis videndum est. Treatise written c. 1349–50, place unknown (Campbell p. 30).
16. Simon de Couvin (XIV-1).

For two other early accounts in Arabic see my notes on Muḥammad ibn Muḥammad of Almeria (XIV-2) and on Muḥammad ibn 'Alī al-Shaqūrī (XIV-2).

ALBERTO DE' ZANCARI

Albertus de Zancariis, de Zanchariis, Albertus Bononiensis.

A physician and anatomist of Bologna. He must not be confused with another Albert of Zancari, son of Enoch, to whom some of the letters of Francesco Filelfo (1399–1481) were addressed.

He came from an aristocratic and medical family; was born about 1280, the son of Galvano de' Zancari, who was likewise a well known physician.

In 1310 he was given the title doctor physicae, and in 1326 he was granted his final medical degree. During the year 1314 he was one of the city doctors of Ravenna. He was still alive in 1348.

Albert was a conscientious and intelligent physician, but his works show that he was not highly original. He had mastered the best learning of his own time but did not add much to it. Boccaccio (Decameron 1, nov. 10) speaks of him (maestro Alberto da Bologna) as "un grandissimo medico e di chiara fama quasi a tutto il mondo."

Like Mondino de' Luzzi, Albert advocated the use of human bodies in demonstrating anatomical principles.

One of his most interesting works is a brief treatise on medical deontology entitled De cautelis medicorum. Although this work bears the same title as a treatise on the same subject which is ascribed to Arnold of Villanova (XIII-2), the contents are quite different. In his work Albert deals first with questions concerning the physician and his contacts with people in general; discussing, in particular, problems arising in connection with uroscopy and abortion. The second section deals with the conduct of the physician in relation to the sick. The conclusion contains a brief discussion on the subject of professional consultations. His principal authorities are Hippocrates, Galen, Serapion the Elder, and Mesuë the Younger.

His regimen on stone, Consilium super passione calculosa, is a very brief statement that the three main remedies are emetics, bloodletting, and purgation. He gives a number of prescriptions. The only authority mentioned is Mesuë the Younger (XI-1).

Albert also wrote a treatise on the plague, De febre pestilentiali super primam fen quarti canonis Avicennae; and one on leprosy in the form of a commentary on a part of Ibn Sīnā's Qānūn, Glossae super librum Avicennae de curatione leprae. Two other commentaries were written by him, Expositiones super librum de pharmacis Hippocratis; and In Galeni libros de accidente et morbo commentarius. Another unpublished work is a series of questions on the Ars medica of Galen, Quaestiones super Techni Galeni.

Frati (Rivista p. 334, 1914) has found a whole series of consilia by this author, dealing with such subjects as stone, pulse, fevers, and similar subjects.

Albert's so-called commentary on the Aphorisms of Hippocrates, Anforismi Ypocratis per ordinem collecti, is, according to his own statement in the introduction, merely a new and reorganized edition of Hippocrates' work. He was apparently the first to think of arranging the aphorisms in topical order, so that they might be more easily remembered. For each main topic, the aphorisms are divided into two groups: theory and practice. The topics are (1) diet and emetics, (2) prognosis and certain causes of diseases, etc., (3) influence of air, season, and time of life, etc., (4) purgation, etc. Albert's example made little if any impression, and the next attempt in the same direction was made only toward the end of the fifteenth century by one Rodolphus magister, also somewhat ineffectually. The idea was not well realized until the seventeenth century: Jean Vigier (Aphorismes d'Hippocrate rangés et disposés par lieux communs, Lyon 1605),[8] Nicolaus Fon-

[8] Date given by Ganscynieč (p. 160, 1921). That edition is otherwise unknown to me. Ganscynieč mentions two later editions, 1620, 1666, which I could identify.

tanus or Fonteyn (Amsterdam 1633), Joh. Ernst Scheffer (Leiden 1633). He may have been the author of a commentary on the first book of Ibn Sīnā's Qānūn; but he was not the author of a commentary entitled Albertus Zancaris Hippocratis librum, quem Articellam vocant, diligenter exposuit, ascribed to him by Giovanni Garzoni (1419–1506).

Text. De cautelis medicorum habendis, Manuel Morris: Die Schrift des Albertus de Zancariis aus Bologna De cautelis (Leipzig diss., 43 p., 1914).

Consilium ad calculum, edited by K. Sudhoff: Ein Konsilium für einen an Blasenstein Leidenden (AGM 8, 125–28, 1914).

Criticism. Giovanni Fantuzzi: Notizie degli scrittori bolognesi (8, 236, Bologna 1790). Michele Medici: Compendio storico della scuola anatomica di Bologna (p. 36–37, 425–30, Bologna 1857). Lodovico Frati: Per una novella del Boccaccio (Nuova antologia 167, fasc. 1002, 275–77, 1913), deals entirely with Albert; Alberto di Zancari (Rivista di storia critica delle scienze 2, 329–38, 1914; Isis 3, 327). R. Ganscynieč: Die Aphorismenausgabe des Albertus de Zanchariis (AGM 13, 159–65, 1921). Justus Niedling: Die mittelalterlichen und frühneuzeitlichen Kommentare zur Techne des Galenos (Leipzig diss., p. 15, Paderborn 1924; Isis 7, 181).

MAGNINO

Milanese physician who lived probably at the beginning of the fourteenth century and composed a Regimen sanitatis, which seems to be different from that of his more famous contemporary Arnold of Villanova. There are no less than 6 incunabula editions of it printed under his own name. Soon afterward, however, Tommaso Murchi of Genoa, physician to Louis XII (king 1498–1515), included it in his edition of Arnold of Villanova's collected works (Lyon 1504, Venice 1505) under the title Liber de regimine sanitatis Arnaldi de Villanova quem Magninus mediolanensis sibi appropriavit, addendo et immutando nonnulla (fol. 54v–79v). This accusation of plagiarism was repeated by later scholars, and some of them went so far as to deny Magnino's existence. Other scholars, led by Philip Argelati (1745), defend Magnino's reality and his authorship of this particular edition of the Regimen sanitatis, and of a few other works, notably a very short treatise on bloodletting, Liber de phlebotomia, and a very long Tractatus de aquis, de aere, de vinis, de pane et leguminibus.

Text. Regimen sanitatis. First edition, Louvain 1482. Reprinted Paris 1483, Louvain 1486, Basel 1493, Lyon 1500, Paris 1500 (Klebs nos. 640.1–6). Then reprinted in the Opera Arnaldi de Villanova (Lyon 1504, Venice 1505, Lyon 1509, 1520, 1532, Basel 1585, etc.).

A Dutch translation, Tregement der gesontheit. Nu yrst ghetranslateert wten latin in duytsche, was printed in Brussels 1514. Reprinted 1554.

De phlebotomia is included with works of Arnaldo in a Gothic edition, without date or place.

The Tractatus de aquis etc. is unpublished. MS no. 6972, Bibliothèque nationale, Paris.

Criticism. Philip Argelati: Bibliotheca scriptorum mediolanensium (2, 830, Milano 1745). Girolamo Tiraboschi: Storia della letteratura italiana (2d ed., 5, 278–80, Modena 1789). Barthélemy Hauréau (HL 28, 27, 54, 58, 104, 1881).

My knowledge of the Dutch translation is derived from the catalogue of an exhibition held in the Bibliothèque royale de Belgique. Auguste Vincent: Histoire des sciences en Belgique jusqu'à la fin du XVIIIe siècle (p. 16, Bruxelles 1938; Isis 29, 526).

ALBINO DA MONTECALIERO

Giacomo Albino, Jacobus Albinus de Montecalerio (or Moncalerio, in the province of Torino, Piedmont). Italian (Piemontese) physician (d. 1348).

Physician to the princes of Acaia from c. 1328 to his death in 1348. He wrote after 1340 (c. 1341–42) a regimen for prince Giacomo di Acaia (ruled 1334–60, 1363–67), entitled De sanitatis custodia. An introductory chapter explains the importance of medicine and the order of the book. Part 1 (in 11 chapters) deals with the regimen of pregnant women, infants, and children (to their fourteenth year). The second part is divided into three distinctions: D. 1 (3 chapters), air, exercise, sleep. D. 2 (11 plus 9 chapters), food and beverages; changes of diet according to the seasons. D. 3 (18 chapters), other counsels concerning sexual life, the requirements of diverse "complexions" (combinations of the qualities hot, cold, moist, dry), hygiene of the eyes, ears, nose, teeth; special advice for travel in cold or hot weather, at sea; for exercise, for persons with morbid tendencies, for pains in the joints. The third part (8 chapters) deals with hygiene of elderly people, with bathing and rubbing; poisons.

This text is not of great importance, but it is a good and elaborate specimen of a kind of medical literature popular in the fourteenth and fifteenth centuries, when each lord wished to have his own regimen.

Text. Giovanni Carbonelli (1859–1933): Il "de sanitatis custodia" di Maestro Giacomo Albini di Moncalieri, con altri documenti sulla storia della medicina negli stati sabaudi nei secoli XIV e XV (Biblioteca della Società storica subalpina vol. 35, 188 p., 8 pl., Pinerolo 1906). Careful edition: the text covers 85 pages and is accompanied by various other documents and a glossary of 18 pages.

Criticism. Giovanni Carbonelli: Magister Jacobus Albinus de Montecalario (Atti della Società di archeologia p. 368–76, Torino 1905). Karl Sudhoff: Eine Herstellungsanweisung für "Aurum potabile" und "Quinta essentia" von dem herzoglichen Leibarzte Albini di Moncalieri (Archiv für Geschichte der Naturwissenschaften 5, 198–201, 1914). Nothing in Carbonelli (1914 or 1925). Wickersheimer (p. 320, 1936).

GUIDO ARETINO

Guido of Arezzo (in Tuscany). Guidus Aretinus cyrurgicus salernitanus. Italian ophthalmologist (fl. Salerno c. 1326).

In 1326, he received a stipend from king Robert "propter laudabilem experientiam artis suae circa oculos maxime curandos aegrotos."

This Guido Aretino may be identical with the author of the "Liber mitis quem edidit Guidus Aretinus in his quae sunt maxime oportuna in medicina volentibus operari. Quae licet vocare 'Celesium' scilicet liber de regulis et ordine medicandi." The Liber mitis is a general medical treatise containing invectives against medical charlatans. Avicenna and Johannitius are frequently quoted. Johannitius, i.e., Ḥunain ibn Isḥāq (IX-2), he probably knew through the lectures (in Bologna) or the commentary by Taddeo Alderotti (XIII-2), who died in 1303. The MS of the Liber mitis in the Laurentiana of Florence is said to have been written in the thirteenth century; that, however, is not incompatible with the identity of the two Guidi. On the other hand, Guido is not an uncommon name, and there may have been many physicians called Guido and born in, or connected with, Arezzo.

Pansier (part 6, p. 109, 1908). Ugo Viviani: Il Liber mitis di Guido Aretino medico (Atti e memorie della R. Accad. Petrarca 1, 241–56, Arezzo 1920); Medici, fisici e cerusici della provincia aretina vissuti dal V al XVII secolo (p. 17–23, 59, Arezzo 1923).

JOHANNES DE CASSO

Nothing is known about his life beyond what he says in the Explicit to his letters. According to this, he wrote in 1346 a treatise on the care of the eyes for Thomas de Corsinis, a doctor of laws who lived in Florence.

This Tractatus de conservatione visus is largely a compilation of extracts from earlier sources, but retold in a briefer and clearer way. After a brief introduction he writes on the following subjects: (Ch. 1) De rebus nocentibus et ipsum diminuentibus oculum: including sunlight in summer; dusty and smoky air; vapors arising from the land and sea, especially from sulphurous and mineral waters; reading small writing; living in a place where there are strong cold winds; eating dry and melancholic foods; sleeping too soon after meals and for too long a time. (Ch. 2) De hiis que adjuvant et confortant visum: looking at things of a comforting color, such as green and hyacinth blue; bathing the eyes in tepid water in which green things have been placed, such as emeralds; bathing them in the distilled water of many different herbs. (Ch. 3) In quo ponuntur aliqua magis precipua que sunt magis ad conservandum et aliqualiter reparandum quod perditum est de visu: how to make good pills from vipers' flesh, and from various herbs, which will be good for people who have poor vision. (Ch. 4) In quo ponuntur medicine et electuaria ad visum conservandum et recuperandum: a number of prescriptions for the eyes. (Ch. 5) De regimine comestionis: what foods to eat and what ones to avoid, in order to protect and increase the vision.

He quotes Aristotle, Dioscorides, Galen, Mesuë the Elder, Serapion the Elder, al-Rāzī, Ḥunain ibn Isḥāq, Ibn Sīnā, Peter of Spain, and the Cyranides;[9] his references to Dioscorides and Ḥunain are indirect, via Mesuë. According to Pansier, this little treatise is superior to the much longer one by Arnold of Villanova (Introd. 2, 895, no. 43).

Text. Tractatus de conservatione sanitatis oculorum, edited by Pansier (fasc. 1, 31–35, 1903).

Criticism. Pansier (fasc. 6, 114, 1908).

BARNABAS OF REGGIO

Barnabas de Reatinis, de Riathinis. Italian physician (d. c. 1365).

Barnabas came originally from Reggio nell' Emilia, lived for a while in Mantua, then was called to Venice by the Collegio medico about 1334 and died there about 1365.

While in Mantua he wrote, in 1331, a brief treatise entitled De conservanda sanitate, based almost entirely on Arabic doctrines. It was dedicated to Simone da Correggio, exiled from Parma in 1329 by the Rossi, returned in 1331, and by 1341 a member of the signory in Parma.

In Venice in 1338, Barnabas wrote De naturis et qualitatibus alimentorum and dedicated it to Guido of Reggio, bishop of Concordia from 1334 to 1347. In this work Barnabas discussed the natures and qualities of many foods: it is arranged in alphabetical order.

In 1340 Barnabas wrote De conservanda sanitate oculorum. This was also written in Venice, and was dedicated to Beltrando di San Genesio, patriarch of

[9] For the Cyranides, see Introd. 2, 347.

Aquileia from 1334 to 1350. This treatise is a mere collection of aphorisms and general statements on the care of the eyes, based on the works of Galen, Isidore of Seville, Ḥunain ibn Isḥāq, Ibn Sīnā, and others. It is divided into two parts, the first one dealing with the nature, color, complexion, etc., of the eyes, the second part with the various ways in which the eyes suffer injuries, the methods of treating the eyes, and various medicaments.

Text. Libellus de conservanda sanitate oculorum, edited by Giuseppe Albertotti (Memorie della R. Accad. di scienze, lettere ed arti in Modena 11, 339–57, 1895).

Criticism. B. Cecchetti: La medicina in Venezia nel 1300 (Archivio veneto 26, 87, 263–70, 1883). Giuseppe Albertotti: Magister Barnabas de Reggio ed il suo Libellus de conservanda sanitate oculorum (Annali di ottalmologia 25, 103–12, Pavia 1896). Pansier (fasc. 6, 115, 1908). Lynn Thorndike: Another treatise by Barnabas (Isis 8, 285–86, 1926), apropos of the treatise on foods, briefly analyzed.

CASTELLO

Bonaventura de' Castelli. Italian balneologist (d. bef. 1353).

Bonaventura (or Tura) was the son of Giacomo de' Castelli and of Margarita di Benno Bufini. He was a doctor of medicine, and professor in Bologna c. 1335–49; sojourned in Avignon c. 1345; died before 1353.

He wrote a little treatise on the waters of Porretta, Receptae (De utilitatibus) aquae balnei de Porretta, which attained considerable success, witness 4 incunabula editions in Latin and 1 in Italian. It was even translated into Hebrew by an unknown person. The Bagni della Porretta are sulphurous springs, altitude 1155 feet, 36½ miles from Bologna on the road to Pistoia and Florence.

Text. First edition of the De utilitatibus or Receptae, Padua 1473. Also with the De balneis of Gentile da Foligno (Padua 1473) and with the Chirurgia of Guy de Chauliac and others (Venice 1498, 1499, 1546, Lyon 1499, 1559, 1572). It is included in the Collectio de balneis (Venice 1553).

Italian version, Recetta dell' aqua del bagno de Porretta (Padua 1473). Reprinted Bologna 1534, 1558.

French version by M. Bonnejoy (Annales de la Société d'hydrologie médicale de Paris 14, 238–55, 1867–68).

Criticism. Steinschneider (p. 834, 1893). Giuseppe Ravaglia: Una monografia sulle terme di Porretta del secolo XIV (Atti e memorie della R. Deputazione di storia patria per le provincie di Romagna 5, 177–98, 1915). Wickersheimer (p. 87, 1936). Klebs (nos. 994–95, 1938).

CORTENOVA

Uberto di Cortenova (or Cortenuova). Count and canon in Bergamo. Author of a veterinary treatise, De aegritudinibus equorum, of uncertain date but found in an early MS together with Rusio's treatise. We do not know the date of Cortenova's activities, but place him tentatively in the first half of the fourteenth century.

His treatise is divided into 89 chapters; many names of diseases occurring in it are very strange.

Text. The treatise is unpublished. There are at least two MSS, one in the San Marco library, Venice, the other in the library of the queen of Sweden in the Vatican.

Criticism. Pietro Delprato: La mascalcia di Lorenzo Rusio (2, 54, Bologna 1867). L. Moulé (part 3, 39, 1900). Leclainche (p. 140, 1936).

RUSIO

Lorenzo Rusio, Italian veterinary doctor (fl. bef. 1342).

His name appears under a multitude of forms, Latin and Italian, Ruzzius, Russo, Ruzo, de Ruccis, Ruse, Rugino, Rosso, Riso, Ruzio, Rusinus, Roscio, Russone, Risi, Risus, Ronzino, Russus, etc. He composed a treatise on the veterinary art, Liber marescalciae equorum, and dedicated it to the cardinal deacon Napoleone Orsini (cardinal from 1288; d. Avignon 1342).

Rusio's Marescalcia is important because there are abundant MSS of it in Latin and Italian, and many early editions in Latin, Italian, and French. In other words, it is important, irrespective of its intrinsic value, which seems but slight, because it was one of the main sources of veterinary knowledge until the end of the sixteenth century, and was used considerably by later writers on the subject. His own text, as preserved in the earlier MSS, is very different from later MSS and from the printed texts. It is clear that the early (i.e., fifteenth- and sixteenth-century) editors did not respect his words very much, but were anxious to transmit his veterinary knowledge, suppressing, adding, or altering passages as they saw fit. This is something different from the ordinary tradition of a scientific text, and comes closer to the technical unwritten traditions.

Rusio's treatise includes 181 chapters, of which 76 are taken almost verbatim from the treatise of Giordano Ruffo (XIII-2) without mention of the latter. The rest is largely derived from Theodoric Borgognoni, Albert the Great, Vincent of Beauvais, Pietro dei Crescenzi (whose Liber cultus ruris was completed between 1304 and 1309), and Maurus (whose own treatise is dated 1316). Hence it was composed after 1316 and before 1342, probably nearer to the second date than to the first. It is still a moot question whether Rusio used the Byzantine Geoponica directly or not.

The scientific level of the whole work is hardly superior to that of Ruffo's. In some respects it is inferior, for there is a larger amount of astrological superstition than in the earlier work.

Text. Moulé enumerates 17 Latin MSS and 4 Italian ones.

Liber marescalciae equorum. First edition, Speier 1489 (Klebs no. 869). Later Latin editions, Paris 1532, 1533.

Italian editions, Venice 1543, 1548, 1569. La mascalcia di Lorenzo Rusio, volgarizzamento del secolo XIV messo per la prima volta in luce da Pietro Delprato, aggiuntovi il testo latino per cura di Luigi Barbieri (2 vols., Bologna 1867). These two volumes are part of the Collezione di opere inedite o rare dei primi tre secoli della lingua pubblicata per cura della R. Commissione pe' testi di lingua nelle provincie dell' Emilia. Vol. 1 (450 p., 1867) contains the Latin and Italian texts on opposite pages; vol. 2 (340 p., 1867), a history of the Italian veterinary authors, and a glossary to Rusio (p. 273–324).

French edition, Paris 1533, 1541, ?, 1560, 1563, 1567, 1583, ?, 1610.

Criticism. Delprato (p. 50–59, 1867). L. Moulé (part 3, 35–39, 1900). Leclainche (p. 139–40, 1936).

MAURUS AND MARCUS

Mauro and Marco. Mysterious authors of a Latin treatise on the veterinary art composed c. 1316.

Maurus was a German, born in Cologne and marshal (i.e., farrier) to the Roman emperor; Marcus, born in Cyprus, was marshal to the Byzantine emperor. This very symmetry does not inspire confidence. It should be added that the two authors have sometimes been fused into one.

The treatise seems to be derived from the Geoponica. It was written in Latin by Maurus and Marcus and translated from Latin into Italian in 1510 by Sergio Stiso of Brescia.

It is divided into four parts and 97 chapters: (I) anatomy, hygiene, breeding (12 chapters); (II) diseases of horses (57 chapters); (III) diseases of cattle (9 chapters); (IV) medicaments (19 chapters). Maurus is quoted four times by Lorenzo Rusio.

Text. Il vero manescalco ammaestrato circà la sua arte, edited by Marcello Lorenzi (Naples 1729). A MS in the library of Siena dated 1345 is entitled Libro de menescalria composto da Marco Greco insieme con Mauro Tedesco.

Criticism. Pietro Delprato: Notizie storiche degli scrittori italiani di veterinaria (in vol. 2 of his edition of Rusio, p. 41–50, Bologna 1867), includes titles of the 97 chapters. L. Moulé (part 3, 34–35, 1900).

The Geoponica were somewhat neglected in my first volume. They were referred to (Introd. 1, 370, 424, 452; 2, 55, 348) but not analyzed and discussed as they should have been. See edition by Heinrich Beck: Geoponica sive Cassiani Bassi scholastici de re rustica eclogae (680 p., Teubner, Leipzig 1895); and article by Eugen Oder in PW (13, 1221–25, 1910).

PIPÌNO

Giacomo Pipìno of Brindisi. Magister Jacobus de Brindusio. South Italian physician (d. c. 1326).

Pipìno was not an important physician and he left no writings, but it is well to list him here in order to stop misunderstandings. For example, he has been, so to speak, split into two personalities, Giovanni Pipìno di Brindisi (1304–09) and Giacomo di Brindisi (1305–9).

Pipìno was physician to the Angevine court, at least from 1296 to 1326. He was physician to king Charles II and especially to the latter's son Philip, prince of Taranto, then later to king Robert. One of his functions as royal physician was to examine medical and surgical candidates and to confer on them, if they deserved it, the privilegium practicandi. He conducted such examinations in Naples four times for medicine and once for surgery. In April 1326 he was asked by the king to replace the grand chancellor and confer the doctor's degree on one Matteo di Giovanni Jannottaro. This is the last thing recorded of him. Hence he died in that year 1326 or afterward.

Criticism. Noè Scalinci: Il magister Jacobus de Brundusio, docente trecentesco di medicina nello studio di Napoli (Rinascenza salentina anno 4, 25 p., Lecce 1937; Isis 28, 174), including text of archival documents.

GIOVANNI DELLA PENNA

Iohannes de Pegna, de Pinna; Giovanni da Penne.

Giovanni was a member of the faculty of medicine at the University of Naples between 1344 and 1387. He died about 1387.

He wrote two Consilia on the Black Death of 1348, in which he refutes most of the theories of Gentile da Foligno concerning the cause of the pestilence and its prevention and cure. He well realized the nosological unity of that epidemic. His work shows that he was a man who exercised great independence of thought and possessed keen powers of observation.

Giovanni said that pestilence is spread by the breath of a diseased person, therefore he advised people to live in the mountains because of the purer air, and in solitary places, so as not to inhale the breath of any sick person. Gentile preferred the theory that the disease was caused by air polluted from causes other than a person's breath. Giovanni noted that robust persons died soonest in a pestilence, owing to the greater disturbance which had been occasioned in their strong natures, although he admitted that decrepit and old persons were very susceptible. He contradicted Gentile da Foligno's theory that a generation of worms occurs in a body stricken with the pestilence, with the statement that the "disease is caused by coleric matter located in the channels of combustion, like the matter of anthrax, mixed with blood in the veins," and that it affects particularly the chest and heart (Campbell p. 79).

His chief methods of treatment were bleeding on the side in which the pain is felt, and purgation. To strengthen the heart during the treatment, he advised the use of various electuaries, such as syrup of roses, juice of buglossa or borage, and sugar mixed with precious stones, bone of a stag's heart,[9a] and many others.

One of Giovanni's consilia on the plague was presented to the University of Perugia by Franciscus de Gianellis (XIV-2) or discussed by him.

Text. Consilium Magistri Johannis della Penna contra pestem, edited by K. Sudhoff: Pestschriften aus den ersten 150 Jahren nach der Epidemie des "schwarzen Todes" 1348 (AGM 5, 341–48, Leipzig 1911).

Tractatus de peste compositus a Magistro Johanne de Penna excellentiore aliis, edited by K. Sudhoff: Pestschriften aus den ersten 150 Jahren nach der Epidemie des "schwarzen Todes" 1348 (AGM 16, 162–67, 1925).

Criticism. Renzi: Storia (p. 550–51, 1857). Gennaro Maria Monti: L'età angioina (Storia della università di Napoli, by F. Torraco and others, p. 85, Naples 1924). Campbell (p. 13–14, 38, 60, 64, 79, 88–90, 1931). Wickersheimer (p. 461, 1936).

A2. Hispanic Peninsula

ALEXANDER OF SPAIN

Magister Alexander Hispanus. Unknown physician who wrote a general medical treatise for domestic use entitled Melleus liquor physicae artis (The sweet liquor of medicine). The best MS (Madrid, Biblioteca nacional, cod. 8769) was written on parchment in the fourteenth century. Hence Alexander flourished in that century if not before. We place him tentatively in the first half of the fourteenth century.

The Melleus liquor begins with a diet and regimen arranged month by month from January to December. Alexander indicates the foodstuffs to avoid and those to partake of for each month, and gives us other advice, e.g., with regard to bathing and sexual intercourse. This is followed by a treatise on complexions (De complexionibus hominum), including references to St. Bernard, Hippocrates, and Galen; another on roots and herbs (De radicibus et herbis); another on fevers (De febribus: cotidiana, terciana, quartana); and chapters on leprosy, urine, blood flux, paralysis, dropsy, consumption.

[9a] Edward Kremers: On the bone of the stag's heart (Isis 23, 256, 1935).

Two later MSS (fifteenth century) in Helmstadt and Wolfenbüttel contain an additional fragment ascribed to Alexander Hispanus, entitled Introductiones in medicinam ad utilitatem pauperum. That title may have been suggested by the work of another Hispanic doctor, the Thesaurus pauperum of Peter of Spain (XIII-2).

Text. Karl Sudhoff: Alexander Hispanus und das Schriftwerk unter seinem Namen. Ein erstes Wort über ihn und Bekanntgabe seiner medizinischen Schriften (AGM 29, 289–312, 1936; 30, 1–25, 1937). This includes also some criticism, and is thus far our only source on the subject. Some pages have been carelessly repeated, 290–91, 24–25.

FIGAROLA

Peter Figarola (or Fagarola, Figuerola), Spanish physician (fl. 1315).

Peter Figarola was a master of arts and of medicine flourishing in Valencia in 1315. In that year he composed a regimen sanitatis for his two sons, who were then students in Toulouse. It contains advice concerning foods or how to eat, sleep (six hours or little more is the natural amount), clothes, physical exercises, accidents of the soul (de accidentibus anime), colds and coughs (de tussi).

Text. The Latin text was edited by Lynn Thorndike: Advice from a physician to his sons (Speculum 6, 110–14, 1931; Isis 16, 487), who also published an English translation of it (Annals of medical history 3, 17–20, 1931; Isis 18, 455).

ALPHONSO OF CORDOVA

A Christian Spanish physician who wrote on the Black Death of 1348. He must not be confused with another Alphonso of Cordova, who was an astrologer in Seville, 1498 (Chevalier p. 164).

According to the explicit of his Epistola et regimen de pestilentia, it was written in Montpellier. The treatise is short and deals primarily with the causes, methods of prevention, and diagnosis of the plague, but contains only a few remarks on possible remedies.

The causes of the plague are: (1) Natural—that is, astrological. An eclipse of the moon in the sign of the lion, together with a conjunction of unlucky planets, will surely cause an epidemic. An earthquake may also cause one. (2) Unnatural—deliberate pollution of air, water, food, and drink by enemies of Christians. For example, he refers to the willful introduction of the plague into a town by the placing of infected objects in its neighborhood on the windward side. This gives us a glimpse of the superstitious fears caused by the plague, and of the gradual understanding of contagion.

He warns Christians not to eat food and drink which might have been poisoned and to take a good deal of medicine to counteract all possible kinds of poison to which they might have been exposed.

Pills against infected air (which can be infected artificially) are made of theriac and bone of a stag's heart.

Alphonso was one of the first to make a distinction between ordinary boils and abscesses and those which appear on plague-stricken patients.

In his short paragraph on remedies, he mentions the opening of boils, bloodletting, and purgation.

Text. K. Sudhoff: Epistola et regimen Alphontii Cordubensis de pestilentia (AGM 3, 223–26, 1909).

Criticism. K. Sudhoff: Pestschrift nr. 8 (AGM 4, 205, 1910; 17, 101, 1925). Campbell (p. 17, 43, 52, 59, 80, 86, 1931).

JACME D'AGRAMONT

Catalan physician who was professor in the faculty of Lérida[10] and wrote the earliest dated treatise on the great plague of 1348, on April 24, 1348 (an undated tract by Gentile da Foligno may be anterior). This treatise, containing brief recommendations for combating the plague, was written at the request of the city council of Lérida. Its earliness is accounted for by the fact that the plague swept the southwestern Mediterranean countries before penetrating into France, Germany, etc. It came from the eastern Mediterranean lands (Agramont says from Aethiopia), via Sicily (October 1347), Sardinia, the Balearic Islands, touched Marseille in November 1347, and by the turn of the year its presence was felt in Almeria, Carthagena, Barcelona; it reached Paris only in June 1348. Agramont explained that the pestilence is spread by polluted air and mists.

This little treatise (28 col. folio in the MS) is entitled Epistola de Maestre Jacme d. Agramont als honrats e discrets seynnors pahers e Conseyll de la ciutat de Leyda, 24 Abril 1348. Its interest is due to its earliness and to its being written in Catalan.

Text. Dr. Arnold C. Klebs (d. 1943) had planned to edit this treatise. From a letter of his dated Jan. 27, 1934, we gather that he had abandoned that project. According to A. Rovira i Virgili (6, 40, 1931), this text was published by Enric Arderiu of Lérida in 1910.

Criticism. Canibell (p. 13, 1918), description in Catalan of the MS kept in the parochial archives of Verdú in Lérida, and facsimile of a page. K. Sudhoff: Pestschriften aus den ersten 150 Jahren nach der Epidemie des schwarzen Todes 1348 (AGM 17, 120–21, 1925; see also ibid., p. 102, 252, 258). Arnold C. Klebs: A Catalan plague-tract of April 24, 1348, by Jacme D'Agramont (Rapport du 6ᵉ Congrès international d'histoire de la médecine, Amsterdam 1927, pp. 229–32, Antwerp 1929). Campbell (p. 9, 12, 32, 1931).

GIRALDES

"Mestre Giraldes." Portuguese writer on the veterinary art and on poultry (fl. 1318).

Giraldes was physician to king Dinis, the "rei lavrador," king of Portugal from 1279 to 1325 (see Introd. 2, 844). He wrote in Lisbon 1318 a veterinary treatise, Libro de alveitaria, divided into two parts and 77 chapters. Part I deals with everything concerning the horse from its birth to the time when it is bridled and saddled; part II, with the horse's ailments and their treatment. He wrote also a treatise on domestic birds, Arte de volateria.

Text. Both texts are unpublished. A MS of the first is available in the National Library of Lisbon (no. 2294).

Criticism. Diogo Barbosa Machado: Bibliotheca lusitana (2, 385, Lisboa 1747). Leclainche (p. 140, 1936). Joaquim Fiadeiro: Subsidios para o estudo da bibliografia veterinária portuguesa (Revista de medicina veterinária vol. 32, no. 282). The last item not available to me. Information kindly given by professor Alberto Pessoa, of Coimbra (letter of Mar. 3, 1939).

[10] The University of Lérida had been founded in 1300 (Introd. 2, 862).

A3. France

BERENGER

Berenger of Thumba. Berengarius. The place Thumba is unknown to me; could it be Tumba not far from Stockholm?[11] This mysterious Berenger was a physician who flourished in Montpellier in 1332.

He wrote Questiones super aphorismos Hippocratis, disputate et compilate in Montepessulano 1332, and a Regimen contra dolorem capitis in sexagenario.

Wickersheimer has suggested his possible identity with one "Berengarius enutritus in Montepessulano" who translated the De cibariis infirmorum of Azaramus, i.e., Abū-l-Qāsim al-Zahrāwī (X-2). That identity is improbable. According to a fourteenth-century MS (Torino H iv 29), that text was translated from Arabic into Catalan (in vulgare Cathalenorum) and from Catalan into Latin by Berengarius. Then this Berengarius came from Catalonia or from another land of "oc." This is confirmed by another MS (Vienna 5434), in which the author of that translation is called Berengarius Eymericus de Valentia.

The name Berenger was not uncommon in mediaeval times. I do not know any place in Catalonia called Thumba or Tumba.

No text is yet published. Giacosa (p. 426, 1901). Wickersheimer (p. 69, 1936). Lynn Thorndike: Catalogue of incipits (p. 352, 1937); Little known medical works in Basel MSS (Annals of medical history 2, 281, 1940).

There is no mention of a Berengarius or Eymericus in Canibell (1918).

NOTE ON THE COLLEGE OF SAINT COSMAS

A guild of surgeons was established in Paris sometime in the thirteenth century, and, being placed under the protection of St. Cosmas (French, Cosme, Côme), it was called Confrérie et Collège de Saint Côme. The name was natural enough, for Cosmas and Damian were from an early time patrons of physicians and especially of surgeons. They were Arabian twins who exercised the medical art in Ayās (on the Gulf of Alexandrette), for love not for money (therefore, they were called ἀνάργυροι). Under Diocletian they suffered martyrdom for their Christian faith, both being beheaded on September 27, c. 287. Their bodies were carried to Rome and deposited during the pontificate of Felix IV (pope 526–30) in an ancient temple which Felix converted into a church, dedicated to them (SS. Cosmas and Damian martyrs, in a side street near the Forum end of via Cavour) and adorned with splendid mosaics. Cosmas and Damian have been sanctified also by the Orthodox church,[12] and hence their patronage of the medical art extends to the

[11] This hypothesis is rejected by my colleague Johan Nordström, of Upsala, in his kind letter of Dec. 20, 1938. The place Tumba near Stockholm is never mentioned in mediaeval documents. Moreover, the name Berengarius was hardly ever used in mediaeval Sweden. Professor Nordström came across only one mediaeval Berengarius, that is, Andreas Berengarius, an Upsala preacher of the beginning of the fourteenth century, about whom nothing else is known.

[12] The Orthodox church has sanctified three different pairs named Cosmas and Damian, originating respectively in Asia, Rome, and Arabia. The corresponding holidays occur on November 1, July 1, October 17; the Catholic holiday is on September 27. We cannot enter into these hagiographic difficulties; see Deubner's book of 1907 cited in the next footnote. Pious physicians wishing to be on the safe side should celebrate four holidays.

whole of Christendom. The legends which developed about them were particularly exuberant.[13]

The Collège de Saint Côme, to return to it, was not a "college" in the educational sense, but a guild established in order to keep up the standards and defend the rights of a definite group of people, the surgeons. Its beginnings are obscure; it may be true or not that St. Louis sponsored it. It is certain that a guild of surgeons existed in the thirteenth century, for its statutes were homologated by the provost of Paris and published by him, Etienne Boileau (XIII-2), in the Livre des métiers together with the statutes of other arts and crafts; yet these statutes do not mention the college of St. Cosmas or St. Cosmas himself.[14] Thus we may be sure that the Collège de Saint Côme did not yet exist under that name c. 1268. It may have been established by Philippe le Bel in 1311. In that year at any rate a college of surgery (a surgical guild) was founded, with definite conditions of admission and the requirement of a preliminary examination, by a special commission then presided over by Jean Pitart. Philippe's edict of 1311 was confirmed by Jean II in 1352, etc. At the beginning the guild met in the church of St. Jacques de la Boucherie, then in the church of St. Côme (near the rue de l'Ecole de médecine). I do not know when the name Collège de Saint Côme was adopted. See article by L. Hahn (Grande encyclopédie 11, 954).

The Collège de Saint Côme tended to create a surgical aristocracy, "chirurgiens de longue robe," who stood halfway between the learned physicians on the one side and the barbers on the other. Hence, the history of their corporation is the history of a protracted fight on two fronts; they tried to obtain more respect and more privileges from the doctors, but also to prevent transgressions from the barbers. In 1372 the latter were definitely permitted to practice minor surgery, which they had always done. The Confrérie et Collège de Saint Côme existed until the French Revolution.

The name Côme brings to mind that college, but also the famous lithotomist "frère Côme" (Jean Baseilhac, 1703–81).[15]

References to an order of chivalry of SS. Cosmas and Damian, supposed to have been founded in Jerusalem c. 1030 for the protection of pilgrims, are erroneous and probably due to a confusion with the Knights of St. John of Jerusalem or Hospitalers (XII-1). Pierre Hélyot, alias Père Hippolyte (1660–1716), proved in his Histoire des ordres monastiques, religieux et militaires (21 vols., Paris 1714) that the Order of SS. Cosmas and Damian never existed.

To illustrate the internationality of Cosmas and Damian, see Karl Sudhoff: Deutsche Verse auf Kosmas und Damianos aus dem 14. Jahrh. als Einführung eines Kräuterrezeptbuches (AGM 1, 385–87, 1908).

The story of SS. Cosmas and Damian is a good example of an inextricable mixture of many legends, Christian and even pagan. It includes elements borrowed from the Homeric story of the Dioscuri (*Διόσκοροι*), Castor and Pollux (*Κάστωρ*, *Πολυδεύκης*). The Egyptian-Greek rite of incubation (Isis 13, 373–75) was prac-

[13] Michele Melga: Leggenda dei Santi Cosma e Damiano scritta nel buon secolo della lingua e non mai fin qui stampata (54 p., Napoli 1857). Ludwig Deubner: Kosmas und Damian. Texte und Einleitung (240 p., Leipzig 1907), critical edition of the Greek texts with an introduction of 83 p. and a glossary. Augusto da Silva Carvalho: O culto de S. Cosme e S. Damião em Portugal e no Brasil. História das sociedades médicas portuguesas (Biblioteca luso-brasileira de história da medicina vol. 2, 344 p., 12 ill., Universidade, Coimbra 1928).

[14] See edition by René de Lespinasse and François Bonnardot (p. xciii, 208–9, Paris 1879).

[15] BL (1, 368).

ticed in their church in Constantinople. Hippolyte Delehaye: Les légendes hagiographiques (p. 143–44, 164, 180, Bruxelles 1927).

JEAN PITART

Jehan Pitard, Iehan Pitart, Picardi, Piccardi, Piquardi, Pitardi.

The earliest famous surgeon in France. Born sometime between 1230 and 1236, died after 1328. He may have been born in Paris, but it is more probable that he came from Normandy. His birthplace was probably in the neighborhood of Carentan (now dépt. Manche), although he has been claimed by Domfront, Bayeux, and Aunay-sur-Odon. He was one of the leading physicians at the courts of Philip the Fair (1285–1314), Philip V (1316–22), and Charles count of Artois.

In 1311 Philip IV issued a decree governing the practice of surgery in Paris and its environs, and Pitart, the royal surgeon, was appointed to convoke and preside over the examining committee.

It is not proved that he was a founder of the College of St. Cosmas, for which see note above; nevertheless his great influence was frequently acknowledged by its members. (At the beginning of the seventeenth century they caused a portrait of him to be painted, and a medallion was struck in 1775.)

Pitart was not a prolific writer, but through his personal influence as a protégé of kings, and his ability as a teacher, he was able to improve the condition of surgery in France. He was one of the first to welcome Lanfranchi (XIII-2) to Paris, and was one of the teachers and friends of Henry of Mondeville. Pitart is frequently cited by the latter, who calls him "Magister peritissimus et expertissimus in arte cyrurgiae."

The Experimenta ascribed to him by Sudhoff has been shown by Thomas to be a later compilation, possibly by one of Pitart's students. The only work of his which survives, according to Thomas, is a very poor attempt at poetry called Le dit de bigamie. It is a defense of a second marriage contracted by one who is a widow or widower, and makes a general defense of marriage, in opposition to some of the objections of the religious orders.

Sudhoff has printed two prescriptions, one a salve for wounds, the other a plaster.

Text. Le dit de bigamie, printed by Adolfo Mussafia: Über eine altfranzösische Handschrift der K. Universitätsbibliothek zu Pavia (Sitzungsberichte der phil.-hist. Cl., Akad. der Wissenschaften, 64, 586–90, Vienna 1870). Parts of this poem are printed by A. Thomas (Janus 22, 291–92; HL 35, 321–22).

Two recipes, Cest listoire de maistre iehan pitart contre toutes bleceures es bras, es iambes, et en autres lieux, et en ot la recepte du roy de France; and Lemplastre qui sensuit est appele lemplastre misire Jehen Pitart, have been printed by K. Sudhoff (AGM 2, 191–93, 1908).

Criticism. Karl Sudhoff: Ein chirurgisches Manual des Jean Pitard, Wundarztes König Phillipps des Schönen von Frankreich (AGM 2, 189–278, 1908), this includes the apocryphal Experimenta magistri Jo. Pickaert qui habuit receptas a rege Francie et valent contra omnes plagas, in Latin and French. Antoine Thomas: Jean Pitart, chirurgien et poète (Comptes rendus de l'Académie des inscriptions p. 95–111, Paris 1916; the same article is in Janus 22, 279–93, 1917, and in HL 25, 310–24, 1921; Isis 4, 405). Wickersheimer (p. 465, 1936).

HENRY OF MONDEVILLE

French surgeon. Henricus de Armondavilla, Amandavilla, Armendaville, Hermondavilla, Mondavilla, Mundeville, Mandeville, and other variations. Born in the second half of the thirteenth century in Normandy, either in Mondeville, near Caen, or in Emondeville (Manche). Was still living in September 1325, but probably did not live much longer (Pagel, p. 401, 1909).

He studied medicine and surgery in Montpellier, and with Lanfranchi (XIII-2) and Jean Pitart in Paris. He also studied surgery in Italy under the direction of Theodoric Borgognoni (XIII-1), who died in Bologna in 1298, being then 93 years old. Henry was one of the main links between Italian and French surgery; thanks to him, and a little later to Chauliac, surgical leadership passed from Italy to France.

From 1301 on he was personal surgeon to, and military surgeon in the armies of, Philip the Fair (1285–1314) and the latter's son Louis X (1314–16); he sometimes accompanied the armies of Charles count of Valois. During these campaigns he employed, for the first time in France, Theodoric's methods of treating wounds, and found them to be most successful.

In 1304, he was lecturing on anatomy and medicine in Montpellier, where he was acquainted with William of Brescia (XIII-2) and Bernard of Gordon. In 1306 he was back in Paris, where he taught for some time. After his course on surgery in 1312 he traveled by the king's order or on other business to Arras, to England, and to various parts of France. An interesting account of his education, teaching, and practice is included in the introduction to his Chirurgia.

He was in poor health, at least from about 1316, being "asmaticus, tussiculosus, ptisicus, et consumptus." This explains the fact that his work remained incomplete.

He was very well educated and had a good literary and philosophical background ("nutritus Parisiis inter philosophos," said Chauliac). He became very much interested in and enthusiastic about surgery, and wished to revive and elevate that subject, which had fallen into great disrepute. His scholastic training was tempered with fantasy and vivacity. He was honest and independent; in spite of his great reputation, he remained poor; he was sometimes a little cynical. He never married, and his frequent criticisms of women and their ways suggest that he was somewhat of a woman-hater.

There is no evidence that he made systematic dissections, but the hazards of war gave him many opportunities for obtaining firsthand anatomical knowledge. In his anatomical teaching he used drawings or charts (at least 13) and a model of a skull.

He was the first French surgeon who wrote a treatise on surgery, and—together with his master Jean Pitart—he was the first to introduce into France Theodoric's new methods of wound treatment. He wrote in Latin, but part of his treatise was translated into French during his own lifetime (in 1314) by an unknown translator, and that anonymous translation is one of the earliest texts of French scientific literature.

He wrote a single textbook on surgery, which we shall now proceed to analyze; then we shall discuss its main characteristics.

Mondeville's Cyrurgia was planned to include five treatises, divided into "doctrines," and the "doctrines" into chapters. He began his work in 1306 and by 1308 had completed the first treatise and the first doctrine of the second treatise; in 1312 he completed the second treatise (introductory generalities and second doctrine); he stopped working c. 1320, but he left the third treatise very incomplete, and he did not write the fourth treatise nor the tenth and last chapter of the fifth.

In the Introduction he states his purpose: to explain briefly all he has learned

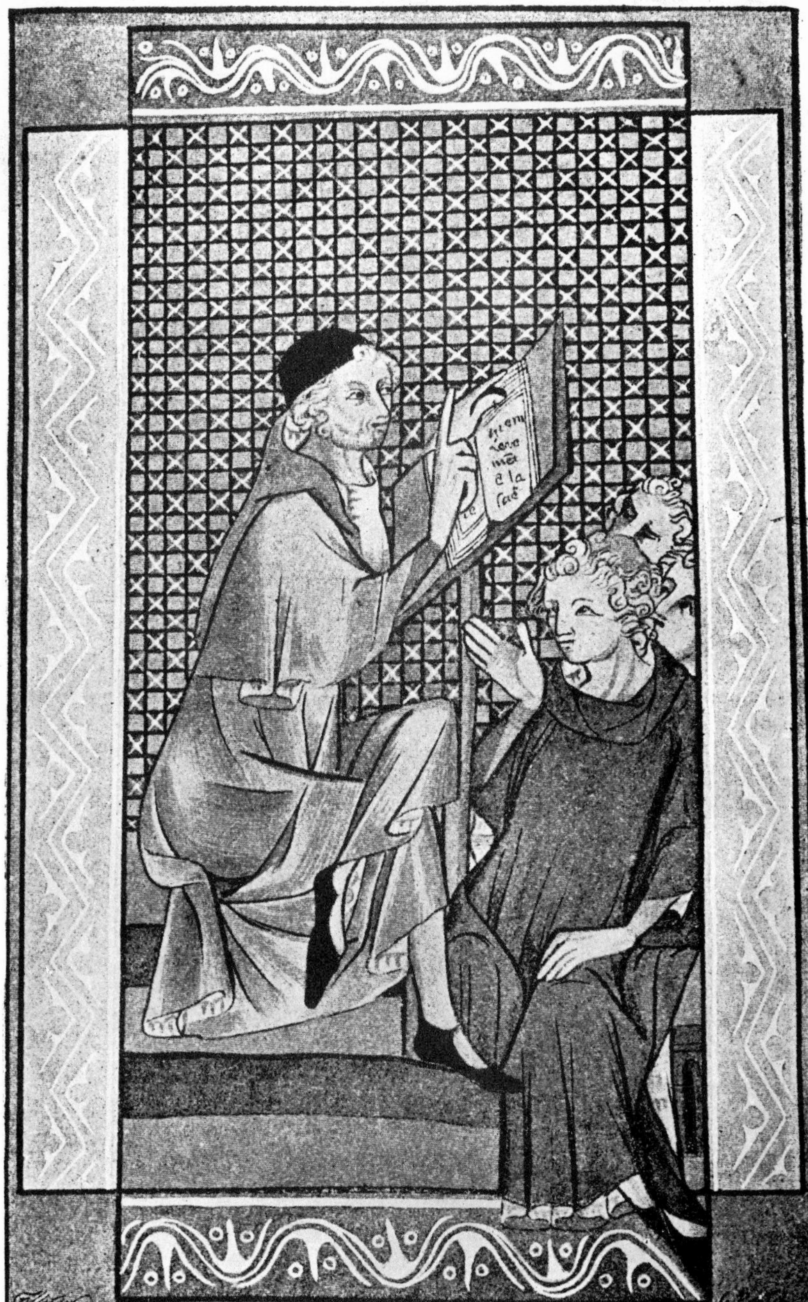

Fig. 21. Portrait of Henri de Mondeville. From a MS (Bibliothèque nationale, Paris, French n° 2030) of his Chirurgie, treatises I and II only, first redaction. That MS was written in 1314, within the author's lifetime. It represents the master facing his students and teaching. Nicaise considers it a very plausible portrait; the same author rejected the Chauliac portraits as implausible.

on surgery either from "doctrine" (authorities) or from personal experience; he discusses the relation of surgeon to patient, and explains the "doctrine of algorism," i.e., the new arithmetic.

Treatise I. Anatomy. One doctrine divided into 12 chapters. This is perhaps the least original part of the whole work, being a summary derived from the first book of Ibn Sīnā's Qānūn. He gives precise definitions of the terms used by him (definitions which are missing in Chauliac) and explains the uses and functions of organs. His definition of nerves includes ligaments and tendons. The system of the portal vein is well indicated. There is a different version of this treatise in the form of the lectures given in Montpellier in 1304.

T. II. General and particular treatment of wounds, ulcers, and contusions. Preceded by generalities concerning the whole of surgical knowledge and practice. This second part is at once the largest (almost the half) of the whole work and the most original.

The generalities include 16 "Notabilia introductoria ad totam cyrurgiam," dealing with medical and surgical deontology, relation between surgeons, or between surgeons and clients, quackery and superstitions, proper fees, superiority of surgery, etc., and 52 "Contingentia," discussing the particular conditions which may influence diseases and cause modifications in their treatment, such as elements, complexion or temperament, humors, age, sex, diet and other habits, weather and seasons, profession. The treatise itself is divided into 2 doctrines, dealing respectively with wounds and contusions in 12 chapters, and with ulcers, bites, fistules, ulcerated cancer in 4 chapters. The second doctrine includes a discussion of rabies.

T. III. Special surgical pathology and therapeutics, divided into 3 doctrines. The first, Doctrina decorationis, in 24 chapters, deals with cosmetics, depilatories, and other tricks of the kind used in "beauty shops"; treatment of various skin diseases and burns; smallpox, measles; scurf, dartre; bloodletting, cauterization, use of leeches and cupping glasses; amputations of members and sections of bones; conservation and preservation of dead bodies, etc. The second doctrine, in 23 chapters, deals with abscesses. After an introduction explaining the theory of humors, the abscesses affecting special parts of the body are considered in the usual order (a capite ad calcem). Apostemes are also classified physiologically according to the humors concerned.[16] The third doctrine was meant to be divided into 43 chapters, on special surgery. Mondeville wrote only a special preface to it and the titles and divisions (more fully developed than the other titles).

T. IV. Fractures and luxations. Remained unwritten. Mondeville, whose strength was waning, proceeded to write the fifth treatise, which was probably already available for his own use.

T. V. Antidotary. To be divided into 10 chapters, of which the last remained unwritten: (1) generalities; (2–8) drugs in pharmacodynamic order: repercussive, resolutive, maturative, mondificative (cleansing), incarnative, caustic, emollient; (9) synonymy and etymology; (10) antidotes considered from other points of view, and various experiments.

The vast scope of this work is clear: it was a medical encyclopaedia for the surgeon's use, the very existence of which was bound to increase the latter's prestige and self-esteem.

[16] See in Nicaise's edition (p. xlvi) tables of the humors and of the apostemes after Mondeville.

The style is brief and generally clear, with occasional dashes revealing the author's vivacity and originality.

Sources. Though the Cyrurgia is much more than a compilation, it refers 1,308 times to 58 authors. I shall name only the authors referred to more than ten times. I give them in chronological order, the figures between parentheses indicating the number of references in the Cyrurgia.

Hippocrates (68), Aristotle (47), Galen (431), Mesuë Major (24), Serapion Senior, al-Rāzī (45), Abū-l-Qāsim (18), 'Alī ibn 'Abbās (12), Mesuë Junior (13), 'Alī ibn Riḍwān (38), Ibn Sīnā (307), Constantine the African (13), Serapion Junior, Ibn Rushd (17), Theodoric Borgognoni (113), Lanfranchi (17). Note the dominance of Galen and Ibn Sīnā (quoted more often than the other 56 authors combined), then, after a long interval, Theodoric Borgognoni.

Mondeville's respect for his authorities was great but conditional. His independent attitude is well expressed in the first chapter of his antidotary. Galen's genius, he remarks, was neither perfect nor final. "Modern authors are to the ancient like a dwarf placed upon the shoulders of a giant: he sees all that the giant sees, and farther still.[17] Thus can we know things which were unknown in Galen's time and it is our duty to consign them to writing." This belief in scientific progress, that it was possible and desirable, was very rare before modern times.

Tradition of Mondeville's Cyrurgia. There are only about nineteen MSS, complete or partial, a relatively small number for a textbook of such usefulness.

The original Latin text was translated into French as early as 1314; the translation being thus necessarily incomplete, as the third and fifth treatises were not yet written at that time. The translator is unknown. It was not Mondeville himself, for the translator was apparently ignorant of anatomy.[18] He was a Norman; perhaps a young student or protégé of Mondeville. The translation is literal and servile, yet very important from the linguistic point of view. It illustrates the transition from the Old French, still half synthetic, to Middle French. It is one of the first French scientific texts and contains many technical terms which are still in use today.

Other early translations: A Provençal translation written in the fourteenth century in the region of Montpellier, Notomia de la surgia de Anric de Mondavilla, that is, the anatomical lessons given by Mondeville in Montpellier 1304 (MS Ashburnham 104, Laurentiana, Florence). Dutch translation of the whole surgery and antidotary in a fourteenth-century MS (British Museum, Galba t. XIII). English translation of the late fifteenth century (Cambridge, Peterhouse 118).

The Cyrurgia was often quoted by Guy de Chauliac (some 86 times), but after Chauliac (d. c. 1368) it was practically forgotten until the Florentine anatomist Antonio Cocchi (1695–1758) rediscovered it in 1746. It was never printed as a living book, but only as a historical document, and that not before 1892.

Its lack of popularity was due partly to the fact that it was incomplete, partly to the existence of the almost contemporary and popular work of Lanfranchi (XIII-2), and finally to its being soon superseded by Chauliac's treatise. Its influence was felt indirectly through that treatise.

[17] Nicaise p. 745. That is the very comparison often ascribed to Newton. It was first made in the Metalogicon, by John of Salisbury (XII-2), who ascribed it to his teacher, Bernard of Chartres (XII-1). See Introd. (1, 248; 2, 195, 466), and Sarton: The history of science and the new humanism (p. 30, New York 1931); Isis (24, 107–9; 25, 451; 26, 147–49).

[18] E.g., he confused the iliac bones with the ileum (last division of the small intestine), translating ilia (when it meant side) by boiaus (§479, 482).

Various characteristics of Mondeville's Cyrurgia. Mondeville's main contribution was his defense of the new method of treating wounds. The ancient method, generally accepted in his time, was based on the belief that the festering of wounds was beneficial. The wound was probed and widened, and suppurative drugs were added. The new method was introduced by Hugh and Theodoric Borgognoni, especially by the latter; it was based on the belief that festering was unnecessary and perhaps harmful; wounds were dressed with warm wine. Jean Pitart taught the new method in Paris, and Mondeville emphasized its importance, insisting that festering should be avoided by all means; the wound should be cleaned without probing, treated without irritant dressings, only with wine, and closed and fomented in order that it might heal promptly by first intention if possible. He realized that the air had a suppurative effect and took pains to keep it out. This treatment, if carefully applied, was semiantiseptic. Mondeville said: When your dressings have been carefully applied, do not interfere with them for some days; keep the air out, for a wound left in contact with air suppurates. Should pain and heat arise, however, open and wash out again, but do not pull your dressings about, nature works better left alone. Take care that your needles are clean, or they will infect the wound.

He introduced the new method in his military and civil practice. Read his own vigorous account of the old and new methods at the beginning of the first doctrine of the second treatise (Nicaise p. 206–26). He witnessed the cure of wounds in the large intestine by means of the new method (T. II, doct. 1, ch. 8; Nicaise p. 363).

Unfortunately the Borgognoni-Mondeville method was rejected by Chauliac, and thus its tradition was stopped.

Mondeville improved the needles and thread holders, invented an instrument to extract arrows, and removed pieces of iron from the flesh by means of a magnet.

He insisted on the necessity of binding the arteries in the case of amputation, but that was not an invention of his (and even less so, of course, of Ambroise Paré, to whom it is sometimes ascribed); that obvious practice can be traced, via the Italian surgeons Oribasios and Archigenes of Apamea, at least as far back as Celsus (I-1).

He was aware of the excessive salivation caused by mercurial ointment, but that had been observed before him by his master Theodoric.

He shared the Hippocratic belief in the vis medicatrix naturae, expressing it wittily as follows: Nature is the fiddler (viollator), and physicians must dance to her tunes (Nicaise p. 192). That is, the physician must learn to play nature's own game, help her, and thus be helped by her, not fight her.

He warned against the complete extirpation of emunctory glands (T. III, doct. 2, ch. 4; Nicaise p. 688), a warning which some of the radical surgeons of today might take to heart.

According to a specialist,[19] "his description of the facies of leprosy, as given by Bloch, is as sharp a description of cutaneous symptoms as can be found, and has not been improved upon: the prominence of the supra-orbital ridges, the loss of hair of the eyebrows, the staring eyes, the thickening of the nose, the nodules in the ali nasi and in the ears, and round white patches in the skin, muscular atrophy between the thumb and first finger, loss of sensation in the extremities." Mondeville complained against the loose terminology of skin ailments (e.g., serpigo, impetigo, pannus), which was confusing and detrimental.

[19] Pusey (p. 39, 1933).

His defense of surgery cannot be praised too much, but his own deontology was not always on the highest level. His methods for insuring payment of fees, and his advice concerning the simulation of virginity (Nicaise p. 588), are not to be recommended, but they illustrate the moral laxity of the age as well as his own, and they also illustrate the relatively low status of the surgeon. The latter, doing manual work, was generally considered an artisan rather than a clerk—an artisan who knew dark secrets and was despised as well as feared. The Cyrurgia is a valuable source for the study of the social aspects of medicine, and of the social conditions of that time in general.

His attitude with regard to various superstitions is typical of his relative independence. He criticizes the superstitious beliefs in St. Eloi's ailment (fistule refusing to heal) and St. Eloi's cure (Nicaise p. 465), yet he cites with approval the cure of rabies practiced in Normandy: plunging about nine times into the sea (Nicaise p. 448); and he refers to the cure of scrofula by royal touching[20] (Nicaise p. 202). One could hardly expect more consistency in his time and circumstances.

The attention of historians of mathematics is drawn to the "doctrine of algorism" which he thought necessary to insert in his Cyrurgia (Nicaise p. 8–10). It is simply an explanation of the new method of writing numbers, not of the operations.

Text. The editio princeps was prepared by Julius Leopold Pagel: Die Anatomie nach einer Handschrift der K. Bibliothek zu Berlin, 1304 (80 p., Berlin 1889); Die Chirurgie des Heinrich von Mondeville nach Berliner, Erfurter und Pariser Codices zum ersten Male herausgegeben. Nebst einer Abhandlung über Synonyma und einem Glossar von M. Steinschneider (xiii + 663 p., Berlin 1892; first published in von Langenbeck's Archiv für klinische Chirurgie, vols. 40, 41, 42, 44, 1890–92). Edouard Nicaise: Chirurgie de Maître Henri de Mondeville, chirurgien de Philippe le Bel, traduction française avec des notes, une introduction et une biographie (lxxxii + 903 p., Paris 1893). This is a modern translation with valuable notes, a study of surgical instruments used in the Middle Ages, and an additional glossary of drugs and their synonyms by Dr. Saint-Lager. Nicaise' edition also includes many variations of the Latin text edited by Pagel.

Alphonse Bos: La Chirurgie de Maître Henri de Mondeville, traduction contemporaine de l'auteur (Société des anciens textes français vol. 41, 2 vols, Paris 1897–98). This is the Old French translation of 1314.

A number of Pagel's students have translated small parts of the Chirurgie into German. A partial list of these translations is as follows: Henri Kleinhans: Die allgemeinen Principien der Wundbehandlung (Berlin 1895). Ernst Rudolph: Das Krebsgeschwür (Berlin 1896). Carl Weber: Spezielle Wundbehandlung (Berlin 1896). W. Diestel-Lämmer: Schusswundenbehandlung (Berlin 1896). Max Rogge: Die Lehre von den vergifteten Wunden (Berlin 1896). Nathan Rawitzki: Über accidentelle Wundkrankheiten (Berlin 1897). Walther Zimmermann: Die Lehre von der Kauterisation (Berlin 1897). Georg Margoniner: Die Behandlung der Quetschungen nach Mondeville (Berlin 1897). Deke Penning Albers: Aus der Anatomie des Heinrich von Mondeville (Berlin 1898). Fritz Hering: Kosmetik nach Heinrich de Mondeville (Berlin 1898). Gustav Leudecke: Wundverband und Wundnaht (Berlin 1898). Ernst Wachsmuth: Aus Mondevilles chirurgischer Deontologie (Berlin 1898). Wilhelm Herda: Die Anatomie des Heinrich von Mondeville (Berlin 1899).

Criticism. Achille Chéreau: Henri de Mondeville (reprint from Mémoires de

[20] With reference to which see Marc Bloch: Les rois thaumaturges. Essai sur le caractère surnaturel attribué à la puissance royale (Strasbourg 1924; Isis 7, 520–21).

la Société des antiquaires de Normandie, 100 p., Paris 1862). Emile Littré: Henri de Mondeville, un des chirurgiens du roi Philippe-le-Bel (HL 28, 325–52, Paris 1881). Gurlt (2, 34–77, 1898). Karl Sudhoff: Ein Beitrag zur Geschichte der Anatomie im Mittelalter (Studien zur Geschichte der Medizin no. 4, 51, 82–89, 1 pl., Leipzig 1908). Deals with Mondeville's use of illustrations in his teaching. Ernest Wickersheimer: La rage et son traitement en Normandie par les bains de mer d'après Mondeville (Bulletin de la société française d'histoire de la médecine 7, 59–61, 1908). Julius Leopold Pagel: Analekten zur Chirurgie des Heinrich von Mondeville (Janus 14, 399–404, 1909). Neuburger (2, 427–29, 488–96, 1911). James J. Walsh: Old time makers of medicine (p. 264–76, New York 1911). Karl Sudhoff: Weitere Beiträge zur Geschichte der Anatomie im Mittelalter (AGM 8, 130–38, 1915); Beiträge zur Geschichte der Chirurgie (part 2, 1918). Frédéric Beaudouin: Henri de Mondeville (19 p., Caen 1920). L. Choulant (p. 43, 44, 58, 1920). C. Singer (p. 73, 1926). August Wilhelm Bock: Diätetische Wundbehandlung im Mittelalter (Kyklos 2, 258–71, Leipzig 1929; Isis 16, 521). William Allen Pusey: History of dermatology (p. 39, Springfield, Ill. 1933; Isis 20, 504–5); Disease, gadfly of the mind. Especially the stimulus of skin-diseases in the development of the mind (British journal of dermatology and syphilis vol. 46, 1934; p. 7 of reprint). Wickersheimer (p. 282, 1936). M. C. Welborn: The long tradition, a study in fourteenth century medical deontology (Medieval essays in honor of James Westfall Thompson p. 344–57, Chicago 1938; Isis 29, 213).

BERNARD OF GORDON

Bernardus Gordonii, de Gordonio, or Gourdon (?). French physician (fl. c. 1283–1308).

Bernard was born possibly at Gordon in Rouergue (a part of Guyenne; now dépt. Aveyron), but there are many other places called Gordon in France. He was educated at Salerno, and taught at Montpellier (c. 1283–1308). The date of his death is unknown (c. 1320).

He was a physician of skill, and of good education. His writings show a wide knowledge of books besides those on medicine, such as the Ethics of Aristotle, the works of Seneca the Younger, Suetonius, St. Augustine. To the ideas which he borrowed from the Arabs he added many scholastic subtilities, as well as some observations of his own. He continued the astrological tendencies of Arnold of Villanova.

His principal work was the Lilium medicinae (sive de morborum prope omnium curatione), written at Montpellier in 1303 (not 1305).[21] This was one of the most popular medical books of the Middle Ages, witness the number of MSS, translations, and printed editions (princeps 1480).

It was a favorite textbook in Ireland, being twice translated into Irish, first by a member of the O'Hickey family in the northern part of Munster, then again in the fifteenth century by Cormac Mac Duinntshleibhe, a distinguished scholar and physician of Ulster. These translations have never been published. Bernard's works were often cited by Irish and Scottish doctors.

It was a favorite also with the Jews, who read it both in the original and in translation. Its Jewish popularity is attested by the existence of two translations. Moses ben Samuel of Roquemaure (XIV-2) translated it under his new name, John of Avignon, at Seville in 1359–1369, and under the title Peraḥ ha-refu'ot (The bud or sprout of health); he changed somewhat the order of the first chapters

[21] According to Renan (p. 732, 1893), the Lilium was completed at Montpellier on February 5, 1304.

of the Lilium. A very different translation was made in 1387 by Jekuthiel ben Solomon of Narbonne (Bonsenhor Salomon, XIV-2) under the title Shoshan ha-refuah (literal translation of Latin title).

A French translation made in 1377 was published in Lyon 1495; a Spanish one was published in Seville 1495.

The Lilium is a textbook of practical medicine, composed in the scholastic manner, but remarkably brief and clear. It is divided into seven particulae, each containing from 12 to 31 chapters. These chapters are very short and are always divided into 4 sections: causa, signa, prognostica, cura. Particula I (31 chapters) deals with fevers, some of the chapter headings being as follows: De febre in generali, De febre effimera, De febribus pestilentialibus, De punctura scorpionis, De punctura apum, etc. Particularly interesting are his discussions of acute fever (bubonic plague), scabies, erysipelas, anthrax, and leprosy. The description of leprosy is especially good; it was mentioned with praise by Guy de Chauliac (XIV-2).

Particula II, De omnibus egritudinibus cerebri usque ad egritudines oculorum (30 chapters). This section deals with the diseases of the head and brain, including chapters on De allopicia, De canicie vel apparatu vel ornatu capillorum, etc., such brain troubles as dolor capitis, scotomia et vertigo, corruptio memorie, stupor, mania et melancholia, ebrietas, epilepsia, apoplexia, and paralysis.

Particula III, De egritudinibus oculorum, aurium, narium, et oris (27 chapters). This part deals with Anothomia oculi, De vulneribus cornee, De debilitate visus, De passione dentium et proprio de dolore. Bernard was probably the earliest writer to mention spectacles in a medical textbook; he called them "oculus berellinus."

Particula IV, De passionibus spiritualium (21 chapters). Some of the chapter headings are: De squinantia, De passionibus uvule, De raucedine et immutatione vocis, De tussi, De ptisi, De difficultate anhelitus et asmate, etc.

Particula V, De passionibus nutritivorum (22 chapters), deals with such subjects as: De difficultate transglutiendi, De debilitate appetitus, De dissinteria, etc.

Particula VI, De passionibus epatis renum et vesice (16 chapters).

Particula VII, De passionibus membrorum generationis in utroque sexu et de antidotis valentibus a capite usque ad pedes (24 chapters). This particula contains one of the first descriptions of a modern truss, which was mentioned by John of Gaddesden but with no direct reference to Gordon, although he probably took his description from the Lilium.

Two lines of the Lilium medicinae enumerating eight[22] contagious diseases have often been quoted:

Febris acuta, ptisis, scabies, pedicon, sacer ignis
Anthrax, lippa, lepra nobis contagia praestant.[23]

Though Bernard was mistaken in considering epilepsy contagious, his discussion of it is remarkable in many respects. His account of the causes is old-fashioned; he repeated the Greek assertion that epilepsy is due to humors blocking passages in the brain and interfering with the supply of air to the limbs; he seems to suggest that nerves exert a mechanical pull on muscles. He was the first to describe seizures of petit mal, or short psychic seizures. He realized the great variety of

[22] The number eight was traditional (Garrison, p. 186, 1929).

[23] That is, acute fevers (such as plague), tuberculosis, scabies, erysipelas, epilepsy, anthrax, trachoma or ophthalmic gonorrhea, leprosy.

precipitating causes and of the forms which a seizure might take. What we now call Jacksonian epilepsy[24] had already been recognized by Galen and again by Bernard, who repeated that an aura arising in a periphery indicates the presence there of poisonous matter. With regard to prognostics, he referred to eclampsia,[25] and considered the premonitory awareness of a seizure as a relatively good omen. He confessed his inability to cure chronic epilepsy. He recommended the avoidance of emotional disturbances, recognizing, e.g., that reflex epilepsy might be precipitated by sudden noise.

Bernard wrote other medical works dealing with such subjects as the diet for febrile patients, prognosis, general therapeutics, hematology, and hygiene. One work, entitled Modus medendi extractus de modo Coffonis,[25a] has not been published. The four medical treatises (1) De phlebotomia, (2) De urinis, (3) De pulsibus, (4) De regimine sanitatis, which are often listed separately, are really the four parts of a single work, De conservatione vitae humanae, written in 1307 (Sudhoff says 1308). Some of Gordon's treatises (in addition to the Lilium) were translated into Hebrew by unnamed translators. According to Leon Joseph of Carcassonne, some of these translations, being made indirectly from versions in the popular language (Provençal is probably meant), were rather poor. According to Steinschneider (p. 786–87, 1893), there are Hebrew translations of the following treatises: Regimen acutarum aegritudinum; Affectus praeter naturam curandi methodus (= De decem ingeniis), dated 1296 or 1299; De prognosticis (= De crisi), dated 1290?, not later than 1299; De conservatione vitae humanae, 1295; De phlebotomia, 1307, translated in 1378; De medicinarum gradibus, 1303.

Text. Practica sive Lilium medicinae, written in 1303. The Lilium was printed for the first time at Naples 1480. There were many other editions: Ferrara 1486, Venice 1496/97, 1498, 1521, 1594, Lyon 1491, 1551, 1574, Paris 1542, Frankfort 1617. (Klebs no. 177.)

There are also editions of separate parts: Liber de febribus, De sterilitate mulierum, De marasmone (which may not be a part of the Lilium), De rheumate.

The French and Spanish translations were first printed in 1495, respectively in Lyon and Seville. Both have Latin titles. (Klebs nos. 178, 179.)

The following works are presented in chronological order:

De urinis et pulsibus, Ferrara 1487.

Tractatus de tyriaca secundum intentionem Averrois et aliorum, Lyon 1491 (with Lilium). Latin and German texts printed by Pagel (Pharmaceutische Post, 1894).

Regimen acutorum morborum, also called Regimen acutorum egritudinum, or De victus ratione et pharmacorum usu in morbis acutis, written 1294, printed Ferrara 1486, Venice 1498, Lyon 1491 (with Lilium), 1574, and in other editions of the Lilium.

Supra prognostica sive De crisi et diebus criticis, written 1295, printed Ferrara 1486, Venice 1498, Lyon 1491 (with Lilium), 1574, and later.

De decem ingeniis seu indicationibus curandorum morborum, written 1299, printed Ferrara 1486, Venice 1498, 1521, Lyon 1574, and later.

De gradibus, written 1303, printed by Pagel (Pharmaceutische Post, 1895).

De conservatione vite humane a die nativitatis usque ad ultimam horam mortis,

[24] Not true epilepsy. Unilateral motor spasms due to local brain irritation. Called after John Hughlings Jackson (1835–1911), of Yorkshire, who described the ailment in 1875; it had been described in 1836 by Richard Bright (Garrison p. 421, 643, 1929).

[25] Fancied perception of flashes of light.

[25a] See note on Copho of Salerno (XII-1).

written in four parts in 1307 or 1308: (1) De phlebotomia, Lyon 1574; (2) De urinis, Ferrara 1487 (Klebs no. 180), Venice 1498, Lyon 1574; (3) De pulsibus, Ferrara 1487, Venice 1498, Lyon 1574; (4) Regimen sanitatis, Leipzig 1570, Lyon 1574, 1580. First complete edition of the four treatises, in the Lyon edition of the Lilium 1574.

Breve compendium de neutralitatibus decidentie (the one ascribed to Bernard in Wolfenbüttel, fol. 171–75, is by Johannes de Tornamira, and the one ascribed to Tornamira, ibid. fol. 168–71, is really by Bernard). Bernard's is printed by Erna Kollert: Zwei Compendien 'De neutralitatibus decidenciae' von Bernhard Gordon und Johann Tornamira (Leipzig diss., 32 p., 1924; Isis 7, 539).

Works which are probably spurious:

De dosi medicinarum is the De medicinis laxativis, a commentary by Johannes de Parma on the work of Mesuë the Younger.

Flores antidotarii.

Uncertain works:

Experimenta.

De confectione ducente ad insenescibilitatem, quantum est possibile per naturam (this is mystical and magical enough to belong to him, according to Sudhoff).

De floribus diaetarum. The edition of Lyon 1574 ascribes it to him, but Schum's Catalogue[25b] lists it as a work of Arnold of Villanova (XIII-2). It is not included in the published works of Arnold.

A fragmentary plague tract, published by Sudhoff in the Sticker Festschrift, p. 47–48, Berlin 1930.

Criticism. Emile Littré: Bernard de Gordon (HL 25, 321–37, 1869). Neubauer-Renan (p. 651–53, 732, 1893). Steinschneider (p. 785, 1893). Gurlt (2, 26–33, 1898). R. von Töply: Die chronologische Reihenfolge der Schriften des Bernard von Gordon (Mitt. 6, 94–95, 1907). H. Carlowitz: Der Lepraabschnitt aus Bernard von Gordons 'Lilium medicinae' (Leipzig 1913). H. I. Bell: The bibliography of Bernard de Gordon's De conservatione vitae humanae (Seventeenth International Congress of Medicine sec. 23, p. 325–37, London 1914). Karl Sudhoff: Zur Schriftstellerei Bernhards von Gordon und deren zeitlicher Folge (AGM 10, 162–88, 1917), supersedes the article by R. von Töply. Martin Eichholtz: Zahnheilkundliches bei Bernard von Gordon (Leipzig diss., 4 p., 1923). Meyer-Steineg and Sudhoff (p. 212–14, 260, 297, 1928). Karl Sudhoff: Mittelalterliche Einzeltexte zur Beulenpest vor 1347/48 (Festgabe Georg Sticker p. 45–48, Berlin 1930), apropos of a plague tract which may have been written by Gordon. Wickersheimer (p. 75, 1936). William Gordon Lennox: Bernard de Gordon on epilepsy (Annals of medical history 3, 372–83, 1941; Isis 34, 46). James F. Ballard: Catalogue of the mediaeval and renaissance MSS (p. 11, 64, Boston 1944; Isis 35, 218), apropos of Hebrew translation of the Lilium written in Spanish rabbinical script, 1468, by Joshua ben David ha-Kohen, and of other Hebrew and Latin MSS and incunabula owned by the Boston Medical Library.

GERALD DE SOLO

Giraldus, Gerardus Bututus de Solo (in Hebrew transcription Sol or Sola), Ghilabat de Sciola, Geraldus Bituricensis, Gherardo Bierne alias de Solo, Géraud, Guiraud. French physician (d. c. 1360).

The adjective Bituricensis (or Bitorinus) refers to the province of Berry; must we conclude that Gerald was a Berrichon? He was nicknamed Expositor because of his commentaries, and also Doctor mansuetus. He became a professor in the medical faculty in Montpellier; he is mentioned in the chartulary of that university as early as 1335. He died c. 1360.

[25b] Wilhelm Schum: Beschreibendes Verzeichniss der Amplonianischen Handschriften-Sammlung zu Erfurt (p. 198, Fol. no. 289, Berlin 1887).

Gerald wrote a medical primer for the students of Montpellier entitled Introductorium juvenum sive de regimine corporis humani in morbis, which is based mainly on the Isagoge of Ḥunain ibn Isḥāq (IX-2). This was translated into Hebrew by Leon Joseph of Carcassonne, in 1402.

His Recepte de febribus, not yet published, is not identical with the Tractatus de febribus, in 5 chapters, which is usually printed in collections of his works. The latter was translated by Abraham Abigdor (XIV-2) in Montpellier or in Arles, in 1379.

Another popular work by Gerald is his commentary on the Latin translation of the ninth book of the Kitāb al-Manṣūrī (Nonus Almansoris) of al-Rāzī (IX-2). A Hebrew translation of this work was begun by Abraham Abigdor and completed by Leon Joseph in 1394; it was possibly revised by the latter in 1402.

Gerald also wrote a commentary on the Viaticum peregrinantis, a translation made by Constantine the African (XI-2) of the Zād al-musāfir of Ibn al-Jazzār (X-2).

In collaboration with Jordanes de Turre, Raymond de Moleriis, and G. de Marceriis, he wrote a diet regimen for a bishop of St.-Paul-Trois-Châteaux (Drôme).

Gerald may have written a commentary on the Aphorisms of Hippocrates. Other works ascribed to him which have not been printed are: De clisteriis, De suppositoriis, Modus medendi, Tractatus de signis humorum, De pestilentia in actu curativo.

Text. Introductorium juvenum sive de regimine corporis humani in morbis, Lyon 1504, Venice 1505, 1520, 1535.

Libellus de febribus, Lyon 1504 (with Nonus Almansoris), Venice 1505, 1520, 1535 (with Introductorium).

Tractatus de gradibus medicinae, Lyon 1504, Venice 1505, 1520, 1535.

Regimen pro domino episcopo Scti. Pauli, qui erat dispositus ad paralisim et colicam passionem, edited by K. Sudhoff (AGM 14, 184–86, 1923).

Commentum super nona particula Almansoris scriptum in 99 capitula distributum, Lyon 1504, Venice 1504, 1505, 1535.

Commentarius super Viatico, Venice 1505, 1520.

Traité des médicines de maistre Girard de Solo réformé et abrégé par monseigneur le chancelier de Montpellier Jehan de Piscis, Paris 1507, 1529.

Le Tresor des Poures . . . avec la cirurgie et plusieurs autres praticqs nouvelles selon maistre Arnoult de Ville Nove, et maistre Girard de Solo, Lyon 1512, Paris 1520?.

Criticism. A. W. E. Th. Henschel: Berühmte Wundärzte und Aerzte des XIII. und XIV. Jahrhunderts (Janus 2, 393–94, 1853). Haeser (1, 688–89, 1875). Cartulaire de l'université de Montpellier (1, 292, Montpellier 1890). Steinschneider (p. 794–98, 1893). Neubauer-Renan (p. 719, 770–75, 1893). Giacosa (p. 485, 1901). Pierre Pansier: Maitres de la faculté de médecine de Montpellier (Janus 9, 544–45, 1904). Neuburger (2, 501, 1911). Wickersheimer (p. 185, 1936).

JORDANES DE TURRE

Jordanes de Turre was a master of medicine at the University of Montpellier c. 1313–15. I leave the name in Latin, as there is no way of knowing whether it was originally French, Italian, or Spanish. Jordanes was quoted by the Hispanic physician Valescus de Taranta, who wrote medical books in 1401 and 1418, but as Valescus himself flourished at Montpellier, this proves nothing.

In 1335 Jordanes was one of four Montpellier consultants who composed a regimen for the bishop of St.-Paul-Trois-Châteaux (26 km. from Montélimar, Drôme), threatened with paralysis. He wrote many medical tracts, to wit: (1) Recepte quas fecit filio suo eunti ad practicam anno 1318, (2) De adiventione graduum in medicinis simplicibus et compositis, (3) Tractatus clysterium, (4) De impregnatione mulierum, (5) De lepra, (6) De urina, (7) Compendium de urinis, (8) Ad curam hydropisis, (9) De febribus, (10) De experimentis, (11) Regimen ad curandum epilepticum.

Text. There are no early editions of any of these texts. Karl Sudhoff published the regimen referred to above, Eine Diätregel für einen Bischof, aufgestellt von vier Professoren von Montpellier in der Mitte des 14. Jahrhunderts (AGM 14, 184–86, 1923).

Criticism. Lynn Thorndike: Vatican Latin MSS (Isis 13, 80, 1929).

Ernest Wickersheimer: Pour éviter la paralysie, Conseils de maitre Pierre de Capestang (Bulletin de la Société française d'histoire de la médecine 18, 103–6, 1924; Isis 7, 192; Introd. 2, 1091); Dictionnaire (p. 513, 1936). Lynn Thorndike: Little known medical works in Basel MSS (Annals of medical history 2, 283, 1940), apropos of MSS on the twenty or sixteen signs of leprosy.

PIERRE DE SAINT FLOUR

French (Auvergnat) physician (fl. Paris 1335–49).

Pierre (not Jean) Gas or Guas, Petrus de Sancto Floro, a clerk of the diocese of St. Flour in upper Auvergne (dépt. Cantal). He was master of arts and procurator of the French nation at the University of Paris in 1335, bachelor in medicine 1342, master of the Paris medical faculty in 1349. The places and dates of his birth and death are unknown.

He is the author of a medical anthology, Colliget florum medicine, also called Concordancie, which is an amplification of (or commentary on) the Concordancie of John of Saint Amand (XIII-2), a collection of sentences extracted mainly from Galen and Ibn Sīnā, arranged in alphabetical order of pathological subjects.

Text. Unpublished. Two MSS in Paris, Sorbonne 133 and Bibliothèque nationale lat. 14734.

Criticism. Emile Littré (HL 21, 258, 1847). Julius Pagel: Die Concordanciae des Johannes de Sancto Amando nebst einem Nachtrage über die Concordantiae des Petrus de Sancto Floro (488 p., Berlin 1894); Neue litterarische Beiträge zur mittelalterlichen Medizin (part 2, Berlin 1896). Wickersheimer (p. 634, 1936).

RAYMOND OF MOLIÈRES

Raymundus de Moleriis, Raimundus de Moleriis (fl. 1335). There are in France many localities called Molière or Molières; e.g., there are Molières in the Drôme, Aveyron, Dordogne, etc.

Raymond was a member of the medical faculty of Montpellier, mentioned as chancellor in 1335. Guy of Chauliac (XIV-2) speaks of him as his teacher.

The only work whose ascription to Raymond has not been challenged is a brief diet regimen for a bishop of St.-Paul-Trois-Châteaux (Drôme) which he wrote in collaboration with three other medical men of Montpellier—Jordanes de Turre, Gerald of Solo, and G. de Marceriis.

The De impedimentis conceptionis, often ascribed to Raymond, also frequently appeared under the name of Arnold of Villanova (XIII-2). According to Diepgen, this work is very similar to other treatises of Villanova, and so far there has been no conclusive evidence that Raymond wrote it.

Another work, De consilio, which has appeared under Raymond's name is a philosophical treatise written by Raymond Lull (XIII-2).

Text. Karl Sudhoff: Eine Diätregel für einen Bischof, aufgestellt von vier Professoren von Montpellier in der Mitte des 14. Jahrhunderts (AGM 14, 184–86, 1923).

Criticism. Marcel Fournier: Les statuts et privilèges des universités françaises (2, 40, Paris 1891). Karl Eduard Arlt: Neuer Beitrag zur Geschichte der medizinischen Schule von Montpellier (p. 13–28, Berlin 1902). Julius Pagel: Raymundus de Moleriis und seine Schrift De impedimentis conceptionis (Janus 8, 530–37, 1903). Pierre Pansier: Les maîtres de la faculté de médecine de Montpellier au moyen âge (Janus 10, 8, 1905). Paul Diepgen: Studien zu Arnald von Villanova (AGM 6, 380–91, 1913). Wickersheimer (p. 677, 1936).

PIERRE CHAUCHAT

Pierre Chauchat (or Chalchat, Calcati). French physician (d. 1363).

The date and place of his birth are unknown. All we know of the early part of his life is that he studied medicine in Paris, having been granted a fellowship by the Collège St. Nicolas-du-Louvre (to which he later bequeathed his medical books). He seems to have practiced medicine mainly in Paris, where he was thrice dean of the medical faculty (1329, 1333, 1342). He was canon in Clermont, then in various Parisian churches, St. Germain l'Auxerrois, St. Marcel, Notre-Dame. In 1352 he was physician to John II (king of France 1350–64).

He composed in 1339 a commentary on the De crisibus (*περὶ κρίσεων*) of Galen, Expositio libri de crisi Galieni.

Criticism. Wickersheimer (p. 625, 1936).

DAMOUZY

Pierre de Damouzy. French physician (d. 1361).

Petrus de Damousis, de Amousis. Pierre originated in Damouzy, near Charleville (dépt. Ardennes). Regent of the medical faculty of Paris 1325–28; he flourished mainly at Reims, where he was chaplain and, in 1343, canon. He enjoyed many other prebends. He died on November 24, 1361, and was buried in the cathedral of Reims.

He wrote on August 16, 1348, a Tractatus de epidemia, the first dealing with the Black Death in the French region. In fact it was written for the sake of prophylaxis before the plague had reached his own district. Unfortunately the author had no clinical experience, and his treatise is nothing but a patchwork of quotations from the Greek, Arabic, and mediaeval physicians. His favorite sources are Aristotle, Galen, 'Alī ibn 'Abbās, Ibn Sīnā, and he is well acquainted with the Lilium medicinae of Bernard of Gordon, which was probably the most recent of his authorities. The treatise is divided into three parts: (1) Cause et signa epydimie, (2) Regimen et preservacio in generali, (3) Regimen et preservacio in particulari. With regard to the causes, he does not insist on the astrological ones, but rather on the meteorological ones, for the air is the main vehicle of contagion. To be sure, the last of the four causes of corruption of the air, according to Ibn Sīnā, the causa remota, is found in the stars, but Damouzy devotes his attention chiefly to nearer causes. For treatment and prevention he recommends bloodletting, purgation, a light diet, and careful living. Moderate out-of-door exercise is helpful before the plague is near; when the danger comes closer it should be avoided. The third part is the longest, and some details of it suggest that it was written a little later, when the danger was greater (the plague spread very rapidly). One should avoid the society of ill people or of people coming from stricken areas; some people may be "carriers" of the contagion without being ill themselves. Damouzy shows how to arrange one's life for safety. He gives various prescriptions for people of different temperaments.

Text. Unpublished. Latin MS 11227, Bibliothèque nationale, Paris, fol. 212–14, middle of the fourteenth century.

Criticism. Wickersheimer (p. 629, 1936). Alfred Coville (HL 37, 327–35, 1938).

A4. England

JOHN OF GADDESDEN

John de Gadesden, de Gabshede, de Gatesden, Joannes Anglicus. English physician (c. 1280–1361).

He must not be confused with another Joannes Anglicus who lived in Bologna about 1316, or with the mathematician Joannes (or Robertus) Anglicus (XIII-2).

John of Gaddesden was born about 1280, probably in Little Gaddesden on the borders of Hertfordshire and Buckinghamshire, where a house is still shown as his. He studied at Merton and by 1300 had received the A.B. degree, by 1303 the A.M., and by 1309 the M.D. He also took a degree in theology, and was in priest's orders, being appointed to a stall in St. Paul's, London, in 1342. From various statements in his Rosa medicinae it is more than likely that he studied for a short time in southern France. He did not study at Montpellier, but inherited its tradition from Gilbert the Englishman (XIII-1), and from Bernard of Gordon.

John practiced in Oxford and then in London, where he was very popular and often praised by his contemporaries; e.g., Chaucer mentions him among the great physicians of all time in the Prologue of the Canterbury Tales (l. 434), "Bernard and Gatesden and Gilbertyn"; but he was derided by Guy de Chauliac. He was the first Englishman to be appointed court physician to an English monarch, Edward II (1307–27). John died in 1361.

About 1314 he composed a medical treatise which he called Rosa medicinae (probably after Gordon's Lilium medicinae, which he quoted), but which is more generally named Rosa anglica. Although the book has been frequently abused and scorned, it is of practically the same caliber as other fourteenth-century medical works, and there are some very good points in it. John was mystical, superstitious, and somewhat of a charlatan, but he was by no means ignorant of the general medical facts of his day.

The Rosa is divided in the following way: De febribus, De universalitate morborum, Tractatus quinque utilissimus et maxime cirurgicis, De morbis particularibus, De preparatione et administratione medicinarum.

John was an exceptionally good observer and his clinical descriptions are often excellent, especially that of a case of ascites with obstructive jaundice. His pathology, however, was generally inaccurate.

His clinical observations of phthisis were equally good, and likewise his remarks on treatment; he knew that a real cure could be effected only if the lung had not yet broken down.

The description of leprosy is especially interesting; he noted the thickening and rapid clotting of the blood of a leper, which might be said to be a partial anticipation of Boeck's and Danielssen's[26] observation of the increase of fibrin ferments in the blood of leper patients.

He recommended urea as a diuretic for a dropsical child.

The discussion of variola is well organized and elaborate. John repeated the popular theory of the therapeutic value of red wrappings and red hangings and applied it to a son of Edward I, whom he cured of the smallpox. John's discussion of the use of red in the cure of smallpox is practically identical with that given by Bernard of Gordon in his Lilium. Gilbert the Englishman (XIII-1) was the first to mention this theory, but says that he learned it "from the old women in the country" (Compendium medicinae). It is tempting to compare this use of red light with Finsen's phototherapy, but that is a curious coincidence, nothing more.[27]

The section on varicella is important because of his description of the eruption called punctilli magni, i.e. petechiae.

Another section deals with the diseases and cures of the mouth, teeth, tongue, and lips. Although he copies much of this from earlier sources, nevertheless he adds some valuable new material; for instance, in his description of the best method of extracting teeth he describes a new instrument which is probably the forerunner of the pelican.

His discussions of stone are paralleled by those of John Jacobi (XIV-2).

He gives four methods of distilling fresh water from sea water, but only one (the fourth) is original with him: "Modo fiat de cera unum vas concavum subtile et ponatur in alio vase pleno aqua salsa, ita quod non intret per orificium superius et tunc intrabit per poros cerae illud quod subile erit, et hoc est dulce et stabit in vase cereo, et istum modum tangit Aristoteles et expositores in secundo metaurorum."

Only a small portion of the Rosa is devoted to surgery; there are brief discussions of tapping, lithotomy, hernia, and the reduction of dislocations. In his treatment of wounds which involve injury to a bone, he is superior to Lanfranchi (XIII-2).

The Antidotarium is extraordinary in its number of prescriptions; he has evidently assembled all the receipts he had ever heard of. Thus the Rosa gives us a valuable picture of fourteenth-century English folk remedies, superstitions, cosmetics, and daily diet.

For some of his most worth-while ideas he depends on Bernard of Gordon and Gilbert the Englishman; some of the poorest parts are taken literally from Gariopontus (XI-1) and from Peter of Spain (XIII-2). He borrowed considerably also from a great many other authors, Hippocrates, Dioscorides, Galen, 'Alī ibn 'Abbās, Ibn Sīnā, Constantine the African, Platearius, Giles of Corbeil, and John of Saint Amand being most frequently quoted.

The most popular medical textbooks in Ireland in the fourteenth and fifteenth centuries were Irish translations of Latin treatises. John's Rosa was translated a number of times—portions of it are still to be found in at least six MSS. Nicholas

[26] Karl Wilhelm Boeck (1808–75); Daniel Cornelius Danielssen (1815–94).

[27] Niels Ryberg Finsen (1860–1904). See William Allen Pusey: History of dermatology (p. 38, 171, Springfield, Ill. 1933; Isis 20, 504).

O'Hickey[28] is said to have translated it into Irish in 1400, and Cormac Mac Duinntshleibhe[29] translated at least parts of it in 1450.

Text. Rosa anglica practica medicine. Editio princeps Pavia 1492 (4 + 173 leaves, double columns; Klebs no. 424). It was reprinted in Venice 1502, Pavia 1517, and Augsburg 1595. Four additional editions (1499, 1506, 1508, 1516) quoted by various authors are uncertain. An Early Modern Irish translation of a section of John's work is edited by Winifred Wulff, in Irish Texts Society vol. 25, London (1923) 1929; Irish translation on one side of page and an English version on the opposite side.

Criticism. John Freind: History of physick (2, 277–93, London 1750). Kurt Sprengel: Histoire de la médecine (2, 449–51, Paris 1815). George Charles Brodrick: Memorials of Merton (p. 37, 176, Oxford 1885). Norman Moore (DNB 20, 347, 1889). Gurlt (2, 158–66, 1898). Byron A. Kinney: The "1516" edition of Gaddesden's Rosa anglica (Bibliographical Society of America, Proceedings and papers 1, 71–73, New York 1904). H. E. Handerson: John of Gaddesden, Variola and the Finsen light-cure (Cleveland medical journal 3, 433–41, 1904). George Dock: Printed editions of the Rosa anglica of John of Gaddesden (Janus 12, 425–35, 1907). Henry P. Cholmeley: John of Gaddesden and the Rosa medicinae (184 p., Oxford 1912). Wilhelm Feldhaus: Zahnärztliches bei John of Gaddesden (Leipzig diss., 14 p., 1922; Isis 6, 150). R. T. Gunther (2, 43, 1923; 3, 11, 20, 1925). Wickersheimer (p. 404, 1936). William G. Lennox: Gaddesden on epilepsy (Annals of medical history 1, 283–307, 1939), containing translation of the text ad hoc taken from the Rosa anglica (p. 157–67, Pavia 1492).

A5. Belgium

JAN YPERMAN

Jehan Yperman, John of Ypres. Flemish surgeon; the father of Netherlandish surgery.

Born in the second half of the thirteenth century; the place of his birth is unknown, but it was in all probability in or near Ypres (Yperen) in West Flanders; he spent most of his life in Ypres and died there at the end of 1330 or in 1331.

He may have studied in Paris under Lanfranchi (XIII-2), although there is no direct evidence for this supposition; in any case he was a faithful follower of Lanfranchi's teaching.

About 1304 he received an appointment as surgeon in the Belle hospital in Ypres. His salary, paid by the municipality, appears on the books down to the year 1329–30. In 1311–12 and again in 1325 he received an additional salary as field surgeon to militia defending the town against the count of Flanders.

Yperman wrote two medical treatises in Flemish (that is, a Dutch or Low German dialect), the first on practical medicine, the second on surgery.

The first of these treatises includes chapters on dropsy, rheumatism, apoplexy, epilepsy, frenzy, lethargy, lung abscesses, and other diseases; and on the treatment of haemorrhages by ligatures and torsions of the arteries.

Most of his therapeutic prescriptions rest upon his own experience; thus, like many of his contemporaries, he was evidently trying to free himself from too great

[28] A member of the O'Hickey family, hereditary physicians to the McCarthys of Carbery.

[29] A distinguished scholar and physician who translated four other Latin medical works into Irish: Walter Agilinus (XIII-1), De dosibus; Thomas Aquinas (XIII-2), On the secrets of nature (?); Bernard of Gordon, Lilium medicinae; Guy de Chauliac (XIV-2), Chirurgia. The Mac Duinntshleibhes were hereditary physicians to the O'Donnells.

dependence upon authority. He borrowed many complicated prescriptions, however, from Dioscorides, Galen, Mesuë, Nicholas of Salerno, Platearius, and numerous other sources.

His Cyrurgia, a much better work than the Medicina, was written for his son in the first quarter of the fourteenth century, not earlier than 1305, since he mentions the Lilium of Bernard of Gordon. It bears witness to the great versatility, independence, and experience of the author.

It is far less ambitious in its scope than Mondeville's. It is divided into seven books: (1) head, 30 chapters; (2) eyes, 25 chapters; (3) nose, 7 chapters; (4) mouth, 20 chapters; (5) ears, 9 chapters; (6) neck and throat, 12 chapters; (7) rest of the body in the usual order downward, 40 chapters. This is followed by 52 unnumbered chapters which occur only in a single MS out of four.

The text is illustrated with a number of drawings of instruments, and with a plate showing the stitching of a wound in the head. Yperman gives good accounts of trephining, arrow wounds, and the healing of harelip. He stresses the use of anaesthesia. He makes fun of the physician who thinks he can cure cataract by purgatives instead of by an operation. His method of treating wounds shows that he had carefully investigated their healing process.

Yperman knew the diagnostic importance of anaesthesia in leprosy, but other physicians of his time shared with him that knowledge borrowed from the Arabs, Abū-l-Qāsim (X-2) and his followers. See my note on leprosy in chapter I, part XI.

Like his contemporary Mondeville and independently of him, he keenly realized the low status of surgery. This was largely due to the ignorance and quackery of many lay surgeons and physicians (leekenmeester). He tried to raise the level of surgery in the same manner as Mondeville: the surgeon should not only know medicine, but be well trained in grammar, logic, rhetoric, and ethics. He describes the physical and moral qualities which the surgeon ought to possess, and gives advice on deontology and bedside manners.

Sources of the Surgery. The main sources were as follows (I quote them in chronological order, the figures between parentheses referring to the number of quotations): Hippocrates (7), Galen (24), Rāzī (3), Ibn Sīnā (29), Benevenutus Grassus (4), Roger of Salerno (5), Roland of Parma (10), William of Congenis (4), Gilbert the Englishman (10), Hugh of Lucca (11), Theodoric Borgognoni (5), Quattuor magistri (13), Bruno da Longoburgo (8), Lanfranchi (17). The main sources in order of frequency were Ibn Sīnā, Galen, Lanfranchi. Outside of Ibn Sīnā and Rāzī no Arabic writer was quoted more than once. It is clear that by far the most of Yperman's learning was obtained from or via the Italian surgeons.

Tradition of the Surgery. In spite of its qualities the Surgery was not popular. Only four MSS have come down to us, all of them in Flemish. The earliest (Brussels) is almost contemporary (1351); the three others date from the fifteenth century. Strangely enough, there is no trace of Yperman's influence in the works of another Flemish surgeon, Thomas Scellinck, who flourished very soon after him (1343). The Surgery remained practically unknown until the Antwerp physician Jean Carolus (1808–63) published an analysis of it in 1854. It was never printed except for antiquarian purposes (1863, 1912).

Text. Corneille Broeckx: Traité de médecine pratique de maître Jean Yperman, publié pour la première fois d'après la copie flamande de la Bibliothèque royale de Bruxelles (147 p., Anvers 1867).

Corneille Broeckx: La chirurgie d'Yperman, publiée pour la première fois d'après la copie flamande de Cambridge (210 p., Annales de l'Académie d'archéologie 20, 128–332, Anvers 1863). E. C. Van Leersum: De Cyrurgie van Meester Jan Yperman (Bibliotheek van middelnederlandsche letterkunde, 330 p., 48 fig., Leiden 1912). This is a critical edition based on the four MSS, including an elaborate introduction, notes, bibliography, and glossary (p. 234–80). A French translation by A. de Mets appeared serially in Hippocrate, Revue d'humanisme médical. I do not know whether that edition was completed, as I have seen only one part of it (no. 9 of vol. 3, Paris Nov. 1935, p. 735–44). A. de Mets: La Chirurgie de Maître Jehan Yperman. Livres I et II (Collection Hippocrate, 121 p., Paris 1936); with an introduction and bibliography.

Criticism. Jean Carolus: La chirurgie d'Yperman mise au jour et annotée (Annales de la Société de médecine de Gand, 195 p., Gand 1854). Haeser (1, 757, 769–72, 801, 1875). Alphonse Vandenpeereboom: Ypriana (1, 208, 211, 376; 2, 62; 4, 368, 375–79, 383–84, 391, Bruges 1880). Gurlt (2, 134–41, 1898). E. C. Van Leersum: Bemerkungen über Broeckx' Ausgabe der Chirurgie des Jan Yperman (Janus 10, 544–49, 1905); Est-ce en 1310 que Jan Yperman est mort? (Janus 14, 393–98, 1909); Meester Jan Yperman, Vlaamsch chirurg uit de 14de eeuw (Nederlandsch Tijdschrift voor Geneeskunde p. 1712–17, 1912); Notes concerning the life of Jan Yperman (Janus 18, 1–15, 1913); Master Jan Yperman's Cyrurgia (Janus 18, 197–209, 1913). Neuburger (2, 430, 519, 1911). E. De Sagher: Note concernant l'année de la mort d'Yperman (Janus 19, 33–34, 1914; Isis 4, 407). William Allen Pusey: History of dermatology (p. 38, 1933; Isis 20, 504–5). Tricot-Royer: Yperman à Namur (9 p. ex Yperman, Anvers s.a.).

SCELLINCK

Thomas Scellinck or Thomas Umbra de Thenismonte. Flemish surgeon.

Born or brought up in Tirlemont (Thienen, 12 miles from Louvain); he traveled in the Brabant and the Namurois and on one occasion went as far as Genoa. He was already practicing in 1317; he practiced for some time in Namur.

In 1343 he completed the composition of a treatise on surgery, in Flemish (Boeck van surgien), divided into four parts which are not easy to analyze as the order is not always quite clear. Part I deals mainly with various wounds; part II with other wounds, apostemes, skin troubles, swellings of glands; part III with the eyes, nose, teeth, mouth, tonsils, ears, skin troubles, lice, fistulas, stone, cramps, etc.; part IV is mainly devoted to the antidotary.

He quotes some twenty-four authorities, most often Hippocrates, Galen, and Ibn Sīnā, then less often al-Rāzī (5 times), Abū-l-Qāsim (7), and Constantine the African (6). He does not quote, and probably was unaware of the existence of his countryman and contemporary Jan Yperman. There are naturally many points in common between Yperman and Scellinck, for they used largely the same sources. Yperman was apparently a little more modern and better acquainted with the Italian school of surgery. Both were agreed in denouncing quacks and other laymen. Both relied on their own experience as well as on the authority of their Greek, Arabic, or Italian predecessors, and they occasionally showed a spirit of independence. Scellinck, however, was less of a surgeon than Yperman, and perhaps more of a physician. "Yperman was ready with the knife, Scellinck prefers the red-hot iron or the chemical caustics. And how cautious is his manner of working. For instance, in order to open up glands or abscessae it is well to administer but a small amount of the caustic on the diseased spot; this is more prudent than too much all at once. And it is advisable to protect the surroundings by a wall of dough against the corroding agent. Yperman dwells at length on ligature of the vessels and the suture of wounds, Scellinck writes on unbloody manipulations for the reposition of broken or distorted limbs. The circumstantial manner in which he deals with operations for stones in the bladder is an exception to his preference for the 'petite chirurgie.' In contrast to Yperman, Scellinck touches anatomy but lightly. On the other hand, his enumeration of wound-healing remedies is very complete, a whole section of his book is devoted to it" (Van Leersum's ed. p. xxi).

Scellinck's book was even less well known than Yperman's. There are only two MSS of it, one in the British Museum, dated 1410, and the other in The Hague, dating from the end of the same century; there is possibly a third one in Oxford (New College). Scellinck himself states at the beginning that he wrote it for his two children, Thomas and Jan. Maybe he had no thought of publication in a broader form, but simply of transmitting his knowledge and experience, the secrets of his profession, to his sons? The Boeck van surgien remained unpublished and practically unknown until 1928.

Text. E. C. Van Leersum: The "Book of surgeries" of Master Thomas Scellinck from Thienen (Opuscula selecta Neerlandicorum de arte medica vol. 7, 378 p., Amsterdam 1928). Critical edition of the Flemish text, with introduction in Dutch and English, and elaborate glossary (Isis 12, 152–53).

Criticism. Sudhoff: Beiträge zur Geschichte der Chirurgie (2, 506, 1918).

BARTHOLOMEW OF BRUGES

Bartholomaeus de Brugis. Flemish physician and philosopher, Aristotelian commentator.

The circumstances of his birth and early years are unknown. He was M.A. in Paris 1307, and obtained a medical degree in Montpellier before 1315. He lectured on Aristotle (Physics, Economics, Meteorology, Poetry, apocryphal De inundatione Nili) in the University of Paris from a little before 1307 to 1309 or later, entered the Sorbonne before 1315. He was canon of Andenne (near Namur), later of Cambrai (1331). From c. 1330 to 1342 he was physician to Guy I of Châtillon (count of Blois 1307–42), and was occasionally consulted by the royal princes. He died at an unknown place and time c. 1354–56.

Many writings are ascribed to him, which have not yet been sufficiently investigated; some of them may be apocryphal.

Medical writings. 1. Notule in Ysagogas Johannitii (i.e., Ḥunain ibn Isḥâq, IX-2), apocryphal?

1 bis. Notule in Tegni Galieni. This is probably the same as no. 1, as Ḥunain's popular treatise was called Isagoge Johannitii ad Tegni Galeni (Introd. 1, 611).

3. Glossule in libros Aphorismorum Ypocratis.

4. Dicta super Prognostica.

5. Commentary on the De regimine acutorum morborum?

6. Scriptum super primum Canonis Avicennae.

7. Remedium epydimie. Brief undated rules. They may have been composed at the time of the Black Death, but there is nothing to prove it. Bartholomew remarks that dying people are more infectious than others, "maxime dum sunt prope mortem vel quando agonizant."

Philosophical writings. 8. Commentary on Aristotle's Economics. The Economics had been translated from Greek into Latin by William of Moerbeke and revised by Durand ḍ'Auvergne in 1295 (HL 25, 58–63, 1869). Bartholomew's elaborate but mediocre commentary was made upon one of the many MSS of that translation; it was entitled Commentum et questiones super librum Yconomicorum Aristotelis, and was dedicated by him in 1309 to a canon of Arras.

9. Questiones et sophismata. Various logical topics.

The commentary on the Physics is preserved in the redaction of a student completed in 1308 at Poitiers, where the curia was then residing.

Text. No text has yet been published except the very short plague regimen, edited by Sudhoff in 1911.

Criticism. No notice in the Biographie nationale de Belgique.

Karl Sudhoff: Pestschriften aus den ersten 150 Jahren nach der Epidemie des "schwarzen Todes" 1348 (AGM 5, 39–41, 1911). Auguste Pelzer: Barthélemy de Bruges, philosophe et médecin du XIVe siècle (Revue néoscolastique de philosophie 36, 459–74, 1934; Isis 24, 207). Wickersheimer (p. 60, 1936). Charles Victor Langlois (HL 37, 238–50, 1936).

SIMON OF COUVIN

Symon de Covino. Simon was born in Couvin, near Dinant in the province of Namur, Belgium (Couvin was then in the diocese of Liége). He received his doctor's degree in Paris and then practiced medicine and astrology in that city. He died in Liége on April 30, 1367, and was buried in the collegiate church of St. Jean, of which he was a canon.

He composed a poem, De iudicio Solis in conviviis Saturni (or De convivio Solis in domo Saturni), of 1,132 hexameters, on the plague of 1348; it was finished in Paris about 1350. He was undoubtedly an eyewitness of the events and conditions which he describes, and his poem gives many interesting and important details of the bubonic plague, which he calls "pestis inguinaria," and also "mors nigra," a name which did not become usual until much later.

In his introduction Simon describes the conjunction of the planets Jupiter and Saturn in Aquarius, which had occurred in 1345, and which was generally supposed to be the main cause of the plague. (Or the "superior root"; the totality of the secondary causes modifying the plague, such as individual temperament, food, age, etc., being called in the astrological language of the day "inferior root.") He says that the coming of this disease was marked by natural phaenomena: heavy mist and clouds, lightning, and falling stars, and deadly south winds. Simon emphasizes the extremely contagious nature of the plague, declaring that it was spread by the breath and clothes of the sick, by furniture, and everything which had been near an infected person. He says that the causes of these great epidemics were not known to the doctors, and that all their usual methods of treatment were of no avail; almost all the Montpellier physicians died. He suggests that the calamity may have been a divine punishment of men's sins and crimes, yet he remarks that it actually increased the license and fury of human passions. He describes in detail the symptoms and course of the illness and insists on the immensity of the catastrophe. According to him, hardly one-third of the people survived; in some places there were more dead people than living ones; towns were emptied of their inhabitants. The mortality was especially heavy among the poorer people, while princes, knights, judges were more often saved: the soft life lasted longer than the hard one.

Simon states that his astrological knowledge was derived from John of Murs, Firmin of Belleval, and Leo the Jew of Montpellier (i.e., Levi ben Gerson).

Text. Libellus de iudicio Solis in conviviis Saturni, sive de horrenda illa peste, quae anno 1348 late per totam Europam grassata est, published by Emile Littré: Opuscule relatif à la peste de 1348 (Bibliothèque de l'Ecole des chartes 2, 201–43, Paris 1840/41).

Criticism. L. A. J. Michon: Documents inédits sur la Grande Peste (p. 14, 21, 32, Paris 1860). Haeser (3, 98, 101, 130, 133, 170, 1882), prints part of the poem. P. Pansier: Les maîtres de la faculté de médecine de Montpellier (Janus 10, 9, 1905). D. D. Brouwers (Biographie nationale de Belgique 22, 538, 1914). Ernest Wickersheimer: Recueil des plus célèbres astrologues et quelques hommes doctes faict par Symon de Phares (p. 22, Paris 1929). Campbell (p. 30–31, 42, 47, 59, 64–65, 80, 86, 1931). Thorndike (3, 305, 311, 1934). Wickersheimer (p. 738, 1936). Alfred Coville (HL 37, 372–82, 1938).

Apropos of "mors nigra," see Stephen d'Irsay: Notes to the origin of the expression "atra mors" (Isis 8, 328–32, 1926).

A6. Germany

JOHN HAKE OF GÖTTINGEN

Johannes Hake von Westerholt, Johann von Göttingen, John Hake, John Griese. German physician who was also interested in political and ecclesiastical affairs in Germany and Avignon (d. 1349).

He was born about 1280 in Göttingen, of bourgeois parents; his father was a member of the council in Göttingen.

John studied medicine in Montpellier, and by 1319 was cited as a professor in the faculties of medicine and of arts in Montpellier. Between 1314 and 1318 he was in Germany as a personal physician of Ludwig of Bavaria, and accompanied him on many campaigns. In 1318 he went to Avignon as the personal physician of cardinal Jacob Gaetani, with whom he remained until he became physician to cardinal Annibaldo of Ceccano.

John himself held two bishoprics, first that of Werden on the Ruhr (1332–40), then that of Freising (1340–49). He spent most of his life, however, in Avignon, where he died of the plague in 1349.

According to contemporary historical accounts, John was an excellent physician. Only fragments of his writings remain: a few brief remarks on renal calculi, still in manuscript; and two tracts on the plague of 1348–49, edited by Sudhoff.

His Ad praeservandum ab epydimia gives a few prescriptions, and some rules for avoiding the disease. The Contra epidimeam contains three prescriptions for the use of those who have the plague.

About 1344, he wrote a letter of warning concerning poisons, De cautela a venenis, to Jan of Luxemburg (king of Bohemia 1310–46).

Text. Ad praeservandum ab epydimia, edited by Karl Sudhoff: Pestratschläge eines Freisinger Bischofs (AGM 5, 37–38, 1911).

Contra epidimeam secundum magistrum Johannem de Gotingen Episcopum Werdensem, printed by Sudhoff (AGM 5, 38–39, 1911).

Joannis de Gottingen episcopi caminensis Epistola ad Joannem I Bohemiae regem de cautela a venenis, edited by Johann Friedrich Schannat: Vindemiae literariae (1, 211–13, Fulda 1723, folio).

Criticism. Karl Wenck: Johann von Göttingen Arzt, Bischof und Politiker zur Zeit Kaiser Ludwigs des Bayern (AGM 17, 141–56, 1925), detailed biography dealing particularly with his political activities, includes an extensive bibliography. Campbell (p. 22–23, 1931). Wickersheimer (p. 416, 1936).

ALBERT OF PARMA

Italian physician who flourished in Alsace (d. c. 1354).

Albert of Parma flourished in Strassburg. He was canon of St. Thomas in 1336 and died on July 26, 1353, 1354, or 1355. He is quoted here as one of the authors of a regimen for the plague of Strassburg, 1349. That regimen was written in German, at the request of the magistrates of Strassburg, by five physicians of that city, to wit "Albertus, Rudolfus, Henricus von Saiszen, Bernhardt von Rostogk und Henricus von Lubelck, alle meyster in der artznye wonende zu Straiszburg"; that is, Albert of Parma, Rudolf Schwenninger (d. not later than 1380), Henry of Saxony (d. in or after 1378), Bernard of Rostock (or Bernhard of Saxony, d. 1370–76), and Henry of Lubelck (the least known of the five). This short text, represented by a single MS in the castle of Berleburg, Westphalia, is not very different from other regimina of that time. Its first recommendation is to go away when the plague comes. If that is not possible, to put in the house and carry about oneself plenty of aromatics, to be moderate in every way and to remain cheerful, to keep the bowels free. At the first sign of infection (bubo on the left side), it is well to take a purgative and an emetic. This little regimen is the earliest monument of Strassburgian medical literature.

Text. Ernest Wickersheimer: La peste noire à Strasbourg et le Régime des cinq médecins strasbourgeois (Proceedings of the Third International Congress of the History of Medicine, London 1922, p. 54–60, Antwerp 1923; Isis 31, 152).
Criticism. Wickersheimer (p. 16, 686, 286, 79, 281, 1936).

B. CHRISTIAN EAST

B1. Byzantium

JOANNES CHUMNOS

Ἰωάννης ὁ Χοῦμνος. Son of Nicephoros Chumnos, and like him in the service of the Palaeologoi, Michael VIII (1261–82) and Andronicos II (1282–1328). John reached the office of *παρακοιμώμενος τῆς μεγάλης σφενδόνης.*

John Chumnos was the author of a number of elegantly written letters, eight of which are printed with the works of his father. The first seven letters deal with philosophical problems, based in large part on the works of Plato. From the eighth letter, *Δίαιτα προφυλακτικὴ εἰς ποδάγραν*, it is evident that he was also interested in medicine; it is a very brief regimen for those afflicted with gout. Part of this letter was taken from the *Σύνταγμα περὶ τῆς ποδάγρας* of Demetrios Pepagomenos (XIII-2). According to John, the chief remedies are a simple diet, purgation, and bloodletting.

John's letters were addressed to the bishops of Ephesos and Philippopolis; to one Cabasilas (*μέγας διοικητής*), chief collector of taxes, different from the great Byzantine mystic; to a philosopher Joseph,[30] and to one Matarancos.

Text. Jean François Boissonade: Anecdota nova (Paris 1844). Almost half of this volume is devoted to Nicephoros' letters. John's letters are edited in p. 203–22, the letter on gout being the last (p. 220–22). Boissonade seems to be in doubt as to the authenticity of that letter (preface p. vii).
Criticism. Krumbacher (p. 482, 1897). M. Treu: Der Philosoph Joseph (Byzantinische Zeitschrift 8, 49–50, Leipzig 1899).

[30] See footnote 32 below.

JOANNES ACTUARIOS

Joannes son of Zacharias, generally called Actuarios, Ἰωάννης ὁ ἀκτουάριος. Byzantine physician, flourished at the court of Constantinople under Andronicos III Palaeologos, emperor from 1328 to 1341. I call him Actuarios, not actuarius, not only because he was a Greek, but also because these words have different meanings in Greek and Latin; actuarius means notary, ἀκτουάριος court physician;[31] his name might thus be Anglicized "John the court physician." One of his teachers was a philosopher named Josephos Rhacendytes[32] (Ῥακενδύτης, dressed in rags), to whom he dedicated one of his medical treatises (see below).

Actuarios' date. Earlier writers (such as Fabricius, Bibl. graec. 12, 636, 1724) placed him in the twelfth century, even in the eleventh; according to K. Sprengel (Histoire de la médecine 2, 242, 1815), he was a contemporary of Nicholas Myrepsos (XIII-2). The dating which is now accepted is based upon the dedication of Actuarios' main work to the chamberlain Apocaucos, who became (1342) a grand duke[33] and is mentioned a great many times in the history of John VI Cantacuzenos. See E. H. F. Meyer (3, 388, 1856) and the edition of Cantacuzenos in the Bonn corpus (vols. 2–4, 1828–32; index, 4, 570: "Apocauchus vel potius Apocaucus").

As Actuarios was the last of the great Byzantine physicians, and as his works were remarkable for their literary quality as well as for their scientific value, it is worth while to discuss his medical philosophy. He continued the traditions of the pneumatic school,[34] which could be readily harmonized with Christian theology, reviving them and developing especially the psychological implications. We shall summarize his views on the subject below apropos of his περὶ ἐνεργειῶν. He was very well acquainted with Greek literature and philosophy, with the Greek medical classics, chiefly Galen, and also (indirectly) with Arabic medicine, yet genuine clinical experience counterbalanced his erudition and helped him to preserve his originality.

His main work is a general medical treatise, Θεραπευτικὴ μέθοδος (Methodus medendi), which he wrote for his friend Apocaucos when the latter was sent on a diplomatic mission to northern Scythia (Russia). It is divided into six books: (1, 2) General diagnosis and summary of special diagnosis (these first two books seem to have circulated independently under the title περὶ διαγνώσεως παθῶν); (3) bloodletting, purgation, enemas, suppositories, gargles, bathing, diet, treatment of fevers, etc.; (4) special pathology and therapeutics; (5, 6) pharmacopoeia (the last two books were the first to be printed; they appeared in Latin translation under the title De medicamentorum compositione, in 1539). Though this work is mainly a compilation derived from Galen and later writings, it contains some novelties and interesting points of view: description of colics due to lead poisoning; first mention of whipworm (Trichocephalus dispar, a nematode parasite of the human

[31] The more usual meaning in modern languages (English, French, German)—computer of insurance risks and premiums—is again different from the Greek and Latin.

[32] This Rhacendytes is very probably identical with Josephos the Philosopher mentioned four times in Krumbacher (p. 481, 497, 549, 552, 1897): letters were addressed to him by Nicephoros Chumnos and Thomas Magistros, and his necrology by Theodoros Metochites is counted one of the latter's best works. Now these three men, Nicephoros, Thomas, and Theodoros, flourished under Andronicos II (1282–1328), and this tallies with Actuarios' own activity during the following reign. See also J. F. K. Hecker (2, 327, 1829).

[33] Τῷ παρακοιμωμένῳ τῷ Ἀποκαύκῳ τῷ καὶ ὕστερον χρηματίσαντι μεγάλῳ δουκί.

[34] Founded by Athenaeos of Attalia in Rome about the middle of the first century (Introd. 1, 260).

intestine); use of gentle purgatives instead of violent ones; distinction between different kinds of squinting; bloodletting by venesection, also by arteriotomy; practice of bloodletting in the vicinity of the ailing part (Hippocratic "revulsion"), or at some distance from it, or in the opposite side or part, e.g. in the foot for headache (Arabic or Byzantine "derivation"); Actuarios used both methods according to circumstances.[35]

Actuarios was a clear writer of the encyclopaedic type, conciliatory rather than aggressive, always aware of the good possibilities of divergent, if not opposite, methods. These fundamental qualities appear also in his treatise on urine.

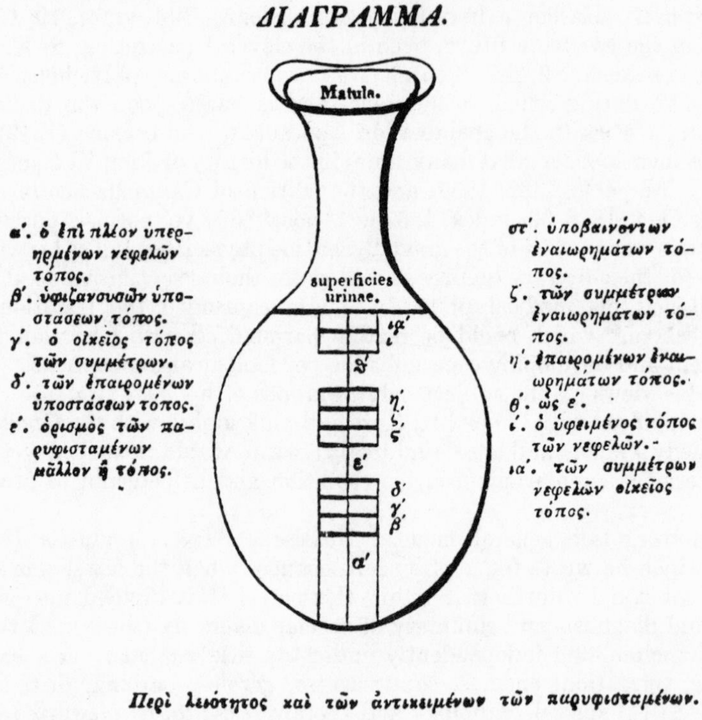

FIG. 22. Diagram for uroscopy, from Actuarios' De urinis (Ideler's edition, 2, 22, 1842). See explanation in text.

The treatise on urine (περὶ οὔρων) is the most elaborate Greek treatise on the subject. It is essentially Galenic, but the author took full advantage of the later Greek writings and of his own not inconsiderable experience. It is divided into seven books: (1) περὶ διαφορᾶς οὔρων, the different kinds of urine, physiological summary; (2, 3) περὶ διαγνώσεως, diagnosis; (4, 5) περὶ αἰτίας, aetiology; (6, 7) περὶ προγνώσεως, prognosis. The differentiations between different kinds of normal and pathological urines as to color, consistency, sediments, and substances (contenta) floating at various levels in the physician's glass (ἀμίς, matula) are very

[35] For the two methods, revulsionary vs. derivative bleeding, see Introd. 2, 77. The conflict became acute c. 1515, when Pierre Brissot (1478–1522) took up the cudgels for the Hippocratic method, or rather against the exclusive practice of "derivation."

minute and complicated. The matula's height is divided into eleven sections which enable one to classify the contenta (the heaviest ones, settling in the four lowest divisions, are the hypostasis; the middle ones, the sublimia or enaeoremata; the lightest ones, the nubes; for the Greek terms relative to each division see diagram, fig. 22). The upper surface of urine in the matula is also elaborately described. The fourth and fifth books include a discussion of the Galenic idea of coction (πέψις) as applied to urology. Urine is an excretion (περιήθημα) from the blood. The most interesting item is a description (the first?) of paroxysmal haemoglobinuria (book 4, ch. 12). In spite of his deep study of the subject, Actuarios was not by any means a fanatical urologist: he fully recognized the value of other methods of diagnosis and prognosis, and emphasized the supreme diagnostic importance of the pulse. This treatise was the first of his to be printed: Latin edition, Venice 1519.

Actuarios' third work, περὶ ἐνεργειῶν καὶ παθῶν τοῦ ψυχικοῦ πνεύματος καὶ τῆς κατ' αὐτὸ διαίτης (De actionibus et affectibus spiritus animalis huiusque nutritione), in two books, dedicated to Rhacendytes, is very important for the history of pneumatism and psychopathology. The old pneumatic theory is developed, the three kinds of pneuma are considered—natural, vital, animal spirits (πνεῦμα φυσικόν, ζωτικόν, ψυχικόν)—but the work is chiefly devoted to the third kind. He discusses the physiological foundation of the πνεύματα and their psychological reactions in health and disease, the normal mechanism of sensation (αἴσθησις), representation (φρόνησις), imagination (φαντασία), judgment (μέρος δοξαστικόν), intellect (διάνοια), and reason (νοῦς). Reason is largely independent of the πνεῦμα ψυχικόν. Attempt at localization of intellectual faculties in various parts of the brain. The second book contains hygienic rules (concerning food, drink, exercise, sleep, bathing, etc.) with special reference to the intellectual life. The περὶ ἐνεργειῶν was the only work of Actuarios to be printed in Greek before the nineteenth century (Paris 1557).

These three works are the only published ones, but a few others are ascribed to Actuarios, e.g., a treatise on bloodletting (περὶ φλεβοτομίας) represented by a Dresden MS.

Text. Methodus medendi. Greek text in J. L. Ideler: Physici et medici graeci minores (2, 353–463, 1842). This contains only books 1 and 2. First Latin edition, restricted to the last two books, by J. Ruellius (Paris 1539, Basel 1540). First complete edition in any language, Latin translation by Corneille Henri Mathys of Bruges (Mathisius, d. 1565) with index (Venice 1554).

E. Teza: I bagni, un capitolo inedito in Greco (Atti del R. Istituto veneto 63, part 2, 299–317, 1904). Greek text of ch. 10 of book 3, together with Mathys' Latin version, an Italian one, and notes. It should be noted that except for this chapter the original Greek text of books 3–6 is still unpublished. A critical edition of the whole work is much to be desired.

De urinis. Greek edition by Ideler (2, 3–192, 1842). Latin translation by Ambrosius Leo of Nola (Venice 1519), many times reprinted (Basel 1520, Paris 1522, Basel 1529, Lyon 1529, Venice 1529, Paris 1548, Basel 1563, Utrecht 1670).

De actionibus et affectibus spiritus animalis. First Greek edition by Jac. Goupylus (Paris 1557). Second Greek edition by J. F. Fischer (Leipzig 1774). Third by Ideler (1, 312–86, 1841). Latin translation by Julius Alexandrinus de Neustain (Venice 1547, again Venice 1554 with the Methodus medendi).

Opera omnia. Only in Latin (Paris 1556, Lyon 1556).

Criticism. J. F. K. Hecker: Geschichte der Heilkunde (2, 335–58, 1829). E. H.

F. Meyer (3, 386–90, 1856). Haeser (1, 481–83, 1875). J. Hirschberg: Die Augenheilkunde bei den Griechen (Archiv für Ophthalmologie, 1887). Krumbacher (p. 615, 618, 620, 1897). A. G. Costomiris: Etudes sur les écrits inédits des anciens médecins grecs (Revue des études grecques 10, 405–45, Paris 1897). Gurlt (1, 591–92, 1898). Iwan Bloch, in Puschmann's Geschichte der Medizin (1, 566–67, 1902). Neuburger (2, 133–37, 1911). E. Desnos: Histoire de l'urologie (p. 192–98, Paris 1914; Isis 2, 466), includes extracts in French translation; see also ibid. p. 200–10, for the history of the matula, with many illustrations. Ralph H. Major: Classic descriptions of disease (p. 500–3, Springfield, Ill. 1932; Isis 19, 518–20), includes English translation of the chapter concerning paroxysmal haemoglobinuria.

C. WESTERN JEWS

C1. Southern France

JACOB BEN JOSEPH HA-LEVI

Judeo-Languedocian physician and translator from Latin into Hebrew, who flourished probably at Alais (Gard), Languedoc, c. 1297–1306. He translated:

1. Arnold of Villanova (XIII-2): Treatise on paralysis, Ma'amar ha-paralisin, in 1297.
2. Mesuë the Third (XIII-1): Cyrurgia Joannis Mesuë. Jacob translated the chapter on the eye from Latin into Hebrew in 1306.
3. Gualterus Agilinus (XIII-1): Treatise on poisons, ma'amar be-eresim. Dealing with four kinds of poisons. Undated.

He composed the following medical treatises:

4. Ma'amar be-ḥazirim ha-niqra maqel shaqed. Treatise on scrofulas called Stick of almond tree. Composed in 1300 at the request of Isaac ben Abraham of Tretz (Bouches-du-Rhône), in Provence.
5. Ma'amar ha-fisṭulas. Treatise on fistulas. Supplement to the preceding treatise, composed in 1301 at Alais, Languedoc, at the request of his father-in-law, rabbi Tanḥum ben Judah.
6. Ma'amar be-hefsed ha-makot. Treatise on the loss (of blood) by wounds. Written in answer to a consultation. Undated.
7. Ma'amar be-mursot. Treatise on abscesses. Authorship uncertain, undated.

Criticism. Neubauer-Renan (p. 655–56, 1893). Steinschneider (p. 780, 801, 1893). Gross (p. 59, 1897). Wickersheimer (p. 316, 1936).

HEZEKIAH HA-MILIABI

Maestre Bonenfant of Milhau (Milhau or Milhaud in dépt. Gard, Languedoc, not Milhau in dépt. Aveyron, Rouergue). Judeo-Languedocian physician and translator from Latin into Hebrew (fl. c. 1343?).

He wrote a Hebrew treatise on tertiary fevers, entitled Gabriel, beginning with the words: "Said Gabriel. I think I must mention what Gordon[35a] wrote on this fever which is half of the tertiary fever hemitritaean." It includes many prescriptions and ends with 92 rules on bloodletting.

He translated freely into Hebrew the Tabula super vita brevis of Arnold of Villanova. That translation, entitled Mabo' Arnauld (Introduction to Arnauld), was completed at Uzès (dépt. Gard, Languedoc) in 1343. According to Gross,

[35a] Gordon is very probably Bernard of Gordon.

however, that translation was made by one Gabriel of Milhaud in 1585 (?). The matter requires investigation. On account of the Hebrew treatise above mentioned, Hezekiah ha-Miliabi could be confused easily with one Gabriel of Milhaud.

Criticism. Steinschneider (p. 782, 1893). Neubauer-Renan (p. 762, 1893). Gross (p. 24, 345, 1897). Isaac Broydé (JE 3, 305, 1902), only 10 lines. Wickersheimer (p. 88, 1936).

ISAAC BEN JUDAH LATTES

Jewish Languedocian physician (fl. 1303).

The surname Lattes or de Lattes (written in Hebrew script with ṭeth and sin) is derived from the place Latte or Lattes between Béziers and Montpellier. Many Jewish scholars of southern France bore it. We have already come across two (Introd. 2, 880, 883), and we shall deal with Isaac's grandson, Isaac ben Jacob (XIV-2), later on.

Isaac was established as a physician in Perpignan (Roussillon) 1303. He was devoting part of his time to Talmudic and scientific studies; he was especially interested in astronomy, probably for astrological reasons. He used talismans for curative purposes, notably a stone upon which a lion was engraved. The religious validity of such a practice caused a controversy between Solomon ben Adret of Barcelona (XIII-2) and Abba Mari ben Moses of Lunel, both conservatives. Isaac posed as a scientist and as a defender of science within Judaism, but his thoughts on the subject were rather muddy, judging from his use of amulets afore-mentioned and from the fact that he signed petitions on both sides of the intense controversy which was then raging between the rabbis on limited rationalism vs. antirationalism or Maimonidism vs. anti-Maimonidism.

He is said to have composed Talmudic commentaries and astronomical writings, but nothing has come to us, and he is mentioned here rather as a good symbol of the intellectual difficulties of that age.

Criticism. Neubauer-Renan (1877, 1893, by index). A. Peiginsky (JE 7, 628, 1904). M. Zobel (EJ 10, 677, 1934). Wickersheimer (p. 311, 1936).

ABRAHAM BEN DAVID CASLARI

Judeo-Languedocian physician of the Caslari family, named after the place Caylar (Hérault) where it originated. (In Hebrew Caslari is generally written with qof and sin.) Abraham may have been the son of David ben Abraham Caslari (XIII-2), yet his grandfather's name was apparently Jahzeel (Yaḥẓe'el), not Abraham.

Abraham ben David was born at Narbonne but flourished at Besalú, near Perpignan, c. 1322–29, perhaps as late as 1349. He was the teacher of Moses ben Joshua of Narbonne.

He wrote three or four medical books:

1. 'Aleh ra'anan (Verdant leaf) or 'Aleh ha-refu'ah (Leaf of healing), a treatise on fevers in five books, 1326.
2. Ma'amar be-qaddaḥot ha-dibriyot u-mine ha-qaddaḥot (Treatise on pestilential and other fevers), also entitled Ma'amar qaẓar lekol ha-qaddaḥot ha-'ippushiyot, composed in 1329, or about the time of the great plague, 1349.
3. Dine ha-haqqazah, rules for bloodletting.
4. Mekalkel maḥalah (Who sustains in illness).

Moses ben Joshua said that his teacher Abraham had assimilated all the recipes of al-Rāzī's antidotary after having translated them into Latin. I do not understand this statement. Maybe Abraham was more familiar with Latin than Arabic, but in any case the Kitāb al-aqrābādhīn had then already been translated into Hebrew at least once, by Moses ibn Tibbon in 1257 (Introd. 2, 849). Abraham had perhaps translated these recipes as a linguistic and mnemonic exercise.

Text. The Ma'amar be-qaddaḥot was edited with a Dutch translation by H. Pinkhof: A. Kashlari over pestachtige koortsen (Amsterdam 1891).
Criticism. Neubauer-Renan (p. 644–67, 1893). Steinschneider (p. 732, 973, 1893). S. Kahn and I. Broydé (JE 3, 599, 1902). EJ (5, 73, 1930).

C2. Hispanic Peninsula

SAMUEL BEN WAQAR

Samuel Ibn Waqar (or Huacar). Judeo-Spanish astrologer, physician, and financier. He was physician and treasurer to Alfonso XI (king of Castile 1312–50). He was still living in Toledo in 1327 and perhaps in 1333.

He may be identical with the unnamed physician who wrote in Arabic the Kitāb al-ṭibb al-qasṭālī al-mulūkī fī-l-umūr al-'amaliya (The royal Castilian book of medicine dealing with practical matters), containing practical recommendations divided into 10 chapters: (1) use of meat, (2) use of wines, (3) bloodletting, (4) cupping, (5) purgatives, (6) baths, (7) emetics, (8) icy drinks, (9) ailments peculiar to certain countries, (10) proper diet for strangers dwelling in those countries. (These chapters 9 and 10, devoted to the consideration of regional diseases or medical geography, are perhaps the most remarkable.) The author of that Arabic treatise was a Toledan Jew, who had an opportunity of treating the young king of Castile, Ferdinand IV (king 1295–1312), the treatment being described by himself in his treatise. That king was born in 1285, and may have been called "fatan" (adolescent)—the term applied to him in the Arabic text—until c. 1305, and even later.

Text. The unpublished Escorial MS written in Toledo 1414 (Spanish era, i.e. A.D. 1376) is described by Casiri (1, 314–15, 1760).
Criticism. Steinschneider (p. 165, 1902). Meyer Kayserling (JE 6, 553, 1904).

SOLOMON IBN YA'ĪSH

In all probability identical with Solomon ben Abraham ben Baruch. In Arabic: Abū-l-Rabī' Sulaimān. Don Soliman. Hispano-Jewish physician, philosopher, and exegete, who flourished in Seville and died there in May 1345 (according to his tombstone).

He wrote in Arabic:

1. An extensive commentary in 6 volumes on Ibn Sīnā's Qānūn. This commentary is philosophical rather than medical. A part of it was copied in Hebrew script during the author's lifetime by Joseph ben Abraham Naḥmias. A summary of Ibn Ya'īsh's commentary on book 1 of the Qānūn was composed in Hebrew by Jacob Qafanton under the title Qiẓẓur bi'ur ha-rishon. (This Jacob Qafanton was the author of an arithmetic; he was already a teacher in 1406 and was no longer alive in 1439; he lived probably in Castile.) A part of the commentary was also translated into Hebrew.

2. A commentary on Abraham ben Ezra's commentary on the Torah. Parts of

it, probably translated by one Jacob Alfandari, were included in the Meqor ḥayyim, a Torah commentary, by Samuel ben Ẓarẓa (called Ibn Sana or Seneh), who flourished at Valencia in the second half of the fourteenth century (JE 12, 638, 1906).

3. A dictionary of difficult words in Arabic poetry.

Text. The Meqor ḥayyim was printed at Mantua in 1559.

Criticism. Steinschneider (p. 686, 774, 939, 1893); (p. 167, 1902). Max Seligsohn (JE 11, 458, 1905). Joseph Heller (EJ 8, 782, 1931).

E. WESTERN MUSLIMS

MUḤAMMAD AL-SHAFRA

Abū 'Abdallāh Muḥammad ibn 'Alī al-Qirbilyānī al-Shafra. Hispano-Muslim surgeon who flourished in the first quarter of the fourteenth century.

The nisba al-Qirbilyānī refers to his native place Crevillente, near Elche, in the province of Alicante. The laqab al-Shafra (or shifra, shufra) is the name of a kind of knife or cutlass, machete, and Renaud suggests that this may be a reference to the knife used by our Muḥammad or his ancestors for digging and cutting roots. Indeed, according to the Iḥāṭa, Muḥammad was a renowned herbalist, who collected his own herbs and roots in the mountains, had become a master in that branch of knowledge, and had filled many books (kanānīsh, pl. of kunnāsh; pandectae) with notes on the subject badly scribbled. These notes have not come down to us.

He flourished mainly in Cadiz during the rule of the Naṣrī sulṭān Naṣr Abū-l-Juyūsh. This Naṣr ruled Granada from 1308 to 1314, when he was deposed and moved to Cadiz, where he died in 1322. Thus our Muḥammad flourished in Cadiz about the years 1314–22. He created there for his prince a botanic garden perfectly arranged, and treated him when a kind of plague (wabā) was desolating that region. He sometimes traveled away from the city to Valencia, Granada, Algeciras, and even to Ceuta across the Straits.

He composed a surgical treatise Kitāb al-istiqṣā' wal-ibrām fī 'ilāj al-jirāḥāt wal-awrām (Book of deepening and consolidation on the treatment of wounds and inflammations or tumors). It is divided into 3 parts, dealing with (1) inflammations and tumors, their causes, symptoms, and treatment; (2) wounds, extraction of arrows, and al-jabr,[36] that is, the reduction of fractures and luxations; (3) simple or composite drugs used in surgery. It is thus a complete treatise on surgery, as that science was understood in mediaeval times. The main literary source is the Taṣrīf of Abū-l-Qāsim of Cordova (X-2), not so much the purely surgical part of it, but rather the pathological part, dealing with inflammations and tumors of many kinds. In addition, Muḥammad was able to draw upon his own personal experience, and he describes many interesting cases cured or witnessed by himself. Abū-l-Qāsim recognized 30 kinds of inflammations and tumors, Muḥammad, 36, some of which are difficult, if not impossible, to identify with our own pathological entities. Among the causes which may delay or prevent the healing of wounds or tumors, Muḥammad, following in this Abū-l-Qāsim, dis-

[36] Hence the Spanish term algebrista, the original meaning of which is bonesetter. The later meaning, as our algebraist, refers to the reduction not of fractures but of equations (Introd. 1, 563).

tinguished local climatic influences; wounds heal better in some places than in others.

Muḥammad al-Shafra composed this book for his son, collecting his many observations and experiences, and often repeating his advice of prudence and even of abstention in critical cases. He was anxious to increase the prestige of his profession, always jeopardized by the cooperation of humbler practicians, barbers, bloodletters, and cuppers (ḥājim or ḥajjām).

Text. The Kitāb al-istiqṣā' is still unpublished. There is a MS of it in the library al-Qarawīyīn in Fez, and there are at least two other Moroccan MSS (Renaud).

Criticism. The main source is the Escorial MS history of Granada by Ibn al-Khaṭīb (XIV-2), Al-iḥāṭa fī ta'rīkh Gharnāṭa. Leclerc (2, 250, 1876), only 8 lines. H. P. J. Renaud: Un chirurgien musulman du royaume de Grenade, Muḥammad ash-Shafra (Hespéris vol. 20, 20 p., 1935; Isis 26, 503), including elaborate analysis of the Istiqṣā'. Brockelmann (suppt. 2, 366, 1938).

IBN KHĀTIMAH

Abū Ja'far Aḥmad ibn 'Alī Ibn Khātimah al-Anṣārī. Hispano-Muslim poet and physician (d. after 1368).

Ibn Khātimah was a descendant of one of the "helpers" of the Prophet and was born in Almeria in 1323/24. He was still alive in 1369, when Ibn al-Khaṭīb spoke enthusiastically of him in the Iḥāṭa. He wrote poems, and two important prose works:

1. A history of Almeria frequently quoted in the Iḥāṭa, entitled Al-maziyyat Almeria 'alā ghairihā min bilād al-Andalusia (The superiority of Almeria over other Andalusian places).

2. A treatise on the plague which raged in Almeria in 1348–49, entitled Taḥṣīl al-gharaḍ al-qāṣid fī tafṣīl al-maraḍ al-wāfid.

The plague treatise is important because it is one of the earliest accounts of the Black Death. (For a list of other early accounts see the note at the end of my article on Gentile da Foligno and the longer note in chapter XXV.) As far as Almeria is concerned, the plague began on June 1, 1348, and it was still raging there when Ibn Khātimah wrote his account of it in the first days of February 1349. Ibn Khātimah's treatise is remarkable not only because of its earliness, but also because of its goodness. It deals with ten questions which are answered at some length: (I) Generalities about the plague, including a discussion of its Arabic name, ṭā'ūn. (II) General and special causes. (III) Why some people fall victims to the plague, while others escape it in spite of equal proximity. Why did the plague reach Almeria faster than other parts of Andalusia? (IV) Contagion. The idea of contagion is well explained, this being somewhat of a novelty in mediaeval literature: "The result of my long experience is that if a person comes into contact with a patient, he is immediately attacked by the disease with the same symptoms. If the first patient expectorated blood, the second will do so. . . . If the first developed buboes, they will appear on the other in the same places. If the first had an ulcer, the second will get the same; and the second patient likewise transmits the disease" (as quoted by Meyerhof, Legacy of Islam p. 341). (V) Prophylaxy. (VI) Therapeutics. The remaining questions or chapters, VII to X, are theological. The treatise occupies an intermediate position between that of Gentile of Foligno and the Compendium de epidimia officially published by the faculty of medicine of Paris in October 1348. Both these treatises were just a little earlier than Ibn Khātimah's, which was more philosophical than the first and more practical than the second. It should be noted that Ibn Khātimah, in spite of his strong theological bias, was not a mere theorist; he had investigated geographical conditions and the comparative incidence of the plague in various places; he was well informed and had made many observations of his own, he was generally reasonable and clear.

There are at least three other Arabic early accounts of the same plague, one by Ibn al-Khaṭīb (XIV-2) and the two others respectively by Muḥammad ibn 'Alī al-Shaqūrī (XIV-2) and Muḥammad ibn Muḥammad of Almeria (XIV-2).

Text. The Arabic text of the plague treatise (Escorial MS 1785, Casiri 1770) is unpublished, except for a fragment edited by Marcus Joseph Müller (Sitzungsberichte der Bayerischen Akad., 1863, 2, 28–31, Munich 1863). Partial German translation by Ṭāhā Dinānah: Die Schrift von Ibn Khātimah über die Pest (AGM 19, 27–81, 1927; Isis 10, 131).

Criticism. Casiri (2, 334, 1770). Gayangos (1, 51, 358, 1840). Pons Boigues (p. 331, 1898). Brockelmann (2, 259, 1902; suppt. 2, 369, 1938). Max Meyerhof: Science and medicine (Legacy of Islam p. 340, Oxford 1931).

F. EASTERN MUSLIMS

'ABDALLĀH IBN 'ABD AL-'AZĪZ

'Abdallāh ibn 'Abd al-'Azīz al-Sīwāsī, i.e., of Sīwās (ancient Sebastia on the upper Halys River). Turkish physician who wrote at the beginning of the fourteenth century an Arabic commentary on the aphorisms of Hippocrates, 'Umdat al-fuḥūl fī sharḥ al-fuṣūl.

Criticism. Brockelmann (suppt. 2, 326, 1938).

MUḤAMMAD IBN MUḤAMMAD AL-KHUJANDĪ

Muḥammad ibn Muḥammad al-Khujandī Najīb al-milla wal-dīn. Transoxianian physician writing in Arabic (fl. 1304–16).

His nisba refers to Khujanda on the Sīr Daryā (Jaxartes). We have met a more famous Khujandī before, Ḥāmid ibn al-Khiḍr (X-2), astronomer and mathematician. This one flourished under the īl-khān Uljāi'tū Khudābanda (ruled 1304–16).

He wrote various medical books in Arabic: a supercommentary on the Qānūn of Ibn Sīnā; then the Mukhtaṣar fī ṣinā'at al-ṭibb; Tarwīḥ al-arwāḥ min 'ilal al-ashbāḥ, etc.

Criticism. Brockelmann (suppt. 2, 219, 1938).

AḤMAD IBN MUḤAMMAD AL-KĪLĀNĪ

This al-Kīlānī dedicated an Arabic commentary on the aphorisms of Hippocrates to Jānī Beg Maḥmūd (khān of the Blue Horde of western Qipčāq 1340–57). He is strangely called al-mutaṭabbib, which means the would-be physician.

Criticism. Brockelmann (suppt. 2, 299, 1938).

IBN-AL-KUTUBĪ

Yūsuf ibn Ismā'īl al-Baghdādī al-Shāfi'ī Ibn al-Kutubī (i.e., son of the bookseller). Muslim Iraqian physician (fl. c. 1311).

He is known to us by a single book which he finished in 1311, a treatise on simple drugs entitled Mā lā yasa'u al-ṭabība jahluhu (What a physician is not allowed to ignore). He was planning to write another book on composite drugs, but did not do so, or else that book has not come down to us.

The Mā lā yasa'u is an abbreviation of the Jāmi' fī-l-adwiya al-mufrada of Ibn al-Baiṭār (XIII-1), which is reduced to about half its size. Ibn al-Kutubī criticizes the repetitions, confusions, inaccuracies, prolixities of Ibn al-Baiṭār's work, but his own work is far less valuable, for in the process of condensation he has mixed indiscriminately various kinds of information the sources of which are lost (whereas in Ibn al-Baiṭār all the authorities are quoted). He has added a few novelties, and seems to have obtained some new data from Bulgarian or Russian sources.

Text. Many MSS but no edition. A critical edition is desirable, but not before the text of Ibn al-Baiṭār is well established and its sources clarified.

Criticism. E. H. F. Meyer (3, 239–45, 1856). Leclerc (2, 261–64, 1876). Brockelmann (2, 169, 1902; suppt. 2, 218, 1938).

MAḤMŪD IBN ILYĀS AL-SHĪRĀZĪ

Najm al-dīn Maḥmūd ibn Ḍiyā' al-dīn Ilyās al-Shīrāzī (or Maḥmūd ibn al-shaikh Ṣā'in al-dīn Ilyās). Persian physician writing in Arabic (d. Shīrāz 1330).

Maḥmūd composed a medical encyclopaedia for the householder entitled Kitāb al-ḥāwī fī 'ilm al-tadāwī (The containing, or "continens," concerning the art of treatment). Also called Al-ḥāwī al-ṣaghīr (The small continens) to distinguish it from the Al-ḥāwī al-kabīr (The great continens) of al-Rāzī (IX-2). One of the MSS (Gotha) is dated 1336–37 and thus is almost contemporary. In spite of its name, the Ḥāwī of our Maḥmūd is not so small, one of the MSS (Bairūt) including 592 very full pages. It is divided into five parts, dealing respectively with (1) generalities, (2) fevers, (3) external infirmities, (4) simple drugs, (5) composite drugs. In part 4 the drugs are arranged in alphabetical order; part 5 is divided into 50 chapters.

Of these 50 chapters, 4 deal with generalities such as the testing of drugs, the properties of viands. The 46 other chapters treat, some of them, pharmaceutical forms, such as oils, robs (Ar. Pers., rubb), troches; others, formulas of remedies serving definite purposes, as emetics, emmenagogues, remedies against sterility, etc. Thus part 5 is at once a codex, wherein drugs are classified according to their pharmaceutical affinities, and a magistral formulary, wherein they are classified according to their pharmacodynamic properties. It is more a codex than a formulary. It includes more than 650 recipes.

Text. Pierre Guigues (1867–1930): Le livre de l'art du traitement de Najm ad-Dyn Mahmoud; Remèdes composés. Texte, traduction, glossaires précédés d'un essai sur la pharmacie arabe (Paris pharmaceutical thesis, 562 p., 240 of them in Arabic, Beyrouth 1902). This is the edition of part 5 based on the MS of St. Joseph College in Bairūt. Includes Arabic-French and French-Arabic glossaries; moreover, the author has added Latin synonyms found in the translation of Serapion Senior (IX-2), Synonima Serapionis, by Gerard of Cremona (XII-2); in the translation of Serapion Junior (XII-1), De simplici medicina, by Simon of Genoa (XIII-2); in the Pandectae of Matthaeus Sylvaticus; and in the commentaries on Dioscorides by Pier Andrea Mattioli (1500–77) (Venice 1554).

This edition had been printed at the author's expense; the remainder of it, stored in his home in Bairūt, was destroyed when his house was pillaged during the war (letter from professor Guigues to me dated Bairūt, Nov. 26, 1927). I obtained a copy of it thanks to the courtesy of the Johns Hopkins Library in Baltimore, Maryland.

Criticism. Hājjī Khalīfa (3, 11, no. 4385, 1842). P. Guigues: Review of his own work (Janus 8, 41–43, 1903). Brockelmann (suppt. 2, 298, 1938).

IBN AL-AKFĀNĪ

Abū 'Abdallāh Shams al-dīn Muḥammad ibn Ibrāhīm al Anṣārī al-Sinjārī al-Miṣrī al-Sakhāwī, called Ibn al-Akfānī or simply al-Akfānī. 'Irāqī physician, naturalist, encyclopaedist (d. 1348–49).

Ibn al-Akfānī was a descendant of one of those who helped the Prophet in Medīna; he was born in or originated in Sinjār in Jazīrah west of Mūṣul; practiced medicine in Cairo, and died of the plague in 1348–49.

He wrote three medical treatises, two on natural history, and a short encyclopaedia (I keep Brockelmann's numbering):

1. Kashf al-rain fī aḥwāl al-'ain (Discovery of the defect in the conditions of the eye). Treatise on eye diseases, divided into 3 books: (I) Description, definition, and anatomy of the eye. The anatomy is taken verbatim from the Qānūn of Ibn Sīnā. (II) Eye diseases, their causes, symptoms, and treatment. The author tried to distinguish as many varieties of diseases as possible, which he succeeded in doing by dividing the varieties recognized by his predecessors into subvarieties. For example, whereas 'Ammar ibn 'Alī (XI-1) recognized 13 eyelid ailments, and 'Alī ibn 'Īsā (XI-1), 29, Ibn al-Akfānī recognized no less than 43; his successor Shādhilī (XIV-2) reduced the number to 36. Some of Ibn al Akfānī's diagnoses are important additions, e.g., the phlegmon (falghamūnī) of the eyelid, the "Persian fire" (carbuncle), twitchings and cramps of the eyelid. He observed ingrowing of eyelashes and the fact that that may cause an inward bending of the cornea requiring surgical intervention. The treatments are very briefly indicated; they are sometimes irrational. (III) Materia medica in alphabetical order, including many more substances than were given by 'Alī ibn 'Īsā, yet omitting a few of these.

A summary or anthology (taghrīḍ) of the Kashf al-rain was made in the following century by one Nūr al-dīn 'Alī al-Munāwī, under the title Wiqāyat al-'ain (Protection of the eye).

2. Kitāb ghunyat al-labīb fī ghaibat (ḥaithu lā yūjad) al-ṭabīb. Domestic medicine for use in the physician's absence.

3. Nihāyat al-qaṣd fī ṣinā'at al-faṣd, on bloodletting.

4. Al-naẓar wal-taḥqīq fī taqlīb al-raqīq. Advice concerning the buying of slaves; this may be of anthropological interest. It is really an application of the science of physiognomy to the art of buying slaves having desirable physical or mental qualities. The unique MS of that work (Ar. 2234, Bibliothèque nationale, Paris) is very incomplete, but the text was expanded in a treatise by Maḥmūd ibn Aḥmad al-'Aintabī al-Amshāṭī (1407–96) (Brockelmann 2, 82, suppt. 2, 93; Mourad p. 33, 55, 1939). See also no. 7.

5. Nukhab al-dhakhā'ir fī aḥwāl al-jawāhir (Selection of treasures concerning the conditions of jewels). Dealing with fourteen precious stones and indicating their qualities.

6. Irshād al-qāṣid ilā asnā'-l-maqāṣid (Guidance for him who tends to the highest purpose). Short encyclopaedic treatise dealing with 60 sciences, of which 10 are called fundamental (aṣlīya), 7 of these speculative (naẓrīya), to wit logic

(manṭiq), metaphysics (al-ilāhī), physics (al-ṭabī'i), mathematics (al-riyāḍa), and its branches (geometry, arithmetic, astronomy, music), 3 practical ('amalīya), to wit politics (siyāsa), ethics (akhlāq), and domestic economy (tadbīr al-manzil). The subdivision of physics into 10 branches (against 7 in Ibn Sīnā) is remarkable. The branches are named in order of growing complexity, the first 2 dealing with simple bodies, the next 7 with compound bodies, the last one with both simple and compound bodies. We thus obtain the list (1) astrology, (2) talismans, (3) phantasmagoria, (4) alchemy, (5) agriculture, (6) veterinary art, breeding of falcons, (7) medicine, (8) physiognomy, (9) oneiromancy, (10) magic (after Mourad p. 27, 1939). The first chapter of the Irshād upholds the importance of science and the dignity of the scientist; the second chapter explains the methods of studying science and of teaching it. The whole work may be considered as a kind of general guide for the student, and may be classified with other Arabic works such as the Ta'līm al-muta'allim of Burhān al-dīn al-Zarnūjī (XIII-1) and the Tadhkirat al-sāmi' wal-mutakallim of Ibn Jamā'a, not to speak of later ones. The author's purpose was simply to indicate the field of each of the sciences and of their divisions and applications, hence the indications given are meager, yet they include much historical information, as he tries to give the names of the main scientists who created or developed each field. For example, for geometry he speaks of Autolycos of Pitane (IV-2 B.C.), Euclid, Archimedes, Apollonios, Menelaos (I-2), and Yūsuf al-Mu'taman (XI-2), king of Saragossa. According to Ḥājjī Khalīfa, some 400 works are quoted in all. In the chapter on astronomy he discusses astrology with as much originality as concision. The study of astronomy may be divided, from the point of view of Muslim theology, into five parts, which are respectively (a) obligatory (wājib), determination of the ritual times; (b) recommended (mandūb), study of the astronomical proofs of the wisdom of God; (c) permitted (mubāḥ), study of the influences which the planets exert upon the earth on account of their trajectories, not of their nature; (d) disapproved (makrūh), study of other planetary influences; (e) forbidden (maḥẓūr), belief in the independent action of the stars, and astrolatry. Thus is astrology condemned, without ambiguity or evasion.

There is an anonymous elaboration of the Irshād al-qāṣid entitled Kitāb al-durr al-naẓīm fī aḥwāl al-'ulūm wal-ta'līm (The well adjusted pearl concerning the conditions of the sciences and of education). Another elaboration was made by the Turkish encyclopaedist Aḥmad ibn Muṣṭafā Tashköprüzāde of Brussa (1495–1561)[37] in the latter's Miftāḥ al-sa'ada wa miṣbāḥ al-siyāda (Key of happiness and beacon of lordship), wherein 150 (or 307) sciences are recognized and defined.

7. Ibn al-Akfānī is probably also the author of a treatise on physiognomy, Kitāb asās al-riyāsa fī 'ilm al-firāsa (Arabic MS 2726, Bibliothèque nationale, Paris), which is very similar to the treatise ad hoc of al-Dimashqī and is derived from the same sources. See also no. 4.

Text. The Irshād al-qāṣid was edited by Aloys Sprenger: A survey of the Muhammedan sciences (Bibliotheca indica no. 21, Calcutta 1849). An English translation well annotated and well indexed is much to be desired.

The Nukhab al-dhakhā'ir was edited by father Louis Cheikho in Al-Mashriq (11, 751–65, 1908). See review of it by Wiedemann in Mitt. (8, 509–11, 1909).

[37] See EI (4, 689, 1929), article by Franz Babinger.

New edition with abundant Arabic notes and Arabic-French glossary by father Anastase Marie de St. Elie (200 p., Baghdād 1939; Isis 32).

The Wiedemann papers cited below contain many extracts from Ibn al-Akfānī's Irshād, and a complete German version of the Nukhab.

Criticism. Hājjī Khalīfa (1, 251, no. 488, 1835). Theodor Haarbrücker: Muhammad's arabische Encyclopädie der Wissenschaften vornehmlich in pädagogischer Beziehung (Jahresbericht über die Luisenst. Realschule, 26 p., Berlin 1859), not available to me. Brockelmann (2, 137, 1902; suppt. 2, 169, 1938). Julius Hirschberg: Die arabischen Lehrbücher der Augenheilkunde (Abhandlungen der Akad. der Wissenschaften, Berlin, 1905, 117 p.; p. 93–95). Ernst Seidel: Studien eines Arztes zu al-Akfānī's Wegweisung für den Zielstrebigen (AGM 12, 10–32, 1920).

Eilhard Wiedemann: Übersetzung und Besprechung der Abhandlung über die Geometrie (Beitr. 5, Erlangen Sitzungsberichte 37, 392–424, 1905); Zu der Astronomie (Beitr .9, ibid. 38, 181–94, 1906); Über die Arithmetik (Beitr. 14, ibid. 40, 29–37, 1908); Übersetzung des Werkes über Mineralogie (Beitr. 30, ibid. 44, 211–29, 1912); Über Physiognomik (Beitr. 42, ibid. 47, 97–100, 1915); Heilkunde der Tiere und der Jagdvögel (Beitr. 53, ibid. vols. 48–49, 242, 1918); Über Landwirtschaft (Beitr. 57, ibid. vols. 50–51, 8–13, 1920); Angaben über die Musik (Beitr. 66, ibid. vols. 54–55, 16–22, 1925). To these should be added Wiedemann's study of Ibn al-Akfānī's alchemy published in another journal (Zeitschrift für praktische Chemie 76, 65, 1907).

Honigmann (p. 181, 1929). Mourad (p. 26–30, 33, 55, 1939). Farmer (p. 52, 1940).

IBN QAYYIM AL-JAWZĪYA

Shams al-dīn Abū 'Abdallāh Muḥammad ibn abī Bakr Ibn Qayyim al-Jawzīya al-Ḥanbalī. Syrian Muslim theologian and physician (1292–1350).

The part of his name by which he is generally called, Ibn Qayyim al-Jawzīya, means "son of the director of the madrasa (school) al-Jawzīya in Damascus." His father (or paternal ancestor) held that position. Ibn Qayyim was born, probably at Damascus, in January 1292. In 1310 he joined Ibn Taimīya, becoming his ardent disciple, sharing his labors and to some extent his sufferings. They were put in prison together in Cairo. He died in September 1350.

Some fifty treatises are ascribed to him, most of which are devoted to the defense of points of Ḥanbalī theology in the spirit of his master Ibn Taimīya. A few others deal with other subjects, e.g.:

1. Kitāb al-ṭuruq al-ḥikmīya fī-l-siyāsa al-shar'īya, on physiognomy and its value to princes.
2. Kitāb al-dā' wal-dawā', on remedy and sickness.
3. Kitab al-ṭibb al-nabawī, medical traditions concerning the Prophet.
4. Kitab ṭibb al-qulūb, medicine of the hearts (spiritual medicine).
5. Tuḥfat al-mawdūd bi-aḥkām al-mawlūd, ritual care of newborn children.
6. Kitāb al-furūsīya al-Muḥammadīya bi-funūn al-qitāl, treatise on horses, horse-riding, and military art.
7. Ḥurmat al-samā', licitness or illicitness of listening to music.

He also wrote books on the manners and conduct of the Prophet (a favorite Muslim subject), e.g., one entitled Zād al-ma'ād fī hady khair al-'ibād (Provision for the journey, or conduct of God's noblest servant), of which there is a very early MS (A.D. 1374) in the British Museum (not listed by Brockelmann).

Text. See Brockelmann.

Criticism. Brockelmann (2, 105–6, 1902; suppt. 2, 126–28, 1938). EI (2, 392, 1918). A. S. Fulton: Two Arabic MS (British Museum quarterly 11, 83–85, 1937). Farmer (no. 222, 1940).

H. CHINA

WANG HAO-KU

Chinese physician who flourished c. 1232–64. Hence he belongs definitely to the thirteenth century; I did not speak of him in volume 2 because I believed that he flourished in 1308. The error—if error it be—is explained below.

Wang Hao-ku, styled Chin-chih, was popularly known as Hai ts'ang hsien shêng. He obtained his chih shih degree. He was a student of Chang Yüan-su and of Li Kao (XIII-2). The dates of his birth and death are unknown.

He is said to have elaborated the old theory of the pulse, connecting it with the eight kinds of wind (?) and stating that all could be felt in the ts'un k'ou or ts'un mo of the left hand. The theory of the pulse was developed very early by the Chinese to a fantastic extent. Their earliest great book on the subject, Mo ching, in 10 chüan, was composed by Wang Shu-ho (III-2), and was the origin of a considerable literature (there are at least 156 Chinese books on the subject). The most remarkable edition of the Mo ching or "pulse classic" is the one prepared in Chinese, Arabic, and Persian by order of Rashīd al-dīn. According to the Mo ching, the pulse can be taken on either hand at three places, ts'un or "inch," at the wrist, kuan or "bar," a little farther, ch'ih or "cubit," farther still; and for each place it can be taken inside or outside, so that there are twelve pulses, six for each hand. Each of these pulses is supposed to be connected with a different organ. This may serve to illustrate the artificial complexity of that theory, which is carried on to absurdity.[38]

Wang Hao-ku wrote the following treatises:

1. A treatise on internal medicine, Yin chêng lüeh li, in one chüan, with a preface dated 1232. The printed text includes a biography of the author, whence the facts of this note are partly derived.

2. A collection of prescriptions for a number of diseases; the arrangement is by diseases, a list of drugs being given for each one. It is called I lei yüang jung, is divided into 12 chüan, and was completed in 1237. (This agrees with the date given by Wylie, "before 1241," but disagrees with the date 1331 given by Hübotter. As far as my experience goes, Wylie is generally accurate, whereas Hübotter is often inaccurate.) The theory dominating the book is the so-called theory of the twelve larger blood vessels. In this treatise Wang refers to Chang Yüan-su as "my teacher."

3. A treatise on fevers, Tz'ŭ shih nan chih, in 2 chüan, explaining Li Kao's theory. It is probably Li Kao's own book edited by Wang Hao-ku; the title,

[38] See Introd. 2, 76. The best short account of the Chinese pulse theory will be found in Wong and Wu (p. 57–66, 1936). That theory was first revealed to the Western world by Michael Boym (S.J., Lemberg 1612–59) in the Specimen medicinae sinicae sive Opuscula medica ad mentem Sinensium, continens I. De pulsibus libros quatuor è sinico translatos . . . , edited by Andrew Cleyer of Cassel (Francfort 1682). Re-edited by Philippe Couplet (S.J.): Clavis medica ad Chinarum doctrinam de pulsibus (1686). Neither edition mentions father Boym's name; both include the translation of the Mo ching. For further information on that Latin translation and others, see Bibliothèque de la Compagnie de Jésus (new ed., 2, 70, Bruxelles 1891) and Isis (15, 202 1931).

meaning "It is hard to understand," was given by Wang. Judging from the two prefaces of the printed text, one of which was written by Wang, it was originally composed by Li Kao; it is difficult to say how many variations were introduced by the editor.

In his preface Wang gives the title of reign Chih ta, corresponding to the years 1308–12, but Wang's biographer (mentioned apropos of item 1) says that Chih ta is an error, and that the title of reign was Chih yüan, corresponding to the years 1264–95. It should be noted that the date 1264 tallies better with the dates of items 1 and 2 (1232, 1237), and with other biographical data. If Wang was a disciple of Chang Yüan-su and Li Kao (and these facts seem well established), and wrote a medical treatise in 1232, he was a very old man (almost a centenarian) in 1308. The date 1308 is not impossible but improbable.

4. A pharmacopoeia, T'ang i pên ts'ao, in 3 chüan. Chüan 1 consists of 3 parts: (1) Li Kao's Yao lei fa hsiang, explaining the theory of yin yang and discussing a number of drugs; (2) Li Kao's Yung yao hsin fa, concerning the use of drugs in general; (3) Wang's own general theory. Chüan 2 and 3 contain detailed studies of different drugs, taken one by one. The properties and usage of each drug are mentioned, together with statements derived from other books, mainly those of Chang Chung-ching (II-2) and Li Kao. As is the case for item 2, the general theory is that of the twelve blood vessels, and various complaints are described in terms of that very artificial system, wherein the agents are called respectively prince, ministers, assistants, etc.

The T'ang i ta fa mentioned by Hübotter as an independent work is probably identical with the T'ang i pên ts'ao.

5. A treatise on children's diseases, Pan lun ts'ui ying.

Text. 1. The Yin chêng lüeh li is included in the Shih wan chüan lou ts'ung shu.

2. The I lei yüang jung was reprinted in 1543, again in 1593, these editions being considerably enlarged.

3. The Tz'ŭ shih nan chih is in I t'ung chêng mo ch'üan shu.

4. The T'ang i pên ts'ao is available in the Library of Congress, in an early edition (probably Ming) bound in 6 volumes.

5. The Pan lun ts'ui ying is in the same collection as item 3.

Criticism. Most information derived from the prefaces to Wang's books, especially the biography attached to the Yin chêng lüeh li. Wylie (p. 98, 1902). Hübotter (p. 41–43, 1924; p. 24, 354, 1929). Wong and Wu (p. 203, 1936).

TSOU HSÜAN

Chinese physician of the Yüan dynasty (fl. c. 1307).

A physician of the northern Sung dynasty, Ch'ên Chih, who flourished during the Yüan fêng period (1078–86), had written a little treatise, Yang-lao fêng ch'in-shu, on the care and feeding of old people. In 1307, Tsou Hsüan added 3 more chüan to that treatise, and the whole work, in 4 chüan, was called Shou-ch'in yang-lao hsin-shu, being first printed under that title in 1342.

Chüan 2 and 3 are included in a volume of the Yung Lo ta tien recently acquired by the Library of Congress; it is the volume comprising chüan 11,618–11,619 of that encyclopaedia. The Shou-ch'in yang-lao hsin-shu occurs in it under the character lao, meaning old. It includes medical and dietetic advice and various prescriptions concerning the preparation of foods and beverages for the health and comfort of aged people. These prescriptions have been frequently copied in Ming medical books.

Text. There is a copy of the original edition of the whole work, dated 1342, in the Kuo-hsüeh library of Nanking. It formerly belonged to the famous collector Ting Ping (1832–99). As stated above, the two middle sections of it are reprinted in a volume of the Yung Lo ta tien available in the Library of Congress. The volume of the Yung Lo ta tien containing the final chapter is, or was, in the Oriental library of the Commercial Press, Shanghai.

Criticism. Wong and Wu (p. 88, 1936). A. W. Hummel: Report of the Library of Congress (p. 157–58, 1940).

WANG YÜ

Chinese physician (fl. 1308).

Wang Yü composed in 1308 (at least this is the date of his preface) a medicolegal work explaining the duties of a coroner, entitled Wu yüan lu. This was probably hardly more than a revised edition of the famous work of Sung Tz'ŭ (XIII-1), Hsi yüan lu. There is still a third work of the same kind, anonymous, entitled P'ing yüan lu. All these titles, Hsi yüan lu, Wu yüan lu, P'ing yüan lu, to which one might add Li yüan lu, are practically equivalent, the word lu meaning record, the two others meaning "clearing up a case" or something amounting to that (e.g., wu yüan means "without injustice"; i.e., the case is cleared).

Text. A new edition of the Wu yüan lu was printed in 1438. There is a Korean re-edition and translation of this edition of 1438, together with additions extracted from the other works above mentioned, in the Library of Congress. It is called Tsêng hsiu wu yüan lu yen chieh (Wu yüan lu, for short); it was published in 1796 and made by the then minister of justice, Hsü Yu-lin, and three other scholars, with some commentary by the minister himself and additions by Chin Chiu-hsia. It is illustrated, and the text is in the Korean syllabary with Chinese characters interspersed. See Courant (no. 1789); but the Library of Congress has only the Korean text (3 books bound in 2 vols.), not the initial volume of Chinese text with prefaces and a postface.

Criticism. Report of the Librarian of Congress (1925, p. 281; Isis 8, 791). Herbert A. Giles: The Hsi yüan lu or Instruction to coroners (Proceedings of the Royal Society of Medicine vol. 17, hist. sec., 59–107, London 1924; Isis 8, 541). Wong and Wu (p. 208, 1936).

WÊN-JÊN KUEI

Chinese physician (fl. c. 1323). He was the author of a treatise on smallpox (or some other contagious diseases?) entitled Wên-jên Shih tou-chên lun, published in 1323.

The data concerning Wên-jên Kuei and his book are doubtful, but there is no doubt that smallpox was known and fought in China long before his time. It is difficult to say when smallpox was introduced into China; the opinion most commonly accepted is that it happened in the 25th year of the rule of Chien Wu (first emperor of the eastern Han, Kuang Wu Ti, 25–58), that is, in 49 during a war with the "barbarians" (Huns?) in Hunan or Hupeh. The first description of smallpox, not only in Chinese literature but in world literature,[39] occurs in the Chou-hou-pei-chi-fang of Ko Hung (IV-1). There are immemorial traditions of the practice

[39] With the possible exception of Herodotos of Rome (I-2)?

of "variolation"[40] in Asia, but the earliest record in China concerns the family of the Sung prime minister Wang Tan, who lived from 957 to 1017 (Giles no. 2230); the event recorded happened during the rule of Chên Tsung (997–1022). The healer lived in the O Mei mountains, Ssŭch'uan. Thus the publication of a new Chinese treatise on smallpox in 1323 is plausible enough.

Text. Ming reprint in 1542.

Criticism. Wylie (p. 103, 1922). Not dealt with by Wong and Wu, though they discuss smallpox in China (p. 82, 215–16, 269, 273–74, 1936).

HU SSŬ-HUI

Chinese physician who flourished during the reign of Jên Tsung of the Yüan dynasty (ruled 1311–20) and (according to the preface of his book) was imperial dietitian from 1314 to 1330.

He wrote and presented to the emperor Wên Ti (T'ien li 1330) a book entitled Yin shan chêng yao (Necessary principles of drink and food = principles of correct diet), derived from data available in the pên ts'ao and other medical books but also from his own personal and administrative experience. He described useful plants as well as methods of preparing them for consumption.

A number of calamities following one another from 1319 to 1330 had caused widespread misery and rendered the publication of this book peculiarly opportune. In 1319, all the roads in Shantung and Huainan were flooded; in 1320, there was a famine in Honan, aggravated by the rebellion of Achakpa (son of the emperor Yesun Timur; emperor himself in 1328 under the Chinese name Yu Chu; Giles no. 4, 1898); in 1322, earthquakes occurred; in 1327, drought, locusts, famine, landslides, and more earthquakes; in 1330, another famine in Honan.

The book is divided into 3 chüan, the second of which is devoted to the cure of diseases by diet. Hu distinguished two kinds of beriberi, known today as the wet and dry forms. The acute or wet form was regarded as due to huo ch'i (or fiery spirit),[41] and the chronic, atrophic, or dry form to the han ch'i (or cold spirit). Hu prescribed various dietary cures for the different forms of beriberi; it is remarkable that these cures were rich in vitamins. This is less surprising when one considers that the Chinese had a traditional knowledge of deficiency diseases and had learned empirically to correct them with appropriate food (that is, food containing sufficient vitamins). For example, such information is already found in the writings of Chang Chung-ching (II-2), the Chinese Galen. The writer Han yü (768–824; Giles no. 632) stated in one of his essays that beriberi is particularly prevalent south of the Yangtze; this was still true in 1935, when a modern Chinese physician

[40] The term variolation is used as distinguished from the more scientific Jennerian inoculation or vaccination (Osiris 1, 533–36, 1936).

[41] The translation of ch'i by spirit or πνεῦμα is insufficient. Chinese medical books ascribe most diseases to disturbances in the normal state of the ch'i characteristic of the region concerned. Thus they speak of p'i ch'i (spleen spirit), kan ch'i (liver spirit), chiao ch'i (foot spirit or beriberi), fêng tu chiao ch'i. These are internal spirits like the archaei or vital forces of Paracelsian medicine; but the Chinese recognize also external spirits, such as huo ch'i (fiery or hot spirit) and han ch'i (cold spirit), which may help to unbalance the organism and cause diseases. Moreover, ch'i has also a meaning comparable to the Aristotelian ψυχή, or rather to its lowest kind, ψυχὴ θρεπτική or vegetative principle. In addition to the ch'i, the animals have a nature of their own, shou hsing (cf. ψυχὴ αἰσθητική), and man has still a higher kind of soul, shan hsing (cf. ψυχὴ διανοητική). These comparisons between Chinese and Greek thought are tentative and somewhat risky, but not useless.

(Hou Hsiang-ch'uan) explained it by the difference in diet between the wheat-eating North and the rice-eating South.

The text of Hu's work was reprinted during the Ming dynasty by order of the emperor Tai Tsung (Ching t'ai 1450–57). The frontispiece of that Ming edition pictures a consultation between two physicians, each with his boy assistant, in the presence of the patient, and bears the inscription "Food cures various diseases"; other illustrations in the book represent plants stimulating various ch'i of the body and remedying deficiencies.

Criticism. This note is derived exclusively from an article by Dr. (Miss) Gwei-djen Lu (Lu Kuei-chên) and Joseph Needham: A contribution to the history of Chinese dietetics (7 ill.), which they sent me in 1939 for publication in Isis. It was mailed to the Belgian printers and proofread, but publication was eventually blocked by the German invasion (Isis 33, 48). As it passed out of my hands, I overlooked it in the first writing of vol. 3. Happily, when Joseph Needham was on his way to China he visited me (Nov. 23, 1942) and kindly placed the MS of their paper again at my disposal.

WEI I-LIN

Chinese physician (fl. c. 1328–37).

Wei I-lin, styled Ta-chai, began in 1328 and completed in 1337 the compilation of a large collection of prescriptions derived from his experience and that of five generations of his ancestors. It is entitled Shih-i tê-hsiao fang and divided into 8 sections: complaints of greater blood vessels; complaints of smaller blood vessels; nervous complaints; gynaecology and obstetrics; eye troubles; mouth, teeth, and throat troubles; bonesetting and cure of arrow wounds; boils and ulcers. The book ends with health rules borrowed from Sun Ssŭ-mo (VII-2). Prescriptions involving acupuncture, hsia chên pien, are scattered throughout the work.[42]

Wei I-lin elaborated the theory of pulse, about which see my note on Wang Hao-ku, adding the consideration of ten more special kinds of pulse as diagnostic signs.

Text. There is in the Library of Congress an early edition of the Shih-i tê-hsiao fang in 20 chüan bound in 24 vols. The preface is dated 1337, no date of printing being given. The text is included also in the Ssŭ k'u ch'uan shu.

Criticism. Wylie (p. 99, 1902). Reports of the Library of Congress (1919, p. 27; 1929, p. 312). Hübotter (p. 41, 1924; p. 24, 354, 1929).

[42] For acupuncture and moxa (two subjects closely related) see Introd. 2, 78. T. Nakayama: Acupuncture et médecine chinoise vérifiées au Japon (85 p., 18 ill., Paris 1934; Isis 25, 262). Georges Soulié de Morant: Précis de la vraie acupuncture chinoise (201 p., 14 fig., Paris 1934; Isis 23, 570). Wong and Wu (p. 227–32, 1936). Both practices are immemorial in China. The earliest Chinese independent treatise is the Chia-i-ching, wherein Huang Fu (III-2) codified ancient traditions. This is the fountainhead of an abundant Chinese and Japanese literature. The practice was introduced into Japan at least as early as 562: it was not explained to Western people till a thousand years later, by the Portuguese Jesuit Luis de Almeida (c. 1523–83) and the German traveler Engelbert Kaempfer (1651–1716).

As examples of the Chinese literature let me cite only the Chên chiu ta ch'êng, 10 vols., by Yang Chi-chou, court physician during the Wan Li period (1573–1620), often reprinted and amplified. Cordier: Bibliotheca sinica (2, col. 1473–75, 1906). For the Japanese tradition see Sasagawa Tomooki: Shin kyū ryōhō taisei (3 vols., Tokyo 1935; Isis 26, 193–96), and Komai Kazuo: Keirasu keiketsu gaku (802 p., abundant ill., Tokyo 1939). For the Korean tradition see Courant (3, nos. 2485, 2526–27, 2534, 2538–39, 1896).

CH'I TÊ-CHIH

Chinese physician (fl. c. 1328–37).

Ch'i Tê-chih wrote in 1328–37 a treatise in 2 chüan entitled Essence of surgery, Wai-k'o ching-i, wherein he discusses among other things various ailments of the genital organs, which, he says, are of three kinds, shih yin ch'uang, tu ching ch'uang, and yin shih-ch'uang. These are three kinds of ch'uang or ulcer. They have nothing to do with syphilis.

Text. His treatise is contained in the I t'ung chêng mo ch'üan shu, books 68–69, edition of 1907.

Criticism. Hübotter (p. 24, 1929). Wong and Wu (p. 218, 1936).

HUA SHOU

Chinese physician (fl. 1341).

Hua Shou, styled Po-jên, wrote many medical works, of which the most important, published in 1341, is the Shih ssŭ ching fa hui in 3 volumes, a practical treatise dealing with the anatomy, physiology, and pathology of blood vessels. This work was popular in Japan as well as in China. He also composed the Nan ching pên i, that is, the best edition with commentary of the ancient medical classic Nan ching, probably written by Pien Ch'iao (V B.C.).

Text. The Chou shih i hsüeh ts'ung shu, edited by Chou Hsüeh-hai, contains the Nan ching pên i, in 2 chüan, as well as another treatise ascribed to the same author, the Chên chia shu yao, in 1 chüan.

Criticism. Hübotter (p. 35, 1924; p. 22, 1929). Wong and Wu (p. 81, 1936).

CHU TAN-CH'I

Chinese physician (1281–1358), the last of the "four famous doctors of the Chin and Yüan dynasties."

Chu Tan-ch'i was not his original name; he was so named because he was popularly known as Tan-ch'i Hsien-sheng. He was styled Chên-hêng and was nicknamed Yen-hsiu.

The "four famous doctors of Chin Yüan," Chin Yüan ssŭ ta chia, that is, the main physicians of the Chin and Yüan dynasties, were Liu Wan-su (XII-2), Chang Tzŭ-ho (XII-2), Li Kao (XIII-1),[43] finally Chu Tan-ch'i.

Chu Tan-ch'i was born in 1281 in I-wu, Chehkiang. He received his first education in his native place, studying the classics with a view to an official career. It is said that he was a Taoist, but that statement is misleading. The fact is that he went to the Pa Hua mountain to sit at the feet of Wên I-kung,[44] who was not a strict Taoist, but an exponent of the eclectic neo-Confucianism of Chu Hsi (XII-2). The story goes that Chu's impulse to study medicine was due to the fact that his master Hsü suffered from a chronic disease which Chu hoped to be able to cure[45] (and later on did cure, hence his fame).

In search of medical knowledge Chu traveled to Soochow, Nanking, and other

[43] I placed him in XIII-2 wrongly (Introd. 2, 1104). When I wrote that note I did not know that Li Kao (= Li Tung Yüan) died in 1251 at the age of 72; he clearly belongs to XIII-1.

[44] His real name was Hsü Chien and he was styled I Chih. After his death he was canonized as Wên I. See Yüan shih, chüan 189.

[45] According to the Hsin Yüan shih, chüan 242, it was his mother, not his master Hsü, who suffered from a chronic disease.

places, finally to Hangchow, where he received lessons from the eccentric doctor Lo Chih-t'i. This Lo had been himself one of the disciples (Li Kao being another) of Chang Yüang-su or Chieh-ku. Chu received from him the traditions of Yüan medicine, and those embodied in the Sung materia medica Ta kuan pên ts'ao.

Yet he developed new theories of his own. For example, the theory of the internal fires, the principal fire chün huo in the heart, and the auxiliary fire hsiang huo in the liver and kidney. Diseases are explained in terms of these fires and their conflicts. Moreover, he claimed that the equilibrium in the body between the two fundamental principles, male or active, yang, and female or passive, yin, was more likely to be disturbed by the predominance of yang, and hence the physician must search for medicines to restrain the yang and support the yin. The medical school adopting this theory of his was called yang yin "to nourish (or support) the yin."[46]

Many medical writings are ascribed to Chu Tan-ch'i and were written by himself or edited by his disciples. The two most important are:

1. Tan-ch'i Hsin fa, edited by his disciples. It is a large medical collection (over 900 p.), divided into 24 chüan, dealing respectively with (1–8) noxious influences from (1,2) outside, (3,4) inside, (4) wind, (5) cold, (6) heat, (7,8) humidity; (9, 10) secretions, excretions, etc., (11) fire, (12) wind, (13) dry heat, (14–17) anxiety and oppression caused by cold, fire, and humidity, (18) accumulations, (19) emptiness, (20, 21) women's diseases, (22, 23) children's diseases, (24) various therapeutical suggestions.

2. Pên ts'ao yen-i pu-i. This materia medica (or herbal) is one of the 42 sources quoted by Li Shih-chên in the great Pên ts'ao kang mu written in 1552–78, which has remained for centuries the Chinese standard book on the subject. Chu Tan-ch'i's herbal is itself in the form of a commentary on the Pên ts'ao yen-i of K'ou Tsung-shih (XII-1), written in 1115. It deals with some 196 drugs, all but very few of them herbs.

Both these works were re-edited by Fang Kuang, styled Yo-chih, and published in 1536 with a preface by Chia Yung, a friend of Fang Kùang. That edition is called Tan-ch'i hsin-fa fu-yü; it includes the Pên ts'ao yen-i pu-i, and also the Ming i tsa chu of Wang Chieh-chai, alias Wang Lun, whose preface is dated 1502.

It will suffice to name his other works:

3. Mo chüeh chih chang ping shih t'u shuo.
4. Ko chih yü lun (in 1347).
5. Chü fang fa hui.
6. I hsüeh fa ming.
7. Chin kuei kou yüan.
8. Huo fa chi yao, and there may be others still.

The most remarkable single feature in Chu Tan-ch'i's work is the earliest mention of chaulmoogra oil, ta fêng tzŭ (extracted from Taraktogenos kurzii, or from Hydnocarpus), for the treatment of leprosy. The use of that drug is very ancient, immemorial, witness various legends relative to its discovery; the name is of Hindu (Bengali) origin. But Chu it was who introduced it into scientific literature; he himself disapproved of the drug because of its irritating effect on the stomach. It is indeed a violent emetic, the smallest dose taken through the mouth causing vomiting. It was only when that and other defects were obviated by the use of a

[46] The non-Chinese reader should be warned that the character yang in the phrase yang yin is different from the one representing the male principle yang; also the tones are different.

mixed ethyl ester that chaulmoogra oil became our best remedy for the cure of leprosy.[47]

According to the Hsin Yüan shih, chüan 242, Chu had a student named Wang Li, styled An Tao, who wrote two medical treatises, Suan hui chi and Pai ping kou yüan, wherein he developed his master's theories.

Text. The Library of Congress has a fine copy of Fan Kuang's edition of Chu's two main works (24 chüan bound in 32 vols., in 4 portfolios, 1536). See A. W. Hummel, Report of the Library of Congress (1929, p. 314, 317).

It also has copies of the Chin kuei kou yüan in vol. 49 of the Chou shih i hsüeh ts'ung shu, and of the Mo yin chêng chih in vols. 25–28 of the Ts'ui lang kan kuan ts'ung shu.

Chu's works mentioned above (nos. 1, 3–8), as well as the Suan hui chi of his disciple Wang Li, are included in the collection I t'ung chêng mo ch'üan shu, edited by Wang K'ên-t'ang, styled Yü t'ai. There is a copy of that collection, dated 1907, in the Harvard-Yenching Library.

Criticism. Hübotter (p. 37–40, 1924; p. 23, 76, 351–54, 1929). Wong and Wu (p. 75, 1932; p. 98, 101–3, 115, 127, 211, 1936). For chaulmoogra see Louis Goodman and Alfred Gilman: The pharmacological basis of pharmacy (p. 943–45, New York 1941).

J. JAPAN

KAJIWARA SHŌZEN

Japanese physician (fl. 1303–38).

Kajiwara is his family name, a name made illustrious by the samurai of Sagami, Kajiwara Kagetoki (d. 1200). Kajiwara Shōzen was physician to the Ashikaga shōgun, which implies that he flourished at least until 1338.

He is the author of two important medical books. In 1303 he compiled the Ton-i shō, a general treatise derived mainly from Chinese sources, but also from his own observations. Two sections of it deal with anatomy and physiology. They contain an account of the five organs in the thorax, the six organs in the abdomen, and the twelve arteries. The structure and functions of the human body are explained in the Chinese manner.

In 1314–15, he wrote a more extensive medical treatise, Man-an-pō, including a pharmacopoeia. It first extended to 62 volumes, but two of these were lost early. This work is also derived from the Chinese examples, but with some original additions and criticisms. In some cases Shōzen did not hesitate to impugn the Chinese authorities.

An additional glimpse into the development of Japanese medicine by the beginning of the fourteenth century is given to us by the statement that the Buddhist priest Ninsei (d. 1303) was a founder of sanitaria for lepers and other incurables and of several charity hospitals.

[47] One first tried to administer the chaulmoogra oil by injection. Victor G. Heiser: Leprosy, its treatment in the Philippine Islands by the hypodermic use of a chaulmoogra oil mixture (U. S. Public Health Service, suppt. 20 to the Public Health reports, 25 p., ill., Washington 1914). The preparation of the ethyl ester was made by Arthur Lyman Dean (1878–), industrial chemist in Hawaii, and was published by him together with Harry T. Hollmann (Journal of cutaneous diseases 37, 374–81, 1919), Dean's section being entitled Preparation of four fatty acid fractions from chaulmoogra oil. See also H. C. de Souza-Araujo: Leprosy, survey made in forty countries 1924–27 (400 p., ill., Instituto Oswaldo Cruz, Rio de Janeiro 1929).

Criticism. Y. Fujikawa: Geschichte der Medizin in Japan (p. 24, 1911; p. 20, 77, 1934). Tase (p. 8–9, 1938).

AKI MORISADA

Japanese physician (d. 1358).

Aki is his family name. Aki Morisada was a court physician, whose specialty was obstetrics. A treatise Jisan hō is attributed to him.

Criticism. Tase (p. 9, 1938).

CHAPTER XII

HISTORIOGRAPHY

(First Half of the Fourteenth Century)

N.B. Only the main articles are grouped in this chapter. The historical contributions of many other men, whose main work was done in other fields, are related in other chapters. For a general survey of historiography in the first half of the fourteenth century, see section XII of chapter I. More information on the men referred to in that section can easily be found by means of the index.

A. WESTERN CHRISTENDOM

A1. Italy

RICCOBALDO DA FERRARA

Ricobaldus Ferrariensis. Italian chronicler and geographer writing in Latin (d. in or after 1312).

Gervasio Riccobaldo originated in Ferrara; according to himself, he witnessed a miracle in Padova 1243, and heard Innocent IV preach in Ferrara 1251, being then still a "giovanetto." Hence he was a man of the thirteenth century, but we include him in our account of the fourteenth century, because we omitted him from our volume 2, and because one of his works at least was continued until 1312. He flourished in Ravenna, where he held a canonry.

He wrote the Pomerium, or Pomerium Ravennatis ecclesiae seu Historia universalis 700–1297, including three parts: (1) history of the German emperors from Charlemagne to 1297; (2) history of the popes from 95 to 1249; (3) Compilatio chronologica from the creation to 1312. This third part was continued to 1469 by Giov. Fil. da Legname of Messina. The first part was translated into Italian by Matteo Maria Boiardo, conte di Scandiano (1434–94), famous author of the Orlando innamorato. It has been claimed that this was not really a translation but a pasticcio ascribed by Boiardo to Riccobaldo, but why should he have done that?

I assume that this same Riccobaldo is the author of the geographical text included in a composite MS of the fourteenth century (Vatican, Ottobon. 2072 lat., fol. 45a–58b), Liber magistri Rycobaldi Ferrariensis de locis orbis et insularum et marium. Like the anonymous geographer of Ravenna (VII-2), whom he quotes, this Riccobaldo divides the earth into twelve zones (twelve day hours and twelve night ones).

Text. The third part was the first to be printed, notably by Joh. Phil. de Lignamine: Chronica summorum pontificum imperatorumque ac de septem aetatibus mundi (Rome 1474; again 1476). This volume is of special interest because it contains the earliest printed account of the invention of printing. Giov. Fil. da Legname was himself a printer in Rome.

The three parts were edited in the Corpus historicum of Joh. Georg Eccard (Würzburg 1729, again Francfort 1743) and in the Rerum italicarum scriptores of L. A. Muratori (Milano 1723–38, vol. 9). The same vol. 9 also contains Boiardo's translation.

G. Parthey: Geographus Ravennas beim Riccobaldus Ferrariensis (Hermes 4, **134–37**, 1870).

Criticism. Potthast (p. 972, 1896). Mario Longhena: L'India nelle enciclopedie di Benzo d'Alessandria, di Ricobaldo da Ferrara e dell' Orbis descriptio (in Pullé 1905, app. 2, p. 8–18). Enciclopedia italiana (29, 252, 1936).

DINO COMPAGNI

Florentine statesman, chronicler, and poet (c. 1260–1324). He was born in Florence about 1260, the youngest of the six sons of Perino Compagni.

Being a silk merchant, he was enrolled in the Arte della seta (the guild of the silk trade) and soon elected its consul; this honor was given to him five more times in the course of the following years. He also became a member of the consiglio del podestà and of various municipal committees. In 1293 he was gonfalonier (gonfaloniere di giustizia, head of the seigniory of the Florentine republic). He died on February 26, 1324, and was buried in S. Trinità.

In his youth Dino wrote verses, sonnets, and ballads. The five sonnets which remain are probably only a small part of a fairly abundant poetical production. The Intelligenza, an allegorical poem of 309 stanzas, usually attributed to him, was written about 1301. In one part of this poem he describes many precious stones, and records their virtues. Material for this part was taken from the Liber de gemmis of Marbode (XI-2), the Roman d'Alexandre, and the Roman de Troie. There is a definite reference in it to the use of Chinese silk (Levasi a lo mattino la donna mia e vestesi di seta cataia . . .). The Intelligenza is the most important poem in nona rima before Spenser's Faerie Queene.

Dino's best-known work is the Cronica delle cose occorrenti ne' tempi suoi, covering the years 1280–1312, which was written between 1310 and 1312. It is probably the only prose work of Dino, since his authorship of the Diceria a Papa Giovanni XXII is very doubtful.

The work is not a chronicle in the strict sense of the word, but the story of the Neri and Bianchi (Black and White), with special reference to the parts played in the struggle by Boniface VIII and later by the emperor Henry VII, and shows the active participation of the author, who, like Dante, was a White. His gentleness and kindness, however, saved him from proscription. His was a Dantesque personality in other respects: ardent patriotism, love of truth, deep conviction, brevity of utterance. His chronicle contains graphic accounts of the main events and an acute analysis of the political situation. Dino draws vivid portraits of the men who took the leading political parts in these years. In spite of obvious inaccuracies and contradictions, and of a hopeless chronology, it is a most remarkable work, suggesting comparison with those of Caesar and Sallust, and opening fittingly the unique series of chronicles which illustrate the peculiar genius of Florence almost as well as the works of her painters. As compared with Villani's chronicle, Compagni's is more exclusively restricted to political events; it is also far more subjective and more dramatic.

There has been considerable discussion as to the genuineness of Compagni's chronicle. Some critics claim that it is a fifteenth-century forgery. They insist that it contains too many errors which an eyewitness of the events could not have made, and that the style is more suggestive of the quattrocento than of the trecento. This matter is not yet settled. It is probable that the chronicle as we have it is not a forgery, but a rifacimento of the original text, and that Compagni was the real author of the latter.

Text. Cronica, first edition in L. A. Muratori: Rerum italicarum scriptores (9, 467–536, Milan 1726); the text is also in the new edition of Muratori edited by I. Del Lungo (Scriptores vol. 9, part 2, Città di Castello 1915). Domenico Maria Manni: Istoria fiorentina (Florence 1728). Isidoro Del Lungo: Dino Compagni e la sua cronica (3 vols. in 4, Florence 1879–87), lengthy introduction, includes Dino's verses, sonnets, and canzoni, elaborate discussion and proof of the authenticity of the Cronica in vol. 3; La cronica, e la canzone morale del pregio dello stesso autore (248 p., Florence 1889; 224 p., 5th ed. revised, Florence 1908; again 1917). Raffaello Piccoli: La cronica, le rime, e l'Intelligenza (206 p., Lanciano 1911). L'Intelligenza, partial edition by Francesco Trucchi (1846). Other editions by Carlo Teoli (Milan 1863), Paul Gellrich (Breslau 1883), Vittorio Mistruzzi (Bologna 1928). German translations of the Cronica have been published by Ida Schwartz: Chronik des Dino Compagni (176 p., Jena 1914) with critical introduction; and by W. Doenniges: Kritik der Quellen für die Geschichte Heinrichs des VII des Luxemburgers (p. 158–313, Berlin 1841).

Criticism. Karl Hillebrand: Dino Compagni, étude historique et littéraire sur l'époque de Dante (439 p., Paris 1862). Paul Scheffer-Boichorst: Florentiner Studien (p. 45–210, Leipzig 1874), first attack on the genuineness of the Cronica. Pietro Fanfani: Dino Compagni vendicato dalla calunnia di scrittore della Cronaca (335 p., Milan 1875); La critica italiana del signore Isidoro Del Lungo (24 p., Florence 1879). Karl von Hegel: Die Chronik des Dino Compagni, Versuch einer Rettung (120 p., Leipzig 1875). Isidoro Del Lungo: La critica italiana nella questione su Dino Compagni (16 p., Florence 1877). Angelo Angelucci: Dino Compagni militare ossia la balestra attorno ed altre voci e locuzioni militari della Cronica (84 p., Florence 1879). Guido Levi: Bonifazio VIII e le sue relazioni col comune di Firenze (Archivio della Società romana di storia patria vol. 5, 116 p., Rome 1882). R. Davidsohn: Forschung zur Geschichte von Florenz (3, 102, 141, 158–59, Berlin 1901). G. Smets: La chronique de Dino Compagni (Revue de l'université de Bruxelles, 1909). Isidoro Del Lungo: Storia esterna vicende avventure d'un piccol libro de' tempi di Dante (2 vols., Milan 1917–18), a general summary of the Dino controversy. Alessandro d'Ancona, Orazio Bacci: Manuale della letteratura italiana (1, 242–57, revised ed., Florence 1928). Domenico Guerri: Dino Compagni, 1260–1324 (95 p., Turin 1932), mainly a collection of extracts from the Cronica. Pouzyna (p. 37, 1935).

GIOVANNI VILLANI

Florentine statesman and chronicler, the greatest Florentine chronicler and one of the greatest of mediaeval times (d. 1348).

Giovanni Villani was born at Florence at an unknown date, probably in the last quarter of the thirteenth century, for he attended the Roman jubilee in 1300 and was then old enough to feel exalted by the majestic ruins of ancient Rome and to conceive then and there his own mission as a historian of Florence. He was educated for business, and traveled in Flanders and France 1302–8 for commercial reasons. From 1316 on he was in the service of Florence in many capacities, being thrice prior, employed in the mint, member of the commission dealing with the famine of 1328, camarlingo (bursar) for the construction of the new city walls 1331; one of his last services to his native city was to be delivered as a war hostage to Mastino II della Scala in Ferrara 1341. He took part in diplomatic negotiations. In addition to the military and political vicissitudes of his country, he witnessed also its economic troubles, the climax of which was the bankruptcy of the Bardi and Bonaccorsi banking houses in 1345 (bankruptcy largely caused by the ruinous wars with the Scala family and with Pisa). After that Villani was thrown into prison. He died of the plague in Florence 1348.

Giovanni Villani immortalized himself by the composition of a chronicle of Florence written in Italian (Nuova cronica; historie fiorentine), also called Cronica universale, because it deals with many European events, as well as with Florentine ones. Indeed, at that time Florence was one of the commercial and financial centers of the world; a cosmopolitan city, one of the best listening posts for the understanding of world affairs. Villani was a Guelf, but not as much a partisan as Dino Compagni, nor as good a writer.

The Nuova cronica is divided into twelve books, and deals with the whole past from the fabulous origins to 1348. As usual, the account of the distant past is simply a compilation from older chronicles. Giovanni's work begins to be truly important with book VII; the six last books deal with the period 1266–1348, which he knew extremely well.

Giovanni's chronicle was continued by his brother Matteo down to the year of the latter's death, also of the plague, in 1363. The events of 1348–63 are dealt with in ten books. A further continuation 1363–65 was provided by Matteo's son Filippo, who will be discussed in chapter XXVI.

The Villani chronicle, and especially Giovanni's part of it, is of fundamental importance for the study of economic conditions, primarily but not exclusively in Florence. It contains a large amount of information, not always well integrated, yet invaluable. For example, the budget of Florence is fully discussed, or rather we are given abundant means for the study of it. There is a wealth of data on Florentine vital and economic statistics. The prosperous industries and wealthy banks of Florence are described, as well as the great bankruptcy of 1345, the repercussions of which were felt all over Europe. Giovanni speaks of marine insurance as having originated in Lombardy in 1182; this proves at least that it was not a novelty. Indeed, international trade and finance had then already attained a high stage of development. While Giovanni was in charge of the mint, in 1317, he caused a list to be made of all Florentine coins. From the point of view of economic history and of statistics as applied to the understanding of a definite society and its vicissitudes, Giovanni's chronicle is unsurpassed, nay unique, in mediaeval literature.

Matteo's chronicle is less important except for his account of the Black Death and its innumerable repercussions: displacement of property, increases in prices, wages, taxes, lawsuits, breakdown of morality, enormous bequests to charities and increase of mortmain, foundation of the University of Florence, etc.

Though Giovanni's main interest was economic, he deals with many other subjects. For example, he gives accounts of the epidemic of flagellants in 1310, and of another religious outburst in 1334. He records the presence of a golden pheasant in Pisa; it is often thought that that bird was not imported from China until the following century. Matteo records the birth of lions in the menagerie of Florence; this helped to destroy mediaeval legends relative to the birth of lions.

Giovanni devoted a chapter (book XII, ch. 41) to the triple conjunction of Saturn, Jupiter, and Mars in 1345. His statements on the subject showed that he shared moderately and cautiously the superstitions of his time. He pointed out that prognostications may be useful if compared in due time with the events themselves. He mentioned the prognostication of great mortality in 1347.

As indicated at the beginning of this notice, Giovanni conceived the idea of writing the history of Florence while standing amid the ruins of Rome in 1300. Compare the resolution taken at the same place on October 15, 1764 by Edward Gibbon!

There remains to be considered the "Malespini question." One of the sources used by Giovanni Villani (as well as by Dante) was the Storia fiorentina composed by Ricordano de Malespini in the period 1270–90, and completed by his nephew Giacotto (or Giachetto) di Francesco Malespini c. 1307. Furthermore, Ricordano himself had used the Cronache di Roma e di Fiesole composed by Fiorello Capocci c. 1280–86, and other sources. These are the conclusions reached by Morghen in 1931. The "Cronaca malispiniana" is thus a real document which was completely absorbed by Villani. The latter used it as a first draft which he corrected and amplified, and which he made so thoroughly his own that the original document almost lost its own existence, just like a discarded draft. The Cronaca malispiniana was not, as claimed by a German scholar in 1874, a forgery posterior to Villani's chronicle, but a document anterior to it and integrated into it.

Arnold Busson: Die florentinische Geschichte der Malespini und deren Benutzung bei Dante (90 p., Innsbruck 1869). Paul Scheffer-Boichorst: Die Geschichte Malispini eine Fälschung (Florentiner Studien, Leipzig 1874). Raffaello Morghen: Note malispiniane (Bullettino dell' Istituto storico italiano no. 40, 105–26, Roma 1921); Dante, il Villani e Ricordano Malispini (ibid. no. 41, 171–94, 1921); Ancora sulla questione malispiniana (ibid. no. 46, 41–92, 1931). See also under "Criticism" at the end of this article.

Text. The first edition of Giovanni's chronicle contained only books I–X (to 1338); it was printed in Venice 1537. First complete edition, books I–XII (2 vols., Florence 1554). Reprinted Florence 1559, 1587 (1090 p.), etc. Edition by Muratori: Rerum italicarum scriptores (vol. 13, Milano 1728). New editions by Ignazio Moutier (8 vols., Florence 1823), and by the same with Francesco Gherardi Dragomanni (4 vols. in 2, Florence 1844–45), again in 7 vols. (Milano 1848), together with Matteo's and Filippo's continuations. References to Villani are generally to the Florentine edition of 1554 and 1587, or to Moutier's editions; there is not yet a critical edition up to present-day requirements.

Selections Englished by Rose E. Selfe, edited by Philip Henry Wicksteed (509 p., Westminster 1906).

First edition of Matteo's chronicle, Florence 1554, etc. Edition by Ignazio Moutier (6 vols., Florence 1825–26), and by F. G. Dragomanni (2 vols., Florence 1846).

Ricordano and Giacotto Malespini, Historia fiorentina. First edition, Florence 1568, again 1592, 1598, 1718. Edition by Muratori: Rerum italicarum scriptores (vol. 8, 1726), etc. Edition by Vincenzio Follini (508 p., Florence 1816), by Antonio Benci (2 vols., Livorno 1830), by Crescentino Giannini (Bologna 1867). Edition with Dino Compagni (Milano 1876).

Criticism. Georg Gottfried Gervinus: Geschichte der florentinischen Historiographie (480 p., Frankfurt 1833). Otto Hartwig: Villani und die leggenda di messer Gianni di Procida (Historische Zeitschrift 25, 233–71, 1871). Oskar Knoll: Beiträge zur italienischen Historiographie im 14. Jahrhundert (Göttingen 1876). Ugo Balzani: Le cronache italiane nel medio evo (Milano 1884). Vittorio Lami: Di un compendio inedito della cronica di Giovanni Villani nelle sue relazioni con la storia fiorentina malispiniana (Archivio storico italiano 5, 369–416, Firenze 1890). Gustave Loisel: Histoire des ménageries (1, 152–53, 1912). Ferdinando Neri: Dante e il primo Villani (Il giornale dantesco 20, 1–31, Firenze 1912). Ernest Mehl: Die Weltanschauung des Giovanni Villani (Beiträge zur Kulturgeschichte des Mittelalters und der Renaissance no. 33, Leipzig 1927). Thorndike (3, 315–16, 1934). Luigi Magnani: La cronaca figurata di G. Villani. Ricerche sulla miniatura fiorentina del Trecento (Codices Vaticanis selecti 24, folio, 42 p., 50 pl., Vatican 1936).

ANDREA DANDOLO

Venetian historian, statesman, and lawyer (d. 1354). He was a scion of an illustrious Venetian family which gave four doges to the republic, being himself the last of these. He studied law under the famous teacher Riccardo Malombra (professor in Bologna, d. 1334), and taught law in Padua.

The exact date of his birth is not known, but we know that he was appointed to positions of high responsibility when he was still very young, and in 1331 he was already procurator of St. Mark's, in 1333 podestà of Trieste, in 1336 provveditore in campo. He finally became doge in 1343 and held this office until his death in 1354.

Andrea did a great deal to encourage the study of classical and contemporary literature. He was greatly praised by Petrarca, and by Venetian chroniclers and writers, such as Lorenzo Mònaci, chancellor of Cándia (1375?–1429), and Marino Sanudo il Giovine (1466–1535).

The Liber blancus and the Liber albus were edited under the direction of Andrea during the time when he was doge. The former contained all the agreements of the Venetian governments with the Western peoples, and the latter those with the Eastern powers. Most of these documents concern Venetian commerce. But the real history of these commercial and political relations was written by Dandolo himself, in two works.

The larger and more important work, the Chronicon, was written while Andrea was doge. Books 1–3 are lost; book 4 begins with an account of St. Mark in Aquileia A.D. 48, and the Chronicon ends with the death of the doge Iacopo Contarini in 1280. The Chronicon includes general history as well as Venetian. A continuation to 1388 was written by Rafaino Caresini (Raphaelis de Caresinis, Raphainus Caresinus), chancellor of Venice, who died in 1390.

The Chronicon is the best source for Venetian political and commercial history of Andrea's own time. A great deal of the material for his works was taken from earlier sources: John the Deacon, Chronica Venetum; Chronicon Altinate; Cronicon Gradense; Martino da Canal's Cronicon; the Liber secretorum fidelium crucis of Marino Sanudo il Vecchio, and the Speculum Paulini.

The so-called Shorter chronicle, only a few sections of which are printed by Muratori, is of little real value since most of the information in it is recounted in the Chronicon in more detail and with more accuracy.

Text. Cronicon Venetum a pontificatu S. Marci ad annum usque 1339, in L. A. Muratori: Rerum italicarum scriptores (12, 13–514, Milan 1728); this includes books 4–10 of Andrea's chronicle (books 1–3 being lost) together with the Continuation, to 1388, written by Rafaino Caresini. New edition by Ester Pastorello in the new Muratori (vol. 12, part 2, Bologna 1922).

Georg Martin Thomas: Commission des Dogen Andreas Dandolo für die Insel Creta vom Jahre 1350 (Abhandlungen der philos.-philol. Cl., K. bayerische Akad. der Wissenschaften 14, 167–224, Munich 1878).

Gottlieb Lukas Friedrich Tafel and Georg Martin Thomas: Der Doge Andreas Dandolo, mit den Original-Registern des Liber albus, des Liber blancus und der Libri pactorum aus dem Wiener Archiv (Abhandlungen der hist. Cl., K. bayerische Akad. der Wissenschaften 8, 1–167, Munich 1856).

Letter of Dandolo to the Commune of Perugia (Archivio storico italiano 16, part 2, 536, Florence 1851).

La cronaca di Raffaino Caresini, in volgare veneziano nel sec. XIV, published by Rinaldo Fulin (100 p., Venice 1877).

Criticism. Henry Simonsfeld: Andreas Dandolo und seine Geschichtswerke (177 p., Munich 1876); Italian translation by Benedetto Morossi (Archivio veneto vol. 14, 102 p., Venezia 1877). Heyd (1, 472, 530, 546, 1885; 2, 104, 1886). E. Winkelmann: Zu Andreas Dandolo (Mittheilungen des Instituts für oesterreichische Geschichtsforschung 9, 320–22, Innsbruck 1888). Domingo Bolfi: L'amor patrio in Francesco Petrarca e le sue epistole ad Andrea Dandolo (28 p., Arezzo 1903). Heinrich Kretschmayer: Geschichte von Venedig (Gotha 1, 1905; 2, 1920, passim).

MUSSATO

Albertino Mussato (1261–1329). Italian diplomat, historian, poet, one of the main forerunners of the humanists.

He was born in the autumn of 1261 near Padova, studied grammar and law, and by 1282 was already a notary in his native city. He became a member of its council and was often sent on diplomatic missions to German and Italian cities. On Christmas 1315 he was given the laurel crown for poetry in Padova, this being the first time that honor was re-established in Italy since ancient days.[1] In 1325 he was banished to Chioggia (on the Adriatic coast, south of Venice), where he died in poverty on May 31, 1329.

His political views were comparable to Dante's. He was an Italian patriot, dreaming of unity, hostile to factions. He was friendly to the emperor Henry VII (ruled 1308–13). He was a moderate Guelf, or as he himself expressed it "Nunc Gelfus nunc Gibolengus ero."

He was a historian but also a writer of Latin verse and prose. His contemporary fame was due primarily to his literary activities, but he owes his permanent fame to his historical writings. Let us consider these first.

They are four in number:

1. The Historia Augusta, or De gestis Henrici VII Caesaris, in 16 books, a narrative of the deeds of Henry VII of Luxemburg in Italy in 1310–13. The first seven books are especially valuable. The Historia Augusta was probably composed not later than 1315.
2. De gestis Italicorum post Henricum VII Caesarem, left unfinished in 14 books, carrying the story down to 1321. It tells the struggles of Lombards and Tuscans after Henry's death.
3. Ludovicus Bavarus. A biography of the emperor Ludwig IV of Bavaria (ruled 1314–47), dealing with the years 1325–29.
4. De traditione Patavii ad Canem Grandem anno 1328 . . . . A sort of pamphlet against the Carraresi who betrayed the city to Can Grande della Scala.

The most important of these works are the first and second, but all are valuable, as composed by a true historian (not a mere chronicler), trying to explain the sequence of events which happened within his own lifetime and, many of them, within his own cognizance. He is comparable to his Florentine contemporaries Dino Compagni and Giovanni Villani, and is perhaps the greatest of the three. He is the first mediaeval historian who tried to renew the classical tradition of historiography, being inspired chiefly by Livy, and his Latin prose is far superior to that of his contemporaries.

He wrote, before 1316, a tragedy in Latin verse, Eccerinis, of real literary and historical interest. It concerns the deeds and downfall of Eccelino III da Romano

[1] Since the days of Statius in the first century. Petrarca was the first to receive the honor in Rome, on Easter Sunday 1341.

(1194–1259), a great Ghibelline leader and cruel tyrant of Padova and Verona. The story is centered on Padova, the people of which appear as a real dramatis persona. The author was influenced mainly by Seneca.

He wrote two philosophical dialogues in prose, De lite inter naturam et fortunam, Contra casus fortuitos. Finally, his letters and elegies (21 in number) reveal many incidents of his life. Two are especially noteworthy, the one addressed Ad mag. Marsilium physicum paduanum (i.e. Marsiglio of Padua), and the other In laudem d. Henrici et commendationem sui operis de gestis ejusdem.

His contemporary fame as a poet may be judged from the fact that Giovanni del Virgilio (of Bologna) commended his verse to Dante, and that Petrarca praised him.

Text. Collected works: Opera, edited by F. Osi and N. Villani, Venice 1636. Separate editions: Historia Augusta sive de gestis Henrici septimi Cesaris, 1310–1313, libri XVI, in J. G. Graevi: Thesaurus (6, 1–198, Lyon 1704); J. Reuber: Veteres scriptores (p. 844–952, Frankfort 1726); L. A. Muratori: Rerum italicarum scriptores (10, 9–568, Milan 1727).

De gestis Italicorum, 1313–1329, libri XII, in Graevi (6, 199–360); Muratori (10, 571–768); books 8–14, edited by Luigi Padrin and A. Medin: Sette libri inediti del De gestis Italicorum post Henricum VII di Albertino Mussato (119 p., Venice 1903).

Ludovicus Bavarus, 1327–29, in Graevi (6, 361–67); Reuber (p. 991–1000); Muratori (10, 769–784); J. F. Boehmer: Fontes rerum germanicarum (1, 170–89, Stuttgart 1843).

Eccerinis tragoedia, Muratori (10, 787–800); edited by Luigi Padrin and Giosuè Carducci (342 p., Bologna 1900).

Translations: German: Historia Augusta, by Walter Friedensburg: Des Albertinus Mussatus Kaisergeschichte, oder Geschichte Kaiser Heinrichs VII, in Das Leben Kaiser Heinrich des Siebenten (part 1, 57–358, Leipzig 1882; 1898). Ludovicus Bavarus, by W. Friedensburg: Quellen zur Geschichte Kaiser Ludwigs des Baiern (p. 1–32, Leipzig 1883).

Italian: Eccerinis, by M. T. Dazzi: L'ecerinide (77 p., Città di Castello 1914).

Criticism. W. Dönniges: Geschichte des deutschen Kaiserthums im 14. Jahrhundert (1, 37–73, Berlin 1841). T. F. A. Wichert: Beiträge zur Kritik der Quellen für die Geschichte Kaiser Ludwigs des Baiern (Forschungen zur deutschen Geschichte 16, 70–82, Göttingen (1876), apropos of Mussato's Ludovicus Bavarus. Andrea Gloria: Documenti inediti intorno a Francesco Petrarca e Albertino Mussato (Atti del R. Istituto veneto di scienze, lettere ed arti 6, 17–52, Venice 1879; 1, 157–78, Venice 1882). J. Wychgram: Albertino Mússato. Ein Beitrag zur italienischen Geschichte des 14. Jahrhunderts (Göttingen diss., Leipzig 1880). G. Weltzien: Untersuchung italienischer Quellen zum Römerzug Ludwig des Baiern (p. 31–35, Halle 1882). F. Novati: La biografia di Albertino Mussato nel De scriptoribus illustribus di Secco Polentone (Archivio storico per Trieste 2, 79–92, Rome 1883); Nuovi studi su Albertino Mussato (Giornale storico della letteratura italiana 6, 177–200; 7, 1–47, 1886). Walter Friedensburg: Zur Kritik der Historia Augusta des Albertino Mussato (Forschungen zur deutschen Geschichte 23, 1–62, Göttingen 1883). M. Minoia: Della vita e delle opere di Albertino Mussato (Rome 1884). Antonio Zardo: Albertino Mussato, studio storico e letterario (388 p., Padua 1884). Eleutero Docimasta: Alcune osservazioni critiche sopra recenti studi intorno Albertino Mussato (2d ed., 66 p., Rome 1892). Manlio Torquato Dazzi: Il Mussato storico, nel VI centenario della sua morte (Archivio veneto anno 59, ser. 5, vol. 6, 357–471, Venezia 1929; reprint 119 p., Venezia 1930). Sapegno (p. 151–54, 1934).

FERRETO DE' FERRETI

Ferreto Vicentino. Italian poet and historian. Born c. 1297 in Vicenza, of a wealthy family. He seems to have spent most of his life in his native city, and he died there in March 1337.

His main title to remembrance is his history, Historia rerum in Italia gestarum, in five books, which he started writing about 1329 and which was interrupted by his death in 1337. He begins his narrative with the year 1250 (the death of Frederick II) and was able to reach the year 1318. It is a general history, though centered upon Italy and more particularly upon Vicenza. His aim was to write a true history "non fictum quicquam nec rogatum aut favore conceptum" (lib. III, see Cipolla's ed. 1, 269). Under the influence of classical historians, particularly Sallustius and Livius, he attempted to write a historical synthesis, not simply a chronicle in the mediaeval style. He was influenced not only by the Roman historians, but also by Dante, whose political views he seems to have shared. He admired the emperor Henry VII, hated factions, dreamed of unity and peace. He showed great skill in selecting and grouping his facts, but the concentration of his narrative upon the events which he considered the most important sometimes gives an impression of one-sidedness. Moreover, he was not always unbiased or truthful.

The first three books of his history were based on unknown sources, but the fourth and fifth were made up largely from the chronicle, Historia Augusta, by Albertino Mussato (1261–1329). Many of Ferreto's incorrect statements were copied from Giovanni Villani (d. 1348) in spite of the fact that those same events were accurately related by Mussato. However, Ferreto recounted many things that he himself had witnessed.

Ferreto was very learned and versed in ancient lore; like Mussato, he tried to write classical Latin, but his purism was carried to the extent of using ancient geographical and ethnographical terms instead of those of his own time. It is interesting to find the same mistake and the same affectation a century later in the writings of Byzantine historians such as Chalcondyles and Critobulos.

He was one of the first to revive the study of Latin poetry in Italy. His mentor in poetry was Benvenuto dei Campesani of Vicenza, concerning whose death in 1330 he wrote two of the poems mentioned below. He wrote many poems, but only a few are extant. They are all on historical subjects. The titles of some of the most interesting ones are as follows: De Scaligerorum origine, in honor of Can Grande della Scala (1291–1329), De morte Benevenuti Campesani poete Vicentini, Ad Mussatum Patavinum de morte Benevenuti Campesani Vicentini poete, Poema circiter annum 1329 scriptum ad Canem Grandem, Bella inter Patavos et Vicentinos, and De morte Dantis poetae Florentini versus centum et decem.

Text. Historia rerum in Italia gestarum ab anno 1250 ad annum usque 1318, edited by L. A. Muratori: Rerum italicarum scriptores (9, 935–1182, Milan 1726). A critical edition by Carlo Cipolla: Le opere di Ferreto de' Ferreti Vicentino (3 vols.: vols. 1, 2, history, and vol. 3, poems; Fonti per la storia d'Italia, Rome 1908, 1914, 1920).

Parts of books 3 and 4 of the history translated by W. Friedensburg: Das Leben Kaiser Heinrich des Siebenten (part I, 377–443, Leipzig 1882; reprinted 1898).

De morte Benevenuti Campesani poetae Vicentini (Muratori 9, 1183–86; Cipolla 3, 103–9).

Ad Mussatum Patavinum de morte Benevenuti Campesani Vicentini poetae (Muratori 9, 1187–88; Cipolla 3, 109–12).

De Scaligerorum origine eroicum in laudem Canis Grandis (Muratori 9, 1197–1218; Cipolla 3, 3–100).

Criticism. Wilhelm Dönniges: Kritik der Quellen für die Geschichte Heinrichs des VII des Luxemburgers (p. 73–89, Berlin 1841). Giacomo Zanella: Di Ferreto de' Ferreti (Vicenza 1861; reprinted in Scritti varii p. 91–107, Florence 1877). Max Laue: Ferreto von Vicenza, seine Dichtungen und sein Geschichtswerk (Halle 1884). Carlo Cipolla: Studi su Ferreto dei Ferreti (Giornale storico della letteratura italiana 6, 53–112, Rome 1885); Ferreto de' Ferreti e l'episodio di Guido da Montefeltro (Bullettino dell' Istituto storico italiano 31, 99–101, Rome 1910); La data della morte di Dante secundo Ferreto dei Ferreti (Atti della R. Accad. delle scienze di Torino 49, 1214–19, Turin 1914). Giovanni Filippi: Politica e religiosità di Ferreto dei Ferreti (Archivio veneto 32, 37–61, 309–27, 1886). Potthast (p. 446, 1895).

GIOVANNI DE MATOCIIS

Giovanni il mansionario veronese. Italian humanist (d. 1337).

This Giovanni was curate (mansionario) of the cathedral of Verona. He died in December 1337. Between 1306 and 1320 he wrote the Historia imperialis, a chronicle from the time of Augustus to that of Charlemagne, derived from a great many pagan and Christian works. Many authors are quoted, the favorite ones being St. Zeno (bishop of Verona 362–80) and the two Plinii.

At that time, i.e. before 1320, Giovanni, like his contemporaries, confused the two Plinii into one, but having discovered the Epistolae he recognized his error and wrote the Brevis adnotatio de duobus Pliniis Veronensibus ex multis hic collecta. He introduced the error of considering the Plinii fellow citizens (Veronesi). As a matter of fact C. Plinius Secundus (Pliny the Elder), author of the Historia naturalis (23–79), and his nephew C. Plinius Caecilius Secundus (Pliny the Younger), author of the Epistolae (61–c. 120), were both born in Como.

Criticism. Sabbadini (chiefly 2, 88–90, 1914).

GIOVANNI DA SAN GIMIGNANO

Italian Dominican, preacher and encyclopaedist (d. 1323).

Giovanni de Goro (or Gorini), Giovanni Coppo (or de' Coppi), Joannes Gorinus de Sancto Geminiano, was born in San Gimignano and assumed the Dominican habit in Siena. He was already middle-aged by the end of the thirteenth century, and by 1314 he was famous as a popular lecturer (contionator) all over Italy. He died in 1323.

He wrote many sermons and orations, also meditations on the Gospels, but his main work is a large encyclopaedia for the use of Dominican preachers entitled Summa de exemplis et rerum similitudinibus, which was completed by 1313 if not earlier. Strangely enough, it was first published under the pseudonym "Helvicus natione Teutonicus," but there seems to be no reason to doubt John's authorship.

It is divided into ten books (I quote the folii from the edition of Venice 1497, printed closely in two columns, to give some idea of the relative size of each book): (I) De coelo et elementis, fol. 3–90; (II) De metallis et lapidibus, fol. 90–113; (III) De vegetabilibus et plantis, fol. 113–59; (IV) De natatilibus et volatilibus, fol. 160–87; (V) De animalibus terrestribus, fol. 187–223; (VI) De homine et membris eius, fol. 223–77; (VII) De visionibus et somniis, fol. 278–314; (VIII) De canonibus et legibus, fol. 315–41; (IX) De artificibus et rebus artificialibus, fol. 341–74; (X)

De actibus et moribus humanis, fol. 375–92. That is, it is a real encyclopaedia of natural, moral, and legal knowledge. Book IX, dealing with inventions and inventors, is of special interest to us, as it is a history of technology which prefigures many others, such as the De inventoribus rerum composed a century and a half later by another Italian, Polidoro Vergilio (John Ferguson in Isis 17, 71–93, 1932; Sarton in Osiris 5, 122, fig. 57, 1938). The arrangement is very curious. For example, book IX is subdivided into 91 chapters, each of which concerns a virtue, or a moral or religious topic, such as active and contemplative life, love of God and of the world, the soul, avarice, confession, perseverance, etc.; but these chapters contain a great many "exempla" derived from the mechanical arts and inventions, such as agriculture, fishing, cultivation of herbs and aromats, clothes, vermin (how to get rid of them), windmills and watermills, ships, painting and limning, arrangement of fortified castles, arms, Greek fire, smithing, glassmaking, weights and measures, etc. There is a reference to spectacles, ocularia (fol. 343r in ed. Venice 1497). Remember that spectacles were invented about the end of the thirteenth century, that a Pisan Dominican, Alessandro della Spina (d. 1313), has been mentioned among the inventors, and that another Pisan Dominican, Giordano da Rivalto, spoke of the invention in 1305 (Introd. 2, 1025). The fundamental purpose of the work is clear enough; it was to provide preachers (the author to begin with) having to prepare sermons on moral and religious subjects with as many appropriate exempla, concrete illustrations, as possible.

Giovanni da San Gimignano is also credited with the legend of a saint of his native town, Santa Fina (i.e., Serafina), a virgin who was born in 1238 and died 15 years later, on March 12, 1253. That text is available in Latin MSS and also in early Italian ones. It was written at the very beginning of the century; it is impossible to say whether Giovanni wrote it in Latin or in Italian, or more generally to determine the priority of either text.

Text. Klebs (no. 562) enumerates 5 incunabula editions of the Summa de exemplis et rerum similitudinibus, Deventer 1477, Cologne 1485, Venice 1497, Basel 1499, Venice 1499. I have examined the second half of the first (books V–X, 265 leaves, folio) and the third (392 leaves, smaller size), each printed in two columns. There are many later editions; e.g., Quétif-Echard quote editions of Venice 1577, 1582, Antwerp 1583, 1599, 1629, Lyon 1585, Cologne 1665, Francfurt 1664.

M. Mansfield: The legend of the holy Fina virgin of Santo Gimignano, now first translated from the trecento Italian of Fra Giovanni di Coppo (174 p., London 1908). Includes the early Italian text, English version, introduction, and notes, as well as information on earlier editions.

Criticism. Quétif-Echard (1, 528–29, 1719). An analysis of the Summa de exemplis is much to be desired, especially of book IX. Adams (p. 73–74, 1938). D. C. Bain: Some notes on the printing of the Summa de exemplis, 1499 (The library 21, 192–98, 1940), typographical study of that particular edition.

PASTRENGO

Guglielmo da Pastrengo (near Verona). Gulielmus Pastregicus Veronensis (c. 1290?–1363).

Friend and correspondent of Petrarca. He was a learned notary in Verona and wrote a short account of illustrious men, including inventors. That kind of effort was continued a little later by Domenico Bandini (XIV-2) and then considerably developed a full century later by Polydore Vergil.

Text. De originibus rerum libellus, in quo agitur de scripturis virorum illustrium, de fundatoribus urbium, de primis rerum nominibus, de inventoribus rerum, de primis dignitatibus, deque magnificis institutionibus (Venice 1547). Not available to me.

Criticism. Sabbadini (1, 4–20, 1905). A. Avena: Guglielmo da Pastrengo e gli inizi dell' umanesimo in Verona (Verona 1907), not seen. John Ferguson: Notes on the work of Polydore Vergil, De inventoribus rerum (Isis 17, 71–93, 1932; p. 91). Thorndike (3, 567, 592, 1934), only a few lines. Sapegno (1934), many short references. Dorothy M. Robathan: Libraries of the Italian renaissance (in J. W. Thompson 1939, p. 519–21).

BENZO D'ALESSANDRIA

Bencius Alexandrinus. Italian historian and humanist (d. c. 1335).

Benzo Cona was born in Alessandria, Piedmont, in the second half of the thirteenth century, of a Lombardian family. We do not know where he was educated, but it was probably in Bologna, for he obtained the diploma of notary. He practiced in Milano in 1311 and before; from 1312 to 1322 he was in Como in the service of Leone Lambertenghi (bishop of Como 1295–1325); from 1325 to 1335 he was in Verona in the chancellery of the Scaligeri. He died in that city in or after 1335.

He was one of the first chancellors to combine humanism with his duties, being exceedingly well prepared for that by a series of travels undertaken by him during the last decade of the thirteenth century in northern and central Italy. These were truly archaeological travels, among the first of their kind. He visited libraries and archives, examining inscriptions and MSS, taking copious notes. For example, he described some of the famous MSS of the cathedral of Verona, MSS of Catullus, Ausonius, and the Scriptores historiae augustae. In fact, Benzo did at the end of the thirteenth century and the beginning of the fourteenth what another Alexandrian, Giorgio Mèrula (1424–94), did again in 1488–93, when he explored Italian libraries and archives for the documentation of his Historia vicecomitum. Benzo was one of the earliest historians of Lombardy, and wrote a tract on the city of Milano (De Mediolano civitate). His humanistic tendencies make of him the most genuine Italian forerunner of Petrarca, and of such men as Giovanni Aurispa and Poggio (both of whom died in 1459).

While he was chancellor of the bishop of Como, he prepared a literary encyclopaedia entitled Chronicon or Historia de moribus et vita philosophorum, divided into three parts. Only the first part has come down to us (Ambrosiana MS), and that part was compiled within the period 1312–22. This book being of greater importance from the literary than the scientific point of view, I do not try to enumerate its numerous classical and mediaeval sources. Benzo's main model was the Speculum historiale of Vincent of Beauvais, but he was far more critical than the latter. He paid special attention to Ausonius (IV-2).

Criticism. Pullé (p. 73–75; app. 2, 1–7, 1905). Sabbadini (2, 128–50, 1914). Note by the same in Enciclopedia italiana (6, 665, 1930).

COLA DI RIENZO

Roman tribune in 1347, slaughtered in 1354.

Cola di Rienzo, that is, Nicola figlio di Lorenzo, was born in Rome 1313/14. His father Lorenzo was a tavern keeper, and his mother Maddalena a laundress and water seller. She died early and Cola was brought up in Anagni. At the time of his father's death he returned to Rome, 1333/34. He had obtained by that time a fair amount of classical learning and a great enthusiasm for ancient Rome. In great contrast with the past glory was the tawdry present. Abandoned by the popes, Rome was ruined by the exactions and the internecine jealousies of the barons, the people being the main victims. Cola dreamed of re-establishing imperial Rome. In 1342/43 he was sent as ambassador to Clement VI in Avignon, representing a popular group, inviting the pope to proclaim a new jubilee and come back. In Avignon he met Petrarca. He was appointed by the pope notary of the camera urbana, and used his position and prestige to prepare a popular revolution, which was accomplished in 1347. On May 20, Cola received full dictatorial powers. At first the pope had helped him, but he was frightened by Cola's ambition. The latter invited the Italian cities to send to him ambassadors to discuss "ad salutem et pacem totius sacrae Italiae." By September, the pope began to oppose him; Cola was accused of heresy; on December 15 he abdicated and fled to the mountains of the Abruzzi.

He spent two years in a Franciscan monastery ruminating a strange mixture of Joachimite and imperial dreams. Finally he set out for Prague in 1350 and tried to persuade Charles IV to revive the empire. He was made a prisoner, then sent to Avignon, where Clement VI confirmed his condemnation. However, Innocent VI (pope 1352–62) took another view of the matter and decided to release him and to use him for his own purposes. In 1354 Cola was sent back to Rome, which he re-entered on August 1 with the title of senator; he was warmly received, but his fantastic ideas and arbitrary ways soon destroyed his popularity. He was lynched by his own people on October 8, 1354.

Cola continued the political and humanistic traditions of Dante and Petrarca, mingling them with the mystical ideas of the Spirituals and strange conceptions of his own. He would not deserve to be dealt with here except for two reasons. The first is the existence of a contemporary anonymous biography of him which is one of the most valuable documents of that time. It is written with remarkable soberness and strength.

The second is Cola's deep interest in the ruins and inscriptions of ancient Rome, an interest as it were awakened by him. It would be wrong to call him an antiquarian or epigraphist; the first Latin epigraphist was the Florentine Poggio Bracciolini (1380–1459).

Text. Vita di Cola di Renzo, tribuno del popolo romano. Scritta in lingua volgare romana di quella età da Tomao Fiortifiocca scribasenato (284 p., small size, Bracciano 1624). That is the first edition; the ascription of authorship to Fiortifiocca (or by others to Pompilio Totti) has not been maintained. Second edition, Bracciano 1631. Reprinted in Muratori: Antiquitates italicae medii aevi (3, 399–548; 6 vols., Milano 1738–42). Later editions, Forli 1828, Firenze 1854, and by Alberto Maria Ghisalberti (Rome 1928).

Annibale Gabrielli: Epistolario (300 p., Roma 1890). Konrad Burdach and Paul Piur: Briefwechsel des Cola di Rienzo (Vom Mittelalter zur Reformation, Forschungen zur Geschichte der deutschen Bildung, II; 5 vols., Berlin 1912–29). Monumental publication. Vol. 1 (748 p., 1913–28) is devoted to Cola's cultural background. Vol. 2 (416 p., 1928) contains a study of the sources and a criticism of Petrarca's letters. Vol. 3 (484 p., 1912), critical edition of Cola's correspondence. Vol. 4 (370 p., 1912), sources for Cola's history. Includes the Latin text of the Oraculum angelicum Cyrilli with commentary by the pseudo-Joachim (p. 223–343).

The lost Greek original is ascribed to Cyril of Constantinople, third general of the Carmelites (d. 1224); the Latin translation was supposedly made by Joachim of Floris (XII-2), who died in 1202. What is certain is that that text circulated in Joachimite circles of southern Italy in the thirteenth century and influenced Cola. Vol. 5 (548 p., 1929), notes. All these volumes are fully indexed.

Criticism. Felix Papencordt: Cola di Rienzi und seine Zeit (375 p., Hamburg 1841). French and Italian translations published in 1845. Emmanuel Rodocanachi: Cola di Rienzo. Histoire de Rome de 1342 à 1354 (467 p., ill., Paris 1888). Mario Emilio Cosenza: Petrarca and the revolution of Cola di Rienzo (344 p., Chicago 1913). Gabriele d'Annunzio: Vite di uomini illustri e di uomini oscuri. La vita di Cola di Rienzo (258 p., Milano 1913). Paul Piur: Cola di Rienzo. Darstellung seines Lebens und seines Geistes (252 p., Wien 1931). Nordström (p. 45, 1933).

A2. Hispanic Peninsula

JUAN MANUEL

Don Juan Manuel (1282–1349). The greatest Spanish writer of his time, chronicler, storyteller, moralist, author of a book on the chase.

Don Juan Manuel was born on May 5, 1282 in the castle of Escalona, New Castile, son of the infante Don Manuel and Beatrix of Savoy, grandson of St. Ferdinand (Ferdinand III, king of Castile and Leon, d. 1252). He was educated by Sancho IV (king 1284–95) and employed by him in the kingdom of Murcia, where his contact with the Arabic world began. Juan Manuel studied Arabic and obtained a good knowledge of Arabic literature. Being regent of Castile during the minority (1312–25) of Alfonso XI, he was involved before 1325, and even more after that date, in an endless series of military affairs and political intrigues. It will suffice to say that at times he was obliged to ally himself with the king of Aragon and even with Muḥammad IV, the Naṣrī king of Granada (1325–33). He finally made his peace with his liege Alfonso XI in 1338 and was loyal to him. He took part in the victory on the Salado River over the Moors in 1340, and in the capture of Algeziras in 1342. He died in Peñafiel (on the upper Douro, east of Valladolid) in 1349 (not 1347; the tomb, now destroyed, in the Dominican church of that city bore the date M.CCC.LXII!).

In spite of his many other activities, he wrote considerably. It will suffice here to mention the Cronica abreviada (c. 1320–24), the Libro de la caza (1325), the Libro del caballero ó del escudero (1326), the Libro de los estados (1329–30), and the most famous of all, El conde Lucanor or Libro de Patronio (c. 1328–35).

The Libro de la caza (1325) is the earliest book on the chase in Castilian, if one does not take into account Los paramientos de la caza, the code promulgated by the king of Navarre, Sancho VI, in 1180 (XII-2). It is divided into twelve chapters: nature of falcons and their varieties, how to know good hawks, how to tame and bring them up, how to molt them, how to feed them and cure them of their ailments (cap. XI). The last chapter describes the best localities for hawking in Spain.

The Libro de los estados betrays the influence of the Blanquerna (c. 1283) of Ramon Lull and of the legend of Barlaam and Ioasaph, which made a Christian saint of the Buddha (Introd. 1, 507).

The Conde Lucanor is a collection of "examples" or stories set in the following frame: The count Lucanor asks his counselor Patronio questions concerning difficult problems of ethics and politics; Patronio answers those questions, telling "examples" for the sake of illustration. The latest date for the Conde Lucanor (1335) is anterior to the earlier date for the Decamerone (1344); Juan Manuel is inferior to Boccaccio as a storyteller, but he is nevertheless a very good one, and the influence of his tales can be traced not only in Spanish literature, but also in Shakespeare (example 35, Taming of the shrew) and Andersen. The diffusion of the Conde Lucanor was far smaller than that of the Decamerone. Our great interest in Juan Manuel's book is due to the abundant Arabic traces which can be detected in it (as well as in his other writings), at one and the same time with regard to style and language and to contents. It is clear that Juan Manuel drank deeply from Arabic literature, or was exposed in other ways to many Arabic influences, e.g., through the Disciplina clericalis of Pedro Alfonso (XII-1), Kalīla wa-Dimna, Syntipas, and Alf laila wa-laila.[2]

The Libro del caballero ó del escudero was partly derived from the Libre del orde cavayleria of Ramon Lull (1274-75). It is clear that Don Juan Manuel used the works of Lull, though he did not share the latter's mysticism.

Text. All the works of Don Juan Manuel were edited by Don Pascual de Gayangos: Escritores en prosa (p. 229-442, Madrid 1860; reprinted 1923).

Libro de la caza. First edited by Don José Gutierrez de la Vega (Biblioteca venatoria vol. 3, 135 p., Madrid 1879). Second edition by Gottfried Baist: Don Juan Manuel: El libro de la caza, zum erstenmale herausgegeben (214 p., Halle 1880).

El conde Lucanor. First edition by Gonzalo de Argote y de Molina (Seville 1575). Second edition, Madrid 1642. Of later editions it will suffice to mention the critical ones by Pascual de Gayangos (Madrid 1860), by Hermann Knust (Leipzig 1900), and by Eugenio Krapf (260 p., Vigo 1902).

French version with elaborate introduction and notes by Adolphe de Puibusque (Paris 1854). New one by count Léon Ostrorog (Paris 1925).

German version by Joseph von Eichendorff in the latter's Sämmtliche Werke (2, 381-569, Leipzig 1864).

English version by James York: Count Lucanor, or the fifty pleasant stories of Patronio (262 p., Westminster 1868; reprinted London 1899, 1924).

Criticism. J. E. Harting (1891). F. Dönne: Syntaktische Bemerkungen zu Don Juan Manuels Schriften (Jahresbericht der Pfeifferschen Anstalt p. 3-24, Jena 1891). Hilda Schulhof: Spanische Prosadichtung des Mittelalters in deutscher Übersetzung (Prager deutsche Studien 34, 64 p., Reichenberg i.Pr. 1925). González Palencia (1928). A. R. Nykl: Arabic phrases in El conde Lucanor (Hispanic review 10, 12-17, 1942).

MUNTANER

Ramón Muntaner (c. 1264-1336). Catalan soldier, historian, and poet.

Muntaner was born in Peralada, Catalonia, in 1264 or 1265. Later his family moved to Valencia. At 20 he joined the Almogávares[3] in the conquest of Minorca. Under Roger de Flor (d. 1306) he fought in Sicily and was made procurator-general.

[2] These Oriental sources have been often referred to in Introd. vols. 1 and 2, but the easiest way of orienting oneself with regard to them is to consult the Encyclopaedia of Islam. For Kalīla wa-Dimna, see Brockelmann (EI 2, 694-98, 1924); for Syntipas or Sindibād-nāme, Carra de Vaux (EI 4, 435, 1927); for the Alf laila wa-laila or the Arabian nights, Johannes Oestrup (EI 1, 252-56, 1909), D. B. Macdonald (EI suppt. vol., p. 17-21, 1934), G. Sarton (Isis 28, 321-29, 1938).

[3] From the Arabic, al-mughāwīr, one who is always ready to fight and make a raid (ghārah). They were mercenary soldiers recruited chiefly in the Pyrénées.

He took part in the siege of Messina in 1300. In 1303 he joined the Catalan Company, organized by Roger, and set out on a crusade to the Near East; in this expedition he took an active part, both in war and in diplomacy. Muntaner abandoned the expedition in Gallipoli, where he spent some time as governor. Later (1311–13) he was made governor of the island of Jerba in the Gulf of Gabes, Tunisia. Between 1322 and 1329 he was active in politics and wars in Valencia. He died in 1336, not on Majorca, but on Iviza, the most westerly of the Balearic Islands.

In 1325, in his 60th year, he began to write, in Catalan, a chronicle entitled Crónica o descriptió dels fets e hazanyes del inclyt rey D. Jacme primer rey Daragó, de Mallorques e de Valencia, comte de Barcelona e de Muntpeller, e de molts de sos descendents. He deals with the period 1204–1328, discussing in great detail the reign of James I of Aragon; with the series of events in which the king was one of the important participants, i.e. the conquests of the kingdoms of Valencia and Murcia; and also with the crusading efforts of the Catalans.

Muntaner's Crónica is more than a history, it is an autobiography and a brief for the glory of Muntaner and Catalonia. It is based mainly on personal experiences and not on earlier or contemporary histories. The Crónica is an excellent history of the formation of the Catalan Company and its expedition to Constantinople, Asia Minor, and Greece; as well as local politics and wars in Valencia, Naples, and Sicily, and the Balearic Islands. Muntaner writes in a highly entertaining and picturesque style. He shows an impartiality of judgment and a veracity not always found in accounts of contemporary events. His Crónica is one of the masterpieces of Catalan literature, as well as one of the main sources of Catalan history.

Muntaner also wrote versified histories, such as the one entitled Sermó del passatge de Sardenya, which has been called the epic of Catalan poetry. This poem, constituting chapter 272 of the Crónica, contains advice to Jaime II and to the infante Anfos III concerning the conquest of Sardinia.

Ramón Muntaner must not be confused with a namesake, Ramón Muntaner of Majorca, who accompanied Jaime I (king 1213–76) in the conquest of Majorca.

Text. Crónica. First edition, Valencia 1558; second edition, Barcelona 1562. Later editions: Karl F. W. Lanz: Chronik des edlen En Ramon Muntaner (586 p., Stuttgart 1844), based on the edition of Valencia; not a critical edition. Antonio de Bofarull y Brocá: Crónica catalana de Ramón Muntaner: texto original y traducción catalana acompañada de numerosas notas (Catalan and Spanish texts in parallel columns, Barcelona 1860). J. Coroleu (640 p., Barcelona 1886). The account of the Catalan expedition has been edited separately by Lluís Nicolau d'Olwer (232 p., Barcelona 1926).

The poem Sermó del passatge de Sardenya (ch. 272 of the Crónica) has been edited separately by Mila y Fontanals: Lo sermo d'En Muntaner (Revue des langues romanes 16, 218–31, 1879; with notes in 17, 38–41, 1880, and 19, 5–12, 1881).

Translations: French: Jean Alexandre Buchon: Chronique (Collection des chroniques vols. 5, 6, Paris 1827); Chronique d'Aragon, de Sicile et de Grèce (Chroniques étrangères, Paris 1840), a new translation by the same author.

German: Karl F. W. Lanz: Chronik des edlen En Ramon Muntaner (2 vols. in 1, 327, 325 p., Leipzig 1842).

Italian: Filippo Moisé: Cronache catalane del secolo XIII. e XIV., una di Raimondo Muntaner l'altra di Bernardo d'Esclot, prima traduzione italiana di Felipo Moisé con note studi e documenti (Florence 1844). Enrico Cardona:

Dell' antica letteratura catalana, studii seguiti dal testo e dalla traduzione della Vita di Giacomo I tolta dalla Cronaca catalana di Ramon Muntaner (p. 131–228, Naples 1878; comprises chapters 6–28 of the Crónica). Partial Sicilian version (86 ch.) of the fifteenth century, edited by V. di Giovanni: Cronache siciliane (p. 221–367, Bologna 1865).

English: Lady Anna Goodenough: The Chronicle of Muntaner (Hakluyt Society second ser.: vol. 1, no. 47, 460 p.; vol. 2, no. 50, 314 p., London 1920–21).

Criticism. Antonio de Bofarull y Brocá: Ramon Muntaner, guerrero y cronista (52 p., Barcelona 1883). Estanislau Aguiló: Alguna noticia més sobre en Ramon Muntaner i sa familia (Revista de bibliografia catalana 3, 26–38, Barcelona 1903). Rubió y Lluch (by index, 1908–21); Paquimeres i Muntaner (Memòries, Institut d'estudis catalans 1, fasc. 2, 33–60, Barcelona 1927), Paquimeres is the Catalan name of Pachymeres (XIII-2). Francisco Almarche y Vasquez: Ramón Muntaner, cronista dels Reys de Aragó, ciutadà de Valencia (Congrés d'historia de la corona d'Aragó 1, 483–505, Barcelona 1909). Rafael Ballester y Castell: Les fuentes narrativas de la historia de España durante la edad media (p. 142–46, Palma de Mallorca 1912). Nicolae Iorga: Ramón Muntaner et l'empire byzantin (Revue historique du sud-est européen, IVe année, 325–55, 1927). Lluis Nicolau d'Olwer: Resum de literatura catalana (p. 51, Barcelona 1928). Carlo Banús y Comas: Expedición de Catalanes y Aragoneses a Oriente a principios del siglo XIV (228 p., Madrid 1929). Rovira i Virgili (vol. 5, by index, 1928; 6, 87–90, 1931). Jaume Massó Torrents: Repertori de l'antiga literatura catalana. I. La poesia (p. 284–90, Barcelona 1932). Vera (2, 97–99, 1934).

A3. France

GEOFFROI OF PARIS

Godefroy of Paris (Geoffrey, Godfrey, etc.). French chronicler (fl. Paris c. 1300–16).

He wrote poems in French and Latin. His most important work is a chronicle of Paris from 1300 to 1316, in French verse (7,918 lines). The chronicle is very interesting because the author was living in a tragic epoch, the rule of Philippe IV and Louis X, and witnessed many extraordinary events, e.g., the condemnation of the Templars. He is witty and his reactions are especially valuable because he is not an official observer, but rather like a novelist (in the old acceptance of that word, a newsmonger). In fact, he is the first Parisian novelist.

Text. Geoffroi's chronicle was first edited by J. A. C. Buchon: Chronique métrique de Godefroy de Paris, suivie de la Taille de Paris en 1313 (Collection des chroniques nationales vol. 9, Paris 1827). Second edition in the Recueil des historiens de la France (22, 87–166, Paris 1865).

Criticism. Natalis de Wailly: Mémoire sur Geoffroi de Paris (Mémoires de l'Académie des inscriptions vol. 18, 41 p., Paris 1849; p. 495). Petit de Julleville (2, 294, 1896). Molinier (3, 192, 1903).

GUIARD

Guillaume Guiart or Guiard. French chronicler (fl. 1304–16).

Guiard was born in Orléans; he took part in the Flemish campaign, and was wounded a short time before the battle of Mons-en-Puelle (near Lille; where Philippe le Bel defeated the Flemings in 1304). Being incapacitated, he lived for a time in Arras, where he began his chronicle. Later he resided in Paris, and this enabled him to rewrite his chronicle in 1306–7, with reference (so he says) to the St. Denis archives. In 1313 he was in poor circumstances in Paris, being called a "menestrel de bouche," which I take to mean a public storyteller; he was still alive in 1316.

His chronicle in verse (21,510 lines), entitled Branche de royaulx lignages, deals with the kings of France from Philippe II Auguste (king 1180–1223) to Philippe IV le Bel (king 1285–1314), in whose honor he composed it. It is important for the period 1296–1304 (to which some 8,000 lines are devoted), especially for the Flemish wars (1301–4).

Text. The part dealing with St. Louis was edited by Ducange in the latter's Joinville (Paris 1668). First complete edition by J. A. C. Buchon: Collection des chroniques nationales (vols. 7, 8, Paris 1828). Second edition of about 13,000 lines by Léopold Delisle (Recueil des historiens de France 22, 171–300, 1865).

Criticism. Paulin Paris (HL 31, 104–43, 1893). Molinier (3, 190, 1903).

JOINVILLE

Jean de Joinville (1224–1319). French chronicler, one of the greatest of mediaeval times, biographer of Saint Louis.

Jean sire de Joinville was born at the castle of Joinville (dépt. Haute-Marne, Champagne) in 1224. He was thus a Champenois like his great predecessor Geoffroi de Villehardouin (XIII-1). Having lost his parents in childhood, he was brought up by his suzerain Thibault IV, count of Champagne. As soon as he was of age he assumed the office of seneschal (i.e., high bailiff or steward) of Champagne, hereditary in his family.

In 1248, he left his home, wife, and children to take part in the Sixth Crusade. He met Louis IX in Cyprus, where the king had established a base. In the following spring (1249) Louis IX sailed to Damietta, which he captured, his plan being to destroy the Muslim power in Egypt. The crusaders, weakened by their indiscipline as well as by dysentery and scurvy, were utterly defeated at al-Manṣūra (on the Damietta branch of the Nile) by the Ayyūbī sulṭān al-Mu'aẓẓam Tūrānshāh, and king Louis was made a prisoner with the remnants of his army. The execution of the treaty of peace was delayed because of the overthrow of Ayyūbī power in Egypt by the Baḥrī Mamlūk dynasty. After the peace Louis and Joinville remained in Palestine, returning to France in 1254. When Louis IX undertook a new crusade (the seventh) in 1267–70, Joinville excused himself and stayed at home; we may recall that Louis died of the plague soon after his landing in Tunis (Carthage) in 1270. In 1283 Philip III the Bold entrusted to Joinville the administration of the county of Champagne during the minority of Jeanne of Navarre.[4] In 1315, being 91 years old, he wrote a letter to king Louis X le Hutin (1314–16) promising to come and fight with him against the Flemings! He died at Joinville in 1319.

Joinville is a man of the thirteenth century, yet if he had died at the age of 76 at the end of that century, he would have remained unnoticed, for his greatest achievement, his Mémoires or Histoire de Saint Louis, was completed in the fourteenth century, as late as October 1309. It is probable that he began to put his reminiscences in order soon after St. Louis' death, and he began their redaction

[4] Jeanne (1272–1305) was the only daughter of the last count of Champagne, Henry I le Gros, who was also king of Navarre. She married, in 1284, Philippe IV le Bel (king 1285–1314). She was thus queen of France from 1285, and the crowns of France, Navarre, and Champagne were then united. Joinville was the liege man not of the king of France, but of the count of Champagne, king of Navarre.

somewhat later at the request of queen Jeanne. At the time of her death, in 1305, the Mémoires were not yet completed; he offered them in 1309 to her son Louis (Louis X).

These reminiscences are a little incoherent and repetitious, which is not surprising considering that the author was an old man telling stories of his youth; indeed, he was often describing events which had happened more than half a century before. They are very valuable, however, because the author was a good observer, very ingenuous and "prime-sautier"; he was a laudator temporis acti, but youthful and imaginative. His Mémoires are divided into three parts, dealing respectively with (1) Louis' character and early life, (2) his adventures in Egypt and Syria, (3) subsequent events of his life. The second part is by far the largest, and the book is thus mainly an account of the Sixth Crusade and an admirable biography of the good king St. Louis,[5] but it is also to a large extent a biography of himself. As painted by Joinville, Louis is a great king and a saint, yet very human, not a kind of saintly abstraction as is so often the case in hagiographical writings. St. Louis, by the way, had been canonized as early as 1297, Joinville being one of the witnesses in the process of canonization. Among many descriptions and observations made by Joinville, we may refer in the first place to his description of scurvy[6] (§291, 299, 300 in the text established by Natalis de Wailly), of the Nile coming from the terrestrial paradise and its periodical floods, the Beduins, the Tatars, etc. There is also an unmistakable reference to fossil fishes, some of which were shown to king Louis while he was in Ṣaidā' in 1253. This is the earliest reference to fossil fishes in mediaeval literature (Sarton 1941).

Joinville's book ranks with those of Villehardouin (XIII-1) and Froissart (XIV-2) as one of the three outstanding classics of mediaeval French historiography. Because of his imagination and the candor of his French prose, he may be considered a harbinger of Montaigne (1533–92) and La Fontaine (1621–95).

Joinville's Mémoires include a text of the Enseignemens of St. Louis (see Introd. 2, 725) somewhat different from the other traditions of that very important treatise written by the good king for the edification of his children.

The Mémoires are the fruit of Joinville's old age; his only other work was a fruit of his youth. That is a commentary on the Credo composed by him in 1250–51 at Acre. It is really a picture book meant to include some 36 edifying illustrations explained by a brief text. The Credo has come to us in a single MS (Bibliothèque nationale, Paris) representing the text as revised in 1287, with only 26 illustrations.

It is worth while to compare Joinville with Jean de Meung (XIII-2), if only to make the reader realize that these two great French writers were contemporaries. Indeed, it is probable that Jean de Meung was born later than Joinville, and was thus his younger contemporary, but it so happened that he wrote his part of the Roman de la rose c. 1268–85 (before 1280?), whereas Joinville did not write his Mémoires until 1309—that is, a full generation later. In spite of that, the aristocrat Joinville is distinctly a man of the past, while the burgher Jean represents the future.

[5] All in all, one of the best mediaeval biographies.

[6] The earliest account of scurvy which is generally quoted (e.g., H. Harold Scott: History of tropical medicine 1, 21, London 1939) is that of Antonio Pigafetta of Vicenza, one of the survivors of Magellan's circumnavigation. That observation of scurvy was made on November 28, 1520. Lord Stanley of Alderley: The first voyage around the world (Hakluyt Society no. LII, p. 64, London 1874). Joinville's account is more than two centuries earlier than Pigafetta's.

Text. Edition by Antoine Pierre de Rieux (Poitiers 1535?, 1547, 1561). Many other early editions, of which I shall cite only the one prepared by Charles du Fresne du Cange (1610–88), the great lexicographer (Paris 1668). Modern editions by Michaud and Poujoulat (Paris 1836), by J. A. C. Buchon (Paris 1838), by Francisque Michel (Paris 1858). These modern editions include translations into modern French. The best critical edition was prepared by Natalis de Wailly: Oeuvres comprenant l'Histoire de Saint Louis, le Credo, et la lettre à Louis X, avec un texte rapproché du français moderne en regard (608 p., Paris 1867). Revised in 1874 and after that often reprinted in extenso or partially. I have used the reprint of 1874, a very beautiful and convenient volume, giving throughout the original text and on opposite pages a version in modern French. The text is illustrated with various contemporary documents and maps, and is followed by 22 "éclaircissements," that is, a series of essays explaining royal politics, coinage, weapons, clothing, Joinville's language and grammar, seals, etc. There is also a glossary (p. 601–58) and a generous index.

Le livre des saintes paroles et des bons faits de notre saint roi Louis, traduction française par André Mary (Paris 1928).

There are translations into Spanish, Italian, English, etc. The English translation by Sir Frank Marzials is included in Everyman's Library (London 1908, etc.). An earlier translation by Thomas Johnes (1748–1816) was printed in his own house at Hafod (near Swansea, Glamorganshire, Wales) in 1807. A new translation by Joan Evans, in a slightly archaic English, has recently appeared (Gregynog Press, Newton, Montgomeryshire 1938), a sumptuous publication with colored armorial bearings of the principal characters.

Criticism. Ambroise Firmin Didot: Etudes sur Joinville (2 vols., Paris 1870), vol. 2 includes a facsimile of the unique MS of the Credo. Henri François Delaborde: Jean de Joinville (Paris 1894). Gaston Paris (HL 32, 291–459, 1898). Langlois (4, 1–46, 1928), apropos of the Credo and of the Enseignemens de Louis IX. Sarton: The earliest reference to fossil fishes (Isis 33, 56–58, 1941), query answered by Frank D. Adams (Isis 33, 335), A. S. Pease (Isis 33, 689–90), Eugene V. Prostov (Isis 34, 24), L. Carrington Goodrich (Isis 34, 25), Robert Eisler (Isis 34, 363).

A4. Germanic Countries

OTTOKAR OF STYRIA

Ottokar von Horneck, or von Steiermark. Didactic poet, born in the forties of the thirteenth century, in Upper Styria, and died c. 1309. He was the son of a popular minnesinger. That his family name was Horneck has been denied by Seemüller and others. Lorenz says that he was a knight, but other writers doubt this claim. From his Reimchronik it is evident that he was a layman, and a vassal of count Otto II of Lichtenstein. Ottokar tells us that he studied the art of poetry under Conrad of Rotenberg (otherwise unknown), who had spent some time in Sicily at the court of king Manfred (king 1258–66).

Ottokar wrote in German verse a chronicle from 1250 to 1309. He probably wrote this between the years 1305 and 1309. The work is divided into four parts: (1) from the death of Frederick II to the fall of Acre (1250–91), c. 45,000 verses; (2) siege and fall of Acre (1281–91), c. 10,000 verses; (3) to the death of Henry, abbot of Admont in Styria (1297), c. 15,000 verses; (4) up to 1309, c. 30,000 verses.

The author's main interest is in the history of Austria and Styria, but he also discusses the affairs of Salzburg, Bohemia, Hungary, the Empire, and the relations of these countries to France, Italy, and the Near East. He treats at some length the relations between the kings and princes; between the kings and various classes of people; between cities and kings; between the Jews and the kings, etc.

His work is not very critical, many of his facts are taken from hearsay. He is not a mere annalist, however, but a historian who organized his material in three ways: according to chronology, subject matter, and geography. This history is quite pragmatic, especially the second part. His facts are drawn from a vast number of annals and chronicles of cities and provinces, monasteries and kings in Austria, Styria, Alsace, Thuringia, Italy, and France. He also used the Schwabenspiegel as one of his sources, a work seldom if ever used by chroniclers. His work is very detailed and inclusive.

In the preface to the Reimchronik, Ottokar says that he wrote another work, the Buoch der Keiser, but so far no manuscript of it has been found. This was a chronicle of the deeds of the Assyrian, Greek, Persian (material from the Latin sources only), Roman kings and emperors, up to the "last" one, Frederick II. He says that he planned to write a similar history of the popes, but this was never begun.

Text. Hieronymus Pez: Scriptores rerum austriacarum (3, 1–844, Leipzig 1745), with extensive glossary and index. Franz Lichtenstein and Joseph Seemüller: Ottokars österreichische Reimchronik (Monumenta Germaniae historica, 2 vols., 1565 p., Hanover 1890–93), long critical introduction.

Criticism. Theodor Schacht: Aus und über Ottokar's von Horneck Reimkronik (355 p., Mainz 1821). Arnold Busson: Beiträge zur Kritik der steyerischen Reimchronik und zur Reichsgeschichte im XIII. und XIV. Jahrhundert (Sitzungsberichte der Kais. Akad. der Wissenschaften, phil.-hist. Cl., vols. 111, 114, 117, 126, Vienna 1885–92). Ottokar Lorenz: Deutschlands Geschichtsquellen im Mittelalter (1, 242–52, Berlin 1886). H. Vildhaut: Quellenkunde zur allgemeinen Geschichte (4, 360–67, Werl 1909). M. Vystijd: Die steirische Reimchronik (Mitteilungen des österreichischen Instituts für Geschichtsforschung vol. 34, Innsbruck 1913). Hans von Voltelini: Ottokars österreichische Reimchronik und der Schwabenspiegel (Zeitschrift der Savigny-Stiftung für Rechtsgeschichte 50, 385–88, Weimar 1930).

PETER OF DUSBURG

Petrus de Dusburg. Prussian historian. Born probably in Duisburg in the duchy of Cleves. He called himself a "priest-brother" of the Teutonic Order, and a "canonicus sambiensis" or "officialis ecclesiae sambiensis" (sambiensis refers to Samland, the province of East Prussia, the center of which is Königsberg). He spent some time in Königsberg, the capital of the order's domain,[7] where he wrote his chronicle. The date and place of his death are unknown.

Peter's Chronica, written in 1326 and dedicated to Hochmeister Werner von Orseln (murdered in 1330), is an important document for the early history of Prussia and the founding of the Teutonic Order c. 1191 and its development up to 1326. It is a history of the government of the territory, its colonization, the cities and their overseas relations, the struggle between the knights and clergy and their feuds with the Polish knights; there is no discussion of foreign or domestic politics.

This Chronica is divided into four parts: In part I there is a detailed account of the founding of the order at Acre by the citizens of Bremen and Lübeck; the establishment of various houses in Armenia, "Romania," Apulia, Austria, Livonia, and Prussia. The principal sources for this part are the statutes of the order, and the De primordiis ordinis theutonici (an earlier work which is now lost).

In part II Dusburg recounts in detail the conquest of the Prussians (up to 1231)

[7] For the order itself, founded in 1191, see my note, Introd. 2, 333.

by the Teutonic Knights, describing the various wars and the final subjection; the donation to the order of East Prussia, Kulm (on the Vistula), and West Prussia in 1230 by Conrad the Polish duke of Masovia is also given.

Part III deals with the war against the Prussians between 1231 and 1326. Dusburg includes brief but interesting descriptions of Prussia and the customs of its inhabitants; the building of various castles and fortifications; the advent of many pilgrims into these lands; the capture of various castles; raids into Poland, and neighboring provinces. In the second half of this part Dusburg describes the war with the Lithuanians; raids into Poland, Livonia, Carsovia,[7a] and the destruction of Memel and other important places; and the devastation of Brandenburg.

The fourth part, entitled De incidentibus, is a brief chronicle of "important" events from 1190 to 1326, culled mostly from the Compendium of Martin of Troppau (XIII-2) and the Historia ecclesiastica of Ptolemy of Lucca (XIII-2). These events include the capture of Constantinople; the death of many Tatars in Spain; the dates of founding of ten religious orders, and the names of the popes in whose times they were organized; supernatural and natural phaenomena; obituary notices of kings and popes; a biography of Conrad, the fifth master-general of the Teutonic Knights; and a description of conditions in the Holy Land.

In the first three parts of his work, Peter depends almost entirely upon his own experience and that of his friends for his information, therefore his history is a valuable contemporary source for the early conquest of Prussia by the Germans.

A Supplementum to this chronicle is found in some manuscripts, which continues the record to 1435; the first 20 chapters (1326–30) were probably written by Dusburg himself, and the rest by Conrad Bitschin, scribe of the city of Kulm. This Supplementum deals primarily with accounts of the destruction of various castles.

Peter's Chronica was translated into German verse by Nicolaus von Jeroschin, chaplain of the order, between 1331 and 1341.

Text. Cronica terrae Prussiae, or Chronicon Prussiae atque Ordinis Teutonici, c. 1190–1326, edited by Christopher Hartknoch (Frankfort and Leipzig, 1679). Critical edition by Max Töppen (Scriptores rerum prussicarum 1, 21–213; Supplementum, chs., 1–20, p. 213–219, Leipzig 1861), with Conrad Bitschin's additions (ibid. 3, 478–506, 1866).

Di Kronike von Pruzinlant, the fourteenth-century translation by Nicolaus von Jeroschin, published by Ernst Strehlke (Scriptores rerum prussicarum 1, 303–648, Leipzig 1861).

Criticism. Michal Wiszniewski: Historya literatury polskiéj (2, 140–46, Cracow 1840). Max Töppen: Geschichte der preussischen Historiographie (p. 1–18, Berlin 1853); Historisch-comparative Geographie von Preussen (Gotha 1858). Walther Fuchs: Zu Peter von Dusburg und das Chronicon olivense[7b]

[7a] Carsovia is the land of Kors or the Kourons, in modern language Kurland or Courland, a Baltic country, south of the Gulf of Riga, then inhabited by Lithuanians or by Letts and perhaps also by Finnish tribes. The name Masovia above refers to a Polish province, main city Warsaw. The name Nattangia below refers to the district of Natangen, south of the Baltic between Frisches Haff and the river Alle. The almost hopeless intricacies of Baltic ethnography are indicated by Alfred Bilmanis: Grandeur and decline of the German Balts (Slavonic and East European review 22, 50–80, 1944).

[7b] Chronicle of the Cistercian monastery of Oliva, near Danzig, founded in 1170–79. That chronicle was completed in 1349, probably by the abbot of that time, Stanislas, not by Gerhard von Braunsvalde, who was prior of Oliva in 1337. Text edited by Theodor Hirsch (Scriptores rerum prussicarum 1, 649–805, 1861). The name of Oliva is familiar to historians because of the treaty of Oliva, concluded in 1660 between Poland and Sweden in that very monastery.

(Altpreussische Monatsschrift 21, 193–260, 421–84; 23, 405–34, Königsberg i.Pr. 1884–86). Carl Beckherrn: Das "Propugnaculum in introitu terre Nattangie" der Chronik des Dusburg (pars III, cap. 133) (Altpreussische Monatsschrift 23, 283–303, Königsberg i.Pr. 1886). Max Perlbach: Zu Peter von Dusburg (Preussisch-Polnische Studien zur Geschichte des Mittelalters 2, 95–119; vol. 3, Halle 1886). Walther Ziesemer: Nicolaus von Jeroschin und seine Quelle (116 p., Berlin 1907).

JOHN OF VICTRING

Johannes Victoriensis, de Victoria, Johannes Schoenfelder, Johann Viktring. Austrian chronicler (d. 1345).

John was born between 1270 and 1280, probably in Lotharingia; and by 1312 was abbot of Victring, a Cistercian monastery near Klagenfurt in Carinthia on the river Gran. Nothing is known about his early life except that he was a student in Victring by 1307 or 1308. He had good opportunities for collecting valuable information for his history, since he was intimately connected with those who made history, that is, with the courts of Carinthia-Tyrol, Vienna, and Aquileia; he was secretary and adviser to count Henry of Carinthia, to count Albert II of Austria, to Bertrand of Aquileia, and to others. He died in 1345, not 1347.

Between 1341 and 1343 John wrote the first redaction of his Liber certarum historiarum, a history of Austria and Carinthia from 1217 to 1342, and dedicated it to Albert II of Austria (duke 1330–58). We have only two fragments of it today, which have been published by Pez under the title Chronica Carinthiae. This redaction was merely a local history, but in the next year John expanded it to include some of the more important events of Spanish, English, and Italian history. This second version was dedicated to the patriarch Bertrand of Aquileia (patriarch 1334–50). He planned to write a third redaction, but of this we have only the preface.

In book I of the second edition, John, after passing over rather hurriedly the main historical events from the time of Charles Martel to the reign of Frederick II, discusses in detail the main events in Styria and Austria; the conquest of Austria by Ottokar of Moravia; the struggles of king Bela of Styria and king Stephen of Hungary, etc. He also has quite a little to say about Italian history, because Italy harbored the papacy. In his account of the Germans he deals at some length with the relations between the empire, the papacy, and the kings. He usually took the side of the papacy in any controversy.

John was an educated man, and from the style of writing used in his histories he had evidently read widely in classical works; he frequently cites Vergil, Horace, Ovid, and others.

For the period before his own time John drew largely upon the works of Isidore of Seville, Einhard, Regino of Prüm, Hermann the Lame, Otto of Freising, and Martin of Troppau. For contemporary history he relies mostly on his own experiences and on information given to him by the important men of his time, among whom he mentions Leopold of Weltingen, bishop Matthew of Brixen, the patriarch Bertrand of Aquileia, count Henry of Carinthia, and the knight Conrad of Aufenstein.

The Liber certarum historiarum is one of the best histories written in the later Middle Ages; it is not merely a compilation of material arranged in chronological order, but a well organized synthesis with some critical exposition.

Text. Hieronymus Pez: Anonymi Leobiensis chronicon, libri VI (Scriptores rerum austriacarum 1, 751–966, Leipzig 1721), contains fragments of the second redaction of the Liber certarum historiarum; continuation of Chronicle to 1347 (ibid. p. 966–72).

J. G. Eccard: Corpus historicum medii aevi (1, 1413–60), prints an extract of the first redaction under the title Continuatio chronici Martini Poloni (Leipzig 1723).

S. A. Würdtwein: Joannis de Schoenfelt equitis austriaci chronicon ab anno MCCC usque ad MCCCXLVI (Nova subsidia diplomatica 3, 201–37, Heidelberg 1782), contains what seems to be another redaction of book III, 3 to VI, 12. Much briefer than the other editions.

Johann Friedrich Böhmer: Johannes Victoriensis und andere Geschichtsquellen Deutschlands im vierzehnten Jahrhundert (Fontes rerum germanicarum 1, 271–450, Stuttgart 1843), a transcription of the larger section of the first redaction. Contains many errors in transcription.

Walter Friedensburg: Das Buch gewisser Geschichten von Abt Johann von Victring (Die Geschichtschreiber der deutschen Vorzeit, Lieferung 82, 362 p., Leipzig 1888; reprinted 1899), a German translation of the Latin edition by Böhmer.

Feodor Schneider: Iohannis abbatis Victoriensis Liber certarum historiarum (Scriptores rerum germanicarum vols. 57, 58, Hanover 1909–10). The only good edition containing all parts of this work.

Criticism. K. Stögmann: Johannes Victoriensis und Peter von Königsaal[7c] (Oester.-Kais. Wiener Zeitung no. 13, 97–99; no. 14, 107–9, Vienna 1856). August Fournier: Abt Johann von Viktring und sein Liber certarum historiarum (166 p., Berlin 1875); Zur Kritik von Johann von Victrings Liber certarum historiarum (Programm, Halle a.S. 1878). Ottokar Lorenz: Deutschlands Geschichtsquellen im Mittelalter (1, 252–60, Berlin 1886). Edmund Aelschker: Abt Johann von Viktring (Neue Carinthia, Zeitschrift für Geschichte Kärntens, Jahrg. 1, 14–26, 58 ff., Klagenfurt 1890). Fedor Schneider: Studien zu Johannes von Victring (Neues Archiv 28, 137–91, Hanover 1903; 29, 397–442, Hanover 1904; part I was printed separately as an inaugural dissertation, Hanover 1902). Ernst Klebel: Zu den Fassungen und Bearbeitungen von Johanns von Viktring "Liber certarum historiarum" (Mitteilungen des oesterreichischen Instituts für Geschichtsforschung, suppt. vol. 11, 354–73, Innsbruck 1929).

MATTHIAS OF NEUENBURG

German chronicler (d. after 1354 and before 1371).

Matthias Neoburgensis. Neuenburg im Breisgau is a place on the Rhine 4 miles below Basel. The dates of Matthias' birth and death are unknown. In 1315–16 he was studying at the University of Bologna, where he became a magister decretorum, that is, a master of canon law. In 1327 he was advocatus (counsel) to the episcopal court of Basel; when Berthold of Bucheck (near Solothurn or Soleure in Switzerland) was appointed bishop of Strassburg, in 1328, Matthias followed him as legal adviser; he was still acting in that capacity in 1350. He visited the curia in Avignon twice, in 1335 and 1338. He was still living on May 9, 1355, but in 1370 was spoken of as dead.

[7c] Reference to the Königsaal chronicle or Chronicon aulae regiae, one of the most important sources for Bohemian history in the fourteenth century. Part of that chronicle was written by Otto von Thüringen, second abbot of the Cistercian abbey of Königsaal (d. 1314); it was continued to 1337 by his successor, Peter von Zittau (d. 1339), and to 1352 by Franz von Prag (d. 1362). Johann Loserth: Die Königsaaler Geschichts-Quellen mit den Zusätzen und der Fortsetzung des Dommherrn Franz von Prag (Fontes rerum austriacarum vol. 8, 627 p., 6 pl., Wien 1875); Loserth (ADB 25, 476–78, 1887). Potthast (p. 508, 1895).

He wrote (or edited) an important Latin chronicle of Germany from 1273 to 1350; there are various continuations of it down to 1378. An excellent biography of his master Berthold, bishop of Strassburg from 1328 to 1353, is also ascribed to him.

There has been considerable discussion with regard to the authorship of the chronicle. It was long ascribed to the count Albrecht of Hohenberg (Albertus Argentinensis), chancellor of Ludwig of Bavaria; it was also ascribed to Jacob of Mainz, notary in Speier (Spires on the Rhine). Though such a question does not admit of a complete and final solution, the evidence now available suggests that Matthias was not only the editor of the chronicle, but also its author or joint author.

The author of the Chronicle defended the emperor Ludwig of Bavaria against the curia, but with moderation; he was unfavorably disposed toward Karl of Luxemburg.

Text. Alberti Argentinensis chronici fragmentum a Rudolpho Habsburgico usque ad . . . 1349, edited by Cuspinian (Johannes Spiesshaymer, c. 1473–1529): De consulibus Romanorum commentarii (p. 667–710, Basel 1552), very incomplete edition. G. Studer: Die Chronik des Matthias von Neuenburg (304 p., Bern 1866). Ludwig Weiland: Die Wiener Handschrift der Chronik (Abhandlungen der Gesellschaft der Wissenschaften, Göttingen, vol. 37, 60 p., 1891); Die vaticanische Handschrift (ibid. vol. 38, 62 p., 1892). New edition by Adolf Hofmeister (Monumenta Germaniae historica, Berlin 1924).

German translation by Georg Grandaur, with introduction by Ludwig Weiland (320 p., Leipzig 1892; reprinted 1899).

Vita sive gesta Bertholdi first edited by Urstisius (Christian Wurstisen, 1544–88): Germaniae historicorum illustrium . . . (2, 167–79, Francfort 1585; reprinted 1670). Also in Studer's edition of the chronicle (p. 220–35, Bern 1866), and in Joh. Friedr. Böhmer: Fontes rerum germanicarum (4, 297–309, Stuttgart 1868).

Criticism. W. Wiegand (ADB 20, 666–68, 1884). Potthast (p. 512, 780, 1896).

JOHN OF WINTERTHUR

Joannes Vitoduranus. Swiss Franciscan chronicler (d. 1348 or after).

John was born in Winterthur, canton of Zürich, c. 1300, assumed the Franciscan habit there in 1315, flourished in the monasteries of Basel, Villingen, Schaffhausen, and Lindau (1340 et seq.) on the Lake of Constance. He died in or after 1348.

He wrote a chronicle covering the period 1198 to 1348. He began his work c. 1340 and wrote the history down to that time, then continued it in the form of annals to 1348; he tried to revise the whole and added a general preface. The chronicle deals mainly with southern Germany, the struggle between the emperor Ludwig and the Avignonese popes, the conflicts between the Swabian nobility and the cities, etc. It is especially valuable for the history of the final period, say, 1300–48. It occasionally contains references to events happening in other countries, special attention being paid to events of Franciscan interest. For example, we owe to it the preservation of a long summary of the first letter written by John of Montecorvino (d. c. 1328) from China (but ascribed to a German brother, perhaps Arnold of Cologne).

John of Winterthur was remarkably impartial on all matters which did not concern his order, and his account is of special interest from the cultural point of view.

Text. Johannis Vito Durani Chronicon quo suorum ac paulo superiorum temporum res gestas describit (40 p., in Gottfried Wilhelm Leibniz: Accessiones historicae vol. 1, Leipzig 1698). The editor is no other than the great mathematician Leibniz (1646–1716). Other editions need not be mentioned here except the critical one by Georg von Wyss: Die Chronik des Minoriten Johannes von Winterthur nach der Urschrift hrg. (Archiv für schweizerische Geschichte vol. 11, 300 p., Zürich 1856).

German translation by Bernhard Freuler (400 p., Winterthur 1866).

Criticism. G. v. Wyss (ADB 14, 483, 1881). Potthast (p. 677, 1896). A. C. Moule (p. 197, 207, 1930).

A5. Low Countries

HOCSEM

Jean de Hocsem. Liégeois (Belgian) chronicler (1279–1348).

Jean de Hocsem or Joannes Hocsemius was born at Hoxem, a hamlet of Hougaerde, near Tirlemont (prov. Brabant, Belgium), in February 1279 n.s.[8] In 1296 he was a student in Paris, and he attended the famous law school of Orléans from 1305 to 1308. In 1305 he visited Clement V in Lyon, where that pope had just been crowned. In 1308 he returned to his country and was appointed rector of one of the altars in St. Germain, Tirlemont, and canon of Incourt in Brabant. His public life began really in 1315, when he became canon in Liége. The rest of his life was largely spent in that city, or in Huy (1325–30) when the chapter could not continue in Liége because of the hostilities between the prince bishop of Liége and the city. He was écolâtre of St. Lambert, i.e., principal of the cathedral school of Liége, from 1317 to 1340. In 1325 he traveled to the curia in Avignon, and had many opportunities of negotiating with John XXII concerning difficulties between the canons, the prince bishop, and the commune of Liége. He died at Liége on October 2, 1348, perhaps of the plague, of which he had witnessed the horrors. His will, dated May 20, 1348, shows that he was a wealthy man; he bequeathed his books to various persons and institutions, e.g., his Catholicon (Introd. 2, 1135) to the cathedral of Liége on condition that it be kept chained.

He wrote three works:

1. Digitus florum utriusque juris sub ordine alphabeti, in 1341. A book of the same kind as the Margarita decreti of Martin of Troppau (XIII-2), to which, however, he does not refer.
2. Flores auctorum et philosophorum. A lost anthology.
3. Chronicon. Gesta pontificum leodiensium. A chronicle of the prince bishops of Liége from 1247 to 1348. This is by far his main work, and his only title to fame. He began it in 1334 and continued it to within a few months of his death. It is of fundamental importance for the history of the principality of Liége during a critical period.

It may be divided into two main parts, 1247 to 1312 and 1312 to 1348, the first of which is less authoritative, though he took considerable pains to check his facts. For the second part he was a witness and to some extent an actor. As secretary of the chapter of Liége, legal adviser, and in many cases negotiator, he had firsthand knowledge of the events reported by him. He used archival sources which he mentions. He took pains with regard to chronology, yet made many technical mistakes. He noted the fluctuations of prices, meteorological data, natural oddities. Though his chronicle is centered on the principality of Liége, he often

[8] I.e., new style. The year is 1279 if counted from Christmas or January 1; it would still be 1278 if the new year began on the Annunciation, March 25.

looked beyond its borders. For example, there are many references to Cola di Rienzo. For outside history he used the chronicle of William of Nangis (to 1300) and the Chronicon pontificum et imperatorum of Martin of Troppau.

At its best, his chronicle comes close to history proper or to the reminiscences of a statesman. He was well informed, conscientious, honest, and tried to determine the causes of events. He had studied Aristotle's Politics. His own ideal of government was one in charge of the good citizens, but he did not explain how to find and employ them. He was well aware of the constant danger of a monarchy's becoming a tyranny, and of an aristocracy's becoming an oligarchy. He was well read in ancient and mediaeval letters and law. Unfortunately his grammar is poor, his style worse, and his accuracy often took the form of pedantism.

In his writings he showed some interest in, and knowledge of, mathematics, and refers to Euclid.

Text. The Chronicon was first edited by Jean de Chapeauville, canon of Liége (1551–1617), in his Gesta pontificum tungrensium, traiectensium et leodiensium (2, 273–514, Liége 1613). New critical edition by Godefroid Kurth: La chronique de Jean de Hocsem (524 p., Commission royale d'histoire, Bruxelles 1927), including indexes and glossary.

Criticism. Stan. Bormans: Les Flores utriusque juris de Hocsem (Bulletin de la Commission royale d'histoire 13, 207–24, 1886–87). Godefroid Kurth (Biographie nationale de Belgique 9, 395–404, 1886–87). Many of Kurth's statements have been corrected by himself in his elaborate preface of 1927. C. Le Paige: Notes pour servir à l'histoire des mathématiques dans l'ancien Pays de Liége (Bulletin de l'Institut archéologique liégeois 21, 457–565, 1888; p. 466–67).

MELIS STOKE

Melis or Amelis, Emil, Aemilius. Dutch chronicler, born c. 1235, died sometime after 1305.

Melis was probably educated in the monastery of Egmond in North Holland; all that we know about his connection with that monastery is that he made use of its chronicle. He later became a clerk at the court of count Floris V (1256–96), son of Willem II of Holland. At this court Melis began his history, which he dedicated to Floris and Willem III (1305–37).

His Rijmkroniek, in ten books, begins with the year 694 and ends with the death of Jan II in 1305. It was written in Dutch, and most of it was finished before 1305. This chronicle is valuable not only because the author was interested in the history of the counts of Holland, but also because he includes discussions of the relations between Holland and the other countries, especially for the period after the year 1250. The account of the reign of Willem II is particularly good.

For the first part of his work, from 694 to 1205, Melis took most of his material from the Latin chronicle of Egmond (Chronicum Egmundanum), which is the earliest Dutch source for Dutch history. This part is brief and was probably intended as an introduction to the whole work. The sources for the part dealing with the years 1205 to 1250 have not yet been identified. The last and best part of the work is based largely on his own experiences. He probably took some of his ideas from the Spieghel historiael of Jacob van Maerlant (XIII-2), though he was obviously an aristocrat, rather than a democrat like Maerlant.

Text. Rijm-kroniek van Holland, first edition by Jan van der Does: Hollandtsche Rijmkronijk (Amsterdam 1591). Second edition, The Hague 1610.

Third edition by Cornelis van Alkemade (Hollandsche Jaarboeken, Leiden 1699), this being the first edition bearing the author's name. Very elaborate edition by Balthazar Huydecoper (3 vols., Leiden 1772). Latest edition by Willem Gerard Brill: Rijmkroniek van Melis Stoke (Werken van het historisch genootschap vol. 40, 42, 766 p., Utrecht 1885).

Criticism. A. J. Van der Aa: Biographisch woordenboek (17, part 2, 1015, 1874). Karl von Richthofen: Die älteren Egmonder Geschichtsquellen (p. 202–7, Berlin 1886). W. J. A. Jonckbloet: Geschiedenis der nederlandsche letterkunde (4th ed., 2, 148–58, Groningen 1887–92). Ottokar Lorenz: Deutschlands Geschichtsquellen im Mittelalter (2, 17–18, Berlin 1887). Jan Romein: Nieuw nederlandsch biografisch woordenboek (8, 1289, 1930).

VELTHEM

Lodewijk van Velthem. Flemish chronicler (fl. 1294–1316).

Lodewijk (i.e., Lewis) of Velthem was a clerk whose origin is not clearly known. In 1294 he was in Paris, presumably for the sake of study. In 1297 we find him in Ghent, where he saw the Welsh soldiers who came with Edward I to fight the French. In 1304 he was assistant priest in Sichem near Diest, and in 1312 he became the parish priest of Velthem near Louvain (whence his name). He was still in Velthem in 1316, when he almost died of the plague.

His main work is a continuation of the Spieghel historiael, a free Dutch translation of the Speculum historiale of Vincent of Beauvais by Jacob van Maerlant (XIII-2). Maerlant had divided the Speculum into four parts; he translated the first and third, and began the fourth. The second part was translated by Philip Utenbroeke of Damme (near Bruges), and the fourth (to c. 1250) was completed by Velthem, at the request of his patroness, the lady Maria van Berlaer of Antwerp (1315).

He then undertook the writing of a fifth part at the request of the patrician Gerard van Voorne, whose chaplain he hoped to become. That fifth part (28,000 lines) is divided into eight books, dealing with the events of the period 1248–1316; it is especially valuable as usual for the end of that period, of which the author had firsthand knowledge, that is, for the fourteenth century. For the anterior part the author depended upon other sources, primarily Latin.

He continued Maerlant's Boek van Merlijn (the Book of Merlin) after verse 10,409, following a French romance, Le livre du roi Artus; he completed that work in 1326 (or should one read 1306?). After his great illness of 1316 he was blind for a time, and then vowed to write poems in praise of Our Lady if he recovered his sight; he did recover it, and wrote the poems (Van onser soeten Vrouwen love). He wrote at least one other poem, dealing with an episode of the Lancelot cycle; this was done probably before 1315. It is possible that his more poetical activities were entirely anterior to 1315, except for the verses to Our Lady (1316); then the date of Merlijn would be 1306, not 1326.

To return to the chronicle, it deals mainly with England, the Low Countries, and the Empire, and is interesting because an observer living near Louvain was more impartial in many respects than one closer to the capitals of the great nations. The most important page is the account of the Battle of the Golden Spurs, when the French chivalry was utterly defeated by the unhorsed Flemish people, near Kortrijk (Courtrai) on July 11, 1302.

Text. Spiegel historiael of rymspiegel, zynde de Nederlansche Rymschronyk van Lodewyk van Velthem. First edition by Isaac le Long (Amsterdam 1727), poor edition. This was followed by critical editions of various parts. A critical edition of the whole work was begun by Herman Vander Linden and Willem de Vreese for the Commission royale d'histoire of Belgium. Vol. 1, edited by them, was published in Brussels 1906; it contains books 1 and 2. The printing of vol. 2 was interrupted by the war; that volume, containing books 3 and 4, appeared in 1931 (preface dated 1932). The third and last volume (460 p.) appeared in 1938. It includes critical notes and index, but not the biography of the author, nor the commentaries on his work, which are badly needed. It was edited by Herman Vander Linden, Paul De Keyser, and Adolf Van Loey.

Criticism. G. J. A. Jonckbloet: Specimen e literis neerlandicis exhibens Ludovici de Velthem chronici quod inscribitur Speculum historiale librum III denuo editum secundum codicem ms unicum (136 p., The Hague 1840), quoted here because of its introduction. Nicolaas Marais Hoogenhout: Untersuchungen zu Lodewijk van Velthem's Spiegel historiael (Strassburg diss., 76 p., Leiden 1902).

Very little is known about Philip Utenbroeke. He was a contemporary and disciple of Jacob van Maerlant, and died before 1315. See J. Vercoullie (Biographie nationale de Belgique 25, 980, 1932).

JAN VAN BOENDALE

Jan de Clerc, Jan de Klerk, Jan Boendaele. Flemish didactic poet and chronicler (c. 1280–1365).

He was born c. 1280 at Boendale, Tervueren, near Brussels. He established himself in Antwerp about the beginning of the century and was secretary to the board of aldermen to his death in 1365. Boendale was deeply influenced by Maerlant (XIII-2), and like him wrote in Flemish various didactic poems dealing with history, philosophy, politics, ethics, etc.

Before 1312, he began his main historical work, a rhymed chronicle which after many interruptions was finally finished in 1350. This chronicle, called Die brabantsche yeesten, contains in five books (16,318 lines) the history of Brabant to 1350; two more books, carrying the narrative to 1432 and 1440 respectively (whole work 46,486 lines), were added later by an unknown writer.

Jan tried, as far as possible, to eliminate all fables and to write a true history, stressing in particular the events about which he had firsthand information; his main purpose being to write a "true genealogy of the dukes of Brabant and their history." He includes, however, considerable material on events which had taken place outside of Brabant; for instance, he has quite a little to say concerning the First Crusade. Books 5 to 7 are especially valuable; in these are found an account of the reign of John III, duke of Brabant from 1312 to 1355.

For the early part of this work, he drew heavily on the Spieghel historiael of Jacob van Maerlant. Boendale, however, revised, corrected, and expanded the text of Maerlant. He also cited other sources, such as the rhymed chronicle of Jan Van Heelu, written in Flemish c. 1291; and the Chronica de origine ducum.

Boendale wrote a number of short didactic poems, historical, philosophical, political, or ethical in content. One of these, Die corte kronyk van Brabant, deals with the period from the time of Hector to 1312. This poem was written at Antwerp in 1322, and is an abridgment of the Yeesten, in 144 verses.

Another poem, written c. 1340–48, is called Van den derden Edewaert. We now have only a fragment of this work, in which are related the important events of the years 1338–40. It is in the nature of an epic poem, dealing with the intervention of the English king, Edward III, in Flanders in order to further his claims to the French throne, which was one of the causes of the Hundred Years' War.

Jan wrote at least three other didactic poems: De lekenspieghel (Mirror of the lay people), which was finished in 1330, dealing with sacred and Christian history, and ethics. The second, Jans teestije of dit is van Woutere ende van Janne (Jan's feelings, or dialogue between Walter and Jan), was written between 1315 and 1325, and deals with philosophical and legal questions, which are discussed in a very original way. The third, Die dietsche doctrinale (Flemish doctrinal), was completed in Antwerp 1345–46, and dedicated to the duke John III; it treats of ethical and religious questions.

His historical poems are the most characteristic product of lay historiography in the Low Countries in the fourteenth century. He is a good representative of the high bourgeoisie of Brabant; he is equally opposed to the French and to the labor leader Jacob van Artevelde; he sets his faith in the merchants and farmers. He does not hesitate to criticize bitterly the clergy and the aristocracy.

Text. De brabantsche yeesten of Rijm-kronijk van Braband (vols. 1 and 2 edited by Jan Frans Willems; vol. 3, by J. H. Bormans; Brussels 1839, 1843, 1869). Vol. 1 contains Jan's own poem; vols. 2 and 3, the continuations.

Korte rymkronyk van Brabant, edited by Ph. Blommaert: Oudvlaemsche Gedichten (p. 84–90, Ghent 1838); and by Willems and Bormans: Brabantsche yeesten (2, cxliii–clv).

Van den derden Edewaert, coninc van Engelant, Rijmkronijk geschreven omtrent het jaer 1347, edited by J. F. Willems (Belg. Museum voor de nederduitsche taal- en letterkunde 4, 298–367, Ghent 1840). Translated into French by Octave Delepierre: Edouard III, roi d'Angleterre, en Belgique (52 p., Ghent 1841).

Die lekenspieghel, leerdicht van den jare 1330, edited by M. De Vries (3 vols., Leiden 1844–50).

Jan's teestije of dit is van Woutere ende van Janne, edited by F. A. Snellaert: Nederlandsche gedichten uit de veertiende eeuw (p. 137–275, Brussels 1869).

Die dietsche doctrinale van den jare 1345, edited by W. J. A. Jonckbloet (375 p., The Hague 1842)

Criticism. O. Delepierre: Edouard III, roi d'Angleterre, en Flandre (Philobiblon Society miscellanies vol. 10, 1866–67), an account of the poem. Ph. Blommaert (Biographie nationale de Belgique 2, 587–91, 1868). Vanderkindere (p. 262, 331, 1879). H. Haerynck: Jan Boendaele, ook geheeten Jan de Clerc: zijn leven, zijne werken en zijn dood (225 p., Ghent 1888). W. J. A. Jonckbloet: Geschiedenis der nederlandsche letterkunde (4th ed., 2, 158–60, 167–82, etc., Groningen 1887–92). Henri Pirenne: Histoire de Belgique (3d ed., 2, 460, Brussels 1922). H. Nélis: Les sources du livre VI des Brabantsche yeesten (Mélanges de Bormans), not seen. Henry S. Lucas: Edward III and the poet chronicler John Boendale (Speculum 12, 367–69, 1937).

A6. Bohemia

CHRONICLE OF DALIMIL

The Chronicle of Dalimil or Kronyka Boleslavská is a rhymed chronicle in the Czech language of Bohemian events from the world's creation down to the end of the reign of Henry of Carinthia and the coronation of John of Luxemburg as king of Bohemia in 1310. It has long been ascribed to Dalimil Mezeřický, knight of St. John, canon of Boleslav. That ascription is now abandoned, though the name, established by long usage, remains. The author was probably a layman, a nobleman; he composed the chronicle between 1308 and 1316. As usual, the chronicle is especially valuable for the final part; the earliest event witnessed by the author occurred in 1279.

This poem is the earliest historical work written in Czech and one of the outstanding monuments of Bohemian literature. It is largely derived from Cosmas of Prague (XII-1) and his continuers. The keynote is intense hatred of the Germans. The enmity between Slavs and Germans which has been for many centuries (and is still today) one of the dominant motives of European history was never more intense than it was in the time when the author of this chronicle lived. It was his ardent nationalism which induced him to write it.

It enjoyed great popularity for two centuries. It was very promptly translated into German, first in prose (c. 1320), then in verse (c. 1330–46).

Text. There are 9 complete MSS of the chronicle, the oldest being in Trinity College, Cambridge.

First edition by Paul Gessin (Pavel Ješin): Kronyka stará klášstera Boleslawského (Prague 1620), suppressed in the same year, after the battle of the White Mountain and the occupation of Prague by Austrian-Spanish troops. Later editions, 1786, 1849, 1851, 1853, 1874. Seventh edition by Josef Jireček: Rýmovaná kronika česká (Fontes rerum bohemicarum 3, 3–224, Prague 1882). Eighth edition by V. E. Mourek: Kronika Dalimilova (182 p., Prague 1892; reprinted 1910).

Rhymed German version. Venceslav Hanka: Dalimils Chronik von Böhmen (253 p., Stuttgart 1859). Jos. Jireček: Tutsch kronik von Behemlant (printed opposite the Czech text above mentioned).

Prose German version. Jos. Jireček: Die pehemische chronik (op. cit., 3, 257–97). Jireček's fundamental edition also contains a number of additional documents, Czech and German.

Criticism. Louis Leger, in Joseph Fricz: La Bohême historique (p. 257–70, 1867). Potthast (p. 361, 1896). L. Leger: Grande encyclopédie (13, 774). Franz Lützow: History of Bohemian literature (London 1899; reprinted 1907; p. 29–35); Lectures on the historians of Bohemia, being the Ilchester lectures for the year 1904 (p. 15–17, London 1905). H. Jelinek: Histoire de la littérature tchèque (vol. 1, Paris 1930). Roman Jakobson: The wisdom of the ancient Czechs (in Czech, 240 p., 4 maps, New York 1943), reviewed by Henri Grégoire (Renaissance 1, 652–55, 1944).

A7. England

Langtoft

Peter of Langtoft. English chronicler in French verse (d. after 1307).

This Peter is called after the village of Langtoft in the East Riding of Yorkshire. He was a canon in the Austin priory of Bridlington near Langtoft. He wrote in barbarous "Yorkshire French" a rhymed chronicle of England from Brutus to 1307. The early part, taken from Geoffrey of Monmouth (XII-1), and the middle part, taken from various sources, are worthless, but the final part, dealing with the rule of Edward I Longshanks (1272–1307), is interesting. It deals mainly with the Scottish wars, the point of view being anti-Scot.

The part 689–1307 was translated into English verse by Robert Mannyng in 1338.

Text. First edition by Thomas Wright (Rolls series, 2 vols., London 1866–68).

Criticism. T. F. Tout (DNB 32, 117, 1892). C. Gross (no. 1808, 1915).

HEMINGBURGH

Walter de Hemingburgh,[9] Walter of Gisburn or Guisborough. English Augustinian canon, chronicler; died after 1313, perhaps much later.

He flourished at St. Mary's, Gisburn (in the West Riding of Yorkshire), c. 1297, and was subprior there in 1302. He presented a volume of sermons to his church in 1307.

He wrote in Latin a chronicle of English affairs extending from the Norman conquest to 1346, but it is not certain that he himself carried it to 1346. There is a strange gap from 1315 to 1327. He almost certainly covered the whole rule of Edward I (1272–1307); the accounts of Edward II and III may have been written by another (John of Tynemouth?).

The earlier part of his chronicle is naturally derived from other chroniclers, such as Eadmer of Canterbury (XII-1), Henry of Huntingdon (XII-2), William of Newburgh (XII-2). From the beginning of Edward I (1272) it has the value of a contemporary record.

Text. Thomas Gale: Scriptores quinque (2, 455–594, 1691), only down to 1272. The remainder was edited by Thomas Hearne: Historia de rebus gestis Edwardi I, II, III (2 vols., Oxford 1731). Complete critical edition by Hans Claude Hamilton (English Historical Society, 2 vols., London 1848–49).

Criticism. W. J. Hardy (DNB 25, 385, 1891). C. Gross (no. 1788, 1915).

TREVET

Nicholas Trevet. English humanist, theologian, and chronicler (d. after 1334).

Nicholas Trevet (or Trivet,[9a] Triveth, and other variants) was born between 1258 and 1268; he was probably educated by the Dominicans and he assumed the Dominican habit. He studied in Paris and in Oxford, where he received his doctor's degree. He seems to have obtained the favor of royal and high ecclesiastical circles. He took part in the quarrel about ecclesiastical poverty before 1323. In that year or soon after he was lector at Blackfriars, Ludgate. He probably survived John XXII, who died on December 4, 1334.

He wrote commentaries on the Old Testament (notably one on Genesis dedicated to John XXII), on Cicero (lost), Livy, Vergil, on Seneca's tragedies, St. Augustine's Civitas Dei, Boetius' Consolatio, and the Sentences of Peter the Lombard.[9b] He showed little originality in these commentaries, except that his interest in the Latin classics was unusual in his time in England; that interest may have been awakened or at least warmed by his contacts with the scholars of Avignon.[9c] He composed Quodlibeta and Quaestiones disputatae; a treatise on the Jewish cal-

[9] The name Hemingford as applied to him was first used in 1548 by John Bale, bishop of Ossory in Ireland (DNB 3, 41–42).

[9a] The form Trivet had first been preferred, as was the case in DNB. At the time of the final rewriting of this note Trevet seemed more acceptable. The form Trivet will be found in the first chapter of this work, which was already proofread when the change to Trevet was decided upon.

[9b] The commentaries on Vergil and on the Sentences ascribed to him are of dubious authorship. The commentary on Ovid formerly ascribed to him is now credited to Pierre Bersuire (R. J. D.).

[9c] At least with the Dominican Niccolò da Prato, born in Prato in 1250, bishop-cardinal of Ostia from 1303 to his death in 1321. In 1304 he visited Florence as the legate of Benedict XI and interdicted the city. He was also sent on a papal mission to England, and Trevet may have known him then.

endar, De computo Hebraeorum; Canones eclipsium ad meridiem Sarum;[10] etc. He and his brother Dominican Thomas of Sutton were among the earliest prominent defenders of Thomism in England.

His best-known work is a chronicle of the first six Plantagenet kings, Annales sex regum Angliae qui a comitibus andegavensibus originem traxerunt, from 1136 to 1307; it is valuable for the last two reigns, Henry III and Edward I, especially for the last one (1272–1307). He refers to a very cold winter in Scotland in 1301.

He composed a history of the world, in French, Les cronicles qe frère Nichol Tryvet escript a dame Marie (i.e., Mary, daughter of Edward I, later a nun at Amesbury, near Salisbury). He also wrote a Latin history (Historia ab orbe condito usque ad Christi nativitatem) dedicated to Hugh of Angoulême, archdeacon of Canterbury.

Out of some 45 works ascribed to him, 29 have survived, represented by a total of at least 300 MSS. Various investigations of these MSS have reduced the number of authentic works to 30, of which 24 are extant.

His reputation was international. One of Dante's many references to Seneca, namely in the letter he wrote before 1319 to Can Grande della Scala, is a quotation from one of the tragedies made not from the original text, but from Trevet's commentary. Petrarca and Boccaccio seem to have been acquainted with some of Trevet's commentaries.

Text. Annales. First edited by Luc d'Achéry in his Spicilegium (8, 411–728, Paris 1668), reprinted in the second edition of that work (3, 143–231, Paris 1723). Second edition by Anthony Hall (2 vols., Oxford 1719–22); the Trevet text is in vol. 1. Fourth edition by Thomas Hog (English Historical Society, 458 p., London 1845).

An edition of the Cronicles was prepared from three MSS by A. Rutherford in 1932, but is not yet published. One of the best MSS (Arundel 56, British Museum, late fourteenth century) was reproduced in facsimile by the care of the Modern Language Association (MLA) of America (no. 111, 76 sheets, 1930).

Extracts from the Cronicles have appeared in various publications. I quote only for the sake of curiosity the one edited by George Webbe Dasent: Theophilus in Icelandic, Low German and other tongues from MSS in the Royal Library of Stockholm (152 p., London 1845; p. 31). This concerns the legend of Theophilos, steward (οἰκονόμος) of the church of Adana in Cilicia in the time of Justinian (VI-1), who sold himself to the Devil, then repented and was redeemed by the Holy Virgin; the French poète Rutebeuf (d. c. 1286) dramatized that legend in his Miracle de Théophile.

The life of Constance, the source of Chaucer's Man of law's tale, edited with translation by Edmund Brock in Frederick James Furnivall: Originals and analogues of some of Chaucer's Canterbury tales (part 1, 1–53, 1872; see also part 13, 221–50, 1876). This is a part of the Cronicles.

Ezio Franceschini: Il commento di Nicola Trevet al Tieste [Thyestes] di Seneca (Orbis romanus, no. XI, 104 p., 6 pl., Università del Sacro Cuore, Milano 1938).

The MS of Trevet's commentary on Livy (Lisbon, B. N. MSS Illum. 134–35) was reproduced in microfilm for MLA (no. add. 52 F, 2 rolls). Other microfilms of Trevet's works made for MLA are being used at present (May 1945) by professor Ruth J. Dean, of Mount Holyoke College, and by professor Edmund T.

[10] Sarum (or Old Sarum), near Salisbury, is one of the oldest towns in England. The bishopric of Sherborne was removed to it in 1078, and the cathedral of Sarum became very important. The ordinal of offices "for the use of Sarum" was the ritual of all southern England until 1550.

Silk, of Yale University. The latter is preparing an edition of Trevet's commentary on Boetius' Consolatio; his work is nearing completion.

The MS of the commentary on Ovid's Metamorphoses (Merton College, Oxford, no. 299, fifteenth century) was reproduced for MLA (no. 50, 135 sheets, 1926). That commentary is now ascribed to Pierre Bersuire, a fact of which I became aware too late to modify the note devoted to the latter in chapter III.

Criticism. Charles Jourdain: Commentaires inédits de Guillaume de Conches et de Nicolas Triveth sur la Consolation de la philosophie de Boèce (Notices et extraits 20, 40–82, 1862), reprinted in his Excursions historiques et philosophiques à travers le Moyen âge (p. 31–68, Paris 1888). Trevet used the commentary of William of Conches (XII-1), but the expression "plagiarized" (Introd. 2, 197) is perhaps a bit strong, considering mediaeval habits. C. L. Kingsford (DNB 57, 234–36, 1899), article needing many corrections. Franz Ehrle: N. Trivet, Sein Leben, seine Quolibet und Quaestiones ordinariae (Beiträge zur Geschichte der Philosophie des Mittelalters suppt. vol. 2, 1–63, Münster 1923). De Wulf (2, 49–52, 1926). Britton (year 1301, 1937). Ezio Franceschini: Studi e note di filologia latina medievale (Milano 1938; Medium aevum 10, 161–68, 1941). The first and longest of these studies deals with the mediaeval commentaries on Seneca's tragedies, the earliest of those commentaries being Trevet's c. 1315; the third deals with the commentary on the Aeneid ascribed to Trevet. Ruth J. Dean: Essay in Anglo-Norman palaeography (Studies in French language and mediaeval literature presented to Mildred Katharine Pope p. 79–87, Manchester University 1939), apropos of two MSS of the Cronicles; Nicholas Trevet, a study of his life and works with special reference to his Anglo-Norman chronicles (University of Oxford, Abstracts of dissertations for D. Phil., 11, 116–19, 1939); MS Bodl. 292 and the canon of Trevet's works (Speculum 17, 243–49, 1942); The earliest medieval commentary on Livy,—by Nicholas Trevet (Medievalia et humanistica part 3, 86–98, 1945; Isis 36); Trevet's life and works, a study of the MSS and extracts from unpublished texts (to appear c. 1946).

Miss Ruth Dean kindly helped me to revise this note in May 1945.

READING

Robert de Reading. English chronicler (d. 1325).

Robert was a monk of Westminster. He is the author of the final portion of the Flores historiarum, dealing with the years 1307–25, that is, the rule of Edward II of Carnarvon. It is a good source for that period; Robert was opposed to the king and to the latter's foster brother and favorite Piers Gaveston, earl of Cornwall (d. 1312), and warmly in favor of Thomas of Lancaster (d. 1322). Robert's style is somewhat pedantic, and foreign words (English, French, Greek) were occasionally inserted by him into the Latin text.

The Flores historiarum is a composite chronicle of England from the creation to 1326, which was long ascribed to an imaginary person Matthew of Westminster, because the earlier part is largely taken from *Matthew* Paris (XIII-2) and the oldest MS came from *Westminster* Abbey. As a matter of fact the oldest MS, down to 1265, was copied in St. Albans, mostly from Matthew Paris; the Flores were continued at Westminster by various chroniclers to 1306; for the period 1307–25 by Robert of Reading, and for 1325–26 by an anonymous writer. The whole part posterior to Matthew Paris, that is, from 1259 to 1326, is a valuable contemporary chronicle.

Robert of Reading should not be confused with another chronicler, John of Reading (d. 1368–69), who has been claimed (by James Tait 1914) to be the real author of the chronicle of the archbishops of Canterbury (597–1369) ascribed to Stephen Birchington.[11]

Text. The Flores historiarum was first edited under the name of Matthew of Westminster by Matthew Parker, archbishop of Canterbury (London 1567). Second much improved edition by same (London 1570), reprinted in Francfort 1601. These editions extend only to 1307.

English translation to 1307 by Charles Duke Yonge (Bohn's library, 2 vols., London 1853).

First edition to 1326, that is, first edition of Robert of Reading, by Henry Richards Luard (Rolls series, 3 vols., London 1890).

The Canterbury chronicle was first edited under Birchington's name by Henry Wharton: Anglia sacra (1, 1–48, London 1691). New edition under the name of John of Reading by James Tait (Manchester University 1914).

The Flores historiarum and the Canterbury chronicle contain many meteorological observations.

Criticism. C. L. Kingsford: Robert de Reading (DNB 47, 365, 1896). William Hunt: Matthew of Westminster (DNB 60, 357, 1899). C. Gross (nos. 1774, 1832a, 2432, 1915). Britton (passim, 1937).

MURIMUTH

Adam Murimuth, Adamus Murimuthensis. English chronicler. Born in Oxfordshire 1274–75; died in 1347.

He was educated at Oxford, where he became a doctor of civil law in 1312 or soon before. From c. 1312 to c. 1318 and even later he spent much time in Avignon, representing the archbishop of Canterbury or the king, and defending English ecclesiastical interests before the curia. By 1323, he was canon in Hereford, and he held other ecclesiastical offices in Exeter and London.

Having observed that the chronicles of Exeter did not extend beyond 1302 and those of Westminster beyond 1305, he decided to write a "continuatio ex visu et auditu mei temporis." This work, entitled Continuatio chronicorum, covers the period from 1303 to 1347. He began to write it c. 1325 and worked at it until the last year of his life. The information for the years 1303–37 is quite meager; for the last ten years the material is more abundant, although he never wrote in great detail. This part of the chronicle is of particular value for the account of the English campaigns in France and of the negotiations between the two countries. The chronicle is of special interest from the ecclesiastical point of view.

There is an anonymous continuation down to 1380.

Text. Continuatio chronicorum, or Chronicon sive historia sui temporis, first edition by Anthony Hall (2 vols., Oxford 1719–22), the Murimuth text is in vol. 2. Better edition to 1346 by Thomas Hog (English Historical Society series, 272 p., London 1846), containing the Continuatio ad 1380. Critical edition by E. Maunde Thompson (Rolls series no. 93, p. 3–275, London 1889), this being the first complete edition to 1347.

Criticism. W. Stubbs: Chronicles of the reigns of Edward I and Edward II (1, lx–lxxiv, London 1882). C. L. Kingsford (DNB 39, 331–33, 1894).

[11] A monk of Christ Church, Canterbury, who came probably from Birchington in the isle of Thanet. He was still living in 1382. William Hunt (DNB 5, 71, 1886).

HIGDEN

Ranulf Higden. English Benedictine, author of the Polychronicon (d. 1364).

There are many variants of the name Higden (Hydon, Higdon, Hygden, Hikeden, etc.) and of course of the Christian name Ranulf (Ralph, Radulf, Randle, etc.). The place and date of his birth are unknown, as well as other circumstances anterior to his assumption of the Benedictine habit at St. Werburg's, Chester, 1299. He visited various parts of England, especially Shropshire, Derbyshire, and Lancashire. He died on March 12, 1363–64, and was buried at St. Werburg.

Many writings are ascribed to him, but only one matters, that is, his Polychronicon, a universal chronicle from the beginning of the world to his own days, in seven books. The first edition apparently ended in 1327, but Higden continued it to 1342 or 1344; further continuations are by other hands, for example, John Malverne (XIV-2) carried it down to 1394.

The Polychronicon has very little value, if any, as a historical source, but it was the most ambitious historical synthesis of its time, and it enjoyed two centuries of genuine popularity (over 100 MSS are extant). It was more than a chronicle, rather a kind of popular encyclopaedia, which reveals to us the scientific outlook of a learned man of that time.

Higden's Mappa mundi is not another work, but simply the first book of his chronicle, largely devoted to geography. This book was illustrated with a map of the world, a wheel map of a very crude type but including many names. Higden's geographical knowledge was antiquated; it was partly derived from a kind of geographical dictionary of the thirteenth century, the Geographia universalis, itself derived from earlier writers, especially Isidore of Seville (VII-1).

Among the many side lights thrown by Higden upon his environment, we may mention his statement that gentlemen's children were taught to speak French from the cradle on. (Indeed, English became the official language of England only toward the end of Edward III's rule, 1327–77. From 1215 French diplomas occasionally replaced Latin ones; they almost superseded the latter in the second half of the century. Edward III ordered occasional pleading in English in 1363, and in the following year Parliament was opened for the first time in the English language).

Another proof of the Polychronicon's popularity is afforded by the existence of three early English translations. The first was made by John of Trevisa in 1387; the second, made at the beginning of the fifteenth century, remained unpublished until recently; the third was a revision of Trevisa's prepared by William Caxton (printed by him in 1482).

Text. For Trevisa's translation see my note on John of Trevisa (XIV-2).

The Latin text was edited, together with Trevisa's translation and the anonymous fifteenth-century translation, by Churchill Babington (vols. 1, 2) and Joseph Rawson Lumby (vols. 3–9) for the Rolls series (9 vols., London 1865–86).

A stanzaic life of Christ, compiled from Higden's Polychronicon and the Legenda aurea, edited from MS Harley 3909 by Frances A. Foster (Early English Text Society no. 166, 500 p., London 1926). This is a compilation made at Chester in the fourteenth century. For the Legenda aurea of James of Voragine see Introd. 2, 1106.

Criticism. C. L. Kingsford (DNB 26, 365, 1891). Beazley (2, 586, 1901; 3, 529, 552, 556, 1906). Nansen (passim, 1911), Higden's map is reproduced, 2, 189. C. Gross (no. 1793, 1915). Michael C. Andrews (1926).

A8. Ireland

CLYN

John Clyn. Irish Franciscan chronicler (d. 1349).

John Clyn or Clynne was living in the Franciscan monastery of Kilkenny. In 1336 he was already sufficiently important to be appointed the first warden of the Franciscan house of Carrick. He died probably in 1349.

He wrote annals of Ireland from the beginning to 1349; they are valuable for the period 1315-49, i.e., from the Scottish invasion to the plague, the ravages of which in Kilkenny he describes. Clyn does not revive the legends of the seanachies (or shanachies, from Ir. seanchuidhe, storyteller), but the early part of his chronicle, from the creation to 1314, is extremely brief. When he stopped his work, in 1349, he left parchment for his successors, but the chronicle was not continued. His chronicle contains many meteorological data.

Text. Annales Hiberniae, edited by Richard Butler: The annals of Ireland by friar John Clyn and Thady Dowling (1544-1628) together with the annals of Ross (Irish Archaeological Society no. 12, Dublin 1849). The text of Clyn's Annales covers 38 p. The annals of Ross (p. 41-46) refer to the years 1265-1480; they were compiled in the Dominican house established in 1267 at New Ross on the Barrow on the borders of Wexford and Kilkenny.

Criticism. Butler's preface (1849). Britton (1937), years 1325-38.

B. EASTERN CHRISTENDOM

B1. Byzantine Historiography

XANTHOPULOS

Nicephoros Callistos Xanthopulos, Νικηφόρος Κάλλιστος ὁ Ξανθόπουλος. Byzantine ecclesiastical historian. Born c. 1256, was a priest in the Hagia Sophia and probably a teacher in the patriarchal school (οἰκουμενικὸν διδασκαλεῖον) in Constantinople. He published his historical work in 1317, certainly not before; it is not known how long he lived afterward.

His main work is an ecclesiastical history in eighteen books, extending to the death of the emperor Phocas in 610. The author had planned five other books reaching to 911. He may have used or plagiarized an anonymous history written c. 920. His sources, directly or indirectly (through the lost anonymous one), were Eusebios (IV-1), Sozomenos, Socrates, and Theodoretos (all three of V-1), and Evagrios (VI-2). He expressed an immense admiration for St. John Chrysostom (347-407). He developed the idea of a universal history of the Christian church, an idea which can be traced back to the fifth century, yet paid but little attention to the Catholic church.

He was also a poet and rhetorician, and composed προγυμνάσματα, that is, rhetorical exercises, which continue the tradition of Hermogenes of Tarsos (Ἑρμογένης, fl. under Marcus Aurelius, II-2) and Aphthonios of Antioch (Ἀφθόνιος, fl. end of third century), a tradition which had never been interrupted in the Byzantine schools.

He wrote commentaries on Gregory of Nazianzos (c. 327-89), the great master of Christian rhetoric.

Text. Ecclesiasticae historiae libri XVIII, first edited in Greek, together with the Latin translation of Joannes Langus, by the French Jesuit Fronton du Duc

(Ducaeus, 1558–1624) posthumously (folio, 2 vols., Paris 1630). Reprinted in PG (vols. 145–47, 1865), together with many minor writings.

Criticism. Krumbacher (p. 291–93, 1897). Eleutheroudakis encyclopaedia: Callistos (7, 125, 1929). J. Glettner: Die Progymnastica des Nikephoros Kallistos Xanthopulos (Byzantinische Zeitschrift 33, 1–12, 255–70, 1933), including first edition of that short text. A. D. Wilson: An illustrated Greek MS of c. 1500 (British Museum quarterly 13, 81, 1939), apropos of a MS of the Synaxaria.

CHRONICLE OF MOREA

At the end of the Fourth Crusade (1202–4), two French knights who had taken part in it, Guillaume de Champlitte and Geoffroy de Villehardouin (the historian's nephew), had managed to conquer the whole of Morea (Peloponnese). In 1205 Guillaume was elected by the other knights prince of Morea (or Achaia); Geoffroy succeeded him in 1209, then Geoffroy's sons Geoffroy II and Guillaume II ruled after him until the latter's death in 1278; Guillaume II's heir was a daughter married to the son of Charles king of Naples. Anarchy followed: competition between the Angevines and other lords, aggravated by the intervention of Catalan, Genoese, Florentine, and Navarrese adventurers.

For the sake of the historian of science who is not familiar with all the vicissitudes of international banditry in the Middle Ages, I may recall that some of the noble Crusaders had taken possession of Athens. In 1205, Bonifacio of Monferrat gave Attica and Boeotia as a fief to Othon de la Roche, who called himself great lord (*μέγας κύριος*) of Athens. The family of de la Roche ruled over Athens until 1308; they assumed the title of grand duke of Athens and Thebes in 1259. In 1311 the duchy of Athens fell into the hands of Catalan pirates, who gave it to their Sicilian overlord; later it passed into Aragonese hands, then into the hands of the Acciajuoli of Florence, finally until 1460 into Venetian power.

To return to Morea, the memory of the French principality is perpetuated to this day by the ruins of fortified castles of astounding size and strength, notably in Mistra. The foundation of the Latin empire of Constantinople (1204–61) and the dramatic events of Morea in the thirteenth century have been described in a chronicle which was written in the first quarter of the fourteenth century and was already available in four languages, Greek, French, Italian, Aragonese (Catalan), before the end of that century.

The Greek and French versions are closely related and complete each other; the Italian one, derived from the Greek, is much shorter. The Aragonese version, which was the latest, differs more from the three others than these differ among themselves. What was the original language of the chronicle, Greek or French? Perhaps there was a lost prototype to the existing texts? Longnon (1911) claims that the lost prototype was written in Venetian. These chronicles contain valuable information not only on the political history and geography of Morea, but also on church affairs, feudal law, fortifications, public and private manners, etc.

The Greek chronicle, in political verses (9,219 verses in the oldest and best text), two versions represented by five MSS, extends from 1095 to 1292. The original text was written before 1326 by a gasmulos (*γασμοῦλος*, offspring of a French father and Greek mother),[11a] whose feelings were violently anti-Greek and pro-French, *Χρονικὸν τῶν ἐν Ῥωμανίᾳ καὶ μάλιστα ἐν τῷ Μορέᾳ πολέμων τῶν Φράγκων.* Some of the

[11a] The term gasmulos is Byzantine slang. For a discussion of it see the Eleutheroudakis encyclopaedia (3, 765, Athens 1928).

statements made in that very biased work can be controlled by reference to the contemporary Catalan chronicles of Bernard Desclot (XIII-2) and Ramón Muntaner and the Venetian one of Marino Sanudo il Vecchio.

The French text, which was at one time believed to be the original, Livre de la conqueste de Constantinople et de l'empire de Romanie et dou pays de la princée de la Morée, is represented by a single MS (library of the dukes of Burgundy, now in Bibliothèque nationale, Paris). The French account extends from 1205 to 1305. It is preceded by a chronological table carried to 1333. The French text was written between 1333 and 1341. The dialect is Picard or Walloon.

The Italian version, Istoria della Morea, exists also in a single MS following the Istoria del regno di Romania of Marino Sanudo.

The Aragonese version is the only one which is not anonymous; it was made in 1393 by Juan Fernandez de Heredia (d. 1396), grand master of the Hospitalers. It includes continuation to 1377 and various interpolations.

Text. I mention the texts of the four versions in the chronological order of the first editions of each:

Greek (1840): First edition by J. A. Buchon: Chroniques étrangères relatives aux expéditions françaises pendant le XIIIe siècle (Paris 1840), imperfect edition of the later and poorer Greek text with French translation, and various other documents; Buchon published in 1845 the better Greek text (see below). Prologue of the Greek version with Latin translation edited by Emmanuel Miller in Recueil des historiens grecs de Croisades (vol. 1, part 2, 581–623, 1875). John Schmitt: The chronicle of Morea, Τὸ χρονικὸν τοῦ Μορέως (722 p., London 1904), edited in two parallel texts, i.e., the two Greek versions from the MSS of Copenhagen and Paris. Adamantios I. Adamantiou: Τὰ χρονικὰ τοῦ Μορέως (Athens 1906).

French: J. A. Buchon: Recherches historiques sur la principauté de Morée et ses hautes baronnies (2 vols., Paris 1845), texts of the French version and the better Greek one. Jean Longnon: Livre de la conqueste de la princée de l'Amorée (Société de l'histoire de France, Paris 1911).

Italian: Karl Hopf: Chroniques gréco-romanes (p. 414–68, Leipzig 1873).

Aragonese: Alfred Morel-Fatio: Libro de los fechos e conquistas del principado della Morea (Société de l'Orient latin, Geneva 1885). Aragonese text and French translation.

Criticism. Potthast (p. 294, 1896). Krumbacher (p. 832–38, 1897). John Schmitt: Die Chronik von Morea als eine Quelle für Faust (Vortrag; Leipzig 1904). Sir Rennell Rodd: The princes of Achaia and the chronicles of Morea (2 vols., London 1907). Erich Stüwe: Die französischen Lehnwörter und Namen in der mittelgriechischen Chronik von Morea (diss., 180 p., Rostock i.M. 1919). Vasiliev (2, 117, 414, 1932), discussing (p. 118) the influence of the Chronicle of Morea on Goethe's Faust. Henri Omont (HL 37, 536–39, 1938).

NICEPHOROS GREGORAS

Nicephoros Gregoras, Νικηφόρος ὁ Γρηγορᾶς. Byzantine polyhistor (1295–1359).

Nicephoros was born at Heraclea Pontica (Eregli) on the southern shore of the Black Sea in 1295, and was educated there and later in Constantinople. He seems to have moved in the highest circles, for no less a person than Joannes XIII Glycys, Γλυκύς (patriarch 1316–20), taught him rhetoric (in 1320 Nicephoros redacted the patriarch's will), and the great chancellor Theodoros Metochites taught him astronomy; in exchange Nicephoros explained the Greek classics to Theodoros' children. Being admitted into the favor of Andronicos II Palaeologos, he shared the latter's disgrace; when Andronicos was deposed in 1328, Nicephoros lost his property, but thanks to Metochites' protection was not exiled. He was associated with his patron in the latter's restoration of the church of St. Saviour in Chora (now Kahrie jami; see my note on Metochites), attending particularly to the gathering of the precious materials which were needed for the embellishment of the sanctuary. After Metochites' death (1332), Nicephoros was acting as a kind of trustee for that church and the monastery attached to it. Unfortunately he became involved in the passionate controversy concerning the Uncreated Light which mystics could recapture in their ecstasies (see note on Barlaam); he rejected those views and as a result was persecuted by Joannes VI Cantacuzenos, who had taken the side of the Hesychasts and shared their fanaticism. In 1351, Nicephoros, then an elderly man, was made a prisoner in the very monastery which he had helped to restore and was treated with contumely and downright cruelty by the "gentle" mystics (in Christ's name?). He was twice visited in secret (1351, 1352) by a friend, Agathangelos, who gave him news from the outside world. He was released in 1354, when Cantacuzenos was dethroned and replaced by Joannes V Palaeologos. He died in 1359 or soon afterward.

He was the greatest of the writers who flourished under the Palaeologoi, that is, during the last two centuries of Byzantine history (1261–1453). When two delegates of the curia arrived in Constantinople in 1333 to explore the possibilities of union between the Orthodox and Catholic churches, he represented the patriarch; the project was defeated, but after the departure of the delegates discussions continued between the Greeks and became more and more heated. Nicephoros was at first bitterly opposed to Barlaam, and their rivalry or enmity never ceased, but he gradually came to favor the union, while the men of power were consolidating themselves against it, especially after Cantacuzenos' accession in 1347. As we have seen, he opposed the Hesychastic tendencies which were menacing the Orthodox church in another way. Later, when these controversies were revived in the quarrel between the Palamites and the Acindynites, he remained neutral, thus incurring the hatred and punishment of both sides. This explains the many persecutions which darkened the end of his life.

His main work was a Byzantine history from 1204 to 1359, which he composed in the St. Saviour monastery, *Ῥωμαϊκὴ ἱστορία*. It is divided into 37 books, of which the first 7 deal with the period 1204–1320; the other 30 with his own times, 1320–59.[12] As the chronicle of Georgios Pachymeres (XIII-2; Introd. 2, 972) ended in 1308, Nicephoros' work may be considered a continuation of it from 1308 to 1359, especially ample for the last thirty years. The style is Platonic or tries to be, but the spirit is not, for Nicephoros wrote like a partisan, and his work is full of the acrimonious theological controversies from which he himself had suffered so much. It could not be otherwise, for those controversies were the main events of domestic and foreign policy.

Nicephoros wrote a eulogy of Theodoros Metochites at the time of the latter's death, in 1332.

Next in importance are his astronomical writings. He had studied the Almagest and took a special interest in the observation and calculation of eclipses. He predicted two lunar eclipses and one solar one in 1330, and they occurred at the

[12] Gibbon used it extensively, but only books 1–24, the later books, 25–37, being still unpublished in his time.

appointed times; he announced other eclipses to occur in 1333 and 1335. His astronomical interests are often revealed in his history (notes on eclipses, etc.). He took pains to defend astronomy against ecclesiastical prejudices on the one side, and against astrological superstitions on the other. There are various remarks to that effect in his history, and he wrote to the metropolite Apros in 1335 a letter against the detractors of astronomy (περὶ τῶν τὴν ἀστρονομίαν ὑβριζόντων; letter 49 in Guilland's edition, p. 188–93).[13]

The reading of Synesios (V-1) suggested to him a treatise on the astrolabe, derived naturally from Ptolemy (II-1) and Philoponos (VI-1). In fact, he wrote two treatises on the astrolabe, in the first of which (before 1335) he explained how tc construct one, πῶς δεῖ κατασκευάζειν ἀστρόλαβον or περὶ κατασκευῆς καὶ γενέσεως ἀστρολάβου. Judging from the number of MSS (at least 26), that treatise was much in demand. Sometime later (c. 1350?) he wrote another treatise wherein he discussed the mathematical method of projection of the lines drawn on a sphere from that sphere upon a plane.

In 1324, he submitted to Andronicos II a treatise on the reform of the calendar, with special reference to the determination of Easter. That treatise is inserted in his history (VIII, 13). It is misleading to consider the treatise an extraordinary anticipation of the Gregorian calendar introduced by pope Gregory XIII in 1582, as was done by scholars who played on the names Gregoras and Gregorius. The need of a reformation of the calendar had been explained by Robert Grosseteste (XIII-1), then again by Roger Bacon (XIII-2), and in 1344 Clement VI ordered John of Meurs and Firmin de Beauval to prepare a report on the subject (Avignon 1345).[14] The idea was in the air at least as early as the thirteenth century in the West, and as early as the fourteenth century in the East. The thing which needs explanation is the great delay in its realization, delay largely due to ecclesiastical prejudices and political vicissitudes. As the reform was finally accomplished in 1582 by the Catholic church, the Orthodox church refused to accept it and has not yet accepted it today, except when compelled by civil governments.

Nicephoros prepared a new computus for Easter which was criticized by Barlaam, and which Isaac Argyros (XIV–2) included in his own computus.

Nicephoros had read some of the ancient Greek mathematicians and Nicomachos of Gerasa (I-2), perhaps with Theodoros Metochites or under the latter's guidance, but he showed no interest in pure mathematics, except for a short text on geometrical arithmetic (building of successive squares by the addition of gnomons, etc.), of no importance. On the other hand, he was interested in music and physics. Ptolemy died before being able to complete his Harmony (ἁρμονικά), the last chapter written by him being chapter 13 of book 3. Nicephoros tried to complete it, and his effort was sharply criticized by his rival Barlaam. In another writing he discussed musical intervals. Finally, a commentary on Ptolemy's geography is ascribed to him. He may have been interested in the mathematical aspect of geography, whereas his contemporaries were probably more interested in itineraria or meager summaries like the Γεωγραφία συνοπτική of Nicephoros Blemmydes (XIII-2).

His other writings must be mentioned more rapidly. Two treatises on grammar:

[13] Is the Παρακλητικὴ περὶ ἀστρονομίας mentioned by Krumbacher (p. 296) another title of the same text, or another text?

[14] Of course this is later than Gregoras' treatise and might have been suggested by it; yet that is very improbable. It is more probable that Clement VI was influenced by the Latin scholars of the preceding century.

Τεχνολογία γραμματικῆς, Περὶ ὀρθογραφίας. Explanation of Odysseus' wanderings, Ἐπίτομος ἐξήγησις εἰς τὰς καθ' Ὅμηρον πλάνας τοῦ Ὀδυσσέως. Commentary on the book of dreams of Synesios of Cyrene (V-1), περὶ ἐνυπνίων. In his youth Nicephoros had composed a philosophical dialogue, Φλωρέντιος ἢ περὶ σοφίας, reviving under fancy names a discussion which had occurred between himself and Barlaam. Toward the end of his life he wrote a little tract in answer to various physical questions asked by the empress Helena, daughter of Joannes Cantacuzenos and wife of Joannes Palaeologos (Isis 29, 486).

In addition to the many theological discussions included in his history, he wrote treatises on theology or ecclesiastical politics which are mostly unpublished, also a good number of letters of value for the study of his times, which have not yet been completely published.

His philosophy was a mixture of Aristotelianism and Platonism; on the whole he was rather a Platonist, but without originality and without strength. He discussed Aristotelian physics and logic.

Text. PG (vols. 148–49, Paris 1865) contains the largest collection of Nicephoros' writings.

History. Latin translation, Paris 1567, Francfort 1578. Partial editions of the Greek text, Basel 1862 (books 1–11), Paris 1702, Venice 1729 (books 1–24). First complete edition of 37 books in Bonn corpus (3 vols., 1829–55), books 1–23 edited in vols. 1–2 by J. Schopen, editio princeps of books 24–37 by Im. Bekker in vol. 3, 1855. Elaborate edition, in Greek and French with notes, of book 37 (= 36 in Bekker's edition) by Valentin Parisot (Notices et extraits des MSS 17, part 2, 1–406, Paris 1851). PG (148, 119–1450; 149, 9–502), Greek-Latin edition with prefaces of earlier editions and indexes. An Italian translation of books 1–11 by Lodovico Dolce appeared in Venice as early as 1569. French translation (Paris 1685) by Louis Cousin (1627–1707).

The necrology of Theodoros Metochites was edited by Jan Meurs (Leiden 1618), then again, together with the text of Michael Glycas (XII-1), in Greek and Latin by Philippe Labbe (Paris 1660).

Eulogy of Hugh IV (king of Cypros 1324–59) edited by Emmanuel Miller and Constantinos Sathas in their edition of the chronicle of Cypros, 1359–1432, of Leontios Machairas (still living in 1434), Λεοντίου Μαχαιρᾶ χρονικὸν Κύπρου (Paris 1882), in Greek and French.

Editions of other eulogies are cited by Guilland.

Florentios in PG (149, 643–48), incomplete. Edition by Albert Jahn (Jahns Jahrbuch suppt. vol. 10, 485–536; 11, 387–92, 1844–45).

Nicephori explicatio in librum Synesii de insomniis, interprete Anthonio Pichonio. Appended to Synesius, Liber de insomniis (Paris 1586). Nicephori versus etiam oneirocritici in Artemedori Daldiani et Achmetis Sereimi F. oneirocritica, edited by Nicolas Rigault (Paris 1603). Edition by Dionysios Petavius (Denys Petau of Orléans, 1583–1652) in Opera Synesii (p. 351–429, Paris 1612). PG (149, 521–642). For Artemidoros Daldianos of Ephesus (II-2) and Aḥmad ibn Sirin (IX-1) above mentioned, see Introd. 1, 295, 558.

Many letters have been published here and there, the best collection being Rodolphe Guilland: Correspondance de Nicéphore Grégoras (416 p., Paris 1927), summaries of 161 letters, most of which are unfortunately anterior to 1345; 18 of these letters are edited; 21 letters to Gregoras, 1 of which is edited.

Latin translations of Nicephoros' logic and of his treatise on the astrolabe by Giorgio Valla (Venice 1498).

St. Bezdechi: Un manuel de philosophie à l'usage des dames. Un échantillon d'arithmetica geometrica (34 p., Cluj 1938; Isis 29, 486), editions of Nicephoros' answers to the empress Helena, and of the short text on geometrical arithmetic. Another mathematical fragment is included in Heiberg's edition of Euclid (5, 723–24, 1888).

The two treatises on the astrolabe have been edited by Armand Delatte, together with three other Byzantine treatises (2, 195–235, 4 figs., 1939).

Criticism. Carl v. Jan: Die Harmonie der Sphären (Philologus vol. 52, 1893). Franz Boll: Studien über Ptolemaeus (Jahns Jahrbuch suppt. vol. 21, 1894). Krumbacher (p. 293–98, 623, etc., 1897). Van Millingen (p. 301–2, 1912). Rodolphe Guilland: Essai sur Nicéphore Grégoras (348 p., Paris 1926), reviewed by Louis Bréhier (Journal des savants, 1928, p. 35–39). Eleutheroudakis encyclopaedia (4, 148, 1928). Konrad Miller: Die ältesten Separatkarten der drei Erdteile wahrscheinlich von Nikephoros Gregoras um 1350 in Konstantinopel entworfen (folio, 7 p., 6 pl., Stuttgart 1931).

B2. Armenian Historiography

HAYTON THE MONK

Armenian historian dictating in French (d. c. 1314).

Hayton or Haiton; Hethum, Hetum, or Hetoum, also same forms without initial h. Haytonus monachus. He was born between 1230 and 1245 in Lesser Armenia, being a nephew of Hayton I (XIII-2), king of Armenia (1223–26 to 1268–70). He was probably the son of Oshin, the king's puisne brother, lord of Corycos. He called himself in French "seigneur de Courc" (or Courcy), the reference being to the place (his native place?) of Corycos,[15] in Cilicia Aspera, a little harbor facing Cyprus in the south. He took part in the wars carried on by his cousin Hayton II (king 1289–97), or at any rate was a witness of many of the events of those wars which he later described. Before 1299, he went on a pilgrimage to France, and upon his return to Cilicia after an absence of two years he wished to become a monk; political and military conditions, however, were so bad in his country that he considered it his duty to face them rather than evade them. In 1305 he assumed the Praemonstratensian habit in the monastery of Bellapais (or Lapais), near Kerýnia, on the northern coast of Cyprus.

In 1307 he went to France and in Poitiers dictated in French his Fleur des histoires de la terre d'Orient to Nicolas Falcon of Toul, who in the same year translated it into Latin (Flos historiarum partium Orientis) for Clement V. In 1351 the Latin text was retranslated by Long John of Ypres (XIV-2) into French; this is not a literal translation, but Long John neither omits important parts nor adds material of his own. This was probably the first Western attempt to write a systematic geography of Asia; it is rudimentary.

Hayton gives an interesting history of the Mongols and of Lesser Armenia, although a rather prejudiced one. He knew many of the men mentioned and took part in, or witnessed, most of the events he describes. He was writing with a definite purpose, to interest the West in Armenia, and to tell them that they could gain the aid of the Tatars in recovering the Holy Land. This alliance with the Mongols appears in many plans for crusades, for instance in those of two other fourteenth-century writers, William Adam and Marino Sanudo; but it is more fully developed in the work of Hayton, who had had personal contact with them and knew their military abilities.

[15] Modern Korgos (many variants), where one may still see the ruins of an Armenian fortified castle, Kys kalé.

The Fleur des histoires is divided into four parts. Part I contains principally geographic and ethnographic information. Hayton discusses the appearance, characteristics, and religious beliefs of the people of each of the fifteen kingdoms or regions of Asia he describes in the following order: Cathay, Tharse (east of Transoxiana), Turkestan, Corasme (Khwārizm, south of the Aral Sea), Gazarie (land of the Khazars, southern Russia), Coumaine (north of the Caucasus and of the Caspian), India, Persia, Media, Armenia, Georgia, Chaldea, Mesopotamia, Turkey, Syria. He must have traveled extensively, not only in and near Lesser Armenia but in more distant countries; for example, he mentions obscure districts in Georgia. His account is very short, however (e.g., Cathay is disposed of in 30 lines), and contains but few novelties.

Part II is a summary of the principal facts of the history of the emperors and kings of the Arabs and of the Turks from the time of Mohammed to the middle of the thirteenth century, and the races to which they belonged.

Part III is a longer and more detailed account of the history of the Mongols or Tatars from the period of Chingiz Khān (XIII-1) to the first years of the fourteenth century; especially concerning their invasions of Western Asia and Europe; their struggle against the caliphs of Baghdād and the sultan of Egypt; their relations with the princes of Lesser Armenia; and their conquest of the Holy Land.

Part IV contains Hayton's plan for the recovery of the Holy Land. The plan was severely criticized by Marino Sanudo in the second book of the Secreta. The first 10 chapters deal with the political and administrative organization of Egypt, and the military power of the sultan in Syria and in Egypt. He includes brief geographical and ethnographical details of the two countries, a very brief history of the sultans of Cairo (c. 1150–1300), certain details of the Crusades, and of the wars against the infidels carried on by the Latin kings of Jerusalem. Chapters 11–28 contain the plan for the crusade: (1) There should first be a swift attack by a small advance guard, using Cyprus and Armenia as military bases. This army should try to take certain important cities on the coast of Syria. (2) The main army should go to the east by sea and stop first in Cyprus. If the advance guard had not been able to secure the coast cities in Syria, the second army should then proceed to Armenia, where they could organize and collect supplies. But in any case the crusaders should make sure of an alliance with the Tatars. In this section all the small details concerning their preparations were worked out.

Hayton probably did not use the books of Marco Polo (XIII-2) and John Pian del Càrpine (XIII-1), but may have used that of William of Rubruquis (XIII-2). It is true that he related certain stories which are also found in these works, such as the account of paper money in use in China; the remains of Noah's Ark on Mt. Ararat; the foundation of Peking, and others. It is possible that all these men were merely relating stories current in the East.

Another work, entitled the Chronographie or Table chronologique, has recently been attributed to Hayton by Avkerian, the Armenian translator of the Fleur des histoires. The Chronographie was written in Armenian about 1296. It contains a brief account of the main events which took place in the East, especially in Armenia, Syria, and Palestine, between 1076 and 1307. Many of these events are connected with the crusades which occurred in this period. It is based on Armenian, French, and Syrian histories.

Hayton did not write the Exordium Jerosolimitani hospitalis ac ordinis, and probably did not write a commentary on the Apocalypse sometimes attributed to him; nor the Memoria, another project for the recovery of the Holy Land.

Text. Les fleurs des hystoires de la terre Dorient compillees par frere Haycon, the original French text, Paris 1501?, 1515?, 1516, c. 1520, 1522, Lyon 1585, 1595. Modern edition by Louis de Backer: L'extrême Orient au moyen âge (p. 125–253, Paris 1877), poor. New edition in Recueil des historiens des croisades, Documents arméniens (2, 113–253, Paris 1906).

Editions of the original Latin text, Liber (sive Flos) historiarum partium Orientis, the Latin text of Nicolas Falcon (sometimes called by mistake Salcon). First edition by Menrad Molther, Hagenau 1529. New edition by Johann Huttich in the collection entitled Novus orbis regionum ac insularum veteribus incognitarum . . . , with preface by Simon Grynaeus, Paris 1532 (two variants), Basel 1532, 1537, 1555. The whole collection was translated into German by Michael Herr (Strassburg 1534), and into Dutch from the German by Cornelis Ablijn (Antwerp 1563). All these editions and translations of the Novus orbis are folios. Third Latin edition by Reiner Reineck (Reineccius) in his Chronicon Hierosolymitanum (quarto, 2 vols., Helmstadt 1585), reprinted in his Historia orientalis (quarto, 2 vols., Helmstadt 1602); Hayton's text is in the second volume of each collection. Edition by Andreas Müller (Berlin 1671), reproducing the text of one of the Basel editions of the Novus orbis. New edition in Recueil des historiens des croisades, Documents arméniens (2, 255–63, Paris 1906).

The translations into other languages will now be dealt with in the chronological order of the first translations into each language. All these translations were made presumably from the Latin text, except when otherwise stated.

French: By Jean Le Long of Ypres (Paris 1529). By Pierre Bergeron: Recueil de divers voyages curieux (Leyden 1729).

English: Translation ascribed to Alexander Barclay (1475?–1552), printed by Richard Pynson (London c. 1520–30). Translation of books I and III in Samuel Purchas: Hakluytus posthumus (folio, 4 vols., London 1625), in vol. 3. The part concerning Cathay was reprinted in Yule (1, cxcv–vi, 1866).

German: The German translation by Michael Herr (1534) has already been mentioned.

Italian: Translation of book III in the collection of Giambattista Ramusio: Delle navigationi e viaggi (vol. 2, Venezia 1559), often reprinted. Other translations by Joseppe Horologgi: Historia degli imperatori greci (Venezia 1562) and by an anonymous writer (Francesco Sansovino?) in a collection bearing the same title (Venezia 1562).

Dutch: Ablijn's translation from the German (Antwerp 1563) has been cited above. There is also a Dutch translation from the English, in the Dutch edition of Samuel Purchas' collection (Amsterdam 1655). There is still another Dutch translation by J. H. Glazemaker: Markus Paulus venetus reizen . . . (Amsterdam 1664).

Spanish: Spanish translation by Amaro Centeno (Cordova 1595), free and incomplete. Wesley Robertson Long: La flor de las ystorias de Orient (223 p., Chicago 1934), Aragonese translation of the last third of the fourteenth century, from the unique Escorial MS, with introduction, bibliography, and notes.

Armenian: Armenian translation by the Mekhitarist priest Avkerian (Jean Baptiste Aucher), S. Làzzaro, Venezia 1842.

Chronographie, or Table chronologique, published as an appendix to the Armenian translation of the Flos historiarum of Avkerian, Venice 1842. Translated into French by V. Langlois (Revue de l'Orient 15, 107–14, 1863); and by E. Dulaurier (Documents arméniens 1, 471–90, Paris 1869).

Criticism. Neumann (p. 207, 1836). Patcanian (p. 83, 1860). Paulin Paris: Hayton, Prince d'Arménie, historien (HL 25, 479–507, Paris 1869). Röhricht (p. 65–67, 1890). Charles Kohler: Hayton (Recueil des historiens des croisades, Documents arméniens, 2, xxiii–cxlii, Paris 1906), includes extensive bibliography. Friedrich Ernest August Krause: Das Mongolenreich nach der Darstellung des Armeniers Haithon (Festschrift für Friedrich Hirth p. 238–67, Berlin 1920; Isis 4, 406). August Vermeylen: Le livre de la Fleur des hystoires de la Terre de Orient, et le problème des influences orientales au Moyen âge (Actes du Congrès d'histoire de l'art 1, 331 ff., Paris 1921). Gustave Soulier: Le moine arménien Hethoum et les apports d'extrême-orient (Revue des études arméniennes 9, 249–54, Paris 1929; T'oung pao 27, 448–49, 1930). Pouzyna (p. 97, 1935). Atiya (p. 62–64 and by index, 1938).

B4. Nestorian Historiography

'AMR IBN MATTĀ

'Amr ibn Mattā al-Ṭīrhānī al-Nusṭūrī. Nestorian chronicler (fl. after 1317). He came from Ṭīrhān on the Tigris, near Sāmarrā. Al-Ṭīrhān was then a Christian center many centuries old.

One of the sources used by Abū-l-Faraj (Barhebraeus, XIII-2) in his great chronicle was the Kitāb al-mijdal (Book of the tower or castle, cf. Hebrew migdal) written by the Nestorian Mārī ibn Sulaimān. The Kitāb al mijdal contains two parts, the first dealing with Nestorian theology, the second with the history of the Nestorian patriarchs down to 1147; hence it was written after 1147 and before 1286, when Abū-l-Faraj composed his own work. 'Amr ibn Mattā revised and abbreviated the Kitāb al-mijdal and continued it to the death of Yaballaha III, in 1317.[16]

Another revision of the same Mijdal was made by another contemporary Nestorian, Ṣalībā ibn Yūḥannā of Mūṣul. It is difficult to disentangle the two versions, which should be considered together. Ṣalībā gives details which are lacking in 'Amr's text, but this may be explained equally well by assuming that Ṣalībā's revision of 'Amr implied amplifications, or that 'Amr's revision of Ṣalībā implied subtractions. From other MSS of his it would seem that Ṣalībā flourished c. 1330 (Cheikho, p. 136, 1924).

Text. Father Henry Gismondi (S.J.), who died in 1914, edited the Arabic text of the historical part of the Kitāb al-mijdal and of the additions and revisions of 'Amr and Ṣalībā and translated them into Latin: Maris Amri et Slibae de patriarchis Nestoriarum commentaria (4 vols. in 2, Rome 1896–99).

Criticism. Duval (p. 200, 1907). Baumstark (p. 6, 1922). Cheikho (p. 136, 149, 185, 1924). James Alan Montgomery: The history of Yaballaha III (p. 20, New York 1927; Isis 10, 129).

B5. Abyssinian Historiography

THE CHRONICLE OF 'AMDA ṢION

'Amda Ṣion was the most important king of Abyssinia in the fourteenth century. He ruled from 1314 to 1344, and made himself famous by his triumphant wars against the Muslims, especially by the crusade of 1332. His rule was made more difficult and memorable by internal disorders due to the rivalry between the northern and southern peoples and to monkish intrigues. The monks began to oppose

[16] We have already met Yaballaha III apropos of Bar Ṣauma (XIII-2; Introd. 2, 1069).

the king because he had married his stepsister, and they quarreled among themselves apropos of the sabbath and the date of Christmas. This led to persecutions by the civil government and the martyrization of some churchmen.

The importance of 'Amda Ṣion's rule is reflected in a kind of government and court manual, Ser'ata mangest, suggesting Byzantine models, e.g., the "Ἔκθεσις τῆς βασιλείου τάξεως of Constantinos VII Porphyrogennetos (X-2). The redaction of that manual is probably posterior to his rule.

The old Ge'ez mythical chronicles, Kebra nagast (Grandeur of the kings), were replaced about this time or a little later by other chronicles, written also in Ge'ez but more objectively. They deal chiefly with the period 1270 to 1344, with later extensions to 1434. The center of interest is 'Amda Ṣion.

These chronicles—which were the earliest objective chronicles of the Abyssinian past—were later revised and rewritten in a conventional language, still Ge'ez in structure but including gradually more and more words of the common Amharic speech; the so-called "chronicle language" or lesāna tārik.

Among the historical works of this time we should mention an anonymous translation of the Sefer Yosippon, originally written in Hebrew, but soon translated into Arabic. The Aethiopic (Ge'ez) version was derived from the Arabic. For the tradition of that strange work see my notes on the Persian Jew Solomon ben Samuel and on the Serbian one Judah ben Moses Mosconi (XIV-2).

Text. Critical edition of the Aethiopic text of Yosippon by Murad Kamil (382 p., 12 pl., New York 1938; Isis 31, 223).

Criticism. Littmann (p. 197, 206–67, 213, 244, 250, 263, 1907). Kammerer (1, xxxvi, 1929).

C. WESTERN ISLĀM

IBN ABĪ ZAR'

Moroccan historian (d. after 1325).

Abū-l-Ḥasan 'Alī ibn 'Abdallāh ibn abī Zar' al-Fāsī. Nothing is known of his life, except that he wrote a chronicle of North Africa under the Idrīsids, the Berber dynasties, the Almoravides, the Almohades, and the Marīnids, from 788 to 1325/26. It is entitled Kitāb al-anīs al-muṭrib bi rauḍ al-qirṭās fi akhbār mulūk al-Maghrib wa ta'rīkh madīnat Fās (The delightful companion in the Paper Garden,[17] or stories of the kings of the Maghrib and annals of Fās). It is especially valuable for the later period, because for the earlier times it is largely derived, to the point of plagiarism, from the Kitāb al-bayān al-mughrib of Ibn al-'Idhārī (XIII-2). It was itself used in the same manner (or shall we say edited?) by Muḥammad ibn Qāsim ibn Zākūr al-Fāsī (d. 1708). It was sometimes quoted by Ibn Khaldūn.

The Anīs muṭrib is ascribed in some MSS and editions to Abū Muḥammad Ṣāliḥ ibn 'Abd al-Ḥalīm al-Gharnāṭī.

Text. Carl Johan Tornberg: Annales regum Mauritaniae a condito Idrisidarum imperio ad annum fugae 726 (2 vols., Upsala 1843–46), Arabic text with Latin version and notes. Edition by Muḥammad ibn al-Ḥusain al-Fāṭimī (304 p., Fās 1888), and by Muḥammad al-Hāshimī al-Filālī (2 vols., Ribāṭ 1936). The last-mentioned edition extends to 1184, i.e., covers about half the work (Hesperis 24, 144–47, 1937).

[17] The rauḍ (or rauḍat) al-qirṭās (or qarṭas) or Paper Garden is a place near Fās.

German translation by Franz von Dombay (2 vols., Agram 1794–95). Portuguese translation by José de Santo Antonio Moura (454 p., Lisboa 1828). French translation by Auguste Beaumier (588 p., Paris 1860).

Criticism. Gayangos (2, 516, 1843). Wüstenfeld (no. 392, 1881). Pons Boigues (p. 420, 1898). Brockelmann (2, 240, 1902; suppt. 2, 339, 1938). René Basset (EI 2, 358, 1916).

D. EASTERN ISLĀM

D1. Arabia

AL-JANADĪ

Abū 'Abdallāh Muḥammad ibn Ya'qūb Bahā' al-dīn al-Janadī (or Jundī?). Arabian historian of Yaman (died 1331/32).

He wrote a political and literary history of Yaman down to 1323/24, entitled Kitāb al-sulūk fi ṭabaqāt al-'ulamā' wal-mulūk. This is a local history, but the umarā' of Yaman were in touch with the 'Abbāsī caliphs; they had a considerable amount of internal difficulties, but were spared the horrors and the brutal and deep discontinuities caused by the Mongol invasions. Al-Janadī's work is partly derived for the earlier times from the Ta'rīkh al-Rāzī (history of Ṣan'ā) by Aḥmad ibn 'Abdallāh al-Rāzī of Ṣan'ā (fl. 1068), the Ta'rīkh al-Yaman by 'Umāra ibn 'Alī al-Yamanī (XII-2), and the biographies of Ibn Khallikān (XIII-2). It was continued to 1335/36, and a further continuation was made by al-Ḥusain ibn 'Abd al-Raḥmān al-Ahdal (d. 1451).

Text. Extract in Arabic and English from the Sulūk concerning the Qarmatians in Henry Cassels Kay: Yaman, its early mediaeval history (London 1892).

Other extracts in Hartwig Derenbourg: 'Oumāra du Yémen, sa vie et son oeuvre (Arabic text, 2, 541–48, 630–49, Paris 1902).

Criticism. Ḥājjī Khalīfa (3, 613, no. 7238, 1842). Wüstenfeld (no. 399a, 1881), very short note. Brockelmann (2, 184, 1902; suppt. 2, 236, 1938). Kammerer (1, 157, 1929).

D2. Mamlūk Historiography

AL-BIRZĀLĪ

Abū Muḥammad al-Qāsim ibn Muḥammad 'Alam al-dīn al-Birzālī al-Shāfi'ī. Hispano-Muslim historian of Berber origin (1267–1339).

The name Birzālī refers to the Berber tribe Birzāla, al Shāfi'ī refers to the legal school (one of the four orthodox schools of Islam, see Introd. 1, 550). Al-Birzālī was born at Seville in February 1267. After having completed his education, he traveled to the Near East. He was in Aleppo in 1286/87, then went to Egypt, made the Pilgrimage in 1290, and finally established himself in Damascus. He spent the rest of his life there, teaching in various madāris. In the course of his fourth or fifth pilgrimage he died between Madīna and Mekka on June 14, 1339.

Among his many children was a daughter, Fāṭima, who distinguished herself as a calligraphist and copied important MSS.

Al-Birzālī's main work is a continuation of the chronicle of Damascus by Abū Shāma (XIII-2), down to 1338, entitled Ta'rīkh Miṣr wa Dimashq or Kitāb al-wafayāt, because it is largely a collection of biographies. It was itself continued for the period 1338–72 by one of his disciples, Muḥammad ibn Rāfi' al-Sallāmī (1305–72).

We owe to al-Birzālī also a shorter chronicle, Mukhtaṣar al-mi'a al-sābi'a, for the period 1204–1335, largely restricted to obituaries and brief notes on the main events; and at least two other writings.

Criticism. Wüstenfeld (no. 403, 1881). Brockelmann (2, 36, 1902; suppt. 2, 34, 1938); EI (1, 727, 1912).

AL-ADFUWĪ

Abū-l-Faḍl Ja'far ibn Tha'lab al-Adfuwī al-Shāfi'ī. Egyptian historian and theologian (1286–1347).

Al-Adfuwī is so called after his birthplace, Edfu on the Nile in Upper Egypt (c. lat. 25°N.), but his family came from Qūṣ, down the river below Luxor. He studied in Cairo under Muḥammad ibn 'Alī ibn Daqīq al-'Īd (d. 1302) and under Abū Ḥaiyān al-Andalusī. He died in Cairo on May 22, 1347 (or 1348?, of the plague?).

He wrote:

1. A collection of biographies of learned men of Upper Egypt, the first collection restricted to that country. It is called Kitāb al-ṭāli' al-sa'īd al-jāmi' li'asmā' nujabā' al-Ṣa'īd (The auspicious star concerning the noble men of Ṣa'īd); it was compiled upon the advice of his shaykh Abū Ḥaiyān, and was completed in 1337, then continued to 1339. It deals mainly with people of Qūṣ and its neighborhood.
2. Al-badr al-sāfir wa tuḥfat al-masāfir, biographies of men of the thirteenth century.
3. Al-imtā' bi-aḥkām al-samā', discussing the licitness of music.
4. Farā'id al fawā'id wa maqāṣid al-qawā'id, a legal commentary on a book of al-Nawawī (XIII-2).

Text. The numbers of the works above mentioned are the same as Brockelmann's. No. 1 was printed in Alexandria 1914.

Criticism. Wüstenfeld (no. 413, 1882), only a few lines. Brockelmann (2, 31, 1902; suppt. 2, 27, 1938). Sarkis (p. 416, 1930). Farmer (no. 217, p. 52, 1940).

AL-ṢAFADĪ

Ṣalāḥ al-dīn Abū-l-Ṣafā' Khalīl ibn Aibak al-Ṣafadī al-Shāfi'ī. Palestinian man of letters and historian (c. 1297–1363).

Al-Ṣafadī was born in Ṣafad, upper Galilee, c. 1297; he was of Turkish ancestry. He made very elaborate literary studies and was an excellent calligrapher. He was secretary in Ṣafad, later in Cairo, Ḥalab, al-Raḥba (on the Euphrates, modern al-Miyādīn), and finally treasurer in Damascus. In spite of these administrative duties he managed to write an almost unbelievable quantity of books, most of which are poetical and rhetorical exercises, compilations, etc. He died at Damascus on July 23, 1363.

His main work, to which we shall come back presently, is an elaborate biographical dictionary, the Wāfī bi-l-wafayāt. It will suffice to mention a few of his other works: (1) A'yān al-'asr wa a'wān al-naṣr, extract from the preceding restricted to the author's contemporaries, like a "Who's who"; (2) Masālik al-abṣār fī mamālik al-amṣār, treatise on geography; (3) Al-tadhkira al-ṣalāḥīya, collection of extracts with commentaries; this includes extracts from a medical work, Iqtiḍāb fī-l-mas'ala wal-jawāb, by one Jamāl al-dīn Ibrāhīm ibn Maḥmūd al-'Aṭṭār. Other books deal with the biographies of blind persons, or of one-eyed persons; he wrote much poetry, grammatical discussions, and erotical compilations. One of the latter, the Law'at al-shākī wa dam'at al-bāqī, a tale of male homosexuality in prose and verse, has often been printed in Tunis (1857), Constantinople, Cairo, etc. I may still mention for the sake of curiosity the Kitāb kashf al-ḥāl fi waṣf al-khāl, treating in a literary manner, with an abundance of puns and allusions, the subject of khāl (naevus, mole, beauty spot). This is a part of physiognomy. Moles were given different symptomatic or prophetic significance according to their situation on this or that organ, on the right or the left, etc.[18] The study of moles might be combined with astrological ideas, as was done, incidentally, by Ibn abī-l-Rijāl (XI-1) in his Kitāb al-bāri' fī aḥkām al-nujūm.

To return to the Kitāb al-wāfī bi-l-wafayāt (meaning the complete book of necrologies), it is an enormous collection of biographies, the largest of its kind in the Arabic language and in Islām. It included many thousands of biographies of people of all kinds and classes. It is so vast that no complete MS is extant, but it has been possible to reconstruct it almost completely (more than 14,000 biographies) from MSS scattered in many libraries; this was done first by Leone Caetani, prince of Teano, duke of Sermoneta (1869–1935), then by Hellmut Ritter. The latter discovered in Istanbul an autograph MS of a good part of the work, as well as of the A'yān al-'aṣr.

The size of this biographical collection will be better appreciated if one compares it with other Arabic collections. The Ikhbār al-'ulamā of Ibn al-Qifṭī (XIII-1) includes 414 biographies; the 'Uyūn al-anbā' of Ibn abī Uṣaibi'a (XIII-1), some 400; the Wafayāt al-a'yān of Ibn Khallikān (XIII-2), 865; the Fawāt al-wafayāt, continuation of the Wafayāt, by Muḥammad ibn Shākir al-Kutubī (XIV-2), 506; finally, the Kitāb al-manhal al-ṣāfī wal-mustawfī ba'd al-wāfī, which is *not* a continuation of al-Ṣafadī's Wāfī, was compiled by the Cairene historian Abū-l-Maḥāsin Jamāl al-dīn Yūsuf ibn Taghrībardī (1411–c. 1469); it includes 2,307 biographies. All together these five collections contain 4,492 biographies; al-Ṣafadī's contains four times more.

Al-Ṣafadī's purpose was not (as has been said) to continue the Wafayāt al-a'yān of Ibn Khallikān, as was done by others, but rather to put together and complete all the biographies available in Arabic literature, most of which were restricted to special "classes" (ṭabaqāt), and to constitute what would be called today a "national biography of Islām." Like our national biographies, it was comprehensive enough to include a number of strangers, in this case non-Muslims who lived in Islamic countries and shared their activities. The arrangement was alphabetical with the following curious exceptions: The first biography is a very elaborate one of the Prophet Muḥammad, then follow all the men who themselves and whose fathers were called after the Prophet, i.e., all the men named Muḥammad ibn Muḥammad (no less than 201!); next come the other Muḥammad in the alphabetic order of their fathers' first names.

The seriousness of the author's purpose in this work, and his thoroughness, appear from his long introduction (muqaddama), divided into 11 sections: (I) calendars used by Muslims, Persians, Jews, etc.; (II) grammatical discussion of the writing of

[18] The subject had been touched by at least one Greek, Melampus (Μελάμπους), date unknown, author of περὶ παλμῶν μαντική and περὶ ἐλαιῶν τοῦ σώματος, in both of which a king Ptolemaios is addressed (PW 29, 399, 1931). Melampus was also a forerunner in the kind of divination called spasmatomancy (in Arabic, 'ilm al-ikhtilāj), derived from the observation of bodily motions, jerks, spasms.

dates; (III) how to date events in writing; (IV) ethnical and topographical names (nisba); (V) proper names, patronymics; kunya; honorary surnames or nicknames (laqab), and the relations of these names; (VI) orthography, writing, abbreviations, and other conventions; (VII) plan of historical works; (VIII) discussion of the word wafā (decease); (IX) usefulness of historiography; (X) qualities of a good historian; (XI) historical bibliography, divided according to subjects (history of the East, of the Maghrib, of Egypt, of the caliphs, . . . , of the governors, judges, learned men, poets, etc.). To his article on the Prophet he also attached a special bibliography of 35 works. For a list of his 282 authorities as quoted by himself see Journal asiatique (19, 243–97, 1912) or Ritter's edition (1, 47–55). In short, we are given here much of what is contained in a manual of historiography, together with the indispensable bibliography. That is very remarkable indeed.

The author of the Wāfī bi-l-wafayāt should not be confused with two other contemporary Ṣafadī. The first of these is al-Ḥasan ibn 'Abdallāh al-Hāshimī al-Ṣafadī, who flourished in Egypt c. 1294–1312 and wrote an account and description of that country (EI 4, 54); the second is Shihāb al-dīn Aḥmad ibn Yūsuf al-Ṣafadī, who flourished in Egypt or Syria and wrote, in 1341, the Kitāb al-wajīz al-muntaqā wal-'azīz al-multaqā, conversation in rhymed prose of a sulṭān with his philosopher on medicine (Brockelmann 2, 137; suppt. 2, 169).

Text. Emile Amar: Prolégomènes à l'étude des historiens arabes par al-Ṣafadī, publiés et traduits d'après les MSS de Paris et de Vienne (Journal asiatique 17, 251–308, 465–531, 1911; 18, 5–48, 1911; 19, 243–97, 1912). This edition is restricted to the muqaddama of the Wāfī bi-l-wafayāt. A complete edition of that gigantic work has been undertaken by Hellmut Ritter in the series Bibliotheca islamica, published in Istanbul, Maṭba'at al-dawlah. The first volume (vol. 6a of the series, 394 p., 7 pl., 1931) contains the muqaddama and the biographies of the men called Muḥammad to Muḥammad ibn Ibrāhīm ibn 'Abd al-raḥmān (no. 246); that is, another volume will be needed before we reach the beginning of the alphabet! Ritter's edition is based on the Istanbul MSS, some of which are the author's autograph, and on an Istanbul MS of the A'yān al-'aṣr, which is also partly an autograph. Ritter has added many notes in Arabic. On account of the importance of that edition, I refer to the following reviews of it: by C. Brockelmann (O. L. Z. 36, 691–93, 1933); by F. Krenkow (J. R. A. S., 1933, p. 190–93); also in J. A. O. S. (54, 214, 1934) and in J. Q. R. (27, 195, 1936).

For a specimen of al-Ṣafadī's work see his biography of Ibn al-Nafīs (XIII-2). Englished by Max Meyerhof (Isis 23, 105–10, 1935).

The Nakt al-himyān fī-l-nukat al-'umyān, 300 biographies of famous blind people, was carefully edited by Aḥmad Zakī pāshā (Cairo 1911).

Criticism. Wüstenfeld (no. 423, 1882). Brockelmann (2, 31–33, 1902; suppt. 2, 27–29, 1938), enumerating 41 works. Ahmed bey Zeki: Dictionnaire biographique des aveugles de l'orient (Presse médicale d'Egypte no. 5, 1911), apropos of his edition cited above. Giuseppe Gabrieli: Como si possa ricostruire dai manoscritti il grande dizionario biografico di al-Ṣafadī (Rendiconti, R. Accad. dei Lincei 21, 685–757, 2 pl., Roma 1913; Isis 6, 151); Indice alfabetico di tutte le biografie (ibid. vols. 22–25, 1913–16; reprint 258 p., Roma 1916); this index, which has not been continued, deals only with the names beginning with A, and lists 3,192 names! F. Krenkow (EI 4, 52–54, 1924), listing 33 works. Sarkis (col. 1210–13, 1928–30). Mourad (p. 37–39, 1939).

BAIBARS AL-MANṢŪRĪ

Al-Amīr Rukn al-dīn Baibars (or Bībars) al-Manṣūrī al-Khaṭī'ī (the sinner). Egyptian minister and historian; Ḥanafī theologian; died at the age of 80 in 1325.

He was a mamlūk (slave) of the sulṭān al-Manṣūr Qalāūn (ruled 1279–90), who freed him and appointed him governor of al-Kerak (east of the Dead Sea). He held various other offices under other salāṭīn of the Baḥrī Mamlūk dynasty, with the usual vicissitudes of fortune.

For example, the sulṭān Khalīl (1290–93) dismissed him, but his successor Nāṣir appointed him chief of his secretariat (dīwān al-inshā) with the title dawādār kabīr (grand secretary of state), and he continued in that office until 1304/5. In 1303/4 he was put in charge of the repairs made necessary by the earthquake of Alexandria. In 1311/12 he was made viceroy (nā'ib al-salṭana), but was thrown into prison in the following year and remained there until 1317/18. He made the Pilgrimage in 1318/19. He endowed a Ḥanafī college in Cairo and died in ramaḍān 725 (August–September 1325).

He wrote two historical works which are still unpublished:

1. Zubdat al-fikra fī ta'rīkh al-hijra, a general history of Islām to 1324, with the collaboration of his Christian secretary Abū-l-Barakāt. This is a very large work in eleven volumes, of which there is no complete MS anywhere; as far as can be judged from the parts extant, it is largely derived from the Kāmil of Ibn al-Athīr (XIII-1).

2. Al-tuḥfa al-mulūkīya fī-l-daula al-Turkīya, a history of the Mamlūk dynasty from the beginning in 1250 to 1321.

Criticism. Wüstenfeld (no. 390, 1881). Brockelmann (2, 44, 1902; suppt. 2, 43, 1938). K. V. Zetterstéen: An Arabic manuscript supposed to contain the Zubdat el-fikra (Monde oriental 3, 264–66, 1909), apropos of a continuation of Baibars' history to 1344 in the Bodleian. D. S. Margoliouth (EI 1, 590, 1911).

IBN AL-WARDĪ

Abū Ḥafṣ Zain al-dīn 'Umar ibn al-Muẓaffar al-Qurashī al-Bakrī al-Ma'arrī Ibn al-Wardī al-Shāfi'ī. Muslim Syrian philologist, writer, and historian (d. 1349).

Ibn al-Wardī was born before 1290 in Ma'arrat al-Nu'mān, in northern Syria (the birthplace also of the famous poet Abū-l-'Alā' al-Ma'arrī, 973–1057); he studied in Ḥamāh, Damascus, and Aleppo, and apparently spent the rest of his life in the last-named city, where he was for a time deputy for the qāḍī Muḥammad ibn al-Naqīb (d. 1343) and where he died of the plague on March 18, 1349. After having received a warning in a dream, he devoted his last years to meditation, research, and writing.

He wrote a good amount of poetry, including a poem on the plague, of which he was to be himself soon afterward one of the victims. This Maqāma fī-l-ṭā'ūn al-āmm was included by the Egyptian polygraph al-Suyūṭī (1445–1505) in the latter's work on the plague. Other poems of his were the occasion of many commentaries.

He also composed writings on grammar, history, law, mysticism, and oneiromancy.

Grammar: Short grammatical poem, Al-tuḥfa al-Wardīya. Adaptation of the famous poem Al-alfīya of Muḥammad ibn 'Abdallāh al-Ṭā'ī al-Jaiyānī (1203–73), etc.

History: Tatimmat al-mukhtaṣar fī akhbār al-bashar. Summary of the chronicle of Abū-l-Fidā' with a continuation to 1348/49.

Law (fiqh): Al bahja al-Wardīya, versification of the small treatise Al-ḥāwī al-ṣaghīr of 'Abd al-Ghaffār ibn 'Abd al-Karīm al-Qazwīnī (d. 1266). Al-masā'il al-mulaqqabāt al-Wardīya fī-l-farā'iḍ, poem on the rules of inheritance. Etc.

In his youth he wrote a book on the interpretation of dreams, Al-muqaddama (al-alfīya) al-Wardīya (or, Manẓūma fī ta'bīr al-ru'yā). The Shihāb al-thāqif wal-'adhāb al-wāqif is a mystical treatise.

It is remarkable how many of his writings bear his own name in the form of the adjective Wardīya. This is rather unusual, such adjectives being used more often to designate patrons than authors. It suggests that Ibn al-Wardī's fame was recognized and capitalized.

The authorship of the Kharīdat al-'ajā'ib has been wrongly ascribed to him. That work was composed—largely plagiarized from the Jāmi' al-funūn of Ibn Shabīb—by another Ibn al-Wardī (fl. 1446), for whom see my note on Ibn Shabīb. This is a source of continual confusion, for references to "Ibn al-Wardī" are almost always references to the Kharīdat al-'ajā'ib, that is, they are references to the younger Ibn al-Wardī or through him to Ibn Shabīb.

I am much perplexed by these two Ibn al-Wardī, supposed to follow each other at a distance of a century, for their names are far too much alike; I repeat them here for comparison, italicizing the parts which they do not have in common:

Zain al-dīn Abū Ḥafṣ 'Umar *ibn al-Muẓaffar* ibn al-Wardī al-Qurashī al-Bakrī al-Ma'arrī *al-Shāfi'ī* (d. 1349).

Sirāj al-dīn Abū Ḥafṣ 'Umar *ibn Muḥammad* ibn al-Wardī al-Qurashī al-Bakrī al-Ma'arrī *al-Ḥalabī* (fl. 1446).

According to Brockelmann, the names are even closer, for he calls both of them 'Umar ibn al-Muẓaffar. I call the second 'Umar ibn Muḥammad, as is done in the catalogue of Arabic books in the British Museum (2, 715, 1901). I have never come across two other Arabic names as closely alike as these two; they may have coalesced because of the confusion of the one man (or name) with the other.

Text. I cite editions of the texts mentioned above, not of other texts such as his Dīwān, or his most popular poem, Al-lāmīya fī-l-naṣīḥa or Naṣīḥat al-ikhwān, a moral poem rhyming in l addressed to his son.

The Maqāma fi-l-ṭā'ūn was published in the Majmū'at al-jawā'ib (Constantinople 1300 H. = 1882/83).

Al-alfīya al-Wardīya, on the interpretation of dreams, Cairo 1326 H. (= 1908/9) and other Cairene editions.

The grammar Al tuḥfa al-Wardīya is included in A collection of nine tracts on Arabic grammar (p. 88–114, Tellicherry 1881). New edition by Rudolf Abicht (Breslau 1891). Edition with commentary by 'Abd al-Qādir al-Afrāmī (or Ifrānī?): Mirqāt al-naḥw (Madras 1906).

Tatimmat al-mukhtaṣar fī akhbār al-bashar (2 vols., Cairo 1868). Second edition (4 vols., Constantinople 1870).

Criticism. Reinaud (1, 154, 1848). Wüstenfeld (no. 412, 1882). Brockelmann (2, 140, 1902; suppt. 2, 174–75, 1938). Moh. ben Cheneb: Ibn al-Wardī (EI 2, 427, 1918).

AL-DHAHABĪ

Shams al-dīn Abū 'Abdallāh Muḥammad ibn Aḥmad al-Dhahabī al-Turkumānī al-Shāfi'ī. Muslim-Turkish traditionist and historian (1274–1348).

The name Turkumānī recalls his Turkish ancestry. Al-Dhahabī was born at Damascus or at Mayyāfāriqīn in October 1274; he studied in Damascus under many teachers, then completed his education by sitting at the feet of many more in other places, such as Ba'albakk, Mekka, Ḥalab, Nābulus, Alexandria, Cairo. It is said that he had more than thirteen hundred teachers, the biographies of whom he collected in his Mu'jam. Such a statement is not as fantastic as it seems, for in the days when oral tradition was supreme, an inquisitive and zealous scholar would go from teacher to teacher, just as now he consults one book after another. Moreover, he may have counted as teachers the teachers of his teachers, etc. Finally he became himself a professor of ḥadīth in Damascus, and had many pupils of his own, one of whom, 'Abd al-Wahhāb ibn 'Alī Tāj al-dīn al-Subkī (1327–70), included his biography in the collection of biographies of Shāfi'ī theologians (Ṭabaqāt al-Shāfi'īya).

Al-Dhahabī was a famous student of history, fiqh, and ḥadīth, but, being struck with blindness c. 1342, he then devoted his time to collecting biographical and other historical information by oral tradition. He died in Damascus in February 1348 (or 1353?) and was buried near the Bāb al-ṣaghīr.

His works are so numerous that it would take too long to enumerate them all. I shall speak only of a few.

1. Al-mushtabih fī asmā' al-rijāl. Alphabetical dictionary of proper names occurring in the aḥādīth.

2. Mīzān al-i'tidāl fī naqd al-rijāl. Alphabetical dictionary of apocryphal or weak traditionists.

3. Tajrīd asmā al-ṣaḥāba. Dictionary of the Prophet's companions, derived from the Usd al-ghāba of Ibn al-Athīr (XIII-1).

4. Tahdhīb tahdhīb al-kamāl fī asmā' al-rijāl. Correction of correction of the names in the traditions recorded in the six canonical books (for a list of these see EI 2, 192). The origin of this compilation may be briefly told, as an example of many other literary developments in Islām. Abū 'Abdallāh Muḥammad ibn Maḥmūd Ibn al-Najjār (1183–1245) had written a collection of biographies of the traditionists entitled Kitāb al-kamāl fī ma'rifat al-rijāl. About a century later abundant corrections and additions to this work were collected by Jamāl al-dīn Yūsuf ibn al-Zakī al-Mizzī (d. 1341–42) and 'Alā' al-dīn Mughulṭā'ī ibn Qilij (d. 1361–62), under the title Kitāb al-tahdhīb, Book of correction (or adjustment). This enormous work (13 vols.) was abbreviated and corrected by al-Dhahabī; this was again corrected by Ibn Ḥajar al-'Asqalānī (1372–1449), who published a Kitāb tahdhīb al-tahdhīb. An abridgment of al-Dhahabī's work was made by Aḥmad ibn 'Abdallāh al-Khazrajī, entitled Khulāṣat tahdhīb al-tahdhīb fi asmā' al-rijāl.

Al-Dhahabī wrote various other works on ḥadīth, which was always his subject of predilection.

5. Mukhtaṣar li ta'rīkh Baghdād. Summary of the history of Baghdād by Muḥammad ibn Sa'īd Ibn al-Dubaithī (1163–1239).

6. Mukhtaṣar akhbār al-naḥwiyyīn li Ibn al-Qifṭī. Summary of the history of grammarians by Ibn al-Qifṭī (XIII-1), a work different from the latter's Ikhbār al-'ulamā, to which historians of science so often refer (Introd. 2, 684).

7. Ta'rīkh al-islām. History of Islām. This was al-Dhahabī's most ambitious work. It is a general history to 1300/1, completed by him in 1340. It was so large a work (in 12 or 20 vols.) that the MS tradition was very irregular. Though there are over 50 MSS, most of them represent only parts of the work, and among them they do not cover the whole text (the decades A.H. 131–40, 231–60, 281–300 are still missing; the decades A.H. 141–70, 261–80 are extant only in part). The MSS of Aya Sophia nos. 3005–14 are autographs of the author.

Unlike his great predecessors al-Ṭabarī (X-1), al-Mas'ūdī (X-1), Ibn al-Jauzī (XII-2), Ibn al-Athīr (XIII-1), whose histories though centered on Islām began with the Creation, extending respectively to A.D. 915, c. 950, 1180, and 1231, al-Dhahabī began his own account with the genealogy of the Prophet, completely neglecting earlier times. His method of exposition, however, is not very different from that used by Ibn al-Jauzī in the Kitāb al-muntaẓam, except that he separates the biographies (al-mutawaffūn) from the general history (al-ḥawādīth al-kā'ina). The history of those seven Muslim centuries (A.H. 1–700, A.D. 622–1300) is divided into 70 classes (ṭabaqāt) of 10 Muslim years each. For each class the general history is given first, then the biographies, covering on the average six or seven times more space (in some MSS all the biographies are put together). For the first three centuries, the account is largely a summary of the Ta'rīkh al-rusul wal-mulūk of al-Ṭabarī; for the following four centuries (A.H. 301–700, A.D. 913–1300), the account is much longer, and the authorities are duly quoted. For each decennial period the author relates the general history of Islām, then the local history of various centers (chiefly Baghdād and Damascus), then the curiosities ('ajā'ib), finally the biographies of the people who died during that period. Al-Dhahabī was specially interested in the history of the Saljūq and Ayyūbī dynasties, and he gave a very valuable account of the tragic events of the Mongol invasion. Though he had necessarily more and better information concerning Syria and Egypt than other countries, and was also better informed concerning Eastern than Western Islām, yet he paid more attention to Western Islām than al-Ṭabarī and even Ibn al-Athīr. He was interested also in Islamic religious divergencies, such as Bāṭinīya and Shī'a.[19] He threw some light on the economic vicissitudes of Baghdād and Damascus, quoting prices of commodities, etc.

The curiosities or wonders ('ajā'ib) include astronomical and meteorological events, droughts, famines, earthquakes (1067/68, 1157, 1169/70). His account of the terrible events of 1200–1 in the Near East (famines, plague, earthquake) is particularly full. Other curiosities are of the kind which always appeal to the man in the street, anywhere, such as the story of a sorcerer, the appearance of an elephant in Damascus, a Baghdād woman who had double twins, etc.

The biographies are very abundant but vary considerably in length. Many are devoted to poets, theologians, and other scholars, but it is not known how many, if any, are devoted to scientists, such as astronomers or physicians.

In addition to the four historians already quoted, al-Dhahabī made full use also of the Kitāb mir'āt al-zamān fī ta'rīkh al-a'yān of Sibṭ Ibn al-Jauzī (XIII-1), a chronicle from the creation to 1256 (Ibn al-Athīr's stopped in 1231). His other sources are too abundant to be enumerated here (see J. R. A. S. 1932, p. 850–55).

On account of its enormous size, discouraging copyists, the Ta'rīkh al-islām was often abbreviated by the author himself, by Taqī al-dīn Ibn Qāḍī Shubha (d. 1448), by Ibn al-Shammā' al-Ḥalabī (d. 1529), by Ildukuz al-Ayyūbī. The abbreviations prepared by al-Dhahabī extended to the whole text, as in the Kitāb duwal al-islām (or al-ta'rīkh al-ṣaghīr) and the Kitāb al-'ibar fī akhbār al-bashar mimman 'abar (or al-ta'rīkh al-awsaṭ, or al-mutawassiṭ), or were restricted to the biographies, as in the Ṭabaqāt al-ḥuffāẓ, Ṭabaqāt al-qurrā, Siyar al-nubalā. There are also a num-

[19] Too long to explain here. For Bāṭinīya, seekers of the inner meaning of the Qur'ān, see B. Carra de Vaux (EI 1, 679, 1911), also my Introd. 1, 593. As to the Shī'a, general name for a group of Muslim sects recognizing 'Alī as the legitimate caliph after the death of the Prophet, see R. Strothmann (EI 4, 350–58, 1926). Shī'a doctrines have often been referred to by me in previous volumes (see index), but not discussed.

ber of continuations: by al-Dhahabī, additional biographies to 1340; by Aḥmad ibn 'Abd al-raḥīm al-'Irāqī (d. 1423) to 1384/85; by Ibn Qāḍī Shubha, etc. Finally, there are translations of the Ta'rīkh al-islām, either partial or abridged, in Persian and Turkish.

8. A treatise entitled Al-ṭibb al-nabawī (or nabī), Medicine of the Prophet, has been ascribed to al-Dhahabī, but in my opinion unconvincingly. That title appears many times in Arabic literature; so much so that Ḥājjī Khalīfa devotes a special section to it (4, 131, 1845), "'ilm ṭibb al-nabī." He ascribes such treatises to Abū Nu'aim Aḥmad ibn 'Abdallāh al-Iṣfahānī (d. 1038/39), to Abū-l-'Abbās Ja'far ibn Muḥammad al-Mustaghfirī (d. 1040/41), to Jalāl al-dīn 'Abd al-Raḥmān ibn abī Bakr al-Suyūṭī (d. 1505), and to four others, but not to al-Dhahabī. On the other hand, the text translated by A. Perron (1860)—the only one I have examined—ascribed by him to one Jalāl al-dīn Abū Sulaimān Dā'ūd is not the kind of text one would expect from a historian and traditionist. It includes a few traditions concerning the Prophet, but not more than might be found in any general medical book written by a Muslim. It is certainly not a book of medical traditions concerning the Prophet, but an elaborate medical treatise which can only have been composed by a physician. It is divided into three parts: (I) medical generalities, hygiene; (II) medicines and foods, that is, an abundant materia medica beginning with general views on practical medicine and the qualities required in a physician; (III) treatment of diseases and prophylaxy. Of course al-Dhahabī may have written an entirely different treatise bearing the same title, but such a treatise has not yet been produced.

Text. 1. Kitāb al-mushtabih. Edited by Pieter de Jong (614 p., Leiden 1863–81).

2. Mīzān al-i'tidāl. Edited by Maulavī Muḥammad Khādim Ḥusain (2 vols., lithog., Lucknow 1884). Other edition, Cairo 1907/8.

3. Tajrīd asmā' al-ṣaḥāba. Printed in Haidarābād (1898).

4. Khulāṣat tahdhīb al-tahdhīb. Abridgment by Aḥmad ibn 'Abdallāh al-Khazrajī, with various glosses (500 p., Būlāq 1884).

August Fischer: Biographien von Gewährsmännern des Ibn Isḥāq, hauptsächlich aus al-Dhahabī (134 p., Leiden 1890); Neue Auszüge aus al-Dhahabī und Ibn al-Najjār (Zeitschrift der Deutschen morgenländischen Gesellschaft 44, 401–45, 1890).

5, 6. Unpublished.

7. Ta'rīkh al-islām. There is no complete edition, but various biographies have been edited, e.g., that of Ibn Rushd by Ernest Renan in his Averroës (app. IV, p. 456–62, stereotyped ed. 1869). The Ṭabaqāt al-ḥuffāẓ (classes of those who know the traditions by heart) was edited by Ferdinand Wüstenfeld: Liber classium virorum qui Korani et traditionum cognitione excelluerunt (3 parts, lith., Göttingen 1833/34).

Kitāb duwal al-islām (2 vols., 566 p., Haidarābād 1919; Isis 8, 542).

8. The apocryphal Al-ṭibb al-nabawī in its first edition (120 p., lith., Cairo 1870?) is ascribed to al-Dhahabī. It was reprinted with the same ascription in the margins of the Tashīl al-manāfi', a compendium of medicine of Ibrāhīm ibn 'Abd al-raḥmān al-Azraqī (Cairo 1887).

French translation by A. Perron: La médecine du Prophète (Gazette médicale de l'Algérie; reprint 228 p., Alger 1860), who ascribed the text to Jalāl al-dīn Abū Sulaimān Dā'ūd.

Criticism. Wüstenfeld (no. 410, 1882). Brockelmann (2, 46–48, 1902; suppt. 2, 45–47, 1938). Mohammed ben Cheneb (EI 1, 954–55, 1912).

Joseph de Somogyi: The Ta'rīkh al-islām of adh-Dhahabī (Journal of the Royal Asiatic Society, 1932, p. 815–55; Isis 19, 534); Ein arabisches Kompendium der Weltgeschichte, das Kitāb duwal al-islām (Islamica 5, 334–53, 1932); The Ta'rīkh al-islām as an authority on the Mongol invasion of the Caliphate (Journal of the Royal Asiatic Society, 1936, p. 595–604; Isis 27, 127); Ein arabischer Bericht über die Tataren im Ta'rīkh al-islām (Der Islam 24, 105–30, 1937). Farmer (no. 221, p. 53, 1940), apropos of a treatise of Dhahabī's on the knowledge of melodies, fī ma'rifat al-anghām, in verse. The Paris MS 2480 contains a staff of eight lines in colors for musical notation. Farmer refers also (no. 230) to another musical treatise, Kitāb fī 'ilm al-mūsīqā wa ma'rifat al-anghām (Science of music and knowledge of melodies), by Muḥammad ibn Muḥmamad ibn Aḥmad al-Dhahabī Ibn al-Ṣabbāḥ, who was probably a son of al-Dhahabī dealt with in this note.

D3. 'Irāq

IBN AL-ṬIQṬAQĀ

'Irāqī Shī'a writer on politics and history (fl. beginning of fourteenth century).

Abū Ja'far Jalāl al-dīn (or Ṣafī al-dīn) Muḥammad ibn 'Alī ibn Ṭabāṭabā Ibn al-Ṭiqṭaqā (or Ṭiqṭaqī) was a descendant of the orthodox caliph 'Alī, through al-Ḥasan and Ibrāhīm Ṭabāṭabā. His father, 'Alī, representing the 'Alī interests in 'Irāq, was the victim of a political murder in 1281. Ibn al-Ṭiqṭaqā was born c. 1262, continued his father's political mission in al-Ḥilla, Najaf, and Kerbelā, married a woman from Khorāsān, traveled to Marāgha in 1297 and in 1301/2 to Mūṣul, where he was detained by inclement weather. Nothing is known of him after that date.

During his forced sojourn in Mūṣul he wrote the book which immortalized him, dedicating it to the Mongol governor of that city, Fakhr al-dīn 'Īsā. Hence the book is called Kitāb al-fakhrī[20] fī-l-ādāb al-sulṭānīya wal-duwal al-islāmīya.

The Fakhrī is divided into two parts, the first being a political treatise (a kind of speculum regale or instructio principum), the second, a history of the Muslim dynasties from 'Alī (656) to the end of the 'Abbāsī caliphate (1258). That history is derived from lost works of al-Mas'ūdī (X-1), from chronicles of Muḥammad ibn Yaḥyā al-Ṣūlī (d. 946) and Hilāl ibn al-Muḥsin al Ṣābī (d. 1056) (see Isis 5, 496), above all from the Kāmil of Ibn al-Athīr (XIII-1). The author does not deal only with the caliphs, but also with their wuzarā'.

The Fakhrī is a very distinguished book; it is well and simply written, sufficiently critical and anecdotic, moderate, practical-minded, agreeable to read. It is also remarkably impartial in spite of the author's Shī'a convictions. To be sure, those convictions made it easy for him to criticize the 'Abbāsī rulers, yet he was not afraid to speak of the atrocities of the sack of Baghdād by the Mongols (February 13–20, 1258). This is the more creditable when we remember that the book was dedicated to a Mongol governor representing the īl-khān Ghāzān Maḥmūd (ruled 1295–1304).

It was soon translated into Persian under the title Tajārib al-salaf, by Hindushāh ibn Sanjar al-Kīrānī for an atābek of Lūristān before 1323.

Text. Extracts printed and translated by Silvestre de Sacy: Chrestomathie arabe (vol. 1, 1806). Other extracts in Arabic and French by Auguste Cherbonneau in Journal asiatique (7, 297–359; 8, 316–38, 1846; 9, 134–47, 1847). Arabic edition by Wilhelm Ahlwardt (456 p., Gotha 1860). Better edition by Hartwig Deren-

[20] Because of that title it was wrongly ascribed to Fakhr al-dīn al-Rāzī (XII-2). It is far more usual for Arabic titles to refer in that way to a patron than to the author.

bourg (548 p., Bibliothèque de l'Ecole des hautes études, sci. phil. fasc. 105, Paris 1895). Other editions, Cairo 1900, 1927, London 1921 (printed Cairo).

French translation by Emile Amar (Archives marocaines vol. 16, 674 p., Paris 1910), carefully annotated and indexed.

Criticism. Wüstenfeld (no. 375a, 1881). Brockelmann (2, 161, 1902; suppt. 2, 201, 1938). Cl. Huart (EI 2, 423, 1918). Browne (2, 463–65, 1906); The Tajaribu's-salaf (Journal of the Royal Asiatic Society, centenary suppt. p. 245–54, 1924). Sarkis (col. 146, 1930).

'ABD AL-RAZZĀQ AL-SHAIBĀNĪ

Kamāl al-dīn abū-l-Faḍā'il 'Abd al-Razzāq ibn Aḥmad ibn Muḥammad, called Ibn al-Fūṭī[21] al-Baghdādī. 'Irāqī historian and librarian (1244–1323).

He was born in Baghdād, June 26, 1244, in a middle-class family. He was a pupil of 'Alī ibn Anjab Ibn al-Sā'ī al-Baghdādī (1197–1275), librarian to the khalīfa al-Mustanṣir (ruled 1226–42). At the time of Hūlāgū's sack of Baghdād, in 1258, he was made a prisoner, being then 14 years old, and sent to Adharbāijān. He was soon liberated by Nāṣir al-dīn al-Ṭūsī (XIII-2), who took him into his service. He spent some 13 years in Marāgha, being the librarian of the observatory. I do not know whether his librarianship ended before Nāṣir al-dīn's death (in 1274) or after; in the second case he would have been a witness of the last days of that institution, which did not outlast Nāṣir al-dīn's sons. He finally returned to his native city, where he continued his studies and writings, and where he died on January 13, 1323.

He wrote in Arabic a number of chronicles:

1. Al-ḥawādith al-jāmi'a wal-tajārib al-nāfi'a min al-mi'a al-sābi'a, dealing with the last 'Abbāsī caliphs, and the beginning of the Mongol domination to 1300.

2. Majma' al-ādāb fī mu'jam al-asmā' wal-alqāb, a kind of biographical dictionary in 50 volumes, of which only one ('ain to qāf) exists. Autograph MS in the Dār al-kutub al-Ẓāhirīya in Damascus.

3. Mukhtaṣar akhbār al-khulafā' al-'Abbāsīyīn. Collection of stories concerning the 'Abbāsī caliphate, written as a continuation or complement to a similar work by his teacher Ibn al-Sā'ī, which was itself a continuation of the Kāmil of Ibn al-Athīr (XIII-1). There is in the Bibliothèque nationale of Paris a partial copy of the Kāmil written by Ibn al-Fūṭī.

He was the author of many other works, historical and philological, which seem to be completely lost.

He was an annalist and anecdotist more than a historian, but his writings are very valuable because there are but few Arabic witnesses of the Mongol period in 'Irāq and Persia which have come down to us. He had watched the terrible events of Hūlāgū's time, been acquainted with the early Mongol chieftains, and later with more civilized rulers from Arghūn to Abū Sa'īd, when the Mongol ferocity was gradually tempered with Islām.

Text. No. 1 was printed in Baghdād 1932.

Criticism. Brockelmann (suppt. 1, 590, 1937; suppt. 2, 202, 1938). The shaykh Muḥammad Riḍā al Shabībī devoted a lecture to 'Abd al-Razzāq in the School of Law of Baghdād, April 23, 1940. That lecture was published in Baghdād but has not reached me. I know it only through a long summary in Al-mustami' al-'arabī (London, Feb. 21, 1941).

[21] Or Fuwaṭī. Mentioned in Introd. 2, 1005, where his name is wrongly spelled Fūtī instead of Fūṭī.

D4. Persia (Histories in Persian)

RASHĪD AL-DĪN

Persian physician, historian, and patron of learning; wrote in Persian and Arabic (1247–1318).

Contents: (1) Life. (2) His learning and patronage of learning. (3) His universal history. (4) Rashīd Ṭabīb, his medical activities. (5) His views on alchemy. (6) His other writings. (7) Systematic diffusion of his works. (8) Note on the Tabrīz school of painting.
(9) Text. (10) Criticism.

1. *Life*

Abū-l-Khair Rashīd al-dīn Faḍl Allāh ibn 'Imād al-dawla al-Hamadānī. Often called Rashīd al-dīn Ṭabīb. He was born c. 1247 in Hamadān (Arabic, Hamadhān; Greek, Ecbatana). His grandfather, Muwaffaq al-dawla 'Alī, had been, together with the great astronomer Nāṣir al-dīn al-Ṭūsī, an unwilling guest of the "Assassins"[22] in their stronghold of Alamūt (near Qazwīn); when Alamūt was captured by the Mongols in 1256, both were taken into Hūlāgū's service. Rashīd al-dīn was also in the service of the īl-khān of Persia, first of Abāgā (ruled 1265–81), being his physician and adviser. His prestige and power increased, and during the rule of Ghāzān Maḥmūd (1295–1304), the greatest of the Mongol rulers of Persia, he became prime minister in 1298. In 1303 he accompanied Ghāzān as Arabic secretary during the latter Syrian campaign, and being in 'Āna on the Euphrates in the spring of that year, he introduced to the īl-khān the historian Waṣṣāf ('Abdallāh ibn Faḍlallāh of Shīrāz). His favor and wealth continued to increase under Ghāzān's successors, but the jealousy, hatred, and intrigues of his enemies increased in proportion, and one of them, 'Alī shāh,[23] finally succeeded in having him demoted (October 1317). Rashīd al-dīn was accused of having poisoned the īl-khān Uljāi'tū (d. 1316)—a doctor failing to cure his royal patient might easily be accused of having caused his death—and he and his son Ibrāhīm were executed on July 18, 1318; their property confiscated, their pious foundations robbed, etc. Another son of Rashīd al-dīn, Ghiyāth al-dīn, was put to death in 1336.

At the time of his persecution Rashīd al-dīn was accused of being a Jew, but it has never been proved that he had Jewish origins. A century later Jalāl al-dīn Mirān shāh (d. 1407/8), a son of Tīmūr Lang, caused the remains of Rashīd al-d n to be exhumed and reburied in the Jewish cemetery.

2. *His learning and patronage of learning*

Rashīd al-dīn offers perhaps the best example of prodigious success followed by complete and abject destruction. The wheel of fortune turned fast in Oriental courts, but no illustration of it is more striking than the case of Rashīd al-dīn, because the latter was successful not only in the material but also in the spiritual sense (this probably aggravated the jealousies against him).

He had accumulated an immense fortune and used part of it to build a suburb of the new īl-khān capital, Sulṭānīyah in Jibāl (founded by Arghūn 1284–91 and

[22] Ismā'īlī, see Introd. 1, 752, 593; 2, 1001.

[23] 'Alī shāh was a colleague of Rashīd al-dīn; it is said that he was the first minister of the Mongol īl-khān to die a natural death (Browne 3, 71). This was probably due to the "accident" of his dying in bed early enough in 1324.

completed by Uljāi'tū 1305); that suburb, a little town in itself, was called after him Rashīdīya. In Tabrīz, which was also a great cosmopolite center of Mongol Persia, he built another suburb, also called after himself, Rab'-i-Rashīdī, which included 24 caravansaries, 1,500 shops, and 30,000 houses, mills, baths, mosques, an elaborate hospital (dār al-shifā) with all kinds of specialists brought from India, China, Egypt, and Syria. There were gathered 6,000 to 7,000 students, and there were enough theologians to fill a whole street, the kūcha-i-'ulamā'. Water had been brought to the suburb from the river Sarāw-rūd through aqueducts hewn in the rocks. He gave to the Rab'-i-Rashīdī a library of 60,000 volumes.

Town planning may have been partly speculative, but, as we have seen, he also built mosques, libraries, hospitals, and endowed pious foundations and libraries. His expenses for the copying of books, translations, illustrations, maps amounted to 60,000 dīnār.

He was very learned in many fields and a true polyglot. He wrote mainly in Persian, but also in Arabic; and it is said that he had some knowledge of Mongolian, Uighūr (Turkish),[24] Hebrew, and even Chinese. It seems unlikely that he was himself able to use Mongolian or Chinese documents, but he was aware of their importance and of the need of taking them into account. In the reading of the Mongolian chronicle Altan däptär he was helped by Pūlād-čink-sānk and perhaps by Ghāzān; he obtained also the collaboration of at least one Hindu scholar and two Chinese ones. He was certainly aware of many peculiarities of the Chinese dialects and of the script serving for them all.[25]

Such learning seems less incredible than it would be otherwise if one remembers the extraordinary mixture of Asiatic peoples caused by the Mongol invasion and continued throughout the Yüan dynasty (1280–1368). It will suffice to recall that Hūlāgū (1256–65) is said to have employed a thousand Chinese engineers in his conquest of Persia and 'Irāq, and that on the other hand Kublai Khān (1257–94) engaged Persian technicians, such as A-lao-wa-ting and I-ssŭ-ma-yin, and that the sons of these men, Ma-ho-sha and Ya-ku, remained in the Mongol service (Introd. 2, 765, and by index). Moreover, polyglot traditions can be traced in Central Asia to earlier times, witness the statement of al-Bīrūnī (XI-1) in his pharmacopoeia (Isis 20, 454).

3. *His universal history*

Rashīd al-dīn's main work is a large historical collection originally composed in Persian, the Jāmi' al-tawārīkh (Collection of histories), comparable in importance and dimension to the Kitāb akhbār al-rusul wal-mulūk, the Arabic annals of al-Ṭabarī (X-1). It is perhaps more important, because of the use made of materials not only Arabic and Persian but also Uighūr, Mongolian, and Chinese. As to size, in spite of the fact that we do not have the complete text, what we have extends over 600,000 words.

The first part of the work, dealing with Mongolian history, was undertaken at the request of Ghāzān Maḥmūd (d. 1304); it was finished only after Ghāzān's death, in 1306, but Ghāzān's successor, Uljāi'tū, to whom it was presented, respected the original dedication, and that part is sometimes entitled Ta'rīkh-i-ghāzānī.

[24] His Persian writings include an unusually large number of Turkish words or idioms.

[25] This appears very clearly in his preface to the (Persian) Tānksūqnāmah discovered in Hagia Sophia and discussed below in section 4, Rashīd Ṭabīb.

The whole work was completed in 1310. A supplement dealing with Uljāi'tū (1304–16) was added in 1312.

According to Browne (3, 73), the contents are briefly as follows:

"Vol. I, ch. i. History of the different Turkish and Mongol tribes, their divisions, genealogies, pedigrees, legends, etc., in a preface and four sections. Ch. ii. History of Chingīz Khān, his ancestors and successors, down to Ghāzān Khān. Vol. II, Preface. On Adam and the Patriarchs and Hebrew Prophets. Part 1. History of the ancient kings of Persia before Islām, in four sections. Part 2. History of the Prophet Muḥammad and of the Caliphate, down to its extinction by the Mongols in 1258; of the post-Muhammadan Persian dynasties of Persia, viz. the Sultans of Ghazna, the Seljūqs, the Khwārazmshāhs, the Salgharid Atābeks of Fārs, and the Isma'īlīs of the West and of the East; of Oghuz and his descendants, the Turks; of the Chinese; of the Jews; of the Franks and their Emperors and Popes; and of the Indians, with a long and full account of Sakyamuni (Buddha) and of the religion which he founded."

This is not only the greatest historical work written in Persian (Arabic copies were soon put in circulation as well as the Persian ones), but also the earliest universal history in any language, for it includes records concerning Europe, the Near East, Central Asia, the Far East. The part dealing with Mongolian history was especially precious, for that subject had been very meagerly dealt with in the (Arabic) Kāmil of Ibn al-Athīr (XIII-1) to 1231 and in the (Persian) Niẓām al-tawārīkh of al-Baiḍāwī (XIII-2) to 1275, and the very valuable Persian chronicle of al-Juwainī (XIII-2), Ta'rīkh-i-jahān gushā, extended only to the middle of the thirteenth century. Rashīd al-dīn's work is our most important source for the study of Chingiz Khān (XIII-1), of Kublai Khān (XIII-2), of Nāṣir al-dīn al-Ṭūsī (XIII-2), and others (see Introd. vol. 2 by index). In addition, it helps us to understand the complicated Isma'īlī affairs, the obscure history of Chinese Islām, etc. We would not consult such a work for European affairs, yet the author's information concerning them is instructive. He was aware of the struggles between popes and emperors, knew that Scotland paid tribute to England, and that there are no snakes in Ireland.

The Jāmi al-tawārīkh contains a clear and elaborate account of Chinese block printing, the earliest notice of such printing,[26] except with regard to paper money; but Rashīd al-dīn saw in this only a means of authenticating historical documents and preserving them in their integrity, rather than a means of diffusing them. Curiously enough, some block printing occurred at Tabrīz in 1294. Both Rashīd al-dīn and Marco Polo must have known of it. It was an issue of paper money with text printed in Chinese and Arabic; the Chinese characters show that this was an imitation of the paper money published by Kublai Khān. The money had to be promptly withdrawn, however, because of the popular uproar against it. Because of that issue, Tabrīz is the only Islamic place where there is a clear, if ephemeral, record of early block printing.[27]

As to the originality of Rashīd al-dīn vs. his fellow Tabrīzī and contemporary al-Banākatī, especially with regard to printing, see my note on the latter.

[26] The relevant text given in chapter VII is taken from al-Banākatī, not from Rashīd al-dīn, but that amounts to the same thing. See article on al-Banākatī.

[27] Carter (p. 128, 1925). Karl Jahn: Das iranische Papiergeld. Ein Beitrag zur Kultur- und Wirtschaftsgeschichte Īrān's in der Mongolenzeit (Archiv orientální 10, 308–40, 1940).

4. *Rashīd Ṭabīb, his medical activities*

Rashīd was a practical physician, employed as such by the īl-khān court. It is probable that when he became prime minister his medical practice had to be stopped or considerably reduced, but some of his letters (no. 7 in the list below) show that he was deeply interested in the organization of hospitals (e.g., in Tabrīz, Shīrāz, Hamadān). He took pains to obtain all kinds of drugs and aromatic oils for the hospital which he had founded in Rab'-i-Rashīdī. These drugs were obtained not only from various Persian localities, but also from 'Irāq, Asia Minor, Syria, India, and even China. Other letters evidence his desire to reward many learned men, not only in the East, but also in Spain and North Africa!

Leclerc (2, 134) ascribes to Rashīd al-dīn a treatise on the advantages and disadvantages of various kinds of food and clothing written for Arghūn Khān, who ruled from 1284 to 1291 (MS in Copenhagen).

One of the most curious writings included in the Rashīdī collection (Jāmi' al-taṣānīf al-Rashīdī) remains to be considered. It is an encyclopaedia of Chinese medicine and government in four volumes. Rashīd al-dīn had realized the importance of Chinese medicine, hitherto unknown in Persia, and had charged a number of translators and copyists to prepare a corpus of it in Persian, Arabic, and Chinese. The four volumes were devoted respectively to (1) Chinese medicine, theory and practice, (2) Chinese materia medica, (3) Mongolian materia medica, (4) theory and practice of Mongolian government. A MS of the Persian translation of volume I has been discovered recently (1939) by Dr. A. Süheil Ünver in the Hagia Sophia library, Istanbul, bearing the title Tānksūqnāmah[28]-i Īlkhān dar funūn-i-'ulūm-i khiṭā'ī (Treasure of the īl-khān on the sciences of Cathay). It was copied at Tabrīz in 1313–14 by Muḥammad ibn Aḥmad ibn Maḥmūd Qawwām al-Kirmānī (who is known to have been one of the copyists employed by Rashīd al-dīn). The volume begins with an introduction explaining the high value of medicine among other sciences, the characteristics of different climates and their influence upon men of different nations, the superiority of the Chinese ideographic writing because of its independence of phonetics and its consequent internationalism, and the excellence of Chinese medicine. Then follow physical and metaphysical discussions, treatises on the pulse, the anatomy of the head, embryology and pregnancy. This volume is entitled in Arabic script Wānk shū khū, which is obviously a transcription of Wang Shu-ho (III-2), name of a famous Chinese physician who lived at the time of the western Chin dynasty (265–317) and composed a treatise on the pulse, Mo ching, in ten books (Introd. 1, 342; 2, 76; Isis 15, 202, 1931). Thus Wang Shu-ho was one of the sources of the Ilkhanic encyclopaedia of medicine, but the real nature of the borrowing (translation, selection, adaptation?) cannot be evaluated until the Chinese and Persian texts have been carefully collated.

5. *His views on alchemy*

In his biography of Hūlāgū Khān, Rashīd al-dīn praises him for his activities as a builder of palaces and especially of the observatory of Marāgha (about which see my note on Nāṣir al-dīn al-Ṭūsī, XIII-2, Introd. 2, 1004; Chinese astronomers

[28] The word tānksūqnāmah does not occur in Steingass' Persian dictionary (which has tansūq and tansūkh), but my young friend Aydin Sayili has found it in the Hibat al-ḥaqā'iq, a Turkish book written in the Uighūr script probably at the beginning of the twelfth century, edited by Najīb 'Āsim in Uighūr script and in Arabic transcription (p. 11 in the Uigbūr text, and p. 30, 108 in the Arabic. Istanbul 1915/16).

were working there together with their Persian colleagues). He praises him also for his love of philosophy and science, but blames him for his interest in alchemy. That fragment (Quatremère p. 401–3) is interesting because it gives some idea of an alchemical laboratory in Mongol Persia, and illustrates Rashīd-al-dīn's rationalism, for to him the alchemists surrounding Hūlāgū were nothing but quacks and knaves.

6. *His other writings*

1. The Kitāb al-aḥyā wal-athār (Book of animals and monuments) has not yet been recovered, but we know that it was a collection, divided into 24 chapters, of data concerning meteorology, agriculture, arboriculture, apiculture, the destruction of insects and other pests, farming, stockbreeding, architecture, fortification, shipbuilding, mining, and metallurgy.

2. The Tawḍīḥāt (Explanations) is a treatise on mystical theology, arranged in the form of 19 letters with a preface. It was written for Uljāi'tū (ruled 1304–16).

3. The Miftāḥ al-tafāsīr (Key to the commentaries) is a book on Qur'ān exegesis wherein the fundamental questions of Islamic theology are discussed. It includes a refutation of metempsychosis, which suggests that that Hindu doctrine was then sufficiently acclimatized in Persia to need refutation.

4. Laṭā'if al-ḥaqā'iq (Subtle truths), 14 letters on theology beginning with an account of a vision experienced by the author on April 11, 1306; he then dreamed that he was presented to the Prophet.

5. Al-risāla al-sulṭānīya. Account of a theological discussion which took place in Uljāi'tū's presence. Written on March 14, 1307.

Nos. 2 to 5 exist in a single Paris MS dated 1310–11, in Arabic, under the general title Majmū'a-i-Rashīdīya. These four texts show that Rashīd al-dīn was much engrossed with theology in Uljāi'tū's time. Apparently his enemies had tried to undermine his power by impeaching his orthodoxy, for there exists a defense of the latter signed by seventy leading 'ulamā.

6. Bayān al-ḥaqā'iq (Elucidation of truths), 17 letters on theology, smallpox, the nature and kinds of heat, etc. Lost.

7. Collection of 53 letters addressed to his sons and other high officials, arranged and edited by his secretary, Muḥammad of Abarqūh (in Fārs, about halfway between Iṣṭakhr and Yazd). They deal with politics, finance, medicine (see medical section above). A register of these letters is given by Browne (3, 80–86).

7. *Systematic diffusion of his works*

One of the most original aspects of Rashīd al-dīn's personality is revealed to us by the multiple measures which he took in order to diffuse and preserve his writings. This is, I believe, unique in mediaeval history. It is not enough to remark that he could do it because of his great wealth, for he might have used his wealth in many other ways, and it is very remarkable that he used a part of it for that singular purpose. He caused several copies of his works to be made and circulated among his friends, who were encouraged to copy them; the Arabic works were translated into Persian and vice versa, and copies were circulated in both languages and deposited in the mosque at Rab'-i-Rashīdī. He ordered collected editions of his works, fully illustrated, to be prepared under the general title Jāmi' al-taṣānīf al-Rashīdī and deposited in public libraries (presumably mosques). He created an endowment the revenues of which were used to make two complete copies of his collected works every year, the one in Arabic, the other in Persian. These additional copies were to be presented to the cathedral mosques of the chief Islamic cities. A number of precautions were taken to make sure that these copies were carefully collated with the originals, well written, bound, etc., and distributed in the best manner. Each copy included a prayer for Rashīd al-dīn composed by himself. Each lecturer supported by his foundation was obliged to prepare new copies, etc.

In short, Rashīd al-dīn had planned in considerable detail a system which would insure the preservation of his works in their integrity, but he had not foreseen that he would be disgraced, his family destroyed,[29] his endowments confiscated, and his noblest purpose systematically traversed. Thus the text of his main work, the universal history, has not reached us in its integrity. There are many MSS of it, however, some of which are illustrated with such beautiful miniatures that they must be taken into account in every history of Persian art.

Considering on the one hand his idée fixe, the wish to transmit to posterity correct and authenticated copies of his works, and on the other hand his knowledge of the best method of doing that, Chinese block printing, it is curious that he did not think of applying that method to his purpose. If he had thought of that, the further development of Islamic (and Christian) culture might have been different; as a matter of fact, the Islamic world seems to have stopped, rather than helped, the westward diffusion of the printing art.

8. *Note on the Tabrīz school of painting*

It was in all probability thanks to the patronage of Rashīd al-dīn that an original school of painting developed in Tabrīz at the beginning of the fourteenth century. At any rate, a good many miniatures were made there at his expense to illustrate "de luxe" copies of his history presented to Mongol princes or famous sanctuaries. Magnificent copies of his history are extant today in the Bibliothèque nationale, Paris, in the libraries of Edinburgh University and of the Royal Asiatic Society, London, and perhaps in other places. The miniatures of these MSS are remarkable because of their obvious originality, their rich range of colors, and also because of the foreign influences which they reveal. These influences came from the East and also from the West. Byzantine, Italian traits can be easily recognized, as well as other particularities which are unmistakably Chinese (e.g., plates LI, LIX, LX, LXI, in Blochet). The Chinese influences confirm the scientific influences mentioned before; the Italian influences were probably due to the Christian missionaries who brought with them illustrated Bibles or Gospels.

The miniatures of the Tabrīz studio are important in themselves, but even more so because they helped to shape the future evolution of Persian art. They also continued the Rashīdī tradition, for the existence of illustrated copies of the history of the Mongols made in Tabrīz excited the emulation of later artists. For example, there is an illustrated MS of that history made in Delhi late in the sixteenth century (Pozzi collection, Paris; Blochet pls. CLXXXIII–V). The Delhi illustrations are more complex, more sophisticated than the Tabrīz ones, but far less beautiful.

Edgar Blochet: Musulman painting (136 p., 200 pl., London 1929). Eustache de Lorey: L'école de Tabriz. L'Islam aux prises avec la Chine (Revue des arts

[29] He enumerated fourteen sons and four daughters; I do not know what happened to each of them.

asiatiques 9, 27–39, 6 pl., Paris 1935). Arthur Upham Pope: A survey of Persian art (Oxford Press 1938–39).

8. *Text*

It is probable that an edition of Rashīd al-dīn's history was printed in Constantinople in 1714, being one of the only two books printed in Islām (outside of China) before 1825 (Carter p. 113, 232).

Etienne Marc Quatremère: Histoire des Mongols de la Perse (vol. 1, folio de luxe, Imprimerie royale, Paris 1836), no more published. Persian text and French translation with abundant notes, to Hūlāgū inclusive. The first part of the book is an elaborate and well documented biography of Rashīd al-dīn, which is the source of all later biographies.

The late Edward G. Browne had made plans for a complete critical edition in Persian, to include 7 vols. Two of these volumes have been admirably edited by Edgar Blochet: Introduction à l'histoire des Mongols (Gibb memorial series vol. 12, 398 p., Leyden 1910); Djami el-tévarikh, Histoire générale du monde par Fadl Allah Rashid ed-Din. Tarikh-i moubarek-i Ghazani, Histoire des Mongols. Tome II. Contenant l'histoire des empereurs mongols successeurs de Tchinkkiz Khaghan (same series, vol. 18, 690 p., Leyden 1911), Persian text with notes in French and many Arabic, Persian, Mongol, and Chinese references. A note in front of that volume announces that vol. 3, including the history of the Mongols of Persia, is printing, and that vol. 1, including the history of Turkish tribes and Chingiz Khān (XIII-1), will appear later.

The history of Ghāzān Maḥmūd (ruled 1295–1304), included in the Ta'rīkh-i-mubārak-i-Ghāzānī, has been edited from the MSS in Istanbul, London, Paris, and Vienna by Karl Jahn (Gibb memorial series vol. 14, 44 p. in German, 388 in Persian, 1940), critical edition with indexes.

Sir Henry Yule: Cathay under the Mongols, in Cathay (2d ed., 3, 107–33, 1914), English extracts based on the French translations by Jules Klaproth (Journal asiatique 11, 335–58, 447–70, 1833) and by Constantin Mouradgea d'Ohsson, in the latter's Histoire des Mongols (Paris 1824; reprinted La Haye 1834–45).

Tanksuknamei ilhan der fünunu ulûmu hatai mukaddimesi. Turkish translation of the Persian version of Chinese medicine, edited by Süheil Ünver, with preface by Baki Gölpinarli (72 p., many plates, Istanbul 1939; Isis 31, 152). The illustrations reproduced from the Hagia Sophia Persian MS 3596 are typically Chinese; compare with the illustrations in Isis (14, 255–63, 1930).

Criticism. Franz von Erdmann: Vollständige Übersicht der ältesten türkischen, tatarischen und mogholischen Völkerstämme nach Raschid ud-din's Vorgange bearbeitet (190 p., Kasan 1841). Henry Yule: An endeavour to elucidate Rashid-uddin's geographical notices of India (Royal Asiatic Society, 17 p., Nov. 1869). Leclerc (2, 133–34, 1876). Brockelmann (2, 200, 1902; suppt. 2, 273, 1938).

E. G. Browne: Suggestions for a complete edition of the Jami'u't-tawarikh (Journal of the Royal Asiatic Society, 1908, p. 17–37); Literary history of Persia (chiefly 3, 68–87, 1920); Arabian medicine (p. 103–29, 1921) or the French translation of that work by H. P. J. Renaud (p. 116–23, 1933).

Ferrand (2, 361–62, 1914). Carra de Vaux (1, 204–11, 1921). Carter (1925). Paul Pelliot: Une ville musulmane dans la Chine du nord sous les Mongols (Journal asiatique vol. 211, p. 261–79, 1927; Isis 15, 407). Reuben Levy: The account of the Isma'ili doctrines in the Jami' al-tawarikh (Journal of the Royal Asiatic Society, 1930, p. 509–36; Isis 15, 410). Storey (sec. II, fasc. 1, 71–78, 1935). E. Berthels: Rashīd al-dīn (EI 3, 1124–25, 1936). K. Jahn: Das iranische Papiergeld (Archiv orientální 10, 308–40, Prague 1938). Walter J. Fischel: On the Iranian paper currency of the Mongol period (Journal of the Royal Asiatic Society, 1939, p. 601–3). Abdulhak Adnan: Sur le Tanksukname (Isis 32, 44–47, 4 fig.). C. A.

Macartney: Where was "Black Wallachia" in the thirteenth century? (Journal of the Royal Asiatic Society, 1940, p. 198–200).

AL-BANĀKATĪ

Fakhr al-dīn Abū Sulaimān Dā'ūd ibn Muḥammad al-Banākatī. Persian historian and poet (d. 1329/30).

Dā'ūd al-Banākatī came from Transoxiana, his name being derived from the place Banākat (Fanākant) on the river Sir Daryā (Greek Jaxartes; Arabic Saiḥūn). In 1301–2 he was appointed malik al-shu'arā' (king of poets, "poet laureate") by Ghāzān Maḥmūd (īl-khān of Persia 1295–1304).

In 1317, during the rule of khān Abū Sa'īd (1316–35), he completed a very elaborate history of the world in Persian, entitled Rawḍat ūli-l-albāb fī tawārīkh al-akābir wal-ansāb (Garden of the intelligent on the histories of the great and on genealogies) but generally called Ta'rīkh-i-Banākatī. It is very largely derived from the Jāmi' al-tawārīkh of Rashīd al-dīn, but contains new information which the author was well placed at the cosmopolitan Mongol court in Tabrīz to obtain. His history is even broader and more cosmopolitan than that of his great contemporary (Rashīd al-dīn completed his own work in 1310/11 and died in 1318).

The Ta'rīkh-i-Banākatī is divided into nine parts: (1) prophets and patriarchs, (2) ancient kings of Persia, (3) the prophet Muḥammad and the caliphs, (4) Persian dynasties contemporary with the 'Abbāsid caliphs, (5) Jews, (6) Christians and Franks (history of the Roman emperors and popes), (7) Hindus, (8) Chinese, (9) Mongols. As contrasted with the other Muslim and Christian historians of the Middle Ages, Banākatī's catholicity is astounding. His judgment of non-Muslim opinions is generally quiet and fair. He refers to many European countries, events, and people generally unknown to the Arabs.

It is claimed that his Chinese information is entirely derived from that given by Rashīd al-dīn. The most interesting item, namely the account of Chinese block printing and its use by the Chinese government for the production of standardized copies, is certainly derived from that source.[30] Nevertheless, al-Banākatī's book, not Rashīd al-dīn's, was the origin of the Western tradition on the subject, for the Chinese part of his Rawḍat was edited in Persian and Latin (under a misleading title) as early as 1677 by August Müller, and the passage of that text relative to Chinese printing was quoted by Gerard Meerman in his Origines typographicae (The Hague 1765).

By the way, this was not the first mention of Chinese printing in Western literature. The first was made in 1550, by Paolo Giovio of Como (Paulus Jovius, 1483–1552) in his Historiae sui temporis (Florence 1550; p. 161 in ed. of 1558). Yet most Western scholars remained unfamiliar with early Chinese printing until the time of Jules Klaproth (1834) and Stanislas Julien (1847); and the great mass of educated people have remained unfamiliar with it until our own days! For the history of that incredibly slow tradition see Carter (p. xiii).

Text. Part 8 was edited by August Müller under the false title: Abdallae Beidavaei Historia sinensis (Jena 1677, again 1689), in Persian and Latin. Müller thought that the author was the famous Persian theologian and historian al-Baiḍāwī

[30] The Chinese clearly realized that the value of printing lay in standardization rather than in diffusion. For a discussion of these two points of view see Sarton (1938). Banākatī's account of Chinese printing has been quoted in chapter VII.

(XIII-2). That error was continued by S. Weston: A Chinese chronicle by Abdalla of Beyza translated from the Persian (38 p., London 1820).

The desirability of a complete edition of the Rawḍat depends upon how much it differs from the Jāmi' al-tawārīkh. A joint edition of the two works would perhaps be the best solution.

Criticism. W. Barthold (EI 1, 645, 1911). Browne (3, 100–3, 1920). Carter (p. 131, 189, 239, 1925).

AL-WAṢṢĀF

Persian historian writing in Persian (fl. 1303–28).

'Abdallāh ibn Faḍlallāh of Shīrāz, generally called Waṣṣāf (good describer or historian, panegyrist), abbreviated from Waṣṣāf-i-ḥaḍrat (court historian). He was a tax collector of the īl-khānī government in Persia, and a protégé of Rashīd al-dīn, who presented him to Ghāzān Maḥmūd (ruled 1295–1304) at 'Āna in 1303 and to Uljāi'tū Khudābanda (ruled 1304–16) at Sulṭānīya in 1312.

He wrote a continuation of the history of the Mongols, Ta'rīkh-i-jahān gushā, of al-Juwainī (XIII-2), dealing with the period 1257–1328 and entitled Tajziyat al-amṣār wa tazjiyat al-a'ṣār (Allotment of lands and propulsion of ages), or more briefly Ta'rīkh-i-Waṣṣāf. It is well informed but badly composed and execrably written in a highly conventional and bombastic style, to the point of being almost unreadable. That style was unfortunately taken as a model by many Persian historians.

Text. Lithographic edition (Bombay 1853). This is the only complete edition, including the 5 vols. of Waṣṣāf's history. Editions of vol. 1 only by Hammer-Purgstall (Vienna 1856), in Persian and German. Other editions of vol. 1, Tabrīz 1885/86, and Lahore before 1928.

Criticism. Ferrand (2, 359–60, 1914). Browne (3, 67, 1928). Clément Huart (EI 4, 1133, 1933). Storey (sec. II, fasc. 2, 267–70, 1936).

E. CEYLON

SIṄHALESE CHRONICLE

In great contrast with India, where historical records are rare and poor, Ceylon produced a great Pāli chronicle, the Mahāvaṃsa, which gives an unbroken record of the Sinhalese (Singhalese, Siṅhalese) past from the mythical beginnings and the fifth century B.C. up to the middle of the eighteenth century, or even up to the end of that century, if the supplement (added in 1877) is taken into account, that is, a period of 23 centuries.

We have dealt with the first part of the Mahāvaṃsa in volume 1 (p. 412), apropos of Mahānāma (V-2). That first part was composed at the Mahāvihāra (the great minster) in Anurādhapura by a bhikkhu or Buddhist monk. The second part, called Cūlavaṃsa,[31] consists of three sections: (I) to 1186, written in the thirteenth century; (II) to 1333, written in the fourteenth century, by one Dhammakitti; (III) to the middle of the eighteenth century, written by the bhikkhu Tibbotuvāvē Sumaṅgala, who flourished in the second half of that century.

The second section constitutes one of the most important historical chronicles of our century. It was written, like the rest, in Pāli verse.

[31] Cūlavaṃsa is the Pāli name; Suḷuvaṃsaya is the Siṅhalese name. Cūlavaṃsa means the lesser dynasty, as opposed to Mahāvaṃsa, the great dynasty.

Text. Princeps of the Cūlavaṃsa by H. Sumangala and Don Andris de Silva Batuwantudawa (Columbo 1877). A much improved edition was prepared for the Pāli Text Society by Wilhelm Geiger (2 vols., London 1925-27), in Roman character. English version by Wilhelm Geiger and Mrs. C. Mabel Rickmers (née Duff), for the Pāli Text Society (2 vols., London 1929-30).

Criticism. G. C. Mendis: Early history of Ceylon (Heritage and life of Ceylon series, p. 1-2, Calcutta 1932), see list of 171 kings from 483 B.C. to 1518 (p. 83-88). G. P. Malalasekera: Pāli literature of Ceylon (p. 215, London 1928). B. C. Law (2, 517-96, 1933).

F. CHINA AND KOREA

LI TSÊ

Annamite historian of his own country writing in Chinese (fl. end of thirteenth century and beginning of fourteenth).

Li Tsê was a descendant of Yüan Fu, governor of Chiao Chou in the eastern Chin dynasty (317-420); he was adopted by Li Pêng and hence named Li. He was styled Ching-kao and nicknamed Tung Shan. He took refuge in China after having betrayed his countrymen to Kublai Khān, who died in 1294 (XIII-2). He wrote in Chinese at the beginning of the fourteenth century a treatise on Annam, An-nan chih-lüeh, dealing with Annamite history, natural and administrative geography, government, institutions, rites, music, education, agriculture, biography, etc. The earliest preface to it (by another hand) is dated 1307.

The work was divided into 20 chapters, as follows: (I) map (lost); generalities, administrative divisions, mountains, rivers, antiquities, division of Annam under the T'ang and Yüan; customs, tributary countries, sundials; (II) edicts of the Yüan and preceding dynasties; (III) Yüan embassies; (IV) expeditions sent out to punish Annam; (V) letters of famous Yüan officials; (VI) letters of the kings of Annam under the Yüan and preceding dynasties; (VII) civil and military governors under the Han and the Three States (202 B.C. to A.D. 265); (VIII) idem under the Six Dynasties (265-618); (IX) idem under the T'ang (621-907); (X) Chinese officials who took refuge in Annam at different times; genealogy of the Chao dynasty, 208-111 B.C. (this is the beginning of the historic period in Annam); usurpers of the time of the Five Dynasties (420-618); (XI) genealogy of the Ting dynasty (968-91), and of the Li (Giles 1912, no. 6942) dynasty (981-1009); (XII) genealogy of the Li (ibid. no. 6884) dynasty (1010-25); (XIII) genealogy of the Ch'ên dynasty (1225-1414); (XIV) public education, public service regulations, uniforms, justice, military organization; embassies under different dynasties; (XV) remarkable men; natural products; (XVI) miscellany; poems by famous men; (XVII) poems by envoys to Annam since 1264, and poems addressed to them at the time of their departure by the Annamite academicians; (XVIII) poems by famous Annamites; sketch of Annamite geography in verse; this ends with the author's biography (incomplete, it stops in 1293); (XX) composition and poems on Annamite history (this chapter is lost).

Another short history of Annam, entitled Yüeh chih lüeh, was written at the beginning of the fourteenth century. It covers the period extending from the later Han dynasty (25-221) to the fourteenth century.

Text. Early prints are very rare; a Japanese edition was derived from one of them in 1884, unfortunately imperfect. Upon that text of 1884 was based a French translation by Camille Sainson: Ngann-nann-tche-lo. Mémoires sur l'Annam

(590 p., Péking 1896). There are but few notes, but all the proper names are given in Chinese script and they are indexed; there is also a list of the Annamite dynasties from 939 to 1342.

There is another edition in the Ssŭ k'u ch'üan shu tsung mu.

The Library of Congress has a Chinese edition in 20 chüan, bound in 4 vols., printed 1884. It also has an edition of the Yüeh chih lüeh in vol. 36 of the Shou shan ko ts'ung shu.

Criticism. Wylie (p. 41, 1902).

CH'ÊN LI

Ch'ên Li, styled Shou Wêng, nicknamed Ting Yü. Chinese Confucianist and historian (1252–1333).

He was born in 1252 in Hsiu-ning, Anhui, and was a kind of infant prodigy, being already a full-fledged scholar in his boyhood. He refused to serve under the Yüan dynasty and devoted himself to teaching, being known to his disciples as Ting yü hsien shêng. He took his master's degree in 1314 at the age of 63, but failed to pass the chin shih examination because of sickness.

1. His main work is a history of China from the beginning to the end of the Sung dynasty (1279). It is entitled Li chao t'ung lüeh, in 4 chüan. It was completed in 1310 and was published by his grandson P'an Chih later.

Other works of his:

2. Shang shu chi ch'üan tsuan su, in 6 chüan. This is a commentary on the canon of history (shang shu), including traditional views and earlier criticisms.

3. Ch'in yu t'ang sui lu, discussing various schools of philosophy.

4. Ting yü chi, in 16 chüan, collection of essays in prose and verse.

Criticism. Yüan shih, chüan 189. Giles (no. 232, 1898). Wieger (p. 422, 1920).

CHANG CHU

Chinese poet and historian (1287–1368).

Chang Chu, whose literary name was Chung Chü, was born in 1287 in Chin-ning, Yünnan; he graduated in the Han-lin academy and held high offices. According to the Yüan shih, chüan 186, and the Hsin Yüan shih, chüan 211, he was a student of Li Ts'un, styled An Jên, a famous scholar of that day, who continued the philosophic tradition of Lu Chiu-yüan (XII-2). Under his direction Chang studied the theory of tao tê and hsing-ming (life).

Chang contributed to the Liao, Chin, and Sung dynastic histories. He wrote a collection of poems called T'o yen tz'ŭ, and the Chung i lu (biographies of loyal and devoted officers).

Criticism. Giles (no. 40, 1898). Wieger (p. 410, 1920).

T'ANG HOU

Chinese painter and historian of painting (fl. 1328).

In 1328 or 1330 T'ang Hou, styled Chün Tsai, wrote a short history of painting from the beginning of the third century to the Yüan dynasty, entitled Hua chien. He explained the characteristics of the different schools of painting in China, making it possible to detect forgeries, and added a brief account of the art of foreign peoples.

Text. The Library of Congress has the Hua chien in vol. 92 of the Shuo fu and in vol. 2 of the Hua hsüeh hsin yin.

Criticism. Wylie (p. 136, 1902). Wieger (p. 401, 495, 1920). Friedrich Hirth: Scraps from a collector's note book (p. 112, Leiden 1905). Herbert A. Giles: Introduction to the history of Chinese pictorial art (London 1918).

G. JAPAN

JAPANESE CHRONICLES

In the note on Fujiwara Tamenari (XII-1) reference was made to the Clear mirror, Masu-kagami, an anonymous chronicle extending from 1184 to 1333. It is one of the Three mirrors (Mitsu kagami, San kyō) or of the Four mirrors (Yotsu kagami, Shi kyō). It has been ascribed to a member of the illustrious Ichijō family, Ichijō Fuyuyoshi (1464–1514). The Masu-kagami is interesting from the literary point of view; for example, it illustrates the preponderance of poetry in the court circle during the Kamakura period.

Another famous chronicle of this time is the Taihei-ki (Records of great peace), in 41 volumes, reciting the events of the troubled period from 1318 to 1368. In another edition, entitled Taihei-ki sō-moku, the narrative is continued to 1382. The historical value of this work is not great, but it has exerted a very considerable influence upon Japanese literature.

There has been much discussion by Japanese scholars concerning the authorship of the Taihei-ki. It is probable that Kitabatake Chikafusa wrote or edited a part of it; it is certain that he could not write the whole of it, for he died in 1354. The ascription to Gen-e is open to the same objection, for Gen-e died in 1352. The Taihei-ki has also been ascribed to the Buddhist monk Kojima, who flourished at the Hiei-zan, main seat of the Tendai sect, and died in 1374; that ascription is now generally rejected. The work is probably of composite authorship.

Criticism. W. G. Aston: Japanese literature (p. 169–83, 1899). Papinot (p. 298, 615, 1909). Brinkley and Kikuchi (p. 366, 1914). Hugh Borton: Survey of Japanese historiography (American historical review 43, 489–99, 1938), contains very little pertinent to this note.

Louis Emile Bertin: Les grandes guerres civiles du Japon, 1156–1392 (428 p., Paris 1894). K. Asakawa: The documents of Iriki, illustrative of the development of the feudal institutions of Japan (592 p., New Haven 1929; Isis 14, 527).

CHAPTER XIII

LAW AND SOCIOLOGY

(First Half of the Fourteenth Century)

N.B. Only the main articles are grouped in this chapter. The contributions to law or sociology of many other men, whose main work was done in other fields, are related in other chapters. For a general survey of law and sociology in the first half of the fourteenth century, see section XIII of chapter I. More information on the men referred to in that section can easily be found by means of the index.

A. CHRISTIAN WEST

A1. Italy

OLDRADO DA PONTE

Oldrado da Lodi. Oldradus de Ponte (or de Laude). Italian jurist born at Lodi near Milano. He studied law in Bologna under Dinus Mugellanus (Dino da Mugello, near Florence, died toward the end of the thirteenth century) and taught law in the same city, then in Padua from 1307 to 1310, then in Siena and Montpellier. Finally he became advocatus consistorialis under John XXII in Avignon; he died in that city in 1335.

He wrote lessons concerning the Infortiatum (middle section of the Pandects of Justinian[1]), questions, and consilia (the early printed editions include 333 consilia).

At an unknown time (about the time of John XXII's decretal Spondent against alchemists, but was it before or after?) he wrote a consilium on sortileges at the beginning of which he gives his opinion of alchemy. He repeats arguments for and against, but concludes in favor of it, remarking that after all the alchemist does nothing but emulate craftsmen who make glass, or worms which make silk. He quotes Augustine's views on the seminal forces which exist in everything and thanks to which all kinds of evolutionary changes are always possible or conceivable: "Insunt enim (ut dicit B. Augustinus) rebus corporeis per omnia elementa quaedam occultae seminariae rationes, quibus cum data fuerit oportunitas temporalis et causalis prorumpunt in species debitas suis modis et finibus. Si ergo ipsi hoc attribuunt Deo non videntur peccare." Alchemy becomes a forbidden science only when it is mixed up with magic. The alchemists who could transmute base metals into gold should be considered public benefactors.

Among his pupils were Guglielmo di Pastrengo and Bàrtolo da Sassoferrato, and among his friends Giovanni d'Andrea and Petrarca, all of whom are dealt with in this volume.

Text. The Consilia were first printed in Rome 1472 and many times afterward. The consilium on alchemy, "Ex Oldrado consil. 74 de sortileg. num. 1," is included in Joannes Chrysippus Fanianus: De iure artis alchemiae, hoc est, variorum authorum et praesertim iuris consultorum iudicia et responsa ad quaestionem,

[1] Mediaeval jurists divided the Pandects into three parts, to wit, Digestum novum, Infortiatum, et Vetus.

An alchemia sit ars legitima. Printed in De arte chemica (Montbéliard 1602); in Zetzner (1, 48–70, 1659); and in Manget (1, 211, 1702). I have seen only this last-named edition, whence my quotation is derived.

Criticism. Savigny (4, 211, 1839). Ferguson (1906). Thorndike (3, 48–49, 1934).

CINO OF PISTOIA

Italian jurist and poet (1270–1336/37).

Guittone de' Sinibaldi da Pistoia. Guittoncino, hence Cino. Born of a noble family at Pistoia, near Florence, in 1270. He was educated at the grammar school of Francesco da Colle; then studied law (c. 1292) at Bologna under Francesco II Accorso, and also in Orléans under Pierre de Belleperche.[2] Like Dante, he was originally a Ghibelline but became a White, and suffered various political vicissitudes. This explains the fact that he became a doctor in laws in Bologna only in 1310. From 1321, he taught law in various schools: Treviso, Siena, Florence, Perugia, Naples. He obtained considerable fame as a jurist; Bàrtolo was one of his disciples.

His main legal work is the Lectura in Codicem, a commentary on the main laws of the first nine books of the Justinian Codex, which was much appreciated for centuries. Another Lectura "in Digestum vetus" is incomplete, and there remain various other consilia. In the course of his study of the lex VII° mense he asked the opinion of Gentile da Foligno and thus elicited from him a treatise which has been called (not quite correctly) the first treatise on forensic medicine. This matter is discussed in the note devoted to Gentile.

He was one of the early "commentatores"; that is, he represented a new school of law, influenced by the French jurists, more philosophical than the old school of the Bolognese "glossatores." He was also somewhat opposed to the canonists. He tended to defend the civil power against the ecclesiastical power. Earlier writers had compared the pope and emperor respectively to the sun and moon; Cino had the audacity to reverse the metaphor: the emperor is the sun, his authority being derived immediately from God.

He was on friendly terms with Dante and Petrarca, both of whom wrote poems in his praise. He was himself famous as a poet, a distinguished representative of the "dolce stil nuovo." His love for Selvaggia Vergiolesi of Pistoia is thus immortalized, even as Dante's love for Beatrice.

He died in Pistoia at the end of 1336 or in 1337. His beautiful tomb in the Duomo of Pistoia by Cellino di Nese is adorned with bas-reliefs illustrating the teaching of law.

Text. Lectura in Codicem. First edition, Lectura super Codice, Pavia 1483. Many later editions: Venice 1493, Strasbourg (s.a., end of fifteenth century), Lyon 1517, 1528, 1547, Francfort a.M. 1578.

Lectura in Digestum vetus. Lyon 1528, 1547, Francfort a.M. 1578.

De successione ab intestato. First edition s.a.l. [Cologne 1485]. Reprinted 6 times in various legal collections from 1549 to 1670.

Separate consilia are included in seven collections enumerated by Monti (p. 15), and to these must be added the consilia edited by Monti himself (p. 233–64, 1924).

There are many editions of Cino's poems; I can cite only a few. See Ciampi,

[2] Pierre de Belleperche, born at Lucenay-lès-Aix (Nièvre) about the middle of the thirteenth century; died in Paris 1307. Famous French jurist, one of the main advisers of Philippe le Bel.

below. Giosuè Carducci: Rime di Cino da Pistoia (705 p., Firenze 1862). Enrico Bindi and Pietro Fanfani: Le rime (Pistoja 1878). This includes Carducci's biography of Cino and a study by C. Witte on Cino the jurist (5 p.). Carducci's edition was reprinted in the series Classici italiani (vol. 76, 451 p., Milan 1916).

I. Del Lungo: Canzone a Dante per la morte di Beatrice. Riproduzione fototipica (folio, 8 facsimile pl., Firenze 1890). Canzoni d'amore e madrigali di Dante Alighieri, di M. Cino da Pistoia, etc. Riproduzione della rarissima edizione del 1518 per cura di Jarro (i.e., Giulio Piccini) (123 p., Firenze 1899).

English version of many poems in D. G. Rossetti: Early Italian poets.

Criticism. Sebastian Ciampi: Memorie della vita di messer Cino da Pistoja (Pisa 1808); Vita e memorie (3ª ed. rivista ed accresciuta, 2 vols., Pistoia 1826; vol. 2 contains Cino's poems). Luigi Chiappelli: Vita e opere giuridiche di Cino da Pistoia, con molti documenti inediti (Pistoia 1881); Nuove ricerche, con testi inediti (vol. 1, 1911; reprinted from the Bullettino storico pistoiese, anni 12, 13). Orazio Bacci: Novi documenti sulla famiglia di Cino da Pistoia (Giornale storico della letteratura italiana vol. 19, 6 p., 1892). Peleo Bacci: Documenti nuovi su Cino Sighibuldi da Pistoia 1332 (Bullettino storico pistoiese, anno 5, 1903). Guido Zaccagnini: Cino da Pistoia (Pistoia 1918). Gennaro Maria Monti: Cino da Pistoia, giurista, con bibliografia e tre appendici di documenti inediti (276 p., Città di Castello 1924); article in the Enciclopedia italiana (10, 374, 1931).

The ascription of Cino's monument to Cellino di Nese has been challenged. See Thieme's Lexikon (6, 277, 1912).

GIOVANNI D'ANDREA

Joannes Andreae (John the son of Andrew). Famous Italian canonist called "fons et tuba iuris," the "archdoctor of the Decretum," born soon after 1270, in a village of the Mugello valley in the Florentine region, but entirely identified with Bologna, where he studied and taught[3] until his death of the plague, on July 7, 1348. He was buried in the Dominican church, where there is a beautiful monument to his memory.

He taught canon law from 1302 on, explaining the Decretales and the Decretum[4] and other parts of the Corpus iuris canonici. Various political missions were entrusted to him by the city of Bologna. One of these missions, to John XXII in 1328, was particularly memorable, for he was attacked near Pavia by Ghibellines and was held a prisoner for eight months. On account of his fame all kinds of stories clustered around his name. Petrarca corresponded with him. In one of his letters Petrarca rebuked Giovanni's presumption and ignorance.[5]

John XXII (pope 1316–34) had directed a decretal, Spondent quas non exhibent . . . , against alchemists and other counterfeiters. A more favorable opinion of alchemy was expressed by Oldrado da Ponte (about whom see note above). Oldrado's arguments were repeated without acknowledgment by Giovanni d'Andrea, who added that Arnold of Villanova (XIII-2; d. 1311) had actually made rods of gold. That story, of little importance in itself, reappears frequently in legal writings on alchemy. Oldrado and Giovanni, in spite of their legal learning, were equally incapable of appreciating the right and wrong of alchemy. Unfortunately their legal fame gave currency and validity to their worthless opinions, and hence the historian must take them into account.

[3] Except for two years (1307–9) when, Bologna being under an interdict, he taught in Padova.

[4] For general definition of these see Introd. 2, 268.

[5] Familiares (IV, 15). English version in J. H Robinson's Petrarch (2d impression, New York 1899; p. 279–87).

Giovanni's main writings are in the form of commentaries on the Corpus iuris canonici: Novella in Decretales, Glossa in Sextum (i.e., the sixth book of Decretals), Novella in Sextum, Glossa in Clementinas (i.e., the Decretals of Clement V, 1313). This last glossa, written in 1326, was the first devoted to the Constitutiones Clementinae, as Clement's decretals are often called. He wrote a life of St. Jerome, Quaestiones mercuriales, etc. One of his last works, if not the last, written in 1346 ("suspicor quod haec possent esse ultima mea scripta"), was the Additiones ad Durantis Speculum, i.e., notes on the Speculum iudiciale of William Durand (XIII-2). This contained the fruits of fifty years of study, plus borrowings from many other writers, particularly Oldrado.

The popularity of Giovanni's writings is proved by the abundance of MSS and early editions. There are no less than 83 incunabula. Though primarily devoted to canon law, they concern law in general, because of their influence on procedure and of their value for the study of the history of law.

Text. The legal texts relative to alchemy were collected by Joannes Chrysippus Fanianus, a lawyer of Basel, who flourished apparently in the second half of the sixteenth century, under the title De iure artis alchemiae (Basel 1576, Montbéliard 1601). Reprinted in various alchemical collections, the De arte chemica libri duo (Montbéliard 1602), Zetzner (1, 48–70, 1659), and Manget (1, 210–16, 1702). I quote the title as I read it in Manget, De iure artis alchemiae, hoc est, variorum authorum et praesertim iuris consultorum iudicia et responsa ad quaestionem, An alchemia sit ars legitima.

There is no room for a complete bibliography of Giovanni's writings. For the incunabula, see GW (2, col. 176–216, nos. 1675–1757, 1926). I quote only the main titles with brief indications.

Additiones ad Durantis Speculum iudiciale, Strassburg 1475.

Arbor sanguinitatis, Nürnberg 1472 or 1473. No less than 46 incunabula, 5 of which are in German. Many of these editions include commentaries. The first German edition (with same Latin title) appeared in Augsburg 1474.

Casus breves super Decretalibus et Clementinis (apocryphal?), Paris c. 1475, c. 1480, Albi c. 1480, Lyon c. 1485.

Hieronymianus sive Vita S. Hieronymi, Cologne 1482.

De modo observandi interdictum, Magdeburg 1483.

Novella super 1–V. Decretalium, Venice 1489, Pavia 1504, 1505, Venice 1581.

Novella super VI. Decretalium, Rome 1476, Pavia 1484, Venice 1491, 1499, 1581.

Quaestiones mercuriales super regulis iuris, Rome 1472, Strassburg 1475, Rome 1476, Venice 1477, Pavia 1483, Venice 1490, Pavia 1491, Venice 1499, 1581 (after the Novella super Sexto). Included in the collection Selectae quaestiones (Cologne 1570, Lyon 1572).

Summa de sponsalibus et matrimoniis, 16 incunabula, the first in Rome 1473.

Criticism. Savigny (4, 217–20, 1839). Thorndike (3, 49, 1934).

ALBERICO DA ROSCIATE

Alberico da Rosciate (near Bergamo). Albericus de Rosate Bergomensis. Italian jurist (d. 1354).

Alberico studied law in Padua under Oldrado da Ponte (c. 1307–10), obtained his doctor's degree, but never taught. He practiced law and took part in the public affairs of Bergamo, helping to reform its statutes. In 1340 he was sent to Avignon to conclude peace with Benedict XII. He visited Rome at the time of the jubilee of 1350. He died in Bergamo in 1354.

He wrote two short grammatical treatises, De orthographia and De accentu, and commentaries on the Digest and the Codex, and he compiled the Opus statutorum, a collection of questions concerning the administration of Bergamo. His fame, however, is based on two dictionaries, devoted respectively to civil and canon law, which were greatly admired in spite of their mediocrity. Such dictionaries may be usefully consulted by the historian of science, to find contemporary legal opinion on such subjects as astrology, alchemy, medical practice, etc. With regard to alchemy Alberico reiterates the opinions of Oldrado da Ponte, and of Andrea de Rampinis of Isernia (44 miles northeast of Gaeta; Abruzzi e Molise), author of a treatise on feudal law (In usus feudorum comm., Naples 1571), who died in 1353. There is nothing wrong in alchemy if dissociated from magic; alchemical gold may be sold as natural gold if it is as pure as the latter, but not if it is not pure! It is clear from such statements that the transmutation of base metals into gold was generally assumed to be possible, if rare and difficult.

Text. The two dictionaries were printed together by an unknown editor, Dictionarium iuris tam civilis quam canonici (Venice 1581). Savigny says that the Dictionarium was often printed but that one should beware of modern editions because of later interpolations.

The texts concerning alchemy are excerpted in the Fanianus alchemical-juridical collection (1602), e.g., Manget (1, 212–13, 1702); for further bibliography see my note on Oldrado above.

Criticism. Savigny (4, 221–22, 1839). Thorndike (3, 50–51, 1934).

TRIONFO

Agostino Trionfo, Augustinus Triumphus, Augustinus de Ancona. Italian Augustinian publicist (1243–1328).

Agostino was born at Ancona, on the Adriatic coast of Italy, in 1243. He assumed the Augustinian habit and went to Paris to complete his theological studies. In 1274 Gregory X invited him to replace Thomas Aquinas, who had just died, at the council of Lyon. Charles II of Anjou (king of Naples 1285–1309) called him to his court to be tutor to the crown prince Robert. Agostino died in Naples, on April 2, 1328.

Though he was a man of the thirteenth century, being already 58 years of age by the end of it, he must be dealt with here because his main work was done for John XXII between 1316 and 1328. That is, the Summa de potestate ecclesiastica, written against the pope's enemies, the emperor Louis the Bavarian, Marsiglio of Padua, and the Spiritual Franciscans. His defense of the papal power is so excessive that modern apologists are obliged to qualify it. As long as the pope is orthodox his power is unlimited and almost Godlike; should he become heretical, however, he would cease ipso facto to be a pope.

During the pontificate of Clement V (1305–14) Trionfo wrote various other treatises: (1) De facto Templariorum ad quem pertinet inquirere et iudicare de heresi; (2) Contra articulos inventos ad diffamandum sanctissimum patrem Bonifacium (Boniface VIII); (3) De duplici potestate prelatorum et laicorum; (4) De potestate collegii mortuo papa; (5) Contra divinatores et sompniatores. The last named is of great interest to the historian of science, for in it Agostino warns Clement V against diviners and dreamers. Though it insists on the danger to the faith of every kind of occultism, it admits some of the premises of astrology and astrological medicine. The Tractatus contra divinatores, divided into 21 chapters, is an excellent summary of the orthodox case against divination and magic. It helps us to remember that the church was in those days the main bulwark against unbridled superstition.

Text. The Summa de ecclesiastica potestate ad Johannem XXII was first printed in Augsburg 1473 and often reprinted: Rome 1473, Cologne 1475, Rome 1479, Venice 1487, c. 1490, Rome 1579, 1582.

The smaller treatise no. 2, Contra articulos inventos, was edited by Heinrich Finke: Aus den Tagen Bonifaz VIII (Münster i.W. 1902). Treatises 1, 3, 4 were edited by Richard Scholz: Die Publizistik zur Zeit Philipps des Schönen und Bonifaz VIII (p. 172–89, 486–516, Stuttgart 1903). Treatise 5, Contra divinatores et sompniatores, was edited by the same in his Unbekannte Streitschriften aus der Zeit Ludwigs des Bayern (2, 481–90, Rome 1914).

Criticism. Emil Friedberg: Die mittelalterlichen Lehren über das Verhältniss von Staat und Kirche. Augustinus Triumphus, Marsilius von Padua (Zeitschrift für Kirchenrecht 8, 69–138, Tübingen 1869). Poole (p. 219–23, 1920). Flick (1, 46, 92, 205, 1930). Thorndike (3, 9–12, 1934).

MARSIGLIO OF PADUA

Italian publicist (c. 1277–c. 1343).

Contents: (1) Life. (2) The Defensor pacis. (3) Other writings. (4) Marsiglio's influence.
(5) Text. (6) Criticism.

1. *Life*

Marsiglio dei Mainardini. Marsilius Patavinus, de Mainardinis, de Raymundinis. Born at Padua between 1275 and 1280, son of Bonmatteo Mainardino, who was notary to the University of Padua. Friend of Albertino Mussato, who addressed some of his verse to him. He studied medicine in Padua, and practiced it at various times, the emperor being one of his patients. He had no legal training, his often-quoted study of law in Orléans being mythical. He was rector of the University of Paris in 1312–13; in 1316 he was appointed a canon of the cathedral of Padua by the new pope John XXII. Sometime after that, he, who was born a Popolano, became a Ghibelline. After writing his magnum opus, the Defensor pacis, in 1324, he and his philosophical adviser John of Jandun placed themselves under the protection of the emperor Ludwig of Bavaria. They were condemned by John XXII in the summer of 1326, their work was lengthily refuted by him in the following year, and they were finally excommunicated and declared to be heretics and heresiarchs. The emperor had at first been frightened by their radicalism and had been tempted to disown them. They continued to enjoy his favor, however, and attended the imperial deposition of John XXII, the coronation of the emperor by the people of Rome in 1328, and the popular election, confirmed by the emperor, of a new pope (the antipope Nicholas V) in the same year. It is possible, but not proved, that the emperor appointed Marsiglio archbishop of Milano. Marsiglio remained attached to the emperor, returning with him to Germany, until the latter was obliged by the new pope Benedict XII to cast him out as heretic and schismatic in 1336. The circumstances of Marsiglio's last years are very obscure. He died probably in the winter of 1342–43.

2. *The Defensor pacis*

The Defensor pacis was completed by Marsiglio of Padua on June 24, 1324. Marsiglio was helped by John of Jandun, who was generally considered in the fourteenth century as coauthor (e.g., both were repeatedly condemned together and bracketed in every attack). In the book itself, however, Marsiglio appears as the sole author. It is probable that Jandun was simply a philosophical adviser. The Defensor pacis was published at a critical time, for an acute conflict had arisen between the pope John XXII and the emperor Ludwig IV, and the latter had just been excommunicated.

It is divided into three "dictiones": (I) rational arguments (theory of the state); (II) arguments taken from the Scriptures and from the fathers of the church (organization of the church, relation between church and state); (III) practical conclusions. There are digressions which disturb the order of the book, but the leading ideas are the following.

The main good of the commonwealth is peace even as health is the main good of the body. Marsiglio's main object is, therefore, the defense of peace, which is jeopardized by the rivalry between pope and emperor. The burden of the Defensor pacis is the defense of imperial and even more of popular and civil rights against papal sovereignty and ecclesiastical privileges. The church has no business to hold property, or wield temporal power, or even to prosecute heresy. A wise distinction is drawn between the elaboration of laws, a technical task which must be left to experts, and their approbation, which should remain the people's prerogative. The laws are made by lawyers, sanctioned by the people, carried into execution by the prince. The clergy should be deprived not only of most of its privileges, but of tithes or other financial help except for a strict minimum (one recognizes here the influence of Franciscan ideas on evangelical poverty, reaffirmed at the chapter of Perugia in 1322). The supreme authority of the church is not the pope but the council, representing by means of delegates (lay as well as clerical) the whole body of the faithful, and summoned by the emperor, not by the pope. The latter is but one bishop among others, primus inter pares. The bishops are to be appointed by the temporal sovereigns. To these radical ideas were added violent reproofs of the vices permeating the ecclesiastical organization.

Few if any of these ideas were new. Many of them had been explained by St. Thomas Aquinas; some of the most radical concerning the pope's power (or lack of power) could be found in the De potestate papae of the Breton Dominican Hervé Nédélec of Tréguier, general of his order from 1318 to his death in Narbonne 1323.

The novelty was in the combination. The Defensor pacis was a vigorous defense of political and ecclesiastical democracy, anticipating the Reformation and even in some respects the French Revolution. It included an elaborate denunciation of the existing defects and abuses of the church. Its purpose was not only to separate the church from the state, but to subordinate the former to the latter. As often happens, the actual hostilities and reprisals between his imperial patron and the pope had carried the author too far. The Defensor pacis was the most important political treatise of the century, and its influence, as we shall see presently, was considerable.

3. *Other writings*

Before discussing Marsiglio's influence, let us consider rapidly his other publications. The Defensor pacis of 1324 was not only the most important one, but also the first in point of time. It was followed by:

a. De translatione imperii romani, almost literally derived from a treatise written by Landolfo Colonna (canon in Chartres c. 1320). The purpose was to prove that the "Holy Roman Empire" is the continuation of the Roman Empire, and thus to exalt the imperial dignity.

b. Defensor minor. Composed in 1328, but including perhaps later interpolations. It is a sort of supplement to the Defensor pacis, dealing with such questions as: ecclesiastical jurisdiction; penitence, indulgences, crusades, pilgrimages; vows; excommunication and interdiction; general council; marriage and divorce. The spirit of the Defensor minor is the same as that of the Defensor pacis; the two treatises should be considered together.

c. De iurisdictione imperatoris in causa matrimoniali. Special plea for the emperor's rights, against the pope, in nuptial law. Written in 1342 to justify conjugal difficulties of the emperor's son.

4. *Marsiglio's influence*

The Defensor pacis of 1324 acted like a powerful explosive; it remained for a long time an enormous cause of scandal; it was too radical, too much ahead of the times, to be immediately effective. The abundance of fourteenth-century MSS testifies to the eagerness with which it was read.

Another witness to its diffusion is given by the number of attacks directed against it. John XXII took the trouble to refute it in 1327, and the authors were repeatedly censured and condemned by various popes. They were attacked by the Italian Augustinian Alessandro Fassitelli da Sant' Elpidio (general of his order 1312, died 1328) in his De iurisdictione imperii et auctoritate summi pontificis, by the Spanish Franciscan Alvaro Paes (grand penitentiary in Avignon 1330, died Seville 1352) in his Collyrium adversus haereses and De planctu Ecclesiae, by the German priest Conrad of Megenberg in his Oeconomica (c. 1355).

On the other hand, it was eagerly read by all those, whose number was steadily growing, who were discontented with the church and anxious to increase civil and popular authority against the ecclesiastical. Thus John Wycliffe was much influenced by it.

The Defensor pacis did not interest simply the clerks; it was soon translated into French,[6] and the French text was translated into Italian by 1363. The first printed edition (Basel 1522) was prepared by Valentin Curio under the pseudonym Licentius Evangelus for the use of the Reformers. The text of that edition was translated into English by William Marshall (1533) for a similar reason, and printed in 1535 thanks to Cromwell's financial help.[6a] An abridged German translation was printed in 1545. In short, the ammunition collected by Marsiglio in 1324 was eagerly used two centuries later by the Reformers of various countries in their struggle against the mother church.

As to Marsiglio's philosophical influence, it cannot be dissociated from that of William of Occam and John of Jandun. It will suffice to say that he introduced their concrete, commonsensical, radical point of view and their logic into the field of political theory.

5. *Text*

Defensor pacis. First edition by Valentin Curio (Basel 1522). Facsimile copy of the first dictio by Alexander Cartellieri: Erstes Buch für Seminarübungen (90 p., Leipzig 1913).

[6] In 1375 Nicole Oresme, Jean Golein, and others were suspected of having made the translation. They denied it under oath.

[6a] Thomas Cromwell, earl of Essex (1485?–1540), was one of the main organizers of the English Reformation (DNB 13, 192–202, 1888).

Second edition by Francis Goemaere (Gomarus) of Bruges (1563–1641), prepared for Henry IV of France (Francfort 1592). Later editions: Heidelberg 1599, Francfort 1612, 1613, 1614 (in Goldast's collection), 1622, 1623, 1692.

Richard Scholz: Defensor pacis für Übungszwecke bearbeitet (138 p., Leipzig 1914).

First critical edition by Charles William Previté-Orton (566 p., Cambridge 1928; Isis 12, 359). Second by Richard Scholz in Fontes iuris germanici antiqui (Hanover 1932–33).

English translation by William Marshall: The defense of peace, lately translated out of Laten into Englysshe (London 1535).

Incomplete German translation by Max Müller von Westendorff: Ain kurtzer Auszug des treffenlichen Wercks und Fridschirmbuches Marsili von Padua (Neuburg a.d. Donau 1545).

Defensor minor. First edition by C. Kenneth Brampton (92 p., Birmingham 1922).

The two smaller treatises are included in Melchior Goldast: Monarchiae S. Romani imperii sive tractatuum de iurisdictione imperiali seu regia et pontificia seu sacerdotali tomus secondus (p. 147–53, 1286–91, Francfort 1614). That collection was reprinted in 1621 and again in 1668. There are many other editions of the De translatione imperii romani, in various collections: Basel 1555, 1566, Heidelberg 1599 (with the Defensor pacis), London 1690. The De iurisdictione imperatoris in causa matrimoniali was first printed in 1598.

The treatise De potestate papae by Hervé Nédélec was printed in 1506.

Landolfo Colonna's treatise was included by Simon Schard in his De iurisdictione autoritate et praeeminentia imperiali (p. 284 ff., Basel 1566) and reprinted by Goldast (2, 88 ff., 1614).

6. *Criticism*

Baldassare Labanca: Marsiglio da Padova, riformatore politico e religioso (240 p., Padova 1882). James Sullivan: Marsiglio and Occam (American historical review 2, 409–26, 593–610, 1897); The MSS and date of the Defensor pacis (English historical review, April 1905, p. 293–307). Noël Valois: Jean de Jandun et Marsile de Padoue (HL 33, 528–623, 1906). Antonio Cappa-Legora: La politica di Dante e di Marsiglio (Roma 1906). Pasquale Villari: Marsiglio e il Defensor pacis (Nuova antologia p. 369–79, Roma 1913). Leopold Stieglitz: Die Staatstheorie des Marsilius (60 p., Leipzig 1914). Ephraim Emerton: The Defensor pacis (82 p., Cambridge, Mass. 1920). Edoardo Ruffini Avondo: Il Defensor pacis (Rivista storica italiana, 1924, p. 113 ff.). Richard Scholz: Zur Datierung und Überlieferung des Defensor pacis (Neues Archiv der Gesellschaft für ältere deutsche Geschichtskunde 46, 490–512, 1926). C. W. Previté-Orton: The authors cited in the Defensor pacis (Essays presented to Reginald Lane Poole p. 405–20, Oxford 1927). Felice Battaglia: Marsilio da Padova e la filosofia politica del medio evo (278 p., Firenze 1928), with long bibliography; Sul Defensor pacis (Nuovi studi di diritto 2, 128 ff., 1929). Alessandro Passerin d'Entrèves: Rileggendo il Defensor pacis (Rivista storica italiana, ser. 4, vol. 5, 1–37, 1934). Georges de Lagarde: La naissance de l'esprit laïc au déclin du Moyen âge (vol. 2, 335 p., St.-Paul-Trois-Châteaux, Drôme 1934). C. W. Previté-Orton: Marsilius of Padova (Proceedings of the British Academy 21, 137–83, 1935). Carlyle (vol. 6, 1936).

A3. France

JEAN FAURE

French (Angoumoisin) civilian (d. c. 1340).

Jean Faure or Joannes Faber or Fabri (Faure is a regional variety of Faber, a name almost as common in France in various disguises as its equivalent Smith in

England, cf. Lefebre, Lefébure, Fabre, Faure, Fauré, etc.). He hailed from Montbron in the Angoumois (dépt. Charente), and called himself Jean de Montbron or Jean de Roussines (de Runcinis), Roussines being the name of his estate in Montbron. The date of his birth is unknown. He studied law in Montpellier; he praised the teachers of Bologna and blamed those of Orléans, but it does not follow that he studied in those two famous law schools. By 1324 his long studies were completed.

He was a lawyer and also a seneschal in the barony of La Rochefoucauld in Angoumois. For many years he was obliged to travel considerably; he was always on the go "itinerans et negocians." He died at Angoulême (the capital of Angoumois) c. 1340, and was buried in the Dominican cloister (destroyed in 1822).

He is the author of two important and popular law books, the Breviarium and the Lectura. The Breviarium is a summary of books I to IX of Justinian's Codex, the Lectura is a commentary on the four books of the Institutiones. Both textbooks were written; they are not teacher's lessons. Faure was very well read not only in the law, civil and canon, but also in ancient and mediaeval literature; he quotes Hippocrates, Aristotle, Cicero, Seneca, the fathers of the church, Hugh of Saint Victor, St. Bernard, etc. The Bartolus references are later interpolations; the latest civilian quoted by him (in the Lectura) is Cino da Pistoia (Cino's Lectura on the Codex c. 1313). He often refers to his older contemporaries Jacques de Revigny, bishop of Verdun (d. 1296), and Pierre de Belleperche, bishop of Auxerre (d. 1307).

The Breviarium was composed at the beginning of his career, c. 1325–30; the Lectura at the end, c. 1335–40. The second book is far richer than the first. In both he shows himself to be a clear and practical mind, more interested in the reality of law than its archaeology. Private law was his main interest, but he also discussed questions of public law, such as sovereignty, papal vs. temporal power. He was very much of a moralist. The study of nature (e.g., the virtues of plants) he approved; but the study of superstitions he disapproved very strongly.

The Repetitio super materia quaestionis seu torturae wrongly ascribed to him and sometimes printed with the Breviarium (e.g., Paris 1516, 1545) is the work of another hand, probably Italian and post-Bartolian.

Faure's influence was great judging from the number of editions, chiefly but not exclusively in France. He was recognized as an authority by the Italian jurists, and was praised extravagantly by the French ones.

Text. Breviarium. Louvain c. 1475, Lyon 1480, Paris 1499, 1516, 1545, Lyon 1520, 1537, 1550, 1597. That is at least 9 editions before the end of the sixteenth century.

Lectura. One undated incunabulum; other editions Venice 1488, 1492, 1496, 1497, 1499, 1526, Milano 1504, Lyon 1513, 1523, 1527, 1531, 1537, 1540, 1543, 1546, 1578, 1593, or 18 editions before the end of the sixteenth century.

Criticism. Paul Fournier (HL 35, 556–80, 1921).

GUILLAUME DE MONTLAUZUN

French (Quercinois) canonist (d. 1343).

Guillelmus de Montelauduno. Cadet of a noble family named after the place Montlauzun in Quercy (dépt. Lot). He studied theology and canon law, probably in Paris, and assumed the Clunisian habit. In 1305 he attended the coronation of Clement V in Lyon. He seems to have traveled considerably, probably as a visitor of his order. In 1308 he was maître de l'oeuvre (i.e., architect and builder) at the abbey of Lézat (diocese of Rieux, dépt. Haute-Garonne). He taught canon law at the University of Toulouse. In 1319 he was elected abbot of Montierneuf in Poitiers, and continued so until his death, on January 2, 1343.

He wrote commentaries on the later decretals (see Introd. 2, 268), namely the Lectura (between 1306 and 1314) on the Sextus of Boniface VIII (pope 1294–1303); the Apparatus (1319 or 1320) on the Septimus (or Clementinae) of Clement V and on the three Extravagantes of John XXII; and a study on a decretal of Benedict XII (1336) concerning Cluny. His most important work is the Sacramentale (c. 1317), which may be described as a theological guide for the use of canonists. The Sacramentale answered a real need, because by this time canon law and theology had both developed so much that it was almost impossible to be a master in both fields. Indeed, it took five or six years of study to become sufficiently familiar with either field. And yet the legend according to which Gratian (XII-1; fl. 1139) and Peter the Lombard (XII-2; d. 1160) were brothers was symbolically true. The two fields were somewhat overlapping, and one could not be a good canonist without knowledge of theology, or vice versa. The Sacramentale was so called because it was centered on the sacraments, which is the subject where law and theology come closest together, and indeed cannot be separated.

The best proof that Montlauzun's work answered a need is its popularity, witnessed by the number of MSS and of references to it in other treatises of the fourteenth and fifteenth centuries. The Sacramentale failed to be printed, however, and therefore its influence dropped rapidly after the fifteenth century.

In his commentaries Montlauzun often introduced historical digressions. For example, in the Apparatus he discusses the origins of the Jewish and Muslim religions, and gives a biography of the prophet Muḥammad.

Text. Lectura super Sexto. Printed in Toulouse 1524, with many additions by Blaise Auriol (d. Toulouse 1540).

Apparatus Clementinarum. Rome 1475, Rouen 1512, Paris 1517, etc. These commentaries are also included in various collections.

Criticism. Johann Wilhelm Bickell: Über die Entstehung und den heutigen Gebrauch der beiden Extravagantensammlungen des Corpus juris canonici (130 p., Marburg 1825). Paul Fournier (HL 35, 467–503, 1921).

JOHN OF PARIS

Joannes Parisiensis (or de Parisiis). French Dominican, Thomist, publicist (c. 1269–1306).

He was nicknamed Pungens asinos ("pique-ânes"), surdus, dormiens ("qui dort"). It is possible that Quidort (Surdus, de soardis) was his family name; it was a Parisian family name of that time and John was apparently a Parisian. In 1290 he was a master of the faculty of arts in Paris, and this implies that he was born not later than 1269, began his university studies not later than 1284, and was not yet a Dominican in 1290. In 1303 he was already one of the fratres celebriores in the Dominican house of St. James, the three others named with him being Durand de Saint Pourçain, Hervé Nédélec, and James of Lausanne.[7] He became licentiate in theology in 1304. Having got into trouble because of his views on the Eucharist, he appealed to the pope, and on his way to the curia he died in Bordeaux, on September 22, 1306.

He is chiefly known because at the end of 1302 (or the beginning of 1303) he

[7] Swiss Dominican (d. 1321). Author of elaborate commentaries on the Holy Writ and the Sentences. Barthélemy Hauréau (HL 33, 459–79, 1906).

wrote a political treatise De potestate regia et papali, wherein he took sides with Philippe le Bel against Boniface VIII. It is derived from Thomas Aquinas but with a strong royalist and French bias. He defined the church as the body of the faithful, not the body of the clergy, and defended the supreme authority of the French king in France against that of pope or emperor. The pope has no title to temporal authority, and his spiritual authority may be overruled by a general council. Priests and bishops are servants of the church rather than of the pope. State and church are two separate domains. Never had the spiritual authority of the pope been analyzed and restricted with as much clearness and strength. There is an early French translation of that treatise by Raoul de Presles (fifteenth-century MS in Lyon).

In 1303 he signed with many other Parisian Dominicans a petition for a general council.

In 1304 John wrote a treatise on the Real Presence, Determinatio de modo existendi corporis Christi in sacramento, wherein he deviated from the doctrine set forth by Innocent III (pope 1198–1216). He was accused of heresy and forbidden to teach and hear confessions. He appealed to the pope, then Clement V (pope 1305–14), but died soon afterward. He has been considered (by Wilhelm Münscher and others) a forerunner of the Lutheran theory of impanation (versus transubstantiation, or consubstantiation).

Though the political treatise of John of Paris, and next to it his treatise on the Real Presence, have attracted more attention, his philosophical and theological writings are perhaps more important, for he was one of the early defenders of Thomism. His main work was probably a commentary on the four books of Sentences. We may also mention a Quodlibetum; a treatise De unitate esse et essentiae in creatis (lost); a summary of Aristotelian physics, Abbreviatio librorum naturalis philosophiae Aristotelis; a commentary on the Meteorology, and a treatise on the rainbow, De yride (iride), both lost. These two may be identical with an anonymous continuation of St. Thomas' commentary on the Meteorology (St. Thomas' commentary extended to the first two books only). Indeed, that continuation also contains a treatise on the rainbow (digressio de coloribus variis iridis), divided into eight questions (Grabmann 1922, p. 23). Various other treatises on the rainbow were composed at about this time, in Latin and Arabic, and it would be worth while to compare them. Finally, John of Paris may be the author of the Correctorium corruptorii (or Quare) written in defense of St. Thomas against the Franciscan William de la Mare (XIII-2); this is a very difficult question, for there are apparently various Correctoria or Correptoria, but it does not concern us.

Text. The Determinatio de modo existendi corporis Christi in sacramento was edited by Petrus Allix (London 1686). This Allix (1641–1717) was one of the French Protestant refugees in England (DNB 1, 334).

The De potestate was first printed together with the works of Durand of Saint Pourçain and others (Paris 1506). Then by Sim. Schardius (d. 1573) in his De iurisdictione etc. (Basel 1566), in his Syntagma (Strassburg 1609), and in his Sylloge (Strassburg 1618). Finally by Melchior Goldast: Monarchia (2, 108–47, Hanau 1612).

Criticism. Félix Lajard (HL 25, 244–70, 1869). Carlo Cipolla: Il trattato De monarchia di Dante Alighieri e l'opuscolo De potestate regia et papali di Giovanni da Parigi (Memorie della R. Accad. di Torino, ser. 2, 42, 325–419, 1892). Martin Grabmann: Studien zu Johannes Quidort von Paris (Sitzungsberichte der Bayerischen Akad., phil. Kl., 1922, vol. 3, 60 p., München 1922), very elaborate study largely derived from MSS. De Wulf (2, 47, 1926). Flick (vol. 1, 1930). Alfons Hufnagel: Studien zur Entwicklung des thomistischen Erkenntnisbegriffes im Anschluss an das Correctorium "Quare" (Beiträge zur Geschichte der Philosophie des Mittelalters vol. 31, no. 4, 140 p., Münster 1935). George Sarton: The tradition of the optics of Ibn al-Haitham (Isis 29, 403–6, 1938).

A4. Germanic Countries

RUPRECHT VON FREISING

Ruprecht (or Rupert) von Freising. German jurist (d. in or after 1329).

Ruprecht was born at Freising in Bavaria c. 1270–75. He completed in 1328 (not 1332) the compilation of a new code in German, the Rechtsbuch, which is important for the history of Bavarian civilization.

Another code, the so-called Landrechtsbuch, previously ascribed to him, is now recognized as a later abbreviated interpretation of Swabian law.

The name of Freising suggests at once a greater man than Ruprecht, the historian Otto of Freising (XII-2), one of the best historians of mediaeval times.

Text. Ruprecht's Rechtsbuch was edited by Lor. Westenrieder in his Beiträge zur vaterländischen Geschichte (no. 7, 250 p., Munich 1802). New edition by Hermann Knapp (145 p., Leipzig 1916).

Georg Ludwig v. Maurer: Das Stadt- und das Landrechtsbuch Ruprechts von Freising (464 p., Stuttgart 1839).

Criticism. v. Rockinger: Ueber die Grundlage des dem Ruprecht von Freising beigelegten Landrechtes (Sitzungsberichte der Münchener Akad., phil. Cl., 1871, p. 463–501), against the authenticity of the second code. Eisenhart (ADB 29, 746–47, 1889).

JOHANN VON BUCH

Johann von Buch (or Buck, Bok, Boich, etc.) the Younger. German jurist (fl. 1321–56).

Johann's father, the margravial high steward Nicolaus (or Claus) von Buch, died in 1314. His own career was spent as chamberlain, legal adviser, judge, etc. in the service of the duke of Braunschweig (Brunswick), then of the margraves of Brandenburg. In 1350 he was excommunicated together with his lord by Clement VI. He was last mentioned in 1356. He flourished mostly in Altmark, Brandenburg.

He exerted a deep influence upon the development and unification of German law, and its gradual impregnation with Roman ideas. The growth of German law had been considerably retarded by the lack of political unity in the Holy Roman Empire, and the existence not only of innumerable territorial divisions, but also of many social cleavages (witness the coexistence of feudal law, Lehnrecht; manorial law, Hofrecht; town law, Stadtrecht, and country law, Landrecht; peasant law, Bauernrecht; guild law, Zunftrecht, etc.).

He wrote in Lower Saxon dialect two important commentaries on the Sachsenspiegel (for which see Eike of Repgow, XIII-1):

1. After 1325, the oldest gloss to the Sachsenspiegel-Landrecht, wherein he tries to explain it with reference to foreign law and to harmonize it with the Leges and Canones.

2. Later, c. 1335, the Richtsteig Landrechts, a systematic account of procedure on the basis of the Sachsenspiegel, this time without reference to foreign law.

A Richtsteig Lehnrechts is also ascribed to him; the oldest gloss to the Sachsenspiegel-Lehnrecht, however, is probably a later production which originated in Upper Saxony.

Text. His gloss to the Sachsenspiegel-Landrecht is printed in the Cologne edition of 1480. The prologue to the gloss has been edited with notes by Carl Gustav Homeyer (Abhandlungen der Preussischen Akad., 58 p., Berlin 1854).

Der Richtsteig Landrechts nebst Cautela und Premis, edited by Carl Gustav Homeyer (674 p., Berlin 1857), with long introduction and glossary.

Criticism. Steffenhagen (ADB 3, 463, 1876). Vinogradoff (lecture 5, 1909).

B. CHRISTIAN EAST

B1. Byzantine Law

BLASTARES

Matthew Blastares, Ματθαῖος ὁ Βλαστάρης. Byzantine jurist (fl. 1335).

As in the case of his contemporary the jurist Armenopulos, about whom we know little beyond the fact that he completed the Hexabiblos in 1345, we know little more about Blastares than that he wrote the preface to his Syntagma in 1335. The little more is simply that Blastares was a monk and priest and lived in Salonica; he possibly died in the St. Isaac monastery of that city.

His main work is the Syntagma, which is a dictionary of canon and civil law, all the information relative to each subject being classified under the word representing that subject in the alphabetical order of these words. E.g., civil and canon law concerning marriage and women are dealt with in the chapters περὶ γάμου and περὶ γυναικῶν under the letter gamma. The sources of the information are seldom indicated; hence a critical study of Blastares' Syntagma is very complicated. According to his own preface, he used the nomocanon of 883, sometimes falsely ascribed to the patriarch Photios (IX-2).

The nomocanones are combinations of civil and canon law, complex codes of church laws (κανόνες) and worldly ones (νόμοι), which are typical of the theocratic Byzantine civilization. The most important nomocanones were the one of 883 and the revision made by Theodoros Bestes in 1090.

The Syntagma is important as one of the latest monuments of Byzantine law, but also because of its influence abroad. It interested Western humanists, but only in an archaeological way; on the contrary, its influence upon the Slavonic peoples was a deep and living one. The code of the Serbian tsar Stephen Dushan Urosh IV (ruled 1331–55), promulgated in 1349, included a selected abridgment of the Syntagma. There are various Slavonic translations of the Syntagma.

Blastares wrote other legal compendia generally appended to the Syntagma in the MSS and editions, and a few other treatises, (a) theological: on the procession of the Holy Spirit, addressed to Guy de Lusignan; (b) ecclesiastical: on the feast of unleavened bread (τὰ ἄζυμα) in the week after Easter, on the colyba (τὰ κόλυβα, boiled wheat distributed to the congregation of Orthodox churches on certain days, usually in remembrance of the dead); (c) apologetical or controversial: against the Jews (also ascribed to Matthew Cantacuzenos), against the Latins (ἔλεγχος τῆς πλάνης τῶν Λατίνων), against Barlaam and his disciples; (d) grammatical: a treatise on rhetoric.

Text. A fragment of the Syntagma was published by Antonius Augustinus of Saragossa (1517–86), archbishop of Tarragona, in his Collectio constitutionum graecarum (Lerida 1567), but the first complete edition was included by William Beveridge (1637–1708), bishop of St. Asaph, in his Συνοδικόν, a collection of canons and decrees of the Orthodox church (2, 1–272, Oxford 1672). Later edition by Rhalli and Potli: Σύνταγμα τῶν θείων καὶ ἱερῶν κανόνων (vol. 6, Athens 1859), reprinted in PG (vols. 144, 145, Paris 1865).

Criticism. Krumbacher (p. 607–8, 1897), only a few lines. L. Petit (DTC 2, 916–17, 1905; reprinted 1923).

ARMENOPULOS

Constantine Armenopulos, Κωνσταντῖνος ὁ Ἀρμενόπουλος. Byzantine jurist (fl. 1345).

The form Ἀρμενόπουλος accepted by Greek scholars is more plausible than the form Ἁρμενόπουλος (Harmenopulos) generally accepted by Western Byzantinists.

Constantine was born c. 1320, his father being major-domo of the imperial court in Constantinople, and his mother, Muzeline (Μουζελίνη), a cousin of John Cantacuzenos. He died in 1383.

His main work, a small compendium of law, was completed in 1345. It is generally called Ἑξάβιβλος because of its subdivision into six books, or manual of laws (πρόχειρον τῶν νόμων, manuale legum), and includes not only civil and criminal codes, but also additional regulations, such as a rural code. It is naturally derived from all previous codifications, such as the Corpus juris of Justinian (VI-1) and the Basilica as revised by order of Constantinos VII Porphyrogennetos (X-2). In fact, it would seem to be derived from earlier texts of the early codes than those which have come down to us, and may thus be used for the criticism of the sources of the Justinian codex.

The Hexabiblos is a mediocre compilation, but it is interesting because it is the latest Byzantine monument of its kind and because it was exceedingly popular and continued to have some influence almost until our own days! It was translated into vulgar Greek c. 1490 by Nicolaos Cunales Critopulos (Νικόλαος Κουνάλης ὁ Κριτόπουλος) together with the manual of canon law of Matthaeos Blastares. Two other translations into modern Greek were made, by Theodosios Zygomalas (Θεοδόσιος Ζυγομαλᾶς) in the sixteenth century, and later by Alexios Spanos (Ἀλέξιος Σπανός). In 1835, it became the official lawbook of Greece, and it is still used (or was until recently) by the judges of that country and of Bessarabia. On the other hand, it attracted the curiosity of many sixteenth-century humanists.

Armenopulos compiled a dictionary wherein the syntactic usage of words was illustrated. He wrote a short treatise on Christian heresies, and theological treatises, including one against Gregorios Palamas. He was naturally involved in the Hesychastic controversy, for Salonica, not very far from the Holy Mountain, was the center of the storm. It would seem that he tried to act as moderator, examining the controversy in a legal way, and concluding that the arguments of both sides were equally wrong. This caused an attack from Gregorios Acindynos, who accused him of trying to introduce a new heterodoxy.

Text. PG (vol. 150, 1865) contains the De haeresibus, De fide orthodoxa, Narratiuncula de tribus tomis synodicis, Tomus in Palamam, Epitome divinorum et sacrorum canonum.

The Hexabiblos or Promptuarium juris civilis was edited in Greek by Theodoricus Adamaeus (428 p., Paris 1540). A Latin translation by Bernhardus a Rey appeared in Cologne 1547. Many later editions in Greek and Latin. It will suffice to cite the critical one, with Latin translation, glossary, etc., by Karl Wilhelm Ernst Heimbach (Leipzig 1851).

A German version appeared in the sixteenth century (Francfort a.M. 1564), Handbuch und Auszug kayserlicher und bürgerlicher Rechte, edited by the German jurist Justinus Göbler (Goblerus, 1503–67).

Spanos' version in modern Greek was printed in Venice 1744 and many times afterward.

Partial English translation by Edwin Hanson Freshfield: A manual of Byzantine law, vol. 6, on torts and crimes (66 p., Cambridge 1930).

The treatise on heresies, περὶ ὧν οἱ κατὰ καιροὺς αἱρετικοὶ ἔδοξαν, De opinionibus haereticorum qui singulis temporibus exstiterunt. First edited (Basel 1578) together with the Legatio ad Armenios of Manuel Comnenos (emperor 1143–80), with translation by the Westphalian Orientalist Joannes Leunclavius (Löwenklau, 1533–93). Re-edited (Helmstadt 1612) together with a treatise on the same subject by Honorius of Autun (XII-1).

Tomus contra Gregorium Palamam, first edited in Greek and Latin by Leon Allatios of Chios (1586–1669) in the latter's Graecia orthodoxa (1, 780–85, Rome 1652).

Criticism. Emil Herzog: Πραγματεία περὶ τοῦ προχείρου ἢ τῆς ἑξαβίβλου Κωνσταντίνου τοῦ Ἀρμενοπούλου (104 p., Munich 1837). Krumbacher (p. 103, 607, 610, 786, 1897). Tafrali (1912). S. Sakellariados: Περὶ τοῦ βίου τοῦ Κ. Ἀρμενοπούλου καὶ τοῦ ἔργου αὐτοῦ (Athens 1916), work known to me only through the summary in the Eleutheroudakis encyclopaedia (2, 478–79, 1927). Vasiliev (2, 412, 1932).

THOMAS MAGISTER

Θωμᾶς ὁ μάγιστρος. Byzantine philologist (fl. first quarter of fourteenth century).

The circumstances of his life are unknown, except that he was a monk and was often called Theodulos monachos (Θεόδουλος ὁ μοναχός), that he flourished in Constantinople under Andronicos II (1282–1328), but mainly in Salonica. There was a friendly rivalry between the men of letters of Salonica and Constantinople (the two main intellectual centers of the empire), and frequent relations between them. Thomas' writings show that he was very familiar with the conditions of life, many of them very unpleasant, in Salonica, and he went sometimes to the capital for political reasons. For example, in or after 1310 his fellow citizens sent him to Constantinople to plead the cause of general Chandrenos, who had successfully defended Salonica against the Catalans, yet had fallen into disgrace.

His main work is a collection of Greek words and phrases arranged in alphabetical order, Ἐκλογὴ ὀνομάτων καὶ ῥημάτων ἀττικῶν, largely derived from the works of the best ancient writers, some of which (see below) he had studied himself, but also from other works of the same kind, even from such recent ones as the Συλλογή and the Περὶ σχεδῶν of Manuel Moschopulos. This would suggest that he was perhaps a little younger than the latter and that his activity continued for some time after 1316.

Thomas wrote many literary exercises, an apology for Chandrenos addressed to Andronicos II, an account of the cruel invasions of Catalans and Turks into Thessaly and Macedonia addressed to the philosopher Joseph,[8] περὶ τῶν ἐν τῇ Ἰταλῶν καὶ Περσῶν ἐφόδῳ γεγενημένων, and two political treatises dealing respectively with the duties of kings (λόγος περὶ βασιλείας) and with the duties of subjects (περὶ πολιτείας).

[8] A correspondent of Nicephoros Chumnos and Joannes Chumnos. Theodoros Metochites wrote his necrology (see p. 889, note 32).

Finally, he compiled scholia to Aeschylos, Sophocles, Euripides, and to the letters of Synesios of Cyrene (V-1).

Text. The Ἐκλογή was first edited by the printer Zacharias Callierges (fl. 1499–1523) in Rome 1517. Many later editions: Paris 1532, Franeker 1690, 1698, Leiden 1757, etc.

Modern editions by Friedrich Ritschl (650 p., Halle i.S. 1832), and by Karl Jacobitz (Leipzig 1833).

The defense of Chandrenos, the account of the Catalan invasion, and other pieces were edited by Jean François Boissonade: Anecdota graeca (2, 188–268, Paris 1830).

The two political treatises, De regis officiis and De subditorum officiis, may be read in PG (vol. 145, 1865), together with many other writings.

For the scholia, see Krumbacher.

Criticism. Krumbacher (chiefly p. 548–50, 1897). Theodor Hopfner: Thomas Magister, Demetrios Triklinios, Manuel Moschopulos; eine Studie über ihren Sprachgebrauch in den Scholien zu Aischylos, Sophokles, Euripides, Aristophanes, Hesiod, Pindar und Theokrit (Sitzungsberichte der Kais. Akad. der Wissenschaften, phil. Kl., vol. 172, 73 p., Wien 1912). Tafrali (1912). Eleutheroudakis encyclopaedia (6, 603, Athens 1929).

D. EASTERN ISLĀM

D1. Mamlūk

IBN JAMĀ'A

Abū 'Abdallāh Muḥammad ibn Ibrāhīm Ibn Jamā'a. Syrian traditionist and student of government (1241–1333).

Ibn Jamā'a was born in Ḥamāh in October 1241, was educated in Damascus, and became there a professor of Shāfi'ī theology. In 1288 he was appointed qāḍī in Jerusalem; in 1291, qāḍī al-quḍāt in Egypt, and later in Damascus. He was also a preacher in the Umaiya mosque. After the death of Ibn Daqīq al-'Īd (1302), he was recalled to Cairo, where he continued the duties of judge and teacher until 1327. He died in February 1333.

His most important work is a treatise on the rights and duties of kings, Taḥrīr al-aḥkām fī tadbīr ahl (or millat) al-islām. It is far less known than the Kitāb al-aḥkām al-sulṭānīya of 'Alī ibn Muḥammad al-Māwardī (XI-2), also a Shāfi'ī doctor, but has the advantage of remaining closer to the realities of government, of being more practical. It covers about 2,400 lines, and is divided into 17 chapters: (1) need of an imām (leader of the Muslim people) and conditions of that leadership; (2) rights and duties of imām and sulṭān; (3) appointment and duties of ministers; (4) use of princes for the preparation of war; (5) preservation of legal institutions and determination of constitutional offices; (6) use of armies and their preparation for the jihād; (7) gifts and investitures of the ruler; (8) gifts to the soldiers and their duties in jihād; (9) use of horses and weapons, armament of the soldiers; (10) organization of the ruler's cabinet (dīwān) and its subdivisions; (11) excellence of the holy war and preparation for it; (12) various kinds of jihād, and its continuance against a brave enemy; (13, 14) booty and its just division; (15) armistices and agreements for the sake of security; (16) fighting against Muslim rulers; (17) conditions of vassalage (dhimma) imposed upon conquered people.

It is remarkable how much of this book on constitutional law is really devoted to holy war (jihād), its preparation, conditions, results. This illustrates the organic aggressiveness of the Muslim community, at least against foreign non-Muslims. That aggressiveness was an unavoidable consequence of the religious, totalitarian, and fanatical nature of the genuine Muslim state.

Among the other works of Ibn Jamā'a I shall mention only a kind of general guidebook for students called Tadhkirat al-sāmi' wal-mutakallim fī ādāb al-'ālim wal muta'allim, composed in 1273, which continued the tradition begun by Burhān al-dīn al-Zarnūjī (XIII-1), exemplified also in his own time by Ibn al-Akfānī.

The profession of judge and professor was continued in the Ibn Jamā'a family, e.g., by a son, 'Abd al-'Azīz (d. 1366), a grandson, Ibrāhīm (d. 1388), a great-grandson, Muḥammad ibn abī Bakr (1357–1416). The last-named one was not only a theologian, but also a physician, established in Cairo, where he died of the plague. The Taḥrīr al-aḥkām of his ancestor was wrongly ascribed to him.

Text. The Taḥrīr al-aḥkām was edited, translated into German, and annotated by Hans Kofler: Handbuch des islamischen Staats- und Verwaltungsrechtes von Badr ad-dīn Ibn Jamā'ah (Islamica 6, 349–414; 7, 1 ff., Leipzig 1934–35; Abhandlungen für die Kunde des Morgenlandes 23, part 6, 18–128, Leipzig 1938).

Criticism. Brockelmann (2, 74, 72, 112, 94, 1902; suppt. 2, 80, 78, 138, 111, 1938). EI (2, 371, 1916). Farmer (no. 229, p. 54, 1940), apropos of a treatise on the licitness of music by the grandson Ibrāhīm ibn 'Abd al-Raḥīm ibn Muḥammad (d. 1388).

IBN AL-UKHUWWA

Ḍiyā' al-dīn Muḥammad ibn Muḥammad al-Qurashī al-Shāfi'ī, generally called Ibn al-Ukhuwwa. Egyptian (or Syrian) author of a book on ḥisba (d. May 2, 1329).

Ibn al-Ukhuwwa's book entitled Ma'ālim al-qurba fī aḥkām al-ḥisba is a guide for the muḥtasib, who was a kind of public censor of morality, especially trade morality, an inspector of weights and measures, trade regulations, etc.[9] It is not known when the function appeared; it probably developed gradually. The subject is already discussed in books of the second half of the eleventh century,[10] to wit, in the Aḥkām al-sulṭānīya of 'Alī ibn Muḥammad al-Māwardī (XI-2) of Baghdād, and in the great theological treatise Iḥyā 'ulūm al-dīn of al-Ghazzālī (XI-2). By the end of the same century a special treatise was devoted to the subject, this being the earliest known to me, by Muḥammad ibn abī Muḥammad al-Saqaṭī of Malaga (Isis 19, 528). Among later treatises I shall mention only the one composed in Seville at the beginning of the twelfth century by Ibn 'Abdūn (Isis 24, 200) and the Nihāyat al-rutba fī ṭalab al-ḥisba written for Ṣalāḥ al-dīn (ruled 1169–93) by 'Abd al-Raḥmān ibn Naṣr (XII-2). Similar topics (regulations relative to arts and trades, falsifications, charlatanism) were discussed in the Kitāb al-ishāra ilā maḥāsin al-tijāra by Ja'far ibn 'Alī al-Dimashqī (XII-2) and in the Kitāb al-mukhtār fī kashf al-asrār by al-Jawbarī (XIII-1).

These books interest the historian of science only indirectly (e.g., with regard to the regulation of the medical professions), but they are of considerable value for the student of economic and social life in Islamic countries. Please note that we find them in 'Irāq, Persia, Syria, Egypt as well as in Spain. In order to illustrate more completely the kind of information which they contain, I reproduce below

[9] The word al-muḥtasib is the root of the Spanish almotacén, meaning an officer of police who inspects weights and measures.

[10] Even before, witness the lost treatise by al-Sarakhsī (IX-2). Franz Rosenthal: Aḥmad ibn al-Ṭayyib al-Sarakhsī (p. 23, 81, American Oriental Society, New Haven, Conn. 1943; Isis 35, 56).

the table of contents of the Ma'ālim al-qurba. It is divided into 70 chapters, as follows: (1) qualifications for the ḥisba and duties of the muḥtasib; (2) enforcement of the law; (3) wine and unlawful musical instruments; (4) duties of and to "protected," non-Muslim, people (dhimmī); (5) funeral rites; (6) forbidden commercial transactions (e.g., usury, purchase in advance, "futures"); (7) practices forbidden to men (as wearing of silk or gold); (8) things forbidden in the markets (sūq, aswāq); (9, 10) weights, measures, moneys; (11) flour merchants and millers; (12) bakers; (13) sellers of roast meat; (14) sausage makers; (15) sellers of liver and appetizers; (16) butchers; (17) sellers of sheep's heads; (18) cookshops; (19) sellers of pickled meats; (20) makers of harīsa (a special dish made with cereals and ground meat); (21) fish fryers; (22) makers of zulābīya (a pastry); (23) makers of ḥalwā (sweets); (24) makers of syrups; (25) makers of drugs and resins; (26) regulations of small trades; (27) milk sellers; (28) drapers; (29) brokers or criers (dallāl); (30) weavers; (31) tailors, repairers, fullers, makers of caps; (32) makers of silk wares; (33) dyers; (34) cotton spinners; (35) flax spinners; (36) money-changers; (37) goldsmiths; (38) coppersmiths and blacksmiths; (39) shoemakers; (40) farriers; (41) brokers dealing in slaves, houses, and animals; (42) bath keepers; (43) lote-leaf sellers (sidr, lotus); (44) bloodletters and cuppers; (45) physicians, oculists, surgeons, and bonesetters; (46) teachers; (47) mosque attendants and muezzins (the latter must have some astronomical knowledge); (48) preachers; (49) astrologers and letter writers (the combination is curious); (50) punishments; (51) judges and witnesses; (52) princes and governors; (53) muḥtasib; (54) shipmen; (55) sellers of earthenware; (56) potters and ceramists; (57) needle makers; (58) spindle makers; (59) sellers of henna (the plant ḥinnā, Lawsonia inermis, used to dye the skin, hair, nails); (60) comb makers; (61) pressers of sesame and olive oil; (62) sieve makers; (63) tanners and makers of leather bottles; (64) felters; (65) furriers; (66) makers of reed mats; (67) straw sellers; (68) sellers of timber, palm logs, and sawdust; (69) carpenters, sawyers, masons, lime burners, etc.; (70) alia.

The chapters vary considerably in length, some (50, 51) extending to many pages, while others consist of only a few lines. It is clear that among them they cover pretty well every aspect of the social life of Muslims. They describe mediaeval conditions, but in many Islamic countries similar conditions obtained until the beginning of our century; indeed, some of these conditions still obtain in some countries and are immediately recognizable by any attentive person who, like myself, has lived in them.

Text. The Ma'ālim al-qurba was edited by Reuben Levy, with English summary, glossary, and index (Gibb memorial, new ser. 12, 378 p., London 1938; Isis 31, 151). The Arabic text covers 240 p.

Criticism. Levy's introduction. For comparisons with other works of the same kind, see Introd. 1, 753, 780; 2, 462–63, 635; Isis 19, 528; 24, 200. Maurice Gaudefroy-Demombynes: Sur quelques ouvrages de ḥisba (Journal asiatique 230, 449–57, 1938, real date 1940; Isis 33, 135).

The office of muḥtasib is mentioned by Bābar (1, 313, 1921).

D2. 'Irāq and Farther East

IBN NUBĀTA

Muḥammad ibn Muḥammad ibn Nubāta al-Fāriqī. Iraqian man of letters (1287–1366).

He was a descendant of the famous preacher Ibn Nubāta (946–84) and was born like him in Maiyāfāriqīn, in Jazīra, region of the upper Tigris. He was born in 1287, educated in Egypt, and in 1316 established himself in Damascus. He spent some time at the court of Abū-l-Fidā' in Ḥamāh. He was a government secretary in Damascus, and later (1360) in Cairo under the Mamlūk sulṭān Nāṣir Ḥasan (second rule 1354–61). He was protected by Abū-l-Fidā' (prince of Ḥamāh 1310–31) and by the latter's son 'Imād al-dīn. At one time he was in control of the church of the Resurrection (kanīsat al-qumāma, for qiyāma) in Jerusalem and of the Christian pilgrimages. He died in 1366.

He wrote many poems, erotic (Sūq al-raqīq), epigrammatic, didactic, rhetorical, of no interest to us. He edited two collections of letters and compliments, the Ta'līq al-dīwān (1342) and the Saj' al-muṭawwaq. He composed a treatise on the duties of princes, Sulūk duwal al-mulūk, divided into six parts: (1) their privileges, and their duties (2) to themselves, (3) to their families, (4) to their servants and courtiers, (5) to the people, (6) to the army.

Criticism. Brockelmann (2, 10, 1902; suppt. 2, 4, 1938).

E. INDIA AND BURMA

CAṆḌEŚVARA

Hindu jurist (fl. c. 1314).

He was a minister to the king Harasiṃhadeva of Mithilā (in Videha, north of the river Ganges). Mithilā was the seat of a Brahmanical college in the fourteenth century. The king Harasiṃha flourished c. 1314–24.

Caṇḍeśvara was a student of law in the broad Oriental sense (like fiqh in Islām, or for that matter like jurisprudentia = rerum divinarum atque humanarum notitia among the Romans). According to Hindu thought, there are three aims (trivarga) in life: dharma or the fulfillment of religious and moral duties; artha or practical matters, including technicalities, domestic economy, politics; kāma, satisfaction of sexual needs. That classification goes back at least to the time of Patañjali (II-2 B.C.). Now, law or jurisprudence cuts across these three divisions because there are rules relative to each, and thus one has three kinds of lawbooks or codes of regulations, called respectively dharmaśāstra (these being the most important), arthaśāstra, kāmaśāstra.

In 1314 Caṇḍeśvara supervised for king Harasiṃha the edition of a book of law of the second kind, the Nītiratnākara (Jewel mine of politics). It deals with the most important part of arthaśāstra, that is, politics or nītiśāstra, the science of government, also called rājanīti, royal politics.

Caṇḍeśvara also wrote in the field of dharmaśāstra, composing an elaborate code called Smṛitiratnākara (that is, written in verse for mnemonic and traditional purposes), and a shorter one, Kṛityacintāmaṇi, restricted to the purely religious duties or observances.

Text. The more strictly legal part of the Smṛitiratnākara, the sixth out of seven, entitled Vivādaratnākara, was edited by Dīnanātha Vidyālaṅkāra (in 7 parts, 681 p., Bibliotheca indica, Calcutta 1885–87). Re-edited in same series (735 p., Calcutta 1931).

Rājanītiratnākara, edited by Kashi-prasad Jayaswal (124 p., Bihar and Orissa Research Society, Patna 1924).

Criticism. Julius Jolly: Recht und Sitte (Grundriss der indo-arischen Philologie vol. 2, part 8, p. 36, 105, 1896). Duff (p. 214, 216, 1899). Winternitz (3, 502, 532, 1922). Dey (p. 130, 1927). Emeneau (nos. 2286, 3290, 1935).

F. CHINA

SU T'IEN-CHIO

Chinese public servant, biographer, writer on government, Buddhist (1294–1352).

Su T'ien-chio, styled Po Hsiu, was born in 1294 in Chên-ting, Chihli. According to the Hsin Yüan shih, chüan 211, he was a student of Wu Ch'êng; he graduated in the Han-lin yüan in 1324. He entered the civil service and finally became a censor, distinguishing himself by his zeal and energy. He was known to his disciples as Tzŭ chi hsien sheng. He died in 1352.

He wrote a collection of biographies of civil servants of the Yüan dynasty, in 15 chüan, Yüan ch'ao ming ch'ên shih lüeh, and a short treatise on the art of government, Chih shih kuei chien.

According to the Yüan shih, chüan 183, he started to write two other works, to wit, a history of Liao and Chin, Liao Chin chi nien, and a detailed account of the Yellow River, Huang Ho yüan wei, but died before completing them.

Criticism. Giles (no. 1788, 1898). Wieger (p. 391, 1920).

G. JAPAN

JAPANESE LAW

A new code, partly based upon the Jōei shikimoku, was compiled in 1336. It was called Kemmu shikimoku, because it was promulgated during the Kemmu era (1334–36). It contains, divided into 17 chapters, a collection of moral and political precepts. It remained in force during the whole Ashikaga period.

The Kemmu era extended from 1334 to 1336 for the Southern court, but this nengō was used for two more years by the Northern court. Japanese chronology, which is difficult enough for the Western scholar, is made still more difficult for the period 1336–93, because of the coexistence of two imperial courts and two series of nengō!

Text. John Carey Hall: Japanese feudal laws. II. The Ashikaga code. Translation of the Kemmu shikimoku, A.D. 1336 (Transactions of the Asiatic Society of Japan 36, 3–25, Tokyo 1908).

Criticism. Papinot (p. 270, 823, 1909). Brinkley and Kikuchi (p. 403, 1914).

KITABATAKE CHIKAFUSA

Japanese statesman and publicist (1292–1354).

The Kitabatake family was a daimyō family of imperial blood. Chikafusa was its first illustrious member, but he counted among his ancestors many distinguished courtiers and priests. He is also called Minamoto no Chikafusa. He was born in 1292, and was appointed tutor to the crown prince. When the latter died, in 1329, Chikafusa assumed the Buddhist habit. He was passionately devoted to the Southern dynasty[11] (whose rule was challenged by the Northern dynasty from

[11] The words Northern and Southern dynasty (or court) should not be taken too literally. The partisans of either were scattered throughout the islands, according to the fancies of their feudal princes (daimyō). See map of their distribution under the rule of the (Southern) emperor Go-Daigo (ruled 1319–38) in Brinkley and Kikuchi (p. 403, 1914).

1331 to 1412), and led an army for its defense. For a time he was established at the Odawara castle in the Sagami province.

It was during his sojourn in Odawara (1340–43) that he wrote his masterpiece, the Jingō shōtō-ki[12] (Correct genealogy of the divine emperor, or record proving that the emperor is the genuine descendant of the gods) in six volumes. The purpose of that work was to prove the divine claim of the sovereign of the Southern court. It includes a history of Japan from the beginning to 1335, and dissertations on government and politics. It explains the national religion, Shintō, and its relations to the imperial power and to other religious sects. The work was written for the special benefit of the young emperor Go-Murakami (b. 1328, ruled 1339–68).

Chikafusa also wrote for the same emperor (thus after 1339) the Shoku-gen shō, describing the development of the governmental offices.

He was the first Japanese to explain the Chinese theory of government and to apply it to Japanese conditions. He was also the first to attempt a philosophical interpretation of Japanese history. He suggested that Shintō, Buddhism, and Confucianism could be welded into a single system.

Text. The Jingō shōtō-ki was not printed until 1649. German translation, Jinnō Shōtōki, Buch von der wahren Gott-Kaiser-Herrschafts-Linie, with introduction and notes by Hermann Bohner (Japanisch-Deutsch-Kultur-Institut, 342 p., Tōkyō 1935).

Criticism. W. G. Aston: Japanese literature (p. 164–69, 1899). Karl Florenz: Geschichte der japanischen Litteratur (p. 341–45, Leipzig 1906). Brinkley and Kikuchi (p. 403, 1914). Dai shakka jiten (1932).

[12] The first syllable, jin, corresponds to the Chinese character shên, meaning spirits, gods, the usual Japanese pronunciation of which is kami; gō or kwō means emperor; shō, correct; tō, line; ki, record. The reading Jinnō is now preferred to Jinkō.

CHAPTER XIV

PHILOLOGY

(First Half of the Fourteenth Century)

N.B. Only the main articles are grouped in this chapter. The philological contributions of many other men, whose main work was done in other fields, are related in other chapters. For a general survey of philology in the first half of the fourteenth century, see section XIV of chapter I, summarizing the facts concerning more than thirty-one languages. More information on the men referred to in that section can easily be found by means of the index.

The following notes deal only with eight kinds of philologists, Latin, Greek, Coptic, Hebrew, Arabic, Turkish, Chinese, and Japanese, instead of thirty-one.

LATIN

YON

French Latin grammarian. Assistant schoolmaster (summonitor) in the school of Soissons (Aisne) in 1301. He wrote in 1301 a long commentary on the Doctrinale puerorum of Alexandre de Villedieu (XIII-1). It is divided into two parts, dealing respectively with chapters I to IX of the Doctrinale, and with chapter X relative to accentuation and punctuation. Chapters XI and XII (prosody and figures) are not commented upon.

Yon often refers to other glosses on the Doctrinale, and to Robert Kilwardby's (XIII-2) commentary on Priscian (VI-1); he was himself quoted by later glossators (under the name Glosa communis or Glosa Antequam ulterius).

Text. Unpublished; for MSS see HL.
Criticism. Léopold Delisle (HL 31, 1–21, 1893).

SIGER OF COURTRAI

Siger of Gulleghem. Flemish logician and grammarian (d. 1341).

Siger was dean of the chapter of Our Lady in Courtrai (on the Lys, Flanders; Kortrijk aan de Leije), from 1308 to 1323; magister of Paris from 1309, member of the Sorbonne and its procurator in 1315. He died on May 30, 1341, bequeathing many books to the Sorbonne (these books still exist, in the Bibliothèque nationale).

He wrote various treatises, Ars priorum, Fallaciae, Sophismata, Summa modorum significandi, which remained unpublished until recently. The last named of these books is apparently the most important. It explains Siger's views on speculative grammar.

I have already dealt with the "speculative grammarians" or "modistae" in my volume 2 (p. 696, 802, 967), though I failed to speak of the real originator, one Pierre Hélie, who taught in Paris about the middle of the twelfth century.[1] I

[1] Pierre Hélie or Petrus Helias is a rather mysterious personality. See short note in HL (12, 486–87, 1830). According to Wallerand (Siger de Courtrai, p. 36), Pierre Hélie was to Priscianus what Ibn Rushd was to Aristotle! As a matter of fact Siger de Courtrai and other modistae called him always the "commentator," no other name being used.

began my own account with John of Garland (XIII-1), and spoke also of Boetius of Dacia (XIII-2) and of the treatise ascribed to Duns Scot. Still another was Michel of Marbais, who is difficult to place.[2] Siger of Courtrai represents almost the end of that interesting, if abortive, movement.

The aim of the modistae was to harmonize grammar with logic, or, to put it otherwise, to reconcile Donatus and Priscian with Aristotle. Their efforts miscarried because of excessive apriorism; they failed to realize that grammar is a descriptive science, like anatomy, and instead conceived a purely rational grammar which would be the same for all languages; they mixed grammar not only with logic, but also with metaphysics! There is, however, some logic in grammar, and it was worth while to bring out what there was of it; to explain the modi significandi and the modi intelligendi.

The teaching of the modistae did not so much supersede that of the old grammarians, Donatus and Priscian (as I put it in Introd. 2, 696), as complete it and attempt a philosophical justification of it. In fact, in Paris it gave a new, if short, lease on life to them as against the versified treatises of the new grammarians, Eberhard of Bethune and Alexander of Villedieu (XIII-1). The old grammarians were banished from the schools of Toulouse in 1328, but in Paris they continued to hold their ground until 1366. On the other hand, the speculative grammarians did not pay sufficient attention to the new logical ideas introduced by Peter of Spain (XIII-2) in his Parva logicalia (De terminorum proprietatibus). Under the influence of Peter of Spain, logic would become more and more exclusively an instrument for the art of discussion. The last of the modistae, Siger de Courtrai, was more moderate than some of his predecessors or contemporaries such as Michel of Marbais, yet he could not save a movement doomed by its own artificiality.

There are so many points of likeness between Siger's work and the Summa totius logicae ascribed to St. Thomas Aquinas that the Summa is now believed to be a later work contemporary with Siger or perhaps even a little later.

Text. G. Wallerand: Les oeuvres de Siger de Courtrai; étude critique et textes inédits (Les philosophes belges vol. 8, 250 p., Louvain 1913). Contains all the texts mentioned above.

Criticism. Alfred Niglis: Siger von Courtrai (76 p., Freiburg i.B. 1903). H. Vercruysse: Etude critique des sources relatives à la personalité de Siger de Courtrai (Mémoires du cercle historique de Courtrai 4, 37–85, 1910). M. De Wulf (Biographie nationale de Belgique 22, 492–94, 1914).

CONRAD OF HEINRICHAU

Silesian Cistercian monk, grammarian and computist (fl. 1340).

Konrad z Henrykowa. Flourished in the Cistercian monastery of Heinrichau near Münsterberg (35 miles south of Breslau). The Compotus novus ecclesiasticus compilatus et scriptus a fratre Conrado de Heinrichowe exists in an autograph MS of the University of Breslau (MS IV Q 92) dated 1340. That MS includes many works written in the same hand, to wit:

1. Vocabularius rerum, Latin and German (chiefly Latin), derived from Isidore of Seville (VII-1), Papias the Lombard (XI-2), Hugutio of Pisa (XII-2), "Brito, magister Moyses grecus et quidam alii fide digni."

[2] Also called Michel of Brabant and Michel of Roubaix (?). See Notices et extraits (22, part 2, 41, 1868; also by index); Wallerand (op. cit.). This Michel, who wrote Quaestiones super Priscianum and a Tractatus supra grammaticam, was apparently the most speculative of the modistae.

2. The Compotus already mentioned, dated 1340.
3. Tables for calculating the golden number.
4. Compotus manualis Joannis de Pulchrorivo (i.e., Schönbach, close to Neumarkt, 18 miles from Breslau).
5. De coelis et sphaeris planetarum et de quatuor elementis.
6. Tables of the signs of the zodiac for each month.
7. Tabula inventionis lunae.
8. Fragment beginning "Ptolemeus dicit in Centiloquio."
9. Brief chronicle of Polish-Silesian history, 970–1326 (De cronica Polonorum; Breve chronicon Silesiae).

Nos. 1, 2, 9 are ascribed to our Conrad; no. 4 to John of Schönbach; the authorship of the other items is uncertain. Conrad copied them all and thus showed his interest in them.

Zinner mentions various MSS ascribed to Joannes de Pulchrorivo (= Schönbach), one of them dated 1279, in his Verzeichnis der astronomischen Handschriften (nos. 8810–15, 1925; Isis 15, 193–95).

Text. None of these texts is published, except the meager annals, edited at various times, e.g. by Gustav Adolf Stenzel: Scriptores rerum silesiacarum (1, 33–37, Breslau 1835).

Criticism. A. W. E. Th. Henschel: Schlesiens wissenschaftliche Zustände im 14. Jahrhundert (p. 14–15, Breslau 1550). Johann Heyne: Dokumentirte Geschichte des Bisthums und Hochstiftes Breslau (2, 200, Breslau 1864). Aleksander Birkenmajer: Astronomowie i astrologowie śląscy w wiekach średnich (40 p., Katowice 1937; p. 15).

GREEK

TRICLINIOS

Demetrios Triclinios, Δημήτριος ὁ Τρικλίνιος. Byzantine philologist who flourished at the beginning of the fourteenth century; the greatest of his time.

Though Triclinios was head and shoulders above his contemporaries Manuel Moschopulos and Thomas Magister in the field of textual criticism, and sometimes anticipated the niceties of modern philology, the circumstances of his life are almost completely unknown. We do not even know where he flourished, though it was probably in Constantinople.

He wrote a number of scholia to Hesiodos, Pindaros, Aeschylos, Sophocles, Aristophanes, and Theocritos. Some of these scholia are abundant, e.g., those relative to Sophocles cover 147 closely printed pages in the Greek Sophocles published by Adrianus Turnebus (1512–65), i.e., Adrien Tournebu of Andelys in Normandy, in Paris 1553.

Text. See Krumbacher. There is no point in citing here the editions of the scholia, which concern more directly the bibliography of the authors commented upon.

Criticism. Krumbacher (p. 554–56, 1897). Theodor Hopfner: Thomas Magister usw. (Sitzungsberichte der Kais. Akad. der Wissenschaften, philos. Kl., vol. 172, 73 p., Wien 1912).

COPTIC

ABŪ-L-BARAKĀT

Coptic theologian and grammarian writing in Arabic (d. 1324).

Abū-l-Barakāt al-shaykh Shams al-Ri'āsa ibn al-shaykh al-As'ad, called Ibn

Kabar.[3] Coptic (Monophysitic) theologian who was secretary to the amīr Baibars al-Manṣūrī.[4] He was a priest in the church al-Mu'allaqa in old Cairo. He died on May 10, 1324.[5]

He wrote various books on theology:

1. Kitāb jalā' al-'uqūl fī 'ilm al-uṣūl, on principles of Christian theology, as the unity of God, the three hypostases (iqnūm, aqānīm), the corporification of Christ; 18 chapters. MSS are dated 1323, 1333.

2. Miṣbāḥ al-ẓulma wa īḍāḥ al-khidma (Lamp of the darkness and explanation of the service). Large theological treatise divided into 24 chapters, explaining the dogmas, the points of agreement and disagreement with other sects, the lives of the apostles, the canons and councils of the church, the organization of the church, the main ecclesiastical writers and their books. In short, it is a sort of religious and ecclesiastical encyclopaedia for the use of Copts. It includes two lists of Christ's seventy disciples, derived respectively from a Syriac and from a Coptic tradition.

3. Treatise against the Jews and the Muslims.

4. Treatise against fatalism.

5. Sermons (mawā'iẓ) for the Coptic holidays.

6. Al-sullam al-kabīr (Scala magna), a Coptic-Arabic vocabulary (c. 1316).

This last item is the most interesting to us, especially because Coptic items are very rare in this work. I referred to the Coptic version of the Bible (c. II-2; Introd. 1, 291), to Horapollon (c. IV-1; Introd. 1, 358), to a Coptic medical papyrus (c. IX-2; Introd. 1, 614), but unfortunately I did not speak of the Coptic texts on grammar and lexicography.

The Coptic language (even as the Syriac) was rapidly and almost completely superseded by the Arabic, both languages being preserved only for liturgical purposes.[6] Thus by the end of the tenth century it was already necessary to teach the Coptic language to the clergy, for they could no longer obtain their knowledge of it from their mothers' lips. The ancient books of Coptic philology available to us date from the eleventh to the fourteenth century, being written by such men as Athanasios of Qūṣ (eleventh century), Anbā Yuḥannā, bishop of Samannūd (c. 1240), Abū-l-Faraj ibn al-'Assāl (c. 1250), Abu Isḥāq ibn al-'Assāl, Ibn Kātib Qaiṣar, al-Wajīh al-Qalyūbī, Ibn al-Duhairī, Abū Shākir ibn al-Rāhib (c. 1280), and finally Abū-l-Barakāt Shams al-Ri'āsa. These men have been named in rough chronological order; all of them except the first and the last belong to the thirteenth century.

Their philological works were derived from Arabic and were of two kinds, grammars called muqaddama (introduction) and vocabularies called ladder (sullam, scala). The term scala as used by Coptic scholars has become more comprehensive; it may refer not only to a vocabulary, but to a grammar as well.

The Coptic scalae may be divided into two groups, those in which the Boḥairī dialect, spoken in the Delta, dominates, and those containing words of the Ṣa'īdī dialect or dialect of Upper Egypt.

The Scala magna of Abū-l-Barakāt belongs to the first group, which is by far the

[3] The vocalization Kabar (not Kabur, Kubr, Kibr, etc.) is the accepted one in the Coptic community of Cairo.

[4] That is, not the sultan Baibars, as fathers Mallon and Cheikho write it, but the dawādār kabīr of the sulṭān Nāṣir. See the note devoted to him.

[5] The date may not be as precise as that, say c. 1324; certainly not 1363 as written by Cheikho. 'Awaḍ says 15 Jumādā I, 724, which equals May 10, 1324 (not 1323 as he puts it).

[6] I believe that that very preservation consecrated their doom for nonliturgical purposes (Osiris 2, 447).

larger. The words which it contains are classified by subjects in 10 books (bāb) and 32 chapters (faṣl). The vocabulary is not restricted to the liturgical language as in the earlier Coptic scalae, but tries to exhaust the language: (I) God, angels, superior and inferior world; (II) man and his vices and virtues, instruments; (III) animals; (IV) plants; (V) minerals; (VI) geography; (VII) liturgy; (VIII) famous men of the Old and New Testaments; (IX) Hebrew and Greek words; (X) words the gender of which is different in Arabic and Coptic.

Text. According to father Cheikho, some sermons have been printed in Cairo by the care of the Coptic patriarchate (no date, before 1925). This may be a reference to the sermons included in the collection Al-jauhara al-nafīsa fī khuṭb al-kanīsa (Cairo 1914). One sermon was edited by Cheikho in al-Mashriq (19, 241–45, 1921).

Dom Louis Villecourt, Eugène Tisserand, and Gaston Wiet: Livre de la lampe des ténèbres (Patrologia orientalis 20, part 4, 579–734, Paris 1928), Arabic text, with French translation and elaborate introduction, of chapters 1 and 2 of the Miṣbāḥ al-ẓulma.

The Magna scala was edited by the pioneer of Coptic studies, the Jesuit father Athanasius Kircher[7] (1602–80), in his great book Lingua aegyptiaca restituta (624 p., Rome 1643; p. 39–272), and thus became one of the bases of Western Coptic erudition. The words are given in Coptic, Arabic, Latin. There is a Latin index at the end referring to all the texts of this volume. Unfortunately Kircher was a careless editor and translator; a critical edition is much to be desired.

Victor Loret: Les livres III et IV (animaux et végétaux) de la Scala magna (Annales du service des antiquités de l'Egypte 1, 48–63, 215–29, Cairo 1900), with Coptic and Arabic indexes.

Criticism. W. Ahlwardt: Verzeichniss der arabischen Handschriften (vol. 9, no. 10184, p. 547–52, Berlin 1897), long description in Arabic of the contents of the Miṣbāḥ al-ẓulma. Anton Baumstark: Abū-l-Barakāts nichtgriechisches Verzeichnis der 70 Jünger (Oriens christianus 1, 240–75, Roma 1901); Abū-l-Barakāts griechisches Verzeichnis der 70 Jünger (ibid. 2, 312–43, 1902). Alexis Mallon: Une école de savants égyptiens (Mélanges de la faculté orientale, Beyrouth, 1, 109–31, 1906; 2, 213–64, 1907; chiefly 2, 260–63); Catalogue des scalae coptes de la Bibliothèque nationale de Paris (ibid. 4, 57–90, 1910). Cheikho (p. 18, 1924), in Arabic. EI (2, 1003, 1927), by G. Wiet.

I owe to my colleague professor W. H. Worrell, of Ann Arbor, Michigan, the communication of an Arabic biography by Girgis Filoteos 'Awaḍ: Ibn Kabar (208 p., ill., Cairo 1930). The author (born in Ṭanṭā 1867) is a very prolific Coptic writer (see Sarkis' Arabic bibliography, col. 1473–75, 1930), and his book is of particular interest in spite of its discursiveness, as it gives us the Coptic tradition concerning Abū-l-Barakāt.

Note on a Ṣa'īdī Scala of the Same Century

The dialect of Upper Egypt is not by any means as well represented as that of Lower Egypt. There are only two important Ṣa'īdī scalae, both in the Bibliothèque nationale, Paris, and one of these, more complete and more correct than the other (Cod. Copt. 44), was edited by Henri Munier: La scala copte 44 (quarto, 262 p., Bibliothèque d'études coptes, dirigée par Pierre Jouguet, vol. 2, Le Caire 1930).[8] This contains only the transcription in Coptic and Arabic. The MS is dated 1389,

[7] He was incredibly versatile. For another aspect of his thought see Harry Beal Torrey: Kircher and the progress of medicine (Osiris 5, 246–75, 1938). Bibliothèque de la Compagnie de Jésus (4, 1046–77, 1893).

[8] I owe communication of this book to professor Worrell and the Library of the University of Michigan, and repeat my thanks to both.

and is a collection of texts, which may be divided into eight parts; Munier's edition contains only parts I to IV, parts V to VIII having been published before. (I) Ecclesiastical Ṣa'īdī scala of Anbā Yuḥannā of Samannūd in the Delṭa; words of the Bible and liturgic words, mostly Coptic (vs. Greek). (II) Ṣa'īdī grammar by same. (III; this is the main part) Book of degrees (βιβλίον τῶν βαθμῶν), anonymous Coptic-Arabic glossary derived from the Scala magna and other scalae. It is divided into 27 chapters dealing respectively with particles, God and qualities of good people, heavens, the earth and its surface (plants, seas, mountains), birds, quadrupeds and insects, the state, punishments and the church, precious stones and professions, perfumes and drugs, craftsmen and colors, anatomy, women and their peculiarities, defects and vices, miseries and diseases, names of towns, agriculture, horticulture, horses and other animals, veterinary art, varia, Biblical and religious words, etc. (IV) Ṣa'īdī grammar by Anbā Athanasios of Qūṣ (on the Nile below Louksor). (V) Boḥairī grammar by same. (VI) Boḥairī grammar by Anbā Yuḥannā of Samannūd. (VII) Ecclesiastical Boḥairī scala. (VIII) Doxology of St. Victor and Phoibammon.[8a]

HEBREW

JOSEPH BEN DAVID HA-YEWANI

Joseph ben David ha-Yewani (i.e., the Greek). Judeo-Greek grammarian who died not long before 1337. He wrote a book entitled Menorat ha-ma'or (Candelabrum of light), which consists of an introduction on Hebrew grammar followed by an uncompleted Hebrew dictionary (to the root ḥshv). He quotes Ḥayyuj (X-2), Ibn Janāḥ (XI-1), Rashi (XI-2), Abraham ben Ezra (XII-1), David Qimḥi (XII-2), Judah ben Solomon ha-Kohen (XIII-1), Moses ben Naḥman (XIII-2), etc.

Criticism. Max Seligsohn (JE 7, 258, 1904). M. Zobel (EJ 9, 336, 1932).

SOLOMON BEN SAMUEL

Judeo-Persian lexicographer who flourished at Urganj, in Khwārizm, about 1339. He completed in that year, at Urganj, a very elaborate Hebrew-Persian dictionary of the Bible, Targum, and Targumic-Midrashic literature. It is written mainly in Hebrew, but contains explanations in Persian (the author's maternal lauguage) and Arabic, all in Hebrew script. It is entitled Sefer ha-mliẓah (Book of allegory, or explanation); in a Persian appendix it is called Sefer agron[9] wa tafsir kal dabar. It includes some 18,000 articles classified in the Hebrew alphabetic order. Solomon had no clear understanding of the triliteral roots, and his grammatical knowledge was not up-to-date, but in spite of these and other weaknesses his lexicographical work is of very great value. Among the sources quoted by the author are the Sefer ha-razim (Book of secrets) and the Book of Asaph, i.e., the medical treatise of Asaph Judaeus (IX-2), for plant names, etc. Outside of the languages already named, this lexicon contains Turkish, Greek, and Romanic (chiefly Italian) vocables. The Romanic vocables were probably derived from Rashi (who is called Solomon

[8a] Φοιβάμμων. Mysterious personality. Is it identical with the one dealt with by Karl Fuhr: Zwei Hermogeneskommentatoren (Rheinisches Museum 51, 50–51, 1896)? The Eleutheroudakis encyclopaedia mentions (12, 655, Athens 1931) a scholiast of that name who flourished in the second half of the fifth century.

[9] Agron, collection, is the word used for dictionary by Saadia ben Joseph (X-1), and by Qaraites like David ben Abraham (X-2). See Introd. 1, 627, 690.

the Frenchman) and Nathan ben Jehiel. The main interest of the Sefer ha-mliẓah lies in its realism; the author's knowledge was not restricted to words, he was acquainted with the things themselves. He had visited the land of the "Uighūr and of the Khitai" and observed there a Buddhist (Lamaist?) temple, and the use of siphons to transfer liquids. More than a thousand words given by Solomon are missing from the dictionaries to the Targum, Talmud, and Midrash; some of these are simply variants of known words, the majority can be traced back to Hebrew roots or are derived from Syriac, Greek, or Arabic words; some cannot be identified at all.

One of the sources quoted by Solomon is the Dibre ha-yamim be-bayit sheni, which seems identical with the Jewish chronicle "Yosippon,"[10] or with another chronicle derived from it.

Text. This dictionary is not represented completely by any MS. The main part is available in a MS of Leningrad. Fragments completing the Leningrad text are included in MSS which Elkan N. Adler obtained in Bukhārā and brought back to London in 1897. A copy of the whole text has been prepared by Wilhelm Bacher, but its publication is very doubtful because of its bulk.

Criticism. Wilhelm Bacher: Ein hebräisch-persisches Wörterbuch aus dem vierzehnten Jahrhundert (XXIII. Jahresbericht der Landes-Rabbinerschule für das Schuljahr 1899/1900, 212 p., Budapest 1900), kindly lent to me by professor Alexander Marx.

ARABIC

IBN ĀJURRŪM

Abū 'Abdallāh Muḥammad ibn Muḥammad ibn Dā'ūd al-Ṣanhājī, known as Ibn Ājurrūm. Moroccan grammarian (d. 1323).

Ibn Ājurrūm was born in Fās 1273/74. He was of Berber origin, the name Ṣanhājī referring to the Berber tribe Ṣanhāja (EI 4, 152, 1925); Ājurrūm is a Berber word meaning poor but also ascetic, like the Arabic faqīr; that name had first been given to his grandfather Dā'ūd.

He studied in Fās and then performed the Pilgrimage, which enabled him to complete his education. Thus, while passing through Cairo he sat at the feet of the grammarian Athīr al-dīn Abū Ḥaiyān Muḥammad ibn Yūsuf of Granada (d. Cairo 1344), who gave him his "master's degree" (ijāza). After his return from Mecca, he taught grammar and the Qur'ān in the Andalusian quarter of Fās. He died there on March 1, 1323, and was buried in that quarter near the Bab al-ḥamrā'.

He wrote various books dealing with grammar, the orthography of the Qur'ān, and its recitation, but his fame rests exclusively on a grammatical summary which it is said he composed in Mecca, entitled Kitāb al-muqaddama al-ājurrūmīya fī mabādī 'ilm al-'arabīya, but generally called for short al-ājurrūmīya. It is very concise, being meant to be learned by heart, and has been memorized by countless youths all over the Dār al-Islām almost to our own days. The succinctness is carried so far that the text would be barely intelligible to beginners, but they were helped by the teacher's explanations and, if they desired, by written commentaries, a good many of which have come down to us (a dozen have been printed and others are available in MSS).

[10] Also called Sefer (Joseph) ben Gorion; pseudo-Joseph. It was probably composed in southern Italy at the beginning of the tenth century; there was possibly a Judeo-Byzantine prototype of the fifth or sixth century. See my note on Judah ben Moses Mosconi (XIV-2).

Besides being popular among Arabic mu'allimīn, the Ājurrūmīya attracted the attention of many Western scholars, who prepared editions and translations of it. Thus that otherwise insignificant text is equally important for the history of Arabic education in Muslim countries and for the history of Arabic scholarship in the West.

Text. The first edition of the Ājurrūmīya was printed in Rome 1592 (24 p., Medici press). Latin translation by Peter Kirsten (Breslau 1610). Arabic and Latin editions by Thomas Erpenius (Leiden 1617), Thomas Obicini[11] (Rome 1631), Christian Schnabel (Amsterdam 1755–56). Arabic-French edition by Louis Vaucelle (Paris 1833). Arabic, by E. Combarel (Paris 1844). Arabic-French, by Louis Jacques Bresnier (Algiers 1846, again 1866). Arabic-English, by John James Stewart Perowne, bishop of Worcester (Cambridge 1852). Arabic-German, by Ernst Trumpp (Munich 1876). Arabic-Italian, by Adolf Grohmann (Rome 1911). There are also many Oriental editions, e.g., Cairo 1861, 1863, 1864, 1865 (completely vocalized), 1871, 1878, 1881, 1884, 1885, Tunis 1873; to which should be added many editions of the commentaries.

Criticism. Brockelmann (2, 237, 1902; suppt. 2, 332, 1938). Moh. ben Cheneb (EI 2, 358–59, 1916). Renaud (p. 113, 1941).

IBN HISHĀM

Jamāl al-dīn Abū Muḥammad 'Abdallāh ibn Yūsuf ibn Hishām. Egyptian grammarian (1309–60).

Ibn Hishām was born in Cairo in April or May 1309; he studied under the Spaniard Abū Ḥaiyān. He was first a Ḥanbalī, joined the Shāfi'ī school, and finally returned to the Ḥanbalī fold. He died on September 17, 1360.

He wrote some 24 treatises, most of them on grammatical subjects. Judging by the number of MSS, commentaries, adaptations, abbreviations, versifications, his writings enjoyed considerable popularity. The most important is perhaps the Mughnī-l-labīb 'an kutub al-a'ārīb, quoted by Ibn Khaldūn (Prolégomènes 3, 273, 312), who considered the author the most eminent grammarian of his time, and comparable to the best of the ancients, such as Ibn Jinnī (X-2).

Text. There are many Oriental editions of some of his writings or commentaries, for which see Brockelmann. I only cite a few Western editions.

Qaṭr al-nadā wa ball al-ṣadā. Translated into French by A. Goguyer: La pluie de rosée et l'étanchement de la soif (Leyde 1887).

Al-i'rāb 'an qawā'id al-i'rāb, a treatise on logical analysis, published and translated by Silvestre de Sacy: Anthologie grammaticale (p. 73–92, 155–223, Paris 1829).

Sharḥ bānat su'ād. Commentary on the poem in honor of the Prophet beginning with the words Bānat su'ād (Su'ād has gone) composed in 630/31 by Ka'b ibn Zuhair. The Sharḥ was edited by Ignazio Guidi: Ibn Hishāmi commentarius in carmen Ka'bi ben Zoheir Bānat su'ād appellatum (254 p., Leipzig 1871).

Criticism. Brockelmann (2, 23–25, 1902; suppt. 2, 16–20, 1938). Moh. ben Cheneb (EI 2, 387, 1918).

AL-JĀRABARDĪ

Aḥmad ibn al-Ḥasan al-Jārabardī al-Shāfi'ī. Persian (?) theologian and grammarian (d. 1345/46).

[11] The Franciscan Thomas Obicini (d. 1632) was the founder of Arabic studies in San Pietro in Montorio, Rome (Isis 29, 190).

I do not understand the nisba Jārabardī. He is said to have been a pupil of al-Baiḍāwī (XIII-2), which would explain his interest in the works of al-Zamakhsharī (XII-1). He was considered the most learned man in Tabrīz, where he died in December 1345 or January 1346.

He wrote an Arabic grammar, Al-mughnī fī 'ilm al-naḥw, which is an adaptation of the short grammar, Al-unmūdhaj, of al-Zamakhsharī, and a commentary (sharḥ) on the famous Qur'ānic work, Al-kashshāf 'an ḥaqā'iq al-tanzīl, of the same author. He also added commentaries to innumerable others on the larger and smaller grammars, Al-kāfiya and Al-shāfiya, of Ibn al-Ḥājib (XIII-1). Finally, he commented on the collection of fatāwā, Al-ḥāwī al-ṣaghīr, of the Shāfi'ī doctor 'Abd al-Ghaffār ibn 'Abd al-Karīm al-Qazwīnī (d. 1266).

Criticism. Brockelmann (2, 193, 1902; suppt. 2, 257, 1938).

KHAṬĪB DIMASHQ

Turkish or Persian rhetorician writing in Arabic (1267–1338).

Jalāl al-dīn Abū-l-Ma'ālī Muḥammad ibn 'Abd al-Raḥmān, called Khaṭīb Dimashq al-Qazwīnī. He was born in Asia Minor or in Qazwīn 1267, and became a qāḍī first in his native country, later in Damascus (1324), finally qāḍī al-quḍāt in Cairo (1327). He exerted a good influence upon al-Nāṣir Muḥammad (Baḥrī Mamlūk, 1309–40), but was compromised by the extravagance of his son 'Abdallāh ibn Muḥammad, and finally obliged to return to Damascus, where he died not long afterward, in November 1338.

His main work is a commentary or summary of the third part of the Miftāḥ al-'ulūm of al-Sakkākī (XIII-1), dealing with rhetoric (parts I and II being devoted to grammar, ṣarf and naḥw). This summary, called Talkhīṣ al-miftāḥ, enjoyed more popularity than the Miftāḥ itself and was the subject of other commentaries. He wrote another work on rhetoric called Al-īḍāḥ fī-l-ma'ānī wal-bayān, commented upon by al-Āqsarā'ī (XIV-2) and others.

Criticism. Ibn Baṭṭūṭa (1, 210). Brockelmann (2, 22, 1902; suppt. 2, 15, 1938).

TURKISH

ABŪ ḤAIYĀN

Spanish Muslim grammarian and theologian. Author of the first Turkish grammar (1256–1344).

Athīr al-dīn Abū Ḥaiyān Muḥammad ibn Yūsuf . . . ibn Ḥaiyān al-Gharnāṭī al-Nafzī al-Jaiyānī. The three nisbāt refer to his birth in Granada in November 1256, and to the fact that he originated from a Berber family, of the Nafza tribe, established in Jaén (Arabic Jaiyān).[12] He was educated in Granada, Velez-Malaga, and Almeria, and became a theologian of the Ẓāhirī persuasion.[13] About 1280 he went to the Maghrib and Egypt, where he traveled extensively, as far as 'Aidhāb on the Red Sea. He made the Pilgrimage and returned to Egypt via Syria. In

[12] The family had probably moved to Granada in or after 1246, when the city of Jaén was conquered by Ferdinand III of Castile. The city was never more in Islamic power after 1246.

[13] Founded by Dā'ūd al-Ẓāhirī of Kūfa (IX-2). The members of the Ẓāhirī school are fundamentalists who derive the law from the literal text (ẓāhir) of the Qur'ān and sunna. Though founded in the East, that school enjoyed no popularity except in Spain and the Maghrib.

Cairo, he taught Muslim tradition and studied under the famous grammarian Ibn al-Naḥḥās, whom he replaced when the latter died, in 1298. He became himself one of the most popular teachers of the Mamlūk capital. One of his two children was a daughter, Nuḍār (1303–39), who distinguished herself by her learning. He died in Cairo, July 11, 1344, and was buried in the ṣūfī cemetery outside the Bāb al-naṣr.

His education as a Ẓāhirī caused him to sympathize with the fundamentalism of Ibn Taimīya, in whose honor he wrote a poem at the time of the latter's rehabilitation in Cairo. He retracted later, however, accused Ibn Taimīya of gross anthropomorphism (tajsīm), and became a Shāfi'ī. He thus reversed the evolution of the Cordovan Ibn Ḥazm (XI-1), who was first Shāfi'ī but became an ardent Ẓāhirī and was largely responsible for the popularity of the latter school in Spain.

The list of Abū Ḥaiyān's works includes 66 items, the majority of which are lost. We shall only speak of a few of them; to begin with, his (lost) autobiography, Al-nuḍār fī maslāt 'an Nuḍār (Pure gold on consolation for the loss of Nuḍār), which was written shortly after the death of his beloved daughter (1339) and wherein he described his youth, travels, and studies.

A good many of his writings deal with theology, the Qur'ān and its recitation. The main one is a very elaborate commentary on the Qur'ān, called the Ocean (Al-baḥr al-muḥīṭ fī tafsīr al-Qur'ān al-'aẓīm), of which he wrote also two abbreviations. As he was primarily a grammarian, many of his Qur'ānic studies are grammatical or lexicographic. A good many others deal with various manners of reading and intoning the sacred text. He composed an abridgment of the Muḥallā of Ibn Ḥazm (XI-1) on Ẓāhirī doctrine, and a commentary on the Kitāb al-taqrīb wal-taisīr of al-Nawawī (XIII-2).

His history of Spain, Al-mubīn fī ta'rīkh al-Andalus, extended to 60 volumes, which are lost. The biographies of his contemporaries are also lost.

A book on alchemy, Shudhūr al-dhahab fī-l-iliksīr (Particles of gold on the elixir), is ascribed to him, but a book bearing the same title is also ascribed to 'Alī ibn Mūsā al-Andalusī by Ḥājjī Khalīfa (no. 7433; who said 'Alī died in 1106/7) and by Brockelmann (1, 313; who said he died in 1274–75); and to 'Alī ibn Mūsā Ibn Arfa' ra'sahu of Fās (d. 1196/97) by myself (Introd. 2, 1046). With regard to the last ascription see note in Introd. (2, 408), where the book is entitled Dīwān shudhūr al-dhahab fī fann al-salāmāt and is said to deal with the philosopher's stone. Are these writings truly alchemical? are they different from one another? was one of them actually written by Abū Ḥaiyān?

We now come to the latter's most important activity. Abū Ḥaiyān was first and last a grammarian, a philologist. It is said that his Western upbringing caused him to speak Arabic imperfectly, e.g., to confuse the letters ḍ and ẓ, or k and q, and this directed his attention to phonetic subjects. One of his lost writings is the kitāb al-irtiḍā fī (farq baina) ḍād wa ẓā (one's satisfaction with regard to these two letters). He wrote a work in four volumes on the Arabic language, Al-tadhkira al-'arabīya, and many others, only four of which are extant: Al-irtishāf al-ḍarab min lisān al-'arab (Degustation of honey concerning the language of the Arabs); Lamḥa fī-l-naḥw (Glance on syntax); Al-nukat al-ḥisān fī sharḥ ghāyat al-iḥsān (The excellent subtleties being a commentary on the [book called the] acme of perfection), composed in 1290;[14] and Al-takhyīl al-mulakhkhas min sharḥ al-tashīl

[14] It is not clear to me whether Abū Ḥaiyān composed the book or the commentary or both, and whether the date 1290 applies to both, or if not, to which it applies.

(The purified ambiguity). This last-named book was a commentary on the Tashīl al-fawā'id wa takmīl al-maqāṣid of the great Spanish grammarian Ibn Mālik.[15] Lost writings deal with prosody, with the grammar of Sībawaihi (VIII-2), with the Spanish grammarians, with meaning and exposition, with the branches of Arabic philology, with syntax, morphology (taṣrīf), etc. Add to these his studies on the words of the Qur'ān and their meanings and peculiarities.

The most original feature of Abu Ḥaiyān's mind is his interest in other languages. This was probably due to his many contacts in Spain and Africa, and especially in the cosmopolitan atmosphere of Cairo, with people who spoke other languages than Arabic, or whose Arabic was contaminated by other languages. He had obtained a good knowledge of Persian, Turkish, and even Aethiopic.

He wrote one or two books (lost) on the last-named language, one of which was entitled Nūr al-ghabash fī lisān al-ḥabash (Light of the end of the night on the language of the Abyssinians). He composed another book (also lost) on the Persian language. He was, however, especially interested in Turkish, perhaps because there was at that time a large Turkish colony in Cairo, many of them emigrants from Central Asia. Thus he devoted no less than five books to Turkish matters; four of them, dealing respectively with Turkish verbs, the Turkish language in general, Turkish syntax, and Turkish life, are lost.

The one Turkish book extant is Abū Ḥaiyān's outstanding contribution. It is written in Arabic, entitled Kitāb al-idrāk lilisān al-Atrāk, and was completed on January 18, 1313. It is the oldest treatise on Turkish grammar that has come down to us.

It is true there are two short grammatical sections in the anonymous Turkish-Arabic, Persian-Mongol glossary which was composed in 1245/46, probably in Egypt. (The Turkish words are explained in Arabic, the Mongolian words in Persian.) The Turkish-Arabic part is divided into four sections: (1) 24 lists of words arranged by subject, as heaven, earth, trees, animals, etc.; (2) imperative of verbs (that form is always the root in Turkish); (3) conjugation of verbs; (4) particles and suffixes.

There is still another Arabic work of the same general kind, the Kitāb ḥilyat al-insān wa-ḥalbat al-lisān, dealing with the Persian, Turkish, and Mongol languages. Five of its MSS (3 Bodleian, 1 Berlin, 1 Paris) are anonymous, but a sixth MS, in the Müzei Humayun, Istanbul, is ascribed to one Jamāl al-dīn Ibn al-Muhannā. According to Melioranski, that text belongs to the end of the thirteenth century or the beginning of the fourteenth.

To return to the Idrāk of Abū Ḥaiyān, we may still call it the first systematic grammar of the Turkish language. It is divided into three parts: (1) Turkish-Arabic glossary of some 2,200 words arranged more or less in alphabetical order; (2) phonetics and morphology; (3) syntax. The method of exposition is imitated from the Arabic grammar; e.g., the verbs are given in the perfect, not in the imperative, which creates artificial difficulties.

The language dealt with is eastern Turkish (Turkī), as somewhat corrupted in Egypt; the author differentiates Turkī from other dialects, mainly Qipčaqī and

[15] Muḥammad ibn 'Abdallāh ibn Mālik al-Ṭā'ī al-Jaiyānī (1203–73). His family, like Abū Ḥaiyān's, originated in Jaén, but at the time of the Christian reconquest or later it had emigrated not to Granada but to the East; Ibn Mālik was born in Damascus, and spent his life there and in Ḥalab (Brockelmann 1, 298).

Turkomānī. The vocabulary naturally includes foreign words; some 20 Arabic, 60 Persian, and a few Mongolian and Greek.

For the study of the eastern Turkish vocabulary we have a much older source, that is, the Dīwān ʻlughāt al-Turk of Maḥmūd al-Kāshgharī, a Turkish-Arabic vocabulary composed at Kāshghar, Chinese Turkestān, in 466 (= 1073/74, not 1066). This includes grammatical information with comparisons between different Turkish dialects. It would seem that Maḥmūd was planning the composition of a syntax; but that idea was not realized or else the book is lost.

On the other hand, the Turkish grammar in Arabic, al-Qawānīn al-kullīya li ḍabṭ al-lugha al-turkīya (Collected rules for the mastery of the Turkish language), though ascribed in the single MS (in the Shahīd 'Alī pāshā library, Istanbul) to Abū-l-Ḥaiyān, is apocryphal. It is a somewhat later production; e.g., there is in it a reference to the sack of Damascus by Tīmūr Lang in 1400. The author, like Abū Ḥaiyān, was an Arab who had obtained his knowledge of Turkish from the Turkish colony in Cairo.

Text. The Kitāb al-idrāk lilisān al-Atrāk was edited by Muṣṭafā bey (213 p., Constantinople 1891–92). Elaborate review by Cl. Huart (Journal asiatique 20, 326–35, 1892). Improved edition by Ahmet Caferoğlu (360 p., Istanbul 1930–31), including elaborate Turkish commentary and indexes. I owe a copy of this edition and of two other Turkish books mentioned below, and also much information on Turkish grammar and its history, to my young friend and disciple Aydin Sayili.

The thirteenth-century glossary was edited by Martinus Theodorus Houtsma: Ein türkisch-arabisches Glossar nach der Leidener Handschrift (Leiden 1894), reviewed by A. Barbier de Meynard (Journal asiatique 4, 183–87, 1894). The Mongolian-Persian part of that work is still unpublished.

The Kitāb ḥilyat al-insān was edited by Platon Mikhailovich Melioranski in 1900–3. I have not seen that edition and do not know whether it is complete or restricted to the second and third parts of the text. A new edition based on the newly discovered Istanbul MS was published with a Turkish preface (8 p.) by Kilisli Mehmed Rifat (242 p., Istanbul 1919–22). Aptullah Battal: Ibnü-Mühenna lûgati (110 p., Istanbul 1934), index of the Turkish part of the Ḥilyat al-insān.

The Qawānīn kullīya wrongly ascribed to Abū-l-Ḥaiyān was edited by Köprülü zade Muḥammad Fu'ād bey (94 p., Istanbul 1928). The author's family name is now Köprülü; he would thus be called Mehmed Fuat Köprülü.

Criticism. Wüstenfeld (part 2, p. 3–5, 1882). Pons Boigues (no. 278, p. 323–26, 1898). Brockelmann (2, 109, 1902; suppt. 2, 135–36, 1938). Lucien Bouvat: Notice sur Athīr ad-dīn Mohammad ibn Yoûsouf (Revue hispanique 10, 471–84, 1903); Une grammaire turque du huitième siècle de l'hégire (Actes du XIVe congrès des orientalistes, Alger 1905, 3, 44–78, Paris 1907). M. Th. Houtsma (EI 1, 88, 1908). Mehmed Fuat Köprülü: Türk edebiyatı tarihi (Istanbul 1929); the same Köprülü has written many important books and papers on Turcology, in Turkish, and articles in EI.

With regard to Maḥmūd al-Kāshgharī, whose Dīwān was published in Istanbul 1915–17, see C. Brockelmann: Mitteltürkischer Wortschatz nach Maḥmūd al-Kāshgharī (Bibliotheca orientalis hungarica vol. 1, 262 p., Kórösi Csoma Gesellschaft, Budapest 1928; Isis 21, 354), Turkish vocabulary extracted from the Dīwān of 1073 for comparison with the Turkish vocabulary of Abū Ḥaiyān. B. Atalay: Türk dili kuralları (110 p., Ankara 1931), in Turkish, discussing the grammatical information included in the Dīwān.

For the sake of comparison, see Ananiasz Zajaczkowski: Manuel arabe de la langue des Turcs et des Kiptchaks (90 p., 4 pl., Warsaw Society of Sciences and

Letters, Warsaw 1938; O. L. Z. 42, 698, 1939). This deals with the Kitāb bulghat al-mushtāq fī lughat al-Turk wal-Qifjāq written by Jamāl al-dīn Abū Muḥammad 'Abdallāh al-Turkī during the Mamlūk period. Zajaczkowski would place it in Syria about the middle of the fourteenth century. It is a Turkish vocabulary wherein the words are grouped according to subjects. The editor gives the text plus a Turkish-Polish-French glossary.

One may also refer to the very curious treatise of A. Cevat Emre: Sur l'origine de l'alphabet vieux-turc, dit alphabet runique de Sibérie (45 p., Istanbul 1938; Muséon 52, 418).

It may be worth while to refer here also to a much earlier work on Uighūr (or old Turkish) by Arminius Vámbéry: Uigurische Sprachmonumente und das Kudatku bilik. Uigurischer Text mit Transcription und Übersetzung nebst einem uigurisch-deutschen Wörterbuche und lithografirten Facsimile aus dem Originaltexte des Kudatku bilik (small folio, 262 p., 1 pl., Innsbruck 1870), including also a list of the 112 Arabic-Persian words occurring with greatest frequency in the Uighūr text. The Kudatku bilik, meaning lucky (favorable) knowledge, is an ethical work in verse, dealing mainly with the duties of a ruler to his people, the qualities required of the people of different estates, the individual vices which harm society, in short, the relations of the individual to the passing world and to destiny. Central-Asian, Turkish views are predominant, betraying Tibetan and Chinese influences rather than Arabic and Persian. Apart from the brief Islamic doxology at the beginning, the text is hardly religious. It was written by one Yūsuf bearing the title Khāṣṣ ḥājib, special chamberlain to one Bughrā Khān, perhaps Maḥmūd I Bughrā Khān, Īlak khān of Turkistān, who ruled until 1057/58 (Zambaur p. 206, 1927); the Viennese MS used by Vámbéry was written in Uighūr script in Herāt 1439–40, but the text is twice self-dated 1070–71. See Introd. 1, 712. Vasilii Vasilyevich Radlov has published a facsimile of the Kudatku bilik after the Uighūr MS in the imperial library of Vienna (folio, 214 p., St. Pétersbourg 1890) and also an edition and translation, Das Kudatku bilik des Jusuf Chass-Hadschib aus Bälasagun. Theil II. Text und Übersetzung nach den Handschriften von Wien und Kairo (folio, 584 p., Petersburg 1900–10).

Sidney Glazer: The Alfiyya commentaries of Ibn 'Aqīl and Abū Ḥayyān (Moslem world 31, 400–8, 1941; Isis 34, 46). The Kitāb al-alfīya is a famous grammatical poem of a thousand lines written by Ibn Mālik, mentioned above. Among the many commentaries devoted to it were one by Abū Ḥaiyān entitled Manhaj al-sālik, and another by the Egyptian theologian 'Abdallāh ibn 'Abd al-Raḥmān Ibn 'Aqīl al-Shāfi'ī (1294–1367), Brockelmann (2, 88). Glazer compares these commentaries, showing that the one by Ibn 'Aqīl was largely derived from the other. Sidney Glazer: A noteworthy passage from an Arab grammatical text (Journal of the American Oriental Society 62, 106–8, 1942), extract from the Manhaj al-sālik in Arabic and English, illustrating the keenness of Abū Ḥaiyān's philological instinct.

CODEX CUMANICUS

The Codex Cumanicus is a MS of 82 paper leaves of slightly different sizes (height 19.5 to 20.5 cm., width 12.5 to 14 cm.), which is a monument of great importance for the study of the Coman language, a form of Turkish, and of Turcology in general. It was begun in July 11, 1303, and once belonged to Petrarca (1304–74), who bequeathed it to the San Marco Library in Venice. By order of Napoleon it was transferred to the Imperial Library in Paris, but later it was restored to the Marciana, of which it is one of the chief treasures (Cod. Marc. lat. DXLIX).

Before speaking of its contents, it is well to recall the circumstances explaining its existence. In the course of the thirteenth century Russia had been overrun by some of the Tatar tribes of the Golden Horde, which had established in southern Russia the western Qipčaq khanate (Blue Horde) with the capital at Sarai on the lower Volga. These Tatars spoke an Ural-Altaic language called Coman, related to Turkish. A variety of it is still spoken by the Tatars of Kazan (Qazān, now capital of the Tatar Soviet Republic). The people speaking that language were called Comani or Cumani in Latin and Polovtzi in Russian.[16] On the other hand, since the re-establishment of the Byzantine empire in 1261, Genoa's trade was flourishing in Constantinople and around the Black Sea. Genoese merchants were active in Crimea, Russia, and even Persia. Hence the need of the work which we shall now describe.

It contains two very different parts. The first and larger (55 leaves against 27) was composed in 1303, by an Italian, probably Genoese. It is a Latin-Persian-Coman dictionary. The first 29 leaves contain the verbs, each with two or three conjugation forms and a few nouns connected with those verbs, in Latin alphabetical order. On page 30r appears the word bitik (writing) in Uighūr script; all the rest is written in Latin script. Then follow adverbs, declension of pronouns and nouns, then list of words in the three languages classified by subjects: religion, heavens, four elements, four temperaments, time, five senses, weather, adjectives, qualities, everyday life, business and bookkeeping, spices and drugs (5 pages), metals and tools of smithcraft, furred animals and furriery, tailoring, shoemaking, carpentry, barber's shop, various arts and crafts, dignitaries and employees, trade, colors, precious stones, parts of the body, family relationships, good and bad qualities, war and weapons, parts of the house, making of clothes, house building, clothing of men, horses and harness, bedroom, covered table, kitchen, tree, fruit culture, vegetables, mammals, reptiles and vermin, birds, grain, milk, and other food. The commercial intention of this first part is clear.

The second part, probably added somewhat later but not very much later, inasmuch as the whole MS reached Petrarca's hands, was written by German Franciscans, who were conducting missionary work among the Qipčaq. The intention is clearly religious. This part is in fact a brief manual for the use of missionaries. It contains texts in Coman, German, and Italian; no trace of Persian except for a few Persian Comanized words. There are samples of the Coman language, not simply words, but phrases, folk riddles, and a whole series of Coman texts for religious needs, such as prayers, hymns, materials for sermons; also religious Latin-Coman vocabularies, and grammatical remarks.

Text. First edition, incomplete, by Julius Klaproth: Vocabulaire latin, persan et coman (Mémoires relatifs à l'Asie 3, 113–256, Paris 1828). First complete edition, by count Géza Kuun: Codex cumanicus (531 p., Hungarian Academy, Budapest 1880); Additamenta (40 p., ibid. 1883); this elaborate edition with long prolegomena and many indexes seemed final, but it is vitiated by incorrect readings. A new edition by V. V. Radlov: Das türkische Sprachmaterial des Codex Cumanicus (Mémoires de l'Académie de St. Pétersbourg vol. 35, no. 6, 1887), being derived from Kuun, has the same defects.

Facsimile edition of the whole MS, with introductions (12 p.) by K. Grønbech, is vol. 1 of the Monumenta linguarum Asiae maioris (folio, Kopenhagen 1936).

Criticism. The editions of Kuun and Radlov started long and acrimonious

[16] That Russian name is familiar to music lovers all over the world because of the Polovtsian dances in the opera Prince Igor of Alexandr Porfiryevich Borodin (1833–87). See my article on Borodin (Osiris 7, 247, 1939). It should not be concluded from my text that the terms Qipčaq, Comani, and Polovtzi always referred to the same peoples; these questions are extremely complicated. The ethnographic and geographic connotations of each term varied in the course of time.

discussions. For example, Willy Bang wrote no less than seven papers on the subject between 1910 and 1914 (list in Pelliot p. 127). J. Marquart: Über das Volkstum der Komanen (Abhandlungen der Kgl. Gesellschaft der Wissenschaften zu Göttingen 13, no. 1, 25–238, 1914). P. Halász: Pharmakognostisches aus dem Codex Cumanicus (AGM 11, 278–85, 1919), study of the abundant vocabulary relative to herbs and drugs. Golubovich (3, 1–28, 1919). Paul Pelliot: A propos des Comans (Journal asiatique 15, 125–85, 1920). Meillet and Cohen (p. 204, 1924). W. Barthold: Qipčaq (EI 2, 1022, 1927). Tadeusz Kowalski: Karaimische Texte im Dialekt von Troki, eingeleitet, erläutert und mit einem karaimisch-polnisch-deutschen Glossar versehen (400 p., Polish Academy of Sciences, Cracow 1929; J. R. A. S., 1929, p. 905–10). Holger Pedersen: Linguistic science in the nineteenth century (p. 110, Harvard Press 1931).

CHINESE

CHOU PO-CH'I

Chou Po-ch'i, style name Po-Wên. Chinese philologist (d. 1370?).

He was born in Jao-chou, Kiangsi, and was vice-minister of the war ministry in 1352. He was sent to suppress the rebellion of Chang Shih-ch'êng (Giles no. 103) in 1357, but was kept prisoner by the rebels until Chang's death in 1367. When the rebellion was completely put down by the first Ming emperor, he retired from public life, and died soon after the establishment of the new dynasty.

He wrote a treatise on orthography, Liu Shu chêng o, in 5 chüan, and another on etymology, Shuo wên tzŭ yüan, in 1 chüan, wherein he investigated the origins of the characters of the Shuo wên, the first Chinese dictionary arranged by radicals, compiled by Hsü Shên (II-1). For the history of the Shuo wên see also my note on Ku Yeh-wang (VI-1).

Both books were published by Yu-wen kung-liang, president of the imperial academy, whose preface is dated 1355. The second book has a preface by Chou himself dated 1349. Both books were reprinted in 1522 with a new preface by Huang Fang, and again in 1634 by Hu Chêng-yen.

Criticism. Giles (no. 421, 1898).

WU-CH'IU YEN

Chinese archaeologist of the Yüan dynasty (fl. c. 1307). He was styled Tzŭ Hsing, and was a native of Ch'ien t'ang, Chehkiang.

He wrote a treatise on Chinese sphragistics, dealing not only with seals but with the characters engraved on them. Indeed, the two subjects are inseparable in Chinese, the word chuan meaning at one and the same time the seal itself (e.g., a seal of office) and the so-called "seal" character. There are two kinds of seal character, the "greater seal," ta chuan, and the "lesser seal," hsiao chuan. The former was invented by Shih Chou, a historian in the service of Hsüan Wang, Chou emperor from 827 to 781 B.C., in order to replace ancient hieroglyphs; the "lesser seal" characters were invented either by Li Ssŭ or by Ch'êng Mo, both of whom flourished under the First Emperor, Shih Huang-ti (ruled 221–209 B.C.). The earliest Chinese dictionary arranged by radicals, the Shuo wên chieh tzŭ, was written by Hsü Shên (II-1) in "lesser seal" at the beginning of the second century.

The treatise on seals of Wu-ch'iu Yen was entitled Hsüeh-ku-pien and divided into nine sections: lesser seal, bells and vases, ancient character, stone inscriptions, instruments, correction of errors, official hand, origin of letters, distinct origins. The work ends with advice for cleaning seals and using them. Supplements to this work on Chinese sphragistics and epigraphy have been published from time to time; indeed, there are quite a number of books on these subjects, which appeal to the imagination of Chinese scholars.

Wu-ch'iu Yen also wrote a treatise on epigraphy, entitled Chou ch'in k'o shih shih yin, his own preface to it being dated 1307. It is a study of the inscriptions on stone of the Chou and Ch'in dynasties. It was based on an earlier work bearing the same title by Yang wên ping.

Text. I do not know of separate editions of the Hsüeh-ku-pien, but its text is included in a dozen ts'ung shu; for example, in vol. 178 of the Hsüeh ching t'ao yüan, and in vol. 15 of I mên kuang tu.

Criticism. Wylie (p. 139, 1902). Wieger (p. 375, 494, 1920).

JAPANESE

YOSHIDA KENKŌ

Japanese Buddhist author (1283-1350).

Yoshida is the family name. The Yoshida family is a branch of the Urabe family, which attained great influence under the Ashikaga; members of the Yoshida family were responsible in the seventeenth century for the reform of Shintō called Yui-itsu-shintō. Kenkō is the religious name, being simply the Chinese reading of his personal lay name, Kaneyoshi. He was also called Urabe Kenkō, and more often Kenkō.

Kenkō was born in 1283, studied literature, and was patronized by Go-Uda (emperor 1275-87); at the death of his patron, in 1324, he assumed the Tendai habit and retired to the Shūgaku-in. In 1340 he withdrew to the foot of the Kunimi-yama in the province of Iga.

He wrote the Tsure-zure-gusa (Weeds of tedium), a collection of essays and anecdotes, which was very popular and notably influenced Japanese education, because it was one of the means of diffusing Buddhist doctrines as well as the sayings of Confucius and Mencius. It is one of the classics of Japanese literature and may be compared to another great classic, the Hōjō-ki of Chōmei Kamo (XIII-1).

Kenkō is one of the four kings of Japanese poetry (wa-ka shi-tennō),[17] the three others being Ton-a (1301-84), Jōben, and Keiun. He has been called rather inaptly the Horace of Japan. His intentions were often satirical and pessimistic.

Text. The Tsuredzure gusa of Yoshida no Kaneyoshi, being the meditations of a recluse in the fourteenth century. Translated by George B. Sansom with notes and an appendix by M. Anesaki on Religious conditions of Japan in the fourteenth century (Transactions of the Asiatic Society of Japan 39, 1-146, 1911).

Criticism. W. G. Aston: Littérature japonaise (p. 175-87, 1902), brief analysis and extracts. Karl Florenz: Geschichte der japanischen Litteratur (p. 329-38, Leipzig 1906). Papinot (p. 705, 756, 1909). Brinkley and Kikuchi (p. 367, 1914). E. Steinilber-Oberlin: Les sectes bouddhiques japonaises (p. 281-92, Paris 1930).

[17] Wa-ka (Ch., ho-ko) designates a 31-syllable ode (tanka); shi-tennō is the Japanese reading of the Chinese characters ssŭ t'ien wang, a Buddhist phrase translating the Sanskrit caturmahārāja, the four heavenly kings. These are the four demon-kings who guard the four quarters of the universe; they were introduced from Ceylon into China only c. 733 by Pu-k'ung (VIII-1) and are now to be seen in the entrance hall, t'ien-wang t'ang (or tien), of every Buddhist temple. For the ssŭ t'ien wang see Reginald Fleming Johnston: Buddhist China (p. 366-75, London 1913). Karl Ludvig Reichelt: Truth and tradition in Chinese Buddhism (p. 179, Shanghai 1934). Soothill and Hodous (p. 145, 1937).